nature

The Living Record of Science

《自然》百年科学经典

英汉对照版　套装共十卷

第十卷

2002-2007

总顾问：李政道（Tsung-Dao Lee）

英方主编：Sir John Maddox　　中方主编：路甬祥
Sir Philip Campbell

外语教学与研究出版社 · 麦克米伦教育 · 自然科研

FOREIGN LANGUAGE TEACHING AND RESEARCH PRESS · MACMILLAN EDUCATION · NATURE RESEARCH

北京 BEIJING

图书在版编目（CIP）数据

《自然》百年科学经典 : 套装共十卷. 第十卷 : 英汉对照 ／（英）约翰·马多克斯（John Maddox），（英）菲利普·坎贝尔（Philip Campbell），路甬祥主编. —— 北京：外语教学与研究出版社，2020.9

ISBN 978-7-5213-2021-3

Ⅰ. ①自… Ⅱ. ①约… ②菲… ③路… Ⅲ. ①自然科学－文集－英、汉 Ⅳ. ①N53

中国版本图书馆 CIP 数据核字（2020）第 154886 号

地图审图号：GS（2020）5244 号

出 版 人　徐建忠
项目统筹　章思英
项目负责　刘晓楠　黄小斌
责任编辑　王丽霞
责任校对　黄小斌
封面设计　高　蕾
版式设计　孙莉明
插图设计　麦克米伦提供原图扫描版
出版发行　外语教学与研究出版社
社　　址　北京市西三环北路 19 号（100089）
网　　址　http://www.fltrp.com
印　　刷　北京华联印刷有限公司
开　　本　787×1092　1/16
印　　张　67
版　　次　2021 年 1 月第 1 版 2021 年 1 月第 1 次印刷
书　　号　ISBN 978-7-5213-2021-3
定　　价　8000.00 元

购书咨询：（010）88819926　电子邮箱：club@fltrp.com
外研书店：https://waiyants.tmall.com
凡印刷、装订质量问题，请联系我社印制部
联系电话：（010）61207896　电子邮箱：zhijian@fltrp.com
凡侵权、盗版书籍线索，请联系我社法律事务部
举报电话：（010）88817519　电子邮箱：banquan@fltrp.com
物料号：320210001

《自然》百年科学经典（英汉对照版）

总顾问：李政道（Tsung-Dao Lee）

英方主编：Sir John Maddox　　　　中方主编：路甬祥

Sir Philip Campbell

编审委员会

英方编委　　　　　　　　**中方编委**（以姓氏笔画为序）

Philip Ball　　　　　　　　许智宏

Vikram Savkar　　　　　　赵忠贤

David Swinbanks　　　　　滕吉文

本卷审稿专家（以姓氏笔画为序）

于　军	王　宇	王晓良	尹凤玲	冯珑珑	邢　松	刘冬生
许　冰	李　然	肖景发	张颖奇	陆培祥	陈含章	陈继征
季江徽	周济林	郑旭峰	胡永云	胡松年	夏俊卿	徐　栋
徐文堪	高树基	曹　俊	曹庆宏	常　江	曾长青	蔡荣根
裴端卿	黎　卓	潘　雷				

编译委员会

Contents
目录

I

Volume X

(2002-2007)

Estimating the Human Health Risk from Possible BSE Infection of the British Sheep Flock

N. M. Ferguson *et al.*

Editor's Note

The neurodegenerative disease bovine spongiform encephalopathy (BSE) was first recognized in British cattle in the 1980s. The government's response was to monitor herds closely and restrict beef sales to ensure that organs known to harbour BSE were not sold. Nevertheless, an outbreak occurred in the late 1980s, leading to the culling of British cattle and a European ban on British beef exports. BSE is believed to trigger a similar, fatal disease in humans called Creutzfeldt-Jakob disease, of which more than 160 people have died following the 1980s BSE outbreak. Here epidemiologist Roy Anderson and colleagues model the likely course of the human epidemic and predict future deaths to be in the range 50–50,000.

Following the controversial failure of a recent study[1] and the small numbers of animals yet screened for infection[2], it remains uncertain whether bovine spongiform encephalopathy (BSE) was transmitted to sheep in the past via feed supplements and whether it is still present. Well grounded mathematical and statistical models are therefore essential to integrate the limited and disparate data, to explore uncertainty, and to define data-collection priorities. We analysed the implications of different scenarios of BSE spread in sheep for relative human exposure levels and variant Creutzfeldt–Jakob disease (vCJD) incidence. Here we show that, if BSE entered the sheep population and a degree of transmission occurred, then ongoing public health risks from ovine BSE are likely to be greater than those from cattle, but that any such risk could be reduced by up to 90% through additional restrictions on sheep products entering the food supply. Extending the analysis to consider absolute risk, we estimate the 95% confidence interval for future vCJD mortality to be 50 to 50,000 human deaths considering exposure to bovine BSE alone, with the upper bound increasing to 150,000 once we include exposure from the worst-case ovine BSE scenario examined.

THE aim of this study was not to evaluate the probability that BSE has entered the sheep flock, but rather, given the pessimistic assumption that infection has occurred, to explore its potential extent and pattern of spread. In this, we used epidemiological parameter estimates from experimental BSE infections of sheep, and, where data are unavailable, assumed (given the observed similarities in BSE and scrapie pathogenesis in sheep) that other aspects of disease epidemiology resemble those of scrapie. Analyses were constrained to be consistent with the failure to detect the BSE agent in a small sample of 180 brains[2] collected between 1996 and 2000 from sheep diagnosed with scrapie (giving

英国羊群可能的 BSE
感染带来的人类健康风险评估

弗格森等

编者按

神经退行性疾病牛海绵状脑病(BSE)于 20 世纪 80 年代首次在英国牛中发现。英国政府的回应是密切监控牧群，限制牛肉销售，以确保患有 BSE 的牛的器官不被出售。然而，20 世纪 80 年代末爆发了一场疫情，导致英国牲畜遭到扑杀，欧洲禁止英国牛肉出口。据信，BSE 在人类中引发了一种类似的致命疾病(称为克雅氏病)。自 20 世纪 80 年代 BSE 爆发以来，已有 160 多人死于这种疾病。流行病学家罗伊·安德森和他的同事们模拟了人类流行病的可能进程，并预测未来因这种疾病死亡的人数将在 50 ~ 50,000 之间。

随着最近一项有争议的研究的失败[1]加上少数动物已经接受过感染筛查[2]，但牛海绵状脑病(BSE)过去是否是通过饲料添加剂传染到羊身上以及现在是否仍然存在都还不能确定。因此，有充分依据的数学和统计学模型对于整合有限的不同数据、探索不确定性以及确定数据收集的重点都是十分必要的。我们分析了 BSE 在羊群中传播的不同方式与相关的人类暴露水平以及变异型克雅氏病(vCJD)患病率之间的关系，我们发现，如果 BSE 进入了羊群并且发生了一定程度的传播，那么羊 BSE 导致的不断增加的公共卫生风险很可能比牛的大，但是通过附加限制羊产品进入食物供应，可以将任何这类风险减少高达 90%。将这个分析延伸到绝对风险，在 95% 置信区间内，我们估计单纯暴露于牛 BSE 的未来 vCJD 死亡率是 50 到 50,000 人，而一旦暴露于最坏方式传播的羊 BSE，则上限增加到 150,000 人。

本研究的目的不是评估 BSE 进入羊群的可能性，而是悲观地假设感染已经发生，以此来研究感染传播的潜在程度和方式。在本文中，我们使用了实验羊的 BSE 感染得出的流行病学参数估计，对于那些无法获得的数据，就假定该病流行病学的这些数据与瘙痒病类似(考虑到羊身上 BSE 和瘙痒病发病机理的相似性)。此次分析的是从 1996 年到 2000 年之间患有瘙痒病的羊中收集的 180 份脑标本[2]，要求在这些脑标本中不能检测到 BSE 病原体的存在(考虑到在明显患有瘙痒病的绵羊

an upper bound for BSE prevalence within apparently scrapie-affected sheep of 2%; Fig. 1a), and are also broadly consistent with an assessment of historical exposure of the ovine population to meat and bonemeal (MBM)[3].

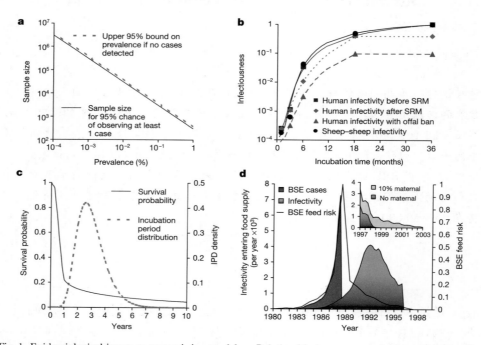

Fig. 1. Epidemiological inputs to transmission model. **a**, Relationship between sample size and detectable prevalence in screening studies. **b**, Infectiousness of sheep as a function of time from infection (see Methods). Sheep and human profiles are separately normalized to give maxima of 1. **c**, Survival probability of sheep as a function of age, and assumed incubation period distribution (IPD) of BSE in sheep. The survivorship function was estimated from annual data from the June census, slaughter, export and disappearance statistics, and data on the seasonality of lamb slaughter. **d**, Before mid-1988, both reported and unreported clinical BSE cases could be used for food (red-shaded curve). After that time, BSE was made notifiable and cases were destroyed, so we assume none entered food. The blue-shaded curve represents the rate of slaughter (per year) of pre-clinical infected cattle weighted by infectiousness relative to disease onset, assuming infectiousness grows at the exponential rate of 4 per year. The over-30-month scheme ended most bovine exposure in 1996, with estimates of residual levels (inset) being dependent on the extent of maternal transmission of BSE. The solid black curve represents the estimated infection hazard to cattle and sheep posed by infectivity in contaminated feed, relative to the maximum level reached in 1988.

Key to our analysis is estimates of the infectivity in animal tissues during disease incubation. Data are limited for BSE in sheep acquired by oral challenge, but using new experimental results and published data from studies of both scrapie[4-7] and sheep BSE[8,9] pathogenesis, we constructed an infectiousness profile. This profile was based on temporal changes in the density of the agent in different tissues, weighted by the proportion of such tissue in the host's body (Fig. 1b). This profile differs from that of BSE in cattle[10,11], with a more rapid rise in overall infectivity early in the incubation period in a wide range of tissues (for example, spleen and lymph nodes). The sheep–human infectiousness profiles (Fig. 1b) adjust for tissue-specific usage in food[12] and the effect of the 1997 specified risk materials (SRM) ban in sheep.

中 BSE 的患病率上限是 2%；图 1a），并且要求与对这些绵羊群曾经与肉类和骨粉（MBM）接触的历史评估大致一样 [3]。

图 1. 传播模型中的流行病学数据。**a**，在筛选研究中样本量和检测到的患病率间的关系。**b**，羊传染性随感染时间的变化（见方法）。羊和人的患病率概况分别归一化到最大值为 1。**c**，羊随着年龄增长的生存概率，以及假设的羊群中 BSE 的潜伏期分布状况（IPD）。生存函数是根据每年 6 月份进行的羊群普查、屠宰、出口和失踪的数据以及羊羔屠宰的季节性数据进行估计的。**d**，1988 年中期之前，报告的和未报告的 BSE 患病牲畜都可以做成食品（红色阴影曲线）。此后，BSE 病例都要上报，并且患畜都被销毁，因此我们假定没有患畜做成食品。蓝色阴影曲线表示临床感染前期牛的屠宰率（每年），以相对于疾病发病的传染性来表示，假设传染性以每年 4 的速度指数式增长。这个超过 30 个月的方案在 1996 年结束了大部分牛群的暴露，而残存水平的估计（插入图）取决于 BSE 母体传播的程度。黑色的实线表示相对于 1988 年达到的最高水平，在受污染饲料中的传染性对牛羊造成的感染风险的估计。

　　我们分析的关键是评估疾病潜伏期内动物组织的传染性。通过进食感染的 BSE 羊群的数据有限，但是根据对瘙痒病 [4-7] 和羊 BSE[8,9] 发病机理研究所获得的新的研究结果和公布的数据，我们构建出了一个传染性的概况。这个概况基于不同组织中病原体密度的暂时性改变，以该组织在宿主体内所占的比例来表示（图 1b）。此概况与牛中的 BSE 感染情况不同 [10,11]，表现为在不同组织（例如脾和淋巴结）的潜伏期早期，总体传染性增加更快。羊–人传染的概况（图 1b）根据食物中特殊组织的含量 [12] 以及 1997 年针对羊的高风险食品（SRM）禁令的效果进行调整。

The distribution of the BSE incubation period in sheep is not well characterized, but on the basis of the limited available data, we used an offset gamma distribution with a mean of 3 years (Fig. 1c) and substantial variance (intended to capture variation caused by dose dependency and host genotype) both for sheep infected by feed and those infected horizontally. Pathogenesis and susceptibility are dependent on the genetic background of the host[13-15], and genotype frequencies of the key polymorphisms vary considerably within and between flocks of different breeds[16,17]. Collation of limited available data suggests that roughly one-third of sheep in Great Britain (England, Scotland and Wales) have BSE-susceptible genotypes (see Supplementary Information). Exposure of the sheep flock to the BSE agent via contaminated feed (Fig. 1d) is assumed to mirror (albeit at a much lower level) that of British cattle, as estimated in back-calculation analyses of the BSE epidemic[18,19]. Exposure is likely to have occurred as far back as the early 1980s, before the disease was identified in cattle[18,19]. As for BSE in cattle[20], host survivorship is important given the long incubation period of the disease. Best estimates (see Supplementary Information) are presented in Fig. 1c (giving a mean life expectancy of 1.5 years), although more precise data are urgently required, perhaps based on a sheep equivalent of the British Cattle Tracing System (http://www.bcms.gov.uk).

Capturing the information in Fig. 1 requires a framework that integrates the temporal evolution of BSE pathogenesis in the individual host (incorporating age-dependent susceptibility and exposure) into a mathematical model of transmission within (including seeding and spread) and between flocks. This model builds on previous analyses of within- and between-flock transmission of scrapie[21,22], and consists of a set of nonlinear partial differential equations detailing the transmission dynamics of the agent and the demography of the sheep flock under time-dependent exposure to BSE-contaminated feed. The dynamics of disease transmission within the sheep population are determined by the magnitude of the respective basic reproduction numbers of the agent within a flock (R_0^A) and between flocks (R_0^F). The reproduction numbers define the average number of secondary cases or flocks generated by one primary case or infected flock in a susceptible flock or population of flocks. We considered three representative scenarios: (I) $R_0^A > 1$, $R_0^F < 1$—self-sustaining transmission within a flock but not between flocks; (II) $R_0^A > 1$, $R_0^F > 1$—the worst-case scenario for future spread, with spread within and between flocks inducing an expanding epidemic; and (III) $R_0^A < 1$, $R_0^F < 1$—the best-case scenario, with non-self-sustaining transmission both within and between flocks (see Fig. 2 for precise parameter values).

For each scenario, the level of flock infection due to MBM exposure was adjusted to give BSE prevalence below 2% of scrapie prevalence at present (consistent with the results of ongoing studies screening sheep brains). Judgements of scenario consistency therefore depend on the estimated prevalence of scrapie in British sheep, with such estimates being based on limited data from detailed surveys of specific flocks (using clinical criteria for diagnosis) and a postal survey of farmers intended to characterize national historical patterns of scrapie incidence[23,24]. The uncertainties in interpreting these data (giving estimates of infection prevalence anywhere between 0.1% and 1%, see Supplementary

羊群中 BSE 潜伏期的分布没有很明显的特征，但是根据有限的可用数据，我们对饲料感染以及水平感染的羊均使用平均数为 3 年的偏移 γ 分布 (图 1c) 以及显著的差异 (试图发现由剂量依赖性和宿主基因型引起的变化)。发病机制和易感性由宿主的遗传背景决定 [13-15]，重要多态性的基因型频率在不同品种的羊群内部和羊群之间的差别相当大 [16,17]。对有限可用数据的整理表明，英国 (英格兰、苏格兰和威尔士) 大约三分之一的羊具有 BSE 易感基因型 (见补充信息)。正如对 BSE 流行病的反算法分析所估计的那样，这些羊群通过污染的饲料暴露于 BSE 病原体中 (图 1d)，这与英国中的情况差不多 (尽管水平要低得多) [18,19]。暴露很可能在 20 世纪 80 年代早期就已经存在，那时尚未在牛群中发现此病 [18,19]。对于牛的 BSE[20]，由于潜伏期很长，宿主的生存概率就显得很重要。尽管迫切需要更加精确的数据，但图 1c 已经显示了最佳估计值 (见补充信息) (平均预期寿命是 1.5 年)，这可能基于在羊群中使用的英国牛群追踪系统 (http://www.bcms.gov.uk)。

获得图 1 所示的信息需要一个模型，而这个模型能够将个体宿主中 BSE 发病机制的时间演变 (包括年龄依赖的易感性和暴露) 整合到在羊群内部 (包括播种和传播) 和羊群之间传播的数学模型中。该模型基于先前对羊群内部和羊群之间瘙痒病传播的分析 [21,22]，并且由一组非线性偏微分方程组成，详细描述了病原体传播的动力学和暴露在受 BSE 污染饲料下的具有时间依赖性的羊群的种群统计学。羊群中疾病传播的动力学是由群内部 (R_0^A) 和群之间 (R_0^F) 病原体各自的基础繁殖数量的大小决定的。繁殖数目定义了以下四种情况的平均数量，或者次要病例，或者由一个主要病例产生的羊群，或者易感群体中受感染的群体，或者种群。我们考虑了三个代表性情况：(I) $R_0^A > 1$，$R_0^F < 1$——群内部是自我维持的传播，而群之间不是；(II) $R_0^A > 1$，$R_0^F > 1$——未来最差的情况，在群内部和群之间传播，导致流行病不断扩大；(III) $R_0^A < 1$，$R_0^F < 1$——最好的情况，群内部和群之间都是非自我维持的传播 (精确的参数值见图 2)。

对于每一种情况，由于 MBM 暴露导致的群体感染的水平都调整到使得 BSE 的患病率低于目前 2% 的瘙痒病患病率 (与正在进行的羊脑筛查的研究结果一致)。因此，对情况一致性的判断就取决于英国羊群中估计的瘙痒病患病率，而这个估计是基于对特定羊群 (使用临床诊断标准进行诊断) 的详细调查以及对农民的邮政调查所得到的有限数据，目的是描述全国瘙痒病发病的历史模式 [23,24]。解释这些数据的不确定性 (感染的患病率估计值在 0.1% ~ 1% 之间，见补充信息) 使得大规模 (图 1a)

Information) make large-scale (Fig. 1a) screening of the national flock for transmissible spongiform encephalopathies (TSEs) a priority. In constructing the scenarios, we assumed a scrapie prevalence of about 0.3%, with scenarios II and III then corresponding to a BSE prevalence of 0.5% that of scrapie, and scenario I to a prevalence of about 2% that of scrapie. Scenario I was thus intended to represent something of a worst case in terms of the numbers of animals infected to date, although we cannot exclude the possibility of even larger epidemics given the limited data currently available.

Figure 2 displays the epidemiological characteristics of these scenarios in terms of within-flock and overall prevalence (Fig. 2a–c), and their implications for human exposure via food (Fig. 2d–f). The estimates of exposure incorporate data on human consumption of ovine material (see Supplementary Information), which indicate that 67% of lambs and 83% of sheep older than 12 months slaughtered for consumption in 1999 were consumed domestically in the UK. Very few live sheep are imported into Great Britain, and most imported lamb meat originates from New Zealand, which has never detected signs of BSE or scrapie infection in either its bovine or ovine populations. Thus the potential risk from BSE-infected sheep arises from home-bred animals.

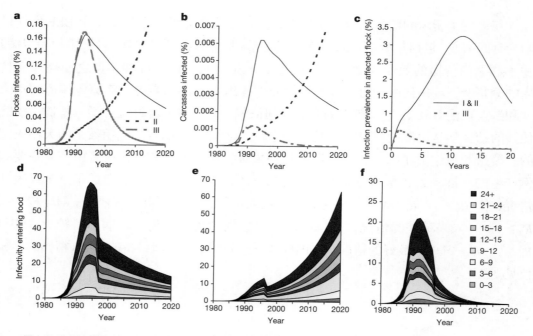

Fig. 2. Epidemiological characteristics of BSE transmission scenarios in sheep. $R_0^A = 2$, $R_0^F = 0.8$ and $\beta_B = 0.2\%$ per year for scenario I; $R_0^A = 2$, $R_0^F = 1.5$ and $\beta_B = 0.025\%$ per year for scenario II; $R_0^A = 0.8$, $R_0^F = 0.5$ and $\beta_B = 0.2\%$ per year for scenario III; where β_B is assumed flock infection incidence rate per unit of feed risk profile shown in Fig. 1c. By comparison, β_B values of 0.2% and 0.025% represent per-animal infection hazards about 50- and 400-fold less than that experienced by cattle. **a**, Proportion of flocks affected through time for scenarios I–III. **b**, Proportion of carcasses entering the food supply infected (at any incubation stage) with BSE. **c**, Prevalence in affected flock as a function of time since initial entry of infection into the flock. **d–f**, Estimated infectivity (in units of maximally infectious carcasses) entering the food supply under scenarios I, II and III, respectively, derived from the infectiousness profiles shown in

筛查全国羊群中的传染性海绵状脑病（TSE）成为优先事项。在构建上述情况时，我们假定瘙痒病的患病率大约是 0.3%，情况 II 和 III 相对应的 BSE 的患病率是瘙痒病的 0.5%，而情况 I 对应的 BSE 患病率是瘙痒病的 2%。因此，情况 I 预期能够代表目前为止感染动物数量的最差状况，尽管我们不能排除由于目前可用的数据有限而发生更大范围流行病的可能性。

图 2 显示了这些情况在群内部和总体患病率方面的流行病学特征（图 2a ～ 2c），以及它们在人类通过食物暴露时的影响（图 2d ～ 2f）。暴露估计包括人类对绵羊身体组成部分进行消费的数据（见补充信息），这表明 1999 年屠宰的 67% 的羊羔和 83% 的超过 12 个月龄的绵羊都是在英国国内消费的。很少有活羊进口到英国，大部分进口的羔羊肉来自新西兰，而新西兰从未在羊群或者牛群中检测到 BSE 或者瘙痒病感染的迹象。因此，BSE 感染的羊的潜在风险都来自于家养动物。

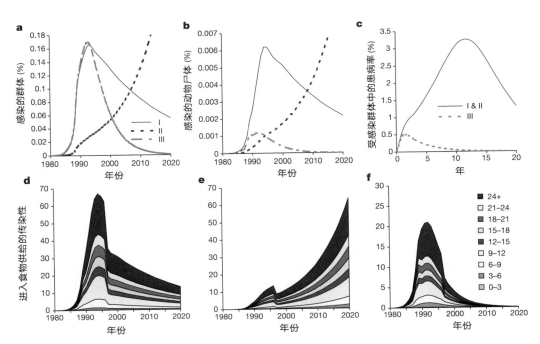

图 2. 羊群中 BSE 传播情况的流行病学特征。情况 I，$R_0^{\wedge} = 2$，$R_0^{F} = 0.8$，$\beta_B = 0.2\%$ 每年；情况 II，$R_0^{\wedge} = 2$，$R_0^{F} = 1.5$，$\beta_B = 0.025\%$ 每年；情况 III，$R_0^{\wedge} = 0.8$，$R_0^{F} = 0.5$，$\beta_B = 0.2\%$ 每年；其中 β_B 是每单位饲料风险分布的假定群体感染发病率，如图 1c 所示。相比之下，β_B 值为 0.2% 和 0.025% 分别表示每个动物感染的风险是牛感染的风险的五十分之一和四百分之一。a，三种情况下，随着时间的推移，受感染群体的比例。b，感染了 BSE 的动物尸体进入食物供给的比例（包括各种潜伏阶段）。c，从感染进入群体开始，受感染群体的患病率随时间的变化的函数。d~f，根据图 1a 所示的传染性概况，在 I、II、III 三种情况下进入食物供给的估计传染性（以最大传染性尸体为单位）。改变受 BSE 感染的羊群的不同比例

Fig. 1a. Varying the proportion of flocks affected with BSE (shown in **a**, and determined by β_B) scales the exposure curves in **d–f** proportionately.

The sudden drop in human exposure in the late 1990s (Fig. 2d–f) is due to the SRM ban for sheep (banning the consumption of the skull, tonsils and spinal column of animals older than 12 months and the spleen of all animals). In the worst-case scenario (II), the degree of risk is still rising steeply, whereas for the other scenarios risk is falling, approaching very low levels in the best case (III). Critically, even in the worst-case scenario, the great majority of past exposure of the human population to BSE arose from cattle (Fig. 1d). However, for all three scenarios considered (and therefore assuming BSE did enter the sheep flock), the number of maximally infectious sheep entering the food supply in Great Britain at present is estimated to be greater than the number of maximally infectious cattle[18,19] (Fig. 1d, inset). This comparison equates the risk from one maximally infectious sheep with that of a cow, despite the difference in body mass, an assumption motivated by the evidence of more widespread distribution of infectivity in sheep.

Potential risk-reduction strategies include restrictions on the age of sheep slaughtered for consumption and enhanced tissue-based controls to reduce the amount of infectivity entering the food supply; additional measures based on flock history or ram genotype might also be possible but are not considered here. Combined tissue- and age-based restrictions are estimated to reduce current and future risk by at least 80% for all three sheep BSE scenarios considered (Fig. 3a). This is encouraging, but the precise values shown depend on the accuracy of the data on the development of infectivity in different tissues of BSE-infected sheep. Furthermore, verifying the age of sheep is difficult without an identification scheme, so in the short term it would be feasible only to exploit seasonal birthing patterns and dental indicators to impose approximate age restrictions. How the impact of 12-month age restrictions might be reduced by compensatory changes in slaughter patterns is shown in Fig. 3b.

Translation of the patterns of relative exposure through time into measures of absolute risk requires estimation of potential vCJD mortality in the human population of Great Britain. Given the uncertainty in the parameters determining such predictions (in particular, the incubation period distribution and human susceptibility), analyses must be based on the best available estimates of temporal changes in human exposure to infected material. The confidence bounds on vCJD mortality shown in Table 1 characterize human exposure by infectivity-weighted estimates of the numbers of BSE-infected cattle (Fig. 1d) and sheep (Fig. 2) slaughtered for consumption through time (correcting for early under-reporting of cattle BSE incidence). We modelled the vCJD epidemic solely in the 40% of the population that are methionine homozygous at prion protein (PrP) codon 129, assuming no other genetic variation in susceptibility. Currently no case data exist with which to constrain epidemic scenarios for other genotypes, but if future cases are diagnosed then upper bounds on epidemic size will increase. Compared with our previous estimates[25], upper bounds on epidemic size in the absence of BSE in sheep have reduced (largely as a result of a change in statistical methods), being in the range 50,000–100,000 depending on the assumptions

（如图 **a** 所示，由 β_B 决定）按比例缩放 **d~f** 的暴露曲线。

20 世纪 90 年代末人类暴露的骤降（图 2d ~ 2f）是因为人们发布了针对羊的 SRM 禁令（禁止食用 12 个月龄以上动物的头骨、扁桃体和脊柱以及所有动物的脾脏）。风险程度在最坏的情况下（II）仍然急剧升高，而在其他情况下都下降了，在最好的情况下（III）达到最低。准确地说，即便是在最坏的情况下，人类既往暴露于 BSE 的大部分情况来源于牛（图 1d）。但是，对所有三种情况来说（假设 BSE 确实进入了羊群），目前英国进入食物供给的受传染的羊的最大数目估计超过了感染的牛的数量 [18,19]（图 1d，插图）。这个比较将一只传染性最强的羊的风险与一头奶牛的风险等同起来，尽管羊和牛的体重差别很大，但是做这一比较是因为有证据表明羊的传染性分布更为广泛。

可能的降低风险的措施包括限制供消费而屠宰的羊的年龄以及加强基于动物组织的控制，以减少进入食物供给的传染性，基于羊群历史以及公羊基因型的其他措施可能也起作用，但是这里不作考虑。对于羊 BSE 三种情况的考虑，结合基于组织和年龄的限制，预计能够将目前和未来的风险降低至少 80%（图 3a）。这很令人鼓舞，但是显示的精确的数值取决于 BSE 感染羊中不同组织传染性发展的数据的准确性。此外，在没有鉴定方案的情况下确定羊的年龄是很困难的，因此在短期内可行的仅仅是根据季节性生育模式以及牙齿指标来施加近似年龄的限制。图 3b 中显示了 12 个月龄限制的效果是如何被屠宰模式的补偿性改变所降低的。

将相对暴露随时间改变的模式转换成绝对风险值需要估计英国人群中潜在的 vCJD 死亡率。考虑到决定这些预测的参数的不确定性（尤其是潜伏期分布以及人类易感性），我们的分析必须基于人类暴露于感染物质的时间变化的最佳现有估计。表 1 显示的 vCJD 死亡率的置信区间以不同时间下屠宰用于消费的 BSE 感染的牛（图 1d）和羊（图 2）数量的传染力加权估计值（对早期牛 BSE 发病率的漏报进行了更正）特征性地描述了人类暴露的情况。我们仅在 40% 的朊蛋白（PrP）密码子第 129 位是蛋氨酸纯合子的人群中模拟 vCJD 流行病，假设这些人在易感性方面没有其他遗传变异。目前，还没有病例数据来限制其他基因型的流行情况，但是如果将来的病例得到诊断，那么流行范围的上限将会增加。与我们之前的估计相比 [25]，在没有疯牛病的情况下，羊疫情的规模上限已经降低（主要是由于统计方法的改变）。根据所作的假设，其范围在 50,000 ~ 100,000 之间。这些数值远远超过了最近发表的估计，它是根据人类先前暴露于 BSE 传染性趋势的粗略描述得出的 [26,27]。2001 ~ 2080 年的

Fig. 3. Impact of risk-reduction measures. **a**, Estimated relative impact of various measures on current exposure to BSE infectivity in sheep food products for scenarios I–III. "Removal of all offals" corresponds to a ban on all internal organs and central nervous system tissue of sheep entering the human food supply, but does not assume removal of lymph nodes. Estimates presented were calculated assuming that age restrictions would not change slaughter patterns. **b**, Estimated impact of imposing age restrictions as a function of the upper age limit imposed for scenario I. Effects on infectivity and total number of infected animals entering the food supply are shown, with dashed curves showing how the impact is reduced if slaughter patterns are adjusted after such a measure, such that all animals currently slaughtered under 12 months old are then slaughtered under the upper age limit imposed.

made. These values are substantially greater than recently published estimates derived assuming a cruder representation of past trends in human exposure to BSE infectivity[26,27]. Best-fit estimates associated with 2001–2080 confidence bounds generally lie in the range 100–1,000, but the fits of the model vary little for fewer than 10,000 deaths. It should be noted (Table 1, E) that large epidemics are still possible even if the mean incubation period is less than 60 years. In the presence of BSE in sheep, the upper bound is substantially increased only if BSE is capable of becoming endemic in the national flock (scenario II).

Table 1. 95% confidence intervals for future vCJD deaths

Cattle only*	2000–2002	2001–2005	2001–2010	2001–2020	2001–2040	2001–2080
A	20–100	40–400	40–1,200	40–5,000	40–20,000	50–50,000
B	20–100	40–400	40–1,200	40–5,000	40–20,000	40–40,000
C	20–100	30–400	40–1,400	40–7,000	40–40,000	40–90,000
D	20–100	30–400	30–1,300	40–7,000	40–40,000	40–100,000
E	20–100	40–350	40–1,100	40–5,000	40–20,000	50–35,000

图 3. 降低风险的措施的效果。a，三种情况下，估计各种措施对于目前羊类食品暴露于 BSE 传染性的相对影响。"去除所有内脏"表示禁止羊的内脏和中枢神经系统组织进入人类的食物供给，但并不意味着要去除淋巴结。显示出来的估计效果是假设年龄限制不会改变屠宰状况的情况下得到的。b，对于情况 I，将年龄限制强行作为年龄上限的函数的估计效果。图中显示了传染性的影响以及进入食物供应的受感染动物总数，而虚线显示的是假如屠宰状况根据下面的措施进行调整后这种影响是如何降低的。该措施是将目前在 12 个月龄以下屠宰的所有动物限定到年龄上限以下屠宰。

置信区间相关的最佳估计在 100～1,000 之间，但对于少于 10,000 的死亡数，这个模型的最佳值变化不大。需要注意的是（表 1，E），大规模的流行仍然是可能的，即便平均潜伏期小于 60 年。羊群中 BSE 存在的情况下，只有 BSE 能够在全国的羊群中流行时，其上限才会大幅度地增加（情况 II）。

表 1. 未来 vCJD 死亡数的 95% 置信区间

仅仅牛 *	2001～2002	2001～2005	2001～2010	2001～2020	2001～2040	2001～2080
A	20～100	40～400	40～1,200	40～5,000	40～20,000	50～50,000
B	20～100	40～400	40～1,200	40～5,000	40～20,000	40～40,000
C	20～100	30～400	40～1,400	40～7,000	40～40,000	40～90,000
D	20～100	30～400	30～1,300	40～7,000	40～40,000	40～100,000
E	20～100	40～350	40～1,100	40～5,000	40～20,000	50～35,000

Continued

Cattle and sheep†	Sheep:cattle infectivity ratio	2001–2020	2001–2040	2001–2080
Scenario I	1:1	40–5,000	40–20,000	40–60,000
	10:1	40–5,000	50–30,000	50–70,000
Scenario II	1:1	20–5,000	20–20,000	20–70,000
	10:1	40–5,000	70–30,000	110–150,000
Scenario III	1:1	40–5,000	40–20,000	40–50,000
	10:1	40–5,000	50–30,000	40–50,000

* Cattle-only calculations assume: A, BSE exposure in humans was proportional to the BSE cases before the mid-1988 in addition to infected animal slaughter rates shown in Fig. 1c; B, as A but excluding exposure to reported BSE cases; C, as A but additionally fitting to at least three vCJD deaths reported before 2001 being infected before 1986, as suggested by analysis of the Queniborough cluster; D, as A but assuming the 1989 specified bovine offal ban reduced human exposure by at least 80%; E, as A but restricting the mean incubation period to be no longer than 60 years.

† Calculations for cattle and sheep assume exposure as A from cattle plus exposure from sheep as in Fig. 2d–f from scenarios I–III, assuming sheep are equally or 10 times as infectious as cattle. Short-term predictions for these scenarios are similar to those excluding sheep.

Although the risk analysis presented here incorporates a wide variety of available information into a single integrated framework, its reliability depends on the quality and volume of data available for parameter estimation. The limited data highlight the need for further studies to measure: (1) scrapie and BSE prevalence in sheep (stratified by age), employing sample sizes sufficiently large to detect low prevalence; (2) sheep survivorship more precisely; (3) BSE infectivity in sheep quantitatively, by stage of incubation, tissue and sheep genotype; (4) age-dependent susceptibility to TSE infection in a variety of species, including sheep and cattle; and (5) historical trends in bovine and ovine tissue consumption. Molecular typing methods giving rapid results[28,29] are clearly valuable for prevalence screening and strain typing (whether for BSE or scrapie), but study design should take account of test sensitivity and therefore consider which tissue should be tested (brain not necessarily being optimal). Given the uncertainty regarding the presence of BSE in the British sheep flock, such large-scale testing is a priority. In the interim, this analysis informs prevalence survey design and policy consideration of the potential benefits of additional risk-reduction measures.

Methods

Additional detail is provided as Supplementary Information.

Modelling transmission of BSE in sheep

Infectiousness of a BSE-infected sheep as a function of time τ since infection (relative to the incubation period T) was estimated by fitting the parametric form $\rho(\frac{\tau}{T}) = \exp\left(a(\frac{\tau}{T})^b/((\frac{\tau}{T})^b + c)\right)$

牛和羊 †	羊：牛传染性比例	2001 ~ 2020	2001 ~ 2040	2001 ~ 2080
情况 I	1 : 1	40 ~ 5,000	40 ~ 20,000	40 ~ 60,000
	10 : 1	40 ~ 5,000	50 ~ 30,000	50 ~ 70,000
情况 II	1 : 1	20 ~ 5,000	20 ~ 20,000	20 ~ 70,000
	10 : 1	40 ~ 5,000	70 ~ 30,000	110 ~ 150,000
情况 III	1 : 1	40 ~ 5,000	40 ~ 20,000	40 ~ 50,000
	10 : 1	40 ~ 5,000	40 ~ 20,000	40 ~ 50,000

* 只计算牛的假设：A，除了图 1c 中所示的受感染动物的屠宰率之外，人类中的 BSE 暴露与 1988 年中期以前的 BSE 病例成比例；B，和 A 一样，但是排除了暴露于已经报告过的 BSE 病例；C，和 A 一样，但是额外地加入了至少 3 例 2001 年前报告的并且在 1986 年前感染的 vCJD 死亡病例，正如对 Queniborough 群体的分析所提示的一样；D，和 A 一样，但是假设 1989 年规定的牛内脏禁令将人类的暴露减少了至少 80%；E，和 A 一样，但是限制平均潜伏期不超过 60 年。

† 计算牛和羊：假设来自牛的暴露和 A 一样，来自羊的暴露如图 2d~2f 所示的三种情况。假定羊的传染性与牛相同或是牛的 10 倍。这些情况下的短期估计值和不包括羊的情况类似。

　　尽管这里所描述的风险分析将很多可用信息整合到了单个的整体框架中，但是其可靠性依赖于用于参数估计的数据的质量和数量。有限的数据强调了进一步测量研究的必要性：(1) 羊的瘙痒病和 BSE 患病率（根据年龄分层），需要足够大的样本量来检测低患病率；(2) 羊的更加精确的生存期；(3) 根据潜伏期的阶段、组织和羊基因型，定量分析羊 BSE 的传染性；(4) 不同物种对于 TSE 感染的年龄依赖的易感性，包括牛和羊；以及 (5) 对牛和羊组织消费的历史趋势。分子分型方法能够快速得出结果 [28,29]，对于患病率筛查和种类分型都非常有价值（无论是 BSE 还是瘙痒病），但是研究设计需要考虑测试的敏感性，因此需要考虑用什么组织进行测试（脑组织并不是最佳选择）。由于英国羊群中是否存在 BSE 仍不确定，这种大规模的测试是需要优先考虑的。在此期间，这个分析为患病率调查的设计以及政策考量提供了依据，说明了额外减少风险措施的潜在好处。

方 法

　　补充信息中提供了详细内容。

BSE 在羊中传播的模型

　　通过将参数式 $\rho(\frac{\tau}{T}) = \exp(a(\frac{\tau}{T})^b/((\frac{\tau}{T})^b+c))$ 与羊 BSE[8,9] 和瘙痒病 [4-7] 发病机制研究的组织特异性的传染力数据进行组合，估算感染后（相对于潜伏期 T）羊 BSE 传染性随时间 τ

to tissue-specific infectivity data from studies of pathogenesis of ovine BSE[8,9] and scrapie[4-7]. The data were weighted by total tissue mass when estimating sheep-to-sheep infectiousness, and by the proportion of tissue mass entering food when estimating human exposure to infectivity (Fig. 1b). This approach captures the impact on overall infectiousness of between-tissue variation in PrP accumulation during pathogenesis of ovine BSE—namely, that some tissues (for example, lymph nodes) rapidly develop detectable infectivity, the growth of which later slows and/or saturates, whereas others (for example, brain) only exhibit high levels of infectivity close to clinical onset.

Because mass-action models cannot capture the observed clustering of cases[20], we developed a model of TSE transmission in sheep that incorporated three relevant tiers: (1) the individual animal—capturing age-dependent susceptibility and exposure, and pathogenesis of disease; (2) the individual flock—capturing within-flock sheep-to-sheep transmission; and (3) the national population of flocks—capturing between-flock transmission and exposure to contaminated feed.

Assuming homogenous mixing within a flock, the deterministic susceptible-infected model is:

$$\frac{\partial x}{\partial t} + \frac{\partial x}{\partial a} = -(\Lambda(t)\kappa(a) + \mu(a))x \qquad x(t, 0) = B \qquad \mu(a) = -\frac{1}{S}\frac{\mathrm{d}S}{\mathrm{d}a}$$

$$\frac{\partial y}{\partial t} + \frac{\partial y}{\partial a} + \frac{\partial y}{\partial \tau} = -(F_A(\tau) + \mu(a))y \qquad F_A(\tau) = \frac{f_A(\tau)}{1 - \int_0^\tau f_A(\tau')\mathrm{d}\tau'}$$

$$y(t, a, 0) = \Lambda(t)\kappa(a)x(t, a)$$

$$\Lambda(t) = \beta_A \int_{\tau=0}^{t} \int_{T=\tau}^{\infty} F_A(T)\,\rho(\tau/T)y(t, a, \tau)\mathrm{d}T\,\mathrm{d}\tau \qquad y(0, a, 0) = \frac{\kappa(a)\,Y_0}{\int \kappa(a)\,\mathrm{d}a}$$

where we denote the densities of susceptible and infected animals of age a at time t by $x(t, a)$ and $y(t, a, \tau)$; time from infection by τ; the incubation period distribution by $f_A(\tau)$ (see Fig. 1c); the force of infection by $\Lambda(t)$; the transmission coefficient for horizontal spread by β_A; the fixed birth rate by B; the mortality rate by $\mu(a)$; and age-dependent susceptibility by $\kappa(a)$ (conservatively assumed to be constant for the first 12 months of life and zero thereafter). The number of animals infected at the start of a flock outbreak is Y_0. Assuming that the infectiousness at time t of a flock infected at $t = 0$ to other flocks is proportional to the within-flock force of infection $\Lambda(t)$, we modelled transmission within a population of 100,000 flocks of 400 animals each. Genetic heterogeneity in susceptibility to infection was modelled at the flock level, with 33,000 flocks assumed to have all animals susceptible and the remainder completely resistant. The introduction of infection into a flock from an external source (contaminated feed or other sheep) was modelled as a rare event, initially infecting 1% of animals.

The infection dynamics of flocks were modelled using an SIRS framework, whereby flocks are initially "susceptible" to infection, enter an "infected" state of extended duration, "recover" and

的变化。估算羊之间的传染性时，数据通过组织总质量进行加权，而在估计人类暴露的传染性时则通过组织进入食物供给的比例进行加权（图 1b）。这种方法捕捉到羊 BSE 发病过程中不同组织间 PrP 聚集的不同对总体传染性的影响——也就是说，一些组织（比如淋巴结）很快就可以检测到传染性，其增长随后放缓和（或）达到饱和，而另一些组织（比如脑）仅仅显示出高水平的传染，接近于临床发作。

由于质量作用模型不能捕捉观察到的病例群[20]，我们建立了一个 TSE 在羊中传播的模型，包含了三个相关的层次：（1）个体动物——得到依赖年龄的易感性和暴露以及疾病的发病机制；（2）独立的羊群——捕捉群内羊之间的传播；（3）全国的羊群——捕捉群间传播以及对污染饲料的暴露。

假定群内的混合是均匀的，那么确定的易感染模型是：

$$\frac{\partial x}{\partial t} + \frac{\partial x}{\partial a} = -(\Lambda(t)\kappa(a) + \mu(a))x \qquad x(t, 0) = B \qquad \mu(a) = -\frac{1}{S}\frac{dS}{da}$$

$$\frac{\partial y}{\partial t} + \frac{\partial y}{\partial a} + \frac{\partial y}{\partial \tau} = -(F_A(\tau) + \mu(a))y \qquad F_A(\tau) = \frac{f_A(\tau)}{1 - \int_0^\tau f_A(\tau')d\tau'}$$

$$y(t, a, 0) = \Lambda(t)\kappa(a)x(t, a)$$

$$\Lambda(t) = \beta_A \int_{\tau=0}^t \int_{T=\tau}^\infty F_A(T)\,\rho(\tau/T)y(t, a, \tau)dT\,d\tau \qquad y(0, a, 0) = \frac{\kappa(a)\,Y_0}{\int \kappa(a)\,da}$$

其中，我们用 $x(t, a)$ 和 $y(t, a, \tau)$ 表示年龄为 a 的易感动物和已感染的动物在 t 时刻的密度；感染后的时间是 τ；潜伏期分布是 $f_A(\tau)$（见图 1c）；感染的强度是 $\Lambda(t)$；水平传播系数是 β_A；固定生产率是 B；死亡率是 $\mu(a)$；依赖年龄的易感性是 $\kappa(a)$（保守地假定生命的前 12 个月为常数，之后是 0）。羊群疫情爆发开始时感染动物的数量是 Y_0。假设一个羊群在 $t = 0$ 时受感染，在 t 时刻对其他羊群的传染性与群内传染性 $\Lambda(t)$ 成正比。我们在含有 100,000 个羊群的群体中建立传播模型，每个羊群中包含 400 只羊。对感染易感性的遗传异质性在羊群水平进行建模，假定 33,000 个羊群中所有的动物都是易感的，而剩余的羊群都是完全耐药的。通过外部来源将感染引入羊群（污染的食物或者其他羊）被建模为小概率事件，最初感染 1% 的动物。

使用 SIRS 框架对羊群的感染动态进行建模，其中羊群最初对感染是"易感状态"，然后进入长时间的"感染"状态，"恢复"，并对再次感染具有耐药性（大约持续 20 年），然后恢复

become resistant to further infection (for a period of 20 years), then revert to the "susceptible" state. The flock-level "recovery" process approximates flock outbreak extinction mechanisms, such as demographic stochasticity (likely to be critical[30] given the low reported prevalence of scrapie), control measures and selection for scrapie-resistant genotypes.

Denoting the number of susceptible flocks at time t by $s(t)$, flocks infected time θ ago by $h(t, \theta)$ (with infectivity $\Lambda(\theta)$ from the within-flock model) and recovered/resistant flocks by $r(t)$, model dynamics are described by:

$$\frac{ds}{dt} = \xi r - \Omega(t)s \qquad\qquad \Omega(t) = \beta_F \int_{\theta=0}^{\infty} \Lambda(\theta)h(t, \theta)d\theta + \beta_B\phi(t)$$

$$\frac{\partial h}{\partial t} + \frac{\partial h}{\partial \theta} = -F_F(\theta)h \qquad\qquad F_F(\theta) = \frac{f_F(\theta)}{1 - \int_0^\theta f_F(\theta')d\theta'}$$

$$\frac{dr}{dt} = \int F_F(\theta)h(t, \theta)d\theta - \xi r \qquad\qquad s(0) = N \quad h(t, 0) = \Omega(t)x \quad h(0, \theta) = 0$$

Here, $f_F(\theta)$ is the "incubation period" distribution for flocks (gamma distributed with mean 6 years; see Supplementary Information); $\Omega(t)$ the force of infection for flocks at time t; β_F and β_B the coefficients for between-flock transmission and exposure of flocks to contaminated feed; $\phi(t)$ the relative risk from contaminated feed at time t (estimates from refs 18, 19); and ξ ($= 0.05$ per year) the rate at which recovered flocks re-enter the susceptible pool. The values of β_A and β_F corresponding to required values of R_0^A and R_0^F were determined numerically.

Exposure of the human population to BSE infectivity in sheep was represented by the number of infected animals slaughtered for food (stratified by age and incubation stage, weighted by infectivity; Fig. 2d–f). The effectiveness of risk-reduction measures was evaluated by examining the distribution of exposure as a function of animal age, and by comparing results obtained from the infectivity profiles corresponding to current SRM controls and a ban on all offal.

It should be noted that this model framework reproduces observed within-flock and overall scrapie incidence patterns well if run to endemicity (results not shown).

Prediction of vCJD incidence

As in earlier work[25], the probability density that an individual develops clinical disease at time t and age a is

$$p(t, a) = S_H(t, a) \int_{t-a}^{t} f(t-u) \, I(u, a-t+u)\exp\left[-\int_0^u I(u', a-t+u')du' \right] du$$

where $S_H(t, a)$ is the probability that someone born at time $t - a$ will survive to age a (derived from

到"易感"状态。羊群水平"恢复"的过程类似于羊群爆发灭绝的机制，比如人口统计学上的随机性（由于报道的瘙痒病的患病率很低，因此这可能很关键[30]）、控制措施和选择耐瘙痒病基因型。

用 $s(t)$ 来表示 t 时刻易感羊群的数量，用 $h(t, \theta)$ 来表示 θ 时刻之前感染的羊群数量（根据羊群内的模型，传染性是 $\Lambda(\theta)$），用 $r(t)$ 来表示恢复的/耐药性的羊群数量，动态模型表示为：

$$\frac{ds}{dt} = \xi r - \Omega(t)s \qquad\qquad \Omega(t) = \beta_F \int_{\theta=0}^{\infty} \Lambda(\theta)h(t, \theta)d\theta + \beta_B \phi(t)$$

$$\frac{\partial h}{\partial t} + \frac{\partial h}{\partial \theta} = -F_F(\theta)h \qquad\qquad F_F(\theta) = \frac{f_F(\theta)}{1 - \int_0^{\theta} f_F(\theta')d\theta'}$$

$$\frac{dr}{dt} = \int F_F(\theta)h(t, \theta)d\theta - \xi r \qquad\qquad s(0) = N \quad h(t, 0) = \Omega(t)x \quad h(0, \theta) = 0$$

这里，$f_F(\theta)$ 是羊群的"潜伏期"分布（平均 6 年的 γ 分布，见补充信息）；$\Omega(t)$ 是 t 时刻的羊群感染强度；β_F 和 β_B 是羊群间传播和羊群暴露于污染食物的系数；$\phi(t)$ 是 t 时刻污染食物的相对风险（从文献 18 和 19 预估）；ξ（= 每年 0.05）是恢复的羊群重新进入易感群体的速度。与 R_0^A 和 R_0^F 的需求值对应的 β_A 和 β_F 的数值用数字来确定。

人群对羊群 BSE 传染性的暴露程度由屠宰后作为食物的感染动物数量来表示（根据年龄和潜伏阶段分层，用传染性加权，图 2d～2f）。降低风险措施的有效性通过以下两种方式评估：检查以动物年龄为函数的暴露分布；将目前 SRM 控制和禁止所有内脏相对应的传染性结果进行比较。

需要注意的是，如果遇到区域性流行，这个模型框架可以很好地复制观察到的羊群内以及总体的瘙痒病发病率模式（结果没有显示）。

vCJD 发病率的预测

如之前的工作所述[25]，个体在 t 时间和 a 年龄发生临床疾病的概率密度是

$$p(t, a) = S_H(t, a) \int_{t-a}^{t} f(t-u) I(u, a-t+u)\exp\left[-\int_0^u I(u', a-t+u')du'\right]du$$

其中 $S_H(t, a)$ 是某个生于时间 $t-a$ 的个体能够活到 a 年龄的可能性（来自于人口普查数据），

census data) and $f(t-u)$ is the incubation period distribution (modified lambda distribution). The infection hazard is given by

$$I(t, a) = \beta g(a) \left(v_c(t) \int \Omega_c(z)\omega_c(z, t)\mathrm{d}z + v_s(t) \int \Omega_s(z)\omega_s(z, t)\mathrm{d}z \right)$$

where β is the transmission coefficient and $g(a)$ an age-dependent susceptibility/exposure function (uniform with gamma-distributed tails). For each infectious species i (C for cattle, S for sheep), $\Omega_i(z)$ is the relative infectiousness of an animal time z from disease onset, $v_i(t)$ is the time-dependent effectiveness of risk-reduction measures (for cattle, this is parameterized as a step reduction in 1989 due to the specified bovine offal ban), and $\omega_i(z, t)$ is the number of animals slaughtered for consumption stratified by time and incubation stage. (Values for sheep were obtained from the above model, and those for cattle used updated back-calculation estimates[18,19], with $\int \Omega_c(z)\omega_c(z, t)\mathrm{d}z$ plotted in Fig. 1d.)

The relative infectiousness of cattle by incubation stage was assumed to increase exponentially from a baseline level to a maximum value before onset of clinical signs[25]. We restricted analysis to the 40% of the population that are methionine homozygous at PrP codon 129, assuming no other genetic variation in susceptibility.

Through numerical solution of the inverse problem (see Supplementary Information or further details), β was calculated as a function of case incidence, allowing incidence of vCJD deaths in any time interval to be treated as a model parameter. This enabled nonlinear optimization techniques to be used to obtain likelihood profiles by fitting the model to the joint age- and time-stratified mortality data to the end of 2000. We obtained 95% confidence bounds from the one-dimensional likelihood profiles. Infection prevalence is poorly constrained by the observed incidence data, and can range from being equal to mortality to 100-fold larger, with little effect on model fit.

(**415**, 420-424; 2002)

N. M. Ferguson, A. C. Ghani, C. A. Donnelly, T. J. Hagenaars & R. M. Anderson
Department of Infectious Disease Epidemiology, Faculty of Medicine, Imperial College of Science, Technology and Medicine, St Mary's Campus, Norfolk Place, London W2 1PG, UK

Received 21 November; accepted 12 December 2001. Published online 9 January 2002, DOI 10.1038/nature709.

References:

1. Frankish, H. Samples blunder renders sheep-BSE study useless. *Lancet* **358**, 1436 (2001).
2. Beckett, M. *House of Commons Hansard Debates, 22 October 2001* 373 (2001)
   ⟨http://www.parliament.the-stationery-office.co.uk/pa/cm200102/cmhansrd/cm011022/debindx/11022-x.htm⟩ .
3. Det Norske Veritas *Assessment of Exposure to BSE Infectivity in the UK Sheep Flock* Report no. C782506 (The Meat and Livestock Commission, London, 1998).
4. Hadlow, W. J., Kennedy, R. C. & Race, R. E. Natural infection of Suffolk sheep with scrapie virus. *J. Infect. Dis.* **146**, 652-664 (1982).
5. van Keulen, L. J. M., Schreuder, B. E. C., Vromans, M. E. W., Langeveld, J. P. M. & Smits, M. A. Scrapie-associated prion protein in the gastrointestinal tract of sheep with natural scrapie. *J. Comp. Pathol.* **121**, 55-63 (1999).
6. van Keulen, L. J. M., Schreuder, B. E. C., Vromans, M. E. W., Langeveld, J. P. M. & Smits, M. A. Pathogenesis of natural scrapie in sheep. *Arch. Virol. Suppl.* **16**, 52-21 (2000).

$f(t-u)$ 是潜伏期分布（修改后的 λ 分布）。感染风险计算如下

$$I(t, a) = \beta g(a) \left(v_c(t) \int \Omega_c(z)\omega_c(z, t)\mathrm{d}z + v_s(t) \int \Omega_s(z)\omega_s(z, t)\mathrm{d}z \right)$$

其中 β 是传输系数，$g(a)$ 是依赖年龄的易感性/暴露函数（与 γ 分布一致）。对于每个感染性物种 i（C 表示牛，S 表示羊），$\Omega_i(z)$ 是疾病出现后 z 时刻某个动物的相对传染性，$v_i(t)$ 是降低风险措施的时间依赖有效性（对牛来说，由于特定的牛内脏禁令，因此在 1989 年发病率骤减），$\omega_i(z, t)$ 是根据时间和潜伏阶段分层的用于消费的动物屠宰数量。（羊的数据从以上的模型得出，而牛的数据用更新后的反算法估计 [18,19]，$\int \Omega_c(z)\omega_c(z, t)\mathrm{d}z$ 在图 1d 中绘出。）

在潜伏期，牛的相对传染性假定从基线水平指数式地增长到临床症状出现前的最高水平 [25]。我们将分析限制在那些 PrP 密码子第 129 位是蛋氨酸纯合的 40% 的人群中，这些人被认为在易感性方面没有其他遗传变异。

通过对反问题的数值解（详情请参阅补充资料），β 以病例发病率的函数来计算，将任意时间段 vCJD 死亡发生率作为模型参数。这使得非线性优化技术通过将截至 2000 年底的年龄和时间分层的死亡率数据套入到该模型中来获得似然分布。我们从单维似然分布中获得了 95% 置信区间。感染的患病率几乎不受观察到的发病率数据的限制，其范围从与死亡率相等到是死亡率的 100 多倍，对模型的拟合影响不大。

（毛晨晖 翻译；肖景发 审稿）

7. Andreoletti, O. *et al.* Early accumulation of PrP^{Sc} in gut-associated lymphoid and nervous tissues of susceptible sheep from a Romanov flock with natural scrapie. *J. Gen. Virol.* **81**, 3115-3126 (2000).

8. Foster, J. D., Parnham, D. W., Hunter, N. & Bruce, M. Distribution of the prion protein in sheep terminally infected with BSE following experimental oral transmission. *J. Gen. Virol.* **82**, 2319-2326 (2001).

9. Jeffrey, M. *et al.* Oral inoculation of sheep with the agent of bovine spongiform encephalopathy (BSE). 1. Onset and distribution of disease-specific PrP accumulation in brain and viscera. *J. Comp. Pathol.* **124**, 280-289 (2001).

10. Fraser, H., Bruce, M. E., Chree, A., McConnell, I. & Wells, G. A. H. Transmission of bovine spongiform encephalopathy and scrapie to mice. *J. Gen. Virol.* **73**, 1891-1897 (1992).

11. Wells, G. A. H. *et al.* Infectivity in the ileum of cattle challenged orally with bovine spongiform encephalopathy. *Vet. Rec.* **135**, 40-41 (1994).

12. Hart, R. J., Church, P. N., Kempster, A. J. & Matthews, K. R. *Audit of Bovine and Ovine Slaughter and By-products Sector (Ruminant Products Audit)* (Leatherhead Food Research Association, London, 1997).

13. Hunter, N. PrP genetics in sheep and the implications for scrapie and BSE. *Trends Microbiol.* **5**, 331-334 (1997).

14. Hunter, N., Goldmann, W., Marshall, E. & O'Neill, G. Sheep and goats: natural and experimental TSEs and factors influencing incidence of disease. *Arch. Virol. Suppl.* **16**, 181-188 (2000).

15. Jeffrey, M. *et al.* Frequency and tissue distribution of infection-specific PrP in tissues of clinical scrapie and cull sheep obtained from scrapie affected farms in Shetland. *J. Comp. Pathol.* (submitted).

16. Baylis, M., Houston, F., Goldmann, W., Hunter, N. & McLean, A. R. The signature of scrapie: differences in the PrP genotype profile of scrapie-affected and scrapie-free UK sheep flocks. *Proc. R. Soc. Lond.* B **267**, 2029-2035 (2000).

17. Hunter, N. *et al.* Is scrapie solely a genetic disease? *Nature* **386**, 137 (1997).

18. Anderson, R. M. *et al.* Transmission dynamics and epidemiology of BSE in British cattle. *Nature* **382**, 779-788 (1996).

19. Ferguson, N. M., Donnelly, C. A., Woolhouse, M. E. J. & Anderson, R. M. The epidemiology of BSE in cattle herds in Great Britain II: Model construction and analysis of transmission dynamics. *Phil. Trans. R. Soc. Lond.* B **352**, 803-838 (1997).

20. Donnelly, C. A. & Ferguson, N. M. *Statistical Aspects of BSE and vCJD—Models for Epidemics* (Chapman & Hall and CRC, London, 2000).

21. Woolhouse, M. E. J. *et al.* Population dynamics of scrapie in a sheep flock. *Phil. Trans. R. Soc. Lond.* B **354**, 751-756 (1999).

22. Gravenor, M. B., Cox, D. R., Hoinville, L. J., Hoek, A. & McLean, A. R. The flock-to-flock force of infection for scrapie in Britain. *Proc. R. Soc. Lond.* B **268**, 587-592 (2001).

23. Hoinville, L. J. A review of the epidemiology of scrapie in sheep. *Rev. Sci. Techn. Office Int. Epizooties* **15**, 827-852 (1996).

24. Hoinville, L. J., Hoek, A., Gravenor, M. B. & McLean, A. R. Descriptive epidemiology of scrapie in Great Britain: results of a postal survey. *Vet. Rec.* **146**, 455-461 (2000).

25. Ghani, A. C., Ferguson, N. M., Donnelly, C. A. & Anderson, R. M. Predicted vCJD mortality in Great Britain. *Nature* **406**, 583-584 (2000).

26. d'Aignaux, J. N. H., Cousens, S. N. & Smith, P. G. Predictability of the UK variant Creutzfeldt–Jakob disease epidemic. *Science* **294**, 1729-1731; published online 25 October 2001 (10.1126/ science.1064748).

27. Valleron, A.-J., Boelle, P.-Y., Will, R. & Cesbron, J.-Y. Estimation of epidemic size and incubation time based on age characteristics of vCJD in the United Kingdom. *Science* **294**, 1726-1728(2001).

28. Hill, A. F. *et al.* Molecular screening of sheep for bovine spongiform encephalopathy. *Neurosci. Lett.* **255**, 159-162 (1998).

29. Maissen, M., Roeckl, F., Glatzel, M., Goldmann, W. & Aguzzi, A. Plasminogen binds to disease-associated prion protein of multiple species. *Lancet* **357**, 2026-2028 (2001).

30. Hagenaars, T. J., Ferguson, N. M., Donnelly, C. A. & Anderson, R. M. Persistence patterns of scrapie in a sheep flock. *Epidemiol. Infect.* **127**, 157-167 (2001).

Supplementary Information accompanies the paper on *Nature*'s website (http://www.nature.com).

Acknowledgements. This work was funded by the Food Standards Agency. N.M.F. and A.C.G. acknowledge funding from The Royal Society. C.A.D., T.J.H. and R.M.A. acknowledge funding from the Wellcome Trust. We are very grateful to M. Bruce, S. Bellworthy and M. Jeffrey for access to pre-publication data on infectivity. We also thank L. Hoinville, J. Wilesmith and R. Will for access to data. We thank N. Hunter, L. Green, J. Anderson, A. James, A. Bromley, H. Mason, P. Comer and members of the Spongiform Encephalopathy Advisory Committee for discussions.

Competing interests statement. The authors declare that they have no competing financial interests.

Correspondence and requests for materials should be addressed to N.M.F. (e-mail: neil.ferguson@ic.ac.uk).

The Role of the Thermohaline Circulation in Abrupt Climate Change

P. U. Clark *et al.*

Editor's Note

The discovery of rapid shifts in climate, some over just a few decades, during the past ice age and the preceding interglacial period has transformed our view of global climate, forcing us to regard it as something potentially unstable that has been unusually quiescent during the present interglacial. The possible implications for human-induced global warming are obvious. The most likely mechanism of these sudden changes involves patterns of water circulation in the North Atlantic Ocean, perhaps caused by changes in the global hydrological cycle. This review article by Peter Clark and coworkers not only supplied an overview of this emerging understanding but also helped to establish the centrality of ocean circulation to the entire process of global climate change.

The possibility of a reduced Atlantic thermohaline circulation in response to increases in greenhouse-gas concentrations has been demonstrated in a number of simulations with general circulation models of the coupled ocean–atmosphere system. But it remains difficult to assess the likelihood of future changes in the thermohaline circulation, mainly owing to poorly constrained model parameterizations and uncertainties in the response of the climate system to greenhouse warming. Analyses of past abrupt climate changes help to solve these problems. Data and models both suggest that abrupt climate change during the last glaciation originated through changes in the Atlantic thermohaline circulation in response to small changes in the hydrological cycle. Atmospheric and oceanic responses to these changes were then transmitted globally through a number of feedbacks. The palaeoclimate data and the model results also indicate that the stability of the thermohaline circulation depends on the mean climate state.

THE ocean affects climate through its high heat capacity relative to the surrounding land, thereby moderating daily, seasonal and interannual temperature fluctuations, and through its ability to transport heat from one location to another. In the North Atlantic, differential solar heating between high and low latitudes tends to accelerate surface waters polewards whereas freshwater input to high latitudes together with low-latitude evaporation tend to brake this flow. Today, the former thermal forcing dominates the latter haline (freshwater) forcing and the meridional overturning in the Atlantic drives surface waters northward, while deep water that forms in the Nordic Seas flows southward as North Atlantic Deep Water (NADW). This thermohaline circulation (THC) is responsible for

温盐环流在气候突变中的作用

克拉克等

编者按

在末次冰期和之前的间冰期期间，气候快速变化的发现已改变了我们对全球气候的看法，其中一些变化仅发生在短短几十年内，这迫使我们将气候变化视为一种潜在的不稳定因素，而这种不稳定因素在目前的间冰期异常沉寂。人类引起的全球变暖产生了显而易见的影响。产生这些突变最可能的机理造成了北大西洋的水循环模式，这个模式也可能是由全球水文循环的变化引起的。彼得·克拉克及其同事的这篇评论文章不仅概述了这一新认识，而且帮助建立了海洋环流在全球气候变化整个过程的中心作用。

许多海洋–大气耦合环流模式的模拟结果指出，大西洋温盐环流的减弱可能是温室气体浓度的增加引起的。但是，要估计未来温盐环流的变化仍有一定困难，这主要是因为模式参数化难以确切，以及气候系统对温室效应响应机制的不确定性。分析过去气候的变化有助于解决这一问题。资料和模式的结果都指出，末次冰期中，气候的突然变化源于大西洋温盐环流的变化对水文循环微小变化的响应。此后，大气和海洋对这些变化的响应通过一系列反馈机制传到全球。古气候资料和模式的结果都指出，温盐环流的稳定性依赖于气候平均态。

海洋通过以下两种途径影响气候：一是通过海洋相对于周围陆地的更大的热容量调节每日的、季节的和年际的温度振荡，二是通过海洋把热量从一地输送到另一地的能力。在北大西洋，高低纬度之间太阳辐射加热的差异使海面的水加速向极地流去，而高纬度的淡水输入和低纬度的蒸腾作用又使水流减速。现在，前者的热力强迫作用超过后者的高盐水（淡水）的强迫作用，大西洋的经向翻转作用使海洋表层水向北流动，而形成于北欧海域的深层水（北大西洋深层水，NADW）则向南流动。温盐环流（THC）负责把大部分大西洋的热量输向极地，输送量峰值在北纬24°达到

much of the total oceanic poleward heat transport in the Atlantic, peaking at about 1.2 ± 0.3 PW (1 PW equals 10^{15} watts) at $24°$N (ref. 1).

No such deep overturning occurs in the North Pacific, where surface waters are too fresh to sink[2]. The lack of a meridional land barrier in the Southern Ocean precludes the existence of strong east–west pressure gradients needed to balance a southward geostrophic surface flow, so that poleward heat transport associated with the THC is small there. Deep-water formation in the Southern Ocean occurs along the Antarctic continental shelf in the Weddell and Ross Seas either through intense evaporation or, more typically, through brine rejection that produces dense water that sinks down and along the slope[3]. In addition, supercooled water may be formed at the base of the thick floating ice shelves during freezing or melting and this dense water may in turn flow downslope[4].

The idea that the Atlantic THC may have many speeds is now a century old[2], but not until the 1960s did a quantitative, albeit idealized, framework emerge to explain the physics behind the potential existence of these multiple equilibria[5]. Subsequently, ocean[6] and coupled atmosphere–ocean general circulation models (GCMs) (ref. 7) were shown to support multiple equilibria. Such studies have revealed that multiple equilibria exist because the atmosphere responds to anomalies of sea surface temperature, but not salinity[8]. They have further shown that transitions between different states are often abrupt and can be induced through small perturbations to the hydrological cycle.

The concept of multiple equilibria of the THC and the transitions between these states is now commonly invoked as a mechanism to explain the abrupt climate changes that were characteristic of the last glaciation[9,10]. Here we refer to an abrupt change as a persistent transition of climate (over subcontinental scale) that occurs on the timescale of decades. Although understanding the mechanisms behind abrupt climate transitions in the past is interesting in its own right, there is a pressing need to gain insight into the likelihood of their future occurrence[11,12]. Most, but not all, coupled GCM projections of the twenty-first century climate show a reduction in the strength of the Atlantic overturning circulation with increasing concentrations of greenhouse gases[13]—if the warming is strong enough and sustained long enough, a complete collapse cannot be excluded[14,15]. The successful simulation of past abrupt events that are found in the palaeoclimate record is the only test of model fidelity in estimating the possibility of large ocean–atmosphere reorganizations when projecting future climate change.

Past Changes in the Thermohaline Circulation

Considerable progress has been made in linking past abrupt changes in North Atlantic surface-ocean and atmospheric temperature with changes in deep ocean circulation, confirming the important role that major reorganizations of the Atlantic THC have played in abrupt climate change. Although a continuum of possible modes of NADW formation may exist[16], palaeoceanographic records suggest that the largest changes in North

1.2 ± 0.3 PW（1 PW = 10^{15} W）（参考文献 1）。

　　北太平洋没有这种翻转作用，那里海洋表层水很淡，不会下沉[2]。在南大洋，经向没有陆地阻隔，因而不存在和向南的地转流相平衡的东西向强气压梯度，因此这里由 THC 引起的向极输送热量较少。在南大洋，深层水形成于威德尔海和罗斯海的南极大陆架附近，它是通过强的蒸发作用或者盐析作用形成的，后一种过程形成的密度大的海水沿着斜坡下沉流动，该过程在南大洋更典型一些[3]。另外，在厚的浮冰大陆架的底部，冰在冻结或融化时可以形成过冷水，这种密度大的水会沿着斜坡向下流动[4]。

　　大西洋 THC 存在多种流速的想法至今已有一个世纪之久了[2]。但直至 20 世纪 60 年代才出现一个定量化、理想化的模式来解释多平衡态的物理原因[5]。此后，海洋环流模式[6] 和海气耦合环流模式（GCMs）（参考文献 7）说明这一多平衡态确实存在。这些研究揭示了，多平衡态是存在的，因为大气是响应于海面温度异常现象，而不是海水盐度[8]。这些研究进一步指出，不同状态之间的转换常常突然发生，而且可能是由水文循环的小扰动引起的。

　　THC 的多平衡态和不同状态之间的转换现在常常用来解释气候突变的机制，这种突变是末次冰期气候的特征[9,10]。此处，我们把发生在几十年尺度的持续的气候（超越次大陆范围）转换叫做气候突变。虽然以往人们把兴趣集中于了解气候突变的机制，但更需要了解的是未来发生气候突变的可能性[11,12]。大部分（并非全部）关于 21 世纪气候的 GCM 耦合模式的结果指出，随着温室气体浓度的增加，大西洋经向翻转流环流的强度将减少[13]，如果增暖足够强，且持续的时间足够长，则不能排除这一环流有完全停滞的可能性[14,15]。当用模式来预测未来气候变化情况下大尺度的海洋–大气重组的可能性时，对古气候记录中的突发事件的成功模拟，是模式逼真度的唯一检验手段。

以往温盐环流的变化

　　将北大西洋洋面和大气温度过去的突变与深海环流的变化联系在一起的研究已取得了很大进展，这些方面的研究证明了大西洋 THC 的重组在气候突变中起了重要作用。虽然可能存在一系列 NADW 模态[16]，但是古海洋记录指出，北大西洋气候的最大变化与三种可能模态之间的转换有关，即现代模态、冰期模态和海因里希模

Atlantic climate were associated with transitions among three possible modes: a modern mode, a glacial mode, and a Heinrich mode[9]. The modern mode is characterized by the formation of deep water in the Nordic Seas and its subsequent flow over the Greenland–Scotland ridge[17]. The newly formed NADW flows into the Labrador Sea where it entrains recirculating, relatively cold and fresh Labrador Sea intermediate waters[17] that are largely confined to the subpolar gyre of the North Atlantic[18] before progressing southward. During the glacial mode, NADW probably formed through open-ocean convection in the subpolar North Atlantic, sinking to depths of less than 2,500 m (ref. 19). Buoyancy loss by brine rejection under sea ice in the Nordic Seas may have provided an additional source of glacial-mode NADW[20]. Finally, during the Heinrich mode, Antarctic-derived waters filled the North Atlantic basin to depths as shallow as 1,000 m (ref. 21).

Changes in the location, depth and volume of newly formed NADW associated with mode shifts are now relatively well constrained, but the magnitude of related changes in the rate of the overturning circulation and deep ocean ventilation remains controversial[22,23]. In this regard, atmospheric radiocarbon (expressed as $\Delta^{14}C_{atm}$, the per mil deviation from a ^{14}C standard after correction for radioactive decay and fractionation) offers great promise for identifying past changes in the globally integrated THC. $\Delta^{14}C_{atm}$ is a function of the production rate of ^{14}C in the upper atmosphere and the sizes of and exchange rates between the major carbon reservoirs. Considerable work yet remains before production-rate effects are quantified so as to yield a residual $\Delta^{14}C_{atm}$ signal that uniquely reflects changes in ocean ventilation back to 22.0 kyr before present (BP), or the period in which existing records show coherent changes in $\Delta^{14}C_{atm}$ (Fig. 1a). As a first approximation, we account for the long-term decrease in ^{14}C production rate that resulted primarily from a gradual increase in the geomagnetic field intensity over the last 22 kyr (ref. 24), isolating changes in $\Delta^{14}C_{atm}$ that, on shorter timescales ($\leqslant 10^3$ yr), are largely due to changes in cosmic radiation or ocean ventilation.

Polar ice core records of the cosmogenic radionuclide ^{10}Be can be used to estimate past changes in cosmic radiation because ^{10}Be is rapidly (1–2 yr) removed from the atmosphere to the ice surface by precipitation. On this basis, the ^{10}Be record from the GISP2 ice core[25] suggests that changes in cosmogenic production rates are an unlikely cause of first-order changes in $\Delta^{14}C_{atm}$ between 15.0 and 22.0 kyr (Fig. 1b). Between 11.5 and 15.0 kyr BP, the ^{10}Be signal in the GISP2 ice core is more strongly influenced by climate, but a detailed analysis suggests that a geomagnetic influence may have been important in explaining the decrease in $\Delta^{14}C_{atm}$ during the Younger Dryas cold event[26,27] (Fig. 1a). The two large increases in ^{10}Be flux at 10.1 and 11.1 kyr BP, which may reflect solar variability[26], correspond to two increases in $\Delta^{14}C_{atm}$ of about 30‰. (The small age offsets indicate that the GISP2 timescale is too old in this interval by about 60 years[26].) In contrast, the fluctuations in $\Delta^{14}C_{atm}$ before 14.6 kyr BP with amplitudes of over 80‰ do not have corresponding fluctuations in ^{10}Be flux, and thus probably reflect changes in the THC, although a geomagnetic influence cannot yet be ruled out for explaining some of the signal.

态 [9]。现代模态的特征是北欧海域有深水区形成以及格陵兰–苏格兰脊地区有相应的流场 [17]。这个新形成的 NADW 流入拉布拉多海，并产生回流，即相对较冷并且较淡的拉布拉多海中层水 [17]，这种水团在向南流之前受到北大西洋副极地环流 [18] 的很大限制。在冰期模态时，NADW 可能是由副极地北大西洋的开阔海洋中的对流形成的，它下沉到不到 2,500 米的深处（参考文献 19）。北欧海域海冰下面的盐析作用引起的浮力减小是形成冰期模态 NADW 的另一个原因 [20]。最后，在海因里希模态时，来自南极的水填满了北大西洋海盆较浅的 1,000 米处（参考文献 21）。

新形成的 NADW 的位置、深度和体积的变化与模态转换相联系，这种联系现在已经了解得相当清楚了，不过它的翻转环流速率和大洋深部的流动性（即深部通风）的变化量级仍有争论 [22,23]。在这方面，大气放射性碳（用 $\Delta^{14}C_{atm}$ 表示，以经过放射性衰减和分馏订正后对 ^{14}C 标准值的偏差来表征，以千分之一计）对弄清全球 THC 过去的变化提供了很大的可能性。$\Delta^{14}C_{atm}$ 是上层大气 ^{14}C 产生率、主要碳库的大小和碳库之间交换率的函数。在使产生率的影响定量化以便得到一个剩余的 $\Delta^{14}C_{atm}$ 信号方面，我们还需要做大量工作。剩余的 $\Delta^{14}C_{atm}$ 信号是唯一能够反映大洋通风在距今 2.2 万年以来变化的量，或者反映这一时期的记录存在 $\Delta^{14}C_{atm}$ 的一致变化量（图 1a）。作一个初步近似，我们给出 ^{14}C 产生率的长期减少趋势，这一结果主要来自 2.2 万年以来地磁场强度的逐渐增加（参考文献 24），而后分离出较短的时间尺度（≤1,000 年）的 $\Delta^{14}C_{atm}$ 变化，这一部分反映了宇宙辐射或者大洋通风的变化。

极地冰芯记录的宇生放射性核素 ^{10}Be 可以用于估计以往宇宙辐射的变化，因为 ^{10}Be 在发生降水时很快（1～2 年）由大气进入冰面。在此基础上，由 GISP2 冰芯 [25] 得出的 ^{10}Be 记录表明，宇生产生率的变化似乎不是 1.5 万到 2.2 万年期间 $\Delta^{14}C_{atm}$ 的一阶变化的原因（图 1b）。距今 1.15 万到 2.2 万年，GISP2 冰芯中 ^{10}Be 的信号受到气候的更大影响，但是详细的分析得出，地磁产生的影响在解释新仙女木冷期事件 $\Delta^{14}C_{atm}$ 的减少也是重要的 [26,27]（图 1a）。距今 1.01 万到 1.11 万年，^{10}Be 通量的两次大的增加，可以反映太阳辐射的变率 [26]，其与两次 $\Delta^{14}C_{atm}$ 约 30‰ 的增加相对应。（小的年代偏离说明 GISP2 时间尺度对于这个时期来讲，相对老了约 60 年的时间 [26]）。相反，距今 1.46 万年振幅超过 80‰ 的振荡并未对应 ^{10}Be 通量的波动，它可能反映的是 THC 的变化，虽然在解释某些信号时地磁的影响不能完全排除。

Fig. 1. Comparison of record of linearly detrended $\Delta^{14}C_{atm}$ to ^{10}Be flux data from the GISP2 ice core. **a,** Linearly detrended records of $\Delta^{14}C_{atm}$ used to infer changes in the global thermohaline circulation between 9.9 and 22.0 kyr BP. Records include tree rings (solid green line)[72], varves from the Cariaco basin (blue circles)[33], varves from Lake Suigetsu, Japan (grey circles with error bars)[73], and U/Th-dated corals (red circles with error bars)[74]. The thin red line is an estimate of production-rate decrease in $\Delta^{14}C_{atm}$ between 11.5 and 12.9 kyr BP (from ref. 26 with age model modified to be on GISP2 timescale); vertical scale is offset by 80‰. We linearly detrended the combined $\Delta^{14}C_{atm}$ records for the interval 5 to 25 kyr in order to account for the long-term decrease in ^{14}C production rate that resulted primarily from a nearly linear increase in the geomagnetic field intensity over this time[24]. Short-term variations in the geomagnetic field intensity may also contribute, but existing geomagnetic records showing variability during this interval are not coherent. **b,** Records of ^{10}Be flux (filled circles) and ice accumulation rate (blue line) from GISP2 ice core. ^{10}Be flux is the product of the ^{10}Be concentration[25] and the ice accumulation rate[75] averaged over the sample interval of the ^{10}Be measurements. We do not show the accumulation rate and ^{10}Be flux records from 14.6 to 11.5 kyr BP because the ^{10}Be flux variations in this interval are dominated by the large variations in snow accumulation rate, thus obscuring production-rate controls on ^{10}Be during this time. Accumulation-rate variability was small before 14.6 kyr BP, thus indicating that there is little potential influence of changes in snowfall rate on ^{10}Be flux.

NADW is presently the major source of ^{14}C to the deep sea[28], and changes in the strength of this water mass (and its preformed properties) probably dominate the variations in $\Delta^{14}C_{atm}$ associated with the global carbon cycle over the last 22.0 kyr. These changes can be modulated by changes in the THC elsewhere, but surface waters in the Southern Ocean and North Pacific are now old[28], and may have been significantly older during glacial periods[29], suggesting that any increase in formation of deep or intermediate waters in these regions will have a lesser impact on the $\Delta^{14}C_{atm}$ budget than changes in NADW.

The hypothesis that changes in $\Delta^{14}C_{atm}$ largely reflect variations in the Atlantic THC is supported by the relation between first-order changes in $\Delta^{14}C_{atm}$ and in proxies that record changes in the volume of NADW and North Atlantic climate (Fig. 2). High $\Delta^{14}C_{atm}$ during the Last Glacial Maximum (LGM) (Fig. 2c) is associated with the glacial mode of NADW[19] and cold North Atlantic atmospheric[30] (Fig. 2d) and sea surface[31] (Fig. 2e) temperatures. The subsequent decrease in $\Delta^{14}C_{atm}$ to essentially interglacial levels was associated with

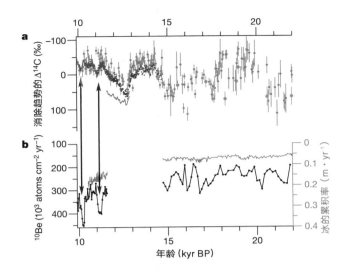

图 1. 消除线性趋势后的 $\Delta^{14}C_{atm}$ 记录和 GISP2（格陵兰冰盖计划）冰芯 ^{10}Be 通量资料的比较。a 图为消除线性趋势后的 $\Delta^{14}C_{atm}$，用于推断距今 0.99 万年到 2.20 万年期间全球温盐环流的变化，其记录包括树木年轮（绿实线）[72]、卡里亚科盆地纹泥（蓝点）[33]、日本水月湖纹泥（带有误差棒的灰点）[73]，以及 U/Th 定年的珊瑚（带有误差棒的红点）[74]。细红线表示距今 1.15 万到 1.29 万年 $\Delta^{14}C_{atm}$ 产生率减少的估量（该指标源于参考文献 26，修改其年代模式以吻合 GISP2 冰芯的时间尺度）；垂直尺度偏移了 80‰。对距今 0.5 万到 2.5 万年期间的综合 $\Delta^{14}C_{atm}$ 记录消除线性趋势是为了估计长期 ^{14}C 产生率的减少，产生率的减少是由这一时间尺度地磁场强度的线性增加造成的[24]。地磁场强度的短期变化对此也有影响，不过已有的地磁场记录指出在这一时期变化不一致。b 图为 GISP2 冰芯的 ^{10}Be 通量记录（实心圈）和冰累积率（蓝线）。^{10}Be 通量由 ^{10}Be 浓度求得[25]，冰的累积率是样本时段 ^{10}Be 的平均观测值[75]。我们没有给出距今 1.46 万到 1.15 万年期间的累积率和 ^{10}Be 通量的记录，因为这一时期 ^{10}Be 通量的变化主要由雪的累积率决定，而掩盖了冰的产生率对 ^{10}Be 的影响。在距今 1.46 万年以前，累积率的变化小，因此降雪率对 ^{10}Be 通量的影响小。

　　NADW 是现今深海 ^{14}C 的主要来源[28]，水团强度的变化（以及其此前形成的性质）可能主导了 2.2 万年以来与全球碳循环相联系的 $\Delta^{14}C_{atm}$ 的变化。这些变化在其他地方受 THC 调制，但在南大洋和北太平洋表层水现在是古老的[28]，而在冰期就更加古老了[29]，这说明在这些区域，深层水或中层水的形成的任何增加对 $\Delta^{14}C_{atm}$ 的影响都没有 NADW 变化的影响大。

　　$\Delta^{14}C_{atm}$ 的变化很大程度上反映大西洋 THC 的变化这一假说，得到了 $\Delta^{14}C_{atm}$ 的一阶变化与记载着 NADW 体积和北大西洋气候变化的代用资料之间关系的支持（图 2）。在末次冰盛期（LGM）（图 2c），$\Delta^{14}C_{atm}$ 的高值与 NADW 冰期模态[19]，北大西洋冷大气的[30]（图 2d）和海面的[31]（图 2e）温度相联系。此后，$\Delta^{14}C_{atm}$ 基本上下降到间冰期水平，这和北大西洋地区增温有关，而随后在距今 1.90 万到 1.47 万年期间，长

warming in the North Atlantic region, while a subsequent long-term increase between 19.0 kyr BP to 14.7 kyr BP coincides with the Oldest Dryas cooling, during which Heinrich event 1 (H1) occurred (~17.5 kyr BP) (Fig. 2b). During H1, $\Delta^{14}C_{atm}$ rapidly increased to levels similar to the LGM (Fig. 2c), whereas the volume of NADW during the Heinrich mode (as inferred from geochemical proxies) was < 50% of that during the LGM[21]. Relative to the glacial mode, these relations suggest that the Heinrich mode reflects some combination of further shallowing of NADW to intermediate depths while maintaining similar rates of overturning, and a compensatory increase in deep-water formation elsewhere.

Fig. 2. Comparison of reconstructed forcings and responses in the Atlantic basin during the last

期的增长则和老仙女木冷期同时发生，在这一时期（距今约 1.75 万年）海因里希 1（H1）事件发生（图 2b）。在海因里希模态时期，$\Delta^{14}C_{atm}$ 迅速上升到类似 LGM（图 2c）的水平，而 NADW 的体积（据地球化学代用资料）小于 LGM 时期的 50%[21]。相对于冰期模态，这些关系说明海因里希模态反映的是 NADW 进一步变浅到中层水深度，同时保持了类似的翻转速度，这种变化得到别处深水形成增加的补偿。

图 2. 末次冰川消退期（距今 1.1 万到 2.2 万年），大西洋海盆的强迫和响应的重建比较。淡水强迫变化

deglaciation (11–22 kyr BP). Time series of changes in freshwater forcing (**a, b**) and response of the THC as inferred by first-order changes in $\Delta^{14}C_{atm}$ (**c**). Panels **d–h** show atmospheric and sea surface temperature changes during the last deglaciation along a north–south transect of the Atlantic basin (72.5° N to 80° S), illustrating the operation of the bipolar seesaw in response to large changes in the Atlantic THC. **a,** Changes in freshwater runoff from North America through the Hudson and St Lawrence Rivers[38]. Two vertical light-grey bars identify intervals of enhanced freshwater flux to the North Atlantic from these sources as well as from icebergs inferred from records (not shown) of total ice-rafted debris (IRD)[37]. **b,** Changes in the amount of IRD containing detrital carbonate lithologies, with large increases identifying times of Heinrich events H1 (identified by darker-grey vertical bar) and H0. The IRD records are from North Atlantic cores VM23-081 (blue curve)[37] and SU8118 (black curve)[31]. **c,** Detrended record of $\Delta^{14}C_{atm}$ from Lake Suigetsu, Japan[73], with first-order changes indicating changes in the meridional overturning of the Atlantic THC (see text); a stronger THC is indicated by more negative values of $\Delta^{14}C_{atm}$. **d,** The GISP2 ice-core oxygen-isotope record[76,77]. Results of calibrating the isotopic palaeothermometer by various methods show a temperature depression of 20 °C at the Last Glacial Maximum ~21.0 kyr BP (ref. 30), a warming of 10 °C at the onset of the Bølling at ~14.6 kyr BP (ref. 32), and a warming of 15 °C at the end of the Younger Dryas ~11.5 kyr BP (ref. 41). **e,** Record of sea surface temperatures (SSTs) derived from alkenones measured in North Atlantic core SU8118 (ref. 31). **f,** Record of SSTs derived from alkenones measured in tropical North Atlantic core M35003-4 (ref. 78). **g,** Record of SSTs derived from alkenones measured in South Atlantic core TN057-21-PC2 (ref. 79). The timescale for this record is provisional (J. Sachs, personal communication). **h,** The Byrd ice-core oxygen-isotope record[50].

A large decrease in $\Delta^{14}C_{atm}$ to interglacial levels coincides with the onset of the Bølling–Allerød warm interval at around 14.7 kyr BP; the abrupt warming recorded in the GISP2 ice core[32] (Fig. 2d) appears to be a nonlinear response to the more gradual increase in the THC (Fig. 2c). A subsequent increase in $\Delta^{14}C_{atm}$ began precisely at the onset of the Younger Dryas cold interval at 13.0 kyr BP (Fig. 2c)[33]. The decrease in $\Delta^{14}C_{atm}$ during the remainder of the Younger Dryas may be the result of an increase in the production rate of ^{14}C (refs 26, 27) (Fig. 1a), suggesting that the THC remained weakened until the end of the Younger Dryas at 11.5 kyr BP when it abruptly switched back to the modern mode[27].

Mechanisms of Past Abrupt Climate Changes

The freshwater budget in the North Atlantic is one of the major components that governs the strength of the Atlantic THC, and dynamical ocean models show that the THC is sensitive to freshwater perturbations on order of 0.1 Sv (1 Sv = 10^6 m^3 s^{-1}) (refs 34–36). A clear goal for understanding past changes in the THC, therefore, is to identify the mechanisms that influenced the North Atlantic freshwater budget. Reconstructions of changes in the freshwater flux from ice sheets around the North Atlantic reveal good agreement with past changes in the THC and North Atlantic climate (Fig. 2a–e), identifying these processes as being important in causing abrupt climate change[37,38]. Paradoxically, although the THC in current models responds to freshwater forcings without delay, the largest deglacial meltwater event on record, referred to as meltwater pulse 1A (MWP-1A), occurs more than 1,000 years before the next significant change in the THC associated with the Younger Dryas cold interval[39]. This paradox may be resolved, however, if MWP-1A originated largely from the Antarctic Ice Sheet[40], where its impact on the Atlantic THC would be substantially reduced.

的时间序列(a 图和 b 图)和 Δ¹⁴C$_{atm}$ 一阶变化所表示的 THC 的响应(c 图)。d~h 图表示末次冰川消退期，沿大西洋海盆的一个南北剖面(北纬 72.5 度到南纬 80 度)上大气和海面温度的变化，说明了在大西洋 THC 大变化响应方面的两极跷跷板作用。a 图为经过哈得孙河和圣劳伦斯河的北美淡水径流的变化[38]。两个垂直的浅灰色柱表示这些源头或者冰山流向北大西洋增加的淡水输入的时间段，冰山流根据冰筏碎屑(IRD)总体的记录[37](未给出)推断而来。b 图为岩屑碳酸盐中 IRD 含量的变化，其增值明显的时期为海因里希事件 H1(用深灰色柱表示)和 H0。IRD 的记录来自北大西洋冰芯 VM23-081(蓝色曲线)[37] 和 SU8118(黑色曲线)[31]。c 图为来自日本水月湖、消除了趋势线的 Δ¹⁴C$_{atm}$ 记录[73]，Δ¹⁴C$_{atm}$ 一阶变化表示北大西洋 THC 经向翻转的变化(见正文)；其中一个较强的 THC 用 Δ¹⁴C$_{atm}$ 的负值标出。d 图为 GISP2 冰芯的氧同位素记录[76,77]。在末次冰盛期距今约 2.10 万年[30]用不同方法算出的同位素古温度有一个 20℃的下降，在距今约 1.46 万年的波令事件开始时增温达到 10℃[32]，在新仙女木事件末期距今约 1.15 万年增温达到 15℃[41]。e 图为根据在北大西洋 SU8118 冰芯中测得的烯酮推断的海面温度记录(SST)[31]。f 图为根据在热带北大西洋 M35003-4 冰芯中测得的烯酮推断的 SST[78]。g 图为根据在南大西洋 TN057-21-PC2 冰芯中测得的烯酮推断的 SST[79]。该记录的时间尺度是临时性的(萨赫斯，个人交流)。h 图为伯德站冰芯的氧同位素记录[50]。

Δ¹⁴C$_{atm}$ 大量减少至达到间冰期水平发生在距今 1.47 万年左右的波令–阿勒罗德暖期；这个 GISP2 冰芯记录的一个突然升温[32](图 2d)看来是对 THC 逐渐增强的非线性响应(图 2c)。其后 Δ¹⁴C$_{atm}$ 的增加与距今 1.30 万年新仙女木冷期的开始精准地一致(图 2c)[33]。新仙女木后期 Δ¹⁴C$_{atm}$ 的减少看来是 ¹⁴C 产生率增加的结果(参考文献 26 和 27)(图 1a)，这说明 THC 直到距今 1.15 万年新仙女木冷期结束时都很弱，而后它又突然转换回现代模态[27]。

过去气候突变的机制

北大西洋淡水注入的多寡是控制大西洋 THC 强度的主要因子之一，动力学海洋模式指出 THC 对量级为 0.1 Sv(1 Sv = 10⁶ m³·s⁻¹)的淡水扰动敏感(参考文献 34~36)。因此，了解过去 THC 的变化是为了弄清影响北大西洋淡水注入多寡的机制。用大西洋周围冰川资料重建的淡水通量的变化与过去 THC 和北大西洋气候的变化相当一致(图 2a~e)，这说明这些过程是导致气候突变的重要因素[37,38]。自相矛盾的是，虽然 THC 的现代模式对淡水强迫没有延迟，然而在记录中显示的最大的冰期融水事件，被称为融水脉动 1A(MWP-1A)，却比而后在新仙女木冷期发生的 THC 显著变化超前了一千多年[39]。不过这一悖论可以解释为：MWP-1A 很大程度上源于南极冰川[40]，它对大西洋 THC 的影响是相当有限的。

Millennial-scale (10^3 yr) changes in the Atlantic THC that involved transitions from modern to glacial modes of NADW are manifested as dramatic fluctuations of North Atlantic climate referred to as Dansgaard–Oeschger (D–O) events, each having a characteristic pattern of abrupt (years to decades) warming followed by gradual (centuries) cooling. The largest changes (> 15 °C over Greenland)[41] occurred during times of intermediate global ice volume, CO_2, or insolation[42]. In Greenland ice core records, abrupt warmings exhibit a preferred waiting time of $1,500 \pm 500$ yr (ref. 43). This spacing is similar to a 1,000–2,000-yr climate cycle identified from marine records during interglacial as well as glacial periods, leading some to speculate that D–O events may be amplified expressions of an ongoing persistent and stable climate cycle[37,43]. However, this timescale of variability does not constrain one mechanism over another. Several mechanisms may have operated jointly, and the relative contribution of potential mechanisms probably changed in response to the large-scale changes in global boundary conditions that accompanied the last deglaciation.

Atmospheric transmission of the D–O signal beyond the North Atlantic region is suggested by high-resolution climate records that display the same structure of change that, within dating uncertainties, is synchronous with the North Atlantic signal. It is also suggested by simulations using atmospheric GCMs[44], although these models have yet to include all potential feedbacks that may be important in transmitting the signal to regions far from the North Atlantic. Greenland ice-core records of methane and $\delta^{18}O$ strongly support the hypothesis of North Atlantic forcing in showing a nearly instantaneous response of the tropical water balance to changes in high-latitude temperature[32,41]. Palaeoclimate records identify additional atmospheric responses to North Atlantic climate that would potentially further amplify and transmit the D–O signal. These include changes in (1) the strength of trade winds and associated oceanic upwelling[45], (2) the position of the Intertropical Convergence Zone, with attendant effects on water vapour transport for the Atlantic to the Pacific basin[46], (3) the strength of the Asian monsoon[47], (4) sea surface temperatures of the Pacific warm pool[48] and (5) ventilation of the North Pacific[49].

A large reduction in the THC during the Heinrich mode (Fig. 2c) causes additional cooling in the North Atlantic[31] (Fig. 2e), while contemporaneous warming observed in some regions of the Southern Hemisphere[9,50] indicates that the large reduction in NADW formation decreased meridional heat transport from the South Atlantic (Fig. 2f–h). A similar "bipolar seesaw" effect may hold for the Younger Dryas event[51] (Fig. 2), but the absence of a comparable thermally antiphased southern signal associated with many of the older D–O events[50] suggests that any changes in oceanic heat transport accompanying the changes from modern to glacial circulation modes were either too small or too short to be clearly registered in existing climate records.

We thus expect to see two mechanisms of variability in climate related to changes in the THC: one associated with atmospheric transmission and one associated with an oceanic seesaw, although these are not independent as an oceanic change necessarily implies an atmospheric response and vice versa. We use empirical orthogonal function (EOF) analysis

NADW 从现代模态到冰期模态的转换中，称为丹斯果–厄施格尔（D–O）事件的北大西洋气候的突然变动，显示了大西洋 THC 千年尺度的变化，其中每一次都有典型的突然（年际到年代际）增温和随之而来的逐渐（世纪尺度）降温。最大的温度变化（在格陵兰 > 15 ℃）[41] 发生在中等大小的全球冰量、CO_2 浓度和太阳辐照量的时期 [42]。在格陵兰冰芯记录中，突然增温通常有一个 $1,500 \pm 500$ 年的酝酿期（参考文献 43）。这段间隔期与源自冰期和间冰期期间的海洋记录中 $1,000 \sim 2,000$ 年的气候循环相似，这使有些人推测 D–O 事件可能是一个持续发展并且稳定的气候循环的放大表现 [37,43]。但是，这一时间尺度变化并不限定于某种特定的机制，而是由若干机制协同控制，每种潜在机制的相对贡献可能随末次冰消期时全球边界条件的大尺度变化而改变。

在北大西洋以外地区，D–O 信号的大气传输，可从高分辨率的气候记录中找到。在一定的定年误差范围内，这些气候记录显示与北大西洋信号同步调的一致变化。这些信号也可由大气环流模式模拟出来 [44]，虽然这些模式尚未能完全包括所有能把信号传到离北大西洋以外很远的地方的重要反馈过程。格陵兰冰芯记录的甲烷和 $\delta^{18}O$ 强烈地支持北大西洋强迫导致热带水的平衡对高纬度温度变化有近乎同时的响应这一假设 [32,41]。古气候记录指出，大气对北大西洋气候另外的响应，说明它能相当大地放大和传输 D–O 信号。这些响应包括以下几种变化：（1）信风和与之相联系的海洋上升流的强度 [45]，（2）热带辐合带的位置，影响着大西洋到太平洋的海盆尺度的水汽输送 [46]，（3）亚洲季风的强度 [47]，（4）太平洋暖池的海面温度 [48]，（5）北太平洋的通风作用 [49]。

海因里希模态期间 THC 的大减弱（图 2c）引起北大西洋的进一步降温 [31]（图 2e），而南半球某些地区同时观测到的增温 [9,50] 说明 NADW 大幅度地减弱了来自南大西洋的经向热量输送（图 2f～h）。类似的"两极跷跷板"效应在新仙女木事件时也有 [51]（图 2），但是没有与许多较古老的 D–O 事件联系的从南面来的反相位的高温信号 [50]，这说明伴随着从现代模态向冰期模态的变化而产生的任何海洋热传输的变化，或者强度太小，或者时间太短，以至在已有的气候记录中找不到。

因此，我们看到两种与 THC 有关的气候变化的机制：一种和大气传输有关，另一种和海洋"跷跷板"效应有关，虽然两者并不是相互独立的，因为海洋的变化意味着大气的响应，或者反过来大气的变化意味着海洋的响应。我们应用经验正交函数

to provide an objective characterization of these modes of climate variability during the last deglaciation by reducing 18 well-dated time series of climate change (Fig. 3) into spatially coherent, orthogonal eigenvectors. Our analysis indicates that the last deglaciation was dominated by two climate responses. The first EOF (68% of variance) captures the global warming from glacial to interglacial conditions that evolved over a timescale of about 10 kyr. Included in this EOF is the interruption of the warming trend by the Younger Dryas. The second EOF (15% of the variance) quantifies the spatial and temporal expression of millennial changes centred at 16 and 12 kyr BP (Fig. 3a). The spatial pattern of this EOF, with negative scores over Antarctica (except Taylor Dome) and in the South Atlantic and positive scores at all other sites (Fig. 4b), is consistent with an atmospheric transmission of the North Atlantic signal except for those areas in the Southern Hemisphere where operation of the seesaw during the last deglaciation produced an antiphased response as predicted by a large change in the THC[52-54]. We find that a similar spatial pattern holds for the interval between 26 and 50 kyr BP, indicating that the seesaw operated during this time as well[50].

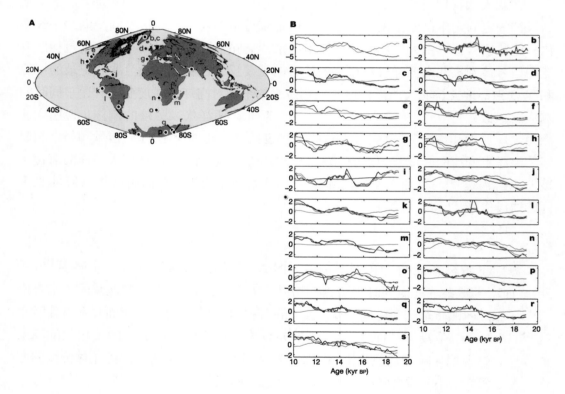

Fig. 3. Time-history of the first two empirical orthogonal functions (EOFs) determined from 18 time series. **A,** Data sampling locations. **B,** Time series. These data sets provide time series of climate change with temporal sampling resolution of about 250 years or less. All time series were interpolated to a constant sampling interval of 125 years. Numerical experiments demonstrate that the results presented here are insensitive to factor-of-2 changes in the selected constant sampling interval. All data sets were then transformed to mean zero and standard deviation of one. We note that where the second EOF is negative, time series are characterized by early warming but a weaker Younger Dryas; where the second EOF is

(EOF)方法将18个记录完好的表示气候变化的历史资料时间序列(图3)加以降维，形成空间上相互关联的正交特征向量，得到了在末次冰消期气候变化模态的客观表征。我们的分析指出，末次冰消期主要有两种气候响应。第一个EOF(可解释68%的方差)捕获了冰期到间冰期1万年以上时间尺度的全球增温，其中包括在新仙女木期增暖趋势的中断。第二个EOF(可解释15%的方差)量化了距今1.6万到1.2万年期间以千年尺度变化的空间和时间的变化(图3a)。EOF空间分布在南极洲(泰勒冰穹除外)和南大西洋为负，在其他地方为正(图4b)。这种分布和北大西洋信号的大气传输方向相同，但南半球的一些地区除外，在这些地区，末次冰消期跷跷板的作用产生了一个反相位的响应，这是由THC的大幅度变化预示的[52-54]。我们还发现了距今2.6万到5.0万年期间类似的空间分布，这说明在这一时期跷跷板的作用也很明显[50]。

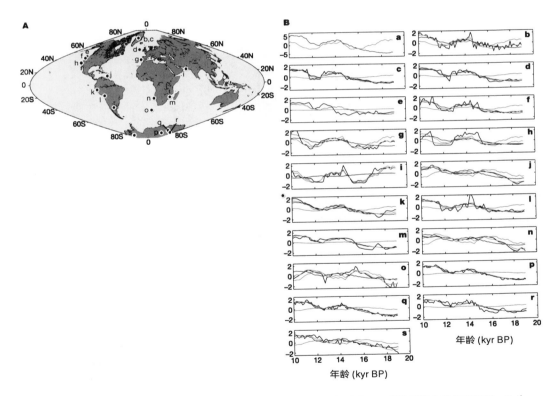

图3. 由18个时间序列求出的前两个经验正交函数(EOF)的时间演变。**A** 为资料样本的地理位置。**B** 为时间序列。这些资料集给出了具有250年左右或更少的采样分辨率的气候变化的时间序列。所有的时间序列都以125年等距时间间隔内插。数值实验说明，此处的结果对选定的等距时间间隔2倍采样率是不敏感的。所有的资料都已换算成平均值为0、标准差为1的序列。我们注意到，在第二个EOF数值为负的地方，其时间序列以早期的增温而后是一个弱的新仙女木期为其特征；在EOF数值为正的地方，新仙女木期趋向一个更强的事件。我们强调，第二个EOF的空间分布强烈地依赖时间尺度的性质和对

positive, the Younger Dryas tends to be a more significant event. We emphasize that the pattern of the second EOF depends strongly on the quality of the timescale and the precision of the synchronization between these palaeoclimatic records (for example refs 80, 81). **a,** The time series for the first two EOFs, where the blue line is the first EOF and the red line is second EOF. The first EOF accounts for 68% of the data variance while the second EOF accounts for 15%. **b–s,** Plots of the original time series and the results of the EOF analysis. The normalized time series from each location (black line), the weighted EOFs using the weights from **a** (blue line is first EOF, red line is second EOF), and the sum of the first two EOFs (green line). **b,** Oxygen-isotope record from the GISP2 ice core[76,77]. **c,** Methane record from the GISP2 ice core[50]. **d,** Percentages of *Neogloboquabrina pachyberma* (s.) from North Atlantic core VM23-81 (ref. 37). **e,** Relative abundance of a radiolarian assemblage identified in northeastern Pacific core EW9504-17PC (ref. 82). **f,** Percentages of *N. pachyberma* (s.) from ODP Site 1019 in the northeastern Pacific[83]. **g,** Alkenone-derived sea surface temperatures from the subtropical northeast Atlantic[31]. **h,** Changes in the bioturbation index from ODP Site 893 in the Santa Barbara basin[49]. **i,** Total organic carbon from Arabian Sea sediments[47]. **j,** Alkenone-derived sea surface temperatures from the tropical North Atlantic[78]. **k,** Oxygen-isotope record from the Huascaran ice core, Peru[84]. **l,** Oxygen isotope record from the Sajama ice core, Bolivia[85]. **m,** Alkenone-derived sea surface temperatures from the tropical Indian Ocean[86]. **n,** Percentages of *N. pachyberma* (s.) from the South Atlantic[87]. **o,** Residual oxygen-isotope record measured on planktonic foraminifera for the South Atlantic[88]. **p,** The Vostok ice-core deuterium record[89]. **q,** Deuterium record from the Dome C ice core[90]. **r,** Oxygen-isotope record from the Taylor Dome ice core[80]. **s,** Oxygen-isotope record from the Byrd ice core[50].

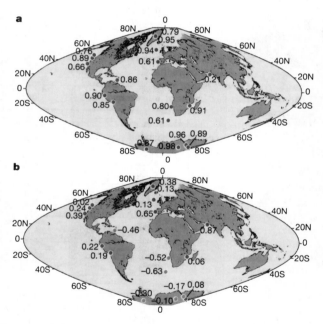

Fig. 4. The spatial pattern of the first two empirical orthogonal functions extracted from the data set (see Fig. 3a). Numbers shown are loadings of the first two EOFs for 18 deglacial time series. Loadings indicate the importance of each EOF in explaining the variations in each time series. To reconstruct the normalized (mean zero and standard deviation of one) time series at any one location, we take the loadings shown in Fig. 3a, multiply them by the time series of the EOFs and add them together. The two loadings next to the Greenland site correspond to the GISP2 oxygen isotope (upper) and methane (lower) records. **a,** First EOF; **b,** second EOF.

这些古气候记录做同时化处理的精度（比如参考文献 80 和 81）。**a** 图为前两个 EOF 的时间序列，蓝线是第一个 EOF 的，红线是第二个 EOF 的。第一个 EOF 可解释 68% 的方差，而第二个 EOF 可解释 15% 的方差。**b ~ s** 图为原始时间序列图和 EOF 分析的结果。每一个测站归一化的时间序列（黑线），应用 **a** 图中的权重求得的加权结果（蓝线是第一个 EOF 的，红线是第二个 EOF 的）和前两个 EOF 的合成结果（绿线）。**b** 图为 GISP2 冰芯的氧同位素记录 [76,77]。**c** 图为 GISP2 冰芯的甲烷记录 [50]。**d** 图为由北大西洋冰芯 VM23-81 获得的左旋厚壁新方球虫百分率（参考文献 37）。**e** 图为由东北太平洋冰芯 EW9504-17PC 获得的放射虫的相对富集丰度（参考文献 82）。**f** 图为东北太平洋大洋钻探计划（ODP）1019 位点获得的左旋厚壁新方球虫百分率 [83]。**g** 图为由烯酮推断的副热带东北大西洋海面温度 [31]。**h** 图为位于圣巴巴拉盆地的大洋钻探计划 893 位点获得的生物扰动指数的变化 [49]。**i** 图为阿拉伯海沉积物中的总有机碳 [47]。**j** 图为由烯酮推断的热带北大西洋海面温度 [78]。**k** 图为秘鲁瓦斯卡兰冰芯的氧同位素记录 [84]。**l** 图为玻利维亚萨哈马冰芯的氧同位素记录 [85]。**m** 图为由烯酮推断的热带印度海海面温度 [86]。**n** 图为南大西洋左旋厚壁新方球虫百分率 [87]。**o** 图为南大西洋浮游有孔虫上残余的氧同位素记录 [88]。**p** 图为东方站冰芯中氘的记录 [89]。**q** 图为冰穹 C 冰芯中氘的记录 [90]。**r** 图为泰勒冰穹冰芯中氧同位素记录 [80]。**s** 图为伯德站冰芯中氧同位素记录 [50]。

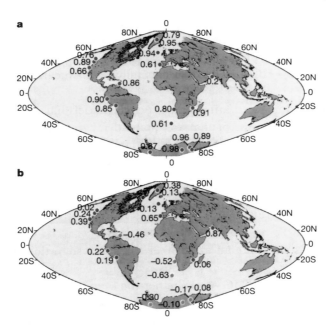

图 4. 由资料集（见图 3a）降维得出前两个经验正交函数的空间分布。图上数字是 18 个间冰期时间序列的前两个 EOF 的载荷。载荷表示每个 EOF 对各个时间序列在解释方差方面的重要程度。为了在任一测站重建归一化（平均值为 0，标准差为 1）的时间序列，我们用图 3a 中测站的载荷乘以 EOF 的时间函数，然后相加。格陵兰测站附近的两个载荷是 GISP2 冰芯的氧同位素记录（上）和甲烷记录（下）。**a** 为第一个 EOF。**b** 为第二个 EOF。

Modelling Abrupt Climate Change

Modelling abrupt climate change faces several challenges: (1) a disparity in timescales between transient states (lasting many centuries) and mode changes (occurring in a few years to decades); (2) a compromise in model complexity due to long integrations and sufficient model resolution to capture abruptness; and (3) uncertainties in initial conditions due to patchy coverage as well as calibration problems in palaeoclimatic proxy data. Although at present there exists no self-consistent model that simulates, without prescribed forcing, changes that resemble the palaeoclimatic record, important progress has been made.

Abrupt change manifests itself in two different ways in climate models: an abrupt transition across a threshold to a new equilibrium state, or a response to a fast forcing. Although multiple equilibria are not necessary for abrupt change[35], the palaeoclimatic records suggest that the ocean–atmosphere system may have preferred modes of operation, that is, the system operates like a "flip-flop" mechanism[55]. This implies the existence of hysteresis of the THC[16,34,56], which appears to be common in coupled climate models. However, the shape and structure of the hysteresis loop strongly depends on model parameters and therefore is still a tunable feature[57] so that the exact location of thresholds cannot yet be determined with current models. Nevertheless, it is clear that thresholds and hence the stability properties of the THC depend fundamentally on the mean climate state[8,58].

A number of ocean and coupled atmosphere–ocean models have found the existence of three distinct modes of the conveyor that are qualitatively the same as the modern, glacial and Heinrich modes identified by palaeoclimate data[16,59,60]. These and other models have also revealed that transitions can be triggered by changes in the freshwater balance of the North Atlantic and changes in modes are associated with changes in the heat budget of the Atlantic basin. For large reductions in NADW formation, this leads to the same "seesaw effect" seen in the data[34,52,53] (Figs 2, 4).

Recent modelling ideas postulate an atmosphere–ocean system during the last glaciation that was extremely close to a threshold, thus requiring very weak freshwater forcing to trigger abrupt changes of the THC[16,60]. Whether the sequence of abrupt events originates from unknown periodic forcing[43,60] or instabilities and feedbacks associated with circum-Atlantic ice sheets[16,38] remains an open question. Furthermore, qualitative consistence with the palaeoclimatic records remains very sensitive to parameter choices in these models. The basic question about the origin of abrupt change is therefore not solved. However, all model simulations until now point towards the key role of the freshwater balance in the Atlantic Ocean. More realistic models and improved reconstructions of the various components of the hydrological cycle (precipitation, run-off, iceberg discharge, sea ice) are urgently needed.

Progress towards a mechanistic understanding of abrupt climate change can be expected from more complete models. These are coupled models with higher resolution, models that no longer require flux adjustments, and models that include biogeochemical cycles.

气候突变的模拟

模拟气候突变面临如下挑战：（1）暂态变化（几个世纪尺度）和模态变化（发生在几年到几十年间）之间时间尺度的差异；（2）如何在长期积分法需要的模式复杂性和为了模拟突变特征而采取精细的模式分辨率之间进行取舍；（3）数据融合涵盖范围和古气候代用资料的校准问题引起的初始条件的不确定性。虽然现在尚无自协调的模式可以在没有事先给定强迫的情况下模拟类似于古气候记录的变化，但研究已经取得了重要的进展。

气候突变本身在气候模式中表现为两种不同的方式：一种是跨过一个阈值时突然转到一个新的平衡态，另一种是对快速强迫的响应。虽然多平衡态对气候突变来说并不是必需的 [35]，但是古气候记录指出海气系统的运行有一定倾向性，即常出现"双稳态"的机制 [55]。这就意味着 THC 的滞后现象 [16,34,56] 的存在，这种情况在耦合气候模式中经常出现。但是这种滞回曲线的形态和结构与模式参数很有关系，因而仍是一种可调特征 [57]，因此阈值的准确位置在当前的模式中仍然是难以确定的。不过，阈值以及由此而来的 THC 的状态稳定性基本上依赖于气候的平均状态 [8,58]。

大量海洋和海气耦合模式已经发现大洋传送带存在着三种不同模态，即与从古气候资料中分析出来的现代模态、冰期模态和海因里希模态 [16,59,60] 大致一样的模态。这些模式和其他模式都指出模态之间的转换由北大西洋淡水平衡的变化启动，而模态内部的变化则和大西洋洋盆的热量收支有关。当 NADW 大量减少时，从记录中看到的"跷跷板效应"就会产生 [34,52,53]（图 2 和 4）。

近期的模拟思路假定了末次冰期期间的大气–海洋系统非常接近一个阈值，因此需要非常弱的淡水强迫来启动 THC 的突然变化 [16,60]。这些突然事件的连续发生究竟是由未知周期的强迫引起 [43,60] 还是由与大西洋周围的冰川有关的不稳定性和反馈作用引起 [16,38]，仍是尚未弄清的问题。再则，模式结果和古气候记录的大致一样，仍然依托于模式中参数的选择。因此，关于突然变化的起因这个基本问题仍然是尚未解决的。但是直到现在，所有模式的模拟结果都指向大西洋淡水平衡这一关键作用上。设计更多的接近实际的模式和改进水文循环中不同成分（降水、径流、冰山冰量的增减、海冰）的重建方法是急需的。

设计更完善的模式有望在了解气候突然变化的机制方面取得进展。这包括更高分辨率的耦合模式、不再要求通量调整的模式和包含生物化学循环的模式。后者能

The latter will enable a direct and quantitative comparison with palaeoclimatic data (for example, the stable isotopes of water and carbon), and significantly facilitate model-based hypothesis testing. The tracer $\Delta^{14}C_{atm}$ affords additional constraints and helps to estimate how much of the observed changes (Fig. 1a) can be associated with changes in the THC[27]. Results based on simplified ocean models show that a shutdown of the Atlantic THC produces a significant increase in $\Delta^{14}C_{atm}$ but the amplitudes are only about half of those observed[27]. Further model simulations are needed to fully explore the dependence of $\Delta^{14}C_{atm}$ changes on model parameters.

Tropical Pacific variability represents the dominant mode of modern climate variability with its effects felt across the globe. Although a basic understanding of the physics of ENSO has been achieved, it is still not clear how ENSO responds in colder and warmer mean climates. For example, some models suggest that tropical Pacific variability will remain similar to the present, whereas others suggest stronger and more frequent warm events could be in store in a warmer future climate. Nevertheless, it is apparent that Atlantic-to-Pacific moisture transport is sensitive to the phase of ENSO[61], so that a persistent trend towards an enhanced frequency of warm events[62] could lead to an increase in net export of moisture from the Atlantic across the Isthmus of Panama, thereby possibly affecting the THC.

Discussion

Publication of the results from the first ice core from Summit, Greenland, detailing abrupt climate change during the last glaciation[63] motivated an intensive investigation for evidence of similar climate instability occurring elsewhere on the globe and its causes. The resulting palaeoclimate records clearly reveal the global extent of millennial-scale climate variability, with varying responses that are consistent with atmospheric and oceanic changes associated with changes in the Atlantic THC (Figs 3, 4). Moreover, the relation between times of increased freshwater flux to the North Atlantic and corresponding decreases in the THC (Fig. 2) supports modelling results showing that the THC was sensitive to small changes in the hydrological cycle (order of 0.1 Sv) during the last glaciation[35,36,60].

With respect to cause and effect, however, our understanding of abrupt climate change remains incomplete. Insofar as the palaeoclimate record provides the fundamental basis for evaluating the ability of models to correctly simulate behaviour of the THC, additional information is needed to address these issues. In particular, several areas that require immediate attention include: (1) an increase in the distribution of sites in the Pacific and Southern Oceans; (2) development of new tools to synchronize palaeoclimatic records and constrain phasing relations; (3) improvements in calibrating the climate signal from proxy records; and (4) further analysis of the $\Delta^{14}C_{atm}$ record for the last 50 kyr BP.

A variety of simulations from coupled models of varying complexities are beginning to simulate the temporal evolution and global signature of millennial-scale change revealed by

够和古气候资料（例如水和碳的稳定同位素）进行直接的定量比较，也能很方便地进行关于模式的假设检验。示踪物 $\Delta^{14}C_{atm}$ 需要更多的约束，有助于估计观测到的变化量（图 1a）与 THC 的变化[27]的联系到底有多大。基于简化海洋模式的结果说明，北大西洋 THC 的停滞将导致 $\Delta^{14}C_{atm}$ 的显著增加，但其模拟到的振幅只是观测结果的一半[27]。为了弄清 $\Delta^{14}C_{atm}$ 的变化对模式参数的依赖性，进一步的模拟是需要的。

热带太平洋的变化代表现代气候变化的主要模态，其对全球都产生影响。我们虽然已对 ENSO（厄尔尼诺–南方涛动）的物理性质有了一个基本的了解，但是仍然不清楚 ENSO 在较冷和较暖的平均气候下会产生什么样的响应。例如，某些模式表明在未来较暖的气候状态下热带太平洋的变化与现代的情况相似，而另一些模式则认为会有更强、更频繁的暖事件发生。但是，大西洋到太平洋的水汽传输对 ENSO 位相的响应非常敏感[61]，这是很清楚的。因此，暖事件频率持续增大的趋势[62]会导致从大西洋穿过巴拿马地峡的水汽净输出增加，因而可能影响 THC 的状态。

讨　论

格陵兰萨米特站的第一个冰芯研究结果的发表，详尽揭示了末次冰期期间气候的突然变化[63]，推动了对发生在全球其他地方类似的气候不稳定性及其原因的广泛研究。已有的古气候记录清楚地说明，全球范围千年尺度气候变率及其不同的响应，与大西洋 THC 变化相联系的大气和海洋的变化有一致性（图 3 和 4）。此外，北大西洋的淡水输入流量增加的时间和相应的 THC 减少的时间的关系（图 2）支持了模拟结果，这些结果说明末次冰期期间 THC 对水文循环的小变化（量级为 0.1 Sv）是敏感的[35,36,60]。

但是，在因果关系方面，我们对气候突变的了解仍然是不完全的。在某种程度上，古气候记录为评估模式是否能够正确模拟 THC 的行为方面提供了重要基础，尚需要增加信息以便弄清这一重要问题。如下几个方面尤其需要重视：（1）增加太平洋和南大洋测站的数目；（2）发展研究新方法以解决古气候记录同时性和确定位相关系；（3）改进用代用资料来校正气候信号的方法；（4）进一步分析距今 5.0 万年以来的 $\Delta^{14}C_{atm}$ 记录。

各种各样的复杂耦合模式得到的不同模拟结果，已经能够初步模拟古气候记录所揭示的千年尺度的时间演变和全球特征，并对这种变化的机制提供了启示。特别

the palaeoclimate record, and provide important insights into the mechanisms of change. In particular, palaeoclimate records and modelling experiments are providing a framework for the possible magnitude of future warming and the response of the interconnected Earth system to such a warming. Moreover, coupled GCM experiments incorporating geologic data (for example, continental runoff history)[36,64] provide new constraints on the mechanisms of abrupt climate change and will lead to model improvements that are essential for achieving the ability to simulate future climate. Nevertheless, modelling past abrupt climate change remains one of the greatest challenges for palaeoclimate modellers. Further progress will probably be realized as fully interactive and non-flux adjusted coupled Earth system models are developed that treat the full range of climate feedbacks[16].

Some modelling experiments find that during the next few centuries, the THC moves to an "off" state in response to increasing greenhouse gases[14,15,65]. A reduction of the meridional heat transport into the circum-Atlantic region would partially compensate the warming due to increasing greenhouse gases, although such a change could have serious climatic consequences for the climate in the circum-Atlantic region through modifying long-established regional air–sea temperature contrasts, seasonal variations in the direction and strength of wind patterns[66] and the location of convective areas[67]. The implication of such changes on regional climate remains largely unexplored. Reorganizations in the THC would also change the distribution of water masses and hence the density in the world ocean. A warmer and more stratified North Atlantic would also take up less anthropogenic CO_2 (ref. 68). On the other hand, other experiments suggest little or no reduction of the THC to the same greenhouse gas forcing[13]. This indicates the possible dominance of negative feedback mechanisms such as changes in the amplitude and frequency of ENSO[69], or modifications of atmospheric variability patterns in the Northern Hemisphere[70].

The fate of the THC in the coming century largely depends on the response of air–sea heat and freshwater fluxes to the increased load of greenhouse gases. Uncertainties in modelled responses are particularly large for the latter[13]. Moreover, the threshold for the occurrence of an abrupt change in a particular climate model depends on poorly constrained parameterizations of sub-grid-scale ocean mixing[57]. Because a complete THC shutdown is a threshold phenomenon, the assessment of the likelihood of such an event must involve ensemble model simulations[71], as well as continued efforts to simulate past abrupt climate changes that so remarkably affected the global climate system.

(415, 863-869; 2002)

Peter U. Clark*, Nicklas G. Pisias[†], Thomas F. Stocker[‡] & Andrew J. Weaver[§]

* Department of Geosciences, Oregon State University, Corvallis, Oregon 97331, USA
[†] College of Oceanic and Atmospheric Sciences, Oregon State University, Corvallis, Oregon 97331, USA
[‡] Climate and Environmental Physics, University of Bern, Physics Institute, Sidlerstrasse 5, 3012 Bern, Switzerland
[§] School of Earth and Ocean Sciences, University of Victoria, PO Box 3055, Victoria, British Columbia V8W 3P6, Canada

是，古气候记录和模拟实验提供了未来增温的可能程度，以及相互联系的地球系统对这种增暖的响应。此外，包含地质资料（如大陆径流的历史演变）的耦合 GCM 实验[36,64]给出了关于气候突变机制的新约束，并将使模式在模拟未来气候的能力方面有本质的改进。不过，模拟过去气候突变对古气候模拟工作者来说仍然是一个很大的挑战。只有考虑完全相互作用和非通量调整的耦合地球系统模式以处理气候反馈的大多数方面，进一步的进展才可能实现[16]。

一些模拟实验得出，在未来的几个世纪，THC 将转向"关闭"的状态以响应温室气体的增加[14,15,65]。沿经线向环大西洋地区热量输送的减少将部分抵消由于温室气体增加引起的增温，然而这种变化将通过下列因素对环大西洋地区的气候造成严重的后果，这些因素是：改变长时间建立的区域性大气–海洋温度差，及风系的方向、强度[66]和对流区位置[67]的季节变化。这些变化对区域气候变化的影响意义仍然有待研究。THC 的重构将改变水团的分布，因而引起世界海水密度的变化。一个更暖和分层更多的北大西洋会吸收更少的人类活动产生的 CO_2（参考文献 68）。但是，也有一些实验指出同样强度的温室气体强迫对 THC 的减少作用不大甚至没有作用[13]。这说明，诸如 ENSO 振幅和频率的变化[69]，或者北半球大气变率分布的变化[70]，这些负反馈机制可能是主要的[70]。

下一世纪 THC 的命运很大程度上取决于大气–海洋中的热量和淡水通量对温室气体浓度增加的响应。模式模拟给出的淡水通量响应的不确定性特别大[13]。而且，在特定的气候模式中发生气候突变的阈值受不够确切的次网格海洋混合参数化的影响[57]。由于 THC 的完全消失是一个临界点的现象，对这一事件的评估需要组合模式的模拟[71]，并需要持续努力以对全球气候系统有显著影响的过去气候突变进行模拟。

（周家斌 翻译；郑旭峰 审稿）

References:

1. Ganachaud, A. & Wunsch, C. Improved estimates of global ocean circulation, heat transport and mixing from hydrographic data. *Nature* **408**, 453-457 (2000).

2. Weaver, A. J., Bitz, C. M., Fanning, A. F. & Holland, M. M. Thermohaline circulation: High latitude phenomena and the difference between the Pacific and Atlantic. *Annu. Rev. Earth Planet. Sci.* **27**, 231-285 (1999).

3. Killworth, P. D. Deep convection in the world ocean. *Rev. Geophys. Space Phys.* **21**, 1-26 (1983).

4. Grumbine, R. W. A model of the formation of high-salinity shelf water on polar continental shelves. *J. Geophys. Res.* **96**, 22049-22062 (1991).

5. Stommel, H. Thermohaline convection with two stable regimes of flow. *Tellus* **13**, 224-250 (1961).

6. Bryan, F. High-latitude salinity effects and interhemispheric thermohaline circulations. *Nature* **323**, 301-304 (1986).

7. Manabe, S. & Stouffer, R. J. Two stable equilibria of a coupled ocean-atmosphere model. *J. Clim.* **1**, 841-866 (1988).

8. Weaver, A. J. in *Natural Climate Variability on Decade-to-Century Time Scales* (eds Martinson, D. G. *et al.*) 365-381 (National Research Council, National Academy Press, Washington DC, 1995).

9. Alley, R. B. & Clark, P. U. The glaciation of the northern hemisphere: a global perspective. *Annu. Rev. Earth Planet. Sci.* **27**, 149-182 (1999).

10. Stocker, T. F. Past and future reorganization in the climate system. *Quat. Sci. Rev.* **19**, 301-319 (2000).

11. Broecker, W. S. Thermohaline circulation, the Achilles heel of our climate system: Will man-made CO_2 upset the current balance? *Science* **278**, 1582-1588 (1997).

12. Alley, R. B. *et al. Abrupt Climate Change: Inevitable Surprises* (National Research Council, National Academy Press, Washington DC, in the press).

13. Cubasch, U. *et al.* in *Climate Change 2001—The Scientific Basis: Contribution of Working Group I to the Third Assessment Report of the Intergovernmental Panel on Climate Change* (eds Houghton, J. T. *et al.*) 525-582 (Cambridge Univ. Press, Cambridge, 2001).

14. Manabe, S. & Stouffer, R. J. Century-scale effects of increased atmospheric CO_2 on the ocean-atmosphere system. *Nature* **364**, 215-218 (1993).

15. Stocker, T. F. & Schmittner, A. Influence of CO_2 emission rates on the stability of the thermohaline circulation. *Nature* **388**, 862-865 (1997).

16. Schmittner, A., Yoshimori, M. & Weaver, A. J. Instability of glacial climate in an earth system model. *Science* (in the press).

17. Dickson, R. R. & Brown, J. The production of North Atlantic deep water: Sources, sinks and pathways. *J. Geophys. Res.* **99**, 12319-12341 (1994).

18. McCartney, M. S. Recirculating components to the deep boundary current of the northern North Atlantic. *Prog. Oceanogr.* **29**, 283-383 (1992).

19. Labeyrie, L. *et al.* Changes in vertical structure of the North Atlantic Ocean between glacial and modern times. *Quat. Sci. Rev.* **11**, 401-413 (1992).

20. Vidal, L., Labeyrie, L. & van Weering, T. C. E. Benthic $\delta^{18}O$ records in the North Atlantic over the last glacial period (60–10 kyr): Evidence for brine formation. *Paleoceanography* **13**, 245-251 (1998).

21. Sarnthein, M. *et al.* Changes in east Atlantic deepwater circulation over the last 30,000 years: Eight time slice reconstructions. *Paleoceanography* **9**, 209-262 (1994).

22. Yu, E. F., Francois, R. & Bacon, M. P. Similar rates of modern and last-glacial ocean thermohaline circulation inferred from radiochemical data. *Nature* **379**, 689-694 (1996).

23. Rutberg, R. L., Hemming, S. R. & Goldstein, S. L. Reduced North Atlantic Deep Water flux to the glacial Southern Ocean inferred from neodymium isotope ratios. *Nature* **405**, 935-938 (2000).

24. Frank, M. Comparison of cosmogenic radionuclide production and geomagnetic field intensity over the last 200,000 years. *Phil. Trans. R. Soc. Lond. A* **358**, 1089-1102 (2000).

25. Finkel, R. C. & Nishiizumi, K. Beryllium 10 concentrations in the Greenland Ice Sheet Project 2 ice core from 3–40 ka. *J. Geophys. Res.* **102**, 26699-26706 (1997).

26. Muscheler, R., Beer, J., Wagner, G. & Finkel, R. C. Changes in deep-water formation during the Younger Dryas event inferred from ^{10}Be and ^{14}C records. *Nature* **408**, 562-520 (2000).

27. Marchal, O., Stocker, T. F. & Muscheler, R. Atmospheric radiocarbon during the Younger Dryas: production, ventilation, or both? *Earth Planet Sci. Lett.* **185**, 383-395 (2001).

28. Broecker, W. S., Mix, A., Andree, M. & Oeschger, H. Radiocarbon measurements on coexisting benthic and planktic foraminifera shells: potential for reconstructing ocean ventilation times over the past 20000 years. *Nucl. Instrum. Methods Phys. Res.* **B5**, 331-339 (1984).

29. Sikes, E. L., Samson, C. R., Guilderson, T. P. & Howard, W. R. Old radiocarbon ages in the southwest Pacific Ocean during the last glacial period and deglaciation. *Nature* **405**, 555-559 (2000).

30. Cuffey, K. M. *et al.* Large Arctic temperature change at the Wisconsin-Holocene glacial transition. *Science* **270**, 455-458 (1995).

31. Bard, E., Rostek, F., Turon, J.-L. & Gendreau, S. Hydrological impact of Heinrich events in the subtropical northeast Atlantic. *Science* **289**, 1321-1324 (1999).

32. Severinghaus, J. P. & Brook, E. J. Abrupt climate change at the end of the last glacial period inferred from trapped air in polar ice. *Science* **286**, 930-934 (1999).

33. Hughen, K. A., Southon, J. R., Lehman, S. J. & Overpeck, J. T. Synchronous radiocarbon and climate shifts during the last deglaciation. *Science* **290**, 1951-1954 (2000).

34. Stocker, T. F. & Wright, D. G. Rapid transitions of the ocean's deep circulation induced by changes in surface water fluxes. *Nature* **351**, 729-732 (1991).

35. Manabe, S. & Stouffer, R. J. Coupled ocean-atmosphere model response to freshwater input: comparison to Younger Dryas event. *Paleoceanography* **12**, 321-336 (1997).

36. Fanning, A. F. & Weaver, A. J. Temporal-geographical meltwater influences on the North Atlantic Conveyor: Implications for the Younger Dryas. *Paleoceanography* **12**, 307-320 (1997).

37. Bond, G. C. *et al.* in *Mechanisms of Global Climate Change at Millennial Timescales* (eds Clark, P. U., Webb, R. S. & Keigwin, L. D.) 35-58 (Geophysical Monograph 112, American Geophysical Union, Washington DC, 1999).

38. Clark, P. U. *et al.* Freshwater forcing of abrupt climate change during the last glaciation. *Science* **293**, 283-287 (2001).

39. Fairbanks, R. G. A 17,000-year glacio-eustatic sea level record: influence of glacial melting rates on the Younger Dryas event and deep ocean circulation. *Nature* **342**, 637-642 (1989).

40. Clark, P. U., Mitrovica, J. X., Milne, G. A. & Tamisiea, M. Sea-level fingerprinting as a direct test for the source of global meltwater pulse 1A. *Science* (submitted).

41. Severinghaus, J. P., Sowers, T., Brook, E. J., Alley, R. B. & Bender, M. L. Timing of abrupt climate change at the end of the Younger Dryas interval from thermally fractionated gases in polar ice. *Nature* **391**, 141-146 (1998).

42. McManus, J. F., Oppo, D. W. & Cullen, J. L. A 0.5-million-year record of millennial-scale climate variability in the North Atlantic. *Science* **283**, 971-975 (1999).

43. Alley, R. B., Anandakrishnan, S. & Jung, P. Stochastic resonance in the North Atlantic. *Paleoceanography* **16**, 190-198 (2001).

44. Hostetler, S. W., Clark, P. U., Bartlein, P. J., Mix, A. C. & Pisias, N. Atmospheric transmission of North Atlantic Heinrich events. *J. Geophys. Res.* **104**, 3947-3952 (1999).

45. Hughen, K. A., Overpeck, J. T., Peterson, L. C. & Trumbore, S. Rapid climate changes in the tropical Atlantic region during the last deglaciation. *Nature* **380**, 51-54 (1996).

46. Peterson, L. C., Haug, G. H., Hughen, K. A. & Rohl, U. Rapid changes in the hydrologic cycle of the tropical Atlantic during the last glacial. *Science* **290**, 1947-1951 (2000).

47. Schulz, H., von Rad, U. & Erlenkeuser, H. Correlations between Arabian Sea and Greenland climate oscillations of the past 110,000 years. *Nature* **393**, 54-57 (1998).

48. Kienast, M., Steinke, S., Stattegger, K. & Calvert, S. E. Synchronous tropical South China Sea SST change and Greenland warming during deglaciation. *Science* **291**, 2132-2134 (2001).

49. Behl, R. J. & Kennett, J. P. Brief interstadial events in the Santa Barbara basin, NE Pacific, during the past 60 kyr. *Nature* **379**, 243-246 (1996).

50. Blunier, T. & Brook, E. J. Timing of millennial-scale climate change in Antarctica and Greenland during the last glacial period. *Science* **291**, 109-112 (2001).

51. Broecker, W. S. Paleocean circulation during the last deglaciation: A bipolar seesaw? Paleoceanography **13**, 119-121 (1998).

52. Crowley, T. J. North Atlantic deep water cools the southern hemisphere. *Paleoceanography* **7**, 489-497 (1992).

53. Schiller, A., Mikolajewicz, U. & Voss, R. The stability of the thermohaline circulation in a coupled ocean-atmosphere general circulation model. *Clim. Dyn.* **13**, 325-347 (1997).

54. Stocker, T. F. The seesaw effect. *Science* **282**, 61-62 (1998).

55. Oeschger, H. *et al.* in *Climate Processes and Climate Sensitivity* (eds Hansen, J. E. & Takahashi, T.) 299–306 (Geophysical Monograph 29, American Geophysical Union, Washington DC, 1984).

56. Mikolajewicz, U. & Maier-Reimer, E. Mixed boundary conditions in ocean general circulation models and their influence on the stability of the model's conveyor belt. *J. Geophys. Res.* **99**, 22633-22644 (1994).

57. Schmittner, A. & Weaver, A. J. Dependence of multiple climate states on ocean mixing parameters. *Geophys. Res. Lett.* **28**, 1027-1030 (2001).

58. Tziperman, E. Inherently unstable climate behaviour due to weak thermohaline ocean circulation. *Nature* **386**, 592-595 (1997).

59. Mikolajewicz, U., Maier-Reimer, E., Crowley, T. J. & Kim, K.-Y. Effect of Drake and Panamanian gateways on the circulation of an ocean model. *Paleoceanography* **8**, 409-426 (1993).

60. Ganopolski, A. & Rahmstorf, S. Rapid changes of glacial climate simulated in a coupled climate model. *Nature* **409**, 153-158 (2001).

61. Schmittner, A., Appenzeller, C. & Stocker, T. F. Enhanced Atlantic freshwater export during El Niño. *Geophys. Res. Lett.* **27**, 1163-1166 (2000).

62. Timmermann, A. *et al.* Increased El Niño frequency in a climate model forced by future greenhouse warming. *Nature* **398**, 694-696 (1999).

63. Johnsen, S. J. *et al.* Irregular glacial interstadials recorded in a new Greenland ice core. *Nature* **359**, 311-313 (1992).

64. Rind, D. *et al.* Effects of glacial meltwater in the GISS coupled atmosphere-ocean model: Part I: North Atlantic Deep Water response. *J. Geophys. Res.* **106**, 27335-27354 (2001).

65. Rahmstorf, S. & Ganopolski, A. Long-term global warming scenarios computed with an efficient coupled climate model. *Clim. Change* **43**, 353-367 (1999).

66. Mikolajewicz, U. & Voss, R. The role of the individual air-sea flux components in CO_2-induced changes of the ocean's circulation and climate. *Clim. Dyn.* **16**, 627-642 (2000).

67. Wood, R. A., Keen, A. B., Mitchell, J. F. B. & Gregory, J. M. Changing spatial structure of the thermohaline circulation in response to atmospheric CO_2 forcing in a climate model. *Nature* **399**, 572-575 (1999).

68. Joos, F., Plattner, G.-K., Stocker, T. F., Marchal, O. & Schmittner, A. Global warming and marine carbon cycle feedbacks on future atmospheric CO_2. *Science* **284**, 464-467 (1999).

69. Latif, M., Roeckner, E., Mikolajewicz, U. & Voss, R. Tropical stabilization of the thermohaline circulation in a greenhouse warming simulation. *J. Clim.* **13**, 1809-1813 (2000).

70. Delworth, T. L. & Dixon, K. W. Implications of the recent trend in the Arctic/North Atlantic Oscillation for the North Atlantic thermohaline circulation. *J. Clim.* **13**, 3721-3727 (2000).

71. Knutti, R. & Stocker, T. F. Limited predictability of the future thermohaline circulation close to an instability threshold. *J. Clim.* **15**, 179-186 (2002).

72. Stuiver, M. *et al.* INTCAL98 radiocarbon age calibration, 24,000 cal BP. *Radiocarbon* **40**, 1041-1083 (1998).

73. Kitigawa, H. & van der Plicht, J. Atmospheric radiocarbon calibration beyond 11,900 cal BP from Lake Suigetsu laminated sediments. *Radiocarbon* **42**, 369-380 (2000).

74. Bard, E., Arnold, M., Hamelin, B., Tisnerat-Laborde, N. & Cabioch, G. Radiocarbon calibration by means of mass spectrometric $^{230}Th/^{234}U$ and ^{14}C ages of

corals: an updated database including samples from Barbados, Mururoa and Tahiti. *Radiocarbon* **40**, 1085-1092 (1998).

75. Cuffey, K. M. & Clow, G. D. Temperature, accumulation, and ice sheet elevation in central Greenland through the last deglacial transition. *J. Geophys. Res.* **102**, 26383-26396 (1992).

76. Grootes, P. M., Stuiver, M., White, J. W. C., Johnsen, S. J. & Jouzel, J. Comparison of oxygen isotope records from the GISP2 and GRIP Greenland ice cores. *Nature* **366**, 552-554 (1993).

77. Meese, D. A. *et al.* The Greenland Ice Sheet Project 2 depth-age scale: Methods and results. *J. Geophys. Res.* **102**, 26411-26423 (1997).

78. Rühlemann, C., Mulitza, S., Muller, P. J., Wefer, G. & Zahn, R. Warming of the tropical Atlantic Ocean and slowdown of thermohaline circulation during the last deglaciation. *Nature* **402**, 511-514 (1999).

79. Sachs, J. P., Anderson, R. F. & Lehman, S. J. Glacial surface temperatures of the southeast Atlantic Ocean. *Science* **293**, 2077-2079 (2001).

80. Steig, E. J. *et al.* Synchronous climate changes in Antarctica and the North Atlantic. *Science* **282**, 92-95 (1998).

81. Mulvaney, R. *et al.* The transition from the last glacial period in inland and near coastal Antarctica. *Geophys. Res. Lett.* **27**, 2673-2676 (2000).

82. Pisias, N. G., Mix, A. C. & Heusser, L. Millennial scale climate variability of the northeast Pacific Ocean and northwest North America based on radiolaria and pollen. *Quat. Sci. Rew.* **20**, 1561-1576 (2001).

83. Mix, A. C. *et al.* in *Mechanisms of Global Climate Change at Millennial Timescales* (eds Clark, P. U., Webb, R. S. & Keigwin, L. D.) 122-148 (Geophysical Monograph 112, American Geophysical Union, Washington DC, 1999).

84. Thompson, L. G. *et al.* Late glacial stage and Holocene tropical ice core records from Huascaran, Peru. *Science* **269**, 46-50 (1995).

85. Thompson, L. G. *et al.* A 25,000-year tropical climate history from Bolivian ice cores. *Science* **282**, 1858-1864 (1998).

86. Bard, E., Rostek, F. & Sonzogni, C. Interhemispheric synchrony of the last deglaciation inferred from alkenone paleothermometry. *Nature* **385**, 707-710 (1997).

87. Little, M. G. *et al.* Trade wind forcing of upwelling seasonality, and Heinrich events as a response to sub-Milankovitch climate variability. *Paleoceanography* **12**, 568-576 (1997).

88. Charles, C. D., Lynch-Stieglitz, J., Ninnemann, U. S. & Fairbanks, R. G. Climate connections between the hemispheres revealed by deep sea sediment core/ice core correlations. *Earth Planet. Sci. Lett.* **142**, 19-22 (1996).

89. Petit, J. R. *et al.* Climate and atmospheric history of the past 420,000 years from the Vostok ice core, Antarctica. *Nature* **399**, 429-436 (1999).

90. Jouzel, J. *et al.* A new 22 ky high resolution East Antarctic climate record. *Geophys. Res. Lett.* **28**, 3199-3202 (2001).

Acknowledgements. We thank G. Bond, J. Jouzel, A. Mix, R. Muscheler, J. Sachs and J. van der Plicht for providing data, the NOAA-NGDC Paleoclimate Program for their data repository, and S. Hostetler, A. Mix, A. Schmittner and R. Stouffer for comments. This work was supported by grants from the Earth System History Program of the US NSF (P.U.C. and N.G.P.), the Swiss NSF (T.F.S.) and the Canadian NSERC (A.J.W.).

Correspondence and requests for materials should be addressed to P.U.C. (e-mail: clarkp@ucs.orst.edu).

Detecting Recent Positive Selection in the Human Genome from Haplotype Structure

P. C. Sabeti *et al.*

Editor's Note

In this paper, geneticist Eric Lander and colleagues present a method for detecting the genetic imprint of natural selection. The technique focuses on haplotypes, sets of closely linked genetic markers present on one chromosome that tend to be inherited together. Knowing that variants of two key genes confer malarial resistance in some individuals, the team looked for evidence that a particular haplotype associated with the resistance variant arose faster in certain populations than would have happened by chance. This "signature" of natural selection was found in both the *G6PD* and CD40 ligand genes, and the team suggest that the test could be used to scan the entire human genome for evidence of recent positive selection.

The ability to detect recent natural selection in the human population would have profound implications for the study of human history and for medicine. Here, we introduce a framework for detecting the genetic imprint of recent positive selection by analysing long-range haplotypes in human populations. We first identify haplotypes at a locus of interest (core haplotypes). We then assess the age of each core haplotype by the decay of its association to alleles at various distances from the locus, as measured by extended haplotype homozygosity (EHH). Core haplotypes that have unusually high EHH and a high population frequency indicate the presence of a mutation that rose to prominence in the human gene pool faster than expected under neutral evolution. We applied this approach to investigate selection at two genes carrying common variants implicated in resistance to malaria: *G6PD*[1] and CD40 ligand[2]. At both loci, the core haplotypes carrying the proposed protective mutation stand out and show significant evidence of selection. More generally, the method could be used to scan the entire genome for evidence of recent positive selection.

THE recent history of the human population is characterized by great environmental change and emergent selective agents[3]. The domestication of plants and animals at the start of the Neolithic, roughly 10,000 years ago, yielded an increase in human population density. Humans were confronted with the spread of new infectious diseases, new food sources and new cultural environments. The last 10,000 years have thus been some of the most interesting times in human biological history, and may be when many important genetic adaptations and disease resistances arose.

We sought to design a powerful approach for detecting recent selection. Our method relies

从单倍型结构检测人类基因组近期的正选择

萨贝提等

编者按

在这篇文章中，遗传学家埃里克·兰德和他的同事们提出了一种检测自然选择的遗传印记的方法。这项技术关注的是单倍型，即存在于一条染色体上的一系列紧密相连的遗传标记，这些标记往往是一起遗传的。研究小组了解到两个关键基因的变异型在某些个体中产生了疟疾抗药性，因此他们寻找证据来证明在某些人群中，与抗药性变异相关的一种特定单倍型出现的速度比偶然出现的速度更快。在 G6PD 和 CD40 配体基因中都发现了这种自然选择的"特征"，研究小组认为，该测试可以用来扫描整个人类基因组，以寻找近期正选择的证据。

检测人群中最近发生的自然选择对于研究人类历史和医学具有深远的意义。这里我们介绍一个通过分析人群中长范围的单倍型来检测最近正选择的基因印记的框架。首先我们在感兴趣的基因座识别单倍型（核心单倍型）。然后我们通过其与该基因座不同距离的等位基因联系的衰减评估每个核心单倍型的年龄，即通过扩展单倍型纯合性（EHH）进行测定。具有异常高的 EHH 和高人群频率的核心单倍型表明，在自然中性进化下，一种突变在人类基因库中上升的速度快于预期。我们应用这种方法研究了两个携带涉及抗疟疾能力的寻常变异型的基因上的选择，G6PD[1] 和 CD40 配体[2]。在这两个基因座上，携带假设的保护性突变的核心单倍型凸现出来并显示出重要的选择证据。一般来说，该方法可以用于扫描整个基因组，以寻找近期正选择的证据。

人类近代史的特点是巨大的环境变化和涌现的选择性媒介[3]。大约 10,000 年前新石器时代开始时，人类培育植物和驯化动物导致人群密度的增长。人类面临着新的传染病、新的食物来源和新的文化环境的传播。因此，过去的 10,000 年成为了人类生物学史上最有意义的一段时间，也可能是许多重要的基因适应和疾病抵抗力出现的时间。

我们试图设计一种强大的方法来检测最近的选择。我们的方法主要基于等位基

on the relationship between an allele's frequency and the extent of linkage disequilibrium (LD) surrounding it. (LD often refers to association between two alleles. Here, we use it to measure the association between a single allele at one locus with multiple loci at various distances.) Under neutral evolution, new variants require a long time to reach high frequency in the population, and LD around the variants will decay substantially during this period owing to recombination[4,5]. As a result, common alleles will typically be old and will have only short-range LD. Rare alleles may be either young or old and thus may have long- or short-range LD. The key characteristic of positive selection, however, is that it causes an unusually rapid rise in allele frequency, occurring over a short enough time that recombination does not substantially break down the haplotype on which the selected mutation occurs. A signature of positive natural selection is thus an allele having unusually long-range LD given its population frequency. The decay of LD, and therefore the relative scale of "short"- and "long"-range LD, is dependent on local recombination rates. A general test for selection on the basis of these principles must therefore control for local variation in recombination rates.

We developed an experimental design to detect positive selection at a locus using the breakdown of LD as a clock for estimating the ages of alleles. We began by genotyping a collection of single nucleotide polymorphisms (SNPs) in a small "core region" to identify the "core haplotypes". We selected SNPs of sufficient density, so that recombination between them would be extremely rare and the core haplotypes could be explained in terms of a single gene genealogy (Supplementary Fig. 1). Zones of very low historical recombination were identified by looking for clusters of SNPs where Hudson's R_M was 0 and $|D'|$ was one[6,7] (see Supplementary Fig. 1).

We then added increasingly distant SNPs to study the decay of LD from each core haplotype. To visualize this process, we generated haplotype bifurcation diagrams that branch to reflect the creation of new, extended haplotypes by historical recombination proximal and distal to the core region. We measured LD at a distance x from the core region by calculating the extended haplotype homozygosity (EHH). EHH is defined as the probability that two randomly chosen chromosomes carrying the core haplotype of interest are identical by descent (as assayed by homozygosity at all SNPs[8]) for the entire interval from the core region to the point x. EHH thus detects the transmission of an extended haplotype without recombination. Our test for positive selection involves finding a core haplotype with a combination of high frequency and high EHH, as compared with other core haplotypes at the locus. An attractive aspect of this approach is that the various core haplotypes at a locus serve as internal controls for one another, adjusting for any unevenness in the local recombination rate.

We applied our approach to two genes that have been implicated in resistance to the malaria parasite *Plasmodium falciparum*. Glucose-6-phosphate dehydrogenase (*G6PD*) is a classical example of a gene where variants can confer malaria resistance[9]. Evidence over the past 40 years has shown that the common variant *G6PD*-202A confers partial protection against malaria, with a case-control study estimating a reduction in disease risk

因的频率与其附近连锁不平衡（LD）程度之间的关系。（LD 通常指两个等位基因间的联系。这里我们用它来测量一个基因座的单个等位基因与不同距离处的多个基因座等位基因之间的联系。）在中性进化下，新的变异型需要一段很长的时间才能达到人群中较高的频率，而且在此期间，变异型附近的 LD 会由于重组大幅度地衰减[4,5]。结果，常见等位基因通常是老的并只有短范围的 LD。很少的等位基因可能是年轻的也可能是老的，因此可能具有长或者短范围的 LD。但是正选择的关键特征是它能引起等位基因频率在足够短的时间内异常快速的增长，以至于重组并未能充分打破这些选择突变发生处的单倍型。因此一个正自然选择的标志就是一个等位基因在其人类频率下具有异常长范围的 LD。LD 的衰减以及因此相对的短和长范围 LD 规模，取决于局部的重组率。根据这个原理设计的选择试验必须控制重组率的局部变异。

　　我们开发了一种实验设计，利用 LD 的分解作为时钟来估算等位基因的年龄，以检测一个基因座的正选择。我们首先在一个小的"核心区域"对一组单核苷酸多态性（SNP）进行基因分型，以识别"核心单倍型"。我们选取具有足够密度的 SNP，这样它们之间的重组会非常少，而且核心单倍型可以用单个基因的谱系来表示（见补充图 1）。通过寻找那些赫德森 $R_M = 0$ 且 $|D'| = 1$ 的 SNP 簇来找出历史重组率非常低的区域[6,7]（见补充图 1）。

　　然后我们加入逐渐增加距离的 SNP 研究每个核心单倍型 LD 的衰减。为了可视化这个过程，我们设计了单倍型分支图，用分支的方式反映核心区域近端和远端通过历史重组产生的新的扩展单倍型。我们通过计算扩展单倍型纯合性（EHH）来测量距离核心区域 x 的 LD。EHH 可以被定义为从核心区域到距离 x 的整个区间内，随机选择的两条携带感兴趣的核心单倍型的染色体在下降过程（通过所有 SNP 的纯合性来测定[8]）中的相同概率。因此，EHH 能够检测不含有重组的扩展单倍型的传播。我们对正选择的检测包含了找到一个与该基因座的其他核心单倍型相比具有高频率和高 EHH 组合的核心单倍型。这种方法令人满意的方面在于一个基因座的多个核心单倍型可以作为相互之间的内部对照，对任何局部重组率上的不均衡进行调节。

　　我们将方法用于与疟疾寄生虫恶性疟原虫的抗药性有关的两个基因上。葡萄糖–6–磷酸脱氢酶（G6PD）是一个基因变异型能够产生疟疾抗性的经典例子[9]。过去 40 年的证据表明常见变异型 G6PD-202A 对疟疾具有部分抗性，其中一项病例对照研究估计可将疾病风险降低约 50%（文献 1）。CD40 配体基因（TNFSF5）编码一种对

of about 50% (ref. 1). The CD40 ligand gene (*TNFSF5*) encodes a protein with a critical role in immune response to infectious agents. One case-control study suggested that a common variant in the promoter region, *TNFSF5*-726C, is associated with a similar degree of protection against malaria[2].

We first studied *G6PD* (Fig. 1). We defined a core region of 15 kilobases (kb) at *G6PD* and genotyped 11 SNPs in 3 African and 2 non-African populations. The SNPs defined 9 core haplotypes (Table 1a) (denoted *G6PD*-CH1 to 9, for core haplotypes 1 to 9). The *G6PD*-202A allele, which has been associated with protection from malaria, was carried on only one core haplotype, *G6PD*-CH8. Notably, *G6PD*-CH8 is common in Africa (18%), where malaria is endemic, but is absent outside of Africa. For carrying out our test for selection, we focused on the three African populations, which did not differ significantly with respect to core haplotype frequencies (by Fisher's exact test[10]) and hence were pooled for the main analysis. (Analyses were also performed separately for each population, yielding qualitatively similar results; see below.)

Fig. 1. Experimental design of core and long-range SNPs for *G6PD* and *TNFSF5*. The core region is highlighted by a cluster of densely spaced SNPs (arrows) at the gene. Additional, widely separated flanking SNPs, used to examine the decay of LD from each core haplotype, are also shown. Markers distal to *G6PD* were within repetitive subtelomeric sequence and could not be genotyped.

Table 1. Core haplotype frequencies in six populations

(a) *G6PD* Core haplotype	Core SNP alleles (kb)											Core haplotype frequencies in six populations						
	-10	-2	-2	-1	0	1	1	3	3	4	4	Total	Beni	Yoruba	Shona	African American	European American	Asian
1	C	G	C	G	G	A	C	C	G	C	C	0.13 (54)	0.15 (9)	0.21 (18)	0.13 (11)	0.13 (12)	0.03 (2)	0.07 (2)
2	–	–	–	–	–	–	–	–	–	–	T	0.16 (67)	0 (0)	0 (0)	0 (0)	0.07 (6)	0.57 (37)	0.80 (24)
3	–	–	–	–	–	–	–	–	–	T	–	0.25 (102)	0.23 (14)	0.24 (21)	0.45 (37)	0.19 (17)	0.17 (11)	0.07 (2)
4	–	–	–	–	–	–	–	T	–	–	–	0.01 (5)	0.02 (1)	0 (0)	0.04 (3)	0.01 (1)	0 (0)	0 (0)
5	–	–	–	–	–	–	–	T	A	–	–	0.10 (41)	0.22 (13)	0.11 (10)	0.06 (5)	0.14 (13)	0 (0)	0 (0)
6	–	–	–	–	–	G	–	–	–	–	–	0.12 (48)	0.17 (10)	0.10 (9)	0.11 (9)	0.22 (20)	0 (0)	0 (0)
7	–	–	T	A	–	G	G	–	–	–	–	0.04 (17)	0.05 (3)	0.07 (6)	0.06 (5)	0.03 (3)	0 (0)	0 (0)
8	–	A*	T	A	A	G	G	–	–	–	–	0.13 (53)	0.17 (10)	0.23 (20)	0.13 (11)	0.13 (12)	0 (0)	0 (0)
9	T	–	–	–	–	–	–	–	–	–	T	0.07 (28)	0 (0)	0.03 (3)	0.02 (2)	0.07 (6)	0.23 (15)	0.07 (2)
											N	415	60	87	83	90	65	30

感染性病原体的免疫应答起关键作用的蛋白。一个病例对照研究表明启动子区域的一个常见变异型 *TNFSF5*-726C 对疟疾具有类似程度的抗性 [2]。

我们首先研究了 *G6PD*（图 1）。在 *G6PD* 上定义了一个 15 千碱基（kb）的核心区域，并在 3 个非洲人群和 2 个非非洲人群中对 11 个 SNP 进行了基因分型。这些 SNP 定义了 9 个核心单倍型（表 1a）（分别表示为 *G6PD*-CH1 到 *G6PD*-CH9，指代核心单倍型 1 到 9）。只有一个核心单倍型（*G6PD*-CH8）携带了 *G6PD*-202A 等位基因，该等位基因与疟疾抗病性相关。显然，*G6PD*-CH8 在疟疾流行的非洲很常见（18%），而在非洲以外地区不存在。为了实施选择测试，我们将重点放在三个非洲人群上，他们在核心单倍型频率上没有显著差异（通过 Fisher 精确测试 [10]），因此被集中在一起进行主要分析。（对每个人群也分别进行了分析，得到了定性上相似的结果；见下文）。

图 1. *G6PD* 和 *TNFSF5* 的核心 SNP 和长范围 SNP 的实验设计。基因的核心区域被一群密集排列的 SNP（箭头）突出显示。此外，图中还显示了高度分离的侧翼 SNP，用于检验每个核心单倍型的 LD 衰减。*G6PD* 远端的标记位于重复的亚端粒序列中，不能进行基因分型。

表 1. 六个群体中的核心单倍型频率

(a) *G6PD* 核心单倍型	核心 SNP 等位基因（kb）										六个群体中的核心单倍型频率						
	−10	−2	−2	−1	0	1	1	3	3	4	4	总计	贝尼人	约鲁巴人	绍纳人	非裔美国人	欧裔美国人	亚洲人
1	C	G	C	G	G	A	C	C	G	C	C	0.13(54)	0.15(9)	0.21(18)	0.13(11)	0.13(12)	0.03(2)	0.07(2)
2	−	−	−	−	−	−	−	−	−	−	T	0.16(67)	0(0)	0(0)	0(0)	0.07(6)	0.57(37)	0.80(24)
3	−	−	−	−	−	−	−	−	T	−	−	0.25(102)	0.23(14)	0.24(21)	0.45(37)	0.19(17)	0.17(11)	0.07(2)
4	−	−	−	−	−	−	−	T	−	−	−	0.01(5)	0.02(1)	0(0)	0.04(3)	0.01(1)	0(0)	0(0)
5	−	−	−	−	−	T	A	−	−	−	−	0.10(41)	0.22(13)	0.11(10)	0.06(5)	0.14(13)	0(0)	0(0)
6	−	−	−	−	G	−	−	−	−	−	−	0.12(48)	0.17(10)	0.10(9)	0.11(9)	0.22(20)	0(0)	0(0)
7	−	−	T	A	−	G	G	−	−	−	−	0.04(17)	0.05(3)	0.07(6)	0.06(5)	0.03(3)	0(0)	0(0)
8	−	A*	T	A	A	G	G	−	−	−	−	0.13(53)	0.17(10)	0.23(20)	0.13(11)	0.13(12)	0(0)	0(0)
9	T	−	−	−	−	−	−	−	−	−	T	0.07(28)	0(0)	0.03(3)	0.02(2)	0.07(6)	0.23(15)	0.07(2)
											N	415	60	87	83	90	65	30

Continued

(b) TNFSF5 Core haplotype	Core SNP alleles (kb)					Core haplotype frequencies in six populations						
	−6	0	1	3	4	Total	Beni	Yoruba	Shona	African American	European American	Asian
1	T	T	T	T	G	0.03 (12)	0.06 (4)	0.03 (3)	0.02 (2)	0.04 (3)	0 (0)	0 (0)
2	C	–	–	–	–	0.50 (200)	0.32 (20)	0.38 (33)	0.46 (38)	0.40 (32)	0.78 (49)	1.00 (28)
3	C	–	–	C	–	0.08 (32)	0.10 (6)	0.12 (10)	0.06 (5)	0.14 (11)	0 (0)	0 (0)
4	–	C*	–	–	–	0.25 (100)	0.38 (24)	0.38 (33)	0.26 (21)	0.27 (22)	0 (0)	0 (0)
5	–	–	C	–	–	0.12 (47)	0.14 (9)	0.07 (6)	0.18 (15)	0.14 (11)	0.10 (6)	0 (0)
6	–	–	C	–	A	0.02 (10)	0 (0)	0 (0)	0.01 (1)	0.01 (1)	0.13 (8)	0 (0)
7	–	C*	C	–	A	0 (1)	0 (0)	0.01 (1)	0 (0)	0 (0)	0 (0)	0 (0)
8	C	–	C	–	–	0 (1)	0 (0)	0 (0)	0 (0)	0.01 (1)	0 (0)	0 (0)
					N	403	63	86	82	81	63	28

Observed core haplotypes at *G6PD* and *TNFSF5* in six populations of African, European and Asian descent. Relative distances of core SNP alleles from the putative malaria resistance mutations are given in kb. Frequencies for haplotypes (and numbers of observations) are given for all populations. There are no apparent recombinants among the *G6PD* core haplotypes, and R_M is 0. There are 2 recombinant haplotypes among the 403 *TNFSF5* chromosomes, and R_M would also be 0 if the 2 haplotypes appearing only once were removed from the analysis[6].
*Both proposed mutations associated with malaria resistance (*G6PD*-202A and *TNFSF5*-726C) are observed only in Africans and occur on *G6PD*-CH8 and on *TNFSF5*-CH4 and *TNFSF5*-CH7, respectively.

G6PD-CH8 demonstrates clear long-range LD (as seen by the predominance of one thick branch in the haplotype bifurcation diagram (Fig. 2a)) and has correspondingly high EHH. The EHH is 0.38 at the largest distance tested; that is, 413 kb (Fig. 2c). For each core haplotype we calculated the relative EHH; specifically, the factor by which EHH decays on the tested core haplotype compared with the decay of EHH on all other core haplotypes combined (Methods).

To test formally for selection, for each core haplotype, we compared the allele frequency to the relative EHH at various distances (Fig. 2e shows the comparison at 413 kb proximal to *G6PD*). *G6PD*-CH8 has a much higher relative EHH than other haplotypes of comparable frequency, but is this statistically significant? To obtain a sense of how unusual our observation is, we simulated haplotypes using a coalescent process (see Methods and Fig. 2e)[11]. The deviation from the simulation results is highly significant and becomes progressively more marked with increasing distance (Fig. 2g) (*P*-values at 413 kb proximal are: constant-sized population, $P < 0.0008$; expansion, $P < 0.0006$; bottleneck, $P < 0.0008$; population structure, $P < 0.0008$; see Methods and Supplementary Table 2 for details of the demographic models we considered). The frequency and LD properties of *G6PD*-CH8 are incompatible with what is expected under a model of neutral evolution for a wide range of demographies. Furthermore, when the three African populations comprising the pooled sample were considered separately, a signal of selection was identified independently in each population (Yoruba, $P < 0.0012$; Beni, $P < 0.0440$; and Shona, $P < 0.0030$, based on

续表

(b) TNFSF5 核心单倍型	核心 SNP 等位基因 (kb)					六个群体中的核心单倍型频率						
	−6	0	1	3	4	总计	贝尼人	约鲁巴人	绍纳人	非裔美国人	欧裔美国人	亚洲人
1	T	T	T	T	G	0.03(12)	0.06(4)	0.03(3)	0.02(2)	0.04(3)	0(0)	0(0)
2	C	—	—	—	—	0.50(200)	0.32(20)	0.38(33)	0.46(38)	0.40(32)	0.78(49)	1.00(28)
3	C	—	—	C	—	0.08(32)	0.10(6)	0.12(10)	0.06(5)	0.14(11)	0(0)	0(0)
4	—	C*	—	—	—	0.25(100)	0.38(24)	0.38(33)	0.26(21)	0.27(22)	0(0)	0(0)
5	—	—	C	—	—	0.12(47)	0.14(9)	0.07(6)	0.18(15)	0.14(11)	0.10(6)	0(0)
6	—	—	C	—	A	0.02(10)	0(0)	0(0)	0.01(1)	0.01(1)	0.13(8)	0(0)
7	—	C*	C	—	A	0(1)	0(0)	0.01(1)	0(0)	0(0)	0(0)	0(0)
8	C	—	C	—	—	0(1)	0(0)	0(0)	0(0)	0.01(1)	0(0)	0(0)
					N	403	63	86	82	81	63	28

在非洲、欧洲和亚洲后代的 6 个群体中观察到 G6PD 和 TNFSF5 的核心单倍型。核心 SNP 等位基因与假定的疟疾抗性突变之间的相对距离用 kb 表示。所有群体的单倍型频率 (以及观察次数) 也显示出来。G6PD 核心单倍型中没有明显的重组，R_M 为 0。在 403 个 TNFSF5 染色体中有两个重组的单倍型，但是如果将仅出现一次的这两个单倍型从分析中去除，R_M 仍然是 0[6]。

* 两种与疟疾抗性相关的假定突变 (G6PD-202A 和 TNFSF5-726C) 仅在非洲人中观察到，分别出现在 G6PD-CH8、TNFSF5-CH4 和 TNFSF5-CH7 中。

G6PD-CH8 具有清晰的长范围 LD (在单倍型分支图中显示为明显的一个粗分支优势型 (图 2a)) 和相应的高 EHH。EHH 在最大的检测距离下是 0.38，也就是 413 kb (图 2c)。对每一个核心单倍型，我们计算了相对的 EHH。具体来说，就是将检测的核心单倍型中 EHH 衰减的因素与所有其他核心单倍型组合起来的 EHH 衰减进行了对比 (见方法)。

为了正式地检测选择，对每一个核心单倍型在不同距离下的等位基因频率与相对 EHH 进行了比较 (图 2e 显示了 G6PD 近端 413 kb 的对比)。G6PD-CH8 与其他具有类似频率的单倍型相比有更高的相对 EHH，但其是否有统计学显著意义？为了了解我们的发现是多么得不寻常，我们用联合的过程模拟了单倍型 (见方法和图 2e)[11]。模拟结果得出的偏离是高度显著的，并且随着距离的增加变得越来越显著 (图 2g) (近端 413 kb 的 P 值：数量稳定的人群 $P < 0.0008$；扩张的人群 $P < 0.0006$；瓶颈效应 $P < 0.0008$；人群结构 $P < 0.0008$；我们使用的人口统计学模型的详细信息见方法和补充表 2)。G6PD-CH8 的频率和 LD 特性与广泛人口分布中的中性进化模型的预期不一致。此外，当把组成融合样本的三个非洲群体分开考虑时，每个群体中各自识别出了一个选择信号 (约鲁巴人 $P < 0.0012$；贝尼人 $P < 0.0440$；绍纳人 $P < 0.0030$，基于数量稳定的群体的模型)，证明选择信号不是将三个群体样本融合

simulation of a constant-sized population), demonstrating that the signal of selection is not an artefact of pooling the three population samples.

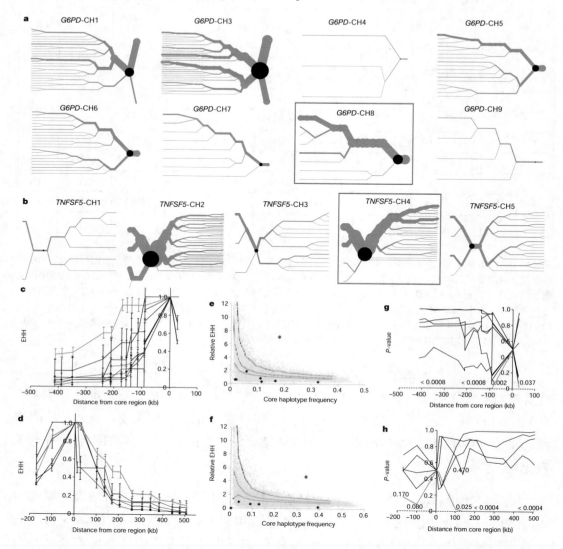

Fig. 2. Core haplotype frequency and relative EHH of *G6PD* and *TNFSF5*. **a**, **b**, Haplotype bifurcation diagrams (see Methods) for each core haplotype at *G6PD* (**a**) and *TNFSF5* (**b**) in pooled African populations demonstrate that *G6PD*-CH8 and *TNFSF5*-CH4 (boxed or labelled in red) have long-range homozygosity that is unusual given their frequency. **c**, **d**, The EHH at varying distances from the core region on each core haplotype at *G6PD* (**c**) and *TNFSF5* (**d**) demonstrates that *G6PD*-CH8 and *TNFSF5*-CH4 have persistent, high EHH values. **e**, **f**, At the most distant SNP from *G6PD* (**e**) and *TNFSF5* (**f**) core regions, the relative EHH plotted against the core haplotype frequency is presented and compared with the distribution of simulated core haplotypes (on the basis of simulation of 5,000 data sets; represented by grey dots and given with 95th, 75th and 50th percentiles). The observed non-selected core haplotypes in our data are represented by black diamonds. **g**, **h**, We calculated the statistical significance of the departure of the observed data from the simulated distribution at each distance from the core. *G6PD*-CH8 (**g**) and *TNFSF5*-CH4 (**h**) demonstrate increasing deviation from a model of neutral drift at further distances from the core region in both directions.

在一起的产物。

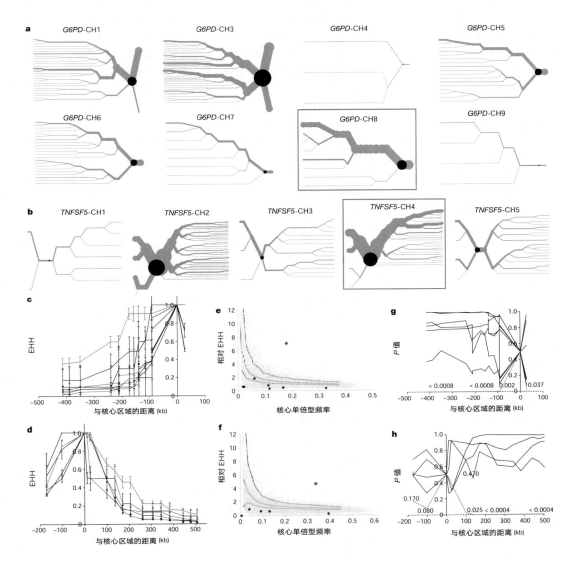

图 2. *G6PD* 和 *TNFSF5* 的核心单倍型频率和相对 EHH。**a**、**b**，在总体非洲人群中，*G6PD*(**a**)和 *TNFSF5*(**b**)的每个核心单倍型的分支图（见方法）表明，*G6PD*-CH8 和 *TNFSF5*-CH4(红色框)具有长范围的纯和性，这在其频率下是不寻常的。**c**、**d**，*G6PD*(**c**)和 *TNFSF5*(**d**)的每个核心单倍型中核心区域不同距离的 EHH 显示了 *G6PD*-CH8 和 *TNFSF5*-CH4 具有持续高水平的 EHH 值。**e**、**f**，*G6PD*(**e**)和 *TNFSF5*(**f**)核心区域最远处的 SNP，其相对 EHH 与核心单倍型的频率进行作图，并与模拟的核心单倍型分布图进行对比(根据 5,000 个数据点的模拟；以灰点表示，并给出第 95、75 和 50 个百分位数)。我们的数据中观察到的非选择的核心单倍型用黑色的菱形表示。**g**、**h**，我们观察到了在离核心单倍型每一距离处模拟分布的数据，并计算了这些数据偏差的显著性差异。*G6PD*-CH8(**g**)和 *TNFSF5*-CH4(**h**)显示出在距离核心区域更远的两个方向上，偏离中性漂移模型的程度更大。

We next applied our approach to the CD40 ligand gene (Fig. 1). We defined a core region of 10 kb and genotyped 5 SNPs. The SNPs defined seven core haplotypes (Table 1b). The *TNFSF5*-726C allele, which has been associated with protection from malaria, was present on *TNFSF5*-CH4, which is common in Africa (34%), but is absent outside of Africa. *TNFSF5*-CH4 demonstrates high LD as seen in the haplotype bifurcation diagrams (Fig. 2b) and has high EHH at long distances (Fig. 2d). *TNFSF5*-CH4 is a clear outlier when compared with other haplotypes (Fig. 2f), and its frequency and LD properties are incompatible with neutral evolution under multiple demographic models (*P*-values at 506 kb distal are: constant-sized population, $P < 0.0012$; expansion, $P < 0.0008$; bottleneck, $P < 0.0012$; population structure, $P < 0.0008$; see Methods and Supplementary Table 2 for details). Again, the *P*-value is increasingly significant at further distances from the core region both proximally and distally (Fig. 2h). When each African population was analysed separately, a signal of selection was significant (Yoruba, $P < 0.0008$; Beni, $P < 0.0023$; Shona, $P < 0.0242$). These results thus provide independent evidence supporting the proposed role of CD40 ligand in malaria resistance[2].

We tested our conclusion of positive selection by performing a similar analysis on 17 randomly chosen control regions across the human genome in the same African populations. We only used data from each control if it was closely matched to our data in terms of the number of chromosomes studied and the homozygosity at the core haplotype and at long distances from the core (Fig. 3). *G6PD*-CH8 and *TNFSF5*-CH4 clearly stand out from the other loci, showing that the *P*-values determined by simulation are also supported by direct, empirical comparison. In measuring *P*-values for the controls where there is no prior hypothesis of selection, a Bonferonni correction for multiple-hypothesis testing was applied. Notably, one core haplotype, from the monocyte chemotactic protein 1 region, shows frequency and LD properties similar to *G6PD* and *TNFSF5*, although this nominally significant result may be simply a false-positive owing to the large number of hypotheses examined.

We used a linkage-disequilibrium-based technique[12] to estimate dates of origin of the two resistance variants. The estimates were about 2,500 years for *G6PD* and about 6,500 years for *TNFSF5* (see Supplementary Information for details). The date for *G6PD* is consistent with a recent independent age estimate for *G6PD*-202A based primarily on microsatellite data[13].

Finally, we explored whether positive selection could have been detected with traditional tests (Supplementary Table 3)[14]. We performed Tajima's *D*-test[15], Fu and Li's *D*-test[16], Fay and Wu's *H*-test[17], the Ka/Ks test[18], the McDonald and Kreitman test[19], and the Hudson–Kreitman–Aguadè (HKA) test[20]. None showed significant deviation from neutral evolution for either *G6PD* or *TNFSF5*, consistent with their low power to detect recent selection.

接下来我们将方法应用到 CD40 配体基因中（图 1）。我们定义了一个 10 kb 的核心区域，对 5 个 SNP 进行基因分型。这些 SNP 确定了 7 个核心单倍型（表 1b）。与疟疾抗性相关的 TNFSF5-726C 等位基因存在于 TNFSF5-CH4 上，后者在非洲很常见（34%），但是在非洲以外地区不存在。TNFSF5-CH4 在单倍型分支图中显示高 LD（图 2b），在长距离时显示高 EHH（图 2d）。TNFSF5-CH4 与其他单倍型相比是一个明确的离群值（图 2f），其频率和 LD 特性在多种人口统计学模型下都与中性进化相矛盾（506 kb 远端的 P 值是：数量稳定的人群 $P < 0.0012$；扩张的人群 $P < 0.0008$；瓶颈效应 $P < 0.0012$；群体结构 $P < 0.0008$；细节见方法及附表 2）。同样，P 值显著性随着距核心区域的距离增加而增加，无论是近端还是远端（图 2h）。当分别分析非洲群体时，选择的信号都有显著性意义（约鲁巴人 $P < 0.0008$；贝尼人 $P < 0.0023$；绍纳人 $P < 0.0242$）。因此这些结果为支持 CD40 配体在疟疾抗性中的作用提供了独立证据 [2]。

我们通过在相同的非洲人群中对人类基因组中的 17 个随机选取的对照区域进行类似的分析，验证了我们关于正选择的结论。只有当对照区域在染色体数目、核心单倍型所在位置以及距离核心区较远处的纯合性方面与我们的数据密切匹配时，我们才使用其数据（图 3）。G6PD-CH8 和 TNFSF5-CH4 与其他基因座明显不同，表明通过模拟得出的 P 值也得到了直接的、实证比较分析的支持。在没有关于选择的优先假设的情况下，我们测量了对照 P 值，并采用邦费罗尼校正方法进行多假设检验。显然，来自单核细胞趋化蛋白 1 区域的一个核心单倍型显示了类似于 G6PD 和 TNFSF5 的频率和 LD 特征，然而这一表面上显著的结果可能仅仅是由于大量的假设被检验，而呈现的假阳性。

我们使用一种基于连锁不平衡的技术 [12] 估计这两个抗性变异体的起源日期。G6PD 估计大约 2,500 年前，TNFSF5 大约 6,500 年前（详情见补充信息）。G6PD 的起源日期与最近主要基于微卫星数据预估的 G6PD-202A 的独立年龄相一致 [13]。

最后，我们探讨了正选择是否能够用传统的方法检测到（补充表 3）[14]。我们进行了 Tajima 的 D 检验 [15]，Fu 和 Li 的 D 检验 [16]，Fay 和 Wu 的 H 检验 [17]，Ka/Ks 检验 [18]，McDonald 和 Kreitman 检验 [19] 以及 Hudson-Kreitman-Aguadè（HKA）检验 [20]。无论是 G6PD 还是 TNFSF5，均未表现出明显的中性进化偏差，这与它们不能检测到最近的选择相一致。

Fig. 3. Control regions: core haplotype frequency against relative EHH. To provide an empirical, non-simulation-based evaluation of the signal of selection, we compared the frequency and relative EHHs for *G6PD* (**a**) and *TNFSF5* (**b**) with patterns observed in randomly chosen genes in the genome (see Methods). **c, d**, We performed the entire analysis again on *G6PD* (**c**) and *TNFSF5* (**d**) for a subset of 78 Yoruban haplotypes (using family trios where phase could be determined). We were able to match 30 to 87 core haplotypes (indicated by outlined diamonds) from the control regions to our data. The 95th, 75th and 50th percentiles for simulated data are also shown. *G6PD*-CH8 and *TNFSF5*-CH4 (indicated by black diamonds) clearly stand out from the pattern seen at other loci in the genome, suggesting a true signal of selection.

Our approach, which we refer to as the long-range haplotype (LRH) test, provides a way to detect recent positive selection by analysing haplotype structure in random individuals from a population. How far back in human history can one detect positive selection?

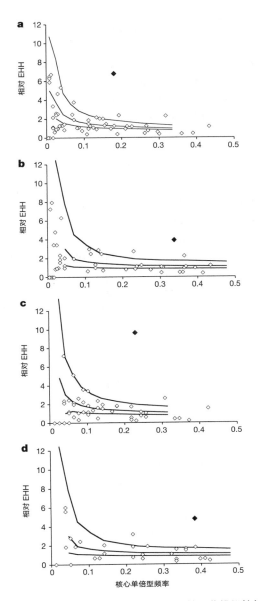

图 3. 对照区域：核心单倍型频率与相对 EHH。为了提供实验性、非模拟性的选择信号评估，我们将 *G6PD* (**a**) 和 *TNFSF5* (**b**) 的频率和相对 EHH 与基因组中随机选择的基因中观察到的模式进行了比较（见方法）。**c**、**d**，我们再次对 78 个约鲁巴人的单倍型子集的 *G6PD*(**c**) 和 *TNFSF5*(**d**) 进行了完整的分析（使用能够确定阶段的三体家系）。我们能够将对照区域的 30 到 87 个核心单倍型(以空心的菱形表示)与我们的数据匹配起来。图中也显示了模拟数据的第 95、75 和 50 个百分位数。*G6PD*-CH8 和 *TNFSF5*-CH4(以黑色菱形表示)与基因组中其他基因座所表现的形式完全不同，表明存在真正的选择信号。

我们称为长范围单倍型(LRH)检测的方法，提供了一种通过分析群体中随机个体的单倍型结构来检测近期正选择的方法。在人类历史上向前追溯多久才能检测到正选择呢？发生在不到 400 代之前的选择性事件(假设 25 年一代的话就是 10,000

Selective events occurring less than 400 generations ago (10,000 years assuming 25 years per generation) should leave a clear imprint at distances of over 0.25 centiMorgans (cM). The signal of such long-range LD should be distinguishable from the background extent of LD for common haplotypes in the genome[21], which are typically tens of thousands of generations old[4] and hence extend 0.02 cM or less. Over many tens of thousands of years, the signal of selection will become lost as recombination whittles the long-range haplotypes to the typical size of haplotype blocks in the human genome[21].

The LRH test can be used to search for evidence of positive selection by testing each common haplotype in a gene, without prior knowledge of a specific variant or selective advantage. Once the signature of selection is found, one must then decipher its cause. The LRH test could be applied to scan the entire human genome for evidence of recent positive selection simply by applying it to each haplotype block in reference data sets from human populations, as will be collected by the Human Haplotype Map project[21]. In this fashion, it should be possible to shed light on how the human genome was shaped by recent changes in culture and environment. The LRH test should also be useful for studying selection in other organisms, including domestic animals and parasites such as the malaria parasite *P. falciparum*[22].

Methods

Human subjects

DNA samples from 252 males from Africa were used in the study: 92 Yoruba and 73 Beni from Nigeria, and 87 Shona from Zimbabwe. Additional DNA samples from 29 Yoruban trios (father–mother–child clusters) were genotyped at the 17 control regions. The Yoruba and Shona males were healthy individuals obtained as part of the International Collaborative Study of Hypertension in Blacks. The Beni samples were from civil servants in Benin City. Samples from four non-African populations and four primates were also used (Supplementary Information).

SNP genotyping

We genotyped 49 SNPs distributed around *G6PD* and 37 SNPs distributed around *TNFSF5* using mass spectrometry (Sequenom)[23]. The SNPs were identified by our own resequencing and through previous discovery efforts[2,24,25]. For *G6PD*, we focused on genotyping SNPs proximal to the gene, as SNPs in the repetitive subtelomeric sequence distal to *G6PD* could not be genotyped. A total of 25 SNPs around *G6PD* and 21 SNPs around *TNFSF5* were successfully genotyped and used in analysis (see Supplementary Information for details).

年)应该在超过 0.25 厘摩 (cM) 的距离上留下明显的印记。这种长范围的 LD 信号应该能够和基因组中普通单倍型的背景长度的 LD 区别开来 [21],因为后者通常有几万代的历史 [4],因此延伸的长度不超过 0.02 cM。经过数万年的时间,随着重组的发生,长范围的单倍型就会变成人类基因组中典型大小的单倍型区域 [21],选择的信号会逐渐丢失。

LRH 检测可以通过分析基因中的每个常见单倍型来寻找正选择的证据,而无须提前知道特定的变异型或者选择优势。一旦发现了正选择的特征,就必须进一步研究其原因。LRH 检测可用于扫描整个人类基因组,仅仅通过将其用于人类群体中参考数据集内的每个单倍型区域,来寻找近期正选择的证据。这些数据信息将收集在人类单倍型图谱计划中 [21]。通过这种方式,我们有可能弄清楚人类基因组是如何被近期的文化和环境变化塑造的。LRH 检测对研究其他生物的选择也有效,包括家畜和寄生虫 (比如恶性疟原虫 [22])。

方　　法

人群对象

研究中使用了 252 名非洲男性的 DNA 样本:来自尼日利亚的 92 名约鲁巴人、73 名贝尼人,来自津巴布韦的 87 名绍纳人。在 17 个对照区对来源于 29 个约鲁巴三体家系 (父亲–母亲–孩子集群) 的额外 DNA 样本进行了基因分型。约鲁巴人和绍纳人是健康的男性,是黑人高血压国际合作研究项目的对象。贝尼人样本来自贝宁城的公务员。还使用了 4 个非非洲人群和 4 个灵长类动物的样本 (补充资料)。

SNP 基因分型

我们使用质谱法 (Sequenom)[23] 对 G6PD 附近的 49 个 SNP 以及 TNFSF5 附近的 37 个 SNP 进行了基因分型。这些 SNP 是通过我们自己的重新测序以及先前的发现相结合鉴定出来的 [2,24,25]。对于 G6PD,我们主要着眼于对基因近端的 SNP 进行基因分型,因为其远端的重复性亚端粒序列中的 SNP 无法基因分型。总共有 G6PD 附近的 25 个 SNP 和 TNFSF5 附近的 21 个 SNP 成功基因分型并用于分析 (详细内容见补充资料)。

Haplotype bifurcation diagrams

To visualize the breakdown of LD on core haplotypes, we created bifurcation diagrams using MATLAB. The root of each diagram is a core haplotype, identified by a black circle. The diagram is bi-directional, portraying both proximal and distal LD. Moving in one direction, each marker is an opportunity for a node; the diagram either divides or not based on whether both or only one allele is present. Thus the breakdown of LD on the core haplotype background is portrayed at progressively longer distances. The thickness of the lines corresponds to the number of samples with the indicated long-distance haplotype.

Extended haplotype homozygosity and relative EHH

EHH at a distance x from the core region is defined as the probability that two randomly chosen chromosomes carrying a tested core haplotype are homozygous at all SNPs[8] for the entire interval from the core region to the distance x. EHH is on a scale of 0 (no homozygosity, all extended haplotypes are different) to 1 (complete homozygosity, all extended haplotypes are the same). Relative EHH is the ratio of the EHH on the tested core haplotype compared with the EHH of the grouped set of core haplotypes at the region not including the core haplotype tested. Relative EHH is therefore on a scale of 0 to infinity.

Coalescent simulations

We used a computer program by Hudson that simulates gene history with recombination[11]. The program was modified to generate data such as we collected. We simulated a long region of DNA (1.3 cM), with one end defined as the "core". We progressively added SNPs at the core until they matched our data (for the *G6PD* or *TNFSF5* core) to within ± 12.5% in terms of the homozygosity. To mimic the SNP selection strategy used by The SNP consortium[25], which was the source of most of the SNPs in our study, we only included simulated SNPs in our analysis if different alleles were observed at two randomly chosen chromosomes from the sample. At longer distances, we added additional SNPs, only choosing SNPs for analysis that matched our data in terms of frequency (within a ± 12.5% window) and also broke down EHH to the same extent as was observed in our data (within ± 12.5%).

We repeated the simulations for 5,000 data sets (each producing typically 6–8 core haplotypes) to generate many data points with which to compare our data. *P*-values were obtained by first binning the simulated data by core haplotype frequency into 30 bins of equal size, each containing about 1,000 data points. We then ranked an observed core haplotype's relative EHH compared with that of all simulated data points within the bin containing haplotypes of the same frequency—the rank determines the *P*-value. For simulations of additional demographic histories, we considered two models of expansion, an extreme bottleneck, and a highly structured population. For expansions, we simulated a population that was constant at size 10,000 until 200 or 5,000 generations ago, when it

单倍型分支图

为了可视化核心单倍型中 LD 的分解，我们使用 MATLAB 创建了分支图。每个图标的根部是核心单倍型，以黑圈表示。图表是双向的，表示近端和远端的 LD。向一个方向移动的话，每个标记都是一个形成节点的机会；图标分支与否取决于存在的等位基因是一个还是两个。因此核心单倍型背景中的 LD 的分解就表示为进行性变长的距离。线条的厚度对应于含有表示的长距离单倍型的样本的数量。

扩展单倍型纯合性和相对 EHH

距离核心区域 x 的 EHH 被定义为从核心区域到距离 x 的整个区间内，两个随机选择的携带被测的核心单倍型的染色体在所有的 SNP 中是纯合的可能性 [8]。EHH 的范围在 0（没有纯合性，所有的扩展单倍型都是不同的）到 1（完全纯合性，所有扩展单倍型都是一样的）之间。相对 EHH 是被测的核心单倍型的 EHH 与不含有被测单倍型的区域内部的核心单倍型集群的 EHH 的比值，因此相对 EHH 的范围是从 0 到无穷大。

联合模拟

我们使用赫德森的计算机程序，通过重组模拟基因历史 [11]。该程序经过修改以生成数据，比如我们之前收集的数据。我们模拟了一个长 DNA 区域（1.3 cM），其一端定义为"核心"。我们逐渐增加核心部位的 SNP，直到它们匹配我们的数据（G6PD 或者 TNFSF5 核心）使得纯合性偏差在 ±12.5% 之内。为了模拟 SNP 联盟使用的 SNP 选择策略 [25]（我们研究中大部分 SNP 来源于此），我们只在样本中随机选择的两个染色体上观察到不同的等位基因时，才将模拟的 SNP 用于分析。在更远的距离处，我们增加额外的 SNP，仅仅选择那些在频率上与我们的数据匹配（±12.5% 之内），而且 EHH 的分解程度与我们数据中观察到的一致（±12.5% 之内）的 SNP 用于分析。

我们对 5,000 个数据集合进行重复模拟（每个通常能够产生 6～8 个核心单倍型）以产生多个数据点，用于和我们的数据进行对比。首先将模拟的数据按照核心单倍型频率分类成 30 个大小相等的集合，每个集合约含有 1,000 个数据点，计算 P 值。然后我们对观察到的核心单倍型的相对 EHH 与含有相同频率单倍型的集合内的所有模拟数据点的 EHH 进行排序，这个排列就确定了 P 值。为了模拟更多的人口统计学历史，我们考虑两种扩张模型，一个极端的瓶颈效应和一个高度结构化的人群。对于扩张，我们模拟了一个人群，在 200 或者 5,000

expanded suddenly by a factor of 1,000. For an extreme bottleneck, we simulated a population that was constant at size 10,000 except for a brief bottleneck (inbreeding coefficient 0.18) that occurred 800 generations ago. (An inbreeding coefficient[26] of 0.18 is generated by dropping the population size to 800 chromosomes for 160 generations.) For a structured population, we simulated two equal-sized populations of size $N/2$ that exchanged migrants throughout history with a probability of $1/8N$ per generation per chromosome.

Results of the simulations remained qualitatively similar when we explored additional demographies and when we varied the stringency of matching to SNP allele frequencies and to haplotype homozygosities. A comprehensive, simulation-based exploration of the LRH test will be presented elsewhere, along with explorations of the statistical power of the test and computer code for implementing the LRH test on other data sets, including those with missing or unphased data (D.E.R., manuscript in preparation).

Control regions

To obtain control data for comparison to the *G6PD* and *TNFSF5* haplotypes, we genotyped the same population samples in 17 randomly chosen autosomal genes (*ACVR2B*, *TGFB1*, *DDR1*, *GTF2H4*, *COL11A2*, *LAMB1*, *WASL*, *SLC6A12*, *KCNA1*, *ARGHDIB*, *PCI*, *PRKCB1*, *NF1*, *SCYA2*, *PAI2*, *IL17R* and *HCF2*) selected previously as part of a genome-wide survey of linkage disequilibrium[26]. For our analyses we randomly picked chromosomes to match the numbers sampled for *G6PD* and *TNFSF5*, and we only included those control regions that we could match to our data in terms of homozygosity at the core and homozygosity at long distance ($\pm 25\%$ stringency of matching). After the filtering process, we evaluated *G6PD* at 240.3 kb proximal to the gene and *TNFSF5* at 343.9 kb distal to the gene, because we could not make enough comparisons to control regions at the further distances. Seven genes matched to *G6PD* and seven genes matched to *TNFSF5*. We repeated the analysis using 78 Yoruban chromosomes for which phase information was known experimentally (because of genotyping in trios) and for which phase for the most part did not have to be inferred computationally. Six genes matched to *G6PD* and six genes matched to *TNFSF5* (see Supplementary Information for details).

(**419**, 832-837; 2002)

Pardis C. Sabeti[*†#], David E. Reich[*], John M. Higgins[*] Haninah Z. P. Levine[*], Daniel J. Richter[*], Stephen F. Schaffner[*], Stacey B. Gabriel[*], Jill V. Platko[*], Nick J. Patterson[*], Gavin J. McDonald[*], Hans C. Ackerman[‡], Sarah J. Campbell[‡], David Altshuler[*§], Richard Cooper[∥], Dominic Kwiatkowski[‡], Ryk Ward[†] & Eric S. Lander[*¶]

[*] Whitehead Institute/MIT Center for Genome Research, Nine Cambridge Center, Cambridge, Massachusetts 02142, USA

[†] Institute of Biological Anthropology, University of Oxford, Oxford, OX2 6QS, UK

[‡] Wellcome Trust Centre for Human Genetics, Roosevelt Drive, Oxford, OX3 7BN, UK

[§] Departments of Genetics and Medicine, Harvard Medical School, Department of Molecular Biology and Diabetes Unit, Massachusetts General Hospital, Boston, Massachusetts 02114, USA

[∥] Department of Preventive Medicine and Epidemiology, Loyola University Medical School, Maywood, Illinois 60143, USA

[¶] Department of Biology, MIT, Cambridge, Massachusetts 02139, USA

[#] Harvard Medical School, Boston, Massachusetts 02115, USA

代之前规模一直稳定在 10,000，然后它突然扩张了 1,000 倍。对于极端的瓶颈效应，我们模拟了一个大小稳定在 10,000 的人群，除了在 800 代前出现了一次短暂的瓶颈效应（近交系数 0.18）。（近交系数 [26] 0.18 的产生是在 160 代内将人群的大小减少至 800 条染色体。）对于结构化的人群，我们模拟了两个大小均是 $N/2$ 的人群，其在整个历史中以每代每个染色体 $1/8N$ 的概率交换迁移者。

当我们探索其他人口统计学时，当我们改变与 SNP 等位基因频率和单倍型纯合性匹配的严格程度时，模拟的结果在定性上保持相似。我们还将对 LRH 测试进行全面的、基于模拟的探索，并探讨该测试的统计能力和在其他数据集（包括那些丢失或者非阶段数据的数据集）上实现 LRH 测试的计算机代码（赖希，稿件准备中）。

对照区域

为了获得对照数据，用来和 G6PD 以及 TNFSF5 单倍型进行比较，我们对同一个人群样本中的 17 个随机选择的常染色体基因进行基因分型（ACVR2B，TGFB1，DDR1，GTF2H4，COL11A2，LAMB1，WASL，SLC6A12，KCNA1，ARGHDIB，PCI，PRKCB1，NF1，SCYA2，PAI2，IL17R 和 HCF2），之前选择它们作为基因组水平连锁不平衡研究的一部分 [26]。对于我们的分析，我们随机选取了匹配 G6PD 以及 TNFSF5 样本数目的染色体，而且我们仅仅使用那些能够在核心的纯合性和长距离的纯合性与我们的数据匹配的对照区域（匹配的严格度是 ±25%）。经过筛选，我们对 G6PD 近端 240.3 kb 处和 TNFSF5 远端 343.9 kb 处进行了评估，因为我们无法对更远距离的对照区域进行比较。发现分别有 7 个基因对应于 G6PD 和 TNFSF5。我们用 78 名约鲁巴人的染色体进行了重复分析，它们的阶段信息已经通过实验得到（因为在三体家系中进行了基因分型），而且大部分的阶段信息不需要通过计算机推断。各有 6 个基因分别对应于 G6PD 和 TNFSF5（详细内容见补充资料）。

（毛晨晖 翻译；胡松年 审稿）

Received 7 June; accepted 19 September 2002; doi:10.1038/nature01140.
Published online 9 October 2002.

References:

1. Ruwende, C. & Hill, A. Glucose-6-phosphate dehydrogenase deficiency and malaria. *J. Mol. Med.* **76**, 581-588 (1998).

2. Sabeti, P. *et al.* CD40L association with protection from severe malaria. *Genes Immun.* **3**, 286-291 (2002).

3. Cavalli-Sforza, L. L., Menozzi, P. & Piazza, A. *The History and Geography of Human Genes* (Princeton Univ. Press, Princeton, 1994).

4. Kimura, M. *The Neutral Theory of Molecular Evolution* (Cambridge Univ. Press, Cambridge/New York, 1983).

5. Stephens, J. C. *et al.* Dating the origin of the CCR5-Delta32 AIDS-resistance allele by the coalescence of haplotypes. *Am. J. Hum. Genet.* **62**, 1507-1515 (1998).

6. Hudson, R. R. & Kaplan, N. L. Statistical properties of the number of recombination events in the history of a sample of DNA sequences. *Genetics* **111**, 147-164 (1985).

7. Lewontin, R. The interaction of selection and linkage. I. General considerations; heterotic models. *Genetics* **49**, 49-67 (1964).

8. Nei, M. *Molecular Evolutionary Genetics* Eqn. 8.4 (Columbia Univ. Press, New York, 1987).

9. Luzatto, L., Mehta, A. & Vulliamy, T. *The Metabolic & Molecular Bases of Inherited Disease* 4517-4553 (McGraw-Hill, New York, 2001).

10. Raymond, M. & Rousset, F. An exact test for population differentiation. *Evolution* **49**, 1280-1283 (1995).

11. Hudson, R. R. Properties of a neutral allele model with intragenic recombination. *Theor. Popul. Biol.* **23**, 183-201 (1983).

12. Reich, D. E. & Goldstein, D. B. *Microsatellites: Evolution and Applications* 128-138 (Oxford Univ. Press, Oxford/New York, 1999).

13. Tishkoff, S. A. *et al.* Haplotype diversity and linkage disequilibrium at human G6PD: recent origin of alleles that confer malarial resistance. *Science* **293**, 455-462 (2001).

14. Rozas, J. & Rozas, R. DnaSP version 3: an integrated program for molecular population genetics and molecular evolution analysis. *Bioinformatics* **15**, 174-175 (1999).

15. Tajima, F. Statistical method for testing the neutral mutation hypothesis by DNA polymorphism. *Genetics* **123**, 585-595 (1989).

16. Fu, Y. X. & Li, W. H. Statistical tests of neutrality of mutations. *Genetics* **133**, 693-709 (1993).

17. Fay, J. C. & Wu, C. I. Hitchhiking under positive Darwinian selection. *Genetics* **155**, 1405-1413 (2000).

18. Hughes, A. L. & Nei, M. Pattern of nucleotide substitution at major histocompatibility complex class I loci reveals overdominant selection. *Nature* **335**, 167-170 (1988).

19. McDonald, J. H. & Kreitman, M. Adaptive protein evolution at the Adh locus in *Drosophila*. *Nature* **351**, 652-654 (1991).

20. Hudson, R. R., Kreitman, M. & Aguade, M. A test of neutral molecular evolution based on nucleotide data. *Genetics* **116**, 153-159 (1987).

21. Gabriel, S. B. *et al.* The structure of haplotype blocks in the human genome. *Science* **23**, 2225-2229 (2002).

22. Wootton, J. C. *et al.* Genetic diversity and chloroquine selective sweeps in *Plasmodium falciparum*. *Nature* **418**, 320-323 (2002).

23. Tang, K. *et al.* Chip-based genotyping by mass spectrometry. *Proc. Natl Acad. Sci. USA* **96**, 10016-10020 (1999).

24. Vulliamy, T. J. *et al.* Linkage disequilibrium of polymorphic sites in the G6PD gene in African populations and the origin of G6PD A. *Gene Geogr.* **5**, 13-21 (1991).

25. Sachidanandam, R. *et al.* A map of human genome sequence variation containing 1.42 million single nucleotide polymorphisms. *Nature* **409**, 928-933 (2001).

26. Reich, D. E. *et al.* Linkage disequilibrium in the human genome. *Nature* **411**, 199-204 (2001).

Supplementary Information accompanies the paper on *Nature*'s website (http://www.nature.com/nature).

Acknowledgements. We thank B. Blumenstiel, M. DeFelice, A. Lochner, J. Moore, H. Nguyen and J. Roy for assistance in genotyping the 17 control regions. We also thank L. Gaffney, S. Radhakrishna, T. DiCesare and T. Lavery for graphics and technical support, B. Ferrell for the Beni samples, and A. Adeyemo and C. Rotimi for helping to collect the Yoruba and Shona samples. Finally, we thank M. Daly, E. Cosman, B. Gray, V. Koduri, T. Herrington and L. Peterson for comments on the manuscript. P.C.S. was supported by grants from the Rhodes Trust, the Harvard Office of Enrichment, and by a Soros Fellowship. This work was supported by grants from the National Institute of Health.

Competing interests statement. The authors declare that they have no competing financial interests.

Correspondence and requests for materials should be addressed to E.S.L. (e-mail: lander@genome.wi.mit.edu).

Initial Sequencing and Comparative Analysis of the Mouse Genome[*]

Mouse Genome Sequencing Consortium

Editor's Note

Here, a high-quality draft sequence of the mouse genome is made freely available for the first time, thanks to the work of an international research consortium. At the time, the data provided an invaluable reference point for geneticists struggling to understand the draft human genome which had been published a year earlier. But it continues to shed light on human biology and disease today, as the mouse remains an invaluable and stalwart model in biomedical research. Comparisons here between the DNA of mouse and man reveal immense similarities, confirming the credentials of this tiny rodent to help fathom the workings of the human genome. But the study also highlights some 300 mouse-specific genes, with the biggest disparities linked to smell, immunity and detoxification.

The sequence of the mouse genome is a key informational tool for understanding the contents of the human genome and a key experimental tool for biomedical research. Here, we report the results of an international collaboration to produce a high-quality draft sequence of the mouse genome. We also present an initial comparative analysis of the mouse and human genomes, describing some of the insights that can be gleaned from the two sequences. We discuss topics including the analysis of the evolutionary forces shaping the size, structure and sequence of the genomes; the conservation of large-scale synteny across most of the genomes; the much lower extent of sequence orthology covering less than half of the genomes; the proportions of the genomes under selection; the number of protein-coding genes; the expansion of gene families related to reproduction and immunity; the evolution of proteins; and the identification of intraspecies polymorphism.

WITH the complete sequence of the human genome nearly in hand[1,2], the next challenge is to extract the extraordinary trove of information encoded within its roughly 3 billion nucleotides. This information includes the blueprints for all RNAs and proteins, the regulatory elements that ensure proper expression of all genes, the structural elements that govern chromosome function, and the records of our evolutionary history.

---

[*] This is a shortened version of the original paper that appeared in *Nature*. In particular, it omits much of the detailed quantitative data in the original figures and tables, and the full list of authors and affiliations has been removed. The original text is freely available in the *Nature* online archive. Citations are numbered herein as they are in the original paper; only those references that are cited in this version are listed in the "References" section.

小鼠基因组的初步测序和对比分析[*]

小鼠基因组测序协作组

编者按

感谢国际协作组的工作，本文首次免费提供一个高质量的小鼠基因组序列草图。当时，这些数据为遗传学家努力理解一年前发表的人类基因组草图提供了宝贵的参考点。但是现在，它仍然继续为揭示人类生物学和疾病提供帮助。因为在生物医学研究中，小鼠始终是一个宝贵而有力的模型。小鼠和人类 DNA 之间的比较揭示了两者巨大的相似性，证实了这种小型啮齿动物能帮助了解人类基因组的运行。但是，该研究也强调了大约 300 个小鼠特异性基因，其中最大的不同与嗅觉、免疫和解毒作用有关。

小鼠基因组序列是理解人类基因组内容的关键信息工具，也是生物医学研究的关键实验工具。在此，我们报告国际合作的成果——一个高质量的小鼠基因组序列草图。我们还对小鼠和人类基因组进行了初步对比分析，描述了从这两个序列中获得的一些启示。我们讨论的主题包括对影响基因组大小、结构和序列的进化力的分析；存在于大部分基因组中的同源染色单体（同线性）的大规模保留；比之低得多只覆盖不到一半基因组的序列直系同源；受选择基因组的比例；蛋白质编码基因的数量；与生殖和免疫相关的基因家族的扩增；蛋白质的进化；物种内多态性的确定。

随着即将掌握人类基因组的完整序列[1,2]，下一个挑战是提取大约 30 亿个核苷酸中编码的非常巨大的信息宝藏。这些信息包括所有 RNA 和蛋白质的蓝图、确保所有基因正确表达的调控元件、控制染色体功能的结构元件以及我们进化史的记录。这些特征当中，一些可以很容易在人类序列中识别，但很多特征是微妙而且难辨别

---

[*] 这是《自然》杂志中原文的缩略版。此版本在于省略了原始图表中的大部分详细量化数据并去除了所有作者及单位名称。原文可在《自然》杂志在线免费获取。参考文献的编码与原文一致，文末"References"仅保留了此版本中有所引用的文献。

Some of these features can be recognized easily in the human sequence, but many are subtle and difficult to discern. One of the most powerful general approaches for unlocking the secrets of the human genome is comparative genomics, and one of the most powerful starting points for comparison is the laboratory mouse, *Mus musculus*.

Metaphorically, comparative genomics allows one to read evolution's laboratory notebook. In the roughly 75 million years since the divergence of the human and mouse lineages, the process of evolution has altered their genome sequences and caused them to diverge by nearly one substitution for every two nucleotides (see below) as well as by deletion and insertion. The divergence rate is low enough that one can still align orthologous sequences, but high enough so that one can recognize many functionally important elements by their greater degree of conservation. Studies of small genomic regions have demonstrated the power of such cross-species conservation to identify putative genes or regulatory elements[3-12]. Genome-wide analysis of sequence conservation holds the prospect of systematically revealing such information for all genes. Genome-wide comparisons among organisms can also highlight key differences in the forces shaping their genomes, including differences in mutational and selective pressures[13,14].

Literally, comparative genomics allows one to link laboratory notebooks of clinical and basic researchers. With knowledge of both genomes, biomedical studies of human genes can be complemented by experimental manipulations of corresponding mouse genes to accelerate functional understanding. In this respect, the mouse is unsurpassed as a model system for probing mammalian biology and human disease[15,16]. Its unique advantages include a century of genetic studies, scores of inbred strains, hundreds of spontaneous mutations, practical techniques for random mutagenesis, and, importantly, directed engineering of the genome through transgenic, knockout and knockin techniques[17-22].

For these and other reasons, the Human Genome Project (HGP) recognized from its outset that the sequencing of the human genome needed to be followed as rapidly as possible by the sequencing of the mouse genome. In early 2001, the International Human Genome Sequencing Consortium reported a draft sequence covering about 90% of the euchromatic human genome, with about 35% in finished form[1]. Since then, progress towards a complete human sequence has proceeded swiftly, with approximately 98% of the genome now available in draft form and about 95% in finished form.

Here, we report the results of an international collaboration involving centres in the United States and the United Kingdom to produce a high-quality draft sequence of the mouse genome and a broad scientific network to analyse the data. The draft sequence was generated by assembling about sevenfold sequence coverage from female mice of the C57BL/6J strain (referred to below as B6). The assembly contains about 96% of the sequence of the euchromatic genome (excluding chromosome Y) in sequence contigs linked together into large units, usually larger than 50 megabases (Mb).

With the availability of a draft sequence of the mouse genome, we have undertaken an

的。解开人类基因组秘密最有力的通用方法之一是比较基因组学，而进行比较最有力的出发点就是实验用小鼠，拉丁文名称为 *Mus musculus*。

打个比方，比较基因组学允许人们阅读进化的实验笔记。在人类和小鼠的谱系分开后的大约 7,500 万年中，进化历程改变了它们的基因组序列，通过几乎每两个核苷酸就替换一个核苷酸（见下文）以及核苷酸的缺失和插入产生分化。分歧率足够低的部分可以比对直系同源序列，但分歧率较高的部分可以通过它们更高的保守性来识别许多功能上重要的元件。对基因组小块区域的研究已经证实了这种跨物种的保守性在识别推测基因或调控元件方面的能力 [3-12]。全基因组范围的序列保守性分析有望系统地揭示所有基因的这类信息。物种之间的全基因组范围比较还可以使得包括突变和选择压力差异在内的形成基因组的关键差异作用更加突出地显示出来 [13,14]。

从字面上看，比较基因组学可以让人们将临床和基础研究人员的实验笔记联系起来。有了这两个基因组的知识，人类基因的生物医学研究可以通过实验操作相应的小鼠基因来补充，加速对于基因功能的理解。在这方面，小鼠是探索哺乳动物生物学和人类疾病无与伦比的模型系统 [15,16]。它的独特优势包括百年的遗传学研究、大量的近交系、成百个自发突变、随机诱变的实用实验技术，以及尤其重要的通过转基因、基因敲除和敲入技术进行的基因组定向操作 [17-22]。

基于这些和其他原因，人类基因组计划（HGP）从一开始就意识到人类基因组的测序需要尽可能快地接着进行小鼠基因组的测序。2001 年初，国际人类基因组测序协作组报告了一份覆盖了 90% 人类常染色质的基因组序列草图，其中 35% 是已经完成了的形式 [1]。从那时起，向着完整人类序列的发展进展迅速，目前大约 98% 的基因组以草图形式提供，约 95% 的基因组以完成图形式提供。

在此，我们报告由美国和英国的多个中心参加的国际合作所产生的一个高质量小鼠基因组序列草图和一个数据分析的广泛科学网络。这个序列草图是由 C57BL/6J 雌性小鼠（以下称为 B6），大约 7 倍的序列覆盖度组装而成。组装结果包括 96% 的常染色质基因组序列（不包括 Y 染色体），由测序序列片段重叠拼接在一起形成大的单元，通常大于 50 兆碱基（Mb）。

利用小鼠基因组的序列草图，我们进行了初步的对比分析，以检测人类和小鼠

initial comparative analysis to examine the similarities and differences between the human and mouse genomes. Some of the important points are listed below.

- The mouse genome is about 14% smaller than the human genome (2.5 Gb compared with 2.9 Gb). The difference probably reflects a higher rate of deletion in the mouse lineage.

- Over 90% of the mouse and human genomes can be partitioned into corresponding regions of conserved synteny, reflecting segments in which the gene order in the most recent common ancestor has been conserved in both species.

- At the nucleotide level, approximately 40% of the human genome can be aligned to the mouse genome. These sequences seem to represent most of the orthologous sequences that remain in both lineages from the common ancestor, with the rest likely to have been deleted in one or both genomes.

- The neutral substitution rate has been roughly half a nucleotide substitution per site since the divergence of the species, with about twice as many of these substitutions having occurred in the mouse compared with the human lineage.

- By comparing the extent of genome-wide sequence conservation to the neutral rate, the proportion of small (50–100 bp) segments in the mammalian genome that is under (purifying) selection can be estimated to be about 5%. This proportion is much higher than can be explained by protein-coding sequences alone, implying that the genome contains many additional features (such as untranslated regions, regulatory elements, non-protein-coding genes, and chromosomal structural elements) under selection for biological function.

- The mammalian genome is evolving in a non-uniform manner, with various measures of divergence showing substantial variation across the genome.

- The mouse and human genomes each seem to contain about 30,000 protein-coding genes. These refined estimates have been derived from both new evidence-based analyses that produce larger and more complete sets of gene predictions, and new *de novo* gene predictions that do not rely on previous evidence of transcription or homology. The proportion of mouse genes with a single identifiable orthologue in the human genome seems to be approximately 80%. The proportion of mouse genes without any homologue currently detectable in the human genome (and vice versa) seems to be less than 1%.

- Dozens of local gene family expansions have occurred in the mouse lineage. Most of these seem to involve genes related to reproduction, immunity and olfaction, suggesting that these physiological systems have been the focus of extensive lineage-specific innovation in rodents.

- Mouse–human sequence comparisons allow an estimate of the rate of protein evolution

基因组之间的相似性和差异。下面列出了一些要点。

- 小鼠基因组大概比人类基因组小约 14%(2.5 Gb 比 2.9 Gb)。这种差异可能反映了小鼠谱系中较高的缺失率。

- 超过 90% 的小鼠和人类基因组可以被划分成相应的保守同线性区域，反映了两个物种所保存的最近共同祖先区段上的基因顺序。

- 在核苷酸水平上，大约 40% 的人类基因组可以比对到小鼠基因组上。这些序列似乎代表了来自于共同祖先的两个谱系中的大部分直系同源序列，余下的序列可能在一个或两个基因组中被删除了。

- 自物种分化以来，每个位点的中性替代率大约是核苷酸替代率的一半，与人类谱系相比较，在小鼠中这些替代出现的次数大概是人类的两倍。

- 通过对全基因组序列的保守程度和中性率进行比较，估计哺乳动物基因组中处于(纯化)选择的小片段(50~100 bp)的比例大约为 5%。这个比例远远高于仅用蛋白质编码序列所能解释的，这意味着基因组很多额外性质(如非翻译区、调节元件、非蛋白质编码基因和染色体结构元件)也受到了生物学功能的选择。

- 哺乳动物基因组正在以不均匀的方式进化，对于分化的不同度量结果显示了基因组中的巨大变化。

- 小鼠和人类的基因组似乎都包含大约 30,000 个蛋白质编码基因。这些精准的估计分别来自基于新证据获得的更大、更完整的基因预测集和不依赖于先前转录或同源性证据的基因重新预测。具有单一可识别直系同源基因的小鼠基因在人类基因组中的比例大约为 80%。没有在人类基因组中检测到任何同源性的小鼠基因的比例似乎小于 1%，反之亦然。

- 小鼠谱系中已经发生了数十个局部基因家族的扩张。大部分看来与生殖、免疫和嗅觉相关，提示这些生理系统是啮齿动物的谱系特异性更新的焦点。

- 小鼠–人类序列的比较可以预测哺乳动物蛋白质的进化速率。某些与生殖、宿

in mammals. Certain classes of secreted proteins implicated in reproduction, host defence and immune response seem to be under positive selection, which drives rapid evolution.

● Despite marked differences in the activity of transposable elements between mouse and human, similar types of repeat sequences have accumulated in the corresponding genomic regions in both species. The correlation is stronger than can be explained simply by local $(G+C)$ content and points to additional factors influencing how the genome is moulded by transposons.

● By additional sequencing in other mouse strains, we have identified about 80,000 single nucleotide polymorphisms (SNPs). The distribution of SNPs reveals that genetic variation among mouse strains occurs in large blocks, mostly reflecting contributions of the two subspecies *Mus musculus domesticus* and *Mus musculus musculus* to current laboratory strains.

The mouse genome sequence is freely available in public databases (GenBank accession number CAAA01000000) and is accessible through various genome browsers (http://www.ensembl.org/Mus_musculus/, http://genome.ucsc.edu/ and http://www.ncbi.nlm.nih.gov/genome/guide/mouse/).

In this paper, we begin with information about the generation, assembly and evaluation of the draft genome sequence, the conservation of synteny between the mouse and human genomes, and the landscape of the mouse genome. We then explore the repeat sequences, genes and proteome of the mouse, emphasizing comparisons with the human. This is followed by evolutionary analysis of selection and mutation in the mouse and human lineages, as well as polymorphism among current mouse strains. A full and detailed description of the methods underlying these studies is provided as Supplementary Information. In many respects, the current paper is a companion to the recent paper on the human genome sequence[1]. Extensive background information about many of the topics discussed below is provided there.

Background to the Mouse Genome Sequencing Project

Origins of the mouse

The precise origin of the mouse and human lineages has been the subject of recent debate. Palaeontological evidence has long indicated a great radiation of placental (eutherian) mammals about 65 million years ago (Myr) that filled the ecological space left by the extinction of the dinosaurs, and that gave rise to most of the eutherian orders[23]. Molecular phylogenetic analyses indicate earlier divergence times of many of the mammalian clades. Some of these studies have suggested a very early date for the divergence of mouse from other mammals (100–130 Myr[23-25]) but these estimates partially originate from the fast molecular clock in rodents (see below). Recent molecular studies that are less sensitive to the differences in evolutionary rates have suggested that the eutherian mammalian radiation

主防御和免疫应答相关的分泌蛋白质似乎是处于正选择，这些推动了蛋白质快速进化。

- 尽管小鼠和人类的转座元件的活性有明显差异，但是两个物种的相应基因组区域中积累了相似类型的重复序列。这种相关性要比简单通过局部（G+C）含量来解释更强，并且指向影响基因组如何被转座子塑造的其他因素。

- 通过对其他品系小鼠的额外测序，我们已经鉴定出了大概 80,000 个单核苷酸多态性（SNP）。SNP 的分布表明小鼠品系间的遗传变异发生在大的区块内，主要反映了两个小鼠亚种：*Mus musculus domesticus* 和 *Mus musculus musculus* 对当前实验室品系的贡献。

小鼠基因组序列可在公共数据库（GenBank 编号 CAAA01000000）中免费获得，并可通过多种基因组浏览器（http://www.ensembl.org/Mus_musculus/，http://genome.ucsc.edu/ 和 http://www.ncbi.nlm.nih.gov/genome/guide/mouse/）访问。

在本文中，我们从基因组序列草图的产生、组装和评估，小鼠和人类基因组之间的同线性保守性，以及小鼠基因组的概貌信息入手。然后，我们探索小鼠的重复序列、基因和蛋白质组，尤其是与人类的比较。接着是对小鼠和人类谱系的选择和突变以及目前小鼠品系中的多态性的进化分析。补充材料对这些研究的方法进行了完整而详细的描述。在很多方面，这篇论文与最近一篇关于人类基因组序列的文章 [1] 的相配套。那里提供了关于下面讨论的许多主题的充分的背景信息。

小鼠基因组测序项目的背景

小鼠的起源

小鼠和人类谱系的确切起源是最近的争论话题。古生物学的证据长期表明，大约 6,500 万年前胎盘哺乳类动物（真兽亚纲动物）的大量扩张，填充了恐龙灭绝留下的生态空间，真兽亚纲大多数目的动物由此产生 [23]。分子系统发育分析表明，许多哺乳动物分支的分化时间较早。其中一些研究表明，小鼠从其他哺乳动物中分化出来的时间非常早（1 亿 ~ 3 亿年前 [23-25]），但是这些估计部分来自于啮齿动物的快速分子钟（见下文）。最近对进化率差异不那么敏感的分子研究表明真兽亚纲动物的扩

took place throughout the Late Cretaceous period (65–100 Myr), but that rodents and primates actually represent relatively late-branching lineages[26,27]. In the analyses below, we use a divergence time for the human and mouse lineages of 75 Myr for the purpose of calculating evolutionary rates, although it is possible that the actual time may be as recent as 65 Myr.

Origins of the mouse genetics

With the rediscovery of Mendel's laws of inheritance in 1900, pioneers of the new science of genetics (such as Cuenot, Castle and Little) were quick to recognize that the discontinuous variation of bred ("fancy") mice was analogous to that of Mendel's peas, and they set out to test the new theories of inheritance in mice. Mating programmes were soon established to create inbred strains, resulting in many of the modern, well-known strains (including C57BL/6J)[30].

Genetic mapping in the mouse began with Haldane's report[31] in 1915 of linkage between the pink-eye dilution and albino loci on the linkage group that was eventually assigned to mouse chromosome 7, just 2 years after the first report of genetic linkage in *Drosophila*. The genetic map grew slowly over the next 50 years as new loci and linkage groups were added—chromosome 7 grew to three loci by 1935 and eight by 1954. The accumulation of serological and enzyme polymorphisms from the 1960s to the early 1980s began to fill out the genome, with the map of chromosome 7 harbouring 45 loci by 1982 (refs 29, 31).

The real explosion, however, came with the development of recombinant DNA technology and the advent of DNA-sequence-based polymorphisms. Initially, this involved the detection of restriction-fragment length polymorphisms (RFLPs)[32]; later, the emphasis shifted to the use of simple sequence length polymorphisms (SSLPs; also called microsatellites), which could be assayed easily by polymerase chain reaction (PCR)[33-36] and readily revealed polymorphisms between inbred laboratory strains.

Origins of mouse genomics

When the Human Genome Project (HGP) was launched in 1990, it included the mouse as one of its five central model organisms, and targeted the creation of genetic, physical and eventually sequence maps of the mouse genome.

By 1996, a dense genetic map with nearly 6,600 highly polymorphic SSLP markers ordered in a common cross had been developed[34], providing the standard tool for mouse genetics. Subsequent efforts filled out the map to over 12,000 polymorphic markers, although not all of these loci have been positioned precisely relative to one another. With these and other loci, Haldane's original two-marker linkage group on chromosome 7 had now swelled to about 2,250 loci.

张发生在整个白垩纪晚期（6,500 万年 ～ 1 亿年前），但啮齿类动物和灵长类动物实际代表了相对较晚的分支谱系[26,27]。在下面的分析中，我们用 7,500 万年的人类和小鼠的谱系分歧时间来计算进化速率，尽管实际时间可能近至 6,500 万年前。

小鼠遗传学的起源

1900 年，随着孟德尔遗传定律的重新发现，遗传的新科学先驱们（如屈埃诺、卡斯尔和利特尔）很快意识到培育出来的精致小鼠的不连续变异类似于孟德尔的豌豆，于是他们开始测试小鼠的新遗传理论。很快建立了交配方案培育近交系，从而产生了很多现代众所周知的品系（包括 C57BL/6J）[30]。

小鼠的遗传作图始于 1915 年霍尔丹[31]关于连锁群上粉色眼稀释和白化基因座之间连锁的报告，该连锁群最终被定位于小鼠 7 号染色体，距首次报道果蝇的遗传连锁仅仅两年。随着新的基因座和连锁群的增加，遗传图谱在随后的 50 年中慢慢发展起来——7 号染色体到 1935 年增长到 3 个基因座，到 1954 年增长到 8 个基因座。从 20 世纪 60 年代到 80 年代早期，血清学和酶学多态性的积累开始充实基因组，到 1982 年，7 号染色体上包含了 45 个基因座（见参考文献 29、31）。

然而，真正的爆发来自于重组 DNA 技术的发展和基于 DNA 序列的多态性的出现。最初，这只涉及限制性内切酶片段长度的多态性（RFLP）检测[32]；后来，重点转移到了简单序列长度多态性（SSLP，也称作微卫星）的应用上，这种多态性可以很容易地通过聚合酶链反应（PCR）进行检测[33-36]，并且容易发现实验室近交系之间的多态性。

小鼠基因组学的起源

1990 年人类基因组计划（HGP）启动时就把小鼠作为五个中心模式生物之一，将构建遗传、物理和最终小鼠基因组序列图谱列为目标。

到 1996 年，已绘制出一个密度包括了常见杂交中顺序排列的近 6,600 个高多态性 SSLP 标记的遗传图谱[34]，为小鼠遗传学提供了标准工具。随后的工作将该图谱上补充为超过 12,000 个多态性标记，尽管并不是所有的基因座都精确地一一相对定位。利用这些和其他基因座，霍尔丹当初在 7 号染色体上的双标记连锁群现在已经扩大到含有约 2,250 个标记。

Physical maps of the mouse genome also proceeded apace, using sequence-tagged sites (STS) together with radiation-hybrid panels[37,38] and yeast artificial chromosome (YAC) libraries to construct dense landmark maps[39]. Together, the genetic and physical maps provide thousands of anchor points that can be used to tie clones or DNA sequences to specific locations in the mouse genome.

With these resources, it became straightforward (but not always easy) to perform positional cloning of classic single-gene mutations for visible, behavioural, immunological and other phenotypes. Many of these mutations provide important models of human disease, sometimes recapitulating human phenotypes with uncanny accuracy. It also became possible for the first time to begin dissecting polygenic traits by genetic mapping of quantitative trait loci (QTL) for such traits.

Continuing advances fuelled a growing desire for a complete sequence of the mouse genome. The development of improved random mutagenesis protocols led to the establishment of large-scale screens to identify interesting new mutants, increasing the need for more rapid positional cloning strategies. QTL mapping experiments succeeded in localizing more than 1,000 loci affecting physiological traits, creating demand for efficient techniques capable of trawling through large genomic regions to find the underlying genes. Furthermore, the ability to perform directed mutagenesis of the mouse germ line through homologous recombination made it possible to manipulate any gene given its DNA sequence, placing an increasing premium on sequence information. In all of these cases, it was clear that genome sequence information could markedly accelerate progress.

Origin of the Mouse Genome Sequencing Consortium

With the sequencing of the human genome well underway by 1999, a concerted effort to sequence the entire mouse genome was organized by a Mouse Genome Sequencing Consortium (MGSC). The MGSC originally consisted of three large sequencing centres—the Whitehead/Massachusetts Institute of Technology (MIT) Center for Genome Research, the Washington University Genome Sequencing Center, and the Wellcome Trust Sanger Institute—together with an international database, Ensembl, a joint project between the European Bioinformatics Institute and the Sanger Institute.

In addition to the genome-wide efforts of the MGSC, other publicly funded groups have been contributing to the sequencing of the mouse genome in specific regions of biological interest. Together, the MGSC and these programmes have so far yielded clone-based draft sequence consisting of 1,859 Mb (74%, although there is redundancy) and finished sequence of 477 Mb (19%) of the mouse genome. Furthermore, Mural and colleagues[45] recently reported a draft sequence of mouse chromosome 16 containing 87 Mb (3.5%).

To analyse the data reported here, the MGSC was expanded to include the other publicly funded sequencing groups and a Mouse Genome Analysis Group consisting of scientists

通过联合使用序列标签位点(STS)、辐射杂交组合[37,38]和酵母人工染色体(YAC)文库来建立高密度标记物图谱[39]，小鼠基因组的物理图谱进展也很快。遗传和物理图谱提供了数千个锚定点，可以将克隆或DNA序列与小鼠基因组中的特定位置联系起来。

有了这些资源，对于可见的、行为的、免疫的以及其他表型的经典单基因突变进行定位克隆变得很直接(但并非总是容易的)。这些突变中的很多突变为人类疾病提供了重要模型，有时以不可思议的精准性描述人类表型。而且，通过进行数量性状基因座(QTL)的遗传作图也使首次开始解析多基因性状成为可能。

持续的进步激发了人们对小鼠基因组完整序列不断增长的渴望。改良的随机诱变方案的发展促成对于感兴趣的新突变的大规模筛选，增加了对更快的定位克隆策略的需求。数量性状基因座绘图实验成功地定位了超过1,000个影响生理性状的基因座，产生了对搜寻大片基因组区域定位基因的高效性技术的需求。而且通过同源重组技术对小鼠胚系进行定向诱变使得人们可以操控给定DNA序列的任何基因，从而增加了对序列信息的重视。所有这些例子中显然基因组序列信息最能显著加速进展。

小鼠基因组测序协作组的起源

1999年，随着人类基因组测序工作的顺利进行，小鼠基因组测序协作组(MGSC)组织协调了对小鼠整个基因组的测序。MGSC最初由三个大型测序中心——怀特黑德研究所／麻省理工学院(MIT)基因组研究中心、华盛顿大学基因组测序中心和威康信托桑格研究所，以及由欧洲生物信息研究所和桑格研究所合作建立的国际数据库Ensembl组成。

除了MGSC在全基因组范围的努力，其他公共资助的团体也一直在生物学感兴趣的特定区域为小鼠基因组测序做贡献。目前为止，MGSC和这些项目一起产生了基于克隆的小鼠基因组的1,859 Mb序列草图(74%，尽管存在冗余)和477 Mb(19%)的完成序列。此外，穆拉及其同事们[45]最近报道了一个包含87 Mb(3.5%)的小鼠16号染色体的序列草图。

为了分析这里报告的数据，MGSC扩大到包括其他公共项目资助的测序小组和

from 27 institutions in 6 countries.

Generating the Draft Genome Sequence

Sequencing strategy

Sanger and co-workers developed the strategy of random shotgun sequencing in the early 1980s, and it has remained the mainstay of genome sequencing over the ensuing two decades. The approach involves producing random sequence "reads", generating a preliminary assembly on the basis of sequence overlaps, and then performing directed sequencing to obtain a "finished" sequence with gaps closed and ambiguities resolved[46]. Ansorge and colleagues[47] extended the technique by the use of "paired-end sequencing", in which sequencing is performed from both ends of a cloned insert to obtain linking information, which is then used in sequence assembly. More recently, Myers and co-workers[48], and others, have developed efficient algorithms for exploiting such linking information.

The ultimate aim of the MGSC is to produce a finished, richly annotated sequence of the mouse genome to serve as a permanent reference for mammalian biology. In addition, we wished to produce a draft sequence as rapidly as possible to aid in the interpretation of the human genome sequence and to provide a useful intermediate resource to the research community. Accordingly, we adopted a hybrid strategy for sequencing the mouse genome. The strategy has four components: (1) production of a BAC-based physical map of the mouse genome by fingerprinting and sequencing the ends of clones of a BAC library[44]; (2) whole-genome shotgun (WGS) sequencing to approximately sevenfold coverage and assembly to generate an initial draft genome sequence; (3) hierarchical shotgun sequencing[46] of BAC clones covering the mouse genome combined with the WGS data to create a hybrid WGS-BAC assembly; and (4) production of a finished sequence by using the BAC clones as a template for directed finishing. This mixed strategy was designed to exploit the simpler organizational aspects of WGS assemblies in the initial phase, while still culminating in the complete high-quality sequence afforded by clone-based maps.

We chose to sequence DNA from a single mouse strain, rather than from a mixture of strains[45], to generate a solid reference foundation, reasoning that polymorphic variation in other strains could be added subsequently (see below). After extensive consultation with the scientific community[52], the B6 strain was selected because of its principal role in mouse genetics, including its well-characterized phenotype and role as the background strain on which many important mutations arose. We elected to sequence a female mouse to obtain equal coverage of chromosome X and autosomes. Chromosome Y was thus omitted, but this chromosome is highly repetitive (the human chromosome Y has multiple duplicated regions exceeding 100 kb in size with 99.9% sequence identity[53]) and seemed an unwise target for the WGS approach. Instead, mouse chromosome Y is being sequenced by a purely clone-based (hierarchical shotgun) approach.

由 6 个国家 27 个科研机构的科学家组成的小鼠基因组分析小组。

生成基因组草图

测序策略

20 世纪 80 年代早期，桑格和同事们研发了随机的鸟枪法测序策略，在随后的 20 年里，它依然是基因组测序的主流手段。该方法包括产生随机序列"读取片段"，基于序列重叠产生初步组装，然后进行定向测序，以获得填补了空缺和解决了歧义的"完成"序列 [46]。安索奇及其同事们 [47] 通过进行"双末端测序"扩展了该技术，从克隆插入片段的两端进行测序，获得连接信息，然后用于序列组装。最近，迈尔斯和同事们 [48] 以及其他人已经开发了利用这种连接信息的有效算法。

MGSC 的最终目标是产生一个完整的、注释丰富的小鼠基因组序列，作为哺乳动物生物学的永久参考。此外，我们希望尽可能快地产生一个序列草图，以帮助解释人类基因组序列，并为学界提供一个有用的中间资源。因此，我们采用混合策略对小鼠基因组进行测序。这个策略包括四个部分：(1) 通过指纹法和对 BAC 文库克隆末端的测序产生基于 BAC 的小鼠基因组物理图谱 [44]；(2) 全基因组鸟枪 (WGS) 测序到大约 7 重覆盖范围，组装产生最初的基因组序列草图；(3) 覆盖小鼠基因组的 BAC 克隆的分级鸟枪测序 [46] 与 WGS 数据结合，以构建 WGS-BAC 组装；以及 (4) 利用 BAC 克隆作为模板进行定向整理，生产完成序列。这种混合策略的设计主要是在初始阶段先解析较为简单的 WGS 组装的组织构架，最终通过克隆图谱获得完整的高质量序列。

我们选择一个单一的小鼠品系进行 DNA 测序，而不是通过品系的混合 [45] 产生坚实的参考基础，理由是随后可以不断添加其他品系的多态性变化 (见下文)。经过科学界的广泛磋商 [52]，B6 品系因其在小鼠遗传中的重要作用而被选中。B6 品系有良好的特征表型，是一个背景品系，许多重要的突变都发生在该品系上。我们选择对雌性小鼠进行测序，以获得 X 染色体和常染色体的相等覆盖率。因此染色体 Y 被省略了，但是这条染色体具有高度重复性 (人类 Y 染色体具有多个重复区域，这些区域超过 100 kb，具有 99.9% 的序列一致性 [53])，似乎并不是 WGS 方法的明智目标。取而代之的是，将通过纯克隆的方法 (分级鸟枪) 对小鼠 Y 染色体进行测序。

Sequencing and assembly

The genome assembly was based on a total of 41.4 million sequence reads derived from both ends of inserts (paired-end reads) of various clone types prepared from B6 female DNA. The inserts ranged in size from 2 to 200 kb. The three large MGSC sequencing centres generated 40.4 million reads, and 0.6 million reads were generated at the University of Utah. In addition, we used 0.4 million reads from both ends of BAC inserts reported by The Institute for Genome Research[54].

A total of 33.6 million reads passed extensive checks for quality and source, of which 29.7 million were paired; that is, derived from opposite ends of the same clone. The assembled reads represent approximately 7.7-fold sequence coverage of the euchromatic mouse genome (6.5-fold coverage in bases with a Phred quality score of > 20)[55]. Together, the clone inserts provide roughly 47-fold physical coverage of the genome.

The sequence reads, together with the pairing information, were used as input for two recently developed sequence-assembly programs, Arachne[56,57] and Phusion[58]. No mapping information and no clone-based sequences were used in the WGS assembly, with the exception of a few reads ($< 0.1\%$ of the total) derived from a handful of BACs, which were used as internal controls. The assembly programs were tested and compared on intermediate data sets over the course of the project and were thereby refined. The programs produced comparable outputs in the final assembly. The assembly generated by Arachne was chosen as the draft sequence described here because it yielded greater short-range and long-range continuity with comparable accuracy.

The assembly contains 224,713 sequence contigs, which are connected by at least two read-pair links into supercontigs (or scaffolds). There are a total of 7,418 supercontigs at least 2 kb in length, plus a further 37,125 smaller supercontigs representing $< 1\%$ of the assembly. The contigs have an N50 length of 24.8 kb, whereas the supercontigs have an N50 length that is approximately 700-fold larger at 16.9 Mb (N50 length is the size x such that 50% of the assembly is in units of length at least x). In fact, most of the genome lies in supercontigs that are extremely large: the 200 largest supercontigs span more than 98% of the assembled sequence, of which 3% is within sequence gaps.

Anchoring to chromosomes

We assigned as many supercontigs as possible to chromosomal locations in the proper order and orientation. Supercontigs were localized largely by sequence alignments with the extensively validated mouse genetic map[34], with some additional localization provided by the mouse radiation-hybrid map[37] and the BAC map[44]. We found no evidence of incorrect global joins within the supercontigs (that is, multiple markers supporting two discordant locations within the genome), and thus were able to place them directly. Altogether, we

测序和组装

基因组组装基于共计 4,140 万个序列读取片段而成，均来自 B6 雌鼠 DNA 制备的各种克隆类型的双末端插入片段（成对末端序列读取片段）。插入片段大小为 2 ~ 200 kb。三个大型 MGSC 测序中心产生了 4,040 万个序列读取片段，犹他大学产生了 60 万个序列读取片段。此外，我们使用了基因组研究所报告的 BAC 插入片段双末端的 40 万个序列读取片段 [54]。

总计 3,360 万个序列读取片段通过了质量和来源的充分检查，其中 2,970 万个是配对的；也就是说，来自同一个克隆的两端。组装了的序列读取片段代表了小鼠常染色体基因组约 7.7 重序列覆盖率（Phred 质量分数大于 20 的碱基覆盖率为 6.5 重）[55]。克隆插入片段总共提供了大约 47 倍的基因组物理覆盖。

序列读取片段以及配对信息被最近开发的两个序列组装程序（Arachne[56,57] 和 Phusion[58]）用来作为输入信息进行组装。除了从少量作为内参的 BAC 中得到一些序列读取片段（小于总数的 0.1%），WGS 组装中不使用图谱信息和基于克隆的序列。在项目过程中，对组装程序进行了中间数据集的测试和比较，从而进行了改进。这些程序在最终的组装中产生可比较的序列输出。Arachne 生成的组装被选为本文所描述的序列草图，因为它产生了更好的短区段和长区段的连续性，具有相当的精确度。

这个组装包括 224,713 个序列重叠群，它们通过至少两个配对序列读取片段连接成超级重叠群（或者支架）。总共有 7,418 个超级重叠群至少 2 kb 长，另外还有 37,125 个代表了小于 1% 组装的较小超级重叠群。重叠群的 N50 长度为 24.8 kb，而超级重叠群的 N50 长度大概是其 700 倍达到 16.9 Mb（如果 N50 长度是 x，则 50% 组装件的长度至少为 x）。事实上，大部分基因组都包括在非常大的超级重叠群中：200 个最大的超级重叠群跨越了 98% 以上的组装序列，其中还有 3% 处于测序空缺区域内。

染色体锚定

我们将尽可能多的超级重叠群按照适当的顺序和方向配到染色体位置上。超级重叠群主要通过与充分验证了的小鼠遗传图谱 [34] 进行比对而定位，一些额外的定位由小鼠辐射杂交图谱 [37] 和 BAC 图谱 [44] 提供。我们没有发现超级重叠群中有不正确的总体连接的证据（即两个不一致位置受到基因组中多个标记的支持），因此可以直接将它们放入染色体中。我们总共放置了 377 个超级重叠群，包括所有长度超过

placed 377 supercontigs, including all supercontigs > 500 kb in length.

Once much of the sequence was anchored, it was possible to exploit additional read-pair and physical mapping information to obtain greater continuity. For example, some adjacent supercontigs were connected by BAC-end (or other) links, satisfying appropriate length and orientation constraints, including single links. Furthermore, some adjacent extended supercontigs were connected by means of fingerprint contigs in the BAC-based physical map. These additional links were used to join sequence into ultracontigs. In the end, a total of 88 ultracontigs with an N50 length of 50.6 Mb (exclusive of gaps) contained 95.7% of the assembled sequence (Fig. 1).

Fig. 1. The mouse genome in 88 sequence-based ultracontigs. The position and extent of the 88 ultracontigs of the MGSCv3 assembly are shown adjacent to ideograms of the mouse chromosomes. All mouse chromosomes are acrocentric, with the centromeric end at the top of each chromosome. The supercontigs of the sequence assembly were anchored to the mouse chromosomes using the MIT genetic map. Neighbouring supercontigs were linked together into ultracontigs using information from single BAC links and the fingerprint and radiation-hybrid maps, resulting in 88 ultracontigs containing 95% of the bases in the euchromatic genome.

500 kb 的超级重叠群。

一旦锚定了大部分序列，就可以利用额外的配对序列读取片段和物理图谱信息来获得更大的连接。例如，一些相邻的超级重叠群通过 BAC 的末端（或者其他）连接相接，如果这些连接包括单连接满足长度和方向约束。此外，在以 BAC 为基础的物理图谱中，一些连接是通过指纹图谱重叠群连接一些相邻延伸的超级重叠群。这些额外的连接用于将序列连成特大超级重叠群。最终，共有 88 个特大超级重叠群，N50 长度为 50.6 Mb（不包括空缺），包括了 95.7% 的组装序列（图 1）。

图 1. 88 个基于序列的特大超级重叠群中的小鼠基因组。MGSCv3 组装的 88 个特大超级重叠群的位置和范围显示在小鼠染色体核型模式图相邻的位置。小鼠所有染色体都是近端着丝粒的，着丝粒位于每条染色体的顶端。利用 MIT 基因图谱，将序列组装的超级重叠群锚定在小鼠染色体上。利用来自单个 BAC 连接、指纹图谱和辐射杂交图谱的信息，将相邻的超级重叠群连在一起形成特大超级重叠群，产生 88 个包括常染色体基因组中 95% 碱基的特大超级重叠群。

Of the 187 Mb of finished mouse sequence, 96% was contained in the anchored assembly. This finished sequence, however, is not a completely random cross-section of the genome (it has been cloned as BACs, finished, and in some cases selected on the basis of its gene content). Of 11,452 cDNA sequences from the curated RefSeq collection, 99.3% of the cDNAs could be aligned to the genome sequence (see Supplementary Information). These alignments contained 96.4% of the cDNA bases. Together, this indicates that the draft genome sequence includes approximately 96% of the euchromatic portion of the mouse genome, with about 95% anchored.

Table 3. Mouse chromosome size estimates

Chromosome	Actual bases in sequence (Mb)	Ultracontigs (Mb)		Gaps within supercontigs		Gaps between supercontigs					Total estimated size (Mb) ‡
		Number	N50 size	Number	Mb	Captured by additional read pairs		Captured by fingerprint contigs*		Uncaptured†	
						Number	Mb	Number	Mb	Number	
All	2,372	88	52.7	176,094	104.5	252	14.0	37	2.30	68	2,493
1	183	6	52.7	13,178	7.8	16	1.1	1	0.32	5	192
2	169	5	111.1	12,141	6.5	4	0.1	1	0.20	4	176
3	149	2	108.9	10,630	6.8	17	0.7	3	0.16	1	157
4	140	3	83.1	10,745	6.3	14	0.4	3	0.26	2	147
5	137	13	17.8	11,288	6.7	11	0.5	3	0.11	12	144
6	138	4	91.4	10,021	6.6	19	1.1	2	0.26	3	146
7	122	5	45.1	9,484	5.7	55	3.4	4	0.12	4	131
8	119	5	35.0	9,186	6.1	7	0.2	2	0.12	4	125
9	116	6	26.8	8,479	4.5	6	0.6	1	0.06	5	121
10	121	4	50.4	9,490	5.4	9	0.6	0	0	3	127
11	115	3	80.4	8,681	4.3	2	0.0	1	0.05	2	119
12	105	2	77.4	7,577	4.0	27	1.2	2	0.00	1	110
13	107	6	28.0	7,910	4.7	13	0.8	4	0.19	5	113
14	107	2	93.6	7,605	4.0	10	0.5	2	0.12	1	112
15	96	3	65.3	7,025	4.3	2	0.1	0	0	2	100
16	91	3	62.3	6,695	4.4	1	0.0	0	0	2	95
17	85	2	80.8	6,584	3.7	17	1.2	4	0.19	1	90
18	84	3	73.5	6,192	3.2	2	0.0	0	0	2	87
19	55	1	57.7	3,934	2.4	7	0.6	2	0.12	0	58
X	134	10	19.9	9,249	7.0	13	0.8	2	0.00	9	142

*These gaps had fingerprint contigs spanning them. The size for 18 out of 37 were estimated using conserved synteny to determine the size of the region in the human genome. The remaining gaps were arbitrarily given the average size of the assessed gaps (59 kb), adjusted to reflect the 16% difference in genome size.

† Uncaptured gaps were estimated by mouse–human synteny to have a total size of 5 Mb. However, because some of these gaps are due to repetitive expansions in mouse (absent in human), the actual total for the uncaptured gaps

在 187 Mb 已完成的小鼠序列中，96% 包含在锚定到染色体的组装中。然而，这个已完成的序列不是一个完全随机的基因组横截面（它已经被克隆成 BAC，完成了测序，并且在一些情况下是根据其基因含量被选择的）。在 RefSeq 数据库收集的 11,452 个 cDNA 序列中，99.3% 的 cDNA 可以和基因组序列比对（见补充信息）。这些比对包含 96.4% 的 cDNA 碱基。这表明基因组序列草图包括小鼠基因组大约 96% 的常染色体部分，其中约 95% 被锚定在染色体上。

表 3. 小鼠染色体长度估算

染色体	序列中实际碱基 (Mb)	特大超级重叠群(Mb)		超级重叠群内的测序空缺		超级重叠群之间的测序空缺					总估计长度 (Mb)‡
		数量	N50 大小	数量	Mb	由其他读取片段对捕获		由指纹图谱重叠群捕获*		未捕获†	
						数量	Mb	数量	Mb	数量	
合计	2,372	88	52.7	176,094	104.5	252	14.0	37	2.30	68	2,493
1	183	6	52.7	13,178	7.8	16	1.1	1	0.32	5	192
2	169	5	111.1	12,141	6.5	4	0.1	3	0.20	4	176
3	149	2	108.9	10,630	6.8	17	0.7	3	0.16	1	157
4	140	3	83.1	10,745	6.3	14	0.4	3	0.26	2	147
5	137	13	17.8	11,288	6.7	11	0.5	3	0.11	12	144
6	138	4	91.4	10,021	6.6	19	1.1	3	0.26	1	146
7	122	5	45.1	9,484	5.7	55	3.4	4	0.12	4	131
8	119	5	35.0	9,186	6.1	7			0.12	4	125
9	116	6	26.8	8,479	4.5	6	0.6	1	0.06	5	121
10	121	4	50.4	9,490	5.4	9	0.6	0	0	3	127
11	115	3	80.4	8,681	4.3	2	0.0		0.05	2	119
12	105	2	77.4	7,577	4.0	27	1.2	2	0.00	1	110
13	107	6	28.0	7,910	4.7	13	0.8	4	0.19	5	113
14	107	2	93.6	7,605	4.0	10	0.5	2	0.12	1	112
15	96	3	65.3	7,025	4.3	2	0.1	0	0	2	100
16	91	3	62.3	6,695	4.4	1	0.0	0	0	2	95
17	85	2	80.8	6,584	3.7	17	1.2	4	0.19	1	90
18	84	3	73.5	6,192	3.2	2	0.0	0	0	2	87
19	55	1	57.7	3,934	2.4	7	0.6	2	0.12		58
X	134	10	19.9	9,249	7.0	13	0.8	2	0.00	9	142

* 这些测序空缺含有横跨的指纹图谱重叠群。利用人类基因组中该区域长度进行保守同线性估计，得到了 37 个中的 18 个的大小。剩余的空缺且用被估算空缺的平均值（59 kb）给出，由此调节反映了基因组的 16% 差异。

† 通过小鼠–人类同线性估计未捕获的测序空缺共有 5 Mb。然而，因为这些空缺中的一部分是由于小鼠中的重复扩张（人类中缺失），所以未捕获空缺的实际总数可能会高得多。例如，1 号染色体(Sp-100rs 区域)上一个大的未捕获空缺就大约有 6 Mb(见正文)。

is probably substantially higher. For example, one large uncaptured gap on chromosome 1 (the Sp-100rs region) is roughly 6 Mb (see text).

‡ Omitting centromeres and telomeres. These would add, on average, approximately 8 Mb per chromosome, or about 160 Mb to the genome. Also omitting uncaptured gaps between supercontigs.

On the basis of the estimated sizes of the ultracontigs and gaps between them, the total length of the euchromatic mouse genome was estimated to be about 2.5 Gb (see Supplementary Information), or about 14% smaller than that of the euchromatic human genome (about 2.9 Gb) (Table 3).

Quality assessment at intermediate scale

Although no evidence of large-scale misassembly was found when anchoring the assembly onto the mouse chromosomes, we examined the assembly for smaller errors.

To assess the accuracy at an intermediate scale, we compared the positions of well-studied markers on the mouse genetic map and in the genome assembly (see Supplementary Information). Out of 2,605 genetic markers that were unambiguously mapped to the sequence assembly (BLAST match using 10^{-100} or better as an E-value to a single location) we found 1.8% in which the chromosomal assignment in the genetic map conflicted with that in the sequence. This is well within the known range of erroneous assignments within the genetic map[34].

We also found 19 instances (0.7%) of conflicts in local marker order between the genetic map and sequence assembly. A conflict was defined as any instance that would require changing more than a single genotype in the data underlying the genetic map to resolve. We studied ten cases by re-mapping the genetic markers, and eight were found to be due to errors in the genetic map. On the basis of this analysis, we estimate that chromosomal misassignment and local misordering affects < 0.3% of the assembled sequence.

At the single nucleotide level in the assembly, the observed discrepancy rates varied in a manner consistent with the quality scores assigned to the bases in the WGS assembly (see Supplementary Information). Overall, 96% of nucleotides in the assembly have Arachne quality scores ≥ 40, corresponding to a predicted error rate of 1 per 10,000 bases. Such bases had an observed discrepancy rate against finished sequence of 0.005%, or 5 errors per 100,000 bases.

Collapse of duplicated regions

The human genome contains many large duplicated regions, estimated to comprise roughly 5% of the genome[59], with nearly identical sequence. If such regions are also common in the mouse genome, they might collapse into a single copy in the WGS assembly. Such artefactual collapse could be detected as regions with unusually high read coverage, compared with the average depth of 7.4-fold in long assembled contigs. We searched for

‡ 去除着丝粒和端粒。这些将使每个染色体平均增加大约 8 Mb，或者基因组增加大约 160 Mb。也除去了超级重叠群之间的未捕获空缺。

以特大超级重叠群和它们之间的空缺的预估尺寸为基础，小鼠常染色体基因组的总长度估计约为 2.5 Gb（见补充信息），或者比人类常染色体基因组（约 2.9 Gb）小了约 14%（表 3）。

中等规模的质量评估

虽然在将组装锚定到小鼠染色体上时没有大规模错误组装的证据，我们还是检查了组装以发现较小的错误。

为了在中等规模上评估准确性，我们比较了小鼠遗传图谱和基因组组装中研究透彻的标记位置（见补充信息）。在明确定位到序列组装的 2,605 个遗传标记中（用 10^{-100} 或更好值作为 E 值与单个位置进行 BLAST 匹配），我们发现遗传图谱中有 1.8% 的染色体分配和序列不符。这完全在遗传图谱已知的错误分配范围内 [34]。

我们还发现局部标记的顺序在遗传图谱和序列组装之间有 19 例（0.7%）不符。矛盾的定义是需要在遗传图谱基础数据中进行多于一个基因型的更改才能解决不符的任何情况。我们通过重新放置映射遗传标记研究了 10 个例子，发现其中 8 个是遗传图谱的错误。在此分析基础上，我们估计染色体分配错误和局部顺序错误影响小于 0.3% 的组装序列。

在组装的单核苷酸水平上，观测到的差异率的变化一定程度上与 WGS 组装中的匹配碱基的质量分数相一致（参见补充信息）。总体来说，该组装中 96% 的核苷酸 Arachne 质量分数 ≥40，相当于预测误差率为每 10,000 个碱基有 1 个错误。这类错误碱基在完成序列上所观测到的差异率为 0.005%，或者每 100,000 个碱基有 5 个错误。

复制区域的分解

人类基因组包含很多大规模的复制区域，估计约占基因组的 5%[59]，它们具有几乎相同的序列。如果这些区域在小鼠的基因组中也很常见，在 WGS 组装中它们可能会分解成单个拷贝。与平均深度 7.4 倍的长组装重叠群相比，这种人工折叠分解会被检测为具有异常高的读取片段覆盖度的区域。我们搜索了长度大于 20 kb 且其

contigs that were > 20 kb in size and contained > 10 kb of sequence in which the read coverage was at least twofold higher than the average. Such regions comprised only a tiny fraction (< 0.0001) of the total assembly, of which only half had been anchored to a chromosome. None of these windows had coverage exceeding the average by more than threefold. This may indicate that the mouse genome contains fewer large regions of near-exact duplication than the human. Alternatively, regions of near-exact duplication may have been systematically excluded by the WGS assembly programme. This issue is better addressed through hierarchical shotgun than WGS sequencing and will be examined more carefully in the course of producing a finished mouse genome sequence.

Unplaced reads and large tandem repeats

We expected that highly repetitive regions of the genome would not be assembled or would not be anchored on the chromosomes. Indeed, 5.9 million of the 33.6 million passing reads were not part of anchored sequence, with 88% of these not assembled into sequence contigs and 12% assembled into small contigs but not chromosomally localized.

Evaluation of WGS assembly strategy

The WGS assembly described here involved only random reads, without any additional map-based information. By many criteria, the assembly is of very high quality. The N50 supercontig size of 16.9 Mb far exceeds that achieved by any previous WGS assembly, and the agreement with genome-wide maps is excellent. The assembly quality may be due to several factors, including the use of high-quality libraries, the variety of insert lengths in multiple libraries, the improved assembly algorithms, and the inbred nature of the mouse strain (in contrast to the polymorphisms in the human genome sequences). Another contributing factor may be that the mouse differs from the human in having less recent segmental duplication to confound assembly.

Notwithstanding the high quality of the draft genome sequence, we are mindful that it contains many gaps, small misassemblies and nucleotide errors. It is likely that these could not all be resolved by further WGS sequencing, therefore directed sequencing will be needed to produce a finished sequence. The results also suggest that WGS sequencing may suffice for large genomes for which only draft sequence is required, provided that they contain minimal amounts of sequence associated with recent segmental duplications or large, recent interspersed repeat elements.

Adding finished sequence

As a final step, we enhanced the WGS sequence assembly by substituting available finished BAC-derived sequence from the B6 strain. In total, we replaced 3,528 draft sequence

中大于 10 kb 序列的读取覆盖度至少是平均值两倍的重叠群。这些区域只包括总组装的小部分（小于 0.0001），其中只有一半锚定在染色体上。这些窗口的覆盖度都没有超过平均值三倍以上。这可能表明小鼠基因组含有比人类更少的近精准复制的大区域。另一种可能是，WGS 组装程序可能已经系统地排除了近精确复制的区域。与 WGS 测序相比，分级鸟枪法能更好解决这个问题，因此将在构建小鼠基因组完成图序列的过程中更仔细地检查这个问题。

未入选的序列读取片段和大串联重复

我们预计基因组中高度重复区域不会被组装或者不会被锚定到染色体上。确实，3,360 万个合格的序列读取中有 590 万个不是被锚定序列的一部分，其中的 88% 不会被组装成序列重叠群，12% 组装成小的重叠群，但是没定位在染色体上。

WGS 组装策略的评估

这里描述的 WGS 组装只涉及随机的序列读取片段，没有任何附加的基于图谱本身的信息。按照很多标准，这种组装是高质量的。超级重叠群的 N50 长度为 16.9 Mb，远远超过之前任何 WGS 组装的结果，并且与全基因组图谱有极好的一致性。组装质量可能归因于几个因素，包括高质量文库的使用、多个文库中插入片段长度的多样性、改进的组装算法以及小鼠品系的近交特性（与人类基因组序列的多态性相比较）。另外一个因素可能是小鼠与人类的不同之处，它具有较少的混淆组装的近期片段复制。

尽管基因组序列草图的质量很高，我们注意到了它包含很多测序空缺、小的组装错误和核苷酸错误。这些问题很可能无法通过进一步的 WGS 测序来解决，因此需要定向测序来产生一个完成图序列。这些结果也提示，WGS 测序对于只需要序列草图的大基因组可能就足够了，前提是近期片段复制或者大量近期分散开的重复元件相关序列最少。

添加完成序列

作为最后一步，我们通过替换来自 B6 品系可用的 BAC 完成序列来增强 WGS 序列组装。总共用组装时能够提供的 210 个完成 BAC 的 48.2 Mb 完成序列替换了

contigs with 48.2 Mb of finished sequence from 210 finished BACs available at the time of the assembly. The resulting draft genome sequence, MGSCv3, was submitted to the public databases and is freely available in electronic form through various sources (see below).

As the MGSC produces additional BAC assemblies and finished sequence, we plan to continue to revise and release enhanced versions of the genome sequence *en route* to a completely finished sequence[66], thereby providing a permanent foundation for biomedical research in the twenty-first century.

Conservation of Synteny between Mouse and Human Genomes

With the draft sequence in hand, we began our analysis by investigating the strong conservation of synteny between the mouse and human genomes. Beyond providing insight into evolutionary events that have moulded the chromosomes, this analysis facilitates further comparisons between the genomes.

Starting from a common ancestral genome approximately 75 Myr, the mouse and human genomes have each been shuffled by chromosomal rearrangements. The rate of these changes, however, is low enough that local gene order remains largely intact. It is thus possible to recognize syntenic (literally "same thread") regions in the two species that have descended relatively intact from the common ancestor.

The earliest indication that genes reside in similar relative positions in different mammalian species traces to the observation that the albino and pink-eye dilution mutants are genetically closely linked in both mouse and rat[67,68]. Significant experimental evidence came from genetic studies of somatic cells[69]. A recent gene-based synteny map[37] used more than 3,600 orthologous loci to define about 200 regions of conserved synteny. However, it is recognized that such maps might still miss regions owing to insufficient marker density.

With a robust draft sequence of the mouse genome and > 90% finished sequence of the human genome in hand, it is possible to undertake a more comprehensive analysis of conserved synteny. Rather than simply relying on known human–mouse gene pairs, we identified a much larger set of orthologous landmarks as follows. We performed sequence comparisons of the entire mouse and human genome sequences using the PatternHunter program[71] to identify regions having a similarity score exceeding a high threshold (> 40, corresponding to a minimum of a 40-base perfect match, with penalties for mismatches and gaps), with the additional property that each sequence is the other's unique match above this threshold. Such regions probably reflect orthologous sequence pairs, derived from the same ancestral sequence.

About 558,000 orthologous landmarks were identified; in the mouse assembly, these sequences have a mean spacing of about 4.4 kb and an N50 length of about 500 bp. The landmarks had a total length of roughly 188 Mb, comprising about 7.5% of the mouse

3,528 个序列草图重叠群。最终的基因组序列草图 MGSCv3 被提交给各公共数据库，并且通过各种资源以电子形式免费提供（见下文）。

随着 MGSC 产生更多的 BAC 组装和完成序列，我们计划继续修订和发布基因组序列的改进版本，使其成为完整的完成序列[66]，从而为二十一世纪的生物医学研究提供永久的基础。

小鼠和人类基因组同线性的保守性

随着序列草图在手，我们开始分析小鼠和人类基因组之间同线性的强保守性。这项研究不仅可以深入了解染色体构造中的进化事件，还可以促进不同物种基因组之间的进一步比较。

从大约 7,500 万年前的共同的祖先基因组开始，小鼠和人类的基因组都被染色体重排彻底改变了。然而，这个改变率相当低，以至于局部基因序列仍然基本保持完整。因此我们才有可能识别两个物种从共同祖先那里相对完整地传下来的同线性区域（字面意思是"同一条线"）。

最早的迹象表明，在不同哺乳动物物种中，基因位于相似的相对位置，这可追溯到对小鼠和大鼠中白化和粉色眼稀释突变都在遗传学上紧密连锁的观察[67,68]。重要的实验证据来自体细胞遗传学研究[69]。最近发布的一项基于基因的同线性图谱[37]使用超过 3,600 个直系同源基因座，定义了约 200 个保守的同线性区域。然而，大家还是意识到由于标记密度不足，这些图谱仍然可能遗漏一些同线性区域。

利用稳定的小鼠基因组序列草图和人类基因组已完成的 90% 的序列，可以进行更全面的保守同线性分析。这项工作并不是简单地依赖于已知的人类–小鼠基因对，而是确定了如下所示的更多数量的直系同源标记物。我们使用 PatternHunter 软件[71]对整个小鼠和人类基因组序列进行对比，识别出相似分值较高（大于 40 分，即至少有 40 碱基完全匹配，错配和空缺会罚分）的序列区域，此外每个序列必须是另一序列高于阈值的唯一匹配。这些区域可能反映了来自同一个祖先序列的直系同源序列对。

我们识别出约 558,000 个直系同源标记；在小鼠基因组组装中，这些序列的平均间隔约为 4.4 kb，N50 长度约为 500 bp。这些标记物总长度大约为 188 Mb，约占小鼠基因组的 7.5%。应当强调的是，这些标记物仅代表了小鼠和人类基因组中可以

genome. It should be emphasized that the landmarks represent only a small subset of the sequences, consisting of those that can be aligned with the highest similarity between the mouse and human genomes. (Indeed, below we show that about 40% of the human genome can be aligned confidently with the mouse genome.)

The locations of the landmarks in the two genomes were then compared to identify regions of conserved synteny. We define a syntenic segment to be a maximal region in which a series of landmarks occur in the same order on a single chromosome in both species. A syntenic block in turn is one or more syntenic segments that are all adjacent on the same chromosome in human and on the same chromosome in mouse, but which may otherwise be shuffled with respect to order and orientation. To avoid small artefactual syntenic segments owing to imperfections in the two draft genome sequences, we only considered regions above 300 kb and ignored occasional isolated interruptions in conserved order (see Supplementary Information). Thus, some small syntenic segments have probably been omitted—this issue will be addressed best when finished sequences of the two genomes are completed.

Marked conservation of landmark order was found across most of the two genomes (Fig. 2). Each genome could be parsed into a total of 342 conserved syntenic segments. On average, each landmark resides in a segment containing 1,600 other landmarks. The segments vary greatly in length, from 303 kb to 64.9 Mb, with a mean of 6.9 Mb and an N50 length of 16.1 Mb. In total, about 90.2% of the human genome and 93.3% of the mouse genome unambiguously reside within conserved syntenic segments. The segments can be aggregated into a total of 217 conserved syntenic blocks, with an N50 length of 23.2 Mb.

Fig. 2. Conservation of synteny between human and mouse. We detected 558,000 highly conserved, reciprocally unique landmarks within the mouse and human genomes, which can be joined into conserved syntenic segments and blocks (defined in text). A typical 510-kb segment of mouse chromosome 12 that shares common ancestry with a 600-kb section of human chromosome 14 is shown. Blue lines connect the reciprocal unique matches in the two genomes. The cyan bars represent sequence coverage in each of the two genomes for the regions. In general, the landmarks in the mouse genome are more closely spaced, reflecting the 14% smaller overall genome size.

The nature and extent of conservation of synteny differs substantially among chromosomes (Fig. 3). In accordance with expectation, the X chromosomes are represented as single, reciprocal syntenic blocks[72]. Human chromosome 20 corresponds entirely to a portion of mouse chromosome 2, with nearly perfect conservation of order along almost the entire length, disrupted only by a small central segment (Fig. 4a, d). Human chromosome 17

用于比对的高度一致序列的一个小子集。(的确，下文中我们表明大约 40% 人类基因组肯定能够与小鼠的基因组比对。)

随后在两个基因组中比较直系同源标记物的位置以识别保守的同线性区域。我们将同线性片段定义为在两个基因组中的单条染色体按相同顺序出现的一系列直系同源标记的最长区域。一个同线性区域首先是一个或多个在人类基因组和小鼠基因组中一条染色体上的毗邻同线性区段，但是在两个基因组上的排列方向和顺序可以打乱而不同。为了避免由两个基因组序列草图不完善而导致的人为的小同线性片段，我们只考虑大于 300 kb 的区域，并忽略保守排列顺序中偶然出现的孤立的中断部分（见补充信息）。因此，一些小的同线性片段可能会被遗漏了，但当两个基因组完整序列的测序完成时，这个问题会得到彻底解决。

我们在两个基因组的大部分序列中发现了标记顺序的显著保守性（图 2）。每个基因组可以被分解为共计 342 个保守的同线性片段。平均每个标记位于包含其他 1,600 个标记的片段中。这些片段长度差异很大，从 303 kb 到 64.9 Mb，平均 6.9 Mb，N50 长度为 16.1 Mb。总体而言，大约 90.2% 的人类基因组和 93.3% 的小鼠基因组明确置于保守的同线性片段中。这些片段可以组成共计 217 个保守的同线区，N50 长度为 23.2 Mb。

图 2. 人类和小鼠之间保守的同线性。我们在小鼠和人类基因组中检测到 558,000 个高度保守且相互独立的标记，这些标记可以连成保守的同线性片段和区块（定义见正文）。这里显示小鼠 12 号染色体一个 510 kb 与人类 14 号染色体的一个 600 kb 片段具有共同祖先的典型片段。深蓝线连接了两个基因组中相互独立匹配的片段。浅蓝色条带代表该区域在每个基因组的序列覆盖度。一般而言，小鼠基因组中的标记间隔更紧密，反映出其总基因组比人类减少了 14%。

不同染色体之间同线性的保守性质和程度有很大差异（图 3）。与预期一致，X染色体表现为单一、相互同线性区块[72]。整条人类 20 号染色体和小鼠 2 号染色体的一部分完全对应，保守性的顺序在整个长度上近乎完美，仅被一个小的中心片段打断（图 4a、4d）。整条人类 17 号染色体与小鼠 11 号染色体的一部分完全对应，但

corresponds entirely to a portion of mouse chromosome 11, but extensive rearrangements have divided it into at least 16 segments (Fig. 4b, e). Other chromosomes, however, show evidence of much more extensive interchromosomal rearrangement than these cases (Fig. 4c, f).

Fig. 3. Segments and blocks > 300 kb in size with conserved synteny in human are superimposed on the mouse genome. Each colour corresponds to a particular human chromosome. The 342 segments are separated from each other by thin, white lines within the 217 blocks of consistent colour.

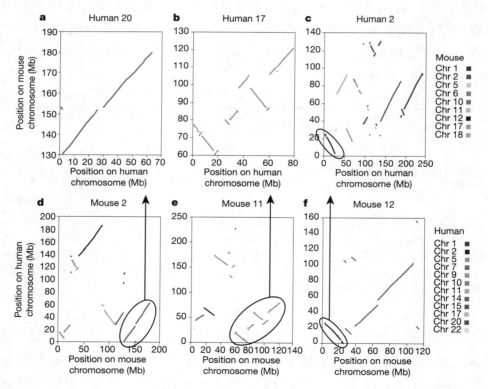

Fig. 4. Dot plots of conserved syntenic segments in three human and three mouse chromosomes. For each of three human (**a**–**c**) and mouse (**d**–**f**) chromosomes, the positions of orthologous landmarks are plotted along the *x* axis and the corresponding position of the landmark on chromosomes in the other genome

是大量的重组将其分成了至少 16 个片段（图 4b、4e）。对其他染色体来说，证据则显示比这些例子更为剧烈的染色体之间的重组（图 4c、4f）。

图 3. 人类基因组中大于 300 kb 的保守同线性片段和区块叠加在小鼠的基因组上。每种颜色对应一个特定的人类染色体。在 217 个具有同一颜色的同线性区块中，共有 342 个同线性片段通过细白线彼此分开。

图 4. 人类三个染色体和小鼠三个染色体中保守同线性片段的点图。x 轴为每条人类（a～c）和小鼠（d～f）染色体上直系同源标记的位置，y 轴为该标记在另一个基因组染色体上的对应位置。不同颜色区分位于同一条染色体上的多个同源标记对应的另一个物种的不同染色体。保守同线性的一个典型例子是

is plotted on the y axis. Different chromosomes in the corresponding genome are differentiated with distinct colours. In a remarkable example of conserved synteny, human chromosome 20 (**a**) consists of just three segments from mouse chromosome 2 (**d**), with only one small segment altered in order. Human chromosome 17 (**b**) also shares segments with only one mouse chromosome (11) (**e**), but the 16 segments are extensively rearranged. However, most of the mouse and human chromosomes consist of multiple segments from multiple chromosomes, as shown for human chromosome 2 (**c**) and mouse chromosome 12 (**f**). Circled areas and arrows denote matching segments in mouse and human.

We compared the new sequence-based map of conserved synteny with the most recent previous map based on 3,600 loci[30]. The new map reveals many more conserved syntenic segments (342 compared with 202) but only slightly more conserved syntenic blocks (217 compared with 170). Most of the conserved syntenic blocks had previously been recognized and are consistent with the new map, but many rearrangements of segments within blocks had been missed (notably on the X chromosome).

The occurrence of many local rearrangements is not surprising. Compared with interchromosomal rearrangements (for example, translocations), paracentric inversions (that is, those within a single chromosome and not including the centromere) carry a lower selective disadvantage in terms of the frequency of aneuploidy among offspring. These are also seen at a higher frequency in genera such as *Drosophila*, in which extensive cytogenetic comparisons have been carried out[73,74].

The block and segment sizes are broadly consistent with the random breakage model of genome evolution[75]. At this gross level, there is no evidence of extensive selection for gene order across the genome. Selection in specific regions, however, is by no means excluded, and indeed seems probable (for example, for the major histocompatibility complex). Moreover, the analysis does not exclude the possibility that chromosomal breaks may tend to occur with higher frequency in some locations.

With a map of conserved syntenic segments between the human and mouse genomes, it is possible to calculate the minimal number of rearrangements needed to "transform" one genome into the other[70,76,77]. When applied to the 342 syntenic segments above, the most parsimonious path has 295 rearrangements. The analysis suggests that chromosomal breaks may have a tendency to reoccur in certain regions. With only two species, however, it is not yet possible to recover the ancestral chromosomal order or reconstruct the precise pathway of rearrangements. As more mammalian species are sequenced, it should be possible to draw such inferences and study the nature of chromosome rearrangement.

Genome Landscape

We next sought to analyse the contents of the mouse genome, both in its own right and in comparison with corresponding regions of the human genome.

All of the mouse genome information is accessible in electronic form through various

人类 20 号染色体(a)仅由来自小鼠 2 号染色体(d)上的三个同源片段组成，其中只有一个很小的片段的顺序不一致。人类 17 号染色体(b)也仅与小鼠一条染色体(11)(e)同源片段共享，不过 16 个片段都被彻底重组了。然而，小鼠和人类大多数染色体由来自多个染色体的多个同源片段组成，如人类 2 号染色体(c)和小鼠 12 号染色体(f)所示。圆圈圈住的区域和箭头表示小鼠和人类相匹配的片段。

我们比较了全新的基于序列保守同线性图谱和最近发布的基于 3,600 个基因座的前期图谱[30]。新图谱展示的保守同线性片段数量增加了很多(342 个比 202 个)，但保守同线性区域数量只有少量增加(217 个比 170 个)。这表明大多数保守同线性区先前已经被识别了，并且与新图谱一致，但是位于区域内的很多重组片段被错过了(特别是 X 染色体)。

发生许多局部重组并不令人意外。就子代间非整倍体频率而言，臂内倒位(即单个染色体内且不包括着丝粒的倒位)相比于染色体间重组(如易位)选择劣势更低。这种局部重组在果蝇等广泛用于细胞遗传学比较的物种中的频率也很高[73,74]。

同源区域和片段的长度与基因进化的随机断裂模型大体一致[75]。总体而言，没有证据表明在基因组中存在广泛的对基因排布顺序的选择。然而，在特殊区域绝不排除这种选择，而且看起来确实可能存在(例如，对主要组织相容性复合体的选择)。此外，分析并不排除染色体断裂可能倾向于在某些位置以更高频率发生的可能性。

利用人类和小鼠基因组之间的保守同线性片段图谱，可以计算将一个基因组"转化"为另一个基因组所需的最小重组数目[70,76,77]。应用于上述的 342 个同线性片段，最简捷的途径有 295 个重组。分析表明，染色体断裂可能倾向于在某个区域重复出现。然而仅凭两个物种不太可能复原祖先染色体上的排列顺序或重建精确的染色体重组过程。随着更多哺乳动物物种的基因组测序完成，理论上可以得出这样的推论并研究染色体重组的特性。

基因组概貌

下一步，我们试图分析小鼠基因组的内容，包括其本身以及与人类基因组的相应区域的比较。

所有小鼠基因组信息可以通过各种浏览器以电子形式访问：Ensembl(http://

browsers: Ensembl (http://www.ensembl.org), the University of California at Santa Cruz (http://genome.ucsc.edu) and the National Center for Biotechnology Information (http:// www.ncbi.nlm.nih.gov). These browsers allow users to scroll along the chromosomes and zoom in or out to any scale, as well as to display information at any desired level of detail. The mouse genome information has also been integrated into existing human genome browsers at these same organizations. In this section, we compare general properties of the mouse and human genomes.

Genome expansion and contraction

The projected total length of the euchromatic portion of the mouse genome (2.5 Gb) is about 14% smaller than that of the human genome (2.9 Gb). To investigate the source of this difference, we examined the relative size of intervals between consecutive orthologous landmarks in the human and mouse genomes. The mouse/human ratio has a mean at 0.91 for autosomes, but varies widely, with the mouse interval being larger than the human in 38% of cases. Chromosome X, by contrast, shows no net relative expansion or contraction, with a mouse/human ratio of 1.03. What accounts for the smaller size of the mouse genome? We address this question below in the sections on repeat sequences and on genome evolution.

(G+C) content

The overall distribution of local (G+C) content is significantly different between the mouse and human genomes. Such differences have been noted in biochemical studies[78-81] and in comparative analyses of fourfold degenerate sites in codons of mouse and human genes[82-85], but the availability of nearly complete genome sequences provides the first detailed picture of the phenomenon.

The mouse has a slightly higher overall (G+C) content than the human (42% compared with 41%), but the distribution is tighter. When local (G+C) content is measured in 20-kb windows across the genome, the human genome has about 1.4% of the windows with (G+C) content > 56% and 1.3% with (G+C) content < 33%. Such extreme deviations are virtually absent in the mouse genome. The contrast is even seen at the level of entire chromosomes. The human has extreme outliers with respect to (G+C) content (the most extreme being chromosome 19), whereas the mouse chromosomes tend to be far more uniform.

There is a strong positive correlation in local (G+C) content between orthologous regions in the mouse and human genomes, but with the mouse regions showing a clear tendency to be less extreme in (G+C) content than the human regions. This tendency is not uniform, with the most extreme differences seen at the tails of the distribution.

In mammalian genomes, there is a positive correlation between gene density and (G+C) www.ensembl.org）、加州大学圣克鲁斯分校（http://genome.ucsc.edu）和美国国家生物技术信息中心（http://www.ncbi.nlm.nih.gov）。这些浏览器允许用户沿着染色体滚动查看，放大或缩小到任何比例，并且以任何期望的细节水平来显示信息。这些组织机构在现有的人类基因组浏览器中也整合了小鼠基因组。在本节中，我们比较了小鼠和人类基因组的一般特性。

基因组扩增和收缩

小鼠基因组的常染色体部分（2.5 Gb）的预计总长度比人类基因组（2.9 Gb）小约14%。为了研究这种差异的来源，我们检测了人类和小鼠基因组中连续直系同源标记之间的间隔的相对大小。常染色体的小鼠/人的比率平均值为0.91，但是变化范围很大，38%的情况是小鼠的间隔大于人类。相比之下，X染色体没有表现出对应的净扩张或收缩，小鼠/人的比率为1.03。小鼠基因组较小的原因是什么？我们在下面关于重复序列和基因组进化部分中讨论了这个问题。

（G+C）含量

小鼠和人类基因组之间的局部（G+C）含量的总体分布有显著差异。在以往生化研究[78-81]以及小鼠与人类基因组密码子的四倍简并位点的比较分析[82-85]中已经注意到了这些差异，但是近乎完整的可用基因组序列为这种现象提供了第一个详细的图像。

小鼠总体（G+C）含量略高于人类（42%比41%），但是分布更紧密。在基因组中以20 kb窗口测量局部（G+C）含量时，人类基因组具有（G+C）含量大于56%的窗口约为1.4%，（G+C）含量小于33%的约1.3%。这种极端偏差在小鼠基因组中几乎不存在。这种差别甚至在染色体水平上都能看到。人类有极端的（G+C）含量的离群值（最极端的是19号染色体），而小鼠的染色体则趋向于更加均匀。

在小鼠和人类基因组的直系同源区域之间，局部（G+C）含量有很强的正相关性，但小鼠区域（G+C）含量的趋势明显不如人类区域那样极端。这种趋势并不均匀，最大差异分布在尾部。

在哺乳动物基因组中，基因密度和（G+C）含量呈正相关[81,86-89]。鉴于人类和小

content[81,86-89]. Given the differences in (G+C) content between human and mouse, we compared the distribution of genes—using the sets of orthologous mouse and human genes described below—with respect to (G+C) content for both genomes. The density of genes differed markedly when expressed in terms of absolute (G+C) content, but was nearly identical when expressed in terms of percentiles of (G+C) content. For example, both species have 75–80% of genes residing in the (G+C)-richest half of their genome. Mouse and human thus show similar degrees of homogeneity in the distribution of genes, despite the overall differences in (G+C) content. Notably, the mouse shows similar extremes of gene density despite being less extreme in (G+C) content.

What accounts for the differences in (G+C) content between mouse and human? Does it reflect altered selection for (G+C) content[90,91], altered mutational or repair processes[92-94], or possibly both? Data from additional species will probably be needed to address these issues. Any explanation will need to account for various mysterious phenomena. For example, although overall (G+C) content in mouse is slightly higher than in human (42% compared with 41%), the (G+C) content of chromosome X is slightly lower (39.0% compared with 39.4%). The effect is even more pronounced if one excludes lineage-specific repeats (see below), thereby focusing primarily on shared DNA. In that case, mouse autosomes have an overall (G+C) content that is 1.5% higher than human autosomes (41.2% compared with 39.7%) whereas mouse chromosome X has a (G+C) content that is 1% lower than human chromosome X (37.8% compared with 36.8%).

CpG islands

In mammalian genomes, the palindromic dinucleotide CpG is usually methylated on the cytosine residue. Methyl-CpG is mutated by deamination to TpG, leading to approximately fivefold under-representation of CpG across the human[1,95] and mouse genomes. In some regions of the genome that have been implicated in gene regulation, CpG dinucleotides are not methylated and thus are not subject to deamination and mutation. Such regions, termed CpG islands, are usually a few hundred nucleotides in length, have high (G+C) content and above average representation of CpG dinucleotides.

We applied a computer program that attempts to recognize CpG islands on the basis of (G+C) and CpG content of arbitrary lengths of sequence[96,97] to the non-repetitive portions of human and mouse genome sequences. The mouse genome contains fewer CpG islands than the human genome (about 15,500 compared with 27,000), which is qualitatively consistent with previous reports[98]. The absolute number of islands identified depends on the precise definition of a CpG island used, but the ratio between the two species remains fairly constant.

The reason for the smaller number of predicted CpG islands in mouse may relate simply to the smaller fraction of the genome with extremely high (G+C) content[99] and its effect on the computer algorithm. Approximately 10,000 of the predicted CpG islands in each species show significant sequence conservation with CpG islands in the orthologous intervals in

鼠之间 (G+C) 含量的差异，我们用下面描述的小鼠和人类的同源基因集合来对比两种基因组的 (G+C) 含量来比较基因的分布。两物种间基因密度就绝对 (G+C) 含量而言，差异显著，但是就 (G+C) 含量百分数而言，几乎相同。例如，两个物种都有 75%～80% 的基因位于它们基因组中 (G+C) 含量最高的一半的区域。因此，尽管在 (G+C) 含量上存在总体差异，但小鼠和人类在基因分布上显示出相似程度的同质性。值得注意的是，尽管在 (G+C) 含量上不那么极端，但在基因密度上，小鼠表现出了相似的极端性。

小鼠和人类 (G+C) 含量差异的原因是什么？它是否反映了对 (G+C) 含量的不同选择 [90,91]，不同的突变或修复过程 [92-94]，或者可能两者都有？可能需要来自于其他物种的数据来解决这些问题。各种神秘现象都需要解释。例如，尽管小鼠总 (G+C) 含量略高于人类 (42% 比 41%)，但是 X 染色体的 (G+C) 含量略低于人类 (39.0% 比 39.4%)。如果排除了特定谱系的重复序列 (见下文)，这一现象更加明显，因此主要关注共享 DNA。在这种情况下，小鼠常染色体总 (G+C) 含量比人类常染色体高 1.5%(41.2% 比 39.7%)，而小鼠 X 染色体的总 (G+C) 含量比人类 X 染色体低 1%(37.8% 比 36.8%)。

CpG 岛

在哺乳动物的基因组中，回文二核苷酸 CpG 通常在胞嘧啶残基上甲基化。甲基化的 CpG 通过脱氨基作用突变为 TpG，导致人类和小鼠基因组中 CpG 的含量大概降低为原来的 1/5[1,95]。在一些与基因调控有关的基因组区域，CpG 二核苷酸不甲基化，因此不受脱氨基和突变的影响。这些区域被称为 CpG 岛，通常是几百个核苷酸的长度，高 (G+C) 含量和高于平均数量的 CpG 二核苷酸。

我们用一个计算机程序根据 (G+C) 含量和任意长度序列 CpG 的含量 [96,97] 识别人类和小鼠基因组序列中非重复部分的 CpG 岛。小鼠基因组包含的 CpG 岛比人类基因组略少 (大约 15,500 比 27,000)，这与之前的报道 [98] 在数量级上是一致的。确定的 CpG 岛的绝对数量依赖于所使用的 CpG 岛的精确界定，但是两个物种之间的比例保持相当一致。

小鼠中预测的 CpG 岛数量较少的原因可能与基因组中仅有较少区域具有极高 (G+C) 含量 [99] 及这一现象对计算机算法的影响有关。每个物种中约有 10,000 个预测的 CpG 岛显示出与其他物种的直系同源区间中的 CpG 岛存在显著的序列保守性，

the other species, falling within the orthologous landmarks described above. Perhaps these represent functional CpG islands, a proposition that can now be tested experimentally[84].

Repeats

The single most prevalent feature of mammalian genomes is their repetitive sequences, most of which are interspersed repeats representing "fossils" of transposable elements. Transposable elements are a principal force in reshaping the genome, and their fossils thus provide powerful reporters for measuring evolutionary forces acting on the genome. A recent paper on the human genome sequence[1] provided extensive background on mammalian transposons, describing their biology and illustrating many applications to evolutionary studies. Here, we will focus primarily on comparisons between the repeat content of the mouse and human genomes.

Mouse has accumulated more new repetitive sequence than human

Approximately 46% of the human genome can be recognized currently as interspersed repeats resulting from insertions of transposable elements that were active in the last 150–200 million years. The total fraction of the human genome derived from transposons may be considerably larger, but it is not possible to recognize fossils older than a certain age because of the high degree of sequence divergence. Because only 37.5% of the mouse genome is recognized as transposon-derived, it is tempting to conclude that the smaller size of the mouse genome is due to lower transposon activity since the divergence of the human and mouse lineages. Closer analysis, however, shows that this is not the case. As we discuss below, transposition has been more active in the mouse lineage. The apparent deficit of transposon-derived sequence in the mouse genome is mostly due to a higher nucleotide substitution rate, which makes it difficult to recognize ancient repeat sequences.

Lineage-specific versus ancestral repeats

Interspersed repeats can be divided into lineage-specific repeats (defined as those introduced by transposition after the divergence of mouse and human) and ancestral repeats (defined as those already present in a common ancestor). Such a division highlights the fact that transposable elements have been more active in the mouse lineage than in the human lineage. Approximately 32.4% of the mouse genome (about 818 Mb) but only 24.4% of the human genome (about 695 Mb) consists of lineage-specific repeats. Contrary to initial appearances, transposon insertions have added at least 120 Mb more transposon-derived sequence to the mouse genome than to the human genome since their divergence. This observation is consistent with the previous report that the rate of transposition in the human genome has fallen markedly over the past 40 million years[1,100].

属于之前描述的直系同源性标记。或许这些区域代表了功能性的 CpG 岛，这个假设可以通过实验进行验证 [84]。

重复序列

哺乳动物基因组中最普遍的特征是它们的重复序列，其中大多数是离散的重复序列，代表着转座元件的"化石"。转座元件是重塑基因组的主要力量，因此它们的化石为测量作用于基因组的进化力提供了有力的报告。最近一篇关于人类基因组序列的论文 [1] 给出了哺乳动物转座子的大量背景，描述了它们的生物学特性并说明了在进化研究中的许多应用。这里，我们将主要关注于小鼠和人类基因组中重复内容之间的比较。

小鼠比人类积累了更多的新的重复序列

目前，大约 46% 的人类基因组是由过去 1.5 亿至 2 亿年中活跃的转座子插入引起的离散重复序列。来自于转座子的人类基因组的总比例可能相当大，但是由于序列的高度分化，不可能识别比某个时代更久远的化石。因为只有 37.5% 的小鼠基因组被认为来自于转座子，很容易得出结论，小鼠基因组更小是由于人类和小鼠谱系分化后，转座子活性降低。然而，更仔细的分析显示情况并非如此。正如我们下面讨论的，转座现象在小鼠谱系中更为活跃。小鼠基因组中转座衍生序列的明显缺失主要是由于更高的核苷酸替换率，以至于很难识别古老的重复序列。

谱系特异性与祖源重复

离散的重复可以分为谱系特异性重复（定义为小鼠和人类分化后通过转座引入的那些重复）和祖源重复（定义为存在于共同祖先中的重复）。这样的划分凸显了一个事实，即转座元件在小鼠谱系中比在人类谱系中更为活跃。约 32.4% 的小鼠基因（大约 818 Mb）但只有 24.4% 的人类基因（大约 695 Mb）由谱系特异性重复组成。与最初的表现相反，自从小鼠和人类的祖先分开之后，在小鼠基因组的转座子插入中，其转座子衍生序列比人类基因组增加了至少 120 Mb。这个观察与之前报道的人类基因组的转座率在过去的 4,000 万年中显著下降一致 [1,100]。

The overall lower interspersed repeat density in mouse is the result of an apparent lack of ancestral repeats: they comprise only 5% of the mouse genome compared with 22% of the human genome. The ancestral repeats recognizable in mouse tend to be those of more recent origin, that is, those that originated closest to the mouse–human divergence. This difference may be due partly to a higher deletion rate of non-functional DNA in the mouse lineage, so that more of the older interspersed repeats have been lost. However, the deficit largely reflects a much higher neutral substitution rate in the mouse lineage than in the human lineage, rendering many older ancestral repeats undetectable with available computer programs.

Higher substitution rate in mouse lineage

The hypothesis that the neutral substitution rate is higher in mouse than in human was suggested as early as 1969 (refs 101–103). The idea has continued to be challenged on the basis that the apparent differences may be due to inaccuracies in mammalian phylogenies[104,105]. The explanation, however, remains unclear, with some attributing it to generation time[101,106] and others pointing to a closer correlation with body size[107,108].

Ancestral repeats provide a powerful measure of neutral substitution rates, on the basis of comparing thousands of current copies to the inferred consensus sequence of the ancestral element. The large copy number and ubiquitous distribution of ancestral repeats overcome issues of local variation in substitution rates (see below). Most notably, differences in divergence levels are not affected by phylogenetic assumptions, as the time spent by an ancestral repeat family in either lineage is necessarily identical.

The median divergence levels of 18 subfamilies of interspersed repeats that were active shortly before the human–rodent speciation indicates an approximately twofold higher average substitution rate in the mouse lineage than in the human lineage, corresponding closely to an early estimate by Wu and Li[109]. In human, the least-diverged ancestral repeats have about 16% mismatch to their consensus sequences, which corresponds to approximately 0.17 substitutions per site. In contrast, mouse repeats have diverged by at least 26–27% or about 0.34 substitutions per site, which is about twofold higher than in the human lineage. The total number of substitutions in the two lineages can be estimated at 0.51. Below, we obtain an estimate of a combined rate of 0.46–0.47 substitutions per site, on the basis of an analysis that counts only substitutions since the divergence of the species.

Assuming a speciation time of 75 Myr, the average substitution rates would have been 2.2×10^{-9} and 4.5×10^{-9} in the human and mouse lineages, respectively. This is in accord with previous estimates of neutral substitution rates in these organisms. (Reports of highly similar substitution rates in human and mouse lineages relied on a much earlier divergence time of rodents from other mammals[104].)

Comparison of ancestral repeats to their consensus sequence also allows an estimate of the

小鼠总的离散重复密度较低归因于祖源重复序列的明显缺乏：它们仅占小鼠基因组的 5%，而在人类基因组中占了 22%。在小鼠基因组中可识别的祖源重复序列倾向于那些更为近期起源的，也就是起源于最接近小鼠和人类分化的那些。这种差异存在的部分可能原因是小鼠谱系中非功能性 DNA 的删除率较高，因此丢失了更多的古老的离散重复序列。但是，这种缺陷很大程度上反映了小鼠谱系中的中性替代率明显高于人类谱系，使得许多更古老的祖源重复无法用可用的计算机程序检测到。

小鼠谱系中的高替代率

早在 1969 年就提出了小鼠的中性替代率高于人类的假说（参考文献 101 ~ 103）。这一观点持续受到挑战，因为这种明显的差异可能是由哺乳动物系统发育不准确造成的 [104,105]。然而，这一解释还是不够清楚，一些人将其归因于世代时间 [101,106]，而另一些人则指出与身体尺寸关系更紧密 [107,108]。

祖源重复序列为中性替代率提供了一个强有力的度量方法，该方法基于将数千份当前拷贝与所推断的祖源元件的共有序列进行比较。祖源重复的大量拷贝数和广泛分布克服了替代率局部差异的问题（见下文）。更值得注意的是，分化水平的差异不受系统发育假设的影响，因为祖源重复家族在任何一个谱系中花费的时间是必然相同的。

在人类-啮齿动物物种形成之前不久活跃的 18 个离散重复序列亚家族的中位分化水平表明，小鼠谱系中的平均替代率大约是人类谱系的两倍，这与 Wu 和 Li[109] 的早期估计非常接近。在人类中，分化最小的祖源重复序列与其共有序列有大约 16% 的错配，相当于每个位点大约 0.17 个替换。相比之下，小鼠的重复序列有至少 26% ~ 27% 的差异或是每个位点大约 0.34 个替换，大约是人类谱系的两倍。这两个谱系的替换总数估计为 0.51。下面，我们根据仅计算物种分化以来产生的替换的分析，得出了每个位点 0.46 ~ 0.47 个替换的综合估计值。

假设物种形成时间为 7,500 万年，人类和小鼠谱系的平均替换率分别为 2.2×10^{-9} 和 4.5×10^{-9}。这与之前对这些生物体的中性替代率的估计是一致的。（关于人类和小鼠谱系中高度相似的替代率的报道取决于啮齿动物与其他哺乳动物更早的分化时间 [104]。）

将祖源重复序列和它们的一致性序列进行比较，还可以估计小片段插入（小于

rate of occurrence of small (< 50 bp) insertions and deletions (indels). Both species show a net loss of nucleotides (with deleted bases outnumbering inserted bases by at least 2–3-fold), but the overall loss owing to small indels in ancestral repeats is at least twofold higher in mouse than in human. This may contribute a small amount (1–2%) to the difference in genome size noted above.

It should be noted that the roughly twofold higher substitution rate in mouse represents an average rate since the time of divergence, including an initial period when the two lineages had comparable rates. Comparison with more recent relatives (mouse–rat and human–gibbon, each about 20–25 Myr) indicate that the current substitution rate per year in mouse is probably much higher, perhaps about fivefold higher (see Supplementary Information). Also, note that these estimates refer to substitution rate per year, rather than per generation. Because the human generation time is much longer than that of the mouse (by at least 20-fold), the substitution rate is greater in human than mouse when measured per generation.

Higher substitution rate obscures old repeats

We measured the impact of the higher substitution rate in mouse on the ability to detect ancestral repeats in the mouse genome. By computer simulation, the ability of the RepeatMasker[100] program to detect repeats was found to fall off rapidly for divergence levels above about 37%. If we simulate the events in the mouse lineage by adjusting the ancestral repeats in the human genome for the higher substitution levels that would have occurred in the mouse genome, the proportion of the genome that would still be recognizable as ancestral repeats falls to only 6%. This is in close agreement with the proportion actually observed for the mouse. Thus, the current analysis of repeated sequences allows us to see further back into human history (roughly 150–200 Myr) than into mouse history (roughly 100–120 Myr).

A higher rate of interspersed repeat insertion does not explain the larger size of the human genome. Below, we suggest that the explanation lies in a higher rate of large deletions in the mouse lineage.

Comparison of mouse and human repeats

All mammals have essentially the same four classes of transposable elements: (1) the autonomous long interspersed nucleotide element (LINE)-like elements; (2) the LINE-dependent, short RNA-derived short interspersed nucleotide elements (SINEs); (3) retrovirus-like elements with long terminal repeats (LTRs); and (4) DNA transposons. The first three classes procreate by reverse transcription of an RNA intermediate (retroposition), whereas DNA transposons move by a cut-and-paste mechanism of DNA sequence (see refs 1, 100 for further information about these classes).

50 bp）和缺失的发生率。两个物种都有核苷酸的净损失（缺失的碱基数量至少是插入碱基的 2～3 倍），但是祖源重复中小片段插入缺失导致的整体损失在小鼠中至少是在人类中的两倍。这可能是导致上述基因组大小差异的一小部分原因（1%～2%）。

应该注意的是，小鼠中大约 2 倍高的替代率代表了自分化时间以来的平均比率，包括两个谱系的替代率相当的初始时期。与最近的近源物种（小鼠–大鼠及人类–猩猩，每个大约 2,000～2,500 万年）的比较表明，小鼠每年的替代率可能要高得多，大约是 5 倍（见补充信息）。此外，注意这些估计指的是每年的替代率，而不是每代的替代率。因为人类的世代时间要比小鼠长很多（至少 20 倍），所以当测量每个世代时，人类的替代率比小鼠高很多。

较高的替代率掩盖了旧的重复

我们测量了小鼠高替代率对检测小鼠基因组祖源重复序列能力的影响。通过计算机模拟，发现当差异水平超过 37% 时，RepeatMasker[100] 程序检测重复的能力迅速下降。如果我们模拟小鼠谱系中的事件时利用人类基因组中的祖源重复来校正小鼠基因组中的高替代水平，那么仍然可识别的祖源重复在基因组中的比例下降到仅有 6%。这与实际观察到的小鼠比例非常一致。因此，对重复序列进行的当前分析，可以让我们追溯人类历史（大约 1.5 亿～2 亿年）到比小鼠历史更远的年代（大约 1 亿～1.2 亿年）。

比较高的散布的重复插入率并不能解释为何人类的基因组比较大。通过下面的分析，我们认为原因在于小鼠谱系中较高的缺失率。

小鼠和人类重复序列的比较

所有哺乳动物基本上都有四类转座元件：（1）自主的长散在核苷酸元件（LINE）一类元件；（2）依赖于 LINE、由短 RNA 衍生的短散在核苷酸元件（SINE）；（3）具有长末端重复（LTR）的逆转录病毒样元件；（4）DNA 转座子。前三类通过 RNA 中间体介导的逆转录（逆转录转座）产生，而 DNA 转座通过 DNA 的剪切–粘贴机制进行（更多信息见参考文献 1、100）。

A comparison of these repeat classes in the mouse and human genomes can be enlightening. On the one hand, differences between the two species reveal the dynamic nature of transposable elements; on the other hand, similarities in the location of lineage-specific elements point to common biological factors that govern insertion and retention of interspersed repeats.

Differences between mouse and human

The most notable difference is in the changing rate of transposition over time: the rate has remained fairly constant in mouse, but markedly increased to a peak at about 40 Myr in human, and then plummeted. This phenomenon was noted in our initial analysis of the human genome; the availability of the mouse genome sequence now confirms and sharpens the observation. Beyond this overall tendency, there are specific differences in each of the four repeat classes.

The first class that we discuss is LINEs. Copies of LINE1 (L1) form the single largest fraction of interspersed repeat sequence in both human and mouse. No other LINE seems to have been active in either lineage. The extant L1 elements in both species derive from a common ancestor by means of a series of subfamilies defined primarily by the rapidly evolving 3' non-coding sequences[110]. The L1 5'-untranslated regions (UTRs) in both lineages have been even more variable, occasionally through acquisition of entirely new sequences[111]. Indeed, the three active subfamilies in mouse, which are otherwise > 97% identical, have unrelated or highly diverged 5' ends[112-114]. L1 seems to have remained highly active in mouse, whereas it has declined in the human lineage. Goodier and co-workers[113] estimated that the mouse genome contains at least 3,000 potentially active elements (full-length with two intact open reading frames (ORFs)). The current draft sequence of the mouse genome contains only 400 young, full-length elements; of these only 12 have two intact ORFs. This is probably a reflection of the WGS shotgun approach used to assemble the genome. Indeed, most of the young elements in the draft genome sequence are incomplete owing to internal sequence gaps, reflecting the difficulty that WGS assembly has with highly similar repeat sequences. This is a notable limitation of the draft sequence.

The second repeat class is SINEs. Whereas only a single SINE (Alu) was active in the human lineage, the mouse lineage has been exposed to four distinct SINEs (B1, B2, ID, B4). Each is thought to rely on L1 for retroposition, although none share sequence similarity, as is the rule for other LINE–SINE pairs[115,116]. The mouse B1 and human Alu SINEs are unique among known SINEs in being derived from 7SL RNA; they probably have a common origin[117]. The mouse B2 is typical among SINEs in having a transfer RNA-derived promoter region. Recent ID elements seem to be derived from a neuronally expressed RNA gene called *BC1*, which may itself have been recruited from an earlier SINE. This subfamily is minor in mouse, with 2–4,000 copies, but has expanded rapidly in rat where it has produced more than 130,000 copies since the mouse–rat speciation[118]. Both B2 and ID closely resemble Ala-tRNA, but seem to have independent origins. The B4 family resembles

对小鼠和人类基因组中这些重复类型进行比较可以获得启发。一方面，两个物种之间的差异揭示了转座元件的动态性质；另一方面，谱系特殊元件位置上的相似性表明控制离散重复的插入和保留具有共同的生物学因素。

小鼠和人类之间的差异

最显著的区别在于转座率随着时间发生的变化：小鼠的转座率保持相当稳定，但人类在大约 4,000 万年的时候，转座率明显增加并达到峰值，然后下降。我们在对人类基因组进行初步分析时注意到了这个现象，小鼠基因组序列的获得则证实并印证了这一观察。除了这个整体趋势外，四个重复类型中的每一个都有特定的差异。

我们首先讨论第一类 LINE。在人类和小鼠中，LINE1（L1）的拷贝构成了离散重复序列中的最大部分。在这两个谱系中似乎都没有其他具有活性的 LINE。两个物种中存在的 L1 元件是从一个共同祖先，通过 3′ 非编码序列的快速进化形成的一系列亚家族衍生而来 [110]。两个谱系中 L1 的 5′ 非翻译区变异性很大，偶尔会获得全新的序列 [111]。事实上，小鼠中三个活跃的亚家族在其他方面的相似性大于 97%，但却具有不相关或者高度分化的 5′ 端 [112-114]。L1 似乎在小鼠中保持高度活性，而在人类谱系中却已经下降了。古迪尔和同事们 [113] 估计，小鼠基因组中至少包含 3,000 个潜在活性元件（全长可达两个完整的开放阅读框）。目前小鼠基因组序列草图只含有 400 个年轻的全长元件，其中只有 12 个含有两个完整的开放阅读框。这可能是用 WGS 鸟枪法组装基因组的一种现象。事实上，由于内部序列空缺，基因组序列草图中大多数年轻元件是不完整的，这反映了 WGS 在组装高度相似重复序列时的难度。这是该序列草图的一个显著不足。

第二类重复是 SINE。虽然人类谱系中只有一个 SINE（Alu）有活性，但是在小鼠谱系中已经显露了四个不同的 SINE（B1、B2、ID、B4）。尽管它们没有共享序列相似性，每个都被认为依赖于 L1 进行逆转录转座，这也是其他 LINE-SINE 配对的规则 [115,116]。小鼠 B1 和人类 Alu 的 SINE 在已知的 SINE 中比较特殊，均衍生于 7SL RNA，所以它们可能有共同起源 [117]。小鼠的 B2 则是 SINE 中比较典型的，具有转运 RNA 衍生的启动子区域。近期出现的 ID 元件似乎来自于神经组织表达的称为 *BC1* 的 RNA 基因，它本身可能是被一个早期 SINE 募集的。这个亚家族在小鼠体内是次要的，有 2～4,000 个拷贝数，但是在大鼠中迅速扩张，自小鼠–大鼠物种形成以来已经产生超过 130,000 个拷贝数 [118]。B2 和 ID 都与 Ala-tRNA（丙氨酸–转

a fusion between B1 and ID[119,120]. We found that 25% of the 75,000 identified ID elements were located within 50 bp of a B1 element of similar orientation, suggesting that perhaps most older ID elements are mislabelled or truncated B4 SINEs.

The third repeat class is LTR elements. All interspersed LTR-containing elements in mammals are derivatives of the vertebrate-specific retrovirus clade of retrotransposons. The earliest infectious retroviruses probably originated from endogenous retroviral-like (ERV) elements that acquired mechanisms for horizontal transmission[121], whereas many current endogenous retroviral elements have probably arisen from infection by retroviruses.

Endogenous retroviruses fall into three classes (I–III), which show a markedly dissimilar evolutionary history in human and mouse. Notably, ERVs are nearly extinct in human whereas all three classes have active members in mouse.

Class III accounts for 80% of recognized LTR element copies predating the human–mouse speciation. This class includes the non-autonomous MaLRs: with 388,000 recognizable copies in mouse, it is the single most successful LTR element. It is still active in mouse (represented by MERVL and the MT and ORR1 MaLRs), but died out some 50 Myr in human[122].

Copies of class II elements are tenfold denser in mouse than in human. In contrast, class I element copies are fourfold more common in the human than the mouse genome (although it is possible that some have not yet been recognized in mouse). In mouse, this class includes active ERVs, such as the murine leukaemia virus, MuRRS, MuRVY and VL30 (several of which have caused insertional mutations in mouse)—no similar activity is known to exist in human.

The fourth repeat class is the DNA transposons. Although most transposable elements have been more active in mouse than human, DNA transposons show the reverse pattern. Only four lineage-specific DNA transposon families could be identified in mouse (the mariner element MMAR1, and the hAT elements URR1, RMER30 and RChar1), compared with 14 in the primate lineage.

For evolutionary survival, DNA transposons are thought to depend on frequent horizontal transfer to new host genomes by means of vectors such as viruses and other intracellular parasites[116,125]. The mammalian immune system probably forms a large obstacle to the successful invasion of DNA transposons. Perhaps the rodent germ line has been harder to infiltrate by horizontal transfer than the primate genome. Alternatively, it is possible that highly diverged families active in early rodent evolution have not been detected yet. Notably, most copies in the human genome were deposited early in primate evolution.

Some of the above differences in the nature of interspersed repeats in human and mouse could reflect systematic factors in mouse and human biology, whereas others may represent

运 RNA) 相似，但似乎是独立起源。B4 家族类似于 B1 和 ID 之间的融合 [119,120]。我们发现，在 75,000 个已经识别的 ID 元件中，25% 定位于具有相似方向的 B1 元件的 50 bp 中，这表明可能大多古老的 ID 元件是错误标记或者截短的 B4 SINE。

第三类重复是 LTR 元件。哺乳动物中所有离散的含 LTR 元件都是脊椎动物特有的逆转录病毒分支的逆转录转座子衍生物。最早的感染性逆转录病毒可能起源于获得了水平传播机制的内源性逆转录病毒 (ERV) 样元件 [121]，而现在很多内源性逆转录病毒元件可能来自于逆转录病毒的感染。

内源性逆转录病毒分为三类 (I ~ III)，显示了人类和小鼠进化史明显不同。值得注意的是，ERV 在人类中几乎灭绝，而这三类在小鼠中都有活跃的成员。

在人类–小鼠物种形成之前，第 III 类元件占可识别的 LTR 元件拷贝数的 80%。这类包括非自主的 MaLR：小鼠中包括 388,000 个可识别的拷贝数，它是唯一最成功的 LTR 元件。仍然活跃在小鼠身上 (以 MERVL、MT 和 ORR1 MaLR 为代表)，但在人类中已经死亡了约 5,000 万年 [122]。

第 II 类元件的拷贝数在小鼠中的密度是人类中的十倍。相比之下，第 I 类元件拷贝数在人类基因组中是在小鼠基因组中的四倍多 (尽管在小鼠中可能还有一些没有被识别)。在小鼠中，这类包括活跃的 ERV (如小鼠白血病病毒)、MuRRS、MuRVY 和 VL30 (其中一些已经导致小鼠插入突变)——在人类中已经没有类似的活性。

第四类重复是 DNA 转座子。尽管大多数转座元件在小鼠体内比在人类中更活跃，但 DNA 转座子显示出相反的模式。在小鼠中，只鉴定出四个谱系特异性 DNA 转座家族 (mariner 元件 MMAR1，hAT 元件 URR1、RMER30 和 RChar1)，而灵长类谱系中有 14 个。

为了进化生存，DNA 转座子被认为依赖于通过病毒和其他细胞内的寄生虫等载体频繁水平转移到新的宿主基因组 [116,125]。哺乳动物的免疫系统可能对 DNA 转座子成功入侵形成巨大的屏障。或许啮齿动物的生殖种系比灵长类基因组更难被水平转移渗透。也可能在啮齿动物进化中活跃的高分化家族可能还没有被检测到。值得注意的是，人类基因组中 DNA 转座子的大多拷贝在灵长类进化早期就被保存下来了。

上述人类和小鼠离散重复的性质差异可以反映小鼠和人类生物学中的系统因素，

random fluctuations. Deeper understanding of the biology of transposable elements and detailed knowledge of interspersed repeat populations in other mammals should clarify these issues.

Similar repeats accumulate in orthologous locations

One of the most notable features about repeat elements is the contrast in the genomic distribution of LINEs and SINEs. Whereas LINEs are strongly biased towards (A+T)-rich regions, SINEs are strongly biased towards (G+C)-rich regions. The contrast is all the more notable because both elements are inserted into the genome through the action of the same endonuclease[126,127].

Such preferences were studied in detail in the initial analysis of the human genome[1], and essentially equivalent preferences are seen in the mouse genome. With the availability of two mammalian genomes, however, it is possible to extend this analysis to explore whether (A+T) and (G+C) content are truly causative factors or merely reflections of an underlying biological process.

Towards that end, we studied the insertion of lineage-specific repeat elements in orthologous segments in the human and mouse genomes. Each insertion represents a new, independent event occurring in one lineage, and thus any correlation between the two species reflects underlying proclivity to insert or retain repeats in particular regions. Visual inspection reveals a strong correlation in the sites of lineage-specific repeats of the various classes. Lineage-specific repeats also correlate with other genomic features, as discussed in the section on genome evolution.

The correlation of local lineage-specific SINE density is extremely strong. Moreover, local SINE density in one species is better predicted by SINE density in the other species than it is by local (G+C) content. The local density of each distinct rodent-specific type of SINE is a strong predictor of Alu density at the orthologous locus in human, although the Alu equivalent B1 SINEs show the strongest correlation ($r^2 = 0.784$).

We interpret these results to mean that SINE density is influenced by genomic features that are correlated with (G+C) content but that are distinct from (G+C) content *per se*. The fact that (G+C) content alone does not determine SINE density is consistent with the observation that some (G+C)-rich regions of the human genome are not Alu rich[128,129].

Simple sequence repeats

Mammalian genomes are scattered with simple sequence repeats (SSRs), consisting of short perfect or near-perfect tandem repeats that presumably arise through slippage during DNA replication. SSRs have had a particularly important role as genetic markers

而其他可能代表了随机波动。对转座元件生物机制更深入的了解和对其他哺乳动物的离散重复序列的详细了解应该可以澄清这些问题。

类似重复在直系同源位置的积累

重复元件的一个最显著的特征是 LINE 和 SINE 的基因组分布差异。LINE 强烈倾向于（A+T）富集区，而 SINE 强烈倾向于（G+C）富集区。这种差异如此显著是因为两种元件都是通过相同的内切核酸酶的作用插入到基因组中[126,127]。

在人类基因组的最初分析中就对这种倾向性进行了详细研究[1]，在小鼠基因组中也发现了类似的倾向。但是，随着两个哺乳动物基因组的获得，就可以扩展这一分析以探索（A+T）和（G+C）含量是真正的影响因素或者仅仅是对于潜在生物学过程的一种反映。

为此，我们研究了在人类和小鼠基因组的直系同源片段中插入的谱系特异性重复元件。每个插入代表了一个新的、独立的事件发生在一个谱系中，因此两个物种之间的任何相关性反映了在特定区域插入或保留重复序列的潜在倾向。目测显示，不同类型的谱系特异的重复位点有很强的相关性。谱系特异的重复也与其他基因组特征相关，如在基因组进化一节中讨论所述。

局部谱系特异的 SINE 密度的相关性非常强。此外，与根据局部（G+C）含量进行预测相比，一个物种的局部 SINE 密度可以通过另一个物种的 SINE 密度进行更好的预测。尽管 Alu 与 B1 SINE 表现出最强的关联性（$r^2 = 0.784$），每种啮齿动物特定类型的 SINE 局部密度都是人类直系同源性基因座上的 Alu 密度的强力预测因子。

我们将这些结果解释为 SINE 密度受到与（G+C）含量相关但与（G+C）含量本身不同的基因组特征的影响。（G+C）含量不单独决定 SINE 密度，这一事实与人类基因组中某些（G+C）富集的区域 Alu 并不富集的观察结果一致[128,129]。

简单序列重复

哺乳动物基因组散在分布着简单重复序列（SSR），可能由 DNA 复制过程中的滑脱引起的短的完全或近似完全的串联重复序列组成。SSR 在小鼠和人类的连锁研

in linkage studies in both mouse and human, because their lengths tend to be polymorphic in populations and can be readily assayed by PCR. It is possible that such SSRs, arising as they do through replication errors, would be largely equivalent between mouse and human; however, there are impressive differences between the two species[135].

Overall, mouse has 2.25–3.25-fold more short SSRs (1–5 bp unit) than human; the precise ratio depends on the percentage identity required in defining a tandem repeat. The mouse seems to represent an exception among mammals on the basis of comparison with the small amount of genomic sequence available from dog (4 Mb) and pig (5 Mb), both of which show proportions closer to human[136] (E. Green, unpublished data).

The analysis can be refined, however, by excluding transposable elements that contain SSRs at their 3′ ends. When these sources are eliminated, the contrast between mouse and human grows to roughly fourfold.

The reason for the greater density of SSRs in mouse is unknown. Analysis of the distribution of SSRs across chromosomes also reveals an interesting feature common to both organisms. In both human and mouse, there is a nearly twofold increase in density of SSRs near the distal ends of chromosome arms. Because mouse chromosomes are acrocentric, they show the effect only at one end. The increased density of SSRs in telomeric regions may reflect the tendency towards higher recombination rates in subtelomeric regions[1].

Mouse Genes

Genes comprise only a small portion of the mammalian genome, but they are understandably the focus of greatest interest. One of the most notable findings of the initial sequencing and analysis of the human genome[1] was that the number of protein-coding genes was only in the range of 30,000–40,000, far less than the widely cited textbook figure of 100,000, but in accord with more recent, rigorous estimates[55,139-141]. The lower gene count was based on the observed and predicted gene counts, statistically adjusted for systematic under- and overcounting.

Our goal here is to produce an improved catalogue of mammalian protein-coding genes and to revisit the gene count. Genome analysis has been enhanced by a number of recent developments. These include burgeoning mammalian EST and cDNA collections, knowledge of the genomes and proteomes of a growing number of organisms, increasingly complete coverage of the mouse and human genomes in high-quality sequence assemblies, and the ability to use *de novo* gene prediction methodologies that exploit information from two mammalian genomes to avoid potential biases inherent in using known transcripts or homology to known genes.

We focus here on protein-coding genes, because the ability to recognize new RNA genes remains rudimentary. As used below, the terms "gene catalogue" and "gene count" refer to

究中作为遗传标记物具有特别重要的作用，因为它们的长度在群体中倾向于多态形式存在，可以轻易地通过 PCR 进行检测。这类 SSR 可能在人类和小鼠之间大致相同，都是由于复制错误而产生的，尽管其序列在两个物种之间存在着显著的差异[135]。

总体而言，小鼠的短 SSR(1～5 bp 单位)是人类的 2.25～3.25 倍；精确比率取决于定义一个串联重复所需的百分比的一致性。根据与狗(4 Mb)和猪(5 Mb)这两个比例都接近于人类的物种[136]的可获得的少量基因组序列的比较，小鼠似乎代表了哺乳动物中的例外。(格林，未发表数据)

然而，通过排除 3′端包含 SSR 的转座元件可以优化分析。当这些来源被消除后，小鼠和人类之间的差异将增加为大约四倍。

小鼠体内的 SSR 密度较大的原因未知。对 SSR 跨染色体分布的分析也揭示了两种生物体共有的一个有趣特征。在人类和小鼠中，靠近染色体臂末端的 SSR 密度几乎增加了两倍。因为小鼠的染色体是近端着丝点的，所以它们仅在一端显示出效果。端粒区的 SSR 密度增加可能反映了亚端粒区高重组率的趋势[1]。

小鼠基因

虽然基因只占哺乳动物基因组的一小部分，但它们是最受关注的焦点。人类基因组初期测序分析[1]最显著的发现之一是，编码蛋白质的基因数量只在30,000～40,000 范围内，远低于被广泛引用的教科书上的数字 100,000，但是符合近期更为严谨的估计[55,139-141]。较低的基因计数是基于对于观察的和预测的基因计数进行系统的不足和过度计数的统计校正。

我们的目标是建立一个改进的哺乳动物蛋白质编码基因目录和重新审视基因计数。最近的很多进展增强了基因组分析能力。这包括迅速发展的哺乳动物 EST 和cDNA 收集，对于越来越多的生物的基因组和蛋白质组的知识，对小鼠和人类基因组的覆盖度越来越完整的高质量序列组装，以及使用新型基因预测方法从两个哺乳动物基因组获取信息，从而避免因使用已知转录本或已知同源基因时固有的潜在偏差的能力。

我们在此关注蛋白质编码基因，因为识别新的 RNA 基因的能力仍然处于初级阶段。如下文所用，术语"基因目录"和"基因计数"仅涉及蛋白质编码基因。我们在

protein-coding genes only. We briefly discuss RNA genes at the end of the section.

Evidence-based gene prediction

We constructed catalogues of human and mouse gene predictions on the basis of available experimental evidence. The main computational tool was the Ensembl gene prediction pipeline[142] augmented with the Genie gene prediction pipeline[143]. Briefly, the Ensembl system uses three tiers of input. First, known protein-coding cDNAs are mapped onto the genome. Second, additional protein-coding genes are predicted on the basis of similarity to proteins in any organism using the GeneWise program[144]. Third, *de novo* gene predictions from the GENSCAN program[145] that are supported by experimental evidence (such as ESTs) are considered. These three strands of evidence are reconciled into a single gene catalogue by using heuristics to merge overlapping predictions, detect pseudogenes and discard misassemblies. These results are then augmented by using conservative predictions from the Genie system, which predicts gene structures in the genomic regions delimited by paired 5′ and 3′ ESTs on the basis of cDNA and EST information from the region.

The computational pipeline produces predicted transcripts, which may represent fragmentary products or alternative products of a gene. They may also represent pseudogenes, which can be difficult in some cases to distinguish from real genes. The predicted transcripts are then aggregated into predicted genes on the basis of sequence overlaps. The computational pipeline remains imperfect and the predictions are tentative.

Initial and current human gene catalogue

The initial human gene catalogue[1] contained about 45,000 predicted transcripts, which were aggregated into about 32,000 predicted genes containing a total of approximately 170,000 distinct exons (Table 10). Many of the predicted transcripts clearly represented only gene fragments, because the overall set contained considerably fewer exons per gene (mean 4.3, median 3) than known full-length human genes (mean 10.2, median 8).

This initial gene catalogue was used to estimate the number of human protein-coding genes, on the basis of estimates of the fragmentation rate, false positive rate and false negative rate for true human genes. Such corrections were particularly important, because a typical human gene was represented in the predictions by about half of its coding sequence or was significantly fragmented. The analysis suggested that the roughly 32,000 predicted genes represented about 24,500 actual human genes (on the basis of fragmentation and false positive rates) out of the best-estimate total of approximately 31,000 human protein-coding genes on the basis of estimated false negatives[1]. We suggested a range of 30,000–40,000 to allow for additional genes.

本节末尾简要讨论了 RNA 基因。

基于证据的基因预测

我们在现有实验证据的基础上构建了人类和小鼠基因预测目录。主要的计算工具 Ensembl 基因预测流程[142]，并用 Genie 基因预测流程[143]加强预测结果。简而言之，Ensembl 系统使用了三层输入。首先，已知编码蛋白质的 cDNA 标记到基因组上。第二，利用 GeneWise 程序[144]，根据在任何生物体中蛋白质相似性预测剩下的蛋白质编码基因。第三，基于 GENSCAN 程序[145]中的由实验证据（如 EST）支持的新基因预测。通过使用试探法合并重叠预测，检测假基因和去掉错误组装，这三组证据被整合成单个基因目录。然后，这些结果通过 Genie 系统的保守预测得到进一步证实。Genie 是基于 cDNA 和 EST 信息，由配对的 5′ 和 3′ EST 界定基因组区域的基因结构预测系统。

计算流程产生预测的转录产物，这些可能代表了一个基因的片段产物或可变产物。它们也可能代表假基因，在某些情况下很难将其与真正的基因区分开。然后预测的转录产物根据序列重叠汇集到预测的基因中。目前计算流程还不完善，因此预测的产物也是试验性的。

初始和目前的人类基因目录

最初的人类基因目录[1]包含大概 45,000 个预测的转录本，被比对到大约 32,000 个预测基因上，其中包括总计约 170,000 个不同的外显子（表 10）。大多数预测的转录本明显只代表基因片段，因为整个序列中每个基因的外显子数目（平均值为 4.3，中位数为 3）比在已知的人类全长基因组上的数目（平均值为 10.2，中位数为 8）少很多。

基于对于碎片化比率、假阳性率和假阴性率的评估，这个初始基因目录被用来估算人类蛋白质编码基因的数量。这种校正非常重要，因为一个典型的人类基因在预测中只代表了其编码序列的一半，或者呈现明显的片段化。分析表明，约 32,000 个预测基因代表了基于假阴性估计的大约 31,000 个人类蛋白编码基因的最佳估计总数[1]中的 24,500 个实际的人类基因（基于碎片化和假阳性率）。我们建议使用 30,000 ~ 40,000 的范围以允许增加其他基因。

Table 10. Gene count in human and mouse genomes

Genome feature	Human		Mouse	
	Initial	Current	Initial*	Extended†
	(Feb. 2001)	(Sept. 2002)	(this paper)	(this paper)
Predicted transcripts	44,860	27,048	28,097	29,201
Predicted genes	31,778	22,808	22,444	22,011
Known cDNAs	14,882	17,152	13,591	12,226
New predictions	16,896	5,656	8,853	9,785
Mean exons/transcript‡	4.2 (3)	8.7 (6)	8.2 (6)	8.4 (6)
Total predicted exons	170,211	198,889	191,290	213,562

* Without RIKEN cDNA set.
† With RIKEN cDNA set.
‡ Median values are in parentheses.

Since the initial paper[1], the human gene catalogue has been refined as sequence becomes more complete and methods are revised. The current catalogue (Ensembl build 29) contains 27,049 predicted transcripts aggregated into 22,808 predicted genes containing about 199,000 distinct exons (Table 10). The predicted transcripts are larger, with the mean number of exons roughly doubling (to 8.7), and the catalogue has increased in completeness, with the total number of exons increasing by nearly 20%. We return below to the issue of estimating the mammalian gene count.

Mouse gene catalogue

We sought to create a mouse gene catalogue using the same methodology as that used for the human gene catalogue (Table 10). An initial catalogue was created by using the same evidence set as for the human analysis, including cDNAs and proteins from various organisms. This set included a previously published collection of mouse cDNAs produced at the RIKEN Genome Center[41].

We also created an extended mouse gene catalogue by including a much larger set of about 32,000 mouse cDNAs with significant ORFs that were sequenced by RIKEN (see ref. 150). These additional mouse cDNAs improved the catalogue by increasing the average transcript length through the addition of exons (raising the total from about 191,000 to about 213,000, including many from untranslated regions) and by joining fragmented transcripts. The set contributed roughly 1,200 new predicted genes. The total number of predicted genes did not change significantly, however, because the increase was offset by a decrease due to mergers of predicted genes. These mouse cDNAs have not yet been used to extend the human gene catalogue. Accordingly, comparisons of the mouse and human gene catalogues below use the initial mouse gene catalogue.

表 10. 人类和小鼠基因组中的基因计数

基因组特性	人类		小鼠	
	初始	现在	初始 *	扩展 †
	（2001 年 2 月）	（2002 年 9 月）	（本文）	（本文）
预测的转录本	44,860	27,048	28,097	29,201
预测的基因	31,778	22,808	22,444	22,011
已知 cDNA	14,882	17,152	13,591	12,226
新预测	16,896	5,656	8,853	9,785
平均外显子数值 / 转录本 ‡	4.2(3)	8.7(6)	8.2(6)	8.4(6)
预测的外显子合计	170,211	198,889	191,290	213,562

* 不包括 RIKEN 的 cDNA 集。

† 包括 RIKEN 的 cDNA 集。

‡ 括号中为中位数。

从最初的文献 [1] 开始，人类基因目录随着序列的完整和方法的修订而不断完善。目前的目录（Ensembl 版本 29）包含 27,049 个预测转录本，比对到 22,808 个预测基因上，其中包含大约 199,000 个不同的外显子（表 10）。预测的转录本更大，外显子的平均数大约翻了一番（至 8.7），目录的完整性增加，外显子的总数增加了近 20%。下面我们重新回到估计哺乳动物基因计数问题。

小鼠基因目录

我们试图利用与人类基因目录相同的方式创建一个小鼠基因目录（表 10）。最初的目录是使用与人类分析相同的证据集合创建的，包括不同生物体的 cDNA 和蛋白质。这一集合包括 RIKEN（日本理化学研究所）基因组中心之前发表的小鼠 cDNA 数据集 [41]。

我们还创建了一个扩展的小鼠基因目录，包括一个由 RIKEN 测序且具有重要开放阅读框的更大的约 32,000 个小鼠 cDNA 的集合（见参考文献 150）。这些额外的小鼠 cDNA 通过增加平均转录本长度，即通过增加外显子（总数从约 191,000 增加到约 213,000，包括许多来自于非翻译区）和通过连接片段化的转录产物来改进目录。该集合贡献了大约 1,200 个新的预测基因。然而，预测基因的总数没有明显变化，因为增加量被预测基因的合并造成的减少相抵消了。这些小鼠 cDNA 尚未用来扩展人类基因目录。因此，下面的小鼠和人类基因目录的比较使用的是初始小鼠基因目录。

127

The extended mouse gene catalogue contains 29,201 predicted transcripts, corresponding to 22,011 predicted genes that contain about 213,500 distinct exons. These include 12,226 transcripts corresponding to cDNAs in the public databases, with 7,481 of these in the well-curated RefSeq collection[151]. There are 9,785 predicted transcripts that do not correspond to known cDNAs, but these are built on the basis of similarity to known proteins.

The new mouse and human gene catalogues contain many new genes not previously identified in either genome. It should be emphasized that the human and mouse gene catalogues, although increasingly complete, remain imperfect. Both genome sequences are still incomplete. Some authentic genes are missing, fragmented or otherwise incorrectly described, and some predicted genes are pseudogenes or are otherwise spurious. We describe below further analysis of these challenges.

Pseudogenes

An important issue in annotating mammalian genomes is distinguishing real genes from pseudogenes, that is, inactive gene copies. Processed pseudogenes arise through retrotransposition of spliced or partially spliced mRNA into the genome; they are often recognized by the loss of some or all introns relative to other copies of the gene. Unprocessed pseudogenes arise from duplication of genomic regions or from the degeneration of an extant gene that has been released from selection. They sometimes contain all exons, but often have suffered deletions and rearrangements that may make it difficult to recognize their precise parentage. Over time, pseudogenes of either class tend to accumulate mutations that clearly reveal them to be inactive, such as multiple frameshifts or stop codons. More generally, they acquire a larger ratio of non-synonymous to synonymous substitutions than functional genes. These features can sometimes be used to recognize pseudogenes, although relatively recent pseudogenes may escape such filters.

To assess the impact of pseudogenes on gene prediction, we focused on two classes of gene predictions: (1) those that lack a corresponding gene prediction in the region of conserved synteny in the human genome (2,705); and (2) those that are members of apparent local gene clusters and that lack a reciprocal best match in the human genome (5,143). A random sample of 100 such predicted genes was selected, and the predictions were manually reviewed. We estimate that about 76% of the first class and about 30% of the second class correspond to pseudogenes. Overall, this would correspond to roughly 4,000 of the predicted genes in mouse.

Comparison of mouse and human gene sets

We then sought to assess the extent of correspondence between the mouse and human gene sets. Approximately 99% of mouse genes have a homologue in the human genome. For 96% the homologue lies within a similar conserved syntenic interval in the human genome.

扩展的小鼠基因目录包括 29,201 个预测转录本，对应的 22,011 个预测基因包含约 213,500 个不同的外显子。这些包括对应于 cDNA 公共数据库中的 12,226 个转录本，其中 7,481 个在 RefSeq 集合[151] 中有很好的注释。有 9,785 个预测转录本与已知的 cDNA 不对应，但这些转录本是建立在已知蛋白质相似性的基础上。

新的小鼠和人类基因目录包括很多新基因，这些新基因以前没有在任何一个基因组中被识别出来。应该强调的是，人类和小鼠基因目录虽然日趋完整，但仍然不完善。两个基因组序列仍然不完整。一些真实的基因缺失，碎片化或以其他方式被错误描述，一些预测基因是假基因或其他形式的假象。下面我们将进一步叙述对这些挑战的分析。

假基因

哺乳动物基因组注释的一个重要问题是区分真基因和假基因，即非活性基因拷贝。经过加工的假基因是通过剪接或部分剪接 mRNA 再逆转录到基因组中而产生的；相比于基因的其他拷贝，假基因经常通过部分或全部内含子的丢失而被识别。未经过加工的假基因产生于基因组区域的重复或是自然选择所释放的某个现存基因的退化。它们有时包含所有的外显子，但是经常遭受缺失和重排，这可能使得很难辨别它们的精确亲缘关系。随着时间的推移，任何一类的假基因都倾向于积累突变，明确显示它们是非活性的，例如存在多个移码或者终止密码子。一般而言，它们比功能能基因获得更大比例的非同义或同义替代。这些特征有的时候会被用来识别假基因，尽管相对较新的假基因可能会逃过这种筛选。

为了评估假基因对基因预测的影响，我们关注两类基因预测：（1）与人类基因组的保守同线性区域内缺乏相应基因预测的（2,705）；（2）在人类基因组中缺乏相互最佳匹配但有明显局部基因簇的成员（5,143）。随机抽取 100 个这样的预测基因样本，并对预测进行人工检查。我们估计大约 76% 的第一类和大约 30% 的第二类与假基因相对应。总体而言，这相当于小鼠中大约有 4,000 个预测基因。

小鼠和人类基因集合的比较

然后，我们试图评估小鼠和人类基因集合之间的对应程度。大约 99% 的小鼠基因在人类基因组中具有同源性。96% 的同源基因位于人类基因组中相似的保守同线性间隔内。对于 80% 的小鼠基因，人类基因组中的最佳匹配反过来在保守同线性间

For 80% of mouse genes, the best match in the human genome in turn has its best match against that same mouse gene in the conserved syntenic interval. These latter cases probably represent genes that have descended from the same common ancestral gene, termed here 1:1 orthologues.

Comprehensive identification of all orthologous gene relationships, however, is challenging. If a single ancestral gene gives rise to a gene family subsequent to the divergence of the species, the family members in each species are all orthologous to the corresponding gene or genes in the other species. Accordingly, orthology need not be a 1:1 relationship and can sometimes be difficult to discern from paralogy (see protein section below concerning lineage-specific gene family expansion).

There was no homologous predicted gene in human for less than 1% (118) of the predicted genes in mouse. Genes that seem to be mouse-specific may correspond to human genes that are still missing owing to the incompleteness of the available human genome sequence. Alternatively, there may be true human homologues present in the available sequence, but the genes could be evolving rapidly in one or both lineages and thus be difficult to recognize.

Mammalian gene count

To re-estimate the number of mammalian protein-coding genes, we studied the extent to which exons in the new set of mouse cDNAs sequenced by RIKEN[132] were already represented in the set of exons contained in our initial mouse gene catalogue, which did not use this set as evidence in gene prediction.

Our estimates suggest that the mammalian gene count may fall at the lower end of (or perhaps below) our previous prediction of 30,000–40,000 based on the human draft sequence[1]. Although small, single-exon genes may add further to the count, the total seems unlikely to greatly exceed 30,000. This lower estimate for the mammalian gene number is consistent with other recent extrapolations[141].

RNA genes

The genome also encodes many RNAs that do not encode proteins, including abundant RNAs involved in mRNA processing and translation (such as ribosomal RNAs and tRNAs), and more recently discovered RNAs involved in the regulation of gene expression and other functions (such as micro RNAs)[165,166]. There are probably many new RNAs not yet discovered, but their computational identification has been difficult because they contain few hallmarks. Genomic comparisons have the potential to significantly increase the power of such predictions by using conservation to reveal relatively weak signals, such as those arising from RNA secondary structure[167]. We illustrate this by showing how comparative

隔中与相同的小鼠基因也具有最佳匹配。后面这些例子可能代表来自同一共同祖先的基因，这里称为 1:1 直系同源性基因。

然而，全面鉴定所有直系同源基因关系具有挑战性。如果单个祖先基因在物种分化后产生了基因家族，则每个物种的家族成员都与相应基因或其他物种中的基因是直系同源的。因此，直系同源不一定是 1:1 关系，有时很难从种内同源中辨别出来（参考下文关于谱系特异性基因家族扩增的蛋白质章节）。

小鼠中，少于 1%(118) 的预测的基因与人类中预测的基因没有同源性。看起来是小鼠特有的基因如果在人类基因中还是缺失状态可能缘于现有的人类基因组序列仍然不完整。也有可能是在现有的序列中存在真正的人源基因，但是基因可能在一个或两个谱系中快速进化，因此很难识别。

哺乳动物基因计数

为了重新估计哺乳动物蛋白编码基因，我们研究了 RIKEN 测序[132]的小鼠 cDNA 新集合中的外显子在我们最初的小鼠基因目录中的外显子集合中的富集程度，而且没有使用这一组数据作为基因预测的证据。

我们的估计表明，哺乳动物基因计数可能会处于（或可能低于）我们先前基于人类序列草图[1]预测的 30,000～40,000 的下限值。虽然小的单外显子基因可能进一步增加计数，但总数似乎不可能大大超过 30,000。对于哺乳动物基因数的这种较低估计与最近的其他推断相符[141]。

RNA 基因

基因组还编码许多不编码蛋白质的 RNA，包括参与 mRNA 加工和翻译的大量 RNA（如核糖体 RNA 和 tRNA），以及最近发现的参与基因表达调控和其他功能的 RNA（例如微 RNA）[165,166]。可能还有很多新 RNA 没有被发现，但由于其特征较少导致它们的计算识别很困难。通过基因组之间的比较，使用保守性来揭示相对较弱的信号（例如由 RNA 二级结构产生的信号[167]）能显著增加此类预测的潜在能力。我们通过展示比较基因组学如何提高一个即便是非常了解的基因家族（tRNA 基因）的识

genomics can improve the recognition of even an extremely well understood gene family, the tRNA genes.

In our initial analysis of the human genome[1], the program tRNAscan-SE[168] predicted 518 tRNA genes and 118 pseudogenes. A small number (about 25 of the total) were filtered out by the RepeatMasker program as being fossils of the MIR transposon, a long-dead SINE element that was derived from a tRNA[169,170].

To improve discrimination of functional tRNA genes, we exploited comparative genomic analysis of mouse and human. True functional tRNA genes would be expected to be highly conserved. Indeed, the 498 putative mouse tRNA genes differ on average by less than 5% (four differences in about 75 bp) from their nearest human match, and nearly half are identical. In contrast, non-genic tRNA-related sequences (those labelled as pseudogenes by tRNAscan-SE or as SINEs by RepeatMasker) differ by an average of 38% and none is within 5% divergence. Notably, the 19 suspect predictions that violate the wobble rules show an average of 26% divergence from their nearest human homologue, and none is within 5% divergence.

On the basis of these observations, we identified the set of tRNA genes having cross-species homologues with < 5% sequence divergence. The set contained 335 tRNA genes in mouse and 345 in human. In both cases, the set represents all 46 expected anti-codons and exactly satisfies the expected wobble rules. The sets probably more closely represent the true complement of functional tRNA genes.

Although the excluded putative genes (163 in mouse and 167 in human) may include some true genes, it seems likely that our earlier estimate of approximately 500 tRNA genes in human is an overestimate. The actual count in mouse and human is probably closer to 350.

Mouse Proteome

Eukaryotic protein invention appears to have occurred largely through two important mechanisms. The first is the combination of protein domains into new architectures. (Domains are compact structures serving as evolutionarily conserved functional building blocks that are often assembled in various arrangements (architectures) in different proteins[174].) The second is lineage-specific expansions of gene families that often accompany the emergence of lineage-specific functions and physiologies[175] (for example, expansions of the vertebrate immunoglobulin superfamily reflecting the invention of the immune system[1], receptor-like kinases in *A. thaliana* associated with plant-specific self-incompatibility and disease-resistance functions[49], and the trypsin-like serine protease homologues in *D. melanogaster* associated with dorsal–ventral patterning and innate immune response[176,177]).

The availability of the human and mouse genome sequences provides an opportunity to

别度来说明这一点。

在我们对人类基因组最初的分析中 [1]，tRNAscan-SE[168] 程序预测了 518 个 tRNA 基因和 118 个假基因。少量（一共 25 个）被 RepeatMasker 程序识别为 MIR 转座子化石（来源于 tRNA 的早已死亡的 SINE 元件 [169,170]）而被过滤。

为了提高对功能性 tRNA 基因的识别，我们进行了小鼠和人类的比较基因组分析。真正的功能性 tRNA 基因预期是高度保守的。事实上，498 个假定的小鼠 tRNA 基因与最接近的人类匹配基因的平均差异度小于 5%（75 bp 中大约有 4 个差异），近一半是完全相同的。相比之下，非 tRNA 基因相关序列（那些被 tRNAscan-SE 标记为假基因或者被 RepeatMasker 标记为 SINE 的序列）平均差异度为 38%，没有一个在 5% 的差异范围内。值得注意的是，违反了摆动法则的 19 个可疑预测显示，与它们最接近的人类同系物的差异度平均为 26%，没有一个在 5% 的差异范围内。

在此观察基础上，我们确定了具有小于 5% 序列差异的跨物种同系物的 tRNA 基因集合。这个集合包括 335 个小鼠 tRNA 基因和 345 个人类 tRNA 基因。这两个集合代表了所有 46 个预期的反密码子，并且完全满足预期的摆动法则。这些集合可能更接近功能性 tRNA 基因的真实补充。

尽管被排除掉的假定基因（小鼠 163 个，人类 167 个）中可能包括一些真正的基因，但我们早期以为人类大约有 500 个 tRNA 基因似乎是高估了。小鼠和人类的实际计数可能更接近 350 个。

小鼠蛋白质学

真核蛋白的出现看来主要通过两个重要机制。第一种是将蛋白质结构域重组到新结构里。（结构域是一种紧凑的结构，作为进化上保守的功能构建块，经常以不同的排列（结构）组装到不同的蛋白质中 [174]。）第二种是伴随着谱系特异功能和生理现象出现的基因家族的谱系特异性扩张 [175]（例如，脊椎动物免疫球蛋白超家族的扩增反映了免疫系统的出现 [1]，拟南芥的受体样激酶与植物特异性自交不亲和性和抗病性功能相关 [49]，黑腹果蝇中的胰蛋白酶样丝氨酸蛋白酶同系物与背腹图案和先天免疫反应相关 [176,177]）。

人类和小鼠这两个密切相关的基因组序列为探索蛋白质进化课题提供了可能，

explore issues of protein evolution that are best addressed through the study of more closely related genomes. The great similarity of the two proteomes allows extensive comparison of orthologous proteins (those that descended by speciation from a single gene in the common ancestor rather than by intragenome duplication), permitting an assessment of the evolutionary pressures exerted on different classes of proteins. The differences between the mouse and human proteomes, primarily in gene family expansions, might reveal how physiological, anatomical and behavioural differences are reflected at the genome level.

Overall proteome comparison

We compared the largest transcript for each gene in the mouse gene catalogue to the National Center for Biotechnology Information (NCBI) database ("nr" set; ftp://ftp.ncbi. nih.gov/blast/db/nr.z) using the BLASTP program[178]. Mouse proteins predicted to be homologues ($E < 10^{-4}$) of other proteins were classified into one of six taxonomic groupings: (1) rodent-specific; (2) mammalian-specific; (3) chordate-specific; (4) metazoan-specific; (5) eukaryote-specific; and (6) other (Fig. 17). The results were similar to those from an analysis of human proteins[1].

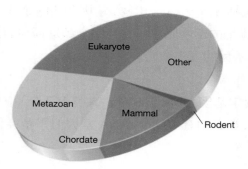

Fig. 17. Taxonomic breakdown of homologues of mouse proteins according to taxonomic range. Note that only a small fraction of genes are possibly rodent-specific (< 1%) as compared with those shared with other mammals (14%, not rodent-specific); shared with chordates (6%, not mammalian-specific); shared with metazoans (27%, not chordate-specific); shared with eukaryotes (29%, not metazoan-specific); and shared with prokaryotes and other organisms (23%, not eukaryotic-specific).

As expected, most of the protein or domain families have similar sizes in human and mouse. However, 12 of the 50 most populous InterPro[179] families in mouse show significant differences in numbers between the two proteomes, most notably high mobility group HMG1/2 box and ubiquitin domains. On close analysis, the differences for six of these families can be accounted for by differential expansion of endogenous retroviral sequences in the genomes. We return below to the issue of expansion of gene families.

这些问题通过研究更密切相关的基因组得到了最好解决。这两个蛋白质组的巨大相似性允许同源蛋白质（那些由共同祖先的单个基因形成而不是基因组内重复形成的蛋白质）进行广泛比较，从而可以评估施加在不同类型蛋白质上的进化压力。小鼠和人类蛋白质组之间的差异，主要是基因家族扩展，可能揭示了生理、解剖和行为的差异如何在基因组水平上反映出来。

总蛋白质组比较

我们使用 BLASTP 程序[178] 将小鼠基因目录中每个基因的最大转录本与美国生物技术信息中心（NCBI）数据库（"nr"集合；ftp://ftp.ncbi.nih.gov/blast/db/nr.z）进行了比较。根据与其他物种蛋白质的同源性（$E < 10^{-4}$）比较，小鼠蛋白质的同系性被分类为六个类群中的一个：（1）啮齿动物特异性；（2）哺乳动物特异性；（3）脊索动物特异性；（4）后生动物特异性；（5）真核生物特异性；（6）其他（图 17）。这些结果与人类蛋白质分析结果相似[1]。

图 17. 按照范围对小鼠蛋白质进行同系物分类。注意，与其他哺乳动物（14%，非啮齿动物特有）共享的基因相比，只有小部分基因可能是啮齿动物特有的（小于 1%）；与脊索动物共享（6%，非哺乳动物特有）；与后生动物共享（27%，非脊索动物特有）；与真核生物共享（29%，非后生动物特有）；与原核生物和其他生物体共享（23%，非真核生物特有）。

正如所料，大多数蛋白质或是其结构域家族在人类和小鼠中的大小相似。然而，小鼠中最常见的 InterPro 家族[179] 的 50 个蛋白质中有 12 个在两个蛋白质组之间的数量上存在显著差异，最显著的是高迁移率一组中 HMG1/2 盒和泛素化结构域。仔细分析，这些家族中的六个的差异可以通过基因组中内源性逆转录病毒序列的差异扩张来解释。下面我们回到基因家族的扩张这一问题。

Evolution of gene families in mouse

As noted above, 80% of mouse proteins seem to have strict 1:1 orthologues in the human genome. Many of the remainder belong to gene families that have undergone differential expansion in at least one of the two genomes, resulting in the lack of a strict 1:1 relationship. Such gene family changes represent an insight into aspects of physiology that have emerged since the last common ancestor.

A well-documented example of family expansion is the olfactory receptor gene family, which represents a branch of the larger G-protein-coupled receptor superfamily tree[193,194]. Duplication of olfactory receptor genes seems to have occurred frequently in both rodent and primate lineages, and differences in number and sequence have been seen as distinguishing the degrees and repertoires of odorant detection between mice and humans. Moreover, an estimated 20% of the mouse olfactory receptor homologues[194] and a higher percentage of human homologues[195,196] are pseudogenes, indicating that there is a dynamic interplay between gene birth and gene death in the recent evolution of this family. The importance of these genes in reproductive behaviour is evident from defects in pheromone responses that result from deletion of the VR1 vomeronasal olfactory receptor gene cluster[197].

To explore systematically recent evolution of the mouse proteome, we searched for mouse-specific gene clusters. We identified genomic regions containing four or more homologous mouse genes that descended from a single gene in the human–mouse common ancestor; these represent local expansions in the mouse lineage. To detect such clusters, we compared all transcripts of each gene with those of five genes on either side (using the BLAST-2-Sequences program with a threshold of $E < 10^{-4}$). A total of 4,563 mouse genes were found to have at least one such homologue within this window. A total of 147 such clusters containing at least four homologues was identified, of which 47 contained multiple olfactory receptor genes, which have been studied elsewhere[193,199] and are not discussed further here. For the remaining 100 clusters, we then constructed dendrograms to examine the evolutionary relationship among the mouse proteins and their human homologues. This allowed us to identify those clusters containing mouse genes that are descendants of a single ancestral gene or for which multiple gene deletions had occurred in the human lineage.

In total, 25 such mouse-specific clusters were identified. In most cases (16), the mouse-specific cluster corresponds to only a single gene in the human genome. Among these 25 clusters, two major functional themes emerge: 14 contain genes involved in rodent reproduction and 5 contain genes involved in host defence and immunity. Each of the 14 "reproduction" clusters contains at least one gene whose expression is modulated by androgens, is involved in the biosynthesis or metabolism of hormones, has an established role in the placenta, gonads or spermatozoa, or has documented roles in mate selection, including pheromone olfaction. The fact that so many of the 25 clusters are related to reproduction is unlikely to be coincidental. Many of the most pronounced physiological differences between rodents and primates relate to reproduction, including substantial

小鼠基因家族的进化

如上所述，80% 的小鼠蛋白质在人类基因组中似乎有严格的 1:1 的直系同源物。其余的大多属于基因家族，它们在两个基因组中的至少一个发生了差异性扩增，导致缺乏严格的 1:1 关系。这种基因家族变化代表了自上一个共同祖先生理学方面出现变化的现象。

一个有文献记载的例子是嗅觉受体基因家族的扩张，它隶属于 G 蛋白偶联受体超家族树的一个分支 [193,194]。嗅觉受体基因的重复似乎在啮齿动物和灵长类动物谱系中经常出现，并且其数量和序列的差异被视为小鼠和人类对于气味的检测程度和组成的区分。此外，估计 20% 的小鼠嗅觉受体同源物 [194] 和更高比例的人类同源物 [195,196] 是假基因，这表明在该家族最近的进化过程中，基因出现和基因死亡之间存在着动态的相互作用。这些基因在生殖行为中的重要性从 VR1 鼻骨的嗅觉受体基因簇的缺失所导致的信息素反应缺陷中显而易见 [197]。

为了系统地探索小鼠蛋白质组的最新进化，我们寻找了小鼠特异性基因簇。我们确定了包含四个或者更多同源小鼠基因的基因组区域，这些同源小鼠基因是人类–小鼠共同祖先中一个单基因的后代；这些基因代表了小鼠谱系中的局部扩增。为了检测这些基因簇，我们将每个基因的所有转录产物与人类和小鼠任意一边的五个基因的转录本进行了比较（使用 BLAST2 序列程序，阈值 $E < 10^{-4}$）。发现总共有 4,563 个小鼠基因在这个窗口中至少有一个这样的同源基因。共计鉴定出 147 个这样的簇，包含至少 4 个同源性基因，其中 47 个包括多种嗅觉受体基因，这些基因已经在别处进行了研究 [193,199]，在此不再作进一步讨论。对于剩下的 100 个簇，我们构建了树状图来研究小鼠蛋白质和它们的人类同源物之间的进化关系。这使我们能够辨别那些小鼠基因簇，它们在小鼠中是单个祖先基因的后代，在人类谱系中则发生了多个基因的删除。

总共鉴定出 25 个这样的小鼠特异性基因簇。在大多数情况下 (16)，小鼠特异性簇只对应人类基因组中的单个基因。在这 25 个簇中，出现了两个主要的功能主题：14 个包括啮齿动物生殖相关基因，5 个包括宿主防御和免疫相关基因。14 个"生殖"簇中的每一个都包含至少一个其表达受雄激素调节的基因，参与荷尔蒙的生物合成或代谢，在胎盘、性腺或者精子中具有确定的作用，或在配偶选择中有确实的作用，包括信息素嗅觉。25 个簇中这么多与生殖相关的事实不太可能是巧合。啮齿动物和灵长类动物之间许多显著的生理差异与生殖相关，包括胎盘结构、产仔数、

variations in placental structures, litter sizes, oestrous cycles and gestation periods. It seems likely that reproductive traits have been responsible for some of the most powerful evolutionary pressures on the mouse genome, and that the demand for innovation has been met through gene family expansions. Examination of the human genome in this way may similarly reveal gene clusters that reflect particular aspects of human reproduction.

The five mouse clusters that encode genes involved in immunity suggest that another major evolutionary force is acting on host defence genes. The five clusters include the major histocompatibility complex (MHC) class Ib genes, two clusters of antimicrobial β-defensins, a cluster of WAP domain antimicrobial proteins and a cluster of type A ribonucleases. Ribonuclease A genes appear to have been under strong positive selection, possibly due to their significant role in host-defence mechanisms[224].

The two major themes—reproduction and immunity—may not be entirely unrelated; that is, the MHC class Ib genes have roles in both pregnancy and immunity. MHC genotype is also known from ethological studies to influence mate selection, although the molecular mechanisms underlying this effect remain unknown. Within the MHC complex, the class I genes are the most divergent, having arisen after the rodent–human divergence[227].

Genome Evolution: Selection

Investigation of the two principal forces that shape the evolution of the mouse and human genomes—mutation and selection—requires looking beyond coarse-scale identification of regions of conserved synteny and purely codon-based analysis of orthologues, to fine-scale alignment of the two genomes at the nucleotide level.

The substantial sequence divergence between the mouse and human genomes is still low enough that orthologous sequences undergoing neutral drift remain conserved enough for them to be aligned reliably. The challenge then is to use such alignments to tease apart the effects of neutral drift, which can teach us about underlying mutational processes, and selection, which can inform us about functionally important elements. It should be emphasized that sequence similarity alone does not imply functional constraint.

In this section, we use whole-genome alignments to explore the extent of sequence conservation in neutral sites (such as ancestral repeat sequences), known functional elements (such as coding regions) and the genome as a whole. By comparing these, we are able to estimate the proportion of regions of the mammalian genome under evolutionary selection (about 5%), which far exceeds the amount attributable to protein-coding sequences. In the next section, we then use the neutral sites to study how mutational forces vary across the genome.

发情周期和妊娠期的实质性变化。生殖相关性状似乎对应了小鼠基因组上受到的一些最强大的进化压力，并且通过基因家族扩张满足了创新的需求。以这种方式对人类基因组进行检查，可以类似地揭示反映人类生殖的特定方面的基因簇。

编码免疫基因的五个小鼠簇显示作用于宿主防御基因的另一个主要的进化力量。这五个簇包括主要组织相容性复合物（MHC）Ib 类基因，两组抗微生物的 β-防御素，一组 WAP 结构域抗微生物蛋白和一组 A 型核糖核酸酶。核糖核酸酶 A 基因似乎一直处于强正选择中，可能是由于它们在宿主防御机制中的重要作用 [224]。

生殖和免疫这两个主题可能并非完全没有关系；也就是说，MHC 中 Ib 类基因在妊娠和免疫中都有作用。从行为学研究中也知道 MHC 基因型会影响配偶选择，尽管这种影响的分子机制仍然不清楚。在 MHC 复合体中，I 类基因是最为分化的，出现在啮齿动物–人类分化之后 [227]。

基因组进化：选择

研究塑造小鼠和人类基因组进化的两个主要力量——突变和选择——需要超越粗略识别保守同线性区域和完全基于密码子的直系同源性分析，达到在核苷酸水平对两个基因组进行精准比对。

小鼠和人类基因组之间的实质性序列差异仍然很小，使得经过中性漂变的同源序列仍足够保守到能够可靠地比对到一起。接下来的挑战就是使用这种比对梳理中性漂变和选择的影响，中性漂变可以告诉我们潜在的突变过程，选择可以告诉我们功能性重要元件。应该强调的是序列相似性本身并不意味着功能约束。

在本节中，我们使用全基因组比对来探索中性位点（例如祖源重复序列）、已知功能元件（例如编码区）和整个基因组的序列保守程度。通过比较这些，我们能够估计哺乳动物基因组受到进化选择的区域的比例（大约 5%），远远超过蛋白质编码序列的数量。在下一节，我们用中性位点来研究突变力如何在基因组中变化。

Fine-scale alignment of genomes

We began by creating a catalogue of sequence alignments between the mouse and human genomes. The alignments were produced by the BLASTZ[328] program by comparing all non-repeat sequences across the genome to identify all high-scoring matches, then, using these as seeds, we extended the alignments into the surrounding regions, including into repeat sequences. Regions that could be aligned clearly at the nucleotide level totalled about 1.1 Gb, corresponding to roughly 40% of the human genome.

Proportion of genome under selection

To investigate the fraction of a mammalian genome under evolutionary selection for biological function, we estimated the proportion of the genome that is better conserved than would be expected given the underlying neutral rate of substitution. We compared the overall distribution S_{genome} of conservation scores for the genome to the neutral distribution $S_{neutral}$ of conservation scores for ancestral repeats using a genome-wide set of 14.3 million non-overlapping 50-bp (human) windows, each containing at least 45 bp (mean 48.67 bp) of aligned sequence. The genome-wide score distribution for these windows has a prominent tail extending to the right, reflecting a substantial excess of windows with high conservation scores relative to the neutral rate. The excess can be estimated by decomposing the genome-wide distribution S_{genome} as a mixture of two components: $S_{neutral}$ and $S_{selected}$ (reflecting windows under selection).

The mixture coefficients indicate that at least 20.8% of the windows are under selection, with the remainder consistent with neutral substitution. Because about 25.2% of all human bases are contained in the windows, this suggests that at least 5.25% (25.2% of 20.8%) of the 50-base windows in the human genome is under selection. Repeating the analysis on more stringently filtered alignments (with non-syntenic and non-reciprocal best matches removed) requiring different numbers of aligned bases per window and with 100-bp windows, yields similar estimates, ranging mostly from 4.8% to about 6.1% of windows under selection (D. Haussler, unpublished data), as does using an alternative score function that considers flanking base context effects and uses a gap penalty[330].

The analysis thus suggests that about 5% of small segments (50 bp) in the human genome are under evolutionary selection for biological functions common to human and mouse. This corresponds to regions totalling about 140 Mb of human genomic DNA, although not all of the nucleotides in these windows are under selection. In addition, some bases outside these windows are likely to be under selection. In a loose sense, these regions might be regarded as containing the "functional" conserved subset of the mammalian genome. Of course, it should be noted that nonconserved sequence may have important roles, for example, as a passive spacer or providing a function specific to one lineage. Notably, protein-coding regions of genes can account for only a fraction of the genome under selection. From

基因组的精细比对

我们首先创建了小鼠和人类基因组之间的序列比对目录。通过 BLASTZ[328] 程序完成比对，该程序通过比较基因组中所有非重复序列来确定所有高得分匹配，然后用这些序列作为种子，我们扩展这些对比到周围区域，包括重复序列在内。在核苷酸水平上可以清楚比对的区域大约为 1.1 Gb，对应于人类基因组的大约 40%。

处于选择的基因组比例

为了研究生物功能进化选择下哺乳动物基因组的比例，我们估计这部分基因组比预期的潜在中性替代更保守。我们使用全基因组的 1,430 万个非重叠的 50 bp（人类）窗口，将基因组保守分数 S_{genome} 的总分布和祖源重复序列的保守分数 $S_{neutral}$ 的中性分布进行了比较，每个窗口包含至少 45 bp（平均 48.67 bp）的比对序列。这些窗口的全基因组得分分布具有向右延伸的突出尾部，反映出相对于中性率而言，具有高保守分数的窗口明显超量。超量值可通过将全基因组分布 S_{genome} 分解为两个成分的混合物——$S_{neutral}$ 和 $S_{selected}$（反映经历选择的窗口）进行估计。

混合系数表明，至少 20.8% 的窗口处于选择中，其余的窗口与中性替换一致。因为人类所有碱基的大约 25.2% 都包含在窗口中，这表明人类基因组中 50 个碱基窗口中至少有 5.25%（20.8% 中的 25.2%）处于选择中。以更严格筛选比对条件重复上述分析（去除了非同线性和单向的最佳匹配），每个窗口需要数量不同的比对碱基和 100 bp 的窗口，得到了类似的估计值，经历选择作用的窗口多数在 4.8% 到 6.1% 范围内（豪斯勒，未发表数据），如同使用一个考虑碱基两端关系效应和使用空缺惩罚的替代评分函数 [330]。

因此，分析表明人类基因组中大约 5% 的小片段（50 bp）正处于人类和小鼠共同具有的生物学功能的选择性进化中。这相当于人类基因组 DNA 总量中的大约 140 Mb 的区域，尽管并非所有处于此窗口的核苷酸都处在选择中。除此之外，这些窗口之外的一些碱基可能也在经历选择。非严格意义上讲，这些区域可能被认为包含哺乳动物基因组的"功能性"保守亚群。当然，应该注意的是，非保守序列可能具有重要作用，例如作为被动间隔子或者在某一特定谱系发挥功能。值得注意的是，基因的蛋白编码区域只占被选择基因组的小部分。从我们对基因的数量和性质的

our analysis of the number and properties of genes, coding regions comprise only about 1.5% of the human genome and account for less than half of the segments under selection.

What accounts for the remainder of the genome under selection? About 1% of the genome is contained in untranslated regions of protein-coding genes, and some of this sequence is under some functional constraint. Another main class of interest are those sequences that control gene expression; if a typical gene contains a few such regulatory sequences, there may be tens to hundreds of thousands of such elements. In addition, conserved sequences probably encode non-protein-coding RNAs (which remain difficult to discern) and chromosomal structural elements. Furthermore, some of the conserved fraction may correspond to sequences that were under selection for some period of time but are no longer functional; these could include recent pseudogenes. Characterization of the conserved sequences should be a high priority for genomics in the years ahead.

The analysis above allows us to infer the proportion of the genome under selection by decomposing the curve S_{genome} into curves $S_{neutral}$ and $S_{selected}$. Importantly, it does not definitively assign an individual conserved sequence as being neutral or selected. One can calculate, for a sequence with conservation score S, the probability $P_{selected}(S)$ that the window of sequence belongs to the selected subset. The probability exceeds 83% for sequences with $S > 3$ and 93% for $S > 4$, but is only 52% for $S = 2$. In other words, some functionally important sequence cannot be separated cleanly from the tail of the distribution of neutral conservation.

Genome Evolution: Mutation

Genome-wide alignments also allow us to investigate how the patterns of neutral substitution, deletion and insertion vary across the genome, providing an insight on the underlying mutational processes.

Substitution rate varies across the genome

Significant variation in the level of sequence conservation has been reported in several small-scale studies of human and mouse genomic regions[10,248-254] and in several larger-scale studies of coding sequences[255-260]. It has not been clear in all cases whether the variation reflects differences in neutral substitution rates or in selection. The human–mouse genome alignments allow us to address the variation more comprehensively and to test for co-variation with the rates of other processes, such as insertions of transposable elements[255] and meiotic recombination[258].

We used the collection of aligned ancestral repeats and aligned fourfold degenerate sites to calculate the apparent neutral substitution rate for about 2,500 overlapping 5-Mb windows across the human genome. To accurately follow fluctuations while accounting for

分析来看，编码区域仅大约占人类基因组的 1.5%，可解释少于一半的处于选择中的片段。

是什么原因导致基因组的剩余部分处于选择中？大约 1% 的基因组是在蛋白质编码基因的非翻译区，其中一些序列受到某些功能限制。另一类引起关注的主要类别是那些控制基因表达的序列；如果一个典型的基因包括一些这样的调节序列，则可能会有数以万计的这种元件的存在。此外，保守序列可能编码非蛋白质的 RNA（这些仍然难以识别）和染色体结构元件。进而，部分这些保守区域可能与某段时间内被选择但不再具有功能的序列相符；这些可能包括最近出现的假基因。未来几年中，解析保守序列应该是基因组学研究的高度优先事项。

上述分析允许我们通过将 S_{genome} 曲线分解为 $S_{neutral}$ 曲线和 $S_{selected}$ 曲线来推断处于选择的基因组的比例。重要的是，它没有明确地将单个保守序列指定为中性或被选择。对于具有保守分数 S 的序列，可以计算出属于选择作用子集的序列窗口的概率 $P_{selected}(S)$。$S > 3$ 的序列概率超过 83%，$S > 4$ 的序列概率超过 93%，但 $S = 2$ 的序列只占 52%。换句话说，一些重要功能序列不能从中性保守分布的尾部被清楚地分离出来。

基因组进化：突变

全基因组的比对还使得我们能够研究中性替代、缺失和插入在基因组中如何发生和变化，从而提供了对潜在突变过程的解析。

替代率在基因组中的变化

在人类和小鼠基因组区域的几个小规模研究 [10,248-254] 和编码序列的几个大规模研究 [255-260] 中，已经报道了序列保守性上的显著变化。尚不清楚在所有情况中，这个变化是否反映了中性替代率或选择上的差异。人类–小鼠基因组比对使我们更全面地研究变异，检测与其他过程比率的共突变情况，例如转座元件的插入 [255] 和减数分裂的重组 [258]。

我们通过收集比对的祖源重复序列和比对的四倍简并位点来计算人类基因组中大约 2,500 个重叠 5 Mb 窗口的中性替代率。为了在考虑碱基组成的区域变化的同时能准确地跟踪波动，通过仅使用窗口中的祖源重复位点（平均大约 280,000 个／窗

regional changes in base composition, the regional nucleotide substitution rate in ancestral repeat sites, t_{AR}, was calculated separately for each 5-Mb window by maximum likelihood estimation of the parameters of the REV model using only the ancestral repeat sites in the window (average of about 280,000 sites per window). The regional nucleotide substitution rate in fourfold degenerate sites, t_{4D}, was calculated similarly from an average of about 3,700 fourfold degenerate sites per window. Windows with fewer than 800 ancestral repeats or fourfold degenerate sites were discarded.

The mean and standard deviations across the windows were $t_{AR} = 0.467 \pm 0.022$ and $t_{4D} = 0.447 \pm 0.067$ substitutions per site. The standard deviation is much larger (over tenfold and threefold, respectively) than would be expected from sampling variance. These data clearly indicate substantial regional fluctuation.

What properties of chromosomal DNA could account for the variation in substitution rate? One possible explanation is local (G+C) content, but previous studies disagree on whether it correlates strongly with divergence[92,255,262,263]. We find that t_{AR} and t_{4D} vary with local (G+C) content, although the dependence is nonlinear[262,264] and is better fitted by regression with a quadratic curve[263]. In other words, the substitution rate seems to be higher in regions of extremely high or low (G+C) content, with the sign of the correlation differing in regions with high versus low (G+C) content. This pattern persists if CpG substitutions are removed from the analysis (data not shown).

All three forces that alter the genome (nucleotide substitution, deletion and insertion) thus vary substantially across the genome. Moreover, they are significantly correlated and tend to co-vary along chromosomes. Notably, these three measures of interspecies divergence are also correlated with recent substitutions in the human genome, as measured by the density of SNPs identified by the SNP Consortium[265].

Possible explanations for variation

What explains the correlation among these many measures of genome divergence? It seems unlikely that direct selection would account for variation and co-variation at such large scales (about 5 Mb) and involving abundant neutral sites taken from ancestral transposon relics. Selection against deleterious mutations can remove linked polymorphisms[270,271], but it is not clear that such effects or related effects[272] could extend to such large scales or to interspecies divergence over such large time periods[273].

It seems more probable that these features reflect local variation in underlying mutation rate, caused by differences in DNA metabolism or chromosome physiology. The causative factors may include recombination-associated mutagenesis[258,266], transcription-associated mutagenesis[274], transposon-associated deletion and genomic rearrangement[275-278], and replication timing[279,280]. Nuclear location may also be involved, including proximity to matrix attachment sites, heterochromatin, nuclear membrane, and origins of replication.

口）对 REV 模型的参数进行最大似然估计，分别计算每 5 Mb 窗口中祖源重复位点 t_{AR} 的区域核苷酸替代率。四倍简并位点 t_{4D} 的区域核苷酸替代率类似地由每个窗口大约 3,700 个四倍简并位点的平均值计算得到。祖源重复或者四倍简并位点少于 800 个的窗口被放弃。

窗口的平均值和标准偏差为每个位点 t_{AR} = 0.467±0.022，t_{4D} = 0.447±0.067 个碱基替换。标准偏差比抽样方差的估计值大很多（分别超过 10 倍和 3 倍）。这些数据明确显示出巨大的区域波动。

染色体 DNA 的哪些特性可以解释替代率的变化呢？一种可能的解释是局部 (G+C) 含量，但之前的研究在它是否与这种变化有很强的相关性上结果并不一致 [92,255,262,263]。我们发现，t_{AR} 和 t_{4D} 随着局部 (G+C) 含量的变化而变化，尽管这种依赖性是非线性的 [262,264]，用二次曲线回归更合适 [263]。换句话说，在 (G+C) 含量极高或极低的区域，替代率似乎更高，在 (G+C) 含量高和低的区域，具有不同的相关性。如果从分析中删除 CpG 位点上的碱基替换，这种模式仍然存在（数据未显示）。

因此，这三种改变基因组的力量（核苷酸替换、删除和插入）在基因组中都有很大的差异。此外，它们之间明显相关而且倾向于沿着染色体共同变异。值得注意的是，这三种变异的种间差异的测量也与人类基因组中的最近替换具有相关性，这是由 SNP 协作组进行的 SNP 密度测量所确定的 [265]。

变化的可能解释

用什么解释基因组分化的各种测量指标之间的关联性？直接选择似乎不太能解释如此大规模（大约 5 Mb）的变异和共变异，而且这些变异还涉及大量从祖源转座子遗物中获取的大量中性位点。对有害突变的选择可以消除连锁多态性 [270,271]，但是尚不清楚这种效应或者相关效应 [272] 能否扩展到如此大的规模或在如此长的时间内 [273] 扩展到种间分化。

这些特征似乎更可能反映了 DNA 代谢或染色体生理学上的差异所引起的潜在突变率的局部变化。诱发因素可能包括重组相关的突变 [258,266]，转录相关的突变 [274]，转座相关缺失和基因组重排 [275-278] 和复制时间 [279,280]。也可能涉及核定位，包括接近基质附着点、异染色质、核膜和复制起始点。

It is clear that the mammalian genome is evolving under the influence of non-uniform local forces. It remains an important challenge to unravel the mechanistic basis and evolutionary consequences of such variation.

Genetic Variation among Strains

Implications for the laboratory mouse

The promise of genomics is the ability to connect phenotypes with genotypes for a wide variety of traits and to use the resulting molecular insights to develop new approaches for the cure and prevention of disease. The laboratory mouse occupies a central place in this vision, both as a prototype for all mammalian biology and as a well-characterized organism for modelling human disease states[15,16,123]. In this section, we briefly discuss ways in which the mouse genome sequence will accelerate biomedical progress in the future. Because the sequence has been made available in public databases in advance of publication, examples for many of the predictions can already be cited.

Positional cloning of genes for mendelian phenotypes

More than 1,000 spontaneously arising and radiation-induced mouse mutants causing heritable mendelian phenotypes are catalogued in the Mouse Genome Informatics (MGI) database (http://www.informatics.jax.org). Largely through positional cloning, the molecular defect is now known for about 200 of these mutants. The availability of an annotated mouse genome sequence now provides the most efficient tool yet in the gene hunter's toolkit. One can move directly from genetic mapping to identification of candidate genes, and the experimental process is reduced to PCR amplification and sequencing of exons and other conserved elements in the candidate interval. With this streamlined protocol, it is anticipated that many decades-old mouse mutants will be understood precisely at the DNA level in the near future. An example of how the draft genome sequence has already been successfully used is the recent identification of the mouse mutation "chocolate" in the melanosome protein Rab38 (ref. 284).

Identification of quantitative trait loci

The availability of more than 50 commonly used laboratory inbred strains of mice, each with its own phenotype for multiple continuously variable traits, has provided an important opportunity to map QTLs that underlie heritable phenotypic variation. A systematic initiative is currently underway[285] to define parameters such as body weight, behavioural patterns, and disease susceptibility among a standard set of inbred lines, and to make these data freely available to the scientific community in the Mouse Phenome Database (www.jax.org/phenome). Appropriate crosses between such lines, followed by genotyping, will enable

很明显，哺乳动物基因组是在非均匀局部力量的影响下进化的。揭示这种变异的机制基础和进化后果仍然是一个很重要的挑战。

品系间遗传变异

对实验小鼠的影响

基因组学的前景是将各种性状的表型和基因型联系起来，并利用由此产生的分子发现来开发治疗和预防疾病的新方案。实验小鼠在这里占据了中心位置，既是作为所有哺乳动物生物学的原型，也是模拟人类疾病状态的具有良好特征的生物体[15,16,123]。在本节中，我们简单讨论小鼠基因组序列在未来将如何加速生物医学进程。因为该序列已经在出版前公布在公共数据库中，所以可以引用许多预测的示例。

孟德尔表型基因的定位克隆

在小鼠基因组信息（MGI）数据库（http://www.informatics.jax.org）中收录了超过1,000个自发产生和辐射诱导产生的小鼠突变体，这些突变体引发可遗传的孟德尔表型。主要通过定位克隆，目前已知大约200个这些突变体的分子缺陷。小鼠基因组序列的注释信息提供了基因猎人工具箱中最有效的工具。研究人员可以直接从基因定位转移到候选基因的鉴定，实验过程简化为对候选区间外显子和其他保守元件进行PCR扩增和测序。通过这种简化的方案，预计在不久的将来，将在DNA水平上精确地解释许多几十年前的小鼠突变体。成功使用基因组序列草图的一个例子就是最近在黑素体蛋白Rab38中鉴定出了小鼠突变体"chocolate"（参考文献284）。

数量性状基因座的鉴定

常用的实验室近交系小鼠超过50种，每种小鼠具有多种连续变化的性状作为自身表型，这为定位可遗传表型的变异的数量性状基因座（QTL）提供了重要机会。目前正在进行一项系统性举措[285]，以确定标准近交系中例如体重、行为模式和疾病易感性等参数，并在小鼠表观数据库（www.jax.org/phenome）中将这些数据免费提供给科学界。这些品系之间适当杂交，然后进行基因分型，能够进行QTL的定位，然

the mapping of QTLs, which can then be subjected to positional cloning. The degree of difficulty is substantially greater for a QTL cloning project than for a mendelian disorder, however, as the responsible intervals are usually much larger, the boundaries more difficult to delineate precisely, and the causative variant often much more subtle[286]. For these reasons, only a handful of the approximately 1,000 mapped QTLs have been identified at the molecular level. The availability of the mouse sequence should greatly improve the chances for future success.

Creation of knockout and knockin mice

The wide application of homologous recombination in embryonic stem cells has provided a remarkable abundance of "custom" mice with specifically engineered loss- or gain-of-function mutations in specific genes of biological or medical interest. Yet this remains a time-consuming process. The design of recombinant DNA constructs for injection has often been delayed by incomplete knowledge of gene structure, requiring tedious restriction mapping or sequencing, and occasionally giving rise to unsatisfying outcomes due to incorrect information. The availability of the mouse genome sequence will both speed the design of such constructs and reduce the likelihood of unfortunate choices. Furthermore, the long-range continuity of the sequence should facilitate the generation of models of contiguous gene-deletion syndromes.

Creation of transgenic animals

For many transgenic experiments, it is important to maintain copy-dependent, tissue-specific expression of the transgene. This is most readily accomplished through BAC transgenesis. The availability of a deep, end-sequenced BAC library from the B6 strain mapped to the genome sequence now makes it straightforward to obtain a desired gene in a BAC for such experiments; end-sequenced BAC libraries from other strains should be available in the future. BACs also provide the ability to make mutant alleles with relative ease, by taking advantage of powerful genetic engineering techniques for custom mutagenesis in the *Escherichia coli* host.

Applications to cancer

The mouse genome sequence also has powerful applications to the molecular characterization of the somatic mutations that result in neoplasia. High-density SNP mapping to identify loss of heterozygosity[288,289], combined with comparative genomic hybridization using cDNA or BAC arrays[290,291], can be used to identify chromosomal segments showing loss or gain of copy number in particular tumour types. The combination of such approaches with expression arrays that include all mouse genes should further enhance the ability to pinpoint the molecular lesions that result in carcinogenesis. Full sequencing of all the exons and

后进行定位克隆。然而，QTL 克隆项目的难度远远大于孟德尔疾病，因为相关的区间通常要大得多，边界更难精确描绘，而致病突变通常也更加微妙[286]。由于这些原因，在大约 1,000 个定位的 QTL 中，只有少数在分子水平上得到鉴定。而小鼠序列的产生在未来应该大大提高成功的机会。

构建敲除和敲入小鼠

同源重组技术在胚胎干细胞中的广泛应用提供了大量"定制"小鼠，它们携带了专门设计的生物学或医学感兴趣的特定基因功能丧失或获得的突变。然而，这仍然是一个耗时的过程。用于注射的重组 DNA 构建体的设计常常因为对基因结构的不完全了解而延迟，需要繁琐的限制性作图或测序，并且偶尔由于不正确的信息而导致令人不满意的结果。小鼠基因组序列的出现将加速这种结构设计并降低产生不幸选择的可能性。此外，序列的长程连续性有助于构建连续基因缺失综合征的模型。

构建转基因动物

对于很多转基因实验来说，保持转基因的拷贝依赖性、组织特异性表达是很重要的。这是最容易通过 BAC 转基因实现的。来自于 B6 品系基因组序列的深度末端测序的 BAC 库的应用，使得现在在此类实验中可以直接获得 BAC 中所需的基因；其他品系的末端测序 BAC 库在将来也将可用。通过利用强大的基因工程技术在大肠杆菌宿主中进行定制诱变，BAC 还能够相对容易地产生突变等位基因。

应用于癌症

小鼠基因组序列在研究导致瘤形成的体细胞突变的分子特征上也具有强大的应用。用于鉴定杂合性缺失的高密度 SNP[288,289] 比对、结合使用 cDNA 或 BAC 阵列的基因组杂交进行比较[290,291] 都可以用于鉴定在特定肿瘤类型中拷贝数缺失或增加的染色体区段。这些方法与包含所有小鼠基因的表达阵列的结合使用，将进一步精确定位导致癌症产生的分子损伤。目前可以对已知肿瘤抑制基因、癌基因和其他候

regulatory regions of known tumour suppressors, oncogenes, and other candidate genes can now be contemplated, as has been initiated in a few centres for human tumours[292].

Making better mouse models

Not all mouse models replicate the human phenotype in the expected way. The availability of the full human and mouse sequences provides an opportunity to anticipate these differences, and perhaps to compensate for them. In some instances, it may turn out that the murine mutation did not reside in the true orthologue of the human disease gene. Alternatively, in a circumstance where the human genome contains only a single gene family member, but the mouse genome contains a paralogue as well as the orthologue, one can anticipate that knockout of the orthologue alone may give a much milder phenotype (or none at all). Such was the case, for instance, with the occulocerebrorenal syndrome described by Lowe and colleagues[296]. Creating double knockout mice may then provide a closer match to the human disease phenotype.

Understanding gene regulation

Of the approximately 5% of windows of the mammalian genome that are under selection, most do not appear to code for protein. Much of this sequence is probably involved in the regulation of gene expression. It should be possible to pinpoint these regulatory elements more precisely with the availability of additional related genomes. However, mouse is likely to provide the most powerful experimental platform for generating and testing hypotheses about their function. An example is the recent demonstration, based on mouse–human sequence alignment followed by knockout manipulation, of several long-range locus control regions that affect expression of the Il4/Il13/Il5 cluster[4].

Conclusion

The mouse provides a unique lens through which we can view ourselves. As the leading mammalian system for genetic research over the past century, it has provided a model for human physiology and disease, leading to major discoveries in such fields as immunology and metabolism. With the availability of the mouse genome sequence, it now provides a model and informs the study of our genome as well.

Comparative genome analysis is perhaps the most powerful tool for understanding biological function. Its power lies in the fact that evolution's crucible is a far more sensitive instrument than any other available to modern experimental science: a functional alteration that diminishes a mammal's fitness by one part in 10^4 is undetectable at the laboratory bench, but is lethal from the standpoint of evolution.

选基因的所有外显子和调控区域进行测序，类似工作在几个人类肿瘤中心已经开始进行[292]。

制作更好的小鼠模型

并非所有的小鼠模型都以预期的方式复制人类表型。完整的人类和小鼠序列提供了一个机会去预测这些差异，并且进行弥补。在某些状况下，可能会发现，小鼠的突变不在人类疾病基因的真正的直系同源物中。或者，在一种情况下，人类基因组仅包含单个基因家族，但是小鼠基因组包含了旁系同源物和直系同源物，人们可以预测单独的直系同源物的敲除可能会产生更温和的表型（或者没有表型）。例如，洛及其同事们[296]描述的闭塞性肾综合征就是这种情况。通过建立双敲除小鼠可以获得与人类疾病表型更接近的模型。

了解基因调控

哺乳动物基因组中大约5%的窗口序列处于选择，大多数的区域似乎不编码蛋白质。大部分这样的序列可能参与基因表达的调控。通过更多相关基因组可以更精准地确定这些调控元件。然而，小鼠很可能提供最强大的实验平台用于产生和测试关于这些元件功能的假设。最近的一个例子是，基于小鼠–人类序列比对后进行的基因敲除证明了影响 Il4/Il13/Il5 基因簇表达的几个长程调控区域[4]。

结　论

小鼠提供了一个独特的镜头，通过它我们可以看到自己。在过去一个世纪里，作为主要的哺乳动物遗传研究系统，它为人类生理和疾病提供了一个模型，从而在免疫学和新陈代谢领域有了重大发现。随着小鼠基因组序列的获得，它正在为我们的基因组研究提供模型和信息。

比较基因组分析可能是了解生物学功能最有力的工具。它的作用在于，进化的熔炉是一种比现代实验科学中任何其他仪器都敏感的仪器：一个会降低哺乳动物身体健康度万分之一的功能性改变是在实验台上检测不到，但是从进化角度来看却是致命的。

Comparative analysis of genomes should thus make it possible to discern, by virtue of evolutionary conservation, biological features that would otherwise escape our notice. In this way, it will play a crucial role in our understanding of the human genome and thereby help lay the foundation for biomedicine in the twenty-first century.

The initial sequence of the mouse genome reported here is merely a first step in this intellectual programme. The sequencing of many additional mammalian and other vertebrate genomes will be needed to extract the full information hidden within our chromosomes. Moreover, as we begin to understand the common elements shared among species, it may also become possible to approach the even harder challenge of identifying and understanding the functional differences that make each species unique.

Methods

Production of sequence reads

Paired-end reads from libraries with different insert sizes were produced as previously described[1] using 384-well trays to ensure linkages.

Availability of sequence and assembly data

Unprocessed sequence reads are available from the NCBI trace archive (ftp://ftp.ncbi.nih.gov/pub/TraceDB/mus_musculus/). Raw assembly data (before removal of contaminants, anchoring to chromosomes, and addition of finished sequence) are available from the Whitehead Institute for Biomedical Research (WIBR) (ftp://wolfram.wi.mit.edu/pub/mouse_contigs/Mar10_02/). The released assembly MGSCv3 is available from Ensembl (http://www.ensembl.org/Mus_musculus/), NCBI (ftp://ftp.ncbi.nih.gov/genomes/M_musculus/MGSCv3_Release1/), UCSC (http://genome.ucsc.edu/downloads.html) and WIBR (ftp://wolfram.wi.mit.edu/pub/mouse_contigs/MGSC_V3/). (See Supplementary Information for detailed Methods.)

(**420**, 520-562; 2002)

Received 18 September; accepted 31 October 2002.

References:

1. International Human Genome Sequencing Consortium Initial sequencing and analysis of the human genome. *Nature* **409**, 860-921 (2001).

2. Venter, J. C. *et al.* The sequence of the human genome. *Science* **291**, 1304-1351 (2001).

3. O'Brien, S. J. *et al.* The promise of comparative genomics in mammals. *Science* **286**, 458-462, 479-481 (1999).

4. Loots, G. G. *et al.* Identification of a coordinate regulator of interleukins 4, 13, and 5 by cross-species sequence comparisons. *Science* **288**, 136-140 (2000).

5. Pennacchio, L. A. & Rubin, E. M. Genomic strategies to identify mammalian regulatory sequences. *Nature Rev. Genet.* **2**, 100-109 (2001).

6. Oeltjen, J. C. *et al.* Large-scale comparative sequence analysis of the human and murine Bruton's tyrosine kinase loci reveals conserved regulatory domains. *Genome Res.* **7**, 315-329 (1997).

7. Ellsworth, R. E. *et al.* Comparative genomic sequence analysis of the human and mouse cystic fibrosis transmembrane conductance regulator genes. *Proc. Natl*

因此，基因组的比较分析应该能够通过进化保守性分辨出我们不会注意到的生物学特征。通过这种方式，它将对我们理解人类基因组发挥重要作用，从而为二十一世纪的生物医学奠定基础。

这里报道的小鼠基因组的初始序列仅仅是这个充满智慧的项目的第一步。我们还需要对许多其他哺乳动物和其他脊椎动物进行测序，以提取隐藏在我们染色体中的全部信息。此外，当我们开始了解物种之间共享的相同元件时，也可能接近识别和理解每个物种所拥有的独特功能及其彼此差异。

方　法

序列读数的产生

如前所述 [1]，利用 384 孔板获得不同片段长度的文库并生成配对末端读取片段，以确保序列的连锁性。

序列和组装数据的可用性

未处理的序列读取片段可以从 NCBI 存档中获得（ftp://ftp.ncbi.nih.gov/pub/TraceDB/mus_musculus/）。原始组装数据（在去掉污染物、锚定染色体和添加完成序列之前）可以从怀特黑德生物医学研究所（WIBR）获得（ftp://wolfram.wi.mit.edu/pub/mouse_contigs/Mar10_02/）。程序集 MGSCv3 可以从 Ensembl（http://www.ensembl.org/Mus_musculus/）、NCBI（ftp://ftp.ncbi.nih.gov/genomes/M_musculus/MGSCv3_Release1/）、UCSC（http://genome.ucsc.edu/downloads.html）和 WIBR（ftp://wolfram.wi.mit.edu/pub/mouse_contigs/MGSC_V3/）获得。（具体方法见补充信息。）

（张瑶楠 翻译；曾长青 审稿）

Acad. Sci. USA **97**, 1172-1177 (2000).

8. Mallon, A. M. *et al.* Comparative genome sequence analysis of the Bpa/Str region in mouse and man. *Genome Res.* **10**, 758-775 (2000).

9. Dehal, P. *et al.* Human chromosome 19 and related regions in mouse: conservative and lineage-specific evolution. *Science* **293**, 104-111 (2001).

10. DeSilva, U. *et al.* Generation and comparative analysis of approximately 3.3 Mb of mouse genomic sequence orthologous to the region of human chromosome 7q11.23 implicated in Williams syndrome. *Genome Res.* **12**, 3-15 (2002).

11. Toyoda, A. *et al.* Comparative genomic sequence analysis of the human chromosome 21 down syndrome critical region. *Genome Res.* **12**, 1323-1332 (2002).

12. Ansari-Lari, M. A. *et al.* Comparative sequence analysis of a gene-rich cluster at human chromosome 12p13 and its syntenic region in mouse chromosome 6. *Genome Res.* **8**, 29-40 (1998).

13. Lercher, M. J., Williams, E. J. & Hurst, L. D. Local similarity in evolutionary rates extends over whole chromosomes in human-rodent and mouse-rat comparisons: implications for understanding the mechanistic basis of the male mutation bias. *Mol. Biol. Evol.* **18**, 2032-2039 (2001).

14. Makalowski, W. & Boguski, M. S. Evolutionary parameters of the transcribed mammalian genome: an analysis of 2,820 orthologous rodent and human sequences. *Proc. Natl Acad. Sci. USA* **95**, 9407-9412 (1998).

15. Rossant, J. & McKerlie, C. Mouse-based phenogenomics for modelling human disease. *Trends Mol. Med.* **7**, 502-507 (2001).

16. Paigen, K. A miracle enough: the power of mice. *Nature Med.* **1**, 215-220 (1995).

17. Hogan, B., Beddington, R., Costantini, F. & Lacy, E. *Manipulating the Mouse Embryo: A Laboratory Manual* (Cold Spring Harbor Laboratory Press, Woodbury, New York, 1994).

18. Joyner, A. L. *Gene Targeting: A Practical Approach* (Oxford Univ. Press, New York, 1999).

19. Copeland, N. G., Jenkins, N. A. & Court, D. L. Recombineering: a powerful new tool for mouse functional genomics. *Nature Rev. Genet.* **2**, 769-779 (2001).

20. Yu, Y. & Bradley, A. Engineering chromosomal rearrangements in mice. *Nature Rev. Genet.* **2**, 780-790 (2001).

21. Bucan, M. & Abel, T. The mouse: genetics meets behaviour. *Nature Rev. Genet.* **3**, 114-123 (2002).

22. Silver, L. M. *Mouse Genetics: Concepts and Practice* (Oxford Univ. Press, New York, 1995).

23. Bromham, L., Phillips, M. J. & Penny, D. Growing up with dinosaurs: molecular dates and the mammalian radiation. *Trends Ecol. Evol.* **14**, 113-118 (1999).

24. Nei, M., Xu, P. & Glazko, G. Estimation of divergence times from multiprotein sequences for a few mammalian species and several distantly related organisms. *Proc. Natl Acad. Sci. USA* **98**, 2497-2502 (2001).

25. Kumar, S. & Hedges, S. B. A molecular timescale for vertebrate evolution. *Nature* **392**, 917-920 (1998).

26. Madsen, O. *et al.* Parallel adaptive radiations in two major clades of placental mammals. *Nature* **409**, 610-614 (2001).

27. Murphy, W. J. *et al.* Molecular phylogenetics and the origins of placental mammals. *Nature* **409**, 614-618 (2001).

29. Morse, H. *The Mouse in Biomedical Research* (eds Foster, H. L., Small, J. D. & Fox, J. G.) 1-16 (Academic, New York, 1981).

30. Morse, H. C. *Origins of Inbred Mice* (ed. Morse, H. C.) 1-21 (Academic, New York, 1978).

31. Haldane, J. B. S., Sprunt, A. D. & Haldane, N. M. Reduplication in mice. *J. Genet.* **5**, 133-135 (1915).

32. Botstein, D., White, R. L., Skolnick, M. & Davis, R. W. Construction of a genetic linkage map in man using restriction fragment length polymorphisms. *Am. J. Hum. Genet.* **32**, 314-331 (1980).

33. Dietrich, W. *et al.* *Genetic Maps* (ed. O'Brien, S.) 4.110-4.142, (1992).

34. Dietrich, W. F. *et al.* A comprehensive genetic map of the mouse genome. *Nature* **380**, 149-152 (1996).

35. Love, J. M., Knight, A. M., McAleer, M. A. & Todd, J. A. Towards construction of a high resolution map of the mouse genome using PCR-analysed microsatellites. *Nucleic Acids Res.* **18**, 4123-4130 (1990).

36. Weber, J. L. & May, P. E. Abundant class of human DNA polymorphisms which can be typed using the polymerase chain reaction. *Am. J. Hum. Genet.* **44**, 388-396 (1989).

37. Hudson, T. J. *et al.* A radiation hybrid map of mouse genes. *Nature Genet.* **29**, 201-205 (2001).

38. Van Etten, W. J. *et al.* Radiation hybrid map of the mouse genome. *Nature Genet.* **22**, 384-387 (1999).

39. Nusbaum, C. *et al.* A YAC-based physical map of the mouse genome. *Nature Genet.* **22**, 388-393 (1999).

41. Kawai, J. *et al.* Functional annotation of a full-length mouse cDNA collection. *Nature* **409**, 685-690 (2001).

44. Gregory, S. G. *et al.* A physical map of the mouse genome. *Nature* **418**, 743-750 (2002).

45. Mural, R. J. *et al.* A comparison of whole-genome shotgun-derived mouse chromosome 16 and the human genome. *Science* **296**, 1661-1671 (2002).

46. Green, E. D. Strategies for the systematic sequencing of complex genomes. *Nature Rev. Genet.* **2**, 573-583 (2001).

47. Edwards, A. *et al.* Automated DNA sequencing of the human HPRT locus. *Genomics* **6**, 593-608 (1990).

48. Huson, D. H. *et al.* Design of a compartmentalized shotgun assembler for the human genome. *Bioinformatics* **17**, S132-S139 (2001).

49. Analysis of the genome sequence of the flowering plant *Arabidopsis thaliana. Nature* **408**, 796-815 (2000).

52. Battey, J., Jordan, E., Cox, D. & Dove, W. An action plan for mouse genomics. *Nature Genet.* **21**, 73-75 (1999).

53. Kuroda-Kawaguchi, T. *et al.* The AZFc region of the Y chromosome features massive palindromes and uniform recurrent deletions in infertile men. *Nature Genet.* **29**, 279-286 (2001).

54. Zhao, S. *et al.* Mouse BAC ends quality assessment and sequence analyses. *Genome Res.* **11**, 1736-1745 (2001).

55. Ewing, B. & Green, P. Analysis of expressed sequence tags indicates 35,000 human genes. *Nature Genet.* **25**, 232-234 (2000).

56. Batzoglou, S. *et al.* ARACHNE: a whole-genome shotgun assembler. *Genome Res.* **12**, 177-189 (2002).

57. Jaffe, D. B. *et al.* Whole-genome sequence assembly for mammalian genomes: Arachne **2**. *Genome Res.* (in the press).

58. Mullikin, J. & Ning, Z. The Phusion Assembler. *Genome Res.* (in the press).

59. Bailey, J. A. *et al.* Recent segmental duplications in the human genome. *Science* **297**, 1003-1007 (2002).

66. Mouse Genome Sequencing Consortium Progress in sequencing the mouse genome. *Genesis* **31**, 137-141 (2001).

67. Clark, F. H. Inheritance and linkage relations of mutant characteristics in the deermouse. *Contrib. Lab. Vert. Biol.* **7**, 1-11 (1938).

68. Castle, W. W. Observations of the occurrence of linkage in rats and mice. *Car. Inst. Wash. Pub.* **288**, 29-36 (1919).

69. Lalley, P. A., Minna, J. D. & Francke, U. Conservation of autosomal gene synteny groups in mouse and man. *Nature* **274**, 160-163 (1978).

70. Nadeau, J. H. & Taylor, B. A. Lengths of chromosomal segments conserved since divergence of man and mouse. *Proc. Natl Acad. Sci. USA* **81**, 814-818 (1984).

71. Ma, B., Tromp, J. & Li, M. PatternHunter: faster and more sensitive homology search. *Bioinformatics* **18**, 440-445 (2002).

72. Ohno, S. *Sex Chromosomes and Sex-Linked Genes* (Springer, Berlin, 1996).

73. Sturtevant, A. H. & Beadle, G. W. The relations of inversions in the X chromosome of *Drosophila melanogaster* to crossing over and disjunction. *Genetics* **21**, 554-604 (1936).

74. Ranz, J. M., Casals, F. & Ruiz, A. How malleable is the eukaryotic genome? Extreme rate of chromosomal rearrangement in the genus *Drosophila*. *Genome Res.* **11**, 230-239 (2001).

75. Nadeau, J. H. & Sankoff, D. The lengths of undiscovered conserved segments in comparative maps. *Mamm. Genome* **9**, 491-495 (1998).

76. Ferretti, V., Nadeau, J. H. & Sankoff, D. *Combinatorial Pattern Matching, 7th Annual Symposium* (eds Hirschberg, D. & Myers, G.) 159-167 (Springer, Berlin, 1996).

77. Bourque, G. & Pevzner, P. A. Genome-scale evolution: reconstructing gene orders in the ancestral species. *Genome Res.* **12**, 26-36 (2002).

78. Thiery, J. P., Macaya, G. & Bernardi, G. An analysis of eukaryotic genomes by density gradient centrifugation. *J. Mol. Biol.* **108**, 219-235 (1976).

79. Salinas, J., Zerial, M., Filipski, J. & Bernardi, G. Gene distribution and nucleotide sequence organization in the mouse genome. *Eur. J. Biochem.* **160**, 469-478 (1986).

80. Sabeur, G., Macaya, G., Kadi, F. & Bernardi, G. The isochore patterns of mammalian genomes and their phylogenetic implications. *J. Mol. Evol.* **37**, 93-108 (1993).

81. Zerial, M., Salinas, J., Filipski, J. & Bernardi, G. Gene distribution and nucleotide sequence organization in the human genome. *Eur. J. Biochem.* **160**, 479-485 (1986).

82. Mouchiroud, D., Fichant, G. & Bernardi, G. Compositional compartmentalization and gene composition in the genome of vertebrates. *J. Mol. Evol.* **26**, 198-204 (1987).

83. Mouchiroud, D., Gautier, C. & Bernardi, G. The compositional distribution of coding sequences and DNA molecules in humans and murids. *J. Mol. Evol.* **27**, 311-320 (1988).

84. Mouchiroud, D. & Gautier, C. Codon usage changes and sequence dissimilarity between human and rat. *J. Mol. Evol.* **31**, 81-91 (1990).

85. Robinson, M., Gautier, C. & Mouchiroud, D. Evolution of isochores in rodents. *Mol. Biol. Evol.* **14**, 823-828 (1997).

86. Bernardi, G. *et al.* The mosaic genome of warm-blooded vertebrates. *Science* **228**, 953-958 (1985).

87. Mouchiroud, D. *et al.* The distribution of genes in the human genome. *Gene* **100**, 181-187 (1991).

88. Zoubak, S., Clay, O. & Bernardi, G. The gene distribution of the human genome. *Gene* **174**, 95-102 (1996).

89. Saccone, S., Pavlicek, A., Federico, C., Paces, J. & Bernard, G. Genes, isochores and bands in human chromosomes 21 and 22. *Chromosome Res.* **9**, 533-539 (2001).

90. Bernardi, G. Compositional constraints and genome evolution. *J. Mol. Evol.* **24**, 1-11 (1986).

91. Bernardi, G., Mouchiroud, D. & Gautier, C. Compositional patterns in vertebrate genomes: conservation and change in evolution. *J. Mol. Evol.* **28**, 7-18 (1988).

92. Wolfe, K. H., Sharp, P. M. & Li, W. H. Mutation rates differ among regions of the mammalian genome. *Nature* **337**, 283-285 (1989).

93. Sueoka, N. Directional mutation pressure and neutral molecular evolution. *Proc. Natl Acad. Sci. USA* **85**, 2653-2657 (1988).

94. Sueoka, N. On the genetic basis of variation and heterogeneity of DNA base composition. *Proc. Natl Acad. Sci. USA* **48**, 582-592 (1962).

95. Bird, A. P. DNA methylation and the frequency of CpG in animal DNA. *Nucleic Acids Res.* **8**, 1499-1504 (1980).

96. Larsen, F., Gundersen, G., Lopez, R. & Prydz, H. CpG islands as gene markers in the human genome. *Genomics* **13**, 1095-1107 (1992).

97. Gardiner-Garden, M. & Frommer, M. CpG islands in vertebrate genomes. *J. Mol. Biol.* **196**, 261-282 (1987).

98. Antequera, F. & Bird, A. Number of CpG islands and genes in human and mouse. *Proc. Natl Acad. Sci. USA* **90**, 11995-11999 (1993).

99. Adams, R. L. & Eason, R. Increased G + C content of DNA stabilizes methyl CpG dinucleotides. *Nucleic Acids Res.* **12**, 5869-5877 (1984).

100. Smit, A. F. Interspersed repeats and other mementos of transposable elements in mammalian genomes. *Curr. Opin. Genet. Dev.* **9**, 657-663 (1999).

101. Laird, C. D., McConaughy, B. L. & McCarthy, B. J. Rate of fixation of nucleotide substitutions in evolution. *Nature* **224**, 149-154 (1969).

102. Kohne, D. E. Evolution of higher-organism DNA. *Q. Rev. Biophys.* **3**, 327-375 (1970).

103. Goodman, M., Barnabas, J., Matsuda, G. & Moore, G. W. Molecular evolution in the descent of man. *Nature* **233**, 604-613 (1971).

104. Kumar, S. & Subramanian, S. Mutation rates in mammalian genomes. *Proc. Natl Acad. Sci. USA* **99**, 803-808 (2002).

105. Easteal, S., Collet, C. & Betty, D. *The Mammalian Molecular Clock* (Landes, Austin, Texas, 1995).

106. Li, W. H., Ellsworth, D. L., Krushkal, J., Chang, B. H. & Hewett-Emmett, D. Rates of nucleotide substitution in primates and rodents and the generation-time effect hypothesis. *Mol. Phylogenet. Evol.* **5**, 182-187 (1996).

107. Martin, A. P. & Palumbi, S. R. Body size, metabolic rate, generation time, and the molecular clock. *Proc. Natl Acad. Sci. USA* **90**, 4087-4091 (1993).

108. Bromham, L. Molecular clocks in reptiles: life history influences rate of molecular evolution. *Mol. Biol. Evol.* **19**, 302-309 (2002).

109. Wu, C. I. & Li, W. H. Evidence for higher rates of nucleotide substitution in rodents than in man. *Proc. Natl Acad. Sci. USA* **82**, 1741-1745 (1985).

110. Smit, A. F., Toth, G., Riggs, A. D. & Jurka, J. Ancestral, mammalian-wide subfamilies of LINE-1 repetitive sequences. *J. Mol. Biol.* **246**, 401-417 (1995).

155

111. Adey, N. B. *et al.* Rodent L1 evolution has been driven by a single dominant lineage that has repeatedly acquired new transcriptional regulatory sequences. *Mol. Biol. Evol.* **11**, 778-789 (1994).

112. Mears, M. L. & Hutchison, C. A. III The evolution of modern lineages of mouse L1 elements. *J. Mol. Evol.* **52**, 51-62 (2001).

113. Goodier, J. L., Ostertag, E. M., Du, K. & Kazazian, H. H. Jr A novel active L1 retrotransposon subfamily in the mouse. *Genome Res.* **11**, 1677-1685 (2001).

114. Hardies, S. C. *et al.* LINE-1 (L1) lineages in the mouse. *Mol. Biol. Evol.* **17**, 616-628 (2000).

115. Ohshima, K., Hamada, M., Terai, Y. & Okada, N. The 3′ ends of tRNA-derived short interspersed repetitive elements are derived from the 3′ ends of long interspersed repetitive elements. *Mol. Cell Biol.* **16**, 3756-3764 (1996).

116. Smit, A. F. The origin of interspersed repeats in the human genome. *Curr. Opin. Genet. Dev.* **6**, 743-748 (1996).

117. Quentin, Y. A master sequence related to a free left Alu monomer (FLAM) at the origin of the B1 family in rodent genomes. *Nucleic Acids Res.* **22**, 2222-2227 (1994).

118. Kim, J. & Deininger, P. L. Recent amplification of rat ID sequences. *J. Mol. Biol.* **261**, 322-327 (1996).

119. Lee, I. Y. *et al.* Complete genomic sequence and analysis of the prion protein gene region from three mammalian species. *Genome Res.* **8**, 1022-1037 (1998).

120. Serdobova, I. M. & Kramerov, D. A. Short retroposons of the B2 superfamily: evolution and application for the study of rodent phylogeny. *J. Mol. Evol.* **46**, 202-214 (1998).

121. Coffin, J. M., Hughes, S. H. & Varmus, H. E. (eds) *Retroviruses* (Cold Spring Harbor Laboratory Press, Cold Spring Harbor, New York, 1997).

122. Smit, A. F. Identification of a new, abundant superfamily of mammalian LTR-transposons. *Nucleic Acids Res.* **21**, 1863-1872 (1993).

123. Hamilton, B. A. & Frankel, W. N. Of mice and genome sequence. *Cell* **107**, 13-16 (2001).

125. Kidwell, M. G. Horizontal transfer. *Curr. Opin. Genet. Dev.* **2**, 868-873 (1992).

126. Feng, Q., Moran, J. V., Kazazian, H. H. Jr & Boeke, J. D. Human L1 retrotransposon encodes a conserved endonuclease required for retrotransposition. *Cell* **87**, 905-916 (1996).

127. Jurka, J. Sequence patterns indicate an enzymatic involvement in integration of mammalian retroposons. *Proc. Natl Acad. Sci. USA* **94**, 1872-1877 (1997).

128. Bernardi, G. The isochore organization of the human genome. *Annu. Rev. Genet.* **23**, 637-661 (1989).

129. Holmquist, G. P. Chromosome bands, their chromatin flavors, and their functional features. *Am. J. Hum. Genet.* **51**, 17-37 (1992).

132. Lyon, M. F. X-chromosome inactivation: a repeat hypothesis. *Cytogenet. Cell Genet.* **80**, 133-137 (1998).

135. Beckman, J. S. & Weber, J. L. Survey of human and rat microsatellites. *Genomics* **12**, 627-631 (1992).

136. Toth, G., Gaspari, Z. & Jurka, J. Microsatellites in different eukaryotic genomes: survey and analysis. *Genome Res.* **10**, 967-981 (2000).

139. Dunham, I. *et al.* The DNA sequence of human chromosome 22. *Nature* **402**, 489-495 (1999).

140. Hattori, M. *et al.* The DNA sequence of human chromosome 21. *Nature* **405**, 311-319 (2000).

141. Roest Crollius, H. *et al.* Estimate of human gene number provided by genome-wide analysis using *Tetraodon nigroviridis* DNA sequence. *Nature Genet.* **25**, 235-238 (2000).

142. Hubbard, T. *et al.* The Ensembl genome database project. *Nucleic Acids Res.* **30**, 38-41 (2002).

143. Kulp, D., Haussler, D., Reese, M. G. & Eeckman, F. H. Integrating database homology in a probabilistic gene structure model. *Pac. Symp. Biocomput.* 232-244 (1997).

144. Birney, E. & Durbin, R. Using GeneWise in the *Drosophila* annotation experiment. *Genome Res.* **10**, 547-548 (2000).

145. Burge, C. & Karlin, S. Prediction of complete gene structures in human genomic DNA. *J. Mol. Biol.* **268**, 78-94 (1997).

150. The FANTOM Consortium and the RIKEN Genome Exploration Research Group Phase I & II Team. Analysis of the mouse transcriptome based on functional annotation of 60,770 full-length cDNAs. *Nature* **420**, 563-573 (2002).

151. Pruitt, K. D. & Maglott, D. R. RefSeq and LocusLink: NCBI gene-centered resources. *Nucleic Acids Res.* **29**, 137-140 (2001).

165. Eddy, S. R. Non-coding RNA genes and the modern RNA world. *Nature Rev. Genet.* **2**, 919-929 (2001).

166. Storz, G. An expanding universe of noncoding RNAs. *Science* **296**, 1260-1263 (2002).

167. Eddy, S. R. Computational genomics of noncoding RNA genes. *Cell* **109**, 137-140 (2002).

168. Lowe, T. M. & Eddy, S. R. tRNAscan-SE: a program for improved detection of transfer RNA genes in genomic sequence. *Nucleic Acids Res.* **25**, 955-964 (1997).

169. Daniels, G. R. & Deininger, P. L. Repeat sequence families derived from mammalian tRNA genes. *Nature* **317**, 819-822 (1985).

170. Lawrence, C., McDonnell, D. & Ramsey, W. Analysis of repetitive sequence elements containing tRNA-like sequences. *Nucleic Acids Res.* **13**, 4239-4252 (1985).

174. Ponting, C. P. & Russell, R. R. The natural history of protein domains. *Annu. Rev. Biophys. Biomol. Struct.* **31**, 45-71 (2002).

175. Lespinet, O., Wolf, Y. I., Koonin, E. V. & Aravind, L. The role of lineage-specific gene family expansion in the evolution of eukaryotes. *Genome Res.* **12**, 1048-1059 (2002).

176. Ponting, C. P., Mott, R., Bork, P. & Copley, R. R. Novel protein domains and repeats in *Drosophila melanogaster*: insights into structure, function, and evolution. *Genome Res.* **11**, 1996-2008 (2001).

177. Rubin, G. M. *et al.* Comparative genomics of the eukaryotes. *Science* **287**, 2204-2215 (2000).

178. Altschul, S. F. *et al.* Gapped BLAST and PSI-BLAST: a new generation of protein database search programs. *Nucleic Acids Res.* **25**, 3389-3402 (1997).

179. Zdobnov, E. M. & Apweiler, R. InterProScan—an integration platform for the signature-recognition methods in InterPro. *Bioinformatics* **17**, 847-848 (2001).

193. Young, J. M. *et al.* Different evolutionary processes shaped the mouse and human olfactory receptor gene families. *Hum. Mol. Genet.* **11**, 535-546 (2002).

194. Zhang, X. & Firestein, S. The olfactory receptor gene superfamily of the mouse. *Nature Neurosci.* **5**, 124-133 (2002).

195. Glusman, G., Yanai, I., Rubin, I. & Lancet, D. The complete human olfactory subgenome. *Genome Res.* **11**, 685-702 (2001).

196. Rouquier, S. *et al.* Distribution of olfactory receptor genes in the human genome. *Nature Genet.* **18**, 243-250 (1998).

197. Del Punta, K. *et al.* Deficient pheromone responses in mice lacking a cluster of vomeronasal receptor genes. *Nature* **419**, 70-74 (2002).

199. Lane, R. P. *et al.* Genomic analysis of orthologous mouse and human olfactory receptor loci. *Proc. Natl Acad. Sci. USA* **98**, 7390-7395 (2001).

224. Zhang, J., Dyer, K. D. & Rosenberg, H. F. Evolution of the rodent eosinophil-associated RNase gene family by rapid gene sorting and positive selection. *Proc. Natl Acad. Sci. USA* **97**, 4701-4706 (2000).

227. Yeager, M. & Hughes, A. L. Evolution of the mammalian MHC: natural selection, recombination, and convergent evolution. *Immunol. Rev.* **167**, 45-58 (1999).

248. Koop, B. F. Human and rodent DNA sequence comparisons: a mosaic model of genomic evolution. *Trends Genet.* **11**, 367-371 (1995).

249. DeBry, R. W. & Seldin, M. F. Human/mouse homology relationships. *Genomics* **33**, 337-351 (1996).

250. Gottgens, B. *et al.* Long-range comparison of human and mouse SCL loci: localized regions of sensitivity to restriction endonucleases correspond precisely with peaks of conserved noncoding sequences. *Genome Res.* **11**, 87-97 (2001).

251. Shiraishi, T. *et al.* Sequence conservation at human and mouse orthologous common fragile regions, FRA3B/FHIT and Fra14A2/Fhit. *Proc. Natl Acad. Sci. USA* **98**, 5722-5727 (2001).

252. Wilson, M. D. *et al.* Comparative analysis of the gene-dense ACHE/TFR2 region on human chromosome 7q22 with the orthologous region on mouse chromosome 5. *Nucleic Acids Res.* **29**, 1352-1365 (2001).

253. Hardison, R. C. Conserved noncoding sequences are reliable guides to regulatory elements. *Trends Genet.* **16**, 369-372 (2000).

254. Chiaromonte, F. *et al.* Association between divergence and interspersed repeats in mammalian noncoding genomic DNA. *Proc. Natl Acad. Sci. USA* **98**, 14503-14508 (2001).

255. Matassi, G., Sharp, P. M. & Gautier, C. Chromosomal location effects on gene sequence evolution in mammals. *Curr. Biol.* **9**, 786-791 (1999).

256. Williams, E. J. & Hurst, L. D. The proteins of linked genes evolve at similar rates. *Nature* **407**, 900-903 (2000).

257. Chen, F. C., Vallender, E. J., Wang, H., Tzeng, C. S. & Li, W. H. Genomic divergence between human and chimpanzee estimated from large-scale alignments of genomic sequences. *J. Hered.* **92**, 481-489 (2001).

258. Lercher, M. J. & Hurst, L. D. Human SNP variability and mutation rate are higher in regions of high recombination. *Trends Genet.* **18**, 337-340 (2002).

259. Castresana, J. Genes on human chromosome 19 show extreme divergence from the mouse orthologs and a high GC content. *Nucleic Acids Res.* **30**, 1751-1756 (2002).

260. Smith, N. G. C., Webster, M. & Ellegren, H. Deterministic mutation rate variation in the human genome. *Genome Res.* **12**, 1350-1356 (2002).

262. Bernardi, G. The human genome: organization and evolutionary history. *Ann. Rev. Genet.* **23**, 637-661 (1995).

263. Hurst, L. D. & Willliams, E. J. B. Covariation of GC content and the silent site substitution rate in rodents: implications for methodology and for the evolution of isochores. *Gene* **261**, 107-114 (2000).

264. Bernardi, G. Misunderstandings about isochores. Part 1. *Gene* **276**, 3-13 (2001).

265. The SNP Consortium An SNP map of the human genome generated by reduced representation shotgun sequencing. *Nature* **407**, 513-516 (2000).

266. Perry, J. & Ashworth, A. Evolutionary rate of a gene affected by chromosomal position. *Curr. Biol.* **9**, 987-989 (1999).

270. Charlesworth, B. The effect of background selection against deleterious mutations on weakly selected, linked variants. *Genet. Res.* **63**, 213-227 (1994).

271. Hudson, R. R. & Kaplan, N. L. Deleterious background selection with recombination. *Genetics* **141**, 1605-1617 (1995).

272. Maynard Smith, J. & Haigh, J. The hitch-hiking effect of a favourable gene. *Genet. Res.* **23**, 23-35 (1974).

273. Birky, C. W. & Walsh, J. B. Effects of linkage on rates of molecular evolution. *Proc. Natl Acad. Sci. USA* **85**, 6414-6418 (1988).

274. Francino, M. P. & Ochman, H. Strand asymmetries in DNA evolution. *Trends Genet.* **13**, 240-245 (1997).

275. Gilbert, N., Lutz-Prigge, S. & Moran, J. Genomic deletions created upon LINE-1 retrotransposition. *Cell* **110**, 315-325 (2002).

276. Symer, D. *et al.* Human l1 retrotransposition is associated with genetic instability *in vivo*. *Cell* **110**, 327-338 (2002).

277. Moran, J. *et al.* High frequency retrotransposition in cultured mammalian cells. *Cell* **87**, 917-927 (1996).

278. Hughes, J. F. & Coffin, J. M. Evidence for genomic rearrangements mediated by human endogenous retroviruses during primate evolution. *Nature Genet.* **29**, 487-489 (2001).

279. Wolfe, K. H. Mammalian DNA replication: mutation biases and the mutation rate. *J. Theor. Biol.* **149**, 441-451 (1991).

280. Gu, X. & Li, W. H. A model for the correlation of mutation rate with GC content and the origin of GC-rich isochores. *J. Mol. Evol.* **38**, 468-475 (1994).

284. Loftus, S. K. *et al.* Mutation of melanosome protein RAB38 in chocolate mice. *Proc. Natl Acad. Sci. USA* **99**, 4471-4476 (2002).

285. Paigen, K. & Eppig, J. T. A mouse phenome project. *Mamm. Genome* **11**, 715-717 (2000).

286. Doerge, R. W. Mapping and analysis of quantitative trait loci in experimental populations. *Nature Rev. Genet.* **3**, 43-52 (2002).

288. Mei, R. *et al.* Genome-wide detection of allelic imbalance using human SNPs and high-density DNA arrays. *Genome Res.* **10**, 1126-1137 (2000).

289. Lindblad-Toh, K. *et al.* Loss-of-heterozygosity analysis of small-cell lung carcinomas using single-nucleotide polymorphism arrays. *Nature Biotechnol.* **18**, 1001-1005 (2000).

290. Heiskanen, M. *et al.* CGH, cDNA and tissue microarray analyses implicate FGFR2 amplification in a small subset of breast tumors. *Anal. Cell Pathol.* **22**, 229-234 (2001).

291. Cai, W. W. *et al.* Genome-wide detection of chromosomal imbalances in tumors using BAC microarrays. *Nature Biotechnol.* **20**, 393-396 (2002).

292. Davies, H. *et al.* Mutations of the *BRAF* gene in human cancer. *Nature* **417**, 949-954 (2002).

296. Janne, P. A. *et al.* Functional overlap between murine Inpp5b and Ocrl1 may explain why deficiency of the murine ortholog for OCRL1 does not cause Lowe syndrome in mice. *J. Clin. Invest.* **101**, 2042-2053 (1998).

328. Schwartz, S. *et al.* Human-mouse alignments with Blastz. *Genome Res.* (in the press).

157

330. Roskin, K. M. Score Functions for Assessing Conservation in Locally Aligned Regions of DNA from Two Species. UCSC Tech Report UCSC-CRL-02-30, School of Engineering, Univ. California (2002).

Supplementary Information accompanies the paper on *Nature*'s website (http://www. nature. com/nature).

Acknowledgements. We thank J. Takahashi and M. Johnston for comments on the manuscript; the Mouse Liaison Group for strategic advice; L. Gaffney, D. Leja and K.-S. Toh for graphical help; B. Graham and G. Roberts for administrative work on sequencing of individual mouse BACs; and P. Kassos and M. McMurtry for secretarial assistance. We thank D. Hill and L. Corbani of the Mouse Genome Informatics Group for their contributions to the GO analysis for mouse and human, and the members of the Bork group at EMBL for discussions. Funding was provided by the National Institutes of Health (National Human Genome Research Institute, National Cancer Institute, National Institute of Dental and Craniofacial Research, National Institute of Diabetes and Digestive and Kidney Diseases, National Institute of General Medical Sciences, National Eye Institute, National Institute of Environmental Health Sciences, National Institute of Aging, National Institute of Arthritis and Musculoskeletal and Skin Diseases, National Institute on Deafness and Other Communication Disorders, National Institute of Mental Health, National Institute on Drug Abuse, National Center for Research Resources, the National Heart Lung and Blood Institute and The Fogarty International Center); the Wellcome Trust; the Howard Hughes Medical Institute; the United States Department of Energy; the National Science Foundation; the Medical Research Council; NSERC; BMBF (German Ministry for Research and Education); the European Molecular Biology Laboratory; Plan Nacional de I+D and Instituto Carlos III; Swiss National Science Foundation, NCCR Frontiers in Genetics, the Swiss Cancer League and the "Childcare" and "J. Lejeune" Foundations; and the Ministry of Education, Culture, Sports, Science and Technology of Japan. The initial threefold sequence coverage was partly supported by the Mouse Sequencing Consortium (GlaxoSmithKline, Merck and Affymetrix) through the Foundation for the National Institutes of Health. We acknowledge A. Holden for coordinating the Mouse Sequencing Consortium. We thank the Sanger Institute systems group for maintenance and provision of the computer resource. The MGSC also used Hewlett-Packard Company's BioCluster, a configuration of 27 HP AlphaServer ES40 systems with 100 CPUs and 1 terabyte of storage. The BioCluster is housed in Hewlett-Packard's IQ Solutions Center, and was accessed remotely. The computing resource greatly accelerated the analysis.

Competing interests statement. The authors declare that they have no competing financial interests.

Correspondence and requests for materials should be addressed to R.H.W. (e-mail: waterston@gs.washington.edu), K.L.T. (e-mail: kersli@genome.wi.mit.edu) or E.S.L. (e-mail: lander@genome.wi.mit.edu).

Authors' contributions. The following authors contributed to project leadership: R. H. Waterston, K. Lindblad-Toh, E. Birney, J. Rogers, M. R. Brent, F. S. Collins, R. Guigó, R. C. Hardison, D. Haussler, D. B. Jaffe, W. J. Kent, W. Miller, C. P. Ponting, A. Smit, M. C. Zody and E. S. Lander.

Detection of Polarization in the Cosmic Microwave Background Using DASI

J. M. Kovac *et al.*

Editor's Note

The characterization of the ripples in the cosmic microwave background radiation, the "afterglow" of the Big Bang, led to quite accurate determination of various cosmological parameters, such as the density of matter and energy, and the speed of expansion. The very success of the standard cosmological model that emerged prompted researchers to look for independent ways of testing it. The model makes very specific predictions about how the microwave background with be polarized (that is, how the oscillating electromagnetic fields of the microwave photons will be aligned). Here John Kovac and coworkers used a telescope at the South Pole to observe this polarization, and confirm that it is just as predicted.

The past several years have seen the emergence of a standard cosmological model, in which small temperature differences in the cosmic microwave background (CMB) radiation on angular scales of the order of a degree are understood to arise from acoustic oscillations in the hot plasma of the early Universe, arising from primordial density fluctuations. Within the context of this model, recent measurements of the temperature fluctuations have led to profound conclusions about the origin, evolution and composition of the Universe. Using the measured temperature fluctuations, the theoretical framework predicts the level of polarization of the CMB with essentially no free parameters. Therefore, a measurement of the polarization is a critical test of the theory and thus of the validity of the cosmological parameters derived from the CMB measurements. Here we report the detection of polarization of the CMB with the Degree Angular Scale Interferometer (DASI). The polarization is deteced with high confidence, and its level and spatial distribution are in excellent agreement with the predictions of the standard theory.

THE CMB radiation provides a pristine probe of the Universe roughly 14 billion years ago, when the seeds of the complex structures that characterize the Universe today existed only as small density fluctuations in the primordial plasma. As the physics of such a plasma is well understood, detailed measurements of the CMB can provide critical tests of cosmological models and can determine the values of cosmological parameters with high precision. The CMB has accordingly been the focus of intense experimental and theoretical investigations since its discovery nearly 40 years ago[1]. The frequency spectrum of the CMB was well determined by the COBE FIRAS instrument[2,3]. The initial detection of temperature anisotropy was made on large angular scales by the COBE DMR

利用 DASI 探测宇宙微波背景的偏振

科瓦奇等

编者按

宇宙微波背景辐射中的连漪特征，又被称为宇宙大爆炸的"余辉"。我们可以非常准确地通过它来测定各种宇宙学参数，例如物质和能量的密度，以及膨胀速度等。标准宇宙学模型的成功进一步促使研究人员去寻找独立检测它的方法。该模型对微波背景如何被偏振（即微波光子产生的振荡电磁场如何排列）进行了非常具体的预测。约翰·科瓦奇及其同事在南极使用望远镜观测了这种偏振，并且确认观测结果与预测一致。

在过去几年已经出现了的标准宇宙学模型中，宇宙微波背景（CMB）辐射在一定的度角尺度上的小温差被理解为是由早期宇宙中热等离子体的声学振荡引起的，而后者又来源于原初密度扰动。最近在该模型下对温度扰动的测量导出了关于宇宙起源、演化和组成的深刻结论。仅仅利用温度扰动的测量，理论框架对预测 CMB 的偏振水平基本上没有自由参数可言。因此，偏振的测量是理论以及从 CMB 测量得到的宇宙学参数的有效性的重要检验。本文中，我们将报道用度角尺度干涉仪（DASI）检测 CMB 所得的探测结果。偏振的检测置信度很高，其水平和空间分布与标准理论的预测非常一致。

CMB 辐射可以作为约 140 亿年前宇宙状态的原始探测仪。现今宇宙复杂结构的种子在当时仅存在于原初等离子体的微小密度扰动中。由于人们已经很好地理解了这种等离子体的物理特性，所以对 CMB 更细节性地测量可以提供宇宙学模型的关键检测，并且可以高精度地确定宇宙学参数的值。自发现至今的将近 40 年时间里，CMB 一直是大量实验和理论研究关注的焦点[1]。CMB 的频谱由宇宙背景探测器（COBE）远红外绝对分光光度计（FIRAS）很好地确定[2,3]。通过 COBE 较差微波辐射计（DMR）[4]，研究人员在大角度尺度上进行了温度各向异性的初始检测，而最近

instrument[4] and recently there has been considerable progress in measuring the anisotropy on finer angular scales[5-10].

In the now standard cosmological model (see, for example, ref. 11), the shape of the CMB angular power spectrum directly traces acoustic oscillations of the photon-baryon fluid in the early Universe. As the Universe expanded, it cooled; after roughly 400,000 years, the intensity of the radiation field was no longer sufficient to keep the Universe ionized, and the CMB photons decoupled from the baryons as the first atoms formed. Acoustic oscillations passing through extrema at this epoch are observed in the CMB angular power spectrum as a harmonic series of peaks. Polarization is also a generic feature of these oscillations[12-18], and thus provides a model-independent test of the theoretical framework[19-21]. In addition, detection of polarization can in principle triple the number of observed CMB quantities, enhancing our ability to constrain cosmological parameters.

CMB polarization arises from Thompson scattering by electrons of a radiation field with a local quadrupole moment[22]. In the primordial plasma, the local quadrupole moment is suppressed until decoupling, when the photon mean free path begins to grow. At this time, the largest contribution to the local quadrupole is due to Doppler shifts induced by the velocity field of the plasma[23]. CMB polarization thus directly probes the dynamics at the epoch of decoupling. For a spatial Fourier mode of the acoustic oscillations, the velocities are perpendicular to the wavefronts, leading only to perpendicular or parallel alignment of the resulting polarization, which we define as positive and negative respectively. We refer to these polarization modes as scalar E-modes in analogy with electric fields; they have no curl component. Because the level of the polarization depends on velocity, we expect that the peaks in the scalar E-mode power spectrum correspond to density modes that are at their highest velocities at decoupling and are thus at minimum amplitude. The location of the harmonic peaks in the scalar E-mode power spectrum is therefore expected to be out of phase with the peaks in the temperature (T) spectrum[15-17].

In light of the above discussion, it is clear that the CMB temperature and polarization anisotropy should be correlated at some level[24]. For a given multipole, the sign of the TE correlation should depend on whether the amplitude of the density mode was increasing or decreasing at the time of decoupling. We therefore expect a change in the sign of the TE correlation at maxima in the T and the E power spectra, which correspond to modes at maximum and minimum amplitude, respectively. The TE correlation therefore offers a unique and powerful test of the underlying theoretical framework.

Primordial gravity waves will lead to polarization in the CMB[14,25] with an E-mode pattern as for the scalar density perturbations, but will also lead to a curl component, referred to as B-mode polarization[26-28]. The B-mode component is due to the intrinsic polarization of the gravity waves. In inflationary models, the level of the B-mode polarization from gravity waves is set by the fourth power of the inflationary energy scale. While the detection of B-mode polarization would provide a critical test of inflation, the signal is likely to be very weak and may have an amplitude that is effectively unobservable[29]. Furthermore, distortions

在更精细的角度尺度上测量各向异性的工作也已经取得了相当大的进展 [5-10]。

在现代标准的宇宙学模型中（如参考文献 11），CMB 角功率谱的形状可以直接追踪到早期宇宙中光子-重子流体的声学振荡。随着宇宙的扩张，它冷却了下来；大约在此 40 万年后，辐射场的强度已经不足以使宇宙保持电离状态，从而在第一个原子形成的同时，CMB 光子与重子退耦。声学振荡在这个时期达到了极值，并在 CMB 角功率谱中的一系列简谐波峰被观察到。偏振也是这些振荡 [12-18] 的普遍特征，因而为理论框架 [19-21] 提供了与模型无关的检测。此外，偏振的探测原则上可以使观察到的 CMB 数量增加到原来的三倍，从而也增强了我们约束宇宙学参数的能力。

CMB 偏振是由具有局部四极矩的辐射场中电子的汤普森散射产生的 [22]。在原始等离子体中，当光子平均自由程开始增加时，局部四极矩被抑制直到退耦。此时，对局部四极矩贡献最大的是由等离子体的速度场引起的多普勒频移 [23]。因此，CMB 偏振将直接探测到退耦时期的动力学过程。对于声学振荡的空间傅里叶模式，速度垂直于波阵面，导致所得偏振按垂直或平行方向排列，我们将其分别定义为正向和负向。这些偏振模式称为标量 E 模式，类似于电场；它们是无旋的。因为偏振水平取决于速度，我们期望标量 E 模式功率谱中的峰值对应于退耦时处于其最高速度的密度模式，也就是处于最小的幅度之时。因此可以预期标量 E 模式功率谱中的谐波峰值的位置与温度 (T) 频谱中的峰值异相 [15-17]。

鉴于上述讨论，很明显可以看出 CMB 温度和偏振的各向异性应该在某种程度上相关联 [24]。对于给定的多极矩，TE 关联的迹象应当取决于退耦时的密度幅度是增加还是减小。所以我们期望 TE 关联中 T 和 E 功率谱中最大值处的变化，分别对应于最大和最小幅度的模式。因此，TE 相关性为基础理论框架提供了独特而强大的检测手段。

原初引力波将导致 CMB 中具有与标量密度扰动有关的 E 模式的偏振 [14,25]，但也将产生一个旋度分量，称为 B 模式偏振 [26-28]。B 模式分量源于引力波的内禀偏振。在暴胀模型中，来自引力波的 B 模式偏振的水平由暴胀能量标度的四次幂决定。虽然 B 模式偏振的探测将为暴胀提供关键的检测，但是其信号可能非常微弱，而且事实上其幅度可能无法有效观测 [29]。此外，宇宙大尺度结构引力透镜的干预对标量 E

to the scalar E-mode polarization by the gravitational lensing of the intervening large scale structure in the Universe will lead to a contaminating B-mode polarization signal which will severely complicate the extraction of the polarization signature from gravity waves[30-33]. The possibility, however, of directly probing the Universe at energy scales of order 10^{16} GeV by measuring the gravity-wave induced polarization (see, for example, ref. 34) is a compelling goal for CMB polarization observations.

Prior to the results presented in this paper, only upper limits have been placed on the level of CMB polarization. This is due to the low level of the expected signal, demanding sensitive instruments and careful attention to sources of systematic uncertainty (see ref. 35 for a review of CMB polarization measurements).

The first limit to the degree of polarization of the CMB was set in 1965 by Penzias and Wilson, who stated that the new radiation that they had discovered was isotropic and unpolarized within the limits of their observations[1]. Over the next 20 years, dedicated polarimeters were used to set much more stringent upper limits on angular scales of order several degrees and larger[36-41]. The current best upper limits for the E-mode and B-mode polarizations on large angular scales are 10 μK at 95% confidence for the multipole range $2 \leqslant l \leqslant 20$, set by the POLAR experiment[42].

On angular scales of the order of one degree, an analysis of data from the Saskatoon experiment[43] set the first upper limit (25 μK at 95% confidence for $l \approx 75$); this limit is also noteworthy in that it was the first limit that was lower than the level of the CMB temperature anisotropy. The current best limit on similar angular scales was set by the PIQUE experiment[44]—a 95% confidence upper limit of 8.4 μK to the E-mode signal, assuming no B-mode polarization. A preliminary analysis of cosmic background imager (CBI) data[45] indicates an upper limit similar to the PIQUE result, but on somewhat smaller scales. An attempt was also made to search for the TE correlation using the PIQUE polarization and Saskatoon temperature data[46].

Polarization measurements have also been pursued on much finer angular scales (of the order of an arcminute), resulting in several upper limits (for example, refs 47 and 48). However, at these angular scales, corresponding to multipoles of about 5,000, the level of the primary CMB anisotropy is strongly damped and secondary effects due to interactions with large-scale structure in the Universe are expected to dominate[11].

In this paper, we report the detection of polarized anisotropy in the CMB radiation with the Degree Angular Scale Interferometer (DASI) located at the National Science Foundation (NSF) Amundsen–Scott South Pole research station. The polarization data were obtained during the 2001 and 2002 austral winter seasons. DASI was previously used to measure the temperature anisotropy from $140 < l < 900$, during the 2000 season. We presented details of the instrument, the measured power spectrum and the resulting cosmological constraints in a series of three papers: refs 49, 6 and 50. Prior to the start of the 2001 season, DASI was modified to allow polarization measurements in all four Stokes parameters over the same

模式偏振的扭曲将导致 B 模式偏振信号的污染，这将严重地使引力波 [30-33] 的偏振特征的提取复杂化。然而，探索能否通过测量引力波引起的偏振（如参考文献 34），进而在 10^{16} GeV 的能量尺度上直接探测宇宙，仍然是 CMB 偏振观测的一个引人入胜的目标。

在本文得出的结果之前，只有关于 CMB 偏振水平上限的报道。这是由于预期信号的水平较低，需要敏锐的仪器并仔细地留意系统不确定性的来源（参考文献 35 给出了有关 CMB 偏振测量的文献综述）。

CMB 偏振程度的第一个极限是由彭齐亚斯和威耳孙在 1965 年确定的，他们阐明其发现的新辐射在观察极限内是各向同性和非偏振的 [1]。在接下来的 20 年中，人们借助专用的起偏器以确定更严格的上限，其角度的量级为几度或者更大 [36-41]。对于多极矩而言，在 $2 \leq l \leq 20$ 的范围中，当前大角度范围内 E 模式和 B 模式偏振的最佳上限为 10 μK，由 POLAR 实验 [42] 给出。

在 1 度量级的角度尺度上，来自萨斯卡通实验的数据分析 [43] 确定了第一个上限（25 μK，置信度为 95%，$l \approx 75$）；这个极限也是值得注意的，因为它是第一个低于 CMB 温度各向异性水平的限制。假设没有 B 模式偏振，当前最佳的情况是由设置了相类似角度标度的 PIQUE 实验 [44] 给出的——E 模式信号上限为 8.4 μK，置信度为 95%。宇宙背景成像仪（CBI）数据 [45] 的初步分析显示了一个类似于 PIQUE 结果的上限，但是在稍微小的尺度上给出的。另外一个尝试是使用 PIQUE 偏振和萨斯卡通温度数据 [46] 研究 TE 相关性。

偏振测量也在更精细的角度范围（1 角分量级）内进行，研究人员已经得到了几个上限（如参考文献 47 和 48）。然而，在这些角度尺度上，对应于大约 5,000 的多极矩，主要的 CMB 各向异性效果被强烈阻尼掉，并且预计与宇宙中的大尺度结构相互作用而产生的次级效应会占主导地位 [11]。

在本文中，我们报告了使用位于美国国家科学基金会（NSF）阿蒙森–斯科特南极研究站的度角尺度干涉仪（DASI）检测到的 CMB 辐射中的偏振各向异性。偏振数据是在 2001 年和 2002 年南半球冬季获得的。DASI 前期用于测量 2000 年观测季中 $140 < l < 900$ 的温度各向异性。我们在三篇系列文章（参考文献 49、6 和 50）中提供了仪器的详细信息、测量的功率谱和由此产生的宇宙学约束。在 2001 观测季开始之前，DASI 被调整为可以在所有四个斯托克斯参数下进行偏振观测，其中 l 的取值范

l range as the previous measurements. The modifications to the instrument, observational strategy, data calibration and data reduction are discussed in detail in a companion paper in this issue[51].

The measurements reported here were obtained within two 3.4° full-width at half-maximum (FWHM) fields separated by 1 h in right ascension. The fields were selected from the subset of fields observed with DASI in 2000 in which no point sources were detected, and are located in regions of low Galactic synchrotron and dust emission. The temperature angular power spectrum is found to be consistent with previous measurements and its measured frequency spectral index is −0.01 (−0.16 to 0.14 at 68% confidence), where 0 corresponds to a 2.73 K Planck spectrum. Polarization of the CMB is detected at high confidence ($\geqslant 4.9\sigma$) and its power spectrum is consistent with theoretical predictions, based on the interpretation of CMB anisotropy as arising from primordial scalar adiabatic fluctuations. Specifically, assuming a shape for the power spectrum consistent with previous temperature measurements, the level found for the E-mode polarization is 0.80 (0.56 to 1.10 at 68% confidence interval), where the predicted level given previous temperature data is 0.9 to 1.1. At 95% confidence, an upper limit of 0.59 is set to the level of B-mode polarization parameterized with the same shape and normalization as the E-mode spectrum. The TE correlation of the temperature and E-mode polarization is detected at 95% confidence and is also found to be consistent with predictions.

With these results contemporary cosmology has passed a long anticipated and crucial test. If the test had not been passed, the underpinnings of much of what we think we know about the origin and early history of the Universe would have been cast into doubt.

Measuring Polarization with DASI

DASI is a compact interferometric array optimized for the measurement of CMB temperature and polarization anisotropy[49,51]. Because they directly sample Fourier components of the sky, interferometers are well suited to measurements of the CMB angular power spectrum. In addition, an interferometer gathers instantaneous two-dimensional information while inherently rejecting large-scale gradients in atmospheric emission. For observations of CMB polarization, interferometers offer several additional features. They can be constructed with small and stable instrumental polarization. Furthermore, linear combinations of the data can be used to construct quantities with essentially pure E- and B-mode polarization response patterns on a variety of scales. This property of the data greatly facilitates the analysis and interpretation of the observed polarization in the context of cosmological models.

DASI is designed to exploit these advantages in the course of extremely long integrations on selected fields of sky. The 13 horn/lens antennas that comprise the DASI array are compact, axially symmetric, and sealed from the environment, yielding small and extremely stable instrumental polarization. Additional systematic control comes from multiple levels of phase

围与之前的研究相同。另一篇与本文一并发表的文章详细讨论了我们在仪器、观测策略、数据校准和数据归算方面的修改 [51]。

本文报告的测量结果是在两个视场获得的，二者具有 3.4°半高宽（FWHM），赤经上间隔 1 小时。这些视场是从 2000 年利用 DASI 观测到的视场的子集中选出的。在这之中没有检测到点源，且位于银河系同步辐射和尘埃辐射较低的区域。温度角功率谱与先前的测量值一致，并且其测量的频率谱指数为 −0.01（置信度为 68% 的参数区间为 −0.16 至 0.14），其中 0 对应 2.73 K 的普朗克谱。基于对原始标量绝热扰动引起的 CMB 各向异性的解释，探测到的 CMB 的偏振具有很高的可信度（ ≥ 4.9σ），并且其功率谱与理论预测一致。具体来讲，假设功率谱的形状与先前的温度测量一致，针对 E 模式的偏振水平为 0.80（置信度为 68% 的参数区间为 0.56 至 1.10），若温度数据为先前给定的数据，预测水平将为 0.9 至 1.1。在 95% 置信度下，与 E 模式谱有着相同的形状和归一化的 B 模式偏振参数化水平的上限被限定为 0.59。温度与 E 模式偏振的 TE 相关性以 95% 置信度被探测到，并且发现与预测一致。

包含这些结果在内，当代宇宙学已经通过了长期的预测和关键的检验。如果没有通过这些检验，那么我们对于宇宙的起源及其早期历史的认知基础恐怕就要动摇了。

用 DASI 测量偏振

DASI 是一款紧凑型干涉测量阵列，是专为测量 CMB 温度和偏振各向异性而优化的 [49,51]。因为它们直接采样天空的傅里叶分量，所以干涉仪非常适合测量 CMB 角功率谱。而且干涉仪会收集瞬时二维信息，同时本身还具有排除大气辐射中大尺度梯度的特性。对于 CMB 偏振的观察，干涉仪提供了几个附加功能。观测数据可以用微小且稳定的仪器偏振构造出来。此外，数据的线性组合可用于在各种尺度上构建具有基本上纯的 E 和 B 模式的偏振响应模式。数据的这种性质极大地方便了在宇宙学模型下分析和解释观察到的偏振。

DASI 旨在利用这些优势，在选定的天空视场进行极长的累积观测。构成 DASI 阵列的 13 个喇叭/透镜天线结构紧凑、轴对称、与环境隔离且密封，产生的仪器偏振非常小而极其稳定。额外的系统化的控制来自多级相位切换和视场作差，目的是

switching and field differencing designed to remove instrumental offsets. The DASI mount is fully steerable in elevation and azimuth with the additional ability to rotate the entire horn array about the faceplate axis. The flexibility of this mount allows us to track any field visible from the South Pole continuously at constant elevation angle, and to observe it in redundant faceplate orientations which allow sensitive tests for residual systematic effects.

Instrumental response and calibration

Each of DASI's 13 receivers may be set to admit either left or right circular polarization. An interferometer measures the correlations between the signals from pairs of receivers, called visibilities; as indicated by equation (4) in the "Theory covariance matrix" subsection recovery of the full complement of Stokes parameters requires the correlation of all four pairwise combinations of left and right circular polarization states (RR, LL, RL and LR), which we refer to as Stokes states. The co-polar states (RR, LL) are sensitive to the total intensity, while the cross-polar states (RL, LR) measure linear combinations of the Stokes parameters Q and U.

Each of DASI's analogue correlator channels can accommodate only a single Stokes state, so measurement of the four combinations is achieved via time-multiplexing. The polarizer for each receiver is switched on a 1-h Walsh cycle, with the result that over the full period of the cycle, every pair of receivers spends an equal amount of time in all four Stokes states.

In ref. 51, we detail the calibration of the polarized visibilities for an interferometer. In order to produce the calibrated visibilities as defined in equation (4) below, a complex gain factor which depends on the Stokes state must be applied to each raw visibility. Although the cross-polar gain factors could easily be determined with observations of a bright polarized source, no suitable sources are available, and we therefore derive the full calibration through observations of an unpolarized source. The gains for a given pair of receivers (a baseline) can be decomposed into antenna-based factors, allowing us to construct the cross-polar gains from the antenna-based gain factors derived from the co-polar visibilities. DASI's calibration is based on daily observations of the bright H_{II} region RCW38, which we described at length in ref. 49. We can determine the individual baseline gains for all Stokes states with statistical uncertainties < 2% for each daily observation. Systematic gain uncertainties for the complete data set are discussed in the "Systematic uncertainties" section.

The procedure for deriving the baseline gains from antenna-based terms leaves the cross-polar visibilities multiplied by an undetermined overall phase offset (independent of baseline). This phase offset effectively mixes Q and U, and must be measured to obtain a clean separation of CMB power into E- and B-modes. Calibration of the phase offset requires a source whose polarization angle is known, and we create one by observing RCW38 through polarizing wire grids attached to DASI's 13 receivers. From the wire-grid observations, we can derive the phase offset in each frequency band with an uncertainty of $\lesssim 0.4°$.

消除仪器错位。DASI 承载底座在高度和方位角上具有完全可操纵性，并且能够围绕面板对整个喇叭阵列进行轴旋转。这种承载架的灵活性使我们能够以恒定的仰角连续追踪来自南极的任何可见的视场，并以其他冗余的面板方向观察它，从而可以对剩余的系统效应进行灵敏性检测。

仪器响应和校准

DASI 的 13 个接收器中的每一个都允许被设置为左或右圆偏振。干涉仪测量的是来自成对的接收器信号之间的相关，称为可视性；如本文"理论协方差矩阵"部分中的等式 (4) 所示，斯托克斯参数的完整获得要求左右圆偏振状态 (RR、LL、RL 和 LR) 的所有四个成对组合相关，我们称之为斯托克斯状态。共极态 (RR、LL) 对总强度敏感，而交叉极态 (RL、LR) 可以测量斯托克斯参数 Q 和 U 的线性组合。

每个 DASI 的模拟相关器通道只能容纳单个斯托克斯状态，因此通过时分多路复用实现四种状态组合的测量。每个接收器的起偏器接通 1 小时沃尔什周期，最终使得在整个周期内，每对接收器在所有的四个斯托克斯状态下花费相等的时间。

在参考文献 51 中，我们详细说明了干涉仪偏振可视性的校准。为了产生如下文的等式 (4) 中定义的校准可视性，必须将依赖于斯托克斯状态的复增益因子应用在每个初始可视性上。尽管通过观察明亮的偏振源可以很容易地确定交叉偏振增益因子，但是没有合适的源可用，因此我们通过观察非偏振源得到完全的校准。一对给定的接收器 (即一条基线) 的增益可以分解为多个天线增益因子，这允许我们从来自共极可视性的天线增益因子来导出交叉偏振增益。DASI 的校准基于每天对 RCW38 的 H_{II} 区域的观测，我们在参考文献 [49] 中对其进行了详细的描述。我们可以确定所有斯托克斯状态的单个基线增益，每日观察的系统不确定性 <2%。"系统不确定性"部分讨论了完整数据集的系统增益不确定性。

从基于天线的项获得基线增益的过程中剩下了交叉偏振可视性乘以未确定的总相位偏移 (与基线无关)。该相位偏移有效地混合 Q 和 U，并且必须进行测量才能获得从 CMB 功率到 E 模式和 B 模式的无污染的分离。相位偏移的校准需要一个偏振角度已知的光源，我们通过观测 DASI 的 13 个接收器附属的偏振丝栅 RCW38 来创建一个这样的光源。根据丝栅观测，我们可以推导出每个频带的相位偏移，不确定度 ≤0.4°。

As an independent check of this phase offset calibration, the Moon was observed at several epochs during 2001–02. Although the expected amplitude of the polarized signal from the Moon is not well known at these frequencies, the polarization pattern is expected to be radial to high accuracy, and this can be used to determine the cross-polar phase offset independently of the wire grid observations. We show in ref. 51 that these two determinations of the phase offset are in excellent agreement.

On-axis leakage

For ideal polarizers, the cross-polar visibilities are strictly proportional to linear combinations of the Stokes parameters Q and U. For realistic polarizers, however, imperfect rejection of the unwanted polarization state leads to additional terms in the cross-polar visibilities proportional to the total intensity I. These leakage terms are the sum of the complex leakage of the two antennas which form each baseline. During the 2000–01 austral summer, DASI's 13 receivers were retrofitted with multi-element broadband circular polarizers designed to reject the unwanted polarization state to high precision across DASI's 26–36 GHz frequency band. Before installation on the telescope, the polarizers were tuned to minimize these leakages.

At several epochs during 2001–02, the antenna-based leakages were determined with a fractional error of 0.3% from deep observations of the calibrator source RCW38. We show in ref. 51 that antenna-based leakages are $\lesssim 1\%$ (of I) at all frequency bands except the highest, for which they approach 2%; this performance is close to the theoretical minimum for our polarizer design. Comparison of the measurements from three epochs separated by many months indicates that the leakages are stable with time.

Given the low level of DASI's leakages, the mixing of power from temperature into polarization in the uncorrected visibilities is expected to be a minor effect at most (see the "Systematic uncertainties" section). Nonetheless, in the analysis presented in this paper, the cross-polar data have in all cases been corrected to remove this effect using the leakages determined from RCW38.

Off-axis leakage

In addition to on-axis leakage from the polarizers, the feeds will contribute an instrumental polarization that varies across the primary beam. Offset measurements of RCW38 and the Moon indicate that the off-axis instrumental polarization pattern is radial, rising from zero at the beam centre to a maximum of about 0.7% near 3°, and then tapering to zero (see also ref. 51).

With the on-axis polarizer leakage subtracted to $\lesssim 0.3\%$ (see above), this residual leakage, while still quite small compared to the expected level of polarized CMB signal (again,

作为这种相位偏移校准的独立检查，在 2001 年 ~ 2002 年期间的几个时期将月球作为观测对象。虽然在这些频率下，来自月球的偏振信号的预期幅度并不十分清楚，但在高精度下预计的偏振模式是发散状的，这可以用来独立地确定丝栅观测的交叉偏振相位偏移。我们在参考文献 51 中表明这两个相位偏移的测定非常一致。

共轴渗漏

对于理想的起偏器，交叉偏振可视性严格正比于斯托克斯参数 Q 和 U 的线性组合。然而，对于真实的起偏器，不需要的偏振态的不完全抑制导致交叉偏振可视性中的附加项与总强度 I 成正比。这些渗漏项是从每个基线形成的两个天线的复合渗漏的总和。在 2000 年 ~ 2001 年南半球夏季期间，研究人员采用多元宽带圆形起偏器更新改造了 DASI 的 13 个接收器，这是为了使通过 DASI 的 26 GHz ~ 36 GHz 频带在高精度时抑制不必要的偏振态。在安装到望远镜上之前，起偏器被调整到最大限度地减少这些渗漏的状态。

在 2001 年 ~ 2002 年间的几个时期内，通过对校准器源 RCW38 的深度观察，天线基线的渗漏被确定会导致 0.3% 的相对误差。参考文献 51 显示天线基线的渗漏在除最高频段之外的所有频段都 $\leqslant 1\%(I)$，而最高频段接近 2%；这种性能接近我们起偏器设计的理论最小值。通过三个时期的测量值（时期之间相隔数个月）的比较，表明渗漏随时间推移是稳定的。

鉴于 DASI 渗漏水平较低，预计未校正的可视性中，从温度到极化的功率混合最多也只是产生次要的影响（见"系统不确定性"部分）。尽管如此，在本文提出的分析方案中，所有情况下都使用 RCW38 确定的渗漏来纠正交叉极化数据，从而消除上述影响。

离轴渗漏

除了来自起偏器的共轴渗漏之外，反馈将导致仪器偏振，这个偏振在横穿初级光束的过程中不断变化。RCW38 和月球的偏移测量表明，离轴仪器偏振模式是径向的，光束中心为 0，在接近 3° 时上升到最大值 0.7%，然后逐渐减小到 0（参考文献 51）。

随着共轴起偏器的渗漏减去 $\leqslant 0.3\%$（见上文）的值，这种残余的渗漏虽然与偏振 CMB 信号的预期水平相比仍然非常小（见"系统不确定性"部分），但却是仪器贡献

see the "Systematic uncertainties" section), is the dominant instrumental contribution. Although the visibilities cannot be individually corrected to remove this effect (as for the on-axis leakage), it may be incorporated in the analysis of the CMB data. Using fits to the offset data (see ref. 51 for details), we account for this effect by modelling the contribution of the off-axis leakage to the signal covariance matrix as described in the "Theory covariance matrix" subsection.

CMB Observations and Data Reduction

Observations

For the observations presented here, two fields separated by 1 h of right ascension, at RA = 23 h 30 min and RA = 00 h 30 min with declination −55°, were tracked continuously. The telescope alternated between the fields every hour, tracking them over precisely the same azimuth range so that any terrestrial signal can be removed by differencing. Each 24-h period included 20 h of CMB observations and 2.3 h of bracketing calibrator observations, with the remaining time spent on skydips and miscellaneous calibration tasks.

The fields were selected from the 32 fields previously observed by DASI for the absence of any detectable point sources (see ref. 49). The locations of the 32 fields were originally selected to lie at high elevation angle and to coincide with low emission in the IRAS 100 μm and 408 MHz maps of the sky[52].

The data presented in this paper were acquired from 10 April to 27 October 2001, and again from 14 February to 11 July 2002. In all, we obtained 162 days of data in 2001, and 109 days in 2002, for a total of 271 days before the cuts described in the next section.

Data cuts

Observations are excluded from the analysis, or cut, if they are considered suspect owing to hardware problems, inadequate calibration, contamination from Moon or Sun signal, poor weather or similar effects. In the "Data consistency and χ^2 tests" section, we describe consistency statistics that are much more sensitive to these effects than are the actual results of our likelihood analysis, allowing us to be certain that the final results are unaffected by contamination. Here we briefly summarize the principal categories of data cuts; we describe each cut in detail in ref. 51.

In the first category of cuts, we reject visibilities for which monitoring data from the telescope indicate obvious hardware malfunction, or simply non-ideal conditions. These include cryogenics failure, loss of tuning for a receiver, large offsets between real/imaginary multipliers in the correlators, and mechanical glitches in the polarizer stepper motors. All data are rejected for a correlator when it shows evidence for large offsets, or excessive noise.

的主要成分。虽然可视性不能通过独立地校正以消除这种影响（对于共轴渗漏），但它却可能包含在 CMB 数据的分析中。使用拟合偏移数据（参考文献 51），我们通过模拟离轴渗漏对信号协方差矩阵的贡献来解释这种影响，如"理论协方差矩阵"部分所述。

CMB 观测和数据归算

观测

这里呈现的观测是在赤经为 23 h 30 min 和 00 h 30 min，赤纬为 -55° 的位置上，对赤经相隔一个小时的两个视场连续追踪所获得的。望远镜每小时在各个视场之间交替观测，在精确相同的方位角上追踪它们，以便通过作差去除所有地面信号。每个 24 小时周期包括 20 小时的 CMB 观察和 2.3 小时的托架校准器观察，剩余的时间用于天空倾角校准和其他校准任务。

这些视场是从 DASI 先前观察到的 32 个视场中选择的，因为缺乏任何可检测的点源（参考文献 49）。这 32 个视场的位置最初被选择为处于高仰角并且与 IRAS 100 μm 和 408 MHz 天图中的低辐射一致的地方 [52]。

本文提供的数据是在 2001 年 4 月 10 日至 10 月 27 日以及 2002 年 2 月 14 日至 7 月 11 日分两次获得的。我们在 2001 年总共获得了 162 天的数据，在 2002 年获得了 109 天的数据，在下一节描述的数据舍弃之前，共计 271 天。

数据舍弃

如果观测结果被认为具有硬件问题、校准不充分、月亮或太阳信号污染、恶劣天气或其他类似的可疑影响，将被排除在分析之外，或者说被舍弃。在"数据一致性和 χ^2 检验"部分中我们指出，比较而言，一致性统计对于这些影响的敏感度要远高于获得这一统计量的似然分析的实际结果，这要求我们要能够确定最终结果不受污染的影响。在这里，我们简要总结一下数据舍弃的主要类别；在参考文献 51 中我们详细描述了每种数据的舍弃。

第一类舍弃的可视性是在具有明显的硬件故障的或仅仅是非理想条件下的望远镜的监测数据。其中包括低温失效、接收机失调、相关器中实/虚乘法器之间的大偏移，以及起偏器步进电机中的机械假信号。当显示有过大偏移或过大噪声的证据时，

An additional cut, and the only one based on the individual data values, is a $> 30\sigma$ outlier cut to reject rare ($\ll 0.1\%$ of the data) hardware glitches. Collectively, these cuts reject about 26% of the data.

In the next category, data are cut on the phase and amplitude stability of the calibrator observations. Naturally, we reject data for which bracketing calibrator observations have been lost due to previous cuts. These cuts reject about 5% of the data.

Cuts are also based on the elevation of the Sun and Moon. Co-polar data are cut whenever the Sun was above the horizon, and cross-polar data whenever the solar elevation exceeded 5°. These cuts reject 8% of the data.

An additional cut, which is demonstrably sensitive to poor weather, is based on the significance of data correlations as discussed in the "Noise model" subsection. An entire day is cut if the maximum off-diagonal correlation coefficient in the data correlation matrix exceeds 8σ significance, referred to gaussian uncorrelated noise. A total of 22 days are cut by this test in addition to those rejected by the solar and lunar cuts.

Reduction

Data reduction consists of a series of steps to calibrate and reduce the data set to a manageable size for the likelihood analysis. Phase and amplitude calibrations are applied to the data on the basis of the bracketing observations of our primary celestial calibrator, RCW38. The raw 8.4-s integrations are combined over each 1-h observation for each of 6,240 visibilities (78 complex baselines × 10 frequency bands × 4 Stokes states). In all cases, on-axis leakage corrections are applied to the data, and sequential 1-h observations of the two fields in the same 15° azimuth range are differenced to remove any common ground signal, using a normalization (field1−field2)/$\sqrt{2}$ that preserves the variance of the sky signal. Except in the case where the data set is split for use in the χ^2 consistency tests in the "χ^2 tests" subsection, observations from different faceplate rotation angles, epochs and azimuth ranges are all combined, as well as the two co-polar Stokes states, LL and RR. The resulting data set has $N \leqslant 4,680$ elements ($6,240 \times 3/4 = 4,680$, where the 3/4 results from the combination of LL and RR). We call this the uncompressed data set, and it contains all of the information in our observations of the differenced fields for Stokes parameters I, Q and U.

Data Consistency and χ^2 Tests

We begin our analysis by arranging the data into a vector, considered to be the sum of actual sky signal and instrumental noise: $\boldsymbol{\Delta} = \mathbf{s} + \mathbf{n}$. The noise vector $\mathbf{n}$ is hypothesized to be gaussian and random, with zero mean, so that the noise model is completely specified by a known covariance matrix $C_N \equiv \langle \mathbf{nn}' \rangle$. Any significant excess variance observed in the

该相关器所有数据都被拒绝。额外的数据舍弃，以及唯一一种基于数据值个体本身的舍弃是 > 30σ 的异常值，以拒绝罕见的（<< 0.1% 的数据）硬件假信号。总的来说，这些舍弃拒绝了大约 26% 的数据。

下一类数据舍弃的依据是校准器观察的相位和幅度稳定性。于是我们拒绝因先前数据舍弃导致托架校准器观察丢失的数据。这些削减拒绝了大约 5% 的数据。

数据也会因为太阳和月亮的升高带来的影响而被舍弃。每当太阳高于地平线时，同极数据都会被舍弃，而当太阳升高超过 5° 时，就会出现交叉偏振数据。这些舍弃拒绝了 8% 的数据。

另一个明显对恶劣天气敏感的舍弃，依据的是"噪声模型"部分对数据相关的显著性的讨论。如果数据相关矩阵中的最大非对角线相关系数的显著性超过 8σ，则视为高斯不相关噪声，全天的数据都将被舍弃。除了被太阳和月球影响而拒绝那些数据之外，该检测总共减少了 22 天的数据量。

归算

数据归算包括一系列步骤，用于校准数据集并将数据集压缩到可管理的大小以进行似然分析。根据我们的初级天体校准器 RCW38 的基础观测，相位和幅度校准将应用在数据上。原始的 8.4 s 集成结合了每小时观测中所有 6,240 种可视性（78 个复基线 ×10 个频带 ×4 个斯托克斯状态）。共轴渗漏校正被正应用于所有情况下的数据，两个视场在相同的 15° 方位角范围内的连续 1 h 观测值相减以消除任何常见的地面信号，并且使用（视场 1 − 视场 2）/√2 来归一化，从而保留天空信号的方差。除了在"χ^2 检验"部分对数据集进行分划以实现 χ^2 一致性检验的情况之外，来自不同的面盘旋转角度、时期和方位角范围的观测结果都被组合起来，同时被组合起来的还包括两个共极斯托克斯状态，LL 和 RR。得到的数据集具有 $N \leqslant 4{,}680$ 个元素（$6{,}240 \times 3/4 = 4{,}680$，其中 3/4 由 LL 和 RR 的组合产生）。我们将其称为未压缩数据集，它包含经过作差处理之后的视场斯托克斯参数 I、Q 和 U 的所有观测信息。

数据一致性和 χ^2 检验

我们通过将数据排列成一个矢量来开始分析，该矢量 Δ 被认为是实际天空信号和仪器噪声的总和：$\Delta = \mathbf{s} + \mathbf{n}$。噪声矢量 $\mathbf{n}$ 被假设为高斯的且随机的，具有零均值，因此噪声模型完全由已知的协方差矩阵 $C_N \equiv \langle \mathbf{nn}^t \rangle$ 确定。在数据矢量 Δ 中观察到的

data vector $\mathbf{\Delta}$ will be interpreted as signal. In the likelihood analysis of the next section, we characterize the total covariance of the data set $C = C_T(\kappa) + C_N$ in terms of parameters κ that specify the covariance C_T of this sky signal. This is the conventional approach to CMB data analysis, and it is clear that for it to succeed, the assumptions about the noise model and the accuracy of the noise covariance matrix must be thoroughly tested. This is especially true for our data set, for which long integrations have been used to reach unprecedented levels of sensitivity in an attempt to measure the very small signal covariances expected from the polarization of the CMB.

Noise model

The DASI instrument and observing strategy are designed to remove systematic errors through multiple levels of differencing. Slow and fast phase switching as well as field differencing is used to minimize potentially variable systematic offsets that could otherwise contribute a non-thermal component to the noise. The observing strategy also includes Walsh sequencing of the Stokes states, observations over multiple azimuth ranges and faceplate rotation angles, and repeated observations of the same visibilities on the sky throughout the observing run to allow checks for systematic offsets and verification that the sky signal is repeatable. We hypothesize that after the cuts described in the previous section, the noise in the remaining data is gaussian and white, with no noise correlations between different baselines, frequency bands, real/imaginary pairs, or Stokes states. We have carefully tested the noise properties of the data to validate the use of this model.

Noise variance in the combined data vector is estimated by calculating the variance in the 8.4-s integrations over the period of 1 h, before field differencing. To test that this noise estimate is accurate, we compare three different short-timescale noise estimates: calculated from the 8.4-s integrations over the 1-h observations before and after field differencing and from sequential pairs of 8.4-s integrations. We find that all three agree within 0.06% for co-polar data and 0.03% for cross-polar data, averaged over all visibilities after data cuts.

We also compare the noise estimates based on the short-timescale noise to the variance of the 1-h binned visibilities over the entire data set (up to 2,700 1-hour observations, over a period spanning 457 days). The ratio of long-timescale to short-timescale noise variance, averaged over all combined visibilities after data cuts, is 1.003 for the co-polar data and 1.005 for the cross-polar data, remarkably close to unity. Together with the results of the χ^2 consistency tests described in the "χ^2 tests" subsection, these results demonstrate that the noise is white and integrates down from timescales of a few seconds to thousands of hours. We find that scaling the diagonal noise by 1% makes a negligible difference in the reported likelihood results (see the "Systematic uncertainties" section).

To test for potential off-diagonal correlations in the noise, we calculate a $6{,}240 \times 6{,}240$ correlation coefficient matrix from the 8.4-s integrations for each day of observations. To increase our sensitivity to correlated noise, we use only data obtained simultaneously for

任何显著的方差超出将被解释为信号。在下一部分的似然分析中，我们依据确定该天空信号协方差 C_T 的参数 κ 来表征数据集的总协方差 $C = C_T(\kappa) + C_N$。这是 CMB 数据分析的传统方法，为了能成功实现，很显然必须彻底检测噪声模型的假设和噪声协方差矩阵的准确性。这对于我们的数据集尤甚，因而为了测量由 CMB 偏振产生的非常小的信号的协方差，我们使用长期积分来达到前所未有的灵敏度水平。

噪声模型

DASI 仪器和观测策略被设计为通过多级作差消除系统误差。慢速和快速相位切换以及视场作差被用于最小化潜在可变的系统偏移，否则可能增加噪声的非热分量。观测策略还包括斯托克斯状态的沃尔什测序，多个方位角范围和面盘旋转角度的观测，以及通过允许检查系统与对偏移与天空信号的检查是可重复的观测，进而实现在整个观测过程中对天空的相同可视性进行重复观测。我们假设在如前一节所描述的数据舍弃之后，剩余数据中的噪声是高斯的白噪声，不同基线、频带、实/虚对或斯托克斯状态之间没有噪声相关。我们仔细检测了数据的噪声属性，以验证该模型的实用性。

通过在视场作差之前 1 小时的时段内计算 8.4 s 积分的方差，组合而成的数据矢量中的噪声方差可以被估算出来。为了检测这种噪声估计是否准确，我们比较了三段不同的短时间尺度内的噪声估计：计算视场差前后 1 h 观测值的 8.4 s 积分以及 8.4 s 积分的连续对。我们发现三者在共极数据中均为 0.06%，在交叉偏振数据中为 0.03%，在数据舍弃后平均了所有可视性。

我们还将基于短时间尺度的噪声估计值与整个数据集中 1 小时分格可视性的方差进行比较（在时间跨度为 457 天的情况下，最多可得到 2,700 个 1 小时观测值）。数据舍弃后，所有组合可视性的长时间尺度与短时间尺度噪声方差的比率可以给出，其中共极数据为 1.003，而交叉偏振数据为 1.005，非常接近于 1。这与“χ^2 检验”部分描述的 χ^2 一致性检验的结果一起表明噪声是白色的，并且随着时间尺度从几秒合并为几千小时，噪声也同时下降。我们发现将对角线噪声缩放 1% 使似然结果产生的差异可以忽略不计（参见“系统不确定性”部分）。

为了检测噪声中潜在的非对角线相关性，我们计算了每天观测的 8.4 s 积分的 $6,240 \times 6,240$ 相关系数矩阵。为了提高数据对相关噪声的灵敏度，我们仅使用特定的一对数据矢量元素同时获得的数据。由于 8.4 s 积分的变量数 M 曾用于计算每个

a given pair of data vector elements. Owing to the variable number of 8.4-s integrations M used to calculate each off-diagonal element, we assess the significance of the correlation coefficient in units of $\sigma = 1/\sqrt{M-1}$. Our weather cut statistic is the daily maximum off-diagonal correlation coefficient significance (see "Data cuts" subsection).

We use the mean data correlation coefficient matrix over all days, after weather cuts, to test for significant correlations over the entire data set. We find that 1,864 (0.016%) of the off-diagonal elements exceed a significance of 5.5σ, when about one such event is expected for uncorrelated gaussian noise. The outliers are dominated by correlations between real/imaginary pairs of the same baseline, frequency band, and Stokes state, and between different frequency bands of the same baseline and Stokes state. For the real/imaginary pairs, the maximum correlation coefficient amplitude is 0.14, with an estimated mean amplitude of 0.02; for interband correlations the maximum amplitude and estimated mean are 0.04 and 0.003, respectively. We have tested the inclusion of these correlations in the likelihood analysis and find that they have a negligible impact on the results, see the "Systematic uncertainties" section.

χ^2 tests

As a simple and sensitive test of data consistency, we construct a χ^2 statistic from various splits and subsets of the visibility data. Splitting the data into two sets of observations that should measure the same sky signal, we form the statistic for both the sum and difference data vectors, $\chi^2 = \Delta' C_N^{-1} \Delta$, where $\Delta = (\Delta_1 \pm \Delta_2)/2$ is the sum or difference data vector, and $C_N = (C_{N1} + C_{N2})/4$ is the corresponding noise covariance matrix. We use the difference data vector, with the common sky signal component subtracted, to test for systematic offsets and mis-estimates of the noise. The sum data vector is used to test for the presence of a sky signal in a straightforward way that is independent of the likelihood analyses that will be used to parameterize and constrain that signal.

We split the data for the difference and sum data vectors in five different ways:

(1) Year—2001 data versus 2002 data;

(2) Epoch—the first half of observations of a given visibility versus the second half;

(3) Azimuth range—east five versus west five observation azimuth ranges;

(4) Faceplate position—observations at a faceplate rotation angle of $0°$ versus a rotation angle of $60°$; and

(5) Stokes state—co-polar observations in which both polarizers are observing left circularly polarized light (LL Stokes state) versus those in which both are observing right circularly polarized light (RR Stokes state).

非对角线元素，故我们以 $\sigma = 1/\sqrt{M-1}$ 为单位评估相关系数的显著性。我们基于天气因素的数据舍弃统计量是每日非对角线相关系数的显著性的最大值（参见"数据舍弃"部分）。

在天气因素的舍弃数据后，所有观测日均使用平均数据相关系数矩阵来检测整个数据集的显著相关性。我们发现 1,864 个（0.016%）非对角线元素具有超过 5.5σ 的显著性，而原本这个相关系数矩阵应该只存在不相关的高斯噪声。异常值主要受相同基线、频带和斯托克斯状态的实/虚对之间的相关性，以及相同基线和斯托克斯状态的不同频带之间的相关性影响。对于实/虚对，最大相关系数幅度为 0.14，估计平均幅度为 0.02；对于带间相关性，最大幅度和估计平均值分别为 0.04 和 0.003。我们已经在似然分析中检测了这些相关性，发现它们对结果的影响可以忽略不计，请参阅"系统不确定性"部分。

χ^2 检验

作为对数据一致性的简单且灵敏的检验，我们从可视性数据的各种划分和子集中构建 χ^2 统计量。将数据分成两组观测值，它们应该测量相同的天空信号，我们构造了和与差数据矢量的统计量，$\chi^2 = \Delta' C_N^{-1} \Delta$，其中 $\Delta = (\Delta_1 \pm \Delta_2)/2$，是和或差数据矢量，而 $C_N = (C_{N1} + C_{N2})/4$ 是相应的噪声协方差矩阵。我们使用差数据矢量，减去公共天空信号分量，来检验系统偏移和噪声的误差估计。数据矢量之和是一种直接用于检验天空信号存在的方式，该方式独立于即将应用于参数化和信号约束的似然分析。

我们以五种不同的方式划分数据矢量的差与和：

（1）年份——2001 年的数据与 2002 年的数据；

（2）时期——对于给定可视性的前半次观测和后半次观测；

（3）方位角范围——东方的和西方的五个观测方位角；

（4）面盘位置——观察面板旋转角度为 0° 和旋转角度为 60°；

（5）斯托克斯状态——共极观测，其中两个起偏器都观察到左旋圆偏振光（LL 斯托克斯状态），而另两个起偏器都观察到右旋圆偏振光（RR 斯托克斯状态）。

These splits were done on the combined 2001–02 data set and (except for the first split type) on 2001 and 2002 data sets separately, to test for persistent trends or obvious differences between the years. The faceplate position split is particularly powerful, since the six-fold symmetry of the (u, v) plane coverage allows us to measure a sky signal for a given baseline with a different pair of receivers, different backend hardware, and at a different position on the faceplate with respect to the ground shields, and is therefore sensitive to calibration and other offsets that may depend on these factors. The co-polar split tests the amplitude and phase calibration between polarizer states, and tests for the presence of circularly polarized signal.

For each of these splits, different subsets can be examined: co-polar data only, cross-polar data only (for all except the Stokes state split), various l-ranges (as determined by baseline length in units of wavelength), and subsets formed from any of these which isolate modes with the highest expected signal to noise (s/n). In constructing the high s/n subsets, we must assume a particular theoretical signal template in order to define the s/n eigenmode basis[53] appropriate for that subset. For this we use the concordance model defined in the "Likelihood parameters" subsection, although we find the results are not strongly dependent on the choice of model. Note that the definitions of which modes are included in the high s/n subsets are made in terms of average theoretical signal, without any reference to the actual data. In Table 1, we present the difference and sum χ^2 values for a representative selection of splits and subsets. In each case we give the degrees of freedom, χ^2 value, and probability to exceed (PTE) this value in the χ^2 cumulative distribution function. For the 296 different split/subset combinations that were examined, the χ^2 values for the difference data appear consistent with noise; among these 296 difference data χ^2 values, there are two with a PTE < 0.01 (the lowest is 0.003), one with a PTE > 0.99, and the rest appear uniformly distributed between this range. There are no apparent trends or outliers among the various subsets or splits.

Table 1. χ^2 Consistency tests for a selection of data splits and subsets

| Split type | Subset | Temperature data | | | | |
| | | Difference | | | Sum | |
		d.f.	χ^2	PTE	χ^2	PTE
Year	Full	1,448	1,474.2	0.31	23,188.7	$< 1 \times 10^{-16}$
	$s/n > 1$	320	337.1	0.24	21,932.2	$< 1 \times 10^{-16}$
	l range 0–245	184	202.6	0.17	10,566.3	$< 1 \times 10^{-16}$
	l range 0–245 high s/n	36	38.2	0.37	10,355.1	$< 1 \times 10^{-16}$
	l range 245–420	398	389.7	0.61	7,676.0	$< 1 \times 10^{-16}$
	l range 245–420 high s/n	79	88.9	0.21	7,294.4	$< 1 \times 10^{-16}$
	l range 420–596	422	410.5	0.65	3,122.5	$< 1 \times 10^{-16}$
	l range 420–596 high s/n	84	73.5	0.79	2,727.8	$< 1 \times 10^{-16}$
	l range 596–772	336	367.8	0.11	1,379.5	$< 1 \times 10^{-16}$

这些划分整合了 2001 年 ~ 2002 年的数据集（除第一种划分类型之外），是 2001 年和 2002 年分开进行的，以检测这两年持续的趋势或者明显的差异。面盘位置的划分方法特别有效，因为 (u, v) 平面覆盖的六重对称允许我们在给定基线上使用不同的接收器对、不同的后端硬件和相对于接地屏蔽的面盘的不同位置来测量天空信号，因此校准和其他偏移可能敏感地取决于这些因素。共极划分检测了起偏器状态之间的幅度和相位校准，并检测圆偏振信号是否存在。

对于上述每一个划分方法，可以检查不同的子集：单一共极数据、单一交叉偏振数据（除了斯托克斯状态划分之外的所有数据）、各种多级矩 l 范围（由波长为单位的基线长度确定），以及由其中具有任意最高的预估信噪比 (s/n) 的孤立模式形成的子集。在构造高 s/n 子集时，我们必须假设特定的理论信号拟合模板，以便定义适合于该子集的 s/n 基本本征模[53]。为此，我们使用"似然参数"部分定义的一致性模型，尽管发现结果并不强烈依赖于模型的选择。需要注意的是，高 s/n 子集中包括哪些模式的定义是根据平均理论信号进行的，而不参考实际数据。在表 1 中，我们给出了划分和子集的代表选择的差值与和值的 χ^2。在每种情况下，我们都给出自由度、χ^2 值以及这个值在 χ^2 累积分布函数的超出概率（PTE）。对于测试的 296 种不同的划分/子集组合，差值数据的 χ^2 值似乎与噪声一致；在这 296 个差值数据的 χ^2 值中，有两个 PTE < 0.01（最低为 0.003），一个 PTE > 0.99，其余均匀分布在该范围之间。各种子集或划分中没有明显的趋势或异常值。

表 1. 用于选择数据划分与数据子集的 χ^2 一致性检验

		温度数据				
划分方式	子集	差值			和值	
		d.f.	χ^2	PTE	χ^2	PTE
年份	完整	1,448	1,474.2	0.31	23,188.7	$< 1 \times 10^{-16}$
	$s/n > 1$	320	337.1	0.24	21,932.2	$< 1 \times 10^{-16}$
	l 范围 0 ~ 245	184	202.6	0.17	10,566.3	$< 1 \times 10^{-16}$
	l 范围 0 ~ 245 高 s/n	36	38.2	0.37	10,355.1	$< 1 \times 10^{-16}$
	l 范围 245 ~ 420	398	389.7	0.61	7,676.0	$< 1 \times 10^{-16}$
	l 范围 245 ~ 420 高 s/n	79	88.9	0.21	7,294.4	$< 1 \times 10^{-16}$
	l 范围 420 ~ 596	422	410.5	0.65	3,122.5	$< 1 \times 10^{-16}$
	l 范围 420 ~ 596 高 s/n	84	73.5	0.79	2,727.8	$< 1 \times 10^{-16}$
	l 范围 596 ~ 772	336	367.8	0.11	1,379.5	$< 1 \times 10^{-16}$

Continued

		Temperature data				
Split type	Subset	Difference			Sum	
		d.f.	χ^2	PTE	χ^2	PTE
Year	l range 596–772 high s/n	67	82.3	0.10	991.8	$< 1 \times 10^{-16}$
	l range 772–1,100	108	103.7	0.60	444.4	$< 1 \times 10^{-16}$
	l range 772–1,100 high s/n	21	22.2	0.39	307.7	$< 1 \times 10^{-16}$
Epoch	Full	1,520	1,546.3	0.31	32,767.2	$< 1 \times 10^{-16}$
	$s/n > 1$	348	366.5	0.24	31,430.0	$< 1 \times 10^{-16}$
Azimuth range	Full	1,520	1,542.6	0.34	32,763.8	$< 1 \times 10^{-16}$
	$s/n > 1$	348	355.2	0.38	31,426.9	$< 1 \times 10^{-16}$
Faceplate position	Full	1,318	1,415.2	0.03	27,446.5	$< 1 \times 10^{-16}$
	$s/n > 1$	331	365.3	0.09	26,270.1	$< 1 \times 10^{-16}$
Stokes state	Full	1,524	1,556.6	0.27	33,050.6	$< 1 \times 10^{-16}$
	$s/n > 1$	350	358.2	0.37	31,722.5	$< 1 \times 10^{-16}$

		Polarization data				
Split type	Subset	Difference			Sum	
		d.f.	χ^2	PTE	χ^2	PTE
Year	Full	2,896	2,949.4	0.24	2,925.2	0.35
	$s/n > 1$	30	34.4	0.27	82.4	8.7×10^{-7}
	l range 0–245	368	385.9	0.25	315.0	0.98
	l range 0–245 high s/n	73	61.0	0.84	64.5	0.75
	l range 245–420	796	862.2	0.05	829.4	0.20
	l range 245–420 high s/n	159	176.0	0.17	223.8	5.4×10^{-7}
	l range 420–596	844	861.0	0.33	837.3	0.56
	l range 420–596 high s/n	168	181.3	0.23	189.7	0.12
	l range 596–772	672	648.1	0.74	704.4	0.19
	l range 596–772 high s/n	134	139.5	0.35	160.0	0.06
	l range 772–1,100	216	192.3	0.88	239.1	0.13
	l range 772–1,100 high s/n	43	32.3	0.88	47.6	0.29
Epoch	Full	3,040	2,907.1	0.96	3,112.2	0.18
	$s/n > 1$	34	29.2	0.70	98.6	3.3×10^{-8}
Azimuth range	Full	3,040	3,071.1	0.34	3,112.9	0.17
	$s/n > 1$	34	38.7	0.27	98.7	3.3×10^{-8}
Faceplate position	Full	2,636	2,710.4	0.15	2,722.2	0.12
	$s/n > 1$	32	43.6	0.08	97.5	1.6×10^{-8}

Results of χ^2 consistency tests for a representative selection of splits and subsets of the combined 2001–02 data set. Visibility data containing the same sky signal is split to form two data vectors; using the instrument noise model, the χ^2 statistic is then calculated on both the difference and sum data vectors. Also tabulated are the number of degrees

温度数据						
划分方式	子集	差值			和值	
		d.f.	χ^2	PTE	χ^2	PTE
年份	l 范围 596～772 高 s/n	67	82.3	0.10	991.8	$< 1 \times 10^{-16}$
	l 范围 772～1,100	108	103.7	0.60	444.4	$< 1 \times 10^{-16}$
	l 范围 772～1,100 高 s/n	21	22.2	0.39	307.7	$< 1 \times 10^{-16}$
时期	完整	1,520	1,546.3	0.31	32,767.2	$< 1 \times 10^{-16}$
	$s/n > 1$	348	366.5	0.24	31,430.0	$< 1 \times 10^{-16}$
方位角范围	完整	1,520	1,542.6	0.34	32,763.8	$< 1 \times 10^{-16}$
	$s/n > 1$	348	355.2	0.38	31,426.9	$< 1 \times 10^{-16}$
面盘位置	完整	1,318	1,415.2	0.03	27,446.5	$< 1 \times 10^{-16}$
	$s/n > 1$	331	365.3	0.09	26,270.1	$< 1 \times 10^{-16}$
斯托克斯状态	完整	1,524	1,556.6	0.27	33,050.6	$< 1 \times 10^{-16}$
	$s/n > 1$	350	358.2	0.37	31,722.5	$< 1 \times 10^{-16}$
偏振数据						
划分方式	子集	差值			和值	
		d.f.	χ^2	PTE	χ^2	PTE
年份	完整	2,896	2,949.4	0.24	2,925.2	0.35
	$s/n > 1$	30	34.4	0.27	82.4	8.7×10^{-7}
	l 范围 0～245	368	385.9	0.25	315.0	0.98
	l 范围 0～245 高 s/n	73	61.0	0.84	64.5	0.75
	l 范围 245～420	796	862.2	0.05	829.4	0.20
	l 范围 245～420 高 s/n	159	176.0	0.17	223.8	5.4×10^{-7}
	l 范围 420～596	844	861.0	0.33	837.3	0.56
	l 范围 420～596 高 s/n	168	181.3	0.23	189.7	0.12
	l 范围 596～772	672	648.1	0.74	704.4	0.19
	l 范围 596～772 高 s/n	134	139.5	0.35	160.0	0.06
	l 范围 772～1,100	216	192.3	0.88	239.1	0.13
	l 范围 772～1,100 高 s/n	43	32.3	0.88	47.6	0.29
时期	完整	3,040	2,907.1	0.96	3,112.2	0.18
	$s/n > 1$	34	29.2	0.70	98.6	3.3×10^{-8}
方位角范围	完整	3,040	3,071.1	0.34	3,112.9	0.17
	$s/n > 1$	34	38.7	0.27	98.7	3.3×10^{-8}
面盘位置	完整	2,636	2,710.4	0.15	2,722.2	0.12
	$s/n > 1$	32	43.6	0.08	97.5	1.6×10^{-8}

结合了 2001 年～2002 年数据集划分和子集的代表性选择的 χ^2 一致性检验结果。包含相同天空信号的可视性数据被划分成两个数据矢量；利用仪器噪声模型，我们计算了数据矢量差值与和值的 χ^2 统计量。这里还列出了自由度（d.f.）的大小与 χ^2 累积分布函数中的超出概率（PTE），来显示结果的显著性（在我们计算的 χ^2 累积分布函数的精度

of freedom (d.f.), and probability to exceed (PTE) the value in the χ^2 cumulative distribution function, to show the significance of the result (PTE values indicated as $< 1 \times 10^{-16}$ are zero to the precision with which we calculate the χ^2 cumulative distribution function). Difference data χ^2 values test for systematic effects in the data, while comparisons with sum data values test for the presence of a repeatable sky signal. Temperature (co-polar) data are visibility data in which the polarizers from both receivers are in the left (LL Stokes state) or right (RR Stokes state) circularly polarized state; polarization (cross-polar) data are those in which the polarizers are in opposite states (LR or RL Stokes state). The "$s/n > 1$" subset is the subset of s/n eigenmodes > 1 and the l range high s/n subsets are the 20% highest s/n modes within the given l range. See "χ^2 tests" section for further description of the data split types and subsets. We have calculated 296 χ^2 values for various split types and subsets, with no obvious trends that would indicate systematic contamination of the data.

The high s/n mode subsets are more sensitive to certain classes of systematic effects in the difference data vector and more sensitive to the expected sky signal in the sum data vector, that otherwise may be masked by noise. Also, the number of modes with expected $s/n > 1$ gives an indication of the power of the experiment to constrain the sky signal. The co-polar data, which are sensitive to the temperature signal, have many more high s/n modes than the cross-polar data, which measure polarized radiation. Within the context of the concordance model used to generate the s/n eigenmode basis, we have sensitivity with an expected $s/n > 1$ to ~340 temperature (co-polar) modes versus ~34 polarization (cross-polar) modes.

Detection of signal

Given that the data show remarkable consistency in χ^2 tests of the difference data vectors, the χ^2 values of the sum data vectors can be used to test for the presence of sky signal, independently of the likelihood analysis methods described below. In the co-polar data, all splits and subsets show highly significant χ^2 values (PTE $< 1 \times 10^{-16}$, the precision to which we calculate the cumulative distribution function).

For the cross-polar data, the sum data vector χ^2 values for the high s/n subsets show high significance, with the PTE $< 1 \times 10^{-6}$ for all $s/n > 1$ subsets in Table 1. This simple and powerful test indicates that we have detected, with high significance, the presence of a polarized signal in the data, and that this signal is repeatable in all of the data splits. The polarization map shown in Fig. 1 gives a visual representation of this repeatable polarization signal. Shown are the epoch split sum and difference polarization maps, constructed using the same using the same 34 modes with $s/n > 1$ of the polarization data in the concordance model s/n eigenmode basis that appear in Table 1. The sum map shows a repeatable polarized signal, while the difference map is consistent with instrument noise.

下，PTE 的值 $<1 \times 10^{-16}$ 即为零）。差值数据 χ^2 值检验的是数据中的系统效应，同时与数据值的和值对照检验是否存在可重复的天空信号。温度（共极）数据是可视性数据，来自两个接收器的起偏器处于左（LL 斯托克斯状态）或右（RR 斯托克斯状态）圆偏振状态；偏振（交叉偏振）数据是起偏器处于相反状态（LR 或 RL 斯托克斯状态）的数据。"$s/n>1$" 子集是 s/n 本征模 >1 的子集，而 l 范围内的高 s/n 子集是给定 l 范围内最高的 20% 的 s/n 模式。有关数据划分类型和子集的进一步说明，请参阅"χ^2 检验"部分。我们计算了各种划分类型和子集的 296 个 χ^2 值，没有明显的趋势表明数据存在系统污染。

高 s/n 模式的子集对差值数据矢量中的某些类别的系统效应更敏感，并且对和值数据矢量中预期的天空信号更敏感，否则它就有可能被噪声掩盖。此外，$s/n>1$ 预期的模式数量表示实验约束天空信号的能力。对温度信号敏感的共极数据比测量偏振辐射的交叉偏振数据的 s/n 模式更高。根据生成 s/n 基础本征模的一致性模型，我们预期约 340 种温度（共极）模式与约 34 种偏振（交叉偏振）模式具有 $s/n>1$ 的灵敏度。

信号检测

假设数据在差值数据矢量的 χ^2 检验中出现了显著的一致性，则可以使用和值数据矢量的 χ^2 值来检测天空信号的存在，而与下面描述的似然分析方法无关。在共极数据中，所有划分和子集显示高度显著的 χ^2 值（PTE $< 1 \times 10^{-16}$，这个精度是我们计算累积分布函数的精度）。

对于交叉偏振数据，高 s/n 子集的和值数据向量 χ^2 值显示出高显著性，表 1 中所有 $s/n>1$ 子集的 PTE $< 1 \times 10^{-6}$。这个简单而强大的检测表示我们已经高度显著地检测到数据中存在偏振信号，并且该信号在所有数据拆分方法中都是可重复的。图 1 中所示的偏振图给出了该可重复偏振信号的视觉呈现，展示出了根据时期划分的和值与差值偏振图，使用相同的 34 种模式构建，其中 $s/n>1$ 的偏振数据在一致性模型 s/n 基础本征模中，如表 1 所示。和值图显示了可重复的偏振信号，而差值图与仪器噪声一致。

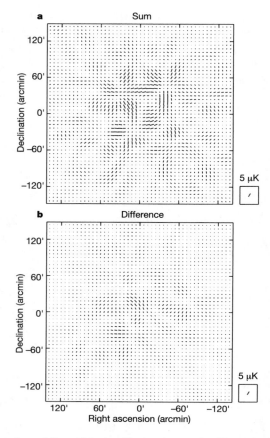

Fig. 1. Polarization maps formed from high signal/noise eigenmodes. Shown are maps constructed from polarized data sets that have been split by epoch, and formed into sum (**a**) or difference (**b**) data vectors, as reported in section "χ^2 tests". In order to isolate the most significant signal in our data, we have used only the subset of 34 eigenmodes which, under the concordance model, are expected to have average signal/noise (s/n) > 1. Because the maps have only 34 independent modes, they exhibit a limited range of morphologies, and unlike conventional interferometer maps, these s/n selected eigenmodes reflect the taper of the primary beam, even when no signal is present. This is visually apparent in the difference map (**b**), which is statistically consistent with noise. Comparison of the difference map to the sum map (**a**) illustrates a result also given numerically for this split/subset in Table 1: that these individual modes in the polarized data set show a significant signal.

It is possible to calculate a similar χ^2 statistic for the data vector formed from the complete, unsplit data set. Combining all the data without the requirement of forming two equally weighted subsets should yield minimal noise, albeit without an exactly corresponding null (that is, difference) test. Recalculating the s/n eigenmodes for this complete cross-polar data vector gives 36 modes with expected s/n > 1, for which $\chi^2 = 98.0$ with a PTE $= 1.2 \times 10^{-7}$. This significance is similar to those from the sum data vectors under the various splits, which actually divide the data fairly equally and so are nearly optimal. It should be noted that our focus so far has been to test the instrumental noise model, and we have not dealt with the small cross-polar signal expected as a result of the off-axis leakage. As noted in the "Off-axis leakage" subsection, it is not possible to correct the data elements directly for this effect,

图 1. 根据高信号/噪声本征模绘制的偏振图。图中显示了由已经按时期划分的偏振数据集所构建的映射，并且生成了和值（**a**）或差值（**b**）数据矢量，如"χ^2 检验"部分中所报告的。为了分离数据中最重要的信号，我们只使用了 34 个本征模的子集，在协调模型下，预计平均信号/噪声（s/n）> 1。因为这个图只有 34 个独立模式，它们表现的形态范围是有限的，并且与传统的干涉仪图不同，即使没有信号存在，这些 s/n 选择的本征模也反映了初级光束的锥度。这在差值图（**b**）中表现得很明显，其在统计上与噪声一致。差值图与和值图（**a**）的比较阐释了表 1 对于该划分/子集数值给出的结果：偏振数据集中的这些独立模式表现为显著的信号。

从一个完整的未划分数据集形成的数据矢量计算出相似的 χ^2 统计量是可能的。没有形成两个同等加权的子集的情况下，组合所有数据应该产生最小的噪声，尽管没有完全对应的零（即差值）检测。重新计算该完整交叉偏振数据矢量的 s/n 本征模，得到 36 个预期 s/n > 1 的模式，其中 $\chi^2 = 98.0$，PTE = 1.2×10^{-7}。这种显著性类似于那些来自各种划分下的和值数据矢量，其实际上相当均等地划分了数据，因此这几乎是最佳的方式。应该指出的是，到目前为止我们的重点是已经检测了的仪器噪声模型，而我们还没有处理能预期到的由于离轴渗漏而产生的小的交叉偏振信号。如"离轴渗漏"部分中所述，不可能直接针对此效应校正数据元素，但我们可以通过计

but we can account for it in calculating these χ^2 results by including the expected covariance of this leakage signal (see "Theory covariance matrix" subsection) in the noise matrix C_N. Again recalculating the s/n eigenmodes, we find 34 cross-polar modes with $s/n > 1$ which give a $\chi^2 = 97.0$ and a $\text{PTE} = 5.7 \times 10^{-8}$, a significance similar to before. The off-axis leakage is also included in the likelihood analyses, where it is again found to have an insignificant impact on the results.

The likelihood analysis described in the following sections makes use of all of the information in our data set. Such an analysis, in principle, may yield statistically significant evidence of a signal even in cases of data sets for which it is not possible to isolate any individual modes which have average $s/n > 1$. However, the existence of such modes in our data set, which has resulted from our strategy of integrating deeply on a limited patch of sky, allows us to determine the presence of the signal with the very simple analysis described above. It also reduces sensitivity to the noise model estimation in the likelihood results that we report next. Finally, it gives our data set greater power to exclude the possibility of no signal than it might have had if we had observed more modes but with less s/n in each.

Likelihood Analysis Formalism

The preceding section gives strong evidence for the presence of a signal in our polarization data. We now examine that signal using the standard tool of likelihood analysis. In such an analysis, the covariance of the signal, $C_T(\kappa)$, is modelled in terms of parameters κ appropriate for describing the temperature and polarization anisotropy of the CMB. The covariance of the data vector is modelled $C(\kappa) \equiv C_T(\kappa) + C_N$; where C_N is the noise covariance matrix. Given our data vector $\boldsymbol{\Delta}$, the likelihood of the model specified by the parameter vector κ is the probability of our data vector given that model:

$$L(\kappa) = P(\boldsymbol{\Delta}|\kappa) \propto \det(C(\kappa))^{-1/2}\exp(-\frac{1}{2}\boldsymbol{\Delta}'C(\kappa)^{-1}\boldsymbol{\Delta}) \tag{1}$$

Although the full likelihood function itself is the most basic result of the likelihood analysis, it is useful to identify and report the values of the parameters that maximize the likelihood (so-called maximum likelihood (ML) estimators). Uncertainties in the parameter values can be estimated by characterizing the shape of the likelihood surface, as discussed further in the "Reporting of likelihood results" subsection.

The CMB power spectra

The temperature and polarization anisotropy of the CMB can be characterized statistically by six angular power spectra: three that give the amplitudes of temperature, E-mode and B-mode polarization anisotropy as a function of angular scale, and three that describe correlations between them. These spectra are written C_l^X, with $X = \{T, E, B, TE, TB, EB\}$. In our likelihood analyses, we choose various parameterizations of these spectra to constrain.

算这些噪声矩阵 C_N 中渗漏信号的预期协方差来计算 χ^2 结果（见"理论协方差矩阵"部分）。接着重新计算 s/n 本征模，我们发现 34 个交叉偏振模式，其中 $s/n > 1$，其给出 $\chi^2 = 97.0$ 及 PTE $= 5.7 \times 10^{-8}$，具有与之前类似的显著性。离轴渗漏也包括在似然分析中，而且再次发现它对结果的影响不大。

以下部分中描述的似然分析使用了我们数据集中的所有信息。即使对于整个数据可能无法分离出任何平均信噪比 $s/n > 1$ 的独立模式，但是原则上这样的分析还是可能得到一个信号具有统计学显著性的证据。但是，在我们数据集当中这种模式的存在，是我们在天空的有限区域中做深度的积分策略造成的，这使我们能够通过上述非常简单的分析来确定信号的存在。它还降低了我们接下来报告的结果中对噪声模型估计敏感的可能性。最后，它使我们的数据集可以更好地排除那些没有信号的可能性，而不是排除那些如果我们观测更多的模且在每个模中具有更小的 s/n 就可以观测到的情况。

似然分析形式化

上一节为我们的偏振数据中存在信号提供了有力证据。我们现在使用似然分析这一标准方法来检查信号。在这样的分析中，信号的协方差 $C_T(\kappa)$ 根据适合于描述 CMB 的温度和各向异性偏振的参数 κ 来建模。建模数据矢量的协方差为 $C(\kappa) \equiv C_T(\kappa) + C_N$；其中 C_N 是噪声协方差矩阵。考虑到我们的数据矢量为 Δ，由参数矢量 κ 给出的模型的似然函数是该模型的数据矢量的概率：

$$L(\kappa) = P(\Delta|\kappa) \; \propto \; \det(C(\kappa))^{-1/2}\exp\left(-\frac{1}{2}\Delta^t C(\kappa)^{-1}\Delta\right) \tag{1}$$

虽然完整的似然函数本身是似然分析的最基本结果，但确定和报告最大似然函数的参数值（所谓的最大似然（ML）估计量）是很有用的。参数值的不确定性可以通过似然函数的边缘概率函数来估计，"似然函数结果报告"部分中会有进一步的讨论。

CMB 功率谱

CMB 的温度和偏振各向异性可以通过六个角功率谱来统计表征：其中三个是温度幅度、E 模式和 B 模式各向异性偏振作为角度尺度的函数，另外三个是它们之间的相关性的描述。这些谱写成 C_l^X，$X = \{T, E, B, TE, TB, EB\}$。在似然分析中，我们选择这些功率谱的不同参数化来进行约束。

For a given cosmological model, these spectra can be readily calculated using efficient, publicly available Boltzmann codes[54]. Details of how to define these spectra in terms of all-sky multipole expansions of the temperature and linear polarization of the CMB radiation field are available in the literature (see refs 15 and 16). For DASI's 3.4° field of view, a flat sky approximation is appropriate[55], so that the spectra may be defined somewhat more simply[26]. In this approximation the temperature angular power spectrum is defined:

$$C_l^T \simeq C^T(u) \equiv \left\langle \frac{\widetilde{T}^*(\mathbf{u})\widetilde{T}(\mathbf{u})}{T_{\text{CMB}}^2} \right\rangle \tag{2}$$

where $\widetilde{T}(\mathbf{u})$ is the Fourier transform of $T(\mathbf{x})$, T_{CMB} is the mean temperature of the CMB, and $l/2\pi = u$ gives the correspondence between multipole l and Fourier radius $u = |\mathbf{u}|$. The order spectra in the flat sky approximation are similarly defined, for example, $C^{TE}(u) \equiv \langle \widetilde{T}^*(\mathbf{u})\widetilde{E}(\mathbf{u})/T_{\text{CNB}}^2 \rangle$. The relationship between $\widetilde{E}$, $\widetilde{B}$ and the linear polarization Stokes parameters Q and U is:

$$\widetilde{Q}(\mathbf{u}) = \cos(2\chi)\,\widetilde{E}(\mathbf{u}) - \sin(2\chi)\,\widetilde{B}(\mathbf{u})$$
$$\widetilde{U}(\mathbf{u}) = \sin(2\chi)\,\widetilde{E}(\mathbf{u}) - \cos(2\chi)\,\widetilde{B}(\mathbf{u}) \tag{3}$$

where $\chi = \arg(\mathbf{u})$ and the polarization orientation angle defining Q and U are both measured on the sky from north through east.

Theory covariance matrix

The theory covariance matrix is the expected covariance of the signal component of the data vector, $\mathbf{C}_T \equiv \langle \mathbf{s}\mathbf{s}' \rangle$. The signals measured by the visibilities in our data vector for a given baseline $\mathbf{u}_i$ (after calibration and leakage correction) are:

$$V^{\text{RR}}(\mathbf{u}_i) = \alpha_i \int d\mathbf{x}\, A(\mathbf{x}, v_i)[T(\mathbf{x}) + V(\mathbf{x})]e^{-2\pi i \mathbf{u}_i \cdot \mathbf{x}}$$
$$V^{\text{LL}}(\mathbf{u}_i) = \alpha_i \int d\mathbf{x}\, A(\mathbf{x}, v_i)[T(\mathbf{x}) - V(\mathbf{x})]e^{-2\pi i \mathbf{u}_i \cdot \mathbf{x}}$$
$$V^{\text{RL}}(\mathbf{u}_i) = \alpha_i \int d\mathbf{x}\, A(\mathbf{x}, v_i)[Q(\mathbf{x}) + iU(\mathbf{x})]e^{-2\pi i \mathbf{u}_i \cdot \mathbf{x}} \tag{4}$$
$$V^{\text{LR}}(\mathbf{u}_i) = \alpha_i \int d\mathbf{x}\, A(\mathbf{x}, v_i)[Q(\mathbf{x}) - iU(\mathbf{x})]e^{-2\pi i \mathbf{u}_i \cdot \mathbf{x}}$$

where $A(\mathbf{x}, v_i)$ specifies the beam power pattern at frequency v_i, $T(\mathbf{x})$, $Q(\mathbf{x})$, $U(\mathbf{x})$, and $V(\mathbf{x})$ are the four Stokes parameters in units of CMB temperature (μK), and $\alpha_i = \partial B_{\text{Plank}}(v_i, T_{\text{CMB}})/\partial T$ is the appropriate factor for converting from these units to flux density (Jy). The co-polar visibilities V^{RR} and V^{LL} are sensitive to the Fourier transform of the temperature signal $T(\mathbf{x})$ and circular polarization component $V(\mathbf{x})$ (expected to be zero). The cross-polar visibilities V^{RL} and V^{LR} are sensitive to the Fourier transform of the linear polarization components

对于给定的宇宙学模型，使用有效的公开可用的玻尔兹曼代码[54]可以很容易地计算这些功率谱。有关如何根据 CMB 辐射场的温度和线性偏振的全天多极展开来定义这些功率谱的细节可在文献中获得（参考文献 15 和 16）。对于 DASI 的 3.4° 视场，平坦天空近似是合适的[55]，因此可以更简单地定义功率谱[26]。在该近似中，温度角功率谱定义为：

$$C_l^T \simeq C^T(u) \equiv \Big\langle \frac{\widetilde{T}^*(\mathbf{u})\,\widetilde{T}(\mathbf{u})}{T_{\mathrm{CMB}}^2} \Big\rangle \tag{2}$$

其中 $\widetilde{T}(\mathbf{u})$ 是 $T(\mathbf{x})$ 的傅里叶变换，T_{CMB} 是 CMB 的平均温度，$l/\pi = u$ 给出了多极矩 l 和傅里叶半径 $u = |\mathbf{u}|$ 之间的对应关系。平坦天空的有序谱定义也是类似的，例如，$C^{TE}(u) \equiv \langle \widetilde{T}^*(\mathbf{u})\widetilde{E}(\mathbf{u})/T_{\mathrm{CNB}}^2 \rangle$。$\widetilde{E}$、$\widetilde{B}$，以及线性偏振斯托克斯参数 Q 和 U 之间的关系是：

$$
\begin{aligned}
\widetilde{Q}(\mathbf{u}) &= \cos(2\chi)\,\widetilde{E}(\mathbf{u}) - \sin(2\chi)\,\widetilde{B}(\mathbf{u}) \\
\widetilde{U}(\mathbf{u}) &= \sin(2\chi)\,\widetilde{E}(\mathbf{u}) - \cos(2\chi)\,\widetilde{B}(\mathbf{u})
\end{aligned}
\tag{3}
$$

其中用来定义 Q 和 U 的 $\chi = \arg(\mathbf{u})$ 与偏振方向角都是从天空上由北到东测量的。

理论协方差矩阵

理论协方差矩阵是数据矢量的信号分量的预期协方差，$\mathbf{C}_T \equiv \langle \mathbf{ss}^t \rangle$。对于给定的基线 $\mathbf{u}_i$，我们的数据矢量中可视性测量的信号（在校准和渗漏校正之后）是：

$$
\begin{aligned}
V^{\mathrm{RR}}(\mathbf{u}_i) &= \alpha_i \int d\mathbf{x}\, A(\mathbf{x}, \nu_i)[T(\mathbf{x}) + V(\mathbf{x})]\mathrm{e}^{-2\pi i \mathbf{u}_i \cdot \mathbf{x}} \\
V^{\mathrm{LL}}(\mathbf{u}_i) &= \alpha_i \int d\mathbf{x}\, A(\mathbf{x}, \nu_i)[T(\mathbf{x}) - V(\mathbf{x})]\mathrm{e}^{-2\pi i \mathbf{u}_i \cdot \mathbf{x}} \\
V^{\mathrm{RL}}(\mathbf{u}_i) &= \alpha_i \int d\mathbf{x}\, A(\mathbf{x}, \nu_i)[Q(\mathbf{x}) + iU(\mathbf{x})]\mathrm{e}^{-2\pi i \mathbf{u}_i \cdot \mathbf{x}} \\
V^{\mathrm{LR}}(\mathbf{u}_i) &= \alpha_i \int d\mathbf{x}\, A(\mathbf{x}, \nu_i)[Q(\mathbf{x}) - iU(\mathbf{x})]\mathrm{e}^{-2\pi i \mathbf{u}_i \cdot \mathbf{x}}
\end{aligned}
\tag{4}
$$

其中 $A(\mathbf{x}, \nu_i)$ 是指定频率 ν_i 下的光束功率模式，$T(\mathbf{x})$、$Q(\mathbf{x})$、$U(\mathbf{x})$ 和 $V(\mathbf{x})$ 是以 CMB 温度 (μK) 为单位的四个斯托克斯参数，且 $\alpha_i = \partial B_{\mathrm{Plank}}(\nu_i, T_{\mathrm{CMB}})/\partial T$ 是从这些单位转换为通量密度 (Jy) 的适当因子。共极性 V^{RR} 和 V^{LL} 对温度信号 $T(\mathbf{x})$ 和圆偏振分量 $V(\mathbf{x})$（预期为零）的傅里叶变换敏感。交叉极性可视性 V^{RL} 和 V^{LR} 对线性偏振分量 Q 和 U 的傅里叶变换敏感。由等式 (3) 可以看出，可视性的成对组合是天空上几乎纯

Q and U. Using equation (3), it can be seen that pairwise combinations of the visibilities are direct measures of nearly pure T, E and B Fourier modes on the sky, so that the data set easily lends itself to placing independent constraints on these power spectra.

We construct the theory covariance matrix as the sum of components for each parameter in the analysis:

$$C_{\mathrm{T}}(\kappa) = \sum_{p} \kappa_{p} B_{\mathrm{T}}^{p} \qquad (5)$$

From equations (2)–(4), it is possible to derive a general expression for the matrix elements of a theory matrix component:

$$B_{\mathrm{T}ij}^{p} = \frac{1}{2} \alpha_{i} \alpha_{j} T_{\mathrm{CMB}}^{2} \int d\mathbf{u} C^{X}(u) \widetilde{A}(\mathbf{u}_{i} - \mathbf{u}, \nu_{i}) \times [\zeta_{1} \widetilde{A}(\mathbf{u}_{j} - \mathbf{u}, \nu_{j}) + \zeta_{2} \widetilde{A}(\mathbf{u}_{j} + \mathbf{u}, \nu_{j})] \qquad (6)$$

The coefficients ζ_{1} and ζ_{2} can take values $\{0, \pm 1, \pm 2\} \times \{\cos\{2\chi, 4\chi\}, \sin\{2\chi, 4\chi\}\}$ depending on the Stokes states (RR, LL, RL, LR) of each of the two baselines i and j and on which of the six spectra (T, E, B, TE, TB, EB) is specified by X. The integration may be limited to annular regions which correspond to l-ranges over which the power spectrum C^{X} is hypothesized to be relatively flat, or else some shape of the spectrum may be postulated.

Potentially contaminated modes in the data vector may be effectively projected out using a constraint matrix formalism[53]. This formalism can be used to remove the effect of point sources of known position without knowledge of their flux densities, as we described in ref. 6. This procedure can be generalized to include the case of polarized point sources. Although we have tested for the presence of point sources in the polarization power spectra using this method, in the final analysis we use constraint matrices to project point sources out of the temperature data only, and not the polarization data (see "Point sources" subsection).

The off-axis leakage, discussed in the "Off-axis leakage" subsection and in detail in ref. 51, has the effect of mixing some power from the temperature signal T into the cross-polar visibilities. Our moolel of the off-axis leakage allow us to write an expression for it analogous to equation (4), and to construct a corresponding theory covariance matrix component to account for it. In practice, this is a small effect, as discussed in the "Systematic uncertainties" section.

Likelihood parameters

In the "Likelihood results" section we present the results from nine separate likelihood analyses involving the polarization data, the temperature data, or both. Our choice of parameters with which to characterize the six CMB power spectra is a compromise between maximizing sensitivity to the signal and constraining the shape of the power spectra. In

的 T、E 和 B 的傅里叶模的直接测量，这使得数据集很容易对这些功率谱设置独立的约束。

在分析中，我们将理论协方差矩阵构造为每个参数部分的总和：

$$C_{\mathrm{T}}(\kappa) = \sum_p \kappa_p \, B_{\mathrm{T}}^P \tag{5}$$

从等式 (2) ~ (4)，可以推导出理论矩阵分量的矩阵元素的一般表达式：

$$B_{\mathrm{T}ij}^p = \frac{1}{2} \alpha_i \alpha_j T_{\mathrm{CMB}}^2 \int \mathrm{d}\mathbf{u}\, C^X(u)\, \widetilde{A}\,(\mathbf{u}_i - \mathbf{u}, v_i) \times [\zeta_1 \widetilde{A}\,(\mathbf{u}_j - \mathbf{u}, v_j) + \zeta_2 \widetilde{A}\,(\mathbf{u}_j + \mathbf{u}, v_j)] \tag{6}$$

系数 ζ_1 和 ζ_2 可取 $\{0, \pm 1, \pm 2\} \times \{\cos\{2\chi, 4\chi\}, \sin\{2\chi, 4\chi\}\}$，取决于两个基线 i 和 j 各自的斯托克斯状态（RR，LL，RL，LR），同时取决于 X 的谱（T, E, B, TE, TB, EB）。积分可以限于环形区域，其对应于范围为 l 的功率谱 C^X；C^X 被假设为相对平坦的，或者可以假设为某种形状的功率谱。

可以使用约束矩阵形式[53] 有效地投射出数据矢量中的潜在污染模式。这种形式可以用来消除已知位置，但不知道它们的通量密度的点源的影响，正如我们在参考文献 6 中所描述的那样。这个程序可以运用推广到包括偏振点源的情况中。虽然我们已经使用这种方法检测了偏振功率谱中点源的存在，但在最后的分析中，我们仅从温度数据中用约束矩阵投射点源，而不是用偏振数据（参见"点源"部分）。

正如在"离轴渗漏"部分中讨论过的，详见参考文献 51，离轴渗漏具有来自温度信号 T 的一些功率混合到交叉偏振可视性中的效果。我们的离轴渗漏的模式允许我们为它写出类似于等式 (4) 的表达式，并构造相应的理论协方差矩阵分量来解释它。在实践中，这是一个很小的影响因素，如"系统不确定性"部分所述。

似然参数

在"似然结果"部分中，我们呈现了九组包括对偏振数据、温度数据或两者联合数据的不同的似然分析结果。对用于描述六张 CMB 功率谱的参数的选择，我们针对信号灵敏度最大化和约束功率谱形状这两方面进行折中。针对不同的分析，我们

the different analyses we either characterize various power spectra with a single amplitude parameter covering all angular scales, or split the l-range into five bands over which spectra are approximated as piecewise-flat, in units of $l(l+1)C_l/(2\pi)$. Five bands were chosen as a compromise between too many for the data to bear and too few to capture the shape of the underlying power spectra. The l-ranges of these five bands are based on those of the nine-band analysis we used in ref. 6; we have simply combined the first four pairs of these bands, and kept the ninth as before. In some analyses we also constrain the frequency spectral indices of the temperature and polarization power spectra as a test for foreground contamination.

The l-range to which DASI has non-zero sensitivity is $28 < l < 1,047$. That range includes the first three peaks of the temperature power spectrum, and within it the amplitude of that spectrum, which we express in units $l(l+1)C_l/(2\pi)$, varies by a factor of about 4. Over this same range, the E-mode polarization spectrum is predicted to have four peaks while rising roughly as l^2 (in the same units), varying in amplitude by nearly two orders of magnitude[17]. The TE correlation is predicted to exhibit a complex spectrum that in fact crosses zero five times in this range.

For the single bandpower analyses which maximize our sensitivity to a potential signal, the shape of the model power spectrum assumed will have an effect on the sensitivity of the result. In particular, if the assumed shape is a poor fit to the true spectrum preferred by the data, the results will be both less powerful and difficult to interpret. For temperature spectrum measurements, the most common choice in recent years has been the so-called flat bandpower, $l(l+1)C_l \propto$ constant, which matches the gross large-angle "scale-invariant" power-law shape of that spectrum. Because of extreme variations predicted in the E and TE spectra over DASI's l-range, we do not expect a single flat bandpower parameterization to offer a good description of the entire data set (although in the "E/B analysis" subsection we describe results of applying such an analysis to limited l-range subsets of data). A more appropriate definition of "flat bandpower" for polarization measurements sensitive to large ranges of $l < 1,000$ might be $C_l \propto$ constant (or $l(l+1)C_l \propto l^2$). Other shapes have been tried, notably the gaussian autocorrelation function (by the PIQUE group[56]) which reduces to $C_l \propto$ constant at large scales and perhaps offers a better fit to the gross shape of the predicted E spectrum.

In our single band analyses, we have chosen a shape for our single bandpower parameters based on the predicted spectra for a cosmological model currently favoured by observations. The specific model that we choose—which we will call the concordance model—is a ΛCDM model with flat spatial curvature, 5% baryonic matter, 35% dark matter, 60% dark energy, and a Hubble constant of 65 km s^{-1}Mpc^{-1}, ($\Omega_b = 0.05$, $\Omega_{cdm} = 0.35$, $\Omega_\Lambda = 0.60$, $h = 0.65$) and the exact normalization $C_{10} = 700$ μK^2. This concordance model was defined in ref. 50 as a good fit to the previous DASI temperature power spectrum and other observations. The concordance model spectra for T, E, and TE are shown in Fig. 4. The five flat bandpower likelihood results shown in Fig. 4, and discussed in the next section, suggest that the concordance shaped spectra do indeed characterize the data better than any

或假设功率谱在全部的角尺度范围上具有相同的幅度参数，或将功率谱的多极矩 l 分为 5 个频段并假设每一段的功率谱(以 $l(l+1)C_l/(2\pi)$ 为单位)基本平坦。之所以选择 5 个频段，是考虑到若分段太多，则需加载的数据太多；若分段太少，则无法捕捉到功率谱的基本形状。这五个频段的 l 的范围是基于我们在参考文献 6 用过的九频段分析。这里，我们只是将这九个频段的前八个频段按四对合并在一起，并保持第九个频段不变。在某些分析中，我们会约束温度和偏振功率谱的谱指数以检验前景污染。

DASI 实验的多极矩探测范围为 $28 < l < 1,047$。这个范围包含了温度功率谱的前三个震荡峰，其中谱的幅度(以 $l(l+1)C_l/(2\pi)$ 为单位)约为四。在同样的多极矩范围内，E 模式偏振功率谱预计会包含四个峰，大致随 l^2(和温度谱相同的单位)上升而上升，其幅度的变化程度几乎达到两个量级 [17]。TE 相关功率谱预计会比较复杂，实际上，它在这段 l 的范围内会有五次等于零。

对于单频段功率分析实现对一个潜在信号的灵敏度的最大化，其分析结果的灵敏度会受到假定的模型功率谱形状的影响，尤其当假设的形状和数据支持的真实功率谱的形状相差甚远时，结果就不太可靠且难以被解释。近几年来，人们普遍选择所谓的"平坦频段功率"方法，即 $l(l+1)C_l \propto$ 常数，来测量温度谱。"平坦频段功率"和温度谱的大角度"标度不变"幂律分布的形状相匹配。根据预测，在 DASI 的 l 范围内 E 和 TE 功率谱变化剧烈，因此我们并不指望一个单平坦频段功率参数化就能很好地描述整个数据集(尽管在"E/B 分析"部分中，我们所描述的结果就是将这种分析方法用于有限 l 范围的数据子集给出的)。对偏振测量敏感的范围($l < 1,000$)，更准确的"平坦频段功率"的定义可以是 $C_l \propto$ 常数(或者 $l(l+1)C_l \propto l^2$)。其他已经被测试过的形状，特别是高斯自相关函数(被 PIQUE[56] 组使用过)，在大尺度上近似为 $C_l \propto$ 常数，或许会更符合 E 谱的总体形状。

作单频段分析的时候，我们会根据目前观测所支持的宇宙学模型预测的功率谱，为单频带功率参数选定一个形状。被选择的特定模型——我们称之为协调模型——是一个 ΛCDM 模型，该模型具有平坦的空间曲率、5% 重子物质、35% 暗物质、60% 暗能量、65 km·s^{-1}·Mpc^{-1} 的哈勃常数(即 $\Omega_b = 0.05$，$\Omega_{cdm} = 0.35$，$\Omega_\Lambda = 0.60$，$h = 0.65$)，以及确定的归一化 $C_{10} = 700\ \mu K^2$。这个协调模型定义在参考文献 50 中，与先前 DASI 温度功率谱和其他观测匹配得很好。图 4 展示了协调模型的 T、E 和 TE 功率谱。五个平坦频段功率似然结果(参见图 4)表明协调模型给出的形状的确比任何幂律分布近似都更符合数据，我们会在下一节对该结果进行讨论。在"E/B 分

power-law approximation. In the "E/B analysis" subsection, we explicitly test the likelihood of the concordance model parameterization against that of the two power laws mentioned above, and find that the concordance model shape is strongly preferred by the data.

It should be noted that the likelihood analysis is always model dependent, regardless of whether a flat or shaped model is chosen for parameterization. To evaluate the expectation value of the results for a hypothesized theoretical power spectrum, we must use window functions appropriate for the parameters of the particular analysis. The calculation of such parameter window functions has previously been described, both generally[57,58], and with specific reference to polarization spectra[59]. In general, the parameter window function has a non-trivial shape (even for a flat bandpower analysis) which is dependent on the shape of the true spectra as well as the intrinsic sensitivity of the instrument as a function of angular scale. Parameter window functions for the E/B and $E5/B5$ polarization analysis are shown in Fig. 2, and will also be made available on our website (http://astro.uchicago.edu/dasi).

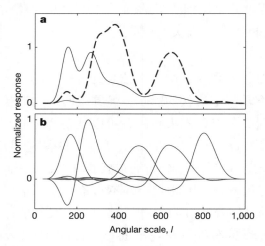

Fig. 2. Parameter window functions, which indicate the angular scales over which the parameters in our analyses constrain the power spectra. **a**, The functions for the E parameter of our E/B analysis, with the solid blue curve indicating response to the E power spectrum and the solid red (much lower) curve indicating response of the same E parameter to the B spectrum. The blue dashed curve shows the result of multiplying the E window function by the concordance E spectrum, illustrating that for this CMB spectrum, most of the response of our experiment's E parameter comes from the region of the second peak ($300 \lesssim l \lesssim 450$), with a substantial contribution also from the third peak and a smaller contribution from the first. **b**, The $E1$ to $E5$ parameter window functions for the E power spectrum (blue) and B power spectrum (red, again much lower) from our $E5/B5$ analysis. All of these window functions are calculated with respect to the concordance model discussed in the text. DASI's response to E and B is very symmetric, so that E and B parameter window functions which are calculated with respect to a model for which $E = B$ are nearly identical, with the E and B spectral response reversed.

Likelihood evaluation

Prior to likelihood analysis, the data vector and the covariance matrices can be compressed

196

析"部分，我们会有明确地检测以比较协调模型参数化和前面提到过的两种幂律参数化的似然。结果表明，数据强烈支持协调模型给出的形状。

需要注意的是，不管采用平坦模型或者给定成形模型来参数化，似然分析总是依赖于模型的。对于一个假设的理论功率谱，为了估计其分析结果的期望值，我们必须采用适用于这个特定分析的参数的窗口函数。这种参数窗口函数的计算方法曾经被概括地描述过 [57,58]，也有特别针对偏振功率谱的文献 [59]。一般而言，参数窗口函数具有非平凡的形状（即使对平坦频段功率分析也是如此），其形状依赖于真实功率谱的形状和仪器的内禀灵敏度，而后者是一个关于角度的函数。E/B、$E5/B5$ 偏振分析的参数窗口函数如图 2 所示，也可以在我们的网站（http://astro.uchicago.edu/dasi）上找到。

图 2. 参数窗口函数，它标示我们分析中的参数约束的是哪一段角度范围上的功率谱。**a**，E/B 分析的 E 参数窗口函数。其中蓝色实线表示对 E 功率谱的响应，红色实线（位置低得多）表示相同的 E 参数对 B 功率谱的响应。蓝色虚线表示的是将 E 窗口函数和协调模型 E 谱相乘的结果，这表明对于此 CMB 功率谱，我们实验的 E 参数的响应大部分来自于第二峰的对应的 l 区域（$300 \leqslant l \leqslant 450$），也有相当一部分来自第三峰，第一峰的贡献更小些。**b**，E 功率谱（蓝色）、B 功率谱（红色，同样位置但低很多）的 $E1$ 到 $E5$ 参数窗口函数。所有这些窗口函数都是根据文中提到过的协调模型计算的。DASI 对 E 和 B 模式的响应非常对称，因此根据 $E = B$ 的模型计算给出的 E 和 B 参数窗口函数基本相同，而 E 和 B 谱响应是相反的。

似然评估

做似然分析之前，通过合并 (u, v) 平面上邻近的、信号高度相关的数据点，我

by combining visibility data from nearby points in the (u, v) plane, where the signal is highly correlated. This reduces the computational time required for the analyses without a significant loss of information about the signal. All analyses were run on standard desktop computers.

For each analysis, we use an iterated quadratic estimator technique to find the ML values of our parameters[53]. To further characterize the shape of the likelihood function, in ref. 6 we used an offset log-normal approximation. Here, for improved accuracy in calculating confidence intervals and likelihood ratios, we explicitly map out the likelihood function by evaluating equation (1) over a uniform parameter grid large enough to enclose all regions of substantial likelihood. A single likelihood evaluation typically takes several seconds, so this explicit grid evaluation is impractical for the analyses which include five or more parameters. For each analysis we also implement a Markov chain evaluation of the likelihood function[60]. We find this to be a useful and efficient tool for mapping the likelihoods of these high-dimensional parameter spaces in the region of substantial likelihood. We have compared the Markov technique to the grid evaluation for the lower-dimensional analyses and found the results to be in excellent agreement. In all cases, the peak of the full likelihood evaluated with either technique is confirmed to coincide with the ML values returned by the iterated quadratic estimator.

Simulations and parameter recovery tests

The likelihood analysis software was extensively tested through analysis of simulated data. The analysis software and data simulation software were independently authored, as a check for potential coding errors.

Simulated sky maps were generated from realizations of a variety of smooth CMB power spectra, including both the concordance spectrum and various non-concordance models, both with and without E and B polarization and TE correlations. Independent realizations of the sky were "observed" to construct simulated visibilities with Fourier-plane sampling identical to the real data. The simulations were designed to replicate the actual data as realistically as possible and include artefacts of the instrumental polarization response and calibration, such as the on-axis and off-axis leakages and the cross-polar phase offset, described in the "Measuring polarization with DASI" section, allowing us to test the calibration and treatment of these effects implemented in the analysis software.

Each of the analyses described in the "Likelihood results" section was performed on hundreds of these simulated data sets with independent realizations of sky and instrument noise, both with noise variances that matched the real data, and with noise a factor of ten lower. In all cases, we found that the means of the ML estimators recovered the expectation values $\langle \kappa_p \rangle$ of each parameter without evidence of bias, and that the variance of the ML estimators was found to be consistent with the estimated uncertainty given by F^{-1} evaluated at $\langle \kappa \rangle$, where F is the Fisher matrix.

们可以压缩数据矢量和协方差矩阵，实现在不显著丢失信号信息的同时，减少分析所需要的计算时间。所有分析计算均在标准台式计算机上运行。

对每一次的分析，我们使用一个迭代二次估计量寻找参数的最大似然（ML）值[53]。为进一步表征似然函数的形状，在参考文献 6 中，我们采用了一个偏移对数正态近似。这里，为提高置信区间和似然比的计算精度，我们在足够大以至覆盖所有实际可能区域的均匀参数网格上求解方程（1）以明确地画出似然函数。一次似然估计一般需要花费几秒钟，因此这种显式网格评估对于包含五个或更多参数的分析是不切实际的。对每次分析我们也用马尔可夫链求似然函数[60]，我们发现它是将这些高维度参数空间的似然函数在实际可能的区域内映射出来的一个高效且实用的工具。对于低维度分析，我们发现马尔可夫法和格点估计法的结果完全吻合。在所有情况下，这两种方法给出的似然函数的峰值和迭代二次估计量给出的最大似然值都相符。

模拟和参数恢复检测

我们用模拟数据对似然分析软件进行了大量检测，分析软件和数据模拟软件被独立编写，以检测潜在的编程错误。

模拟的天图是通过各种光滑的 CMB 功率谱的实现生成的，功率谱包括协调模型的，各种非协调模型的，包括或者不包括 E、B 模式偏振和 TE 相关性的。我们通过和真实数据同样的傅里叶平面采样"观测"独立的天图的实现来构造模拟的可视度。模拟旨在尽可能真实地重复实际数据，并加入仪器偏振响应和校准的人造信号，比如"用 DASI 测量偏振"部分中讲到过的共轴渗漏、离轴渗漏和交叉偏振相位偏移效应，这样做使我们可以检测分析软件执行过程中对这些效应的校准和处理。

"似然结果"部分中描述的每个分析都是在数百个模拟数据集上进行的，模拟数据都由独立的天图实现和仪器误差给出，两者的噪声方差都和实际数据相匹配，其中噪声低于信号的十分之一。我们发现，在任何情况下，最大似然估计量给出的均值和每个参数的均值 $\langle \kappa_p \rangle$ 相比均无明显偏差，并且最大似然估计量的方差和用 F^{-1} 方法在 $\langle \kappa \rangle$ 处估算给出的不确定度一致，这里，F 是费希尔矩阵。

Reporting of likelihood results

Maximum likelihood (ML) parameter estimates reported in this paper are the global maxima of the multidimensional likelihood function. Confidence intervals for each parameter are determined by integrating (marginalizing) the likelihood function over the other parameters; the reported intervals are the equal-likelihood bounds which enclose 68% of this marginal likelihood distribution. This prescription corresponds to what is generally referred to as the highest posterior density (HPD) interval. When calculating these intervals we consider all parameter values, including non-physical ones, because our aim is simply to summarize the shape of the likelihood function. Values are quoted in the text using the convention "ML (HPD-low to HPD-high)" to make clear that the confidence range is not directly related to the maximum likelihood value.

In the tabulated results, we also report marginalized uncertainties obtained by evaluating the Fisher matrix at the maximum likelihood model, that is, $(F^{-1})_{ii}^{1/2}$ for parameter i. Although in most cases, the two confidence intervals are quite similar, we regard the HPD interval as the primary result.

For parameters which are intrinsically positive we consider placing (physical) upper limits by marginalizing the likelihood distribution as before, but excluding the unphysical negative values. We then test whether the 95% integral point has a likelihood smaller than that at zero; if it does we report an upper limit rather than a confidence interval.

We also report the parameter correlation matrices for our various likelihood analyses to allow the reader to gauge the degree to which each parameter has been determined independently. The covariance matrix is the inverse of the Fisher matrix and the correlation matrix, R, is defined as the covariance matrix normalized to unity on the diagonal, that is, $C = F^{-1}$ and $R_{ij} = C_{ij}/\sqrt{C_{ii}C_{jj}}$.

Goodness-of-fit tests

Using the likelihood function, we wish to determine if our results are consistent with a given model. For example, we would like to examine the significance of any detections by testing for the level of consistency with zero signal models, and we would like to determine if the polarization data are consistent with predictions of the standard cosmological model. We define as a goodness-of-fit statistic the logarithmic ratio of the maximum of the likelihood to its value for some model $\mathcal{H}_0$ described by parameters κ_0:

$$\Lambda(\mathcal{H}_0) \equiv -\log\left(\frac{L(\kappa_{\mathrm{ML}})}{L(\kappa_0)}\right)$$

The statistic Λ simply indicates how much the likelihood has fallen from its peak value down

200

似然结果汇报

本文中报告的最大似然（ML）参数估计是多维似然函数的全局最大值。每个参数的置信区间是将似然函数对其他参数求积分（边缘化）确定的。本文报告的区间包含 68%边缘似然分布的等概率边界，这个区间一般被认为是最高后验概率密度（HPD）区间。我们的目标仅仅是给出似然函数的形状，因此在计算这个区间的时候，我们会考虑所有的参数值，包括非物理的参数。本文约定用"ML（HPD 低到 HPD 高）"的格式引述参数值，以此来说明置信区间和最大似然值之间并没有直接关系。

通过计算最大似然模型处的费希尔矩阵，即对参数 i 求 $(F^{-1})_{ii}^{1/2}$，我们给出边缘化后的不确定度，也将其报告在结果列表中。虽然在大多数情况下，这两个置信区间非常相近，但我们采用 HPD 区间作为基本结果。

对于那些固有取正的参数，我们考虑通过如前所述的似然函数边缘化的方法来设置（物理）上界，消去非物理的负值。然后我们检查 95% 积分点的似然是否比参数值为零处的小。如果是，则报告一个上限而不是置信区间。

我们还报告了各个似然分析的参数相关矩阵，方便读者能够评估每个参数被独立测定的程度。协方差矩阵是费希尔矩阵的逆，把它的对角元素归一化后的矩阵被定义为相关矩阵 R，即 $C = F^{-1}$，$R_{ij} = C_{ij}/\sqrt{C_{ii}C_{jj}}$。

拟合优度检验

我们想使用似然函数来确定我们的结果是否支持一个给定的模型。比如说，我们想检查所有探测信号的显著性，则需要检测与零信号模型一致的程度。此外，我们想确定偏振数据是否和标准宇宙学模型预言的一致。我们定义了一个拟合优度统计量，它是似然函数的最大值和某些模型 $\mathcal{H}_0$ 的似然的对数比，记模型 $\mathcal{H}_0$ 的参数为 κ_0，则有：

$$\Lambda(\mathcal{H}_0) \equiv -\log\left(\frac{L(\kappa_{ML})}{L(\kappa_0)}\right)$$

简单来说，统计量 Λ 表明当参数从最大似然处的值变为 κ_0 时，似然函数下降的程度。

to its value at κ_0. Large values indicate inconsistency of the likelihood result with the model $\mathscr{H}_0$. To assess significance, we perform Monte Carlo (MC) simulations of this statistic under the hypothesis that $\mathscr{H}_0$ is true. From this, we can determine the probability, given $\mathscr{H}_0$ true, to obtain a value of Λ that exceeds the observed value, which we hereafter refer to as PTE.

When considering models which the data indicate to be very unlikely, sufficient sampling of the likelihood statistic becomes computationally prohibitive; our typical MC simulations are limited to only 1,000 realizations. In the limit that the parameter errors are normally distributed, our chosen statistic reduces to $\Lambda = \Delta\chi^2/2$. The integral over the χ^2 distribution is described by an incomplete gamma function;

$$\text{PTE} = \frac{1}{\Gamma(N/2)} \int_\Lambda^\infty e^{-x} x^{\frac{N}{2}-1} dx$$

where $\Gamma(x)$ is the complete gamma function, and N is the number of parameters. Neither the likelihood function nor the distribution of the ML estimators is, in general, normally distributed, and therefore this approximation must be tested. In all cases where we can compute a meaningful PTE with MC simulations, we have done so and found the results to be in excellent agreement with the analytic approximation. Therefore, we are confident that adopting this approximation is justified. All results for PTE in this paper are calculated using this analytic expression unless otherwise stated.

Likelihood Results

We have performed nine separate likelihood analyses to constrain various aspects of the signal in our polarization data, in our temperature data, or in both analysed together. The choice of parameters for these analyses and the conventions used for reporting likelihood results have been discussed in "Likelihood parameters" and "Reporting of likelihood results" subsections. Numerical results for the analyses described in this section are given in Tables 2, 3 and 4.

Polarization data analyses and E and B results

E/B analysis. The E/B analysis uses two single-bandpower parameters to characterize the amplitudes of the E and B polarization spectra. As discussed in the "Likelihood parameters" subsection, this analysis requires a choice of shape for the spectra to be parameterized. DASI has instrumental sensitivity to E and B that is symmetrical and nearly independent. Although the B spectrum is not expected to have the same shape as the E spectrum, we choose the same shape for both spectra in order to make the analysis also symmetrical.

We first compute the likelihood using a $l(l+1)C_l/2\pi = \text{constant}$ bandpower (commonly referred to as "flat" bandpower) including data only from a limited l range in which DASI

Λ 值大，则暗示似然结果不支持模型 $\mathscr{H}_0$。为了评估显著性程度，我们在 $\mathscr{H}_0$ 为真的假设下对该统计量进行蒙特卡罗（MC）模拟。这样，我们可以求出当 $\mathscr{H}_0$ 为真的情况下得到一个比观测到的 Λ 值更大的值的概率大小。我们后面称这个概率为 PTE。

考虑在数据十分不支持的模型的情况下，似然统计的充分抽样在计算上会变得难以承受，我们标准的 MC 模拟次数限制在仅 1,000 次实现。在参数误差是正态分布的情况下，我们选择的统计量 Λ 简化为 $\Lambda = \Delta\chi^2/2$。对 χ^2 分布的积分可以描述为一个不完全伽马函数：

$$\text{PTE} = \frac{1}{\Gamma(N/2)} \int_{\Lambda}^{\infty} e^{-x} x^{\frac{N}{2}-1} dx$$

其中 $\Gamma(x)$ 是完全伽马函数，N 是参数的数目。由于似然函数和最大似然估计量的分布一般都不是正态分布，我们还需要验算这个近似是否成立。任何情况下，我们都可以用 MC 模拟计算出一个有意义的 PTE，这样处理后，我们发现 MC 给出的结果和解析近似的结果非常一致。因此我们认为这个近似是可信的。若无特殊说明，本文中 PTE 的结果都是用这个解析表达式计算得到的。

似然结果

我们已经进行了九次不同的似然分析，对偏振数据、温度数据或两者的联合数据的各个方面作出约束。我们已经在"似然参数"和"似然结果报告"部分中对这些分析的参数的选择和报告似然结果所使用的约定进行了讨论。本节讨论似然分析的数值结果并在表 2、3 和 4 中给出。

偏振数据分析和 E、B 结果

E/B 分析 E/B 分析用到两个单频带功率参数描述 E 和 B 偏振谱的幅度。如同"似然参数"部分所讨论过的，该分析需选择要被参数化的功率谱的形状。DASI 对 E 和 B 的仪器灵敏度是对称的且几乎独立的。虽然 B 功率谱的形状预计和 E 功率谱的不同，但为使该分析是对称的，我们还是为这两种功率谱选择了相同的形状。

我们首先用 $l(l+1)C_l/2\pi = $ 常数频段功率（一般称为"平坦频段功率"）来计算似然函数，数据仅包括来自 DASI 且具有高灵敏度的有限的 l 范围上的数据，见图 2。利

has high sensitivity; see Fig. 2. Using the range $300 < l < 450$ which includes 24% of the complete data set, we find the ML at flat bandpower values $E = 26.5\ \mu K^2$ and $B = 0.8\ \mu K^2$. The likelihood falls dramatically for the zero polarization "nopol" model $E = 0$, $B = 0$. Marginalizing over B, we find $\Lambda(E = 0) = 16.9$ which, assuming the uncertainties are normally distributed, corresponds to a PTE of 5.9×10^{-9} or a significance of E detection of 5.8σ. As expected, changing the l range affects the maximum likelihood values and the confidence of detection; for example, shifting the centre of the above l range by ± 25 reduces the confidence of detection to 5.6σ and 4.8σ, respectively. Clearly it is desirable to perform the analysis over the entire l range sampled by DASI using a well motivated bandpower shape for the parameterization.

We considered three *a priori* shapes to check which is most appropriate for our data: the concordance E spectrum shape (as defined in "Likelihood parameters"), and two power law alternatives, $l(l+1)C_l \propto$ constant (flat) and $l(l+1)C_l \propto l^2$. For each of these three cases, the point at $E = 0$, $B = 0$ corresponds to the same zero-polarization "nopol" model, so that the likelihood ratios Λ(nopol) may be compared directly to assess the relative likelihoods of the best-fit models. For the $l(l+1)C_l \propto$ constant case, the ML flat bandpower values are $E = 6.8\ \mu K^2$ and $B = -0.4\ \mu K^2$, with Λ(nopol) $= 4.34$. For the $l(l+1)C_l \propto l^2$ case, the ML values are $E = 5.1\ \mu K^2$ and $B = 1.2\ \mu K^2$ (for $l(l+1)C_l/2\pi$) at $l = 300$, with Λ(nopol) $= 8.48$. For the concordance shape, the ML values are $E = 0.80$ and $B = 0.21$ in units of the concordance E spectrum amplitude, with Λ(nopol) $= 13.76$. The likelihood of the best-fit model in the concordance case is a factor of 200 and 12,000 higher than those of the $l(l+1)C_l \propto l^2$ and $l(l+1)C_l \propto$ constant cases, respectively, and so compared to the concordance shape either of these is a very poor model for the data. The data clearly prefer the concordance shape, which we therefore use for the E/B and other single bandpower analyses presented in our results tables.

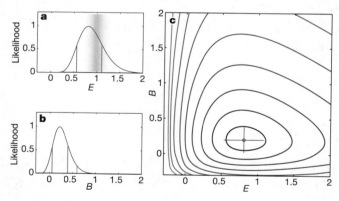

Fig. 3. Results from the two-parameter shaped bandpower E/B polarization analysis. An E-mode power spectrum shape as predicted for the concordance model is assumed, and the units of amplitude are relative to that model. The same shape is assumed for the B-mode spectrum. **c**, The point shows the maximum likelihood value with the cross indicating Fisher matrix errors. Likelihood contours are placed at levels $\exp(-n^2/2)$, $n = 1,2...$, relative to the maximum, that is, for a normal distribution, the extrema of these contours along either dimension would give the marginalized n-sigma interval. **a**, **b**, The corresponding single parameter likelihood distributions marginalized over the other parameter. Note

用 $300 < l < 450$（含完整数据集的 24%）的数据，我们发现平坦频段功率的最大似然值为 $E = 26.5\ \mu K^2$，$B = 0.8\ \mu K^2$。零偏振（$E = 0$，$B = 0$）的"无偏振"模型的似然值急剧下降。把 B 边缘化后，我们得到 $\Lambda(E = 0) = 16.9$。若假设误差呈正态分布，则该值对应的 PTE 为 5.9×10^{-9}，或者说探测到 E 的显著程度为 5.8σ。正如我们预计的，改变 l 范围会改变最大似然值和探测的显著水平。举个例子，把上面的 l 范围中心值移动 ± 25，则探测的显著水平分别下降至 5.6σ 和 4.8σ。采用一个合理的频段功率形状进行参数化，并在 DASI 采样的整个 l 范围内做这样的分析，这显然是我们所希望实现的。

我们考虑了三个先验形状来检查哪个最适合我们的数据，它们分别是协调模型的 E 谱（定义在"似然参数"部分中）、$l(l+1)C_l \propto$ 常数（平坦）和 $l(l+1)C_l \propto l^2$。后两者为幂律分布。对这三种情况，$E = 0$，$B = 0$ 的点都对应偏振为零的"无偏振"模型，因此直接比较似然比 Λ（无偏振）就可以估计最佳拟合模型的相对似然值。对 $l(l+1)C_l \propto$ 常数的情况，其在 $l = 300$ 处的最大似然值为 $E = 6.8\ \mu K^2$，$B = -0.4\ \mu K^2$，Λ（无偏振）$= 4.34$；对 $l(l+1)C_l \propto l^2$ 模型，同样在 $l = 300$ 处的最大似然值是 $E = 5.1\ \mu K^2$，$B = 1.2\ \mu K^2$，Λ（无偏振）$= 8.48$。对于协调模型形状，取协调模型 E 谱幅度为单位幅度，ML 值为 $E = 0.8$，$B = 0.21$，Λ（无偏振）$= 13.76$。协调模型最佳拟合下的似然比模型 $(l+1)C_l \propto l^2$ 和 $l(l+1)C_l \propto$ 常数分别增大为原来的 200 倍和 12,000 倍，因此比起协调形状，其他两个幂律模型都很糟糕。数据明显支持协调模型形状，故我们将此模型用于那些展示在结果列表中的 E/B 及其他单频段功率的分析。

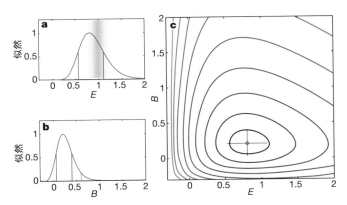

图 3. 双参数成形频段功率 E/B 偏振分析结果。假设 E 模式功率谱形状由协调模型给出，其幅度的单位是相对于该模型的幅度，假设 B 模式功率谱也具有相同的形状。**c**，图中的点表示最大似然值，十字表示费希尔矩阵误差。似然等高线设置为最大似然值的 $\exp(-n^2/2)$ 水平上，其中 $n = 1$，$2\cdots$。对于一个正态分布，沿着任何一个方向，这些等高线的极值就是边缘化的 n-σ 区间。**a** 与 **b**，单参数似然分布（将其余参数边缘化）图。注意似然函数朝着低功率值快速下降，这种似然函数形状（和 χ^2 分布类似）是那

the steep fall in likelihood toward low power values; this likelihood shape (similar to a χ^2 distribution) is typical for positive-definite parameters for which a limited number of high s/n modes are relevant. The grey lines enclose 68% of the total likelihood. The red line indicates the 95% confidence upper limit on B-mode power. The green band shows the distribution of E expectation values for a large grid of cosmological models weighted by the likelihood of those models given our previous temperature result (see ref. 50).

Figure 3 illustrates the result of the E/B concordance shape polarization analysis. The maximum likelihood value of E is 0.80 (0.56 to 1.10 at 68% confidence). For B, the result should clearly be regarded as an upper limit; 95% of the $B > 0$ likelihood (marginalized over E) lies below 0.59.

Figure 2a shows the parameter window functions relevant for this analysis. Note that the E parameter has very little sensitivity to B and vice versa—the purity with which DASI can separate these is remarkable. This is also demonstrated by the low correlation (-0.046) between the E and B parameters (see Table 2).

Table 2. Results of likelihood analyses from polarization data

Analysis	Parameter	l_{low}–l_{high}	ML est.	68% interval				Units
				$(F^{-1})_{ii}^{1/2}$ error	Lower	Upper	UL(95%)	
E/B	E	–	0.80	± 0.28	0.56	1.10	–	Fraction of concordance E
	B	–	0.21	± 0.18	0.05	0.40	0.59	Fraction of concordance E
$E5/B5$	$E1$	28–245	-0.50	± 0.8	-1.20	1.45	2.38	μK^2
	$E2$	246–420	17.1	± 6.3	11.3	31.2	–	μK^2
	$E3$	421–596	-2.7	± 5.2	-10.0	4.3	24.9	μK^2
	$E4$	597–772	17.5	± 16.0	3.8	40.3	47.2	μK^2
	$E5$	773–1,050	11.4	± 49.0	-32.5	92.3	213.2	μK^2
	$B1$	28–245	-0.65	± 0.65	-1.35	0.52	1.63	μK^2
	$B2$	246–420	1.3	± 2.4	-0.7	5.0	10.0	μK^2
	$B3$	421–596	4.8	± 6.5	-0.6	13.5	17.2	μK^2
$E5/B5$	$B4$	597–772	13.0	± 14.9	1.6	31.0	49.1	μK^2
	$B5$	773–1,050	-54.0	± 28.9	-77.7	-4.4	147.4	μK^2
E/β_E	E	–	0.84	± 0.28	0.55	1.08	–	Fraction of concordance E
	β_E	–	0.17	± 1.96	-1.63	1.92	–	Temperature spectral index
Scalar/ Tensor	S	–	0.87	± 0.29	0.62	1.18	–	Fraction of concordance S
	T	–	-14.3	± 7.5	-20.4	-3.9	25.4	$T/(S = 1)$

些只和有限个高信噪比模式相关的、定义为正的参数所特有的。灰色线是 68% 置信区间边界，红色线表示 B 模式功率的 95% 置信上限。绿色的带是大量的宇宙学模型给出的 E 期望值的分布，其权重是用以前的温度结果计算得到的这些模型的似然值（参考文献 50）。

　　图 3 示意了 E/B 协调形状偏振分析的结果。E 的最大似然值为 0.8（置信度为 68% 的参数区间为 0.56 至 1.10）。对于 B，结果显然应该视为上限；$B>0$ 的概率为 95%（将 E 边缘化）时，B 小于 0.59。

　　图 2a 展示了和本次分析相关的参数窗口函数。注意 E 参数几乎和 B 参数无关，反之亦然——DASI 区分两者的能力是非凡的，这一点也反映在 E 和 B 参数之间相关关系（相关系数为 0.046）弱上（见表 2）。

表 2. 偏振数据似然分析结果

分析	参数	$l_{low} \sim l_{high}$	ML est.	68% 区间				
				$(F^{-1})_{ii}^{1/2}$ 误差	下界	上界	UL(95%)	单位
E/B	E	–	0.80	±0.28	0.56	1.10	–	一致的 E 的比例
	B	–	0.21	±0.18	0.05	0.40	0.59	一致的 E 的比例
$E5/B5$	$E1$	$28 \sim 245$	−0.50	±0.8	−1.20	1.45	2.38	μK^2
	$E2$	$246 \sim 420$	17.1	±6.3	11.3	31.2	–	μK^2
	$E3$	$421 \sim 596$	−2.7	±5.2	−10.0	4.3	24.9	μK^2
	$E4$	$597 \sim 772$	17.5	±16.0	3.8	40.3	47.2	μK^2
	$E5$	$773 \sim 1,050$	11.4	±49.0	−32.5	92.3	213.2	μK^2
	$B1$	$28 \sim 245$	−0.65	±0.65	−1.35	0.52	1.63	μK^2
	$B2$	$246 \sim 420$	1.3	±2.4	−0.7	5.0	10.0	μK^2
	$B3$	$421 \sim 596$	4.8	±6.5	−0.6	13.5	17.2	μK^2
$E5/B5$	$B4$	$597 \sim 772$	13.0	±14.9	1.6	31.0	49.1	μK^2
	$B5$	$773 \sim 1,050$	−54.0	±28.9	−77.7	−4.4	147.4	μK^2
E/β_E	E	–	0.84	±0.28	0.55	1.08	–	一致的 E 的比例
	β_E	–	0.17	±1.96	−1.63	1.92	–	温度谱指数
标量/张量	S	–	0.87	±0.29	0.62	1.18	–	一致的 S 的比例
	T	–	−14.3	±7.5	−20.4	−3.9	25.4	$T/(S=1)$

Continued

					The four corresponding parameter correlation matrices						
E1	E2	E3	E4	E5	B1	B2	B3	B4	B5	E	B
1	−0.137	0.016	−0.002	0.000	−0.255	0.047	−0.004	0.000	0.000	1	−0.046
	1	−0.117	0.014	−0.002	0.024	−0.078	0.004	0.000	0.000		1
		1	−0.122	0.015	−0.003	0.010	−0.027	0.003	−0.001		
			1	−0.119	0.000	−0.001	0.002	−0.016	0.003	E	β_E
				1	0.000	0.000	0.000	0.002	−0.014	1	−0.046
					1	−0.226	0.022	−0.002	0.000		1
						1	−0.097	0.011	−0.002		
							1	−0.111	0.018	S	T
								1	−0.164	1	−0.339
									1		1

ML est., maximum likelihood estimate. $(F^{-1})_{ii}^{1/2}$, Fisher matrix uncertainty for parameter i is evaluated at ML. UL, upper limit.

Assuming that the uncertainties in E and B are normally distributed ("Goodness-of-fit tests" section), the likelihood ratio Λ(nopol) = 13.76 implies a probability that our data are consistent with the zero-polarization hypothesis of PTE = 1.05×10^{-6}. Our data are highly incompatible with the no-polarization hypothesis. Marginalizing over B, we find $\Lambda(E = 0) = 12.1$ corresponding to detection of E-mode polarization at a PTE of 8.46×10^{-7} (or a significance of 4.92σ).

The likelihood ratio for the concordance model gives $\Lambda(E = 1, B = 0) = 1.23$, for which the Monte Carlo and analytic PTE are both 0.28. We conclude that our data are consistent with the concordance model.

However, given the precision to which the temperature power spectrum of the CMB is currently known, even within the ~7-parameter class of cosmological models often considered, the shape and amplitude of the predicted E-mode spectrum are still somewhat uncertain. To quantify this, we have taken the model grid generated for ref. 50 and calculated the expectation value of the shaped band E parameter for each model using the window function shown in Fig. 2. We then take the distribution of these predicted E amplitudes, weighted by the likelihood of the corresponding model given our previous temperature results (using a common calibration uncertainty for the DASI temperature and polarization measurements). This yields a 68% credible interval for the predicted value of the E parameter of 0.90 to 1.11. As illustrated in Fig. 3a, our data are compatible with the expectation for E on the basis of existing knowledge of the temperature spectrum.

E5/B5. Figure 4a and b show the results of a ten-parameter analysis characterizing the E and B-mode spectra using five flat bandpowers for each. Figure 2b shows the corresponding parameter window functions. Note the extremely small uncertainty in the measurements of the first bands $E1$ and $B1$.

四个对应参数的相关矩阵											
E1	E2	E3	E4	E5	B1	B2	B3	B4	B5	E	B
1	−0.137	0.016	−0.002	0.000	−0.255	0.047	−0.004	0.000	0.000	1	−0.046
	1	−0.117	0.014	−0.002	0.024	−0.078	0.004	0.000	0.000		1
		1	−0.122	0.015	−0.003	0.010	−0.027	0.003	−0.001		
			1	−0.119	0.000	−0.001	0.002	−0.016	0.003	E	β_E
				1	0.000	0.000	0.000	0.002	−0.014		−0.046
					1	−0.226	0.022	−0.002	0.000		1
						1	−0.097	0.011	−0.002		
							1	−0.111	0.018	S	T
								1	−0.164	1	−0.339
									1		1

ML est.，最大似然估计。$(F^{-1})_{ii}^{1/2}$，在 ML 处参数 i 的费希尔矩阵不确定度。UL，上限。

假定 E 和 B 的不确定度呈正态分布（见"拟合优度检验"部分），似然比 Λ（无偏振）= 13.76 意味着我们的数据和零偏振假设一致的概率 PTE = 1.05×10^{-6}，我们的数据和无偏振的假设非常不相容。将 B 边缘化，我们发现 $\Lambda(E=0) = 12.1$，意味着探测到 E 模式偏振的 PTE 为 8.46×10^{-7}（或者说显著程度为 4.92σ）。

协调模型给出的似然比为 $\Lambda(E=1, B=0) = 1.23$，蒙特卡洛和解析近似给出的 PTE 都是 0.28，由此推断我们的数据支持协调模型。

然而，考虑到目前 CMB 的温度功率谱的精度，即使是经常被考虑的具有 ~ 7 个参数的这类宇宙学模型，预计给出 E 模式谱的形状和幅度仍然有些不确定。为了量化这种不确定性，我们采用了为参考文献 50 构造的模型网格，并使用图 2 所示的窗口函数计算每个模型的成形的频带 E 参数的期望值。然后我们取这些 E 模式幅度的预测值，并根据原先给出温度结果的对应模型下的似然值作加权（对 DASI 的温度和偏振测量使用相同的校准不确定度）。这样做给出一个 E 参数的 68% 置信区间为 0.90 到 1.11。如图 3a 所示，基于目前我们对温度谱的知识给出的 E 的期望值和我们的数据是相匹配的。

$E5/B5$　图 4a 和 b 是 E 和 B 模式在分别使用五个平坦频段功率时的十参数分析结果。表 2b 是对应的参数窗口函数。注意第一频带 E1 和 B1 的测量不确定度非常小。

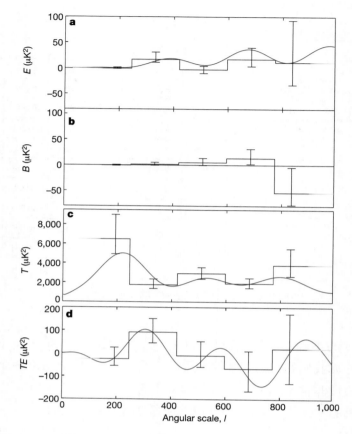

Fig. 4. Results from several likelihood analyses. The ten-parameter $E5/B5$ polarization analysis is shown in **a** and **b**. The $T5$ temperature analysis is shown in **c** and the five TE bands from the $T/E/TE5$ joint analysis are shown in **d**. All the results are shown in flat bandpower units of $l(l+1)C_l/(2\pi)$. The blue line shows the piecewise flat bandpower model for the maximum likelihood parameter values, with the error bars indicating the 68% central region of the likelihood of each parameter, marginalizing over the other parameter values (analogous to the grey lines in Fig. 3a and b). In each case the green line is the concordance model.

Table 3. Results of likelihood analyses from temperature data

Analysis	Parameter	$l_{\text{low}} - l_{\text{high}}$	ML est.	68% interval			
				$(F^{-1})_{ii}^{1/2}$ error	Lower	Upper	Units
T/β_T	T	–	1.19	±0.11	1.09	1.30	Fraction of concordance T
	β_T	–	−0.01	±0.12	−0.16	0.14	Temperature spectral index
$T5$	$T1$	28–245	6,510	±1,610	5,440	9,630	μK^2
	$T2$	246–420	1,780	±420	1,480	2,490	μK^2
	$T3$	421–596	2,950	±540	2,500	3,730	μK^2
	$T4$	597–772	1,910	±450	1,530	2,590	μK^2
	$T5$	773–1,050	3,810	±1,210	3,020	6,070	μK^2

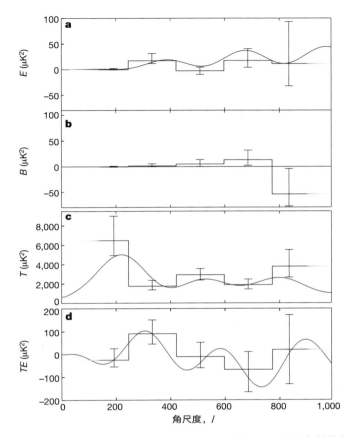

图 4. 数个似然分析的结果。**a** 和 **b** 展示了十参数 *E*5/*B*5 偏振分析。*T*5 温度分析结果在 **c** 中，*T*/*E*/*TE*5 联合分析的五个 *TE* 频段结果在 **d** 中。图示所有结果都以 $l(l+1)C_l/2\pi$ 为单位。蓝色线表示最大似然参数值给出的分段平坦模型下的形状，误差棒是各个参数 68% 置信区间范围的区域大小（将其他参数边缘化，和图 3a 和 b 中的灰色线类似）。每个图中的绿色线，都对应协调模型给出的形状。

表 3. 温度数据似然分析结果

分析	参数	$l_{low} \sim l_{high}$	ML est.	68% 区间			
				$(F^{-1})_{ii}^{1/2}$ 误差	下界	上界	单位
T/β_T	T	–	1.19	±0.11	1.09	1.30	一致的 T 的比例
	β_T	–	−0.01	±0.12	−0.16	0.14	温度谱指数
T5	T1	28 ~ 245	6,510	±1,610	5,440	9,630	μK^2
	T2	246 ~ 420	1,780	±420	1,480	2,490	μK^2
	T3	421 ~ 596	2,950	±540	2,500	3,730	μK^2
	T4	597 ~ 772	1,910	±450	1,530	2,590	μK^2
	T5	773 ~ 1,050	3,810	±1,210	3,020	6,070	μK^2

Continued

The two corresponding parameter correlation matrices						
$T1$	$T2$	$T3$	$T4$	$T5$	T	β_T
1	−0.101	0.004	−0.004	−0.001	1	0.023
	1	−0.092	−0.013	−0.011		1
		1	−0.115	−0.010		
			1	−0.147		
				1		

To test whether these results are consistent with the concordance model, we calculate the expectation value for the nominal concordance model in each of the five bands, yielding $E = (0.8, 14, 13, 37, 16)$ and $B = (0, 0, 0, 0, 0)\ \mu K^2$. The likelihood ratio comparing this point in the ten-dimensional parameter space to the maximum gives $\Lambda = 5.1$, which for ten degrees of freedom results in a PTE of 0.42, indicating that our data are consistent with the expected polarization parameterized in this way. The $E5/B5$ results are highly inconsistent with the zero-polarization "nopol" hypothesis, for which $\Lambda = 15.2$ with a PTE = 0.00073. This statistic is considerably weaker than the equivalent one obtained for the single band analysis in the "E/B analysis" section, as expected from the higher number of degrees of freedom in this analysis. In this ten-dimensional space, all possible random deviations from the "nopol" expectation values $E = (0, 0, 0, 0, 0)$, $B = (0, 0, 0, 0, 0)$ are treated equally in constructing the PTE for our Λ statistic. Imagining the "nopol" hypothesis to be true, it would be far less likely to obtain a result in this large parameter space that is both inconsistent with "nopol" at this level and at the same time is consistent with the concordance model, than it would be to obtain a result that is merely inconsistent with "nopol" in some way at this level. It is the latter probability that is measured by the PTE for our Λ(nopol), explaining why this approach to goodness-of-fit weakens upon considering increasing numbers of parameters.

E/β_E. We have performed a two-parameter analysis to determine the amplitude of the E-mode polarization signal as above and the frequency spectral index β_E of this signal relative to CMB (Fig. 5). As expected, the results for the E-mode amplitude are very similar to those for the E/B analysis described in the previous section. The spectral index constraint is not strong; the maximum likelihood value is $\beta_E = 0.17$ (-1.63 to 1.92). The result is nevertheless interesting in the context of ruling out possible foregrounds (see the "Diffuse foregrounds" subsection below).

两个对应参数的相关矩阵						
$T1$	$T2$	$T3$	$T4$	$T5$	T	β_T
1	−0.101	0.004	−0.004	−0.001	1	0.023
	1	−0.092	−0.013	−0.011		1
		1	−0.115	−0.010		
			1	−0.147		
				1		

为了检测这些结果是否与协调模型一致，我们计算了五个频段中每个频段的（名义上的）协调模型的期望值，得到 $E = (0.8, 14, 13, 37, 16)$，$B = (0, 0, 0, 0, 0)$ μK²。该点（在十维参数空间上）和最大处相比得到似然比 $\Lambda = 5.1$，对于十个自由度下对应的 PTE 为 0.42，表明我们的数据和这种参数化方式给出的预测是相符的。$E5/B5$ 结果和零偏振的"无偏振"模型高度不一致，其中 $\Lambda = 15.2$，PTE = 0.00073。该统计量远低于"E/B 分析"部分中单频段分析给出的对应的值，正如从该分析中较高的自由度数目所能预期的那样。在这个十维空间中，为我们的 Λ 统计量构造 PTE 时候，所有来自"无偏振"期望值 $E = (0, 0, 0, 0, 0)$，$B = (0, 0, 0, 0, 0)$ 的可能的随机偏离都有相同的贡献。假设"无偏振"是正确的，在这样一个大参数空间中获得一个既在上述的水平上与"无偏振"模型相悖，同时又和协调模型匹配的结果，比按照同样的方法得到一个仅仅和"无偏振"模型相悖的结果的可能性要小得多，我们的 Λ（无偏振）对应的 PTE 是用后者的概率给出的，这解释了为什么增加参数数量情况下该拟合优度方法的结论会减弱。

E/β_E　我们已经进行了双参数分析以确定如上所述的 E 模式极化信号的幅度以及该信号相对于 CMB 的谱指数 β_E（图 5）。正如我们预测的，E 模式幅度的结果和上一部分"E/B 分析"给出的差不多，谱指数的约束不是很强，最大似然估计值为 $\beta_E = 0.17$（置信度为 68% 的参数区间为 −1.63 到 1.92）。不管怎样，若不考虑前景（参见"弥散前景"部分）的可能性，这个结果还是值得关注的。

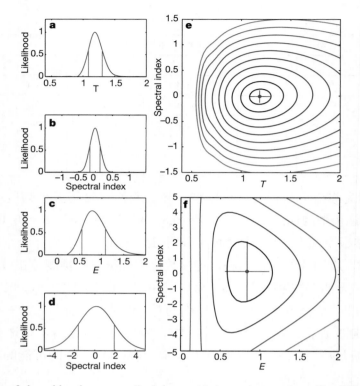

Fig. 5. Results of shaped bandpower amplitude/spectral-index analyses. **a**, **b**, **e**, The T/β_T temperature analysis assuming the T power spectrum shape as predicted for the concordance model, and in units relative to that model. The layout of the plot is analogous to Fig. 3. Spectral index is relative to the CMB blackbody—in these units, synchrotron emission would be expected to have an index of approximately −3. **c**, **d**, **f**, Results of the similar E/β_E analysis performed on the polarization data.

Scalar/tensor. Predictions exist for the shape of the E and B-mode spectra which would result from primordial gravity waves, also known as tensor perturbations, although their amplitude is not well constrained by theory. In a concordance-type model such tensor polarization spectra are expected to peak at $l \approx 100$. Assuming reasonable priors, current measurements of the temperature spectrum (in which tensor and scalar contributions will be mixed) suggest $T/S < 0.2$ (ref. 61), where this amplitude ratio is defined in terms of the tensor and scalar contributions to the temperature quadrupole C_2^T. We use the distinct polarization angular power spectra for the scalars (our usual concordance E shape, with $B = 0$) and the tensors (E_T and B_T) as two components of a likelihood analysis to constrain the amplitude parameters of these components. In principle, because the scalar B-mode spectrum is zero, this approach avoids the fundamental sample variance limitations arising from using the temperature spectrum alone. However, the $E5/B5$ analysis (see subsection "$E5/B5$") indicates that we have only upper limits to the E- and B-mode polarization at the angular scales most relevant ($l \lesssim 200$) for the tensor spectra. It is therefore not surprising that our limits on T/S derived from the polarization spectra as reported in Table 2 are quite weak.

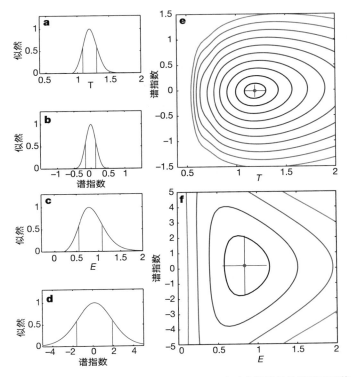

图 5. 成形带功率幅度/谱指数分析结果。图 **a**、**b**、**e**，假设温度功率谱满足协调模型下的 T/β_T 温度分析结果，与模型相对单位一致。此图的布局和图 3 相似，谱指数对应 CMB 黑体谱。在这些单位下，预计同步加速辐射的谱指数约为 −3。图 **c**、**d**、**f**，对偏振数据做类似 E/β_E 分析的结果。

标量/张量　对于 E 和 B 模式谱的形状存在多个预测，预测认为这些谱可能由原初引力波（即张量扰动）产生，尽管理论并不能很好地就它们的幅度给出约束。在协调型模型中，这种张量偏振谱预计在 $l = 100$ 处有峰值。假定一个合理的先验，目前的温度谱（张量和标量的贡献混合在一起）测量暗示 $T/S < 0.2$（参考文献 61），这个幅度比的定义是依据张量和标量对温度四极矩 C_2^T 的贡献给出的：我们把标量（我们惯用的协调模型 E 的形状，$B = 0$）和张量（E_T 和 B_T）各自的偏振角功率谱作为似然分析的两个部分来约束这两个组分的幅度参数。原则上，由于标量 B 模式功率谱是零，这个方法能够避免单独使用温度谱引入基本样本方差的局限性。但是 E5/B5 分析（参见"E5/B5"部分）暗示我们在张量功率谱最相关的 $l \leqslant 200$ 的角尺度上，只能得到 E 和 B 模式的上限。这样，在表 2 中报告中，我们从偏振谱得到的 T/S 的限制相当弱也就不令人费解了。

Temperature data analyses and results for *T* spectrum

T/β_T.   Results are shown in Fig. 5 for a two-parameter analysis to determine the amplitude and frequency spectral index of the temperature signal. The bandpower shape used is that of the concordance T spectrum, and the amplitude parameter is expressed in units relative to that spectrum. The spectral index is relative to the CMB, so that 0 corresponds to a 2.73-K Planck spectrum. The amplitude of T has a maximum likelihood value of 1.19 (1.09 to 1.30), and the spectral index $\beta_T = -0.01$ (−0.16 to 0.14). Although the uncertainty in the temperature amplitude is dominated by sample variance, the spectral index is limited only by the sensitivity and fractional bandwidth of DASI. Owing to the extremely high s/n of the temperature data, the constraints on the spectral index are superior to those from previous DASI observations (ref. 6).

T5.   Fig. 4c shows the results of an analysis using five flat bands to characterize the temperature spectrum. These results are completely dominated by the sample variance in the differenced field. They are consistent with, although less precise than our previous temperature power spectra described in ref. 6; we include them here primarily to emphasize that DASI makes measurements simultaneously in all four Stokes parameters and is therefore able to measure temperature as well as polarization anisotropy. Note that these results and those for T/β_T have not been corrected for residual point sources.

Joint analyses and cross spectra results

T/E/TE.   Figure 6 shows the results of a three-parameter single bandpower analysis of the amplitudes of the T and E spectra, and the TE cross-correlation spectrum. As before, bandpower shapes based on the concordance model are used. The T and E constraints are, as expected, very similar to those from the E/B, E/β_E and T/β_T analyses described above. The new result here is TE which has a maximum likelihood value of 0.91 (0.45 to 1.37). Note that in contrast to the two-dimensional likelihoods shown in other figures, here the contours show apparent evidence of correlation between the two parameters; the parameter correlation coefficients from Table 4 are 0.28 for E/TE and 0.21 for T/TE.

Table 4. Results of likelihood analyses from joint temperature-polarization data set

Analysis	Parameter	l_{low}−l_{high}	ML est.	68% interval			
				$(F^{-1})_{ij}^{1/2}$ error	Lower	Upper	Units
	T	–	1.13	±0.10	1.05	1.29	Fraction of concordance T
$T/E/TE$	E	–	0.77	±0.27	0.57	1.10	Fraction of concordance E
	TE	–	0.91	±0.38	0.45	1.37	Fraction of concordance TE

温度数据分析和 T 谱结果

T/β_T 限制温度信号的幅度和谱指数的双参数分析，结果如图 5 所示，选用协调模型 T 谱的频带功率形状，幅度参数以该谱相对应的单位来表示。该谱的谱指数是相对于 CMB 的，因此 0 对应 2.73 K 的普朗克谱。T 幅度的最大似然估计值为 1.19（置信度为 68% 的参数区间为 1.09 到 1.30），谱指数 $\beta_T = -0.01$（置信度为 68% 的参数区间为 -0.16 到 0.14）。尽管温度幅度的误差主要来源于样本误差，但是谱指数的误差仅受限于 DASI 的灵敏度和带宽比。得益于温度数据极高的信噪比，温度谱指数的限制优于从先前 DASI 观测给出的（参考文献 6）。

T5   图 4c 展示了一个用五平坦频带描述温度谱的分析结果。这些结果完全由离散区域内的样本方差主导。尽管不如我们先前在参考文献 6 中所描述的温度功率谱那么精确，但它们是吻合的。我们把它们列在此处，主要是为了强调 DASI 同时测量四个斯托克斯参数，因此能够在测量温度的同时测量偏振的各向异性。注意，这些结果以及 T/β_T 的结果还未做残留点光源校准。

联合分析和交叉谱结果

T/E/TE   图 6 为功率 T 谱、E 谱和 TE 相关谱的幅度的三参数单频带分析结果。和前面一样，频带功率选用协调模型的形状。和预想的一样，T 和 E 的约束与前面描述过的 E/B、E/β_E 和 T/β_T 分析非常相似。这部分的新结果是 TE 的最大似然估计值，为 0.91（置信度为 68% 的参数区间为 0.45 到 1.37）。注意和其他图中的二维似然分布相反，这里两个参数的二维（似然）等高线图呈现明显的相关关系，从表 4 可知，参数的相关系数为 0.28（E/TE）和 0.21（T/TE）。

表 4. 温度–偏振数据集联合似然分析结果

分析	参数	$l_{low} \sim l_{high}$	ML est.	68% 区间			单位
				$(F^{-1})_{ij}^{1/2}$ 误差	下界	上界	
$T/E/TE$	T	–	1.13	± 0.10	1.05	1.29	一致的 T 的比例
	E	–	0.77	± 0.27	0.57	1.10	一致的 E 的比例
	TE	–	0.91	± 0.38	0.45	1.37	一致的 TE 的比例

Continued

Analysis	Parameter	$l_{low}-l_{high}$	ML est.	68% interval			
				$(F^{-1})_{ij}^{1/2}$ error	Lower	Upper	Units
T/E/TE5	*T*	–	1.12	±0.10	1.09	1.31	Fraction of concordance *T*
	E	–	0.81	±0.28	0.71	1.36	Fraction of concordance *E*
	TE1	28–245	−24.8	±32.2	−55.3	24.7	μK²
	TE2	246–420	92.3	±38.4	44.9	151.1	μK²
	TE3	421–596	−10.5	±48.2	−60.1	52.0	μK²
	TE4	597–772	−66.7	±74.3	−164.6	9.5	μK²
	TE5	773–1,050	20.0	±167.9	−130.3	172.3	μK²
T/E/B/ TE/TB/EB	*T*	–	1.13	±0.10	1.03	1.27	Fraction of concordance *T*
	E	–	0.75	±0.26	0.59	1.19	Fraction of concordance *E*
	B	–	0.20	±0.18	0.11	0.52	Fraction of concordance *E*
	TE	–	1.02	±0.37	0.53	1.49	Fraction of concordance *TE*
	TB	–	0.53	±0.32	0.08	0.82	Fraction of concordance *TE*
	EB	–	−0.16	±0.16	−0.38	0.01	Fraction of concordance *E*

The three parameter correlation matrices

T	*E*	*TE1*	*TE2*	*TE3*	*TE4*	*TE5*	*T*	*E*	*B*	*TE*	*TB*	*EB*
1	0.026	−0.071	0.202	−0.018	−0.075	0.008	1	0.026	0.004	0.230	0.136	0.033
	1	−0.067	0.339	−0.023	−0.090	0.008		1	−0.027	0.320	−0.040	−0.182
		1	−0.076	0.006	0.011	−0.001			1	−0.027	0.219	−0.190
			1	−0.078	−0.039	0.004				1	−0.150	0.109
				1	−0.056	0.004					1	0.213
					1	−0.066						1
						1						

T	*E*	*TE*
1	0.017	0.207
	1	0.282
		1

Marginalizing over T and E, we find that the likelihood of TE peaks very near 1, so that $\Lambda(TE = 1) = 0.02$ with a PTE of 0.857. For the "no cross-correlation" hypothesis, $\Lambda(TE = 0) = 1.85$ with an analytic PTE of 0.054 (the PTE calculated from Monte Carlo simulations is 0.047). This result represents a detection of the expected TE correlation at 95% confidence and is particularly interesting in that it suggests a common origin for the observed temperature and polarization anisotropy.

It has been suggested that an estimator of TE cross-correlation constructed using a $TE = 0$ prior may offer greater immunity to systematic errors[59]. We have confirmed that applying

分析	参数	$l_{low} \sim l_{high}$	ML est.	68% 区间			
				$(F^{-1})_{ij}^{1/2}$ 误差	下界	上界	单位
	T	–	1.12	±0.10	1.09	1.31	一致的 T 的比例
	E	–	0.81	±0.28	0.71	1.36	一致的 E 的比例
	$TE1$	$28 \sim 245$	−24.8	±32.2	−55.3	24.7	μK^2
$T/E/TE5$	$TE2$	$246 \sim 420$	92.3	±38.4	44.9	151.1	μK^2
	$TE3$	$421 \sim 596$	−10.5	±48.2	−60.1	52.0	μK^2
	$TE4$	$597 \sim 772$	−66.7	±74.3	−164.6	9.5	μK^2
	$TE5$	$773 \sim 1,050$	20.0	±167.9	−130.3	172.3	μK^2
	T	–	1.13	±0.10	1.03	1.27	一致的 T 的比例
	E	–	0.75	±0.26	0.59	1.19	一致的 E 的比例
$T/E/B/TE/TB/EB$	B	–	0.20	±0.18	0.11	0.52	一致的 E 的比例
	TE	–	1.02	±0.37	0.53	1.49	一致的 TE 的比例
	TB	–	0.53	±0.32	0.08	0.82	一致的 TE 的比例
	EB	–	−0.16	±0.16	−0.38	0.01	一致的 E 的比例

三参数的相关矩阵

T	E	$TE1$	$TE2$	$TE3$	$TE4$	$TE5$	T	E	B	TE	TB	EB
1	0.026	−0.071	0.202	−0.018	−0.075	0.008	1	0.026	0.004	0.230	0.136	0.033
	1	−0.067	0.339	−0.023	−0.090	0.008		1	−0.027	0.320	−0.040	−0.182
		1	−0.076	0.006	0.011	−0.001			1	−0.027	0.219	−0.190
			1	−0.078	−0.039	0.004				1	−0.150	0.109
				1	−0.056	0.004					1	0.213
					1	−0.066						1
						1						

T	E	TE
1	0.017	0.207
	1	0.282
		1

将 T 和 E 边缘化，我们发现 TE 峰处的似然非常接近 1，因而 $\Lambda(TE=1)=0.02$，PTE 为 0.857。在 T 和 E "无交叉相关关系" 的假设下，$\Lambda(TE=1)=1.85$，其解析 PTE 为 0.054(用蒙特卡洛模拟计算出的 PTE 为 0.047)。这个结果表明在 95% 置信度下，TE 具有相关性。更为有趣的是，这暗示着观测到的温度和偏振各向异性具有相同的起源。

也有人提出，使用 $TE=0$ 的先验构造的一个 TE 交叉相关估计量或许对系统误差更不敏感[59]。我们已经证明对我们的数据使用这样的技巧会产生和上面的似然分

such a technique to our data yields similar results to the above likelihood analysis, with errors slightly increased as expected.

T/E/TE5. We have performed a seven-parameter analysis using single shaped band powers for T and E, and five flat bandpowers for the TE cross-correlation; the TE results from this are shown in Fig. 4d. In this analysis the B-mode polarization has been explicitly set to zero. Again, the T and E constraints are similar to the values for the other analyses where these parameters appear. The TE bandpowers are consistent with the predictions of the concordance model.

T/E/B/TE/TB/EB. Finally, we describe the results of a six shaped bandpower analysis for the three individual spectra T, E and B, together with the three possible cross-correlation spectra TE, TB and EB. We include the B cross-spectra for completeness, though there is little evidence for any B-mode signal. Because there are no predictions for the shapes of the TB or EB spectra (they are expected to be zero), we preserve the symmetry of the analysis between E and B by simply parameterizing them in terms of the TE and E spectral shapes. The results for T, E, B and TE are similar to those obtained before, with no detection of EB or TB.

Systematic Uncertainties

Noise, calibration, offsets and pointing

To assess the effect of systematic uncertainties on the likelihood results, we have repeated each of the nine analyses with alternative assumptions about the various effects that we have identified which reflect the range of uncertainty on each.

Much of the effort of the data analysis presented in this paper has gone into investigating the consistency of the data with the noise model as discussed in the "Noise model" subsection. We find no discrepancies between complementary noise estimates on different timescales, to a level $\ll 1\%$. As discussed in the "χ^2 tests" subsection, numerous consistency tests on subsets of the co-polar and cross-polar visibility data show no evidence for an error in the noise scaling to a similar level. When we re-evaluate each of the analyses described in the "Likelihood results" section with the noise scaled by 1%, the shift in the maximum likelihood values for all parameters is entirely negligible.

In the "Noise model" subsection, we reported evidence of some detectable noise correlations between real/imaginary visibilities and between visibilities from different bands of the same baseline. When either or both of these noise correlations are added to the covariance matrix at the measured level, the effects are again negligible: the most significant shift is in the highest-l band of the E spectrum from the $E5/B5$ analysis (see the "$E5/B5$" subsection), where the power shifts by about $2\ \mu K^2$.

析类似的结果，不过和预测的一样，误差会稍稍增大。

T/E/TE5　我们也进行了一个七参数分析，其中对 *T* 和 *E* 采用了单形状频带功率，对 *TE* 交叉相关谱采用了五平坦频段功率的形状，*TE* 结果见图 4d。此分析中，*B* 模式偏振被明确地设置为零。同样，对 *T* 和 *E* 的约束与其他出现这两个参数的分析类似，*TE* 频段功率和调和模型给出的理论预言一致。

T/E/B/TE/TB/EB　最后，我们描述了对 *T*、*E* 和 *B* 三个功率谱以及三个可能的交叉相关谱 *TE*, *TB* 和 *EB* 的六个成型频带功率分析。虽然几乎没有迹象表明存在 *B* 模式信号，但是为了完备性，我们还是把 *B* 交叉谱列入了分析。由于没有对 *TB* 谱和 *EB* 谱的形状的预测（它们被认为是零），我们简单地根据 *TE* 和 *E* 谱形状对它们进行参数化，以保持 *E* 和 *B* 之间分析的对称性。*T*、*E*、*B* 和 *TE* 的结果与之前得到结果的类似，*EB* 和 *TB* 没有被探测到。

系统不确定度

噪声、校准、补偿和指向

为了评估系统不确定度对似然结果的影响，我们重复了这九组的每一个分析，但是对那些我们已经知道的反映各自不同的不确定范围的效应作了替代的假设。

本文展示的大部分数据分析都尝试研究数据和噪声模型（在"噪声模型"部分讨论）的一致性。我们发现不同时间尺度的互补噪声估计量之间并无差异，均为 $\ll 1\%$ 的水平。正如"χ^2 检验"部分讨论过的，我们对自相关偏振和交叉相关偏振的可视性数据的子集进行了大量的一致性检验，没有迹象表明有一个噪声误差能够达到类似的水平。我们将噪声按比例缩放 1%，重复"似然结果"部分的每一个分析，发现所有参数的最大似然估计值的偏移完全可以忽略不计。

在"噪声模型"部分，我们报告了存在于实部/虚部可视度之间，以及相同基线上不同频带之间可视性的某些可探测噪声相关性的证据。把这些噪声相关的其中一个或两个全部添加到协方差矩阵（在实际测量到的水平上），它们的影响再次可以忽略不计：最显著的偏移出现在 *E5/B5* 分析中 *E* 谱的最高 *l* 频段上（参见"*E5/B5*"部分），其中功率偏移了约 $2\ \mu K^2$。

Errors in the determination of the absolute cross-polar phase offsets will mix power between E and B; these phase offsets have been independently determined from wire-grid calibrations and observations of the Moon, and found to agree to within the measurement uncertainties of about 0.4° (ref. 51). Reanalysis of the data with the measured phase offsets shifted by 2° demonstrates that the likelihood results are immune to errors of this magnitude: the most significant effect occurs in the highest-l band of the TE spectrum from the T, E, $TE5$ analysis (see the "$T/E/TE5$" subsection), where the power shifts by about 30 μK^2.

The on-axis leakages described in the "On-axis leakage" subsection will mix power from T into E and B, and the data are corrected for this effect in the course of reduction, before input to any analyses. When the likelihood analyses are performed without the leakage correction, the largest effects appear in the shaped TE amplitude analysis (see "$T/E/TE$" subsection), and the lowest-l band of $TE5$ from the T, E, $TE5$ analysis (see the "$T/E/TE5$" subsection); all shifts are tiny compared to the 68% confidence intervals. As the leakage correction itself has little impact on the results, the uncertainties in the correction, which are at the $< 1\%$ level, will have no noticeable effect.

As described in the "Off-axis leakage" subsection, the off-axis leakage from the feeds is a more significant effect, and is accounted for in the likelihood analysis by modelling its contribution to the covariance matrix. When this correction is not applied, the E, B results (see "E/B analysis" subsection) shift by about 4% and 2%, respectively, as expected from simulations of this effect. Although this bias is already small, the simulations show that the correction removes it completely to the degree to which we understand the off-axis leakage. Uncertainties in the leakage profiles of the order of the fit residuals (see ref. 51) lead to shifts of less than 1%.

The pointing accuracy of the telescope is measured to be better than 2 arcmin and the root-mean-square tracking errors are < 20 arcsec; as we discussed in refs 49 and 6, this is more than sufficient for the characterization of CMB anisotropy at the much larger angular scales measured by DASI.

Absolute calibration of the telescope was achieved through measurements of external thermal loads, transferred to the calibrator RCW38. The dominant uncertainty in the calibration is due to temperature and coupling of the thermal loads. As reported in ref. 6, we estimate an overall calibration uncertainty of 8% (1σ), expressed as a fractional uncertainty on the C_l bandpowers (4% in $\Delta T/T$). This applies equally to the temperature and polarization data presented here.

Foregrounds

Point sources. The highest-sensitivity point-source catalogue in our observing region is the 5-GHz PMN survey[62]. For our first-season temperature analysis described in refs 49

确定绝对交叉–偏振相位补偿时的误差会混合在 E 和 B 的功率之间，这些相位补偿是通过导线网格校准和对月球的观测独立确定的，且发现其在约 0.4° 的测量误差值（参考文献 51）之内。用测量到的偏移量为 2° 的相位补偿对数据进行重新分析表明，似然结果不受这个程度的误差影响：最显著的影响发生在 T、E、$TE5$ 分析（参见"$T/E/TE$"部分）中 TE 谱的最高 l 频段上，其中功率偏移了约 $30\ \mu K^2$。

"共轴渗漏"部分描述过的共轴渗漏会将 T 功率混入到 E 和 B 功率中，在作任何分析之前，数据会在还原过程中校正掉该效应。若似然分析之前并未做渗漏校准，受影响最显著的是在成形的 TE 幅度分析（参见"$T/E/TE$"部分）和 T、E、$TE5$ 分析（参见"$T/E/TE5$"部分）中 $TE5$ 的最低 l 频段上。相比较于 68% 置信区间，所有的偏移都是微小的。由于渗漏校准本身对结果几乎没有影响，校准时候的误差——小于 1% 的程度——将不会有明显的影响。

如同在"离轴渗漏"部分中所描述的，来自馈源的离轴渗漏是一个更加显著的效应。我们根据其在协方差矩阵的贡献进行建模以解释该效应对似然分析的影响。若不使用该校准，如同模拟该效应时所预料的那样，E、B 结果（参见"E/B 分析"部分）分别偏移约 4% 和 2%。虽然这种偏差已经很小，但模拟表明，就我们所理解的离轴渗漏的程度，校正能将其完全消除。达到拟合残差（参考文献 51）量级的渗漏带来的不确定性会导致的偏移小于 1%。

我们测得望远镜的指向精度优于 2 角分，均方根跟踪误差 <20 角秒。正如我们在参考文献 49 和 6 中所讨论的那样，这个精度对刻画在 DASI 测量的更大角尺度上的 CMB 各向异性已经足够了。

望远镜的绝对校准是通过测量外部热负荷给出的，并传输到 RCW38 定标器上。校准的最重要的不确定性来源于温度和热负荷的耦合。如参考文献 6 中报告的，我们估计存在 8%（1σ）的总体校准不确定度，C_l 频段功率的不确定度表示为分数（在 $\Delta T/T$ 中占 4%）。这同样适用于温度和偏振数据。

前景

点源 我们观测区域中灵敏度最高的点源星表是 5 GHz PMN 巡天[62]。对于参考文献 49 和 6 所描述的第一季度温度分析，我们就是利用此目录来剔除已知点源

and 6 we projected out known sources using this catalogue. We have kept this procedure for the temperature data presented here, projecting the same set of sources as before.

Unfortunately the PMN survey is not polarization sensitive. We note that the distribution of point-source polarization fractions is approximately exponential (see below). Total intensity is thus a poor indicator of polarized intensity and it is therefore not sensible to project out the PMN sources in our polarization analysis.

Our polarization fields were selected for the absence of any significant point-source detections in the first-season data. No significant detections are found in the 2001–02 data, either in the temperature data, which are dominated by CMB anisotropy, or in the polarization data.

To calculate the expected contribution of undetected point sources to our polarization results we would like to know the distribution of polarized flux densities, but unfortunately no such information exists in our frequency range. However, to make an estimate, we use the distribution of total intensities, and then assume a distribution of polarization fractions. We know the former distribution quite well from our own first-season 32-field data where we detect 31 point sources and determine that $dN/dS_{31} = (32 \pm 7)S^{(-2.15\pm0.20)}$ $\mathrm{Jy^{-1}sr^{-1}}$ in the range 0.1 to 10 Jy. This is consistent, when extrapolated to lower flux densities, with a result from the CBI experiment valid in the range 5–50 mJy (ref. 63). The distribution of point source polarization fractions at 5 GHz can be characterized by an exponential with a mean of 3.8% (ref. 64); data of somewhat lower quality at 15 GHz are consistent with the same distribution[65]. Qualitatively, we expect the polarization fraction of synchrotron-dominated sources initially to rise with frequency, and then reach a plateau or fall, with the break point at frequencies $\ll 5$ GHz (see ref. 66 for an example). In the absence of better data we have conservatively assumed that the exponential distribution mentioned above continues to hold at 30 GHz.

We proceed to estimate the effect of point sources by Monte Carlo simulation, generating realizations using the total intensity and polarization fraction distributions mentioned above. For each realization, we generate simulated DASI data by adding a realization of CMB anisotropy and appropriate instrument noise. The simulated data are tested for evidence of point sources and those realizations that show statistics similar to the real data are kept. The effect of off-axis leakage, which we describe and quantify in ref. 51, is included in these calculations.

When the simulated data are passed through the E/B analysis described in the "E/B analysis" subsection, the mean bias of the E parameter is 0.04 with a standard deviation of 0.05; in 95% of cases the shift distance in the E/B plane is less than 0.13. We conclude that the presence of point sources consistent with our observed data has a relatively small effect on our polarization results.

Diffuse foregrounds. In ref. 51, we find no evidence for contamination of the

的。我们对这里所呈现的温度数据保留了同样的处理，和以前一样剔除掉了相同的点源集。

很遗憾的是，PMN 巡天对偏振并不敏感，我们注意到，点源偏振部分的分布大致呈指数分布（见下文），故而总强度不能代表偏振强度，因此做偏振分析时，剔除 PMN 源是不明智的。

在第一季度数据中没有发现任何显著的点源信号，据此我们选择偏振视场。在 2001 年～2002 年数据中，无论是由 CMB 各向异性主导的温度数据还是偏振数据，我们未发现显著的信号。

为了预先计算未被检测到的点源对我们的偏振结果的贡献，我们希望知道被偏振的通量密度的分布，但遗憾的是在我们的频率范围内并不存在这样的信息。但是，为了对其进行估算，我们使用总强度的分布，然后假设偏振部分的分布函数。从第一季度 32 视场数据中，我们对前者的分布有了很好的了解，在那里我们探测到 31 个点源并确定在 0.1 到 10 Jy 范围内有 $dN/dS_{31} = (32 \pm 7)S^{(-2.15 \pm 0.20)} Jy^{-1} \cdot sr^{-1}$。当外推到较低的通量密度时，它的结果和从 CBI 实验（参考文献 63）在 5～50 mJy 范围的结果是一致的。5 GHz 处的点源偏振部分的分布可以用平均值为 3.8%（参考文献 64）的指数分布表征，15 GHz 处的那些质量稍低的数据具有相同的分布[65]。定性地说，我们预计同步加速机制主导的源的偏振部分首先随着频率上升而增大，然后达到平稳水平或达到频率 <<5 GHz 的转折点后下降（例子请参见参考文献 66）。在没有更好的数据的情况下，我们保守地假设上面提到的指数分布直到 30 GHz 仍适用。

我们继续使用蒙特卡罗模拟估计点源的影响，使用上面提到的总强度和偏振部分的分布生成实现。对于每个实现，我们通过加入一个 CMB 各向异性信号和适当的仪器噪声来生成模拟的 DASI 数据。我们就点源的痕迹对模拟数据进行检测，然后保留那些具有同实际数据相近的统计量的实现。离轴渗漏——我们在文献 51 中对其进行描述和量化——的影响已经包含在这些计算中了。

当模拟数据通过"E/B 分析"部分描述的方法进行 E/B 分析时，E 参数的平均偏差为 0.04，其中标准差为 0.05；在占 95% 的案例中，E/B 平面中的偏移距离小于 0.13。我们得出结论，若点源与我们观察到的数据一致，则它们的存在对我们的偏振结果的影响相对较小。

弥散前景　正如"T/β_T"部分对温度谱指数的限制所证实的，在参考文献 51 中，

temperature data by synchrotron, dust or free–free emission, as confirmed by the limits on the temperature spectral index presented in the "T/β_T" subsection. The expected fractional polarization of the CMB is of order 10%, while the corresponding number for free–free emission is less than 1%. Diffuse thermal dust emission may be polarized by several per cent (see for example ref. 67), although we note that polarization of the admixture of dust and free–free emission observed with DASI in NGC 6334 is ≪ 1% (see ref. 51). Likewise, emission from spinning dust is not expected to be polarized at detectable levels[68]. Therefore if free–free and dust emission did not contribute significantly to our temperature anisotropy results they are not expected to contribute to the polarization. Synchrotron emission on the other hand can in principle be up to 70% polarized, and is by far the greatest concern; what was a negligible contribution in the temperature case could be a significant one in polarization.

There are no published polarization maps in the region of our fields. Previous attempts to estimate the angular power spectrum of polarized synchrotron emission have been guided by surveys of the Galactic plane at frequencies of 1–3 GHz (refs 69 and 70). These maps show much more small-scale structure in polarization than in temperature, but this is mostly induced by Faraday rotation[71], an effect which is negligible at 30 GHz. In addition, because synchrotron emission is highly concentrated in the disk of the Galaxy it is not valid to assume that the angular power spectrum at low Galactic latitudes has much to tell us about that at high latitudes[72].

Our fields lie at Galactic latitude −58.4° and −61.9°. The brightness of the IRAS 100 μm and Haslam 408 MHz (ref. 52) maps within our fields lie at the 6% and 25% points, respectively, of the integral distributions taken over the whole sky. There are several strong pieces of evidence from the DASI data set itself that the polarization results described in this paper are free of significant synchrotron contamination. The significant TE correlation shown in Fig. 6 indicates that the temperature and E-mode signal have a common origin. The tight constraints on the temperature anisotropy spectral index require that this common origin has a spectrum consistent with CMB. Galactic synchrotron emission is known to have a temperature spectral index of −2.8 (ref. 73), with evidence for steepening to −3.0 at frequencies above 1–2 GHz (ref. 74). At frequencies where Faraday depolarization is negligible (> 10 GHz), the same index will also apply for polarization. The dramatically tight constraint on the temperature spectral index of $\beta_T = 0.01$ (−0.16 to 0.14) indicates that any component of the temperature signal coming from synchrotron emission is negligibly small in comparison to the CMB. More directly, the constraint on the E-mode spectral index $\beta_E = 0.17$ (−1.63 to 1.92) disfavours synchrotron polarization at nearly 2σ. A third, albeit weaker, line of argument is that a complex synchrotron emitting structure is not expected to produce a projected brightness distribution which prefers E-mode polarization over B-mode[75]. Therefore, the result in Fig. 3 could be taken as further evidence that the signal we are seeing is not due to synchrotron emission.

我们没有发现同步加速、尘埃或者自由–自由辐射污染温度数据的迹象。CMB 的偏振部分预计达到 10% 的程度，而自由–自由辐射对应的偏振部分小于 1%。尽管我们注意到用 DASI 观察到的 NGC 6334 尘埃和自由–自由辐射的混合偏振 <<1%（参考文献 51），但是弥散的热尘埃辐射可能会被偏振几个百分点（如参考文献 67）。同样地，自旋尘埃辐射的偏振程度预计不会达到可探测水平[68]。因此，如果自由–自由和尘埃热辐射对我们的温度各向异性结果没有显著贡献，则可以预料它们不会对偏振产生影响。另一方面，同步加速辐射的偏振率原则上可以高达 70%，这也是目前最被关注的问题。它对温度的贡献可以忽略不计，但可能对偏振有显著贡献。

我们视场区域不存在已经公布过的偏振天图。之前尝试估计计划的同步辐射角功率谱是根据频率为 1–3 GHz 的银道面巡天（参考文献 69 和 70）来做的。这些天图显示的偏振结构尺度比温度的更小，但这主要是由法拉第旋转[71]引起的，该效应在 30 GHz 处可以忽略不计。此外，由于同步辐射高度集中在银河星系盘中，因此通过假设的低银河系纬度的角功率谱是无法知道高纬度地区的角功率谱的[72]。

我们的视场位于银河纬度 −58.4° 和 −61.9° 之间。在我们的视场内，IRAS 100 μm 和哈斯拉姆 408 MHz（参考文献 52）天图的亮度分别占整个天空 6% 和 25% 点的分布。几个来自 DASI 自身数据集的有力证据表明本文所述的偏振结果没有受到显著的同步辐射污染。图 6 所示的 *TE* 强相关性表明温度和 *E* 模信号具有共同的起源。对温度各向异性谱指数的严格约束要求这个共同起源具有与 CMB 相一致的频谱。已知银河同步辐射的温度谱指数为 −2.8（参考文献 73），有证据表明它在频率高于 1～2 GHz 时变陡峭，谱指数为 −3.0（参考文献 74）。在对法拉第消偏振可忽略不计（> 10 GHz）的频率处，相同的谱指数同样适用于偏振。在温度谱指数 $\beta_T = 0.01$（置信度为 68% 的参数区间为 −0.16 至 0.14）的严格约束下，与 CMB 相比，任何来自同步辐射的温度信号都可忽略不计。更直接地，*E* 模式谱指数 $\beta_E = 0.17$（置信度为 68% 的参数区间为 −1.63 至 1.92）的限制在近 2σ 水平下和同步辐射偏振不符。第三个（虽然较弱的）论证思路是，复杂的同步辐射结构预计不会产生一个 *E* 模式优于 *B* 模式的投影亮度分布[75]。因此，图 3 中的结果可以进一步证明我们看到的信号不是来自同步辐射。

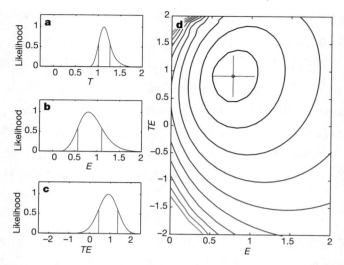

Fig. 6. Results from the three-parameter shaped bandpower $T/E/TE$ joint analysis. Spectral shapes as predicted for the concordance model are assumed (**a–c**) and the units are relative to that model. The layout of the plot is analogous to Fig. 3. The two-dimensional distribution in **d** is marginalized over the T dimension.

Discussion

This paper presents several measures of the confidence with which CMB polarization has been detected with DASI. Which measure is preferred depends on the desired level of statistical rigour and independence from *a priori* models of the polarization. The χ^2 analyses in the "χ^2 tests" subsection offer the most model-independent results, although the linear combinations of the data used to form the s/n eigenmodes are selected by consideration of theory and the noise model. For the high s/n eigenmodes of the polarization data, the probability to exceed (PTE) the measured χ^2 for the sum of the various data splits ranges from 1.6×10^{-8} to 8.7×10^{-7}, while the χ^2 for the differences are found to be consistent with noise. The PTE for the χ^2 found for the total (that is, not split) high s/n polarization eigenmodes, corrected for the beam offset leakage, is 5.7×10^{-8}.

Likelihood analyses are in principle more model dependent, and the analyses reported make different assumptions for the shape of the polarization power spectrum. Using theory to select the angular scales on which DASI should be most sensitive, we calculate the likelihood for a flat bandpower in E and B over the multipole range $300 < l < 450$ and find that data are consistent with $B = 0$ over this range, but that $E = 0$ can be rejected with a PTE of 5.9×10^{-9}.

The choice of the model bandpower is more important when the full l range of the DASI data is analysed. In this case, the likelihood analyses indicate that a $l(l+1)C_l \propto l^2$ model for the E-mode spectrum is 60 times more likely than a $l(l+1)C_l =$ constant model. Further, a bandpass shape based on the concordance model is found to be 12,000 times more

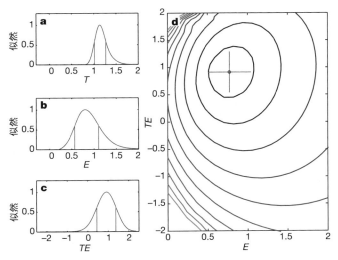

图 6. 三参数型频带功率 $T/E/TE$ 联合分析的结果。假设谱形状满足协调模型（**a** ~ **c**），而单位则是相对于该模型的。该图的布局类似于图 3。**d** 中的二维分布是边缘化 T 维度得到的。

讨　论

本文提出了用 DASI 检测 CMB 偏振的几种置信度测量方法。首选哪种测量方法取决于所需的统计精度和是否独立于偏振的先验模型。尽管用于构成信噪比 (s/n) 本征模的数据的线性组合是基于理论和噪声模型来选择的，"χ^2 检验"部分中的 χ^2 分析还是给出了一个最不依赖于模型的结果。对于偏振数据的高信噪比本征模，用不同数据分割的求和计算给出的超过测量得到的 χ^2 的概率（PTE）范围从 1.6×10^{-8} 到 8.7×10^{-7} 不等。另外，对分割数据的差值计算给出的 χ^2 被发现和噪声是一致的。将光束偏移渗漏校准后，全部的（即不是分割的）高信噪比偏振本征模给出的 χ^2 的 PTE 是 5.7×10^{-8}。

似然分析原则上更加依赖于模型，且就本文报告的分析，我们对偏振功率谱的形状做出了不同的假设。根据理论来选择 DASI 理应最为敏感的角度范围，我们计算了多极矩范围为 $300 < l < 450$ 的一个平坦频段模型的 E 和 B 的似然函数。我们发现，在此范围内数据与 $B = 0$ 一致，但是 $E = 0$ 的 PTE 为 5.9×10^{-9}，故该假设可以被拒绝。

分析完整 l 范围的 DASI 数据时，模型频段功率的选择更为重要。在这种情况下，似然分析表明对于 E 模式频谱，$l(l+1)C_l \propto l^2$ 的模型是 $l(l+1)C_l =$ 常数的模型的可能性的 60 倍。此外我们发现，基于协调模型的带通形状是平坦频段功率的可能性

likely than the flat bandpower. The likelihood ratio test leads to a PTE of 8.5×10^{-7} for the concordance shaped bandpower, corresponding to a confidence of detection of 4.9σ. In all three of these tests, B is found to be consistent with zero, as expected in the concordance model.

The concordance model is also supported by the results of the five-band piecewise-flat analyses, $E5/B5$. The upper limit for the first E band at $28 \leqslant l \leqslant 245$ is only 2.38 μK^2, a factor of 30 lower in power than the previous upper limit. The next band at $246 \leqslant l \leqslant 420$ is detected with a maximum likelihood value of 17.1 μK^2. Such a sharp rise in power with increasing l is expected in the E-mode spectrum (see Fig. 4) owing to the length scale introduced by the mean free path to photon scattering. The polarization of the larger modes is suppressed because the velocity differences are not as large on the scale of the mean free path. In fact, the E spectrum is expected to increase as $l(l+1)C_l \propto l^2$ at small l. This dependence is not expected to continue to the higher l values to which DASI is sensitive, owing to diffusion damping, which suppresses power on scales smaller than the mean free path. The maximum likelihood values of the higher l bands of the DASI five-band E analysis are consistent with the damped concordance model, but lie below a simple extrapolation of the l^2 power law. Again, the five-band B-mode spectrum is consistent with the concordance prediction of zero.

The TE analysis provides further confidence in our detection of CMB polarization and for the concordance model. From the $T/E/TE$ likelihood analysis, the $TE = 0$ hypothesis is rejected with a PTE of 0.054. Note that TE could be negative as well as positive and therefore the $TE \leqslant 0$ hypothesis is rejected with higher confidence.

Lastly, the measured T frequency spectral index, 0.01 (-0.16 to 0.14), is remarkably well constrained to be thermal and is inconsistent with any known foregrounds. The E frequency spectral index, 0.17 (-1.63 to 1.92), is also consistent with the CMB, and although less well constrained than the T index, is inconsistent with diffuse foreground synchrotron emission at nearly 2σ.

In summary, the analyses reported in this paper all indicate a robust detection of E-mode CMB polarization with a confidence level $\geqslant 4.9\sigma$. The measured properties of the polarization are in good agreement with predictions of the concordance model and, as discussed in the "Foregrounds" subsection, are inconsistent with expectations from known sources of foreground emission. These results therefore provide strong support for the underlying theoretical framework for the generation of CMB anisotropy. They lend confidence to the values of the cosmological parameters and to the extraordinary picture of the origin and structure of the Universe derived from CMB measurements. The prospect of further refining our understanding of the Universe using precision polarization measurements is the goal of many ongoing and planned CMB experiments. The detection of polarization at the predicted level reported in this paper points to a promising future for the field.

(**420**, 772-787; 2002)

的 12,000 倍。似然比检验给出一致形状频段功率的 PTE 为 8.5×10^{-7}，对应探测置信度为 4.9σ。在所有这三个检验中，我们发现，正如在协调模型中所预期的那样，B 与零一致。

五频段分段–平坦分析 ($E5/B5$) 的结果同样支持协调模型。在 $28 \leqslant l \leqslant 245$ 处的第一个 E 频段的上限仅为 2.38 μK²，功率是前一个上限的三十分之一。在 $246 \leqslant l \leqslant 420$ 处的第二个频段的最大似然值为 17.1 μK²。由于光子散射的平均自由程引入的长度标度，出现在 E 模式功率谱（参见图 4）的这种随着 l 的增加功率急剧上升的现象是在预料之中的。由于较大模式上的速度差异没有平均自由程尺度上的那么大，因此这些模式的偏振会被抑制。实际上，l 较小时，E 谱预计会以 $l(l+1)C_l \propto l^2$ 形式上升，但由于扩散阻尼抑制了小于平均自由程尺度上的功率，故这种依赖性不会保持到 DASI 敏感的较高的 l 值。在 DASI 五频段 E 分析中，较高 l 频段的最大似然值的和带阻尼的协调模型一致，但位于 l^2 幂律的简单外推模型的下方。同样，正如协调模型所预测的，五频段 B 模式功率谱与零一致。

TE 分析进一步使我们增强了对于 CMB 偏振信号的存在和协调模型的信心。根据 $T/E/TE$ 似然分析，TE 为零的假设以 0.054 的 PTE 被拒绝。注意，TE 可正可负，因此 $TE \leqslant 0$ 假设以更高的置信度被拒绝。

最后，T 的谱指数的测量值为 0.01（置信度为 68% 的参数区间为 −0.16 至 0.14），极好地被约束在热的且不属于任何已知的前景。E 的谱指数为 0.17（置信度为 68% 的参数区间为 −1.63 至 1.92）也与 CMB 一致，虽然比起 T、E 的谱指数约束得不那么好，但与弥散前景同步辐射存在近 2σ 的不一致性。

总之，本文报道的分析均表明存在一个显著的 CMB 的 E 偏振模式信号，其中置信水平 $\geqslant 4.9\sigma$。测量到的偏振的特性和调和模型给出的预测非常一致，并且如"前景"部分所讨论的那样，与目前已知的前景辐射都不匹配。因此，这些结果为 CMB 各向异性的起源的基础理论框架提供了强而有力的支持，从而使得从 CMB 测量推导得出的宇宙学参数的值以及宇宙起源和结构的庞大图景更为可信。使用精确偏振测量进一步完善我们对宇宙的理解是许多正在进行的和计划中的 CMB 实验的目标。本文报道的探测到预计水平的偏振信号为该领域的光明未来指明了方向。

（谭秀慧 吕孟珍 翻译；夏俊卿 审稿）

Detection of Polarization in the Cosmic Microwave Background Using DASI

J. M. Kovac[*†‡], **E. M. Leitch**[§†‡], **C. Pryke**[§†‡||], **J. E. Carlstrom**[§*†‡||], **N. W. Halverson**[¶†] & **W. L. Holzapfel**[¶†]

[*] Department of Physics; [†] Center for Astrophysical Research in Antarctica; [‡] Center for Cosmological Physics; [§] Department of Astronomy & Astrophysics and [||] Enrico Fermi Institute, University of Chicago, 5640 South Ellis Avenue, Chicago, Illinois 60637, USA

[¶] Department of Physics, University of California at Berkeley, Le Conte Hall, California 94720, USA

Received 7 October; accepted 5 November 2002; doi:10.1038/nature 01269.

References:

1. Penzias, A. A. & Wilson, R. W. A measurement of excess antenna temperature at 4080 Mc/s. *Astrophys. J.* **142**, 419-421 (1965).

2. Mather, J. C. *et al.* Measurement of the cosmic microwave background spectrum by the COBE FIRAS instrument. *Astrophys. J.* **420**, 439-444 (1994).

3. Fixsen, D. J. *et al.* The cosmic microwave background spectrum from the full COBE FIRAS data set. *Astrophys. J.* **473**, 576-587 (1996).

4. Smoot, G. F. *et al.* Structure in the COBE differential microwave radiometer first-year maps. *Astrophys. J.* **396**, L1-L5 (1992).

5. Miller, A. D. *et al.* A measurement of the angular power spectrum of the cosmic microwave background form l = 100 to 400. *Astrophys. J.* **524**, L1-L4 (1999).

6. Halverson, N. W. *et al.* Degree angular scale interferometer first results: A measurement of the cosmic microwave background angular power spectrum. *Astrophys. J.* **568**, 38-45 (2002).

7. Netterfield, C. B. *et al.* A measurement by BOOMERANG of multiple peaks in the angular power spectrum of the cosmic microwave background. *Astrophys. J.* **571**, 604-614 (2002).

8. Lee, A. T. *et al.* A high spatial resolution analysis of the MAXIMA-1 cosmic microwave background anisotropy data. *Astrophys. J.* **561**, L1-L5 (2001).

9. Pearson, T. J. *et al.* The anisotropy of the microwave background to l = 3500: Mosaic observations with the cosmic background imager. *Astrophys. J.* (submitted); preprint astro-ph/0205388 at ⟨http://xxx.lanl.gov⟩ (2002).

10. Scott, P. F. *et al.* First results from the Very Small Array - III. The CMB power spectrum. *Mon. Not. R. Astron. Soc.* (submitted); preprint astro-ph/0205380 at ⟨http://xxx.lanl.gov⟩ (2002).

11. Hu, W. & Dodelson, S. Cosmic microwave background anisotropies. *Annu. Rev. Astron. Astrophys.* **40**, 171-216 (2002).

12. Kaiser, N. Small-angle anisotropy of the microwave background radiation in the adiabatic theory. *Mon. Not. R. Astron. Soc.* **202**, 1169-1180 (1983).

13. Bond, J. R. & Efstathiou, G. Cosmic background radiation anisotropies in universes dominated by nonbaryonic dark matter. *Astrophys. J.* **285**, L45-L48 (1984).

14. Polnarev, A. G. Polarization and anisotropy induced in the microwave background by cosmological gravitational waves. *Sov. Astron.* **29**, 607-613 (1985).

15. Kamionkowski, M., Kosowsky, A. & Stebbins, A. Statistics of cosmic microwave background polarization. *Phys. Rev. D.* **55**, 7368-7388 (1997).

16. Zaldarriaga, M. & Seljak, U. All-sky analysis of polarization in the microwave background. *Phys. Rev.D.* **55**, 1830-1840 (1997).

17. Hu, W. & White, M. A CMB polarization primer. *New Astron.* **2**, 323-344 (1997).

18. Kosowsky, A. Introduction to microwave background polarization. *New Astron. Rev.* **43**, 157-168 (1999).

19. Hu, W., Spergel, D. N. & White, M. Distinguishing causal seeds from inflation. *Phys. Rev. D* **55**, 3288-3302 (1997).

20. Kinney, W. H. How to fool cosmic microwave background parameter estimation. *Phys. Rev. D* **63**, 43001 (2001).

21. Bucher, M., Moodley, K. & Turok, N. Constraining isocurvature perturbations with cosmic microwave background polarization. *Phys. Rev. Lett.* **87**, 191301 (2001).

22. Rees, M. J. Polarization and spectrum of the primeval radiation in an anisotropic universe. *Astrophys. J.* **153**, L1-L5 (1968).

23. Zaldarriaga, M. & Harari, D. D. Analytic approach to the polarization of the cosmic microwave background in flat and open universes. *Phys. Rev. D* **52**, 3276-3287 (1995).

24. Coulson, D., Crittenden, R. G. & Turok, N. G. Polarization and anisotropy of the microwave sky. *Phys. Rev. Lett.* **73**, 2390-2393 (1994).

25. Crittenden, R., Davis, R. L. & Steinhardt, P. J. Polarization of the microwave background due to primordial gravitational waves. *Astrophys. J.* **417**, L13-L16 (1993).

26. Seljak, U. Measuring polarization in the cosmic microwave background. *Astrophys. J.* **482**, 6-16 (1997).

27. Kamionkowski, M., Kosowsky, A. & Stebbins, A. A probe of primordial gravity waves and vorticity. *Phys. Rev. Lett.* **78**, 2058-2061 (1997).

28. Seljak, U. & Zaldarriaga, M. Signature of gravity waves in the polarization of the microwave background. *Phys. Rev. Lett.* **78**, 2054-2057 (1997).

29. Lyth, D. H. What would we learn by detecting a gravitational wave signal in the Cosmic Microwave Background anisotropy? *Phys. Rev. Lett.* **78**, 1861-1863 (1997).

30. Zaldarriaga, M. & Seljak, U. Gravitational lensing effect on cosmic microwave background polarization. *Phys. Rev. D* **58**, 23003 (1998).

31. Hu, W. & Okamoto, T. Mass reconstruction with cosmic microwave background polarization. *Astrophys. J.* **574**, 566-574 (2002).

32. Knox, L. & Song, Y. A limit on the detectability of the energy scale of inflation. *Phys. Rev. Lett.* **89**, 011303 (2002).

33. Kesden, M., Cooray, A. & Kamionkowski, M. Separation of gravitational-wave and cosmic-shear contributions to cosmic microwave background polarization. *Phys. Rev. Lett.* **89**, 011304 (2002).

34. Kamionkowski, M. & Kosowsky, A. The cosmic microwave background and particle physics. *Annu. Rev. Nucl. Part. Sci.* **49**, 77-123 (1999).

35. Staggs, S. T., Gunderson, J. O. & Church, S. E. *ASP Conf. Ser. 181, Microwave Foregrounds* (eds de Oliveira-Costa, A. & Tegmark, M.) 299-309 (Astronomical Society of the Pacific, San Francisco, 1999).

36. Caderni, N., Fabbri, R., Melchiorri, B., Melchiorri, F. & Natale, V. Polarization of the microwave background radiation. II. An infrared survey of the sky. *Phys. Rev. D* **17**, 1908-1918 (1978).

37. Nanos, G. P. Polarization of the blackbody radiation at 3.2 centimeters. *Astrophys. J.* **232**, 341-347 (1979).

38. Lubin, P. M. & Smoot, G. F. Search for linear polarization of the cosmic background radiation. *Phys. Rev. Lett.* **42**, 129-132 (1979).

39. Lubin, P. M. & Smoot, G. F. Polarization of the cosmic background radiation. *Astrophys. J.* **245**, 1-17 (1981).

40. Lubin, P., Melese, P. & Smoot, G. Linear and circular polarization of the cosmic background radiation. *Astrophys. J.* **273**, L51-L54 (1983).

41. Sironi, G. *et al.* A 33 GHZ polarimeter for observations of the cosmic microwave background. *New Astron.* **3**, 1-13 (1997).

42. Keating, B. G. *et al.* A limit on the large angular scale polarization of the cosmic microwave background. *Astrophys. J.* **560**, L1-L4 (2001).

43. Wollack, E. J., Jarosik, N. C., Netterfield, C. B., Page, L. A. & Wilkinson, D. A measurement of the anisotropy in the cosmic microwave background radiation at degree angular scales. *Astrophys. J.* **419**, L49-L52 (1993).

44. Hedman, M. M. *et al.* New limits on the polarized anisotropy of the cosmic microwave background at subdegree angular scales. *Astrophys. J.* **573**, L73-L76 (2002).

45. Cartwright, J. K. *et al.* Polarization observations with the cosmic background imager. in *Moriond Workshop 37, The Cosmological Model* (in the press).

46. de Oliveira-Costa, A. *et al.* First attempt at measuring the CMB cross-polarization. *Phys. Rev. D* (submitted); preprint astro-ph/0204021 at ⟨http://xxx.lanl.gov⟩ (2002).

47. Partridge, R. B., Richards, E. A., Fomalont, E. B., Kellermann, K. I. & Windhorst, R. A. Small-scale cosmic microwave background observations at 8.4 GHz. *Astrophys. J.* **483**, 38-50 (1997).

48. Subrahmanyan, R., Kesteven, M. J., Ekers, R. D., Sinclair, M. & Silk, J. An Australia telescope survey for CMB anisotropies. *Mon. Not. R. Astron. Soc.* **315**, 808-822 (2000).

49. Leitch, E. M. *et al.* Experiment design and first season observations with the degree angular scale interferometer. *Astrophys. J.* **568**, 28-37 (2002).

50. Pryke, C. *et al.* Cosmological parameter extraction from the first season of observations with the degree angular scale interferometer. *Astrophys. J.* **568**, 46-51 (2002).

51. Leitch, E. M. *et al.* Measurement of polarization with the Degree Angular Scale Interferometer. *Nature* **420**, 763-771 (2002).

52. Haslam, C. G. T. *et al.* A 408 MHz all-sky continuum survey. I—Observations at southern declinations and for the north polar region. *Astron. Astrophys.* **100**, 209-219 (1981).

53. Bond, J. R., Jaffe, A. H. & Knox, L. Estimating the power spectrum of the cosmic microwave background. *Phys. Rev. D* **57**, 2117-2137 (1998).

54. Seljak, U. & Zaldarriaga, M. A line-of-sight integration approach to cosmic microwave background anisotropies. *Astrophys. J.* **469**, 437-444 (1996).

55. White, M., Carlstrom, J. E., Dragovan, M. & Holzapfel, W. H. Interferometric observation of cosmic microwave background anisotropies. *Astrophys. J.* **514**, 12-24 (1999).

56. Hedman, M. M., Barkats, D., Gundersen, J. O., Staggs, S. T. & Winstein, B. A limit on the polarized anisotropy of the cosmic microwave background at subdegree angular scales. *Astrophys. J.* **548**, L111-L114 (2001).

57. Knox, L. Cosmic microwave background anisotropy window functions revisited. *Phys. Rev. D* **60**, 103516 (1999).

58. Halverson, N. W. *A Measurement of the Cosmic Microwave Background Angular Power Spectrum with DASI.* PhD thesis, Caltech (2002).

59. Tegmark, M. & de Oliveira-Costa, A. How to measure CMB polarization power spectra without losing information. *Phys. Rev. D* **64**, 063001 (2001).

60. Christensen, N., Meyer, R., Knox, L. & Luey, B. Bayesian methods for cosmological parameter estimation from cosmic microwave background measurements. *Class. Quant. Gravity* **18**, 2677-2688 (2001).

61. Wang, X., Tegmark, M. & Zaldarriaga, M. Is cosmology consistent? *Phys. Rev. D* **65**, 123001 (2002).

62. Wright, A. E., Griffith, M. R., Burke, B. F. & Ekers, R. D. The Parkes-MIT-NRAO (PMN) surveys. 2: Source catalog for the southern survey ($-87.5° < \delta < -37°$). *Astrophys. J. Suppl.* **91**, 111-308 (1994).

63. Mason, B. S., Pearson, T. J., Readhead, A. C. S., Shepherd, M. C. & Sievers, J. L. The anisotropy of the microwave background to l = 3500: Deep field observations with the cosmic background imager. *Astrophys. J.* (submitted); preprint astro-ph/0205384 at ⟨http://xxx.lanl.gov⟩ (2002).

64. Zukowski, E. L. H., Kronberg, P. P., Forkert, T. & Wielebinski, R. Linear polarization measurements of extragalactic radio sources at λ6.3 cm. *Astron. Astrophys. Suppl.* **135**, 571-577 (1999).

65. Simard-Normandin, M., Kronberg, P. P. & Neidhoefer, J. Linear polarization observations of extragalactic radio sources at 2 cm and at 17-19 cm. *Astron. Astrophys. Suppl.* **43**, 19-22 (1981).

66. Simard-Normandin, M., Kronberg, P. P. & Button, S. The Faraday rotation measures of extragalactic radio sources. *Astrophys. J. Suppl.* **45**, 97-111 (1981).

67. Hildebrand, R. H. *et al.* A primer on far-infrared polarimetry. *Publ. Astron. Soc. Pacif.* **112**, 1215-1235 (2000).

68. Lazarian, A. & Prunet, S. *AIP Conf. Proc. 609, Astrophysical Polarized Backgrounds* (eds Cecchini, S., Cortiglioni, S., Sault, R. & Sbarra, C.) 32-43 (AIP, Melville, New York, 2002).

69. Tegmark, M., Eisenstein, D. J., Hu, W. & de Oliveria-Costa, A. Foregrounds and forecasts for the cosmic microwave background. *Astrophys. J.* **530**, 133-165 (2000).

70. Giardino, G. *et al.* Towards a model of full-sky Galactic synchrotron intensity and linear polarisation: A re-analysis of the Parkes data. *Astron. Astrophys.* **387**, 82-97 (2002).

71. Gaensler, B. M. *et al.* Radio polarization from the inner galaxy at arcminute resolution. *Astrophys. J.* **549**, 959-978 (2001).

72. Gray, A. D. *et al.* Radio polarimetric imaging of the interstellar medium: Magnetic field and diffuse ionized gas structure near the W3/W4/W5/HB 3 complex. *Astrophys. J.* **514**, 221-231 (1999).

73. Platania, P. *et al.* A determination of the spectral index of galactic synchrotron emission in the 1–10 GHz range. *Astrophys. J.* **505**, 473-483 (1998).

74. Banday, A. J. & Wolfendale, A. W. Fluctuations in the galactic synchrotron radiation—I. Implications for searches for fluctuations of cosmological origin. *Mon. Not. R. Astron. Soc.* **248**, 705-714 (1991).

75. Zaldarriaga, M. The nature of the E-B decomposition of CMB polarization. *Phys. Rev. D* (submitted); preprint astro-ph/0106174 at ⟨http://xxx.lanl.gov⟩ (2001).

Acknowledgements. We are grateful for the efforts of B. Reddall and E. Sandberg, who wintered over at the National Science Foundation (NSF) Amundsen–Scott South Pole research station to keep DASI running smoothly. We are indebted to M. Dragovan for his role in making DASI a reality, and to the Caltech CBI team led by T. Readhead, in particular, to S. Padin, J. Cartwright, M. Shepherd and J. Yamasaki for the development of key hardware and software. We are indebted to the Center for Astrophysical Research in Antarctica (CARA), in particular to the CARA polar operations staff. We are grateful for contributions from K. Coble, A. Day, G. Drag, J. Kooi, E. LaRue, M. Loh, R. Lowenstein, S. Meyer, N. Odalen, R. Pernic, D. Pernic and E. Pernic, R. Spotz and M. Whitehead. We thank Raytheon Polar Services and the US Antarctic Program for their support of the DASI project. We have benefitted from many interactions with the Center for Cosmological Physics members and visitors. In particular, we gratefully acknowledge many conversations with W. Hu on CMB polarization and suggestions from S. Meyer, L. Page, M. Turner and B. Winstein on the presentation of these results. We thank L. Knox and A. Kosowsky for bringing the Markov technique to our attention. We thank the observatory staff of the Australia Telescope Compact Array, in particular B. Sault and R. Subrahmanyan, for providing point source observations of the DASI fields. This research was initially supported by the NSF under a cooperative agreement with CARA, a NSF Science and Technology Center. It is currently supported by an NSF-OPP grant. J.E.C. gratefully acknowledges support from the James S. McDonnell Foundation and the David and Lucile Packard Foundation. J.E.C. and C.P. gratefully acknowledge support from the Center for Cosmological Physics.

Competing interests statement. The authors declare that they have no competing financial interests.

Correspondence and requests for materials should be addressed to J.M.K. (e-mail: john@hyde.uchicago.edu).

Upper Limits to Submillimetre-range Forces from Extra Space-time Dimensions

J. C. Long *et al.*

Editor's Note

Gravity is the weakest of the four fundamental forces, being 40 orders of magnitude weaker than the electromagnetic force. In string theory—an attempt to unify the description of particles and forces—this weakness arises because the force is dissipated in six extra spatial dimensions that are "curled up" and therefore invisible to us. It has been suggested that the effect of these curled-up dimensions might become evident at very small length scales, whereby objects would feel more gravitation force at those scales. Here physicist Joshua Long and colleagues describe an experiment that looked for a deviation of the gravitational force from its familiar inverse-square law on length scales of 100 micrometres. They found no such deviation.

String theory is the most promising approach to the long-sought unified description of the four forces of nature and the elementary particles[1], but direct evidence supporting it is lacking. The theory requires six extra spatial dimensions beyond the three that we observe; it is usually supposed that these extra dimensions are curled up into small spaces. This "compactification" induces "moduli" fields, which describe the size and shape of the compact dimensions at each point in space-time. These moduli fields generate forces with strengths comparable to gravity, which according to some recent predictions[2-7] might be detected on length scales of about 100 μm. Here we report a search for gravitational-strength forces using planar oscillators separated by a gap of 108 μm. No new forces are observed, ruling out a substantial portion of the previously allowed parameter space[4] for the strange and gluon moduli forces, and setting a new upper limit on the range of the string dilaton[2,3] and radion[5-7] forces.

THE combined potential energy V due to a modulus force and newtonian gravity may be written:

$$V = -\int d\mathbf{r}_1 \int d\mathbf{r}_2 \, \frac{G\rho_1(\mathbf{r}_1)\rho_2(\mathbf{r}_2)}{r_{12}} \, [1 + \alpha\exp(-r_{12}/\lambda)] \tag{1}$$

The first term is Newton's universal gravitation law, with G the gravitational constant, r_{12} the distance between two points $\mathbf{r}_1$ and $\mathbf{r}_2$ in the test masses, and ρ_1, ρ_2 the mass densities of the two bodies. The second term is a Yukawa potential, with α the strength of the new force relative to gravity, and λ the range. As for any force-mediating field, the range of the modulus force is related to its mass m by $\lambda = \hbar/mc$. Previous tests of Newtonian gravity

来自额外空间维度在亚毫米尺度上力程的上限

朗等

编者按

引力是四种基本力中最弱的，比电磁力要小四十个数量级。在弦论——一个试图统一描述粒子和力的尝试——中，引力的弱性是由于引力向着六个额外的卷曲不可见维度泄漏导致的。已经有一些建议说这些卷曲维度的效应可能在很小的尺度下会变得很明显，在这些尺度上物体将会感受到更大的引力。本文中，物理学家乔舒亚·朗和合作者们介绍了一个实验，这个实验在 100 μm 的尺度上寻找引力偏离通常熟知的平方反比律的迹象。他们发现没有这样的偏离。

弦理论是人们一直在寻找的、统一自然界四种力和基本粒子的最有希望的方法 [1]，但是现在仍然缺乏直接支持它的证据。除了我们观察到的三个维度之外，弦理论还要求存在六个额外空间维度。通常假定这些额外的维度卷曲成了很小的空间。这个"紧致化"诱导出了"模"场，用来描述时空中每一点紧致维度的大小和形状。根据最近的预测 [2-7]，这些模场产生了和引力大小可比的力，可能能在 100 μm 尺度上被探测到。本文中，我们报告了以下工作：用相隔 108 μm 的两个平面振子来搜寻这一引力强度量级的力。结果未观察到新的力，从而排除了一大块之前对于奇异模力和胶子模力来说是允许的参数空间 [4]，对弦伸缩子力 [2,3] 和径向子力 [5-7] 的力程给出了一个新的上限。

由模力和牛顿引力结合得到的势能 V 可以写作

$$V = -\int d\mathbf{r}_1 \int d\mathbf{r}_2 \frac{G\rho_1(\mathbf{r}_1)\rho_2(\mathbf{r}_2)}{r_{12}} [1+\alpha\exp(-r_{12}/\lambda)] \tag{1}$$

第一项是牛顿万有引力定律，G 是引力常数，r_{12} 是检验质量位置 $\mathbf{r}_1$ 和 $\mathbf{r}_2$ 两点间的距离，ρ_1，ρ_2 是两个物体的质量密度。第二项是汤川势，α 是新的力相对于引力的强度，λ 是力程。对于任何传递相互作用的场，模力的力程和它的质量 m 存在如下关系 $\lambda = \hbar/mc$。之前关于牛顿引力的检验和对于新的宏观力的搜寻涵盖了从光年到纳

and searches for new macroscopic forces have covered length scales from light-years to nanometres[8-10], and it has been found that new forces of gravitational strength can be excluded for ranges λ from 200 μm to nearly a light-year[8,11,12], but limits on new forces become poor very rapidly below 200 μm (refs 9, 13).

The strange and gluon moduli arise in a scenario where supersymmetry (a hypothesized symmetry incorporated in string theory that relates bosons to fermions) is broken at 10–100 TeV, and all compactification occurs near the ultrahigh Planck scale of 10^{19} GeV where gravity is unified (in these scenarios) with other forces. In this case a range of approximately a millimetre is specifically predicted. The dilaton is a scalar field required for the consistency of string theory whose vacuum value fixes the strength of the interaction between strings. It may be interpreted as the modulus describing the size of the tenth space dimension that is compactified in M-theory to yield string theory in nine space dimensions. (M-theory is the structure that unifies the various types of string theory into a single framework[1].) The strength α associated with the dilaton can be computed, but the range λ at present can only be constrained by experiment; little is known about the mechanism which gives the dilaton mass. The radion results from a very different scenario in which one or more dimensions compactify at TeV energy scales, but here a range λ accessible to our experiment is again predicted.

The special significance of millimetre scales derives from a mass formula of the form $m \approx M^2/M_P$, where M_P is the mass associated with the Planck scale, 10^{19} GeV/c^2, and M is a mass of 1–100 TeV/c^2, leading to λ in the centimetre to micrometre range. In the strange and gluon moduli case, M is the scale where supersymmetry breaking occurs, whereas in the radion modulus case it corresponds to the size of one or more compact dimensions. This formula also applies to the ADD theory[14] (named for its authors) in which two compact extra dimensions of millimetre size modify gravity itself. In the ADD theory M is the fundamental length scale where all physics is unified while m is a mass corresponding to the size of the large compact extra dimensions. Many scenarios of compactification, symmetry breaking and mass generation are still viable, so although the possibility of observing new forces at millimetre scales is exciting, such experiments cannot currently falsify string theory.

The planar geometry of our source and detector masses (Fig. 1) is chosen to concentrate as much mass density as possible at the length scale of interest. It is approximately null with respect to the $1/r^2$ newtonian background, a helpful feature in the context of a new force search. A cantilever mode (similar to the motion of a diving board) of the tungsten source mass is driven to a tip amplitude of 19 μm at the resonant frequency of the detector mass. The tungsten detector mass is a double torsional oscillator[15]; in the resonant mode of interest the two rectangular sections of the detector counter-rotate about the torsion axis, with most of the amplitude confined to the smaller rectangle under the source mass and shield. Torsional motion of the detector will be driven if a mass coupled force is present between the source and detector. The motions are detected with a capacitive transducer, followed by a preamplifier, filters and a lock-in amplifier. To suppress background forces due to electrostatics and residual gas, a stiff conducting shield is fixed between the test masses. With

238

米的尺度[8-10]，已有结果表明，在 200 µm 到接近一个光年的尺度范围内不存在引力强度量级的新力[8,11,12]，但是在 200 µm 之下的尺度，对出现新力的限制会快速变弱（参考文献 9 和 13）。

奇异模空间和胶子模空间出现在 10 ~ 100 TeV 下超对称（一个弦论中猜想的将玻色子和费米子联系起来的对称性）破缺的时候，而所有的紧致化过程则是发生在临近超高普朗克尺度（10^{19} GeV）上的（这些情况下的引力和其他力是统一的）。在这种情况下，可以预测出一个大约是毫米级的力程。伸缩子是弦理论自洽性所要求的一个标量场，它的真空值决定了弦之间相互作用的强度。它或许可以被理解成是 M 理论中描述第十个空间维度的尺度的模参数，这个空间维度在 M 理论中被做了紧致化来得到具有九个空间维度的弦论（M 理论是将所有不同的弦论整合成一个框架的理论结构[1]）。和伸缩子相关的强度 α 可以通过计算得到，但是力程 λ 目前只能通过实验来限制，并且我们几乎不知道给出伸缩子质量的机制是什么。径向子是由一个完全不同的机制得到的，这一机制下一个或者多个额外维度的紧致化发生在 TeV 能标尺度上，但这里实验可以得到的力程 λ 也是预测出来的。

毫米尺度特殊的重要性可以通过形如 $m \approx M^2/M_P$ 的质量公式导出，这里 M_P 是和普朗克尺度相关的质量 10^{19} GeV$/c^2$，M 是 1 ~ 100 TeV$/c^2$ 的质量，导致 λ 的尺度在厘米到微米范围之间。在奇异模空间和胶子模空间中，M 是超对称破缺发生的尺度，而在径向子模空间的情况下，它对应于一个或者多个紧致维度的尺度。这个公式适用于 ADD 理论[14]（根据其提出者们的姓名命名），这一理论中两个毫米尺度的紧致化额外维会修改引力。在 ADD 理论中，M 是一个基本尺度，在这个尺度上所有的物理理论都是统一起来的，而 m 是对应于大的紧致化额外维尺度的质量。在许多紧致化图像中，对称性破缺和质量产生依然是可靠的，因此，尽管在毫米尺度上观察到新力的可能性是令人激动的，但这些实验目前还不能证伪弦理论。

我们选择的源和探测器质量呈现为图 1 所示的平面几何，是为了使其尽可能地在感兴趣的尺度上集中更高的质量密度。它几乎不受 $1/r^2$ 牛顿背景的影响，这在寻找一个新力的时候是一个有帮助的特征。钨制的源的悬臂模式（和跳水板的运动类似）在探测器共振频率的驱动下出现了 19 µm 的尖端振幅。钨探测器是双扭转振子[15]，在我们感兴趣的共振模式下，探测器的两个矩形部分绕着扭转轴反转，绝大部分振幅都被限制在防护屏和源下面的小矩形中。如果源和探测器之间存在一个质量耦合力的话将会驱动探测器的扭转运动。运动用电容传感器探测，跟着是一个前置放大器、过滤器和锁定放大器。为了压低由于静电和剩余气体产生的背景力，一个刚性的导电防护屏固定在两个检验质量之间。对于静止的源，源和探测器的距离

the source at rest, the gap between source and detector is adjusted to 108 µm, and the entire apparatus is placed in a vacuum enclosure and maintained at pressures below 2×10^{-7} torr.

Fig. 1. Major components of the apparatus. The smaller rectangle of the tungsten detector (under the shield) is 11.455 mm wide, 5.080 mm long and 195 µm thick. The detector is annealed at 1,300 °C to increase its mechanical Q to 25,000. In operation the 1,173.085-Hz resonant frequency of the detector is stabilized by actively controlling the detector temperature to 305 K. The tungsten source mass is 35 mm long, 7 mm wide and 305 µm thick. The source mass resonant frequency is tuned to the detector and driven by the PZT (lead zirconate titanate) piezoelectric bimorph. The shield is a 60-µm-thick sapphire plate coated with 100 nm of gold on both sides. The test masses and the shield are supported by three separate five-stage passive vibration isolation stacks[23], each providing approximately 200-dB attenuation at 1 kHz. Mechanical probes are used to directly measure the relative orientation and position of each component, and to measure the source mass amplitude. Detector motions are sensed by a cylindrical capacitive probe supported 100 µm above a rear corner of the large rectangle of the detector mass. The probe is biased at 200 V through a 100 GΩ resistor, and connected to an SK 152 junction field-effect transistor (JFET) through a blocking capacitor. The JFET noise temperature of 100 mK is more than sufficient to detect 305 K thermal motions of the detector mass. The JFET preamplifier is followed by a second preamplifier, filters, and finally a two-phase lock-in amplifier. The total voltage gain from the capacitive probe to the lock-in input is approximately 1,600. A crystal-controlled oscillator provides a reference signal for the lock-in amplifier and drives the source mass PZT through a 1:10 step-up transformer.

Figure 2 shows histograms of the raw data, collected with the source mass drive tuned both on and off the detector resonant frequency. Each plot contains data from one channel of the lock-in amplifier, corresponding to one of two orthogonal phases of the detector motion at the drive frequency. The widths of the off-resonance distributions are due to preamplifier noise, whereas the on-resonance distributions are due to the sum of preamplifier noise and detector thermal motions. The on- and off-resonance means shown in Fig. 3 agree within their standard deviations, indicating the absence of a significant resonant force signal.

调整到 108 µm，整个仪器放在真空罩中，然后将压强控制在 2×10^{-7} torr 以下。

图 1. 仪器的主要构成。钨探测器的小矩形（在防护屏下面）有 11.455 mm 宽，5.080 mm 长，195 µm 厚。探测器在 1,300 ℃ 下退火以便增加它的机械品质因子 Q 到 25,000。在操作上，探测器 1,173.085 Hz 的共振频率是通过主动地将探测器的温度控制在 305 K 来稳定下来的。钨制的源有 35 mm 长，7 mm 宽，305 µm 厚。源的共振频率调制到探测器的共振频率，并由锆钛酸铅（PZT）压电双晶片驱动。防护屏是一个 60 µm 厚的蓝宝石板，两侧镀上了 100 nm 厚的金。检验质量和防护屏由三个分立的五步被动隔振层支撑 [23]，每一个在 1 kHz 时提供了大约 200 dB 的噪音减弱。机械探头用来直接探测每个组分的相对取向和位置，还用来测量源的振幅。探测器的运动通过在探测器大矩形后面的角的上方 100 µm 处的一个圆柱形电容式探头来感知。探头通过一个 100 GΩ 的电阻在 200 V 电压上偏置，并且通过一个隔直流电容器连着一个 SK 152 的结型场效应晶体管（JFET）。JFET 100 mK 的噪声温度足够用来探测 305 K 的探测器的热运动了。JFET 前置放大器接着第二个前置放大器、过滤器，最后是一个两相锁定放大器。从电容式探头到锁定放大器输入的总电压放大了约 1,600 倍。一个晶体调控的振子给锁定放大器提供了一个参考信号，并且通过一个 1:10 的升压变压器驱动源质量的 PZT。

图 2 展示了原始数据的直方图，当源的驱动频率在探测器的共振频率时和不在探测器的共振频率时都收集了数据。每个图都包含来自锁定放大器的一个通道的信号，对应于在驱动频率下探测器运动的两个正交模式中的一个。非共振分布的展宽是因为前置放大器的噪声，而共振分布的展宽来自前置放大器的噪声和探测器的热运动之和。图 3 中这个共振和非共振的平均值在标准偏差之内是吻合的，表明不存在一个显著的共振力的信号。

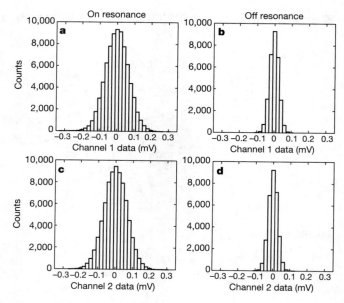

Fig. 2. Distributions of data samples. Data were recorded at 1 Hz with a lock-in bandwidth chosen to include the noise power of the detector thermal oscillations, which was used for calibration. Each data cycle began with five 120-sample diagnostic runs with a direct-current bias of 5–10 V applied to the shield to induce a large test force, transmitted from source to detector via deflections of the shield. The biased runs were recorded at five drive frequencies separated by 15 mHz to cover the detector resonance. The shield was then grounded and the cycle continued with 720 samples with the drive tuned on-resonance (**a, c**) and 288 samples with the drive tuned 2 Hz below the detector resonance (**b, d**). The off-resonance run provided a continuous zero check. A total of 108 such cycles were acquired over five days yielding 77,760 on-resonance samples. The biased diagnostic data show that the source mass amplitude, the detector Q and resonant frequency, and the electronic gain were all stable throughout the data set.

Fig. 3. Means of the off- and on-resonance data samples. The circular point with the larger standard deviations is the on-resonance mean. Correlations between nearby samples have been accounted for in computing the standard deviations shown by error bars. The small offset from the origin is due to leakage of the reference signal internal to the lock-in. Measurements with the shield removed and a bias voltage between the source and detector show that the phase for an attractive force is 189°. The on-resonance mean minus the off-resonance mean at 189° is -0.44 ± 0.82 μV. Based on calibration via the equipartition

图 2. 数据样本的分布。数据在 1 Hz 处收集，选取的锁定带宽包含了探测器热振动的噪声功率以用于校正。每个数据周期从 120 个样本的 5 次诊断运行开始，在防护屏上应用 5～10 V 的直流偏压，用来产生一个很大的检测力，然后通过防护屏的偏转在源到探测器之间传递。偏置运行在五个驱动频率下记录，这五个驱动频率之间间隔 15 mHz 从而覆盖探测器共振频率。防护屏之后接地，然后这个周期继续在驱动频率调到共振频率的 720 个样本（**a** 和 **c**）和驱动频率调到探测器共振频率以下 2 Hz 处的 288 个的样本（**b** 和 **d**）中进行。非共振运行提供了一个连续的零检验。五天时间内获得了共 108 个这样的循环，产生了 77,760 个共振样本。偏置诊断的数据显示源质量的振幅、探测器的品质因子 Q 和共振频率以及电子增益在整个数据集上都是稳定的。

图 3. 非共振和共振数据样本的平均值。具有更大标准偏差的圆点是共振的平均值。邻近样本之间的关联在计算标准偏差时已经考虑进去了，标准偏差用误差棒来体现。原点处的微小偏移来源于锁定放大器内部的参考信号的溢出。去掉防护屏，并在源和探测器之间加上偏置电压进行了探测，结果显示吸引力的相位是 189°。在 189°，共振的平均值减去非共振的平均值是 −0.44 ± 0.82 μV。基于通过能均分定理

theorem this corresponds to a lumped force amplitude at the edge of the detector (smaller rectangle in Fig. 1) of -1.2 ± 2.2 fN, where the negative sign indicates repulsion.

Additional cycles of data were acquired with the source mass on the opposite side of the detector, with a larger, 1-mm gap, and with reduced overlap between the source and detector. No resonant signal was observed in any of these sessions, making it unlikely that the observed null result is due to a fortuitous cancellation of surface potential, magnetic, and/or acoustic effects. Several on-resonance runs were acquired with different transducer probe bias voltage settings. The observed linear dependence on bias voltage of the root-mean-square (r.m.s.) fluctuations in these data is consistent with detector motion due only to thermal noise and rules out additional motion from transducer back-action noise. This check is important because the magnitude of the detector thermal motion is used for calibration.

Data from diagnostic runs with a bias voltage applied to the shield can be used to estimate the minimum size of the residual potential difference between the shield and the (grounded) test masses needed to produce a resonant signal. We find that at least 1.5 V would be needed to generate an effect above detector thermal noise, about an order of magnitude larger than the residual potential difference actually measured between the shield and test masses. The most important magnetic background effect involves eddy currents generated when the source mass moves in an external magnetic field. Fields produced by the source currents create eddy currents in the detector, which then interact with the external field. Studies of this effect with large applied magnetic fields show that the ambient field actually present cannot generate a signal greater than one-fifth of the thermal-noise-limited sensitivity.

The instrument can be calibrated in several ways, but the most accurate method is to use the r.m.s. thermal motion of the detector, which dominates the on-resonance distributions in Fig. 2. According to equipartition, the average kinetic energy in each normal mode of the detector is equal to $\frac{1}{2}kT$; where k is Boltzmann's constant and T is the temperature. The normal mode amplitude corresponding to the thermal energy can be calculated, and by comparing this with the observed voltage fluctuations a calibration can be established relating mode amplitude to voltage. A further calculation must be done to find the mode amplitude resulting from any hypothesized force.

For given values of α and λ the driving force due to equation (1) is computed at 30 values of the source mass phase using Monte Carlo integration, and then the Fourier amplitude of the driving force at the resonant frequency is computed. Using the observed statistics of the data we construct a likelihood function for α for each value of λ and compute 95% confidence-level upper limits on α, assuming a uniform prior probability density function (PDF) for α. This analysis is complicated by the presence of uncertainties in the geometrical and mechanical parameters needed to compute the driven displacement. To include these effects we actually construct a likelihood function of α and the uncertain parameters, and then integrate out the uncertain parameters using prior PDFs based on their experimental uncertainties. The most important of these parameters is the 108-

的校正，这对应于一个在探测器边缘（图 1 中的小矩形）大小为 -1.2 ± 2.2 fN 的集总力振幅，负号表明它是排斥力。

更多的数据周期通过将源放在探测器的另外一侧获得，源和探测器之间有一个比之前大的、大小为 1 mm 的间隙，并且有着更小的交叠。在这些测量中都没有看到任何的共振信号，使得观测到的零结果不太可能源于表面势、磁和（或）声学效应的偶然抵消。设定不同的传感器探头的偏置电压获得了几次共振。在这些数据中观测到的方均根误差的涨落对于偏置电压的线性依赖和只由热噪声产生的探测器运动是自洽的，排除了传感器反作用噪声导致的额外运动。这个检查是重要的，因为探测器热运动的大小是被用来做校正的。

来自诊断运行（在防护屏上施加偏置电压）的数据可以用来估计防护屏和（接地的）检验质量之间的剩余电势差的最小尺度，这个电势差是需要的，它可以产生一个共振信号。我们发现至少需要 1.5 V 的电压来产生一个高于探测器热噪声的效应，1.5 V 大约比测得的在防护屏和检验质量之间的剩余电势差高一个数量级。最重要的磁背景效应是当源在外磁场运动时产生的涡流。源电流产生的场在探测器中产生了涡流，涡流之后会和外部的场相互作用。关于这个大施加磁场带来的效应的研究表明，周围实际存在的场所产生的信号，不能大于热噪声限制给出的灵敏度的五分之一。

这个实验器材可以通过几种方式校正，但是最准确的方法是用探测器的方均根热运动进行校正，它在图 2 的共振分布中占主导。根据能均分定理，每个探测器正则模式的平均动能等于 $\frac{1}{2}kT$；k 是玻尔兹曼常数而 T 是温度。对应于热能的正则模式的振幅可以算出来，比较它和观测到的电压涨落，可以通过将模式振幅和电压联系起来建立一个校正。如果要寻找任何假设存在的力所产生的模式振幅，需要进行更进一步的计算。

对于给定的 α 和 λ 的值，由方程（1）给出的驱动力在源相位取的 30 个值下用蒙特卡罗积分计算，然后算出驱动力在共振频率下的傅里叶振幅。用观测到的数据统计，我们对每个 λ 的值构建了一个 α 的似然函数，然后在假定了一个 α 的均匀先验概率密度分布函数（PDF）的基础上，在 95% 的置信度上计算了 α 的上限。由于计算驱动位移时所需要的几何和动力学参数存在不确定性，这个分析会变得复杂。为了包括这些效应，我们实际上构建了一个 α 和这些不确定参数的似然函数，然后基于实验不确定性，利用先验概率密度分布函数积掉了不确定的参数。这些参数中最重要的是在源和探测器之间具有 6 μm 不确定性的 108 μm 平衡间隙。分析方法的进一

μm equilibrium gap between source and detector which has a 6-μm uncertainty. Further details of our analysis methods are given elsewhere[16].

Our results are shown in Fig. 4, together with other experimental limits and the theoretical predictions. Our limit is the strongest available between 10 and 100 μm. When the gluon and strange moduli forces were first proposed, the areas of their allowed regions in the (α, λ) parameter space were 4.4 and 5.2 square decades respectively. By now they are nearly excluded with only 0.75 and 1.4 square decades still available. Our limit on the dilaton range for $\alpha = 2,000$ is $\lambda < 23$ μm (corresponding to $m > 8.6$ meV), a factor of two better than the previous limit. For the radion modulus we set an upper limit on λ of 88 μm, close to the value of 40 μm estimated in the theory (for one extra dimension). For the ADD theory with two large extra compact dimensions, we do not quite reach the limit on the size of these dimensions already set in refs 11 and 12.

Fig. 4. Current limits on new gravitational strength forces between 1 μm and 1 cm. Our result is a 95% confidence-level upper limit on the Yukawa strength α as a function of range λ (solid bold curve). It is shown together with limits from previous experiments (Lamoreaux[24], Washington[12], Irvine[25]) and theoretical predictions newly constrained (gluon modulus[4], strange modulus[4], string dilaton[2], radion modulus[7]). An unpublished limit from the Stanford experiment[26] is also shown; it is derived in the presence of a background force. The dilaton strength is somewhat model-dependent and there is a range of values reported in the literature[2]. We have chosen the region $200 < \alpha < 3,000$, which includes most values. Also shown are predictions from the ADD theory with two large compact extra dimensions[14,27,28], axion mediated forces[20,21], and the λ region corresponding to a cosmological energy density between 1.0 and 0.1 times the closure density[17]. For the moduli, dilaton, and ADD theories, the upper bounds on λ of the regions shown are set at the experimental limits that were known at the time the theories were proposed.

Besides forces from extra dimensions, two other ideas have suggested new weak forces at submillimetre scales. The cosmological energy density needed to close the universe, if converted to a length by taking its inverse fourth root (in natural units where $\hbar = c = 1$), corresponds to about 100 μm. This fact has led to repeated attempts[17-19] to address difficulties connected with the very small observed size of Einstein's cosmological constant

步细节在其他论文中给出 [16]。

图 4 展示了我们的结果，其中也包括其他实验的限制和理论的预言。我们的限制在 10 μm 到 100 μm 范围内是已知的方法中最强的。当胶子模力和奇异模力第一次被提出的时候，它们在 (α, λ) 参数空间中所允许的区域分别是 4.4 和 5.2 个单位。现在它们除了 0.75 和 1.4 个允许的单位外，其余的都被排除了。关于 $\alpha = 2,000$ 的伸缩子的范围，我们的限制是 $\lambda < 23$ μm（对应于 $m > 8.6$ MeV），比之前的极限好上一倍。对于径向子的模空间，我们给出了一个 $\lambda=88$ μm 的上限，接近理论（一个额外维）预言的 40 μm 的值。对于有两个大的额外紧致维度的 ADD 理论，我们并没有达到文献 11 和 12 中给出的关于这些维度的大小的极限。

图 4. 目前 1 μm 到 1 cm 之间的新引力强度的限制。我们的结果是一个在 95% 置信度上汤川强度 α 函数的上限，它是关于力程 λ 的函数（粗体实线）。之前的实验（拉莫罗 [24]，华盛顿 [12]，欧文 [25]）给出的极限以及理论预言给出的新极限也一并展示在图中（胶子模 [4]，奇异模 [4]，弦伸缩子 [2]，径向子模 [7]）。一个来自斯坦福的未发表的实验 [26] 也展示在图中，它是在存在背景力的前提下得到的。伸缩子的强度某种意义上是依赖于模型，在文献中有一个取值范围 [2]。我们选择区域 $200 < \alpha < 3,000$，它包含了大部分的值。图中也展示了分别由具有两个大的紧致额外维度的 ADD 理论 [14,27,28]，轴子传递的力 [20,21] 以及宇宙学能量密度在 1.0 到 0.1 倍闭合能量密度之间的 λ 区域 [17] 所给出的预言结果。对于模空间、伸缩子和 ADD 理论，展示的 λ 区域的上界设置在理论提出时人们已知的实验所能达到的极限。

除了来自额外维的力，还有其他两个想法可以在亚毫米尺度给出新的弱的相互作用。用来闭合宇宙的宇宙学（临界）能量密度，如果通过做它的负四次方根来得到一个长度（在自然单位制下 $\hbar = c = 1$），结果大概是 100 μm。这个事实使得人们不断尝试 [17-19] 通过引入一个力程大约 100 μm 的力来解决爱因斯坦的宇宙学常数的观测

by introducing new forces with a range near 100 µm. Our result is the best upper bound on α in this region, but we have not quite reached gravitational sensitivity. Finally, the oldest of these predictions, still out of reach, is the very feeble axion-mediated force[20,21]. The axion is a field intended to explain why the violation of charge-parity symmetry is so small in quantum chromodynamics, the theory of the strong nuclear force.

Experiments of the sort reported here constrain string-inspired scenarios by setting very restrictive limits on predicted submillimetre forces. Of course, the actual observation of any new force would be a major advance. Because several theoretical scenarios point especially to these length scales, it is an important goal for the future to reach gravitational strength at even shorter distances, perhaps down to 10 µm. Experiments attempting to reach such distances will confront rapidly increasing background forces, especially electrostatic forces arising from the spatially non-uniform surface potentials of metals[22]. Electric fields due to surface potentials can be shielded with good conductors, but because of the finite stiffness of any shield they still cause background forces to be transmitted between test masses. Stretched membranes (as used by the Washington group) are more effective than stiff plates at the shortest distances, but it remains to be seen down to what distance the background forces can be effectively suppressed.

(**421**, 922-925; 2003)

Joshua C. Long*†, **Hilton W. Chan***†, **Allison B. Churnside***, **Eric A. Gulbis***, **Michael C. M. Varney*** & **John C. Price***

* Physics Department, University of Colorado, UCB 390, Boulder, Colorado 80309, USA

† Present addresses: Los Alamos Neutron Science Center, LANSCE-3, MS-H855, Los Alamos, New Mexico 87545, USA (J.C.L.); and Physics Department, Stanford University, Stanford, California 94305, USA (H.W.C.)

Received 21 October 2002; accepted 13 January 2003; doi:10.1038/nature01432.

References:

1. Greene, B. *The Elegant Universe: Superstrings, Hidden Dimensions, and the Quest for the Ultimate Theory* (Norton, New York, 1999).

2. Kaplan, D. B. & Wise, M. B. Couplings of a light dilaton and violations of the equivalence principle. *J. High Energy Phys.* **8**, 37 (2000).

3. Taylor, T. R. & Veneziano, G. Dilaton couplings at large distances. *Phys. Lett. B* **213**, 450-454 (1988).

4. Dimopoulos, S. & Giudice, G. Macroscopic forces from supersymmetry. *Phys. Lett. B* **379**, 105-114 (1996).

5. Antoniadis, I. A possible new dimension at a few TeV. *Phys. Lett. B* **246**, 377-384 (1990).

6. Antoniadis, I., Dimopoulos, S. & Dvali, G. Millimeter-range forces in superstring theories with weak-scale compactification. *Nucl. Phys. B* **516**, 70-82 (1998).

7. Chacko, Z. & Perazzi, E. Extra dimensions at the weak scale and deviations from Newtonian gravity. Preprint hep-ph/0210254 available at ⟨arXiv.org⟩ (2002).

8. Fischbach, E. & Talmadge, C. *The Search for Non-Newtonian Gravity* (Springer, New York, 1999).

9. Bordag, M., Mohideen, U. & Mostepanenko, V. M. New Developments in the Casimir effect. *Phys. Rep.* **353**, 1-205 (2001).

10. Long, J. C., Chan, H. W. & Price, J. C. Experimental status of gravitational-strength forces in the sub-centimeter regime. *Nucl. Phys. B* **539**, 23-34 (1999).

11. Hoyle, C. D. *et al.* Sub-millimeter tests of the gravitational inverse-square law: A search for "large" extra dimensions. *Phys. Rev. Lett.* **86**, 1418-1421 (2001).

12. Adelberger, E. G. Sub-mm tests of the gravitational inverse-square law. Preprint hep-ex/0202008 available at ⟨arXiv.org⟩ (2002).

13. Fischbach, E., Krause, D. E., Mostepanenko, V. M. & Novello, M. New constraints on ultrashort-ranged Yukawa interactions from atomic force microscopy. *Phys. Rev. D* **64**, 075010 (2001).

14. Arkani-Hamed, N., Dimopoulos, S. & Dvali, G. The hierarchy problem and new dimensions at a millimeter. *Phys. Lett. B* **429**, 263-272 (1998).

15. Kleiman, R. N., Kaminsky, G. K., Reppy, J. D., Pindak, R. & Bishop, D. J. Single-crystal silicon high-Q torsional oscillators. *Rev. Sci. Instrum.* **56**, 2088-2091 (1985).

16. Long, J. C. *et al.* New experimental limits on macroscopic forces below 100 microns. Preprint hep-ph/0210004 available at ⟨arXiv.org⟩ (2002).

17. Beane, S. R. On the importance of testing gravity at distances less than 1 cm. *Gen. Rel. Grav.* **29**, 945-951 (1997).

18. Sundrum, R. Towards an effective particle-string resolution of the cosmological constant problem. *J. High Energy Phys.* **7**, 1 (1999).

值很小所带来的困难。我们的结果是这个区域内能得到的最好的上界，但是我们还没有达到引力的灵敏度。最后，这些预言中最古老的一个，也是目前依然探测不到的，是很微弱的轴子传递的相互作用[20,21]。轴子的引入是为了解释为什么在量子色动力学（强核力的理论）中电荷–宇称对称性的破缺是如此的微小。

    本文报道的这类实验对预测在亚毫米尺度上存在额外力的类弦理论给出了一个很强约束性的极限。当然，能够观测到任何新的力都将是一个巨大的进步。因为一些理论特别地指向了这些尺度，未来在更小的距离（可能低至 10 μm 以下）上到达引力的强度将是一个重要的目标。试图到达这个距离的实验将会面临更快速增长的背景力，尤其是由于金属表面空间不均匀的势所产生的静电力[22]。表面势产生的电场可以被良导体屏蔽，但是由于任何防护屏都有有限的刚性系数，它们依然会造成表面力在检验质量之间传递。延展的膜（即华盛顿课题组所使用的材料）在小距离下比刚性的盘更加有效，但是低至多大的距离下背景力可以被有效地压低还不能确定。

（安宇森 翻译；蔡荣根 审稿）

19. Schmidhuber, C. Old puzzles. Preprint hep-th/0207203 available at ⟨arXiv.org⟩ (2002).

20. Moody, J. E. & Wilczek, F. New macroscopic forces? *Phys. Rev. D* **30**, 130-138 (1984).

21. Rosenberg, L. J. & van Bibber, K. A. Searches for invisible axions. *Phys. Rep.* **325**, 1-39 (2000).

22. Price, J. C. in *Proc. Int. Symp. on Experimental Gravitational Physics* (eds Michelson, P., En-ke, H. & Pizzella, G.) 436-439 (World Scientific, Singapore, 1988).

23. Chan, H. W., Long, J. C. & Price, J. C. Taber vibration isolator for vacuum and cryogenic applications. *Rev. Sci. Instrum.* **70**, 2742-2750 (1999).

24. Lamoreaux, S. K. Demonstration of the Casimir force in the 0.6 to 6 μm range. *Phys. Rev. Lett.* **78**, 5-8 (1997).

25. Hoskins, J. K., Newman, R. D., Spero, R. & Shultz, J. Experimental tests of the gravitational inverse-square law for mass separations from 2 to 105 cm. *Phys. Rev. D* **32**, 3084-3095 (1985).

26. Chiaverini, J., Smullin, S. J., Geraci, A. A., Weld, D. M. & Kapitulnik, A. New experimental constraints on non-Newtonian forces below 100 microns. Preprint hep-ph/0209325 available at ⟨arXiv.org⟩ (2002).

27. Floratos, E. G. & Leontaris, G. K. Low scale unification, Newton's law and extra dimensions. *Phys. Lett. B* **465**, 95-100 (1999).

28. Kehagias, A. & Sfetsos, K. Deviations from the $1/r^2$ Newton law due to extra dimensions. *Phys. Lett. B* **472**, 39-44 (2000).

Acknowledgements. We thank E. Lagae for work in the laboratory, and C. Briggs, T. Buxkemper, L. Czaia, H. Green, S. Gustafson and H. Rohner of the University of Colorado and JILA instrument shops for technical assistance. We also gratefully acknowledge discussions with S. de Alwis, B. Dobrescu and S. Dimopoulos. This work is supported by grants from the US National Science Foundation.

Competing interests statement. The authors declare that they have no competing financial interests.

Correspondence and requests for materials should be addressed to J.C.P. (e-mail: john.price@colorado.edu).

An Extended Upper Atmosphere Around the Extrasolar Planet HD209458b

A. Vidal-Madjar *et al.*

Editor's Note

The extrasolar planet HD 209458b crosses (transits) its parent star as seen from our perspective on Earth, which enables astronomers to determine its mass and radius. Here Alfred Vidal-Madjar and colleagues show that the planet has an extended atmosphere—the first such observation for an extrasolar planet. They obtained a spectrum of the parent star during three transits, and saw that some of the light was absorbed by the planet's atmosphere. They propose that the extended atmosphere probably consists of hydrogen atoms escaping from the planet's gravitational field, though it was later proposed that the atoms were ions from the stellar wind that pick up electrons in the outer atmosphere of the planet. Which explanation is correct is still debated.

The planet in the system HD209458 is the first one for which repeated transits across the stellar disk have been observed[1,2]. Together with radial velocity measurements[3], this has led to a determination of the planet's radius and mass, confirming it to be a gas giant. But despite numerous searches for an atmospheric signature[4-6], only the dense lower atmosphere of HD209458b has been observed, through the detection of neutral sodium absorption[7]. Here we report the detection of atomic hydrogen absorption in the stellar Lyman α line during three transits of HD209458b. An absorption of $15 \pm 4\%$ (1σ) is observed. Comparison with models shows that this absorption should take place beyond the Roche limit and therefore can be understood in terms of escaping hydrogen atoms.

FAR more abundant than any other species, hydrogen is well-suited for searching weak atmospheric absorptions during the transit of an extrasolar giant planet in front of its parent star, in particular over the strong resonant stellar ultraviolet Lyman α emission line at 1,215.67 Å. Depending upon the characteristics of the planet's upper atmosphere, an H_I signature much larger than that for Na_I at 0.02% (ref. 7) is foreseeable. Three transits of HD209458b (named A, B and C hereafter) were sampled in 2001 (on 7–8 September, 14–15 September and 20 October, respectively) with the Space Telescope Imaging Spectrograph (STIS) onboard the Hubble Space Telescope (HST); the data set is now public in the HST archive. To partially overcome contamination from the Earth's Lyman α geocoronal emission, we used the G140M grating with the $52'' \times 0.1''$ slit (medium spectral resolution: ~ 20 km s^{-1}). For each transit, three consecutive HST orbits (named 1, 2 and 3 hereafter) were scheduled such that the first orbit (1,780 s exposure) ended before the first contact to serve as a reference, and the two following ones (2,100 s exposures each) were

太阳系外行星 HD209458b 扩展的
高层大气研究

维达尔-马贾尔等

编者按

在地球上观测到太阳系外行星 HD209458b 穿越其母恒星圆面的现象（凌星）可以帮助天文学家确定行星的质量与半径。本文中，阿尔弗雷德·维达尔-马贾尔与他的同事报道了一颗具有扩展大气层的行星，这也是第一次在太阳系外观测到这样的星体。他们从三次凌星过程中获得了母恒星的光谱，发现某些光线被行星的大气层吸收了。他们提出行星扩展大气层中可能包含有从行星重力场中逃逸出来的氢原子。尽管不久之后有研究指出这些原子是源于行星外层大气中携带电子的恒星风的离子，然而两种假说的正确性尚无定论。

位于 HD209458 系统中的行星是第一颗被观测到多次横越恒星圆面的行星[1,2]。结合凌星观测与视向速度法[3]，可以确定这颗行星的半径和质量，从而确认该行星是一颗气态巨行星。尽管人们对 HD209458 系统的大气特征进行了大量研究[4-6]，但这些研究仅是通过中性钠原子的吸收探测到 HD209458b 存在稠密的低层大气[7]。本文报道的是在 HD209458b 三次凌星过程中，探测到恒星莱曼 α 线被氢原子吸收，观测到的吸收强度为 15±4% (1σ)。通过与模型的模拟结果对比，发现这种吸收应该在超过洛希极限时才会发生，因此可以认为是逃逸的氢原子的吸收。

在宇宙中，氢的丰度远高于其他元素。因此，在太阳系外巨行星的凌星过程中，氢非常适合于探测较弱的大气吸收，尤其是在强共振恒星紫外莱曼 α 发射线（1,215.67Å）波段。根据该行星的上层大气特征，可以预测 H I 的特征谱线比 Na I 的特征谱线要强 0.02%[7]。通过哈勃空间望远镜（HST）上装载的空间望远镜成像光谱仪（STIS），分别在 2001 年 9 月 7 日~8 日、9 月 14 日~15 日和 10 月 20 日对 HD209458b 的三次凌星（分别命名为 A、B、C）进行了采样，这些数据现在已经在 HST 档案库中公开。为了部分地避免地冕莱曼 α 发射线的干扰，我们采用了 G140M 光栅，其缝隙大小为 52″×0.1″（光谱分辨率约为 20 km·s⁻¹）。在每次凌星过程中，安排哈勃望远镜进行连续三个轨道周期（下文以 1、2、3 编号）的观测，其中第一周期（曝光 1,780 s）在发现凌星前就结束以便提供参考，而随后两个周期的观测（分别

partly or entirely within the transit.

The observed Lyman α spectrum of HD209458 is typical for a solar-type star, with a double-peaked emission originating from the stellar chromosphere (Fig. 1). It also shows a wide central absorption feature due to neutral hydrogen in the interstellar medium. The geocoronal emission filled the aperture of the spectrograph, resulting in an extended emission line perpendicular to the dispersion direction. The extent of this emission along the slit allowed us to remove it at the position of the target star. We evaluated its variation both along the slit and from one exposure to another, and excluded the wavelength domain where the corresponding standard deviation per pixel is larger than 20% of the final spectrum. We concluded that the geocoronal contamination can be removed with high enough accuracy outside the central region $1{,}215.5\ \text{Å} < \lambda < 1{,}215.8\ \text{Å}$, labelled "Geo" in Figs 2, 4).

Fig. 1. The HD209458 Lyman α emission line. This high-resolution spectrum (histogram) was obtained with the E140M echelle grating and the $0.2'' \times 0.2''$ wide slit with a spectral resolution of 5 km s^{-1}; it was not used in the present analysis, but it allows the different components of the line profile to be seen. The continuum is a double-peaked emission line originating from the stellar chromosphere: the temperature increase in the lower chromosphere causes an emission line with a central dip due to the high opacity of the abundant hydrogen atoms (solid line). The observed spectrum also has a narrow absorption line (1,215.3 Å, barely seen at lower resolution) and a central wide absorption line (1,215.6 Å) due to the interstellar deuterium and hydrogen, respectively (dashed lines). The grey zone represents the fraction of the spectrum contaminated by the geocoronal emission, which is double-peaked in that case because the plotted spectrum is the average of four exposures obtained at two different epochs. The inset shows a small portion of the 2D image of a G140M first-order spectrum containing the stellar Lyman α profile and a sample of the geocoronal signal. This spectrum is one of the nine spectra used for this analysis. The G140M spectra have lower spectral resolution but higher signal-to-noise ratio. The stellar spectrum is seen as a horizontal line where the two peaks are resolved from the geocoronal emission (vertical line along the slit). The one-dimensional spectra are obtained by vertically adding around ten pixels within the A band. Measurements along the slit direction (~800 pixels available), for example at the position of the B band, allow us to estimate the geocoronal contamination and the background subtraction as well as the corresponding uncertainties.

曝光 2,100 s) 则部分或全部在凌星期间内。

如图 1 所示,观测到的 HD209458 莱曼 α 谱线是典型的类太阳恒星光谱,具有恒星色球层产生的特征双峰发射。同时我们发现在中心位置附近还存在一个较宽的吸收带,这是因为在星际介质中存在中性氢。由于地冕发射线进入摄谱仪孔径,垂直色散方向的发射线发生扩展。沿光栅缝隙的发射线的这种扩展使得我们能够将其从观测目标恒星的位置移除。我们计算出发射线沿缝隙以及两次不同曝光之间的变化情况,同时去除波长域中对应单位像素标准差比最终光谱大 20% 的部分。我们从而得出以下结论:对于波长中心区域(1,215.4 Å < λ < 1,215.8 Å,在图 2、4 中用"Geo"标出)以外的波段,地冕引起的干扰可以很大程度地被消除掉。

图 1. HD209458 的莱曼 α 发射线。这幅高分辨率光谱图(直方图)由 E140M 阶梯光栅得到的,该光栅的缝隙尺寸为 0.2″×0.2″,光谱分辨率为 5 km·s⁻¹,可以分离谱线轮廓的不同分量(尽管本次分析中并未使用)。图中连续发射谱具有双峰结构,这是由恒星色球层产生的,即由于大量氢原子的不透明度较高,底层色球层温度升高,这将使得发射线具有中心下陷结构(实线)。同时,观察到光谱还具有一个非常窄的吸收线(位于 1,215.3 Å,较低分辨率下很难观察到)和一个较宽的中心吸收谱线(1,215.6 Å,虚线),二者分别是由于星际间的氘和氢所引起的。图中灰色区域表示混杂着地冕干扰的光谱部分,由于光谱是在两个不同的纪元得到的四次曝光的平均,因此显示出双峰结构。右上角小框图给出了 G140M 一级光谱二维图像的一小部分,包含了恒星莱曼 α 廓线和部分地冕干扰信号。该光谱是我们用于分析的九个光谱之一,尽管 G140M 光谱具有较低的谱分辨率,但是具有较高的信噪比。该恒星光谱可以看作一条水平线,其中可以在地冕发射线中分辨出两个光谱峰(沿缝隙的垂直方向)。通过将 A 条带区域内的大约 10 个像素相加可以得到一维光谱图。通过沿缝隙方向测量(大约 800 个像素),例如在 B 条带位置,可以使我们估算出地冕干扰和背景影响,以及相应的不确定度。

Fig. 2. The HD209458 Lyman α profile observed with the G140M grating. The geocoronal emission has been subtracted; the propagated errors are consequently larger in the central part of the profile, particularly in the Geo domain (see text). Δλ represents the spectral resolution. **a,** The thin line shows the average of the three observations performed before the transits (exposures A1, B1 and C1); the thick line shows the average of the three observations recorded entirely within the transits (exposures A2, B3 and C3). Variations are seen in the In domain as absorption over the blue peak of the line and partially over the red peak (between −130 km s⁻¹ and 100 km s⁻¹). Quoted velocities are in the stellar reference frame, centred on −13 km s⁻¹ in the heliocentric reference frame. **b,** ±1σ error bars. **c,** The ratio of the two spectra in the In domain, the spectra being normalized such that the ratio is 1 in the Out domain. This ratio is plotted as a function of λ_1 using $\lambda_2 = 1,216.10$ Å (triangles), and as a function of λ_2 using $\lambda_1 = 1,215.15$ Å (circles). The ratio is always significantly below 1, with a minimum at $\lambda_1 = 1,215.15$ Å (−130 km s⁻¹) and $\lambda_2 = 1,216.10$ Å (100 km s⁻¹). In the domain defined by these values, the Lyman α intensity decreases during the transits by 15 ± 4%. The detection does not strongly depend on a particular selection of the domain. While the decrease of the Lyman α intensity is not sensitive to the position of λ_2, it is more sensitive to the position of λ_1, showing that most of the absorption occurs in the blue part of the line. Using the whole domain where the absorption is detected, the exoplanetary atmospheric hydrogen is detected at more than 3σ.

From the two-dimensional (2D) images of the far-ultraviolet (FUV) multi-anode microchannel array (MAMA) detector, the STIS standard pipeline extracts one-dimensional spectra in which the dark background has not been removed. The background level was systematically increasing from one exposure to the next within each of the three visits, but still remained below 2% of the peak intensity of the stellar signal. We therefore reprocessed the 2D images by using two independent approaches. The first one uses the 2D images provided by the standard pipeline and interpolates the background (including the Earth's geocoronal emission) with a polynomial fitted per column above and below the spectrum region. The second method starts from the 2D raw images to which is applied a dark

图 2. 利用 G140M 光栅观测到的 HD209458 的莱曼 α 轮廓。其中，地冕发射的干扰已经被剔除，因此传递误差在廓线中心附近变大，特别是在"Geo"区域，Δλ 表示光谱分辨率。**a.** 图中细线给出了凌星前进行的三次观测（即 A1、B1、C1 三次曝光）的平均；粗线表示凌星中的三次观测（即 A2、B3、C3 三次曝光）的平均。很明显，两条曲线在"In"域存在较大变化，特别是在谱线蓝峰以及部分红峰附近（速度在 $-130 \text{ km} \cdot \text{s}^{-1}$ 到 $100 \text{ km} \cdot \text{s}^{-1}$ 之间）。括号里的速度是相对恒星参考系的速度，在以太阳为中心的参考系中心速度为 $-13 \text{ km} \cdot \text{s}^{-1}$。**b.** 该图给出了 $\pm 1\sigma$ 的误差棒。**c.** 该图给出了两条光谱曲线在"In"域的比值，归一化满足"Out"域比值为 1。其中，带三角标志的曲线表示 $\lambda_2 = 1{,}216.10 \text{ Å}$ 条件下比值与 λ_1 的关系，而带实心圆标志的曲线给出了 $\lambda_1 = 1{,}215.15 \text{ Å}$ 条件下比值与 λ_2 的关系，两种情况下比值的最小值分别于 $\lambda_1 = 1{,}215.15 \text{ Å}$（对应 $-130 \text{ km} \cdot \text{s}^{-1}$）和 $\lambda_2 = 1{,}216.10 \text{ Å}$（对应 $100 \text{ km} \cdot \text{s}^{-1}$）处获得。在这两个最小值定义域范围内，莱曼 α 谱线强度在凌星过程中减小了 15±4%。值得注意的是，探测结果本身与特定的光谱域并没有很强的关联性。莱曼 α 谱线强度的减小对 λ_2 的位置并不敏感，而对于 λ_1 的位置则相对敏感，这说明更多地吸收发生于谱线蓝端部分。对整个探测到吸收的区域的分析表明，系外行星大气氢在大于 3σ 的情况下可以被测度。

根据远紫外（FUV）多阳极微通道阵（MAMA）探测器捕获到的二维图像，STIS 标准通道从二维图像中提取出一维光谱，其中的暗背景并未去除。尽管三次凌星的背景水平从某次曝光到下一次曝光会系统性地增加，但是仍然低于星体信号峰值强度的 2%。因此，我们采用了两种独立的方法对二维图像进行了重新处理。第一种方法采用标准通道提供的二维图像，利用多项式拟合方法对背景光谱区上下各区间（包括地冕发射）进行插值。第二种方法是对二维原始图像进行暗背景校正，这种校正参照一种超暗图像（通过周期观测建立），同时减去沿光栅缝隙测量得到的地冕发

background correction from a super-dark image (created for the period of the observations) as well as a subtraction of the geocoronal emission measured along the slit, away from the stellar spectrum. The differences between the results of both approaches are negligible, showing that systematic errors generated through the background corrections are small compared to the statistical errors. Those errors are dominated by photon counting noise to which we added quadratically the error evaluated for both the dark background and geocoronal subtractions.

The Lyman α line profiles observed before and during the transits are plotted in Fig. 2. The three exposures outside the transits (exposures A1, B1 and C1) and the three entirely within the transits (A2, B3 and C3) were co-added to improve the signal-to-noise ratio. An obvious signature in absorption is detected during the transits, mainly over the blue side of the line, and possibly at the top of the red peak.

To characterize this signature better, we have defined two spectral domains: "In" and "Out" of the absorption. The In domain is a wavelength interval limited by two variables λ_1 and λ_2 (excluding the Geo geocoronal region). The Out domain is the remaining wavelength coverage within the interval 1,214.4–1,216.8 Å, for which the Lyman α line intensity can be accurately measured at the time of the observation. The corresponding In/Out flux ratio derived for each exposure is shown in Fig. 3, revealing the absorption occurring during the transits. To evaluate whether this detection is sensitive to a particular choice of λ_1 and λ_2, we averaged the three ratios before the transits and the three ratios entirely within the transits. We calculated the averaged pre-transits over mid-transits ratio as a function of λ_1 and λ_2 and propagated the errors through boot-strap estimations of the ratio calculated with 10,000 randomly generated spectra according to the evaluated errors over each individual pixel (Fig. 2c). The averaged ratio is always significantly below 1, with the minimum at $\lambda_1 = 1,215.15$ Å and $\lambda_2 = 1,216.1$ Å. In the interval defined by these two wavelengths, the Lyman α line is reduced by $15 \pm 4\%$ (1σ) during the transit. This is a larger-than-3σ detection of an absorption in the hydrogen line profile during the planetary transits.

HD209458 (G0V) is close to solar type, for which time variations are known to occur in the chromospheric Lyman α line[8]. We thus evaluated the In/Out ratio in the solar Lyman α line profile as measured over the whole solar disk by the Solar Ultraviolet Measurements of Emitted Radiation (SUMER) instrument onboard the Solar and Heliospheric Observatory (SOHO)[9] during the last solar cycle from 1996 to 2001, that is, from quiet to active Sun. During this time, the total solar Lyman α flux varies by about a factor of two, while its In/Out ratio varies by less than $\pm 6\%$. Within a few months, a time comparable to our HD209458 observations, the solar In/Out ratio varies by less than $\pm 4\%$. This is an indication that the absorption detected is not of stellar origin but is due to a transient absorption occurring during the planetary transits.

A bright hot spot on the stellar surface hidden during the planetary transit is also excluded. Such a hot spot would have to contribute about 15% of the Lyman α flux over 1.5% of

射线的干扰。以上两种方法所得到的结果差异小到可以忽略不计，表明背景校正产生的系统误差小于统计误差。这些误差受光子计数噪声控制，我们在这些噪声中加入了暗背景和地冕删除两次误差评估。

图 2 给出了凌星前和凌星中观测到的莱曼 α 线廓线。为改善信噪比，我们把三次凌星前的曝光（分别表示为 A1、B1、C1）和三次凌星过程之中的曝光（分别表示为 A2、B3、C3）叠加在了一起。在凌星过程中，一个清晰的吸收信号被探测到，主要位于光谱的蓝端，也可能位于红端峰的顶部。

为了更好地描述该吸收信号特征，我们定义了光谱吸收域"In"和"Out"。其中"In"区域位于波长 λ_1 和 λ_2 之间（不包括"Geo"区域），"Out"区域位于波长 λ_1 和 λ_2 外侧，两区域均位于 1,214.4 ~ 1,216.8 Å 之间，该波段的莱曼 α 线强度在观测期间可以精确测量。图 3 给出了每次曝光相对应的 In/Out 通量比，结果表明在凌星过程中发生了吸收现象。为了评估这次探测对于我们选择的 λ_1、λ_2 值是否敏感，我们将凌星前的三个比值和凌星中的三个比值分别进行平均。然后计算出凌星前与凌星中比值的平均值，并将其作为关于 λ_1 和 λ_2 的函数。根据每个独立像素的估计误差，利用比值的自举估算来传递误差，其中比值是由 10,000 个随机产生的光谱计算产生（图 2c）。平均比值始终显著地小于 1，其中最小值位于位置 λ_1 = 1,215.15 Å 和 λ_2 = 1,216.1 Å。在 λ_1 和 λ_2 之间的波段，凌星过程中莱曼 α 线强度减弱了 15±4% （1σ）。这是一个在行星凌星中对氢吸收廓线所做的大于 3σ 的探测。

HD209458(G0V) 是类太阳恒星，其色球莱曼 α 线强度随时间发生变化[8]。在最近一个太阳活动周期（1996 ~ 2001 年），太阳活动从宁静变得逐渐活跃。在这段时间，太阳和日球层探测器（SOHO）上搭载的太阳紫外辐射光谱仪对整个日面进行了测量，从而可以求出太阳莱曼 α 线轮廓中的 In/Out 比率。结果表明，在该活动周期内，太阳莱曼 α 总通量变化因子大约为 2，其 In/Out 比值变化小于 ±6%。在和 HD209458 观测时间差不多的几个月内，太阳的 In/Out 比值起伏变化小于 ±4%。这说明，探测到的吸收光谱并不是由恒星本身产生，而是在凌星过程中产生的短暂吸收。

我们同时也排除了在凌星过程中恒星表面可能存在明亮热斑的可能性。因为

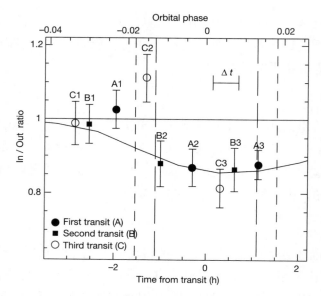

Fig. 3. Relative flux of Lyman α as a function of the HD209458's system phase. The averaged ratio of the flux is measured in the In (1,215.15–1,215.50 Å and 1,215.80–1,216.10 Å) and the Out (1,214.40–1,215.15 Å and 1,216.10–1,216.80 Å) domains in individual exposures of the three observed transits of HD209458b. The central time of each exposure is plotted relative to the transit time. The vertical dashed lines indicate the first and the second contact at the beginning and the end of the transit; the exposures A1, B1 and C1 were performed before the transits, and the exposures A2, B3 and C3 were entirely within the transits. The ratio is normalized to the average value of the three observations completed before the beginning of the transits. The $\pm 1\sigma$ error bars are statistical; they are computed through boot-strap estimations (see text). The In/Out ratio smoothly decreases by around 15% during the transit. The thick line represents the absorption ratio modelled through a particle simulation which includes hydrogen atoms escaping from the planet. In this simulation, hydrogen atoms are sensitive to the radiation pressure above an altitude of 0.5 times the Roche radius, where the density is assumed to be 2×10^5 cm^{-3}; these two parameters correspond to an escape flux of $\sim 10^{10}$ g s^{-1}. The stellar radiation pressure is taken to be 0.7 times the stellar gravitation. The mean lifetime of escaping hydrogen atoms is taken to be 4 h. The model yields an atom population in a curved comet-like tail, explaining why the computed absorption lasts well after the end of the transit.

the stellar surface occulted by the planet, in contradiction with Lyman α inhomogeneities observed on the Sun[10]. Furthermore, this spot would have to be perfectly aligned with the planet throughout the transit, at the same latitude as the Earth's direction, and with a peculiar narrow single-peaked profile confined over the In spectral region. It seems unlikely that a stellar spot could satisfy all these conditions.

图 3. 莱曼 α 谱线的相对通量与 HD209458 系统相位的函数关系。HD209458b 每次凌星过程中，在 In (1,215.15 ~ 1,215.50 Å 和 1,215.80 ~ 1,216.10 Å) 和 Out(1,214.40 ~ 1,215.15 Å 和 1,216.10 ~ 1,216.80 Å) 域上测量每次曝光，可以得到通量平均比值。图中每次曝光过程中的中心时间点是相对整个凌星的时间值，垂直虚线表示凌星开始和结束时的第一次和第二次接触。图中 A1、B1、C1 三次曝光是在凌星前进行，而 A2、B3、C3 是完全在凌星中进行。其中，图中比值相对凌星前完成的三次观测的平均值进行了归一化。±1σ 误差棒所示为统计误差，它们通过自举估算计算得到。可以看出，在整个凌星过程中，In/Out 比值平滑地降低了大约 15%。图中粗线表示通过粒子仿真模型计算得到的吸收比值，其中该模型考虑了从行星逃逸的氢原子。在该仿真中，氢原子对于海拔高度大于 0.5 倍洛希半径处的辐射压较为敏感，其密度假定为 $2 \times 10^5 \ cm^{-3}$，对应的逃逸通量约为 $10^{10} \ g \cdot s^{-1}$。恒星辐射压设为 0.7 倍于恒星引力。逃逸氢原子的平均寿命取 4 h。该模型计算表明，大量逃逸氢原子构成了一个类似弯曲彗尾的结构，这就解释了为什么凌星完成后还观测到吸收现象。

如果恒星表面被行星遮挡了 1.5% 的话，那么这样一个热斑将会贡献莱曼 α 通量的 15%，然而这与观测到的太阳的莱曼 α 非均匀性相矛盾[10]。而且，如果有热斑存在的话，那么在整个凌星过程中，位于地球方向上的相同纬度，热斑都需要与该行星严格对准，此外在 In 光谱区域还会有一个宽度很窄的特征单峰。这些条件过于苛刻，恒星上的热斑不太可能满足所有的这些条件。

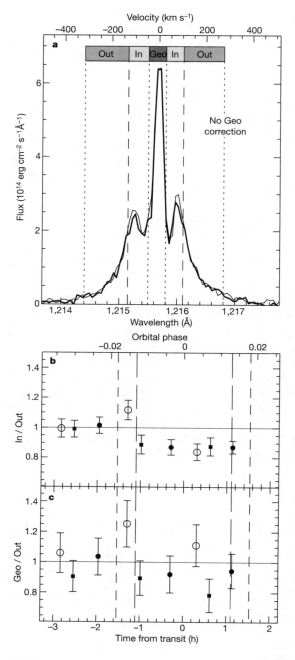

Fig. 4. Spectra and ratios with no geocoronal correction. To investigate the possibility that a bad estimate of the geocoronal correction may cause the detected signal, the spectra and ratios are plotted without this correction. First, note that the geocoronal emission is of the order of the stellar flux, and its peak value is never larger than three times the stellar one. Consequently, the correction is very small outside the Geo domain. **b** shows the same evaluation of the In/Out ratios as made in Fig. 3, with no geocoronal and no background correction. It appears that the impact of the geocoronal correction on these ratios is negligible. To further show that the "wings" of the geocoronal emission do not carry the detected transit signal, **c** shows the Geo/Out ratios, where Geo is the total flux due to the geocorona. If the flux in the In

图 4. 未进行地冕校正的光谱和比值。为了研究不良的地冕校正对于探测信号的影响，图中给出了未经校正的光谱和比值。首先，值得注意的是地冕发射通量与恒星通量量级相同，而且其峰值不会高于恒星峰值的三倍。因此，在 Geo 域外的校正很小。图 b 给出了 In/Out 比值（与图 3 计算相同），但没有进行地冕和背景校正。从图中可见，地冕校正对于比值的影响可以忽略。为了进一步说明地冕发射的"两翼"并不具有探测到的凌星信号，图 c 给出了 Geo/Out 比值，其中 Geo 代表地冕发射的总通量。如果 In 区域内的通量受地冕发射的严重影响，则会发现 Geo/Out 比值与图 3 中比值相似。从图中可知，Geo/Out 比值在 A1、B1 和 C1 平均值附近随机起伏，并没有随地冕变化出现始终一致的凌星特征。类

domain was significantly affected by the geocorona, the Geo/Out ratios should present a signal similar to the In/Out ratios plotted in Fig. 3. The Geo/Out ratios are found to be random fluctuations around the average of the A1, B1 and C1 values. There is no consistent signature of the transit in the geocoronal variations. As in Fig. 2a, **a** shows the average of the three spectra obtained before and during the transits (thin and thick lines, respectively). Quoted velocities are in the stellar reference frame. Here the spectra are without any geocoronal correction. A simple constant has been subtracted to compensate for the mean background levels in order to have matching spectra in the Out domain. This clearly shows that the absorption signature is present even without the geocoronal correction.

Finally, we confirmed with various tests that there are no correlations between the geocoronal variations and the detected signature in absorption. One method is presented in Fig. 4, showing that a contamination of the In domain by the geocorona is excluded. We thus conclude that the detected profile variation can only be related to an absorption produced by the planetary environment.

The observed 15% intensity drop is larger than expected *a priori* for an atmosphere of a planet occulting only 1.5% of the star. Although the small distance (8.5 stellar radii) between the planet and the star results in an extended Roche lobe[11] with a limit at about 2.7 planetary radii (that is, 3.6 Jupiter radii), the filling up of this lobe gives a maximum absorption of about 10% during the planetary transit. Because a more important absorption is detected, hydrogen atoms must cover a larger area: a drop of 15% corresponds to an occultation by an object of 4.3 Jupiter radii. This is clearly beyond the Roche limit as theoretically predicted[6]. Thus some hydrogen atoms should escape from the planet. The spectral absorption width shows independently that the atoms have large velocities relative to the planet. Thus hydrogen atoms must be escaping the planetary atmosphere.

We have built a particle simulation in which we assumed that hydrogen atoms are sensitive to the stellar radiation pressure inside and outside the Roche lobe. Their motion is evaluated by taking into account both the planetary and stellar gravities. The Lyman α radiation pressure is known to be 0.7 times the stellar gravity, the escape flux and the neutral hydrogen lifetime being free parameters. The lifetime of hydrogen is limited to a few hours owing to stellar extreme ultraviolet ionization. Escaping hydrogen atoms expand in an asymmetric comet-like tail and progressively disappear when moving away from the planet. This simple scenario is consistent with the observations (Fig. 3). In this model, atoms in the evaporating coma and tail cover a large area of the star, and most are blueshifted because of the radiation pressure repelling them away from the star. The detection of most of the absorption in the blue part of the line is consistent with these escaping atoms. On the other hand, more observations are needed to clarify whether an absorption is also present in the red part of the line.

To account for the observed absorption depth, the particle simulation implies a minimum escape flux of around 10^{10} g s^{-1}. However, owing to saturation effects in the absorption line, a flux larger by several orders of magnitude would produce a similar absorption signature. So, to evaluate the actual escape flux, we need to estimate the vertical distribution of hydrogen atoms up to the Roche limit, in an atmosphere extended by the stellar tidal forces

似图 2a，图 **a** 给出了凌星前和凌星中获得的三个光谱的平均值，分别用细线和粗线画出。图中速度相对恒星参考系。这里的光谱没有进行任何地冕校正。为了在 Out 域获得匹配光谱，我们在光谱中减去了一个常数以补偿背景平均水平。这清楚地表明，即使没有经过地冕校正也存在特征吸收。

最终，我们通过各种检验确认探测到的特征吸收与地冕的变化没有相关性。图 4 给出了其中的一种方法，表明可以消除 In 区域内地冕造成的干扰。因此，我们得出以下结论：探测到的光谱廓线变化只可能与行星环境产生的吸收有关。

鉴于这颗恒星表面被行星大气遮挡住 1.5% 的情况，观测到的光谱强度减小了 15%，这比预期的值要大。尽管行星与恒星之间的短距离（8.5 恒星半径）造成了洛希瓣扩展 [11]，扩展的上限为 2.7 倍行星的半径（即木星半径的 3.6 倍），而对洛希瓣的填充会引起行星凌星过程的最大吸收，约为 10%。探测到的强吸收意味着氢原子一定覆盖着更大的面积，15% 的减小对应着一个 4.3 倍于木星半径的天体被遮挡，这显然超出了洛希极限的理论值 [6]。所以，一部分氢原子应该从这颗行星发生了逃逸。另外，光谱的吸收宽度独立地表明这些原子相对这颗行星具有较大的速度。因此氢原子必定从这颗行星的大气层逃逸了。

为此，我们建立了一个粒子仿真，在该仿真中我们假设氢原子对洛希瓣内外的恒星辐射压较为敏感。通过考虑行星和恒星的引力作用，可以计算出这些氢原子的运动情况。已知莱曼 α 辐射压是恒星引力的 0.7 倍，氢原子的逃逸通量和中性氢原子的寿命都是自由参量。由于恒星极端紫外电离，氢原子的寿命一般为数小时。逃逸的氢原子扩展形成一个非对称的彗状尾，并随着行星的远离逐渐消失。这一图景与图 3 中的观测相符。在这一模型中，位于蒸发中的彗发和彗尾中的逃逸氢原子覆盖了恒星很大的表面积，并且这些原子被辐射压从恒星表面排斥开，因此大多发生蓝移，蓝移可以解释为辐射压将这些原子从恒星上排斥出来。对蓝端部分谱线吸收的检测结果与这些逃逸中原子的检测结果相吻合。另一方面，对于大多数观测需要弄清是否在谱线红端部分也存在吸收现象。

考虑观测到的吸收深度，粒子仿真表明需要存在最小逃逸通量，其值大约为 10^{10} g·s^{-1}。由于吸收光谱存在饱和效应，即使比最小通量大若干个数量级的通量也会产生相似的特征吸收。所以，为了计算实际的逃逸通量，我们需要估计氢原子在洛希极限以内的大气层垂直分布。大气层由于受到恒星潮汐力作用而扩展，同时由于许多可能的机制而被加热，这些效应都可能引起更大的逃逸通量。对于通量的详

and heated by many possible mechanisms. These effects may lead to a much larger escape flux. A detailed calculation is beyond the scope of this Letter. This raises the question of the lifetime of evaporating extrasolar planets which may be comparable to the star's lifetime itself. If so, the so-called "hot Jupiters" could evolve faster than their parent star, eventually becoming smaller objects, which could look like "hot hydrogen-poor Neptune-mass" planets. This evaporation process, more efficient for planets close to their star, might explain the very few detections[12,13] of "hot Jupiters" with orbiting periods shorter than three days.

(**422**, 143-146; 2003)

A. Vidal-Madjar*, A. Lecavelier des Etangs*, J.-M. Désert*, G. E. Ballester†, R. Ferlet*, G. Hébrard* & M. Mayor‡

* Institut d'Astrophysique de Paris, CNRS/UPMC, 98bis boulevard Arago, F-75014 Paris, France

† Lunar and Planetary Laboratory, University of Arizona, 1040 E. 4th St., Rm 901, Tucson, Arizona 85721-0077, USA

‡ Observatoire de Genève, CH-1290 Sauverny, Switzerland

Received 13 September 2002; accepted 27 January 2003; doi:10.1038/nature01448.

References:

1. Henry, G. W., Marcy, G. W., Butler, R. P. & Vogt, S. S. A transiting "51 Peg-like" planet. *Astrophys. J.* **529**, L41-L44 (2000).

2. Charbonneau, D., Brown, T. M., Latham, D. W. & Mayor, M. Detection of planetary transits across a Sun-like star. *Astrophys. J.* **529**, L45-L48 (2000).

3. Mazeh, T. *et al.* The spectroscopic orbit of the planetary companion transiting HD 209458. *Astrophys. J.* **532**, L55-L58 (2000).

4. Bundy, K. A. & Marcy, G. W. A search for transit effects in spectra of 51 Pegasi and HD 209458. *Proc. Astron. Soc. Pacif.* **112**, 1421-1425 (2000).

5. Rauer, H., Bockelée-Morvan, D., Coustenis, A., Guillot, T. & Schneider, J. Search for an exosphere around 51 Pegasi B with ISO. *Astron. Astrophys.* **355**, 573-580 (2000).

6. Moutou, C. *et al.* Search for spectroscopical signatures of transiting HD 209458b's exosphere. *Astron. Astrophys.* **371**, 260-266 (2001).

7. Charbonneau, D., Brown, T. M., Noyes, R. W. & Gilliland, R. L. Detection of an extrasolar planet atmosphere. *Astrophys. J.* **568**, 377-384 (2002).

8. Vidal-Madjar, A. Evolution of the solar lyman alpha flux during four consecutive years. *Sol. Phys.* **40**, 69-86 (1975).

9. Lemaire, P. *et al.* in *Proc. Symp. SOHO 11, From Solar Min to Max: Half a Solar Cycle with SOHO* (ed. Wilson, A.) 219-222 (ESA SP-508, ESA Publications Division, Noordwijk, 2002).

10. Prinz, D. K. The spatial distribution of Lyman alpha on the Sun. *Astrophys. J.* **187**, 369-375 (1974).

11. Paczynski, B. Evolutionary processes in close binary systems. *Annu. Rev. Astron. Astrophys.* **9**, 183-208 (1971).

12. Cumming, A., Marcy, G. W., Butler, R. P. & Vogt, S. S. The statistics of extrasolar planets: Results from the Keck survey. Preprint astro-ph/0209199 available at ⟨http://xxx.lanl.gov⟩ (2002).

13. Konacki, M., Torres, G., Jha, S. & Sasselov, D. D. An extrasolar planet that transits the disk of its parent star. *Nature* **421**, 507-509 (2003).

Acknowledgements. This work is based on observations with the NASA/ESA Hubble Space Telescope, obtained at the Space Telescope Science Institute, which is operated by AURA, Inc. We thank M. Lemoine, L. Ben Jaffel, C. Emerich, P. D. Feldman and J. McConnell for comments, J. Herbert and W. Landsman for conversations on STIS data reduction, and J. Valenti for help in preparing the observations.

Competing interests statement. The authors declare that they have no competing financial interests.

Correspondence and requests for materials should be addressed to A.V.-M. (e-mail: alfred@iap.fr).

细计算已经超出了本文的研究范围。这也引出了关于太阳系外蒸发中的行星的寿命问题，其寿命可能与母恒星的寿命相当。如果确实如此，这些所谓的"热木星"就会比其母恒星演化更快，最终演变为更小的天体，而这些"热而缺氢"行星和海王星的质量差不多。如果行星距离恒星更近的话，以上蒸发过程将会更快。这也可能解释为什么轨道周期短于三天的"热木星"很少被探测到 [12,13]。

（金世超 翻译；胡永云 审稿）

The Principle of Gating Charge Movement in a Voltage-dependent K$^+$ Channel

Y. Jiang *et al.*

Editor's Note

Proteins in cell membranes that act as gates for alkali-metal ions, opening and shutting in response to changes in the electrochemical potential (voltage) across the membrane, play key roles in important biological processes of higher organisms, such as muscle action and nerve signal transmission. But the mechanism by which these "ion channels" operate was not fully known before these papers from biochemist Roderick MacKinnon and colleagues. This understanding demanded a detailed picture of the molecular structure of the proteins, which was hard to obtain because membrane proteins seldom crystallize well for X-ray diffraction studies. Nonetheless, having succeeded in obtaining a detailed crystal structure, reported in a companion paper to this one, the researchers here describe the changes in molecular shape that control potassium-ion movement through the central pore.

The steep dependence of channel opening on membrane voltage allows voltage-dependent K$^+$ channels to turn on almost like a switch. Opening is driven by the movement of gating charges that originate from arginine residues on helical S4 segments of the protein. Each S4 segment forms half of a "voltage-sensor paddle" on the channel's outer perimeter. Here we show that the voltage-sensor paddles are positioned inside the membrane, near the intracellular surface, when the channel is closed, and that the paddles move a large distance across the membrane from inside to outside when the channel opens. KvAP channels were reconstituted into planar lipid membranes and studied using monoclonal Fab fragments, a voltage-sensor toxin, and avidin binding to tethered biotin. Our findings lead us to conclude that the voltage-sensor paddles operate somewhat like hydrophobic cations attached to levers, enabling the membrane electric field to open and close the pore.

VOLTAGE-DEPENDENT K$^+$ channel opening follows a very steep function of membrane voltage[1]. To allow channels to switch to the open state, gating charges—charged amino acids on the channel protein—move within the membrane electric field to open the pore[1-3]. The crystal structure of KvAP, a voltage-dependent K$^+$ channel, suggests how these gating charge movements might occur[4]. Four arginine residues are located on a predominantly hydrophobic helix–turn–helix structure called the voltage-sensor paddle. One paddle on each subunit is present at the outer perimeter of the channel. By moving across the membrane near the protein–lipid interface, the paddles could carry the arginine residues through the electric field, coupling pore opening to membrane voltage. We test this

电压依赖性 K$^+$ 通道的门控电荷运动的原理

姜有星等

编者按

那些位于细胞膜中的、对碱金属离子起着门控作用、随着膜两侧电化学势（电压）的变化而开放和关闭的蛋白质在高等生物的重要生物过程中起着关键作用，比如肌肉动作和神经信号传导。但是，在生物化学家罗德里克·麦金农及其同事们发表相关的文章之前，这些"离子通道"运转的机制并不完全为人们所知。对这种机制的了解需要有对蛋白质的分子结构的详细描述，然而这一点很难做到，因为膜蛋白很难得到足够好的晶体进行 X 射线衍射分析。尽管如此，研究者们还是成功地获得了其详细的晶体结构并在本文的姊妹篇中进行了报道，在本文中他们则描述了这些蛋白分子形状的变化，这些变化控制了钾离子穿过中央小孔的运动。

通道开放对膜电压的严格依赖使电压依赖性 K$^+$ 通道像开关一样打开。其开放受门控电荷运动驱动，门控电荷来自这个蛋白的 S4 螺旋片段上的精氨酸残基。每个 S4 片段在通道的外围形成半个"电压感受桨"。在这里，我们证明当通道关闭时，电压感受桨位于膜内，接近细胞内表面，当通道打开时桨从内向外跨膜移动很大的距离。将 KvAP 通道重建到平面脂质膜中，并用单克隆的 Fab（抗原表位）片段、电压传感器毒素和连接了生物素的抗生物素蛋白对 KvAP 通道进行研究。通过研究结果我们可以得出这样的结论：电压感受桨的运转有点像疏水性阳离子依附到杠杆上，使得膜电场可打开和关闭孔道。

电压依赖性 K$^+$ 通道开放严格受控于膜电压[1]。为了让通道切换到开放状态，门控电荷——通道蛋白上的带电氨基酸——在膜电场内运动以打开孔道[1-3]。KvAP 的晶体结构（一种电压依赖性 K$^+$ 通道），可能表明了这些门控电荷运动是如何发生的[4]。四个精氨酸残基位于一个显著疏水的被称为电压感受桨的螺旋-转角-螺旋结构上。每个亚基上有一个桨位于通道外围。通过跨膜运动接近蛋白-膜脂质界面，桨可携带精氨酸残基通过电场，将孔道开放与膜电压耦联。我们通过测定通道关闭和打开时膜内电压感受桨的位置来验证该门控电荷运动假说。

hypothesis for the movement of gating charges by estimating the positions of the voltage-sensor paddles inside the membrane when the channel is closed and opened.

Using Fabs and a Toxin to Detect Paddle Motions

Two monoclonal Fabs, 6E1 and 33H1, were used to crystallize and determine the structures of the full-length KvAP channel and the isolated voltage sensor, respectively[4]. Both Fabs were found attached to the same epitope on the tip of the voltage-sensor paddle between S3b and S4. We used these same Fabs to examine the position of the voltage-sensor paddles when the KvAP channel functions in lipid membranes (Fig. 1a), and to assess whether they change their position when the channel gates open in response to membrane depolarization. Figure 1b shows that both the 6E1 and 33H1 Fabs inhibit channel function when applied to the external solution. By contrast, neither Fab affected channel function from the internal solution.

Inhibition by external Fabs requires membrane depolarization (Fig. 1c). When the 33H1 Fab is added to the external chamber while the channel is held closed at −100 mV for 10 min (Fig. 1c, interval between the black and red data points), no inhibition is observed. The slightly larger current of the first red data point (20-min point) reflects recovery from a small amount of steady-state inactivation of channels occurring during the control pulse period (0–10-min data points)[5]. The important point, however, is that inhibition of current is detectable only on the second pulse following the addition of the Fab, as if the channel has first to open in order for the Fabs to bind. Inhibition progresses as the membrane is repeatedly depolarized. We also observe gradual recovery from inhibition if, once the Fabs are bound, the membrane is held at a negative voltage for a prolonged period (30–40-min interval), implying that negative membrane voltages destabilize the interactions between channels and Fabs, causing the Fabs to dissociate. The same properties of inhibition are observed for Fab 6E1. Based on these results, we conclude that the voltage-sensor paddles must remain inaccessible as long as the channel is held closed by the negative membrane voltage, and that the entire epitope (two helical turns of S3b and one turn of S4) becomes exposed to the external side in response to depolarization.

Why do the Fabs inhibit the channel? If they bind to the voltage-sensor paddles from the external side when the membrane is depolarized, why do the Fabs not simply hold the channel permanently open? Inhibition can be explained by the fact that the KvAP channel, like most voltage-dependent K⁺ channels, inactivates[5]. That is, its pore stops conducting ions spontaneously during prolonged depolarizations of the membrane, even though the voltage sensors remain in their open conformation. Inactivation could also occur when the Fabs bind and hold the voltage sensors in their open conformation, thus explaining inhibition.

使用 Fabs 和毒素检测桨的运动

两个单克隆的 Fabs 片段——6E1 和 33H1，分别用于结晶并确定全长 KvAP 通道和独立的电压传感器的结构 [4]。我们发现两个 Fabs 都附在位于 S3b 和 S4 之间的电压感受桨末端的相同抗原表位。当 KvAP 通道在脂质膜内起作用时，我们用相同的 Fabs 检查电压感受桨的位置（图 1a），并评估当膜去极化使通道开放时它们是否改变自己的位置。图 1b 显示，当 Fabs 片段 6E1 和 33H1 被加入外侧溶液中时都能抑制通道功能。相反，当被加入内侧溶液中时两个 Fabs 片段都不影响通道功能。

外侧 Fabs 抑制需要膜去极化（图 1c）。当 33H1 Fab 加到外侧，同时通道在 –100 mV 保持关闭 10 min 时（图 1c，黑色和红色的数据点之间的间隔），没有观察到抑制。第一个红色数据点所显示的略大的电流（20 min 点）反映了在控制脉冲周期内发生的从小量通道稳态失活的恢复（0 ~ 10 min 数据点）[5]。然而，重点是电流抑制只在加入 Fab 后的第二个脉冲检测到，好像通道必须首先打开才能使得 Fabs 进行结合。当膜反复去极化时抑制会继续。若是一旦 Fabs 被结合，且使膜维持更长时间的负电压（30 ~ 40 min 间隔），我们还可以观察到从抑制中逐渐恢复的过程，这意味着负的膜电压使通道和 Fabs 间相互作用不稳定，造成 Fabs 脱离。在 Fab 6E1 的实验中也观察到了相同的抑制特性。基于这些结果，我们得出这样的结论：只要通道通过负膜电压保持关闭，电压感受桨必定是难以接近的，只有去极化时整个抗原表位（S3b 的两个螺旋转角和 S4 的一个转角）才会相应地暴露在外侧。

为什么 Fabs 会抑制通道？当膜去极化时，如果它们从外侧结合到电压感受桨，那为什么 Fabs 不能简单地维持通道永久开放？抑制可以解释为，KvAP 通道会像大多数电压依赖性 K⁺ 通道一样失活 [5]。即当膜去极化时间延长，即使电压传感器保持其开放构象，其孔道也会自发停止导通离子。当 Fabs 结合并保持电压传感器开放的构象中，失活也会发生，从而解释了抑制现象。

Fig. 1. Inhibition of KvAP channels by Fabs and a tarantula venom toxin that bind to the voltage-sensor paddles. **a**, Experimental strategy: Fab (green) is added to the external or internal side of a planar lipid membrane to determine whether the epitope is exposed. **b**, Fabs used in crystallization (6E1 and 33H1) inhibit from the external (red traces) but not the internal (blue traces) side of the membrane. Currents before (black traces) and after the addition of about 500 nM Fab (red and blue traces) were elicited by membrane depolarization to 100 mV from a holding voltage of −100 mV. **c**, Fab 33H1 binds to the voltage-sensor paddle only when the membrane is depolarized. Current elicited by depolarization from −100 mV to 100 mV at times indicated by the stimulus trace (above) in the absence (black symbols) or presence of 500 nM Fab (red symbols) is presented as a function of time. Selected current traces corresponding to the numbered symbols are shown (inset). **d**, VSTX1 binds from the external side only when the membrane is depolarized. Currents, normalized to the average control value, were elicited by a 100-ms depolarization to 100 mV every 120 s (diamonds) or every 600 s (triangles). VSTX1 (30 nM) was added to the external solution at the point indicated by the arrow.

It is interesting that tarantula venom toxins also bind to residues on S3 and S4 (ref. 6), which we now know to be on the voltage-sensor paddles[4]. On addition of an approximately half-inhibitory concentration of the tarantula venom toxin VSTX1 to the external side of KvAP, we observe that the rate of inhibition is faster if the membrane is depolarized at a higher frequency (Fig. 1d). Therefore, the toxins, like the Fabs, require membrane depolarization.

We conclude from experiments with Fab fragments and a tarantula venom toxin that the voltage-sensor paddles are exposed to the extracellular solution during membrane depolarization (positive inside) but not during hyperpolarization (negative inside). In view of the KvAP crystal structure[4], these results imply that the voltage-sensor paddles can move a large distance across the lipid membrane. How deep inside the membrane do the paddles sit

图 1. 结合到电压感受桨的 Fabs 和狼蛛毒液毒素对 KvAP 通道的抑制。**a**，实验策略：将 Fab（绿色）加入平面脂质膜的外侧或内侧，以确定抗原表位是否暴露出来。**b**，结晶所使用的 Fabs（6E1 和 33H1）从膜的外侧（红色轨迹）抑制而非内侧（蓝色轨迹）。加入约 500 nM Fab 之前（黑色轨迹）和之后（红色和蓝色轨迹）的电流是由膜从 –100 mV 钳制电压去极化到 100 mV 时产生的。**c**，只有当膜去极化时，Fab 33H1 才结合到电压感受桨。从 –100 mV 到 100 mV 去极化时产生的电流，在不存在（黑色符号）或存在（红色符号）500 nM Fab 时表示为时间的函数。图中对应于数字符号的电流值，来自选定的电流轨迹（插图中）。**d**，只有当膜去极化时，VSTX1 才从外侧结合。100 ms 去极化至 100 mV，将每 120 s（菱形）或每 600 s（三角形）时间点产生的电流归一化到平均值。在箭头所指示的时间点，将 VSTX1（30 nM）加到外侧溶液。

　　有趣的是，狼蛛毒液毒素也结合 S3 和 S4 的残基（参考文献 6），现在我们知道它们位于电压感受桨上 [4]。另外加入大约一半抑制浓度的狼蛛毒液毒素 VSTX1 到 KvAP 外侧，我们看到，如果膜的去极化频率越高，则抑制速率也越快（见图 1d）。因此，毒素像 Fabs 一样需要膜去极化。

　　我们从 Fab 片段和狼蛛毒液毒素实验可得出结论，电压感受桨在膜去极化时（内部为正），而不是超极化时（内部为负）暴露在细胞外的溶液中。鉴于 KvAP 晶体结构 [4]，这些结果意味着，电压感受桨可以跨越脂质膜移动一段较大的距离。当膜

when the membrane is hyperpolarized, and how far do they move when the channel opens?

Using Biotin and Avidin to Measure Paddle Motions

Finkelstein and co-workers used avidin binding to biotinylated colicin to examine the movements of its components across the lipid bilayer[7-9]. We subjected the KvAP channel to a similar analysis. The idea behind the experiments is outlined in Fig. 2a. We introduce cysteine residues at specific locations in the channel, biotinylate the cysteine, reconstitute channels into planar lipid membranes, and then determine whether avidin binds from the internal or external side, and whether binding depends on membrane depolarization. Wild-type KvAP channels contain a single cysteine on the carboxy-terminus, which was mutated to serine (without affecting function) to work with a channel without background cysteine residues.

Fig. 2. Using avidin and tethered biotin as a molecular ruler to measure positions of the voltage-sensor paddles. **a**, Experimental strategy: KvAP channels with biotin tethered to a site-directed cysteine can be "grabbed" by avidin in solution to affect channel function. **b**, Stereo view of an avidin tetramer (Cα trace, Protein Data Bank code 1AVD) with biotin (red) in its binding pockets. Chemical structure of biotin and its PEO-iodoacetyl linker with buried (inside avidin) and exposed segments indicated. **c**, Representative traces

超极化时，桨在膜内多深的地方？通道打开时它们会移动多远？

利用生物素和抗生物素蛋白测量桨运动

芬克尔斯坦和他的同事们用结合大肠杆菌生物素的抗生物素蛋白来检测其组成部分跨越脂质双层的运动 [7-9]。我们对 KvAP 通道做了类似的分析。图 2a 概述了实验构想。我们在通道的特殊位置引入半胱氨酸残基，用生物素标记这些半胱氨酸，将通道重建到平面脂质膜，然后确定抗生物素蛋白是从内侧还是从外侧结合，以及结合是否取决于膜的去极化。野生型 KvAP 通道蛋白在羧基末端包含一个半胱氨酸，将它突变成丝氨酸（不影响功能），与无本底半胱氨酸残基背景的通道一起进行实验。

图 2. 用结合了生物素的抗生物素蛋白作为分子尺来测量电压感受桨的位置。**a**，实验策略：生物素定点结合到 KvAP 通道的半胱氨酸上，就可以被溶液内抗生物素蛋白"捕获"进而影响通道功能。**b**，抗生物素蛋白四聚体（α 碳原子示踪，蛋白质数据库索引号 1AVD）与结合在其口袋处的生物素（红色）的立体构象。生物素及其 PEO–碘乙酰基连接接头的化学结构，其中隐藏的（即在抗生物素蛋白内的）和暴

showing the effects of avidin on wild-type and mutant biotinylated KvAP channels. Currents were elicited with depolarizing steps in the absence (black traces) or presence of internal (blue traces) or external (red traces) avidin.

The crystal structure of avidin and the chemical structure of biotin attached to its linker are shown in Fig. 2b. Biotin binds within a deep cleft inside the core of avidin, a rigid protein molecule[10]. The atom on the biotin molecule to which the linker is attached is 7 Å beneath the surface of avidin (Fig. 2b). Therefore, when avidin binds to a biotinylated cysteine on the channel, the distance from the cysteine α-carbon to the surface of avidin is 10 Å; this is the pertinent linker length from the α-carbon to avidin. Since avidin is large (the tetramer is a 57-kDa protein), it cannot fit into clefts on the channel and therefore cannot penetrate the surface. The important point is that, for avidin to bind to a tethered biotin, the cysteine α-carbon has to be within 10 Å of the bulk aqueous solution on either side of the membrane. Applying this restraint, we used linked biotin and avidin as a molecular ruler to measure positions of the voltage-sensor paddles.

Detection of avidin binding to biotinylated channels depends on the demonstration of a functional effect when avidin "grabs" tethered biotin. Control experiments and examples are illustrated in Fig. 2c. Our convention for representing data will be black, red and blue traces corresponding to control (no avidin), external and internal avidin, respectively. Biotinylated wild-type channels are not affected by external avidin and show a small reduction in current when avidin is applied to the internal solution. On the basis of protein gel assays, we conclude that the wild-type channels do not contain detectable biotin on them after the biotinylation procedure (not shown). Three examples of biotinylated cysteine mutant channels are shown. The G112C mutant is inhibited completely by external but not internal avidin; the small reduction by internal avidin is similar to the wild-type control. The I127C mutant is inhibited completely by internal but not by external avidin. The L103C mutant shows an outcome different from complete inhibition: external avidin reduces the current but does not abolish it, and changes the kinetics of current activation. Another outcome that is observed at certain positions is partial inhibition by avidin without changing the gating kinetics (Fig. 3). These cases probably reflect incomplete biotinylation of buried cysteine residues. We excluded the possibility that "no effect" (that is, internal avidin on G112C or external avidin on I127C) represents "silent" avidin binding by adding avidin first to the "no effect" side of the membrane and then to the opposite side (not shown). Because avidin binding to biotin is essentially irreversible, silent binding to one side should protect from binding to the other, but this was never observed. Thus, "no effect" signifies no binding.

露的部分在图中标示出来了。c，代表性电流轨迹显示了抗生物素蛋白对野生型和突变体生物素标记的 KvAP 通道的影响。在没有(黑色轨迹)或存在内侧(蓝色轨迹)或外侧(红色轨迹)抗生物素蛋白的情况下，去极化可以引起电流。

抗生物素蛋白的晶体结构和结合到其接头的生物素的化学结构如图 2b 所示。生物素结合在一个刚性蛋白分子——抗生物素蛋白——核心处的一个深深的裂缝内[10]。生物素分子上与接头结合的原子在距抗生物素蛋白表面 7 Å 处(图 2b)。因此，当抗生物素蛋白结合到通道上的生物素化的半胱氨酸时，从半胱氨酸 α 碳到抗生物素蛋白表面的距离就是 10 Å；这是从 α 碳到抗生物素蛋白的合适连接长度。因为抗生物素蛋白很大(该四聚体是一个 57 kDa 的蛋白)，它不能进入通道上的裂缝，因此不能穿越表面。重要的一点是，为使抗生物素蛋白结合到与通道绑定的生物素上，半胱氨酸的 α 碳必须位于膜任意一侧距大量水溶液 10 Å 范围内。运用这个尺度，我们将连接的生物素和抗生物素蛋白作为分子尺来测量电压感受桨的位置。

检测结合到生物素标记通道的抗生物素蛋白取决于当抗生物素蛋白"捕获"绑定的生物素时的功能影响的论证。对照组和实验组如图 2c 所示。我们给出的代表性数据中黑色、红色和蓝色的轨迹分别为对照(无抗生物素)、外侧和内侧加入抗生物素蛋白。生物素标记的野生型通道不受外部抗生物素蛋白影响，并且当抗生物素加入内侧溶液后电流轻微减弱。在蛋白质凝胶电泳分析基础上，我们得出这样的结论：野生型通道在生物素化处理后不含有可检测的生物素(未显示)。这里显示了三个生物素化半胱氨酸突变通道实例。G112C 突变体被外侧的抗生物素蛋白完全抑制，而内侧抗生物素蛋白无此作用；内侧抗生物素蛋白引起的轻微减弱类似于野生型对照。I127C 突变体被内侧的抗生物素蛋白完全抑制，而外侧抗生物素蛋白无此作用。L103C 突变体显示了与完全抑制不同的结果：外侧抗生物素蛋白降低电流，但并不完全消除电流，它还改变了电流激活的动力学。另一项结果是观察到的某些位置被抗生物素蛋白部分抑制而不改变门控动力学(见图 3)。这些例子可能反映了包埋的半胱氨酸残基不能被生物素完全标记。我们通过先将抗生物素蛋白加到膜"没有影响"的一侧然后加到另一侧，排除了"没有影响"(内侧抗生物素蛋白对 G112C 或外侧抗生物素蛋白对 I127C)代表"沉默"抗生物素蛋白结合的可能性(未显示)。由于抗生物素蛋白结合生物素基本上是不可逆的，沉默结合到一侧时应不再结合到另一侧，事实上也从未被观察到，因此，"没有影响"意味着没有结合。

Fig. 3. Accessibility of voltage-sensor paddle residues to the internal and external sides of the membrane. Membrane was depolarized every 120 s in the absence (control) or presence of avidin on the internal and external side of each biotinylated mutant. Red side chains on the voltage-sensor paddle and selected traces indicate inhibition by avidin from the external side only; blue side chains and selected traces indicate inhibition by avidin from the internal side only; yellow side chains and blue and red traces indicate inhibition by avidin from both sides. Black traces show control currents before avidin addition and coloured traces show currents after adding avidin. Each trace is the average of 5–10 measured traces, with the exception of the single traces for position 121.

Data from a scan of the voltage-sensor paddles from amino-acid position 101 on S3b to position 127 on S4 are shown in Fig. 3. Positions were mutated individually to cysteine, biotinylated and studied in planar lipid membranes. Certain biotinylated mutants showed altered gating even before avidin addition (for example, valine 119), or appeared to be less abundant in the membrane (for example, leucine 121). But in all cases, channels could be held closed at negative membrane voltages (typically −100 mV) and opened by membrane depolarizations (typically 100 mV for 200 ms) every 120 s. To compensate for mutations that shifted the voltage-activation curve, we sometimes held the membrane as negative as −140 mV, or used opening depolarizations as positive as 200 mV. Avidin bound to the

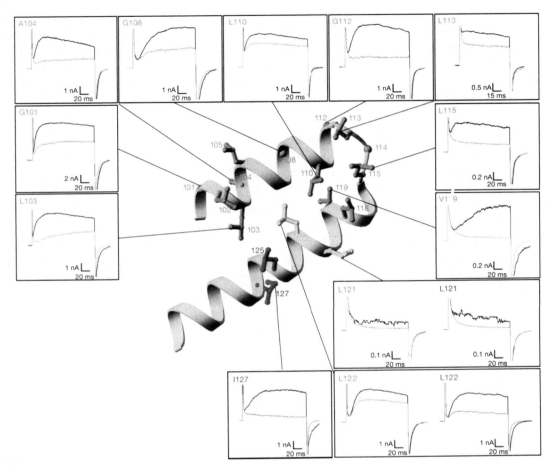

图 3. 电压感受桨残基与膜内侧和外侧的可结合性。在每个生物素标记的突变体内侧和外侧没有（对照）或存在抗生物素蛋白的情况下，每 120 s 膜被去极化。电压感受桨上的红色侧链和对应的电流轨迹表明抗生物素蛋白仅从外侧抑制，蓝色侧链和对应的电流轨迹表明抗生物素蛋白仅从内侧抑制，黄色侧链及蓝色和红色的轨迹表明抗生物素蛋白从两侧抑制。黑色轨迹表明抗生物素蛋白加入前的对照电流，彩色轨迹表明加入抗生物素蛋白后的电流。每个轨迹是 5～10 个测量轨迹的平均值，除了位点 121 是单一的轨迹外。

    图 3 显示了对电压感受桨从 S3b 上 101 位点到 S4 上 127 位点的氨基酸进行扫描得到的数据。对突变为半胱氨酸的位点，用生物素标记后在平面脂质膜内对其进行了研究。某些生物素标记的突变体甚至在加入抗生物素蛋白之前就显示了门控的改变（例如，缬氨酸 119），或在膜中的含量减少（例如，亮氨酸 121）。但在所有情况下，通道可以在负膜电压时维持关闭（通常为 –100 mV），并通过每 120 s 一次的膜去极化（通常为 100 mV，200 ms）而开放。为了抵消突变体电压激活曲线的移动，我们有时将膜电位维持在 –140 mV，或使用更高的去极化电位（200 mV）使其开放。

tethered biotin and affected channel function at all positions studied. In many cases, avidin caused complete inhibition, and in some cases partial inhibition with altered kinetics. Partial inhibition at certain sites (for example, leucine 110 and leucine 122) can be explained on the basis of incomplete biotinylation because the side chain is buried within the "core" of the voltage-sensor paddle between S3b and S4. This finding is consistent with the proposal that S3b and S4 move together as a voltage-sensor paddle unit.

We are most interested in whether a particular position on the voltage-sensor paddle allows binding to avidin from the external or internal solution. Amino acids on the paddle are colour-coded according to the membrane side from which avidin bound: red, outside; blue, inside; yellow, both. For avidin binding from the external side, we examined whether membrane depolarization is required, by studying the effect of depolarization frequency on the rate of channel inhibition by avidin (Fig. 4). Inhibition from the external solution required depolarization: higher frequencies gave higher rates of inhibition. In other words, the voltage-sensor paddles can be protected from external avidin binding by keeping the membrane at negative voltages, and the paddles are exposed to external avidin at positive voltages. This was the case for all external positions (Fig. 3, red and yellow).

Fig. 4. Exposure of the voltage-sensor paddle to the external solution occurs only when the membrane is depolarized. For the biotinylated G112C mutant, normalized (to the average control) currents elicited by depolarization to 100 mV every 60 s (circles), 120 s (diamonds) and 600 s (triangles) are shown before and after the addition of avidin to the external side.

However, protection from inhibition by external avidin, Fabs and a voltage-sensor toxin, by holding the membrane at negative voltages, is incomplete. In particular, if the wait at negative voltages is long enough, inhibition occurs but at a low rate (Fig. 4). This finding is explained on the basis of thermal fluctuations of the voltage sensors. Probably four voltage-sensor paddles have to move to open the pore[1,11-13]. But individual paddle movements must occasionally occur even at negative voltages. These sensor movements underlying incomplete protection are consistent with gating currents preceding pore opening[2], and longer delays before pore opening when the membrane is depolarized from more negative

抗生物素蛋白结合到绑定的生物素上，在被研究的所有位点上影响通道功能。在许多情况下，抗生物素蛋白引起完全抑制，而在另一些情况下，通过改变分子动力学而引起部分抑制作用。在某些位点上（例如，110 位亮氨酸和 122 位亮氨酸）部分抑制可以在不完全生物素标记的基础上进行解释，因为其侧链被包埋在位于 S3b 和 S4 之间的电压感受桨的"核心"内。这一发现与认为 S3b 和 S4 作为电压感受桨单元一起移动的观点一致。

我们最感兴趣的是抗生物素蛋白是否从外侧或内侧溶液中结合到电压感受桨上某一特定位置。根据抗生物素蛋白从膜的哪一侧结合，对桨上的氨基酸进行了颜色标记：红色，外侧；蓝色，内侧；黄色，两侧。对于抗生物素蛋白从外侧结合，我们通过研究去极化频率对抗生物素蛋白抑制通道的程度的影响，观察膜的去极化是否必需（图 4）。从外侧溶液抑制需要去极化：频率越高抑制率也越高。换言之，通过保持膜的负电压可以保护电压感受桨免受外侧抗生物素蛋白结合，而正电压时桨暴露于外侧的抗生物素蛋白中。这是所有外侧位置的情况（图 3，红色和黄色）。

图 4. 只有当膜去极化时，才会发生电压感受桨暴露在外侧溶液中的情况。对于生物素标记的 G112C 突变体，图中显示了抗生物素蛋白加入外侧前后，由每 60 s（圆圈）、120 s（菱形）、600 s（三角形）去极化到 100 mV 所引起的归一化（至平均值）电流。

然而，通过维持膜负电压，并不能完全避免外侧抗生物素、Fabs 和电压传感器毒素造成的抑制。特别是，如果在负电压保留的时间足够长，抑制可发生但发生率低（图 4）。这个发现可用电压传感器的热波动来解释。大概有 4 个电压感受桨必须移动以打开孔道 [1,11-13]。但是，即使在负电压下也必然会偶尔发生个别的桨运动。这些不完全保护下的传感器运动与先于孔道开放的门控电流一致 [2]，且当膜从更负的

holding voltages, a phenomenon known as the Cole–Moore effect[14].

Biotin molecules tethered at two positions were captured by avidin from both sides of the membrane (121 and 122; Fig. 3, yellow). At these positions, inhibition was complete from either side alone, because subsequent addition of avidin to the opposite side caused no further inhibition. Thus, the dual accessibility cannot be ascribed to two structurally distinct populations of channels. We conclude that positions 121 and 122 actually drag biotin and its linker all the way across the lipid membrane from the solution on one side to that on the other when the channel gates. This finding is very important, because it indicates that the voltage-sensor paddles must move a large distance through the membrane, and that they must move through a lipid environment where a bulky chemical structure such as biotin and its linker (Fig. 2b) would be unimpeded. Biotin and its linker could not be dragged through the core of a protein, as would be required by conventional models, which invoke an S4 helix buried within the protein.

Discussion

Positional constraints on the voltage-sensor paddles are summarized in Fig. 5a, b. Horizontal solid lines show the external and internal surfaces of the cell membrane (~35 Å thick) and dashed lines show the 10 Å limit from the membrane surface set by the linker length (Fig. 2b). If the α-carbon of a cysteine residue comes within 10 Å of the membrane surface, then avidin can bind to the attached biotin, otherwise the biotin is inaccessible. Avidin is too large to enter crevices on the channel, so it cannot penetrate below the membrane surface.

At negative membrane voltages when the channel is closed, no positions are accessible to the external side; all residues on the voltage-sensor paddles in their channel-closed position must lie deeper in the membrane than the 10-Å limit below the external surface (Fig. 5a). At negative voltages, the blue and yellow residues on S4 bind from inside, and therefore must come within 10 Å of the internal solution. The red residues, including all of S3b, the tip of the paddle and the first helical turn into S4, are protected from both sides at negative voltages and must therefore lie further than 10 Å from both surfaces; that is, between the two dashed lines. This pattern of accessibility in the closed (negative voltage) conformation constrains the voltage-sensor paddles to lie near the internal surface of the membrane with S3b above S4, as shown (Fig. 5a), similar to the orientation in the crystal structure[4].

At positive membrane voltage when the channel is opened, the entire S3b helix, the tip of the paddle and the first two-and-a-half helical turns of S4 become accessible to external avidin and must therefore be within 10 Å of the external solution (Fig. 5b). The next helical turn on S4 (positions 125 and 127, blue residues) remains more distant than 10 Å from the external surface. The Fabs inform us that, in the opened conformation, two helical turns of S3b and one turn of S4 must actually protrude clear into the external solution, otherwise the epitope would not be exposed (Fig. 1b). The Fabs and pattern of avidin accessibility in

保持电压去极化时孔道开放前的延迟更长，这一现象被称为科尔-摩尔效应[14]。

抗生物素蛋白从膜两侧捕获标记在两个位置的生物素分子（121 位和 122 位；图 3，黄色）。在这些位置，来自任一侧的抑制都是完全的，因为随后在对侧加入抗生物素蛋白并没有引起进一步的抑制。因此，双重可结合性不能归因于两种在结构上截然不同的通道类型。我们断定当通道处于门控状态时，位于 121 位和 122 位的氨基酸残基实际上拖动生物素和其接头一路跨越脂质膜，从一侧溶液到达另一侧溶液。这一发现很重要，因为它说明电压感受桨必须移动很长一段距离穿过膜，必须移动通过脂质环境，在该脂质环境里大的化学结构如生物素及其接头（图 2b）不受阻碍。生物素及接头无法通过蛋白质的核心，正如传统模型所述，该过程要借助于包埋在蛋白质内的 S4 螺旋。

讨　论

图 5a 和 b 总结了电压感受桨上的位置约束。水平实线显示了细胞膜的外表面和内表面（内外表面间的厚度约 35 Å），虚线显示了由接头长度决定的距离膜表面的 10 Å 距离（图 2b）。如果半胱氨酸残基 α 碳到达距膜表面 10 Å 的范围内，那么抗生物素蛋白可以结合到与它连接的生物素上，否则无法接近生物素。抗生物素蛋白太大不能进入通道裂缝，所以不能穿透膜表面。

当膜电压为负，通道关闭时，没有可连接到外侧的位点；电压感受桨上所有残基在通道处于关闭位置时均处于膜外表面下 10 Å 以下的深处（图 5a）。负电压时，S4 上蓝色和黄色残基可从内侧结合，因此，必须到达距细胞内液 10 Å 以内。红色的残基，包括所有 S3b，桨的尖端和 S4 的第一个螺旋，在负电压时它们的两侧都受到保护，因此必须位于离两个表面远于 10 Å 的地方，即两虚线之间。在关闭（负电压）构象中，S3b 在上、S4 在下形成的电压感受桨处于接近膜内表面附近，如图所示（图 5a），类似于晶体结构中的取向[4]。

当膜电压为正，通道开放时，整个 S3b 螺旋、桨的末端和 S4 最初的两个半螺旋转角变得易于接触到外侧抗生物素蛋白，因此必然在距外侧溶液 10 Å 内（图 5b）。S4 上紧接的一个螺旋转角（125 位和 127 位，蓝色残基）与外表面保持着超过 10 Å 的距离。结合位点告诉我们，在开放构象中，S3b 的两个螺旋转角和 S4 的一个转角需从膜内突出进入外侧溶液，否则抗原表位将不会暴露出来（图 1b）。在开放（正电压）构象时，抗原表位和抗生物素蛋白的可结合模式迫使电压感受桨以一个更加垂

the opened (positive voltage) conformation constrain the voltage-sensor paddles to be near the external membrane surface with a more vertical orientation, as shown (Fig. 5b).

Fig. 5. Positions within the membrane of the voltage-sensor paddles during closed and opened conformations, and a hypothesis for coupling to pore opening. **a**, **b**, Closed (**a**) and opened (**b**) positions of the paddles derived from the tethered biotin–avidin measurements, and structural and functional measurements with Fabs. A voltage-sensor paddle is shown as a cyan ribbon with side chains colour-coded as in Fig. 3. Grey side chains show four arginine residues on the paddle, and the green ribbon (**b**) shows part of a bound Fab from the crystal structures. Solid horizontal lines show the external and internal membrane surfaces, and dashed lines indicate the 10-Å distance from the surfaces set by biotin and its linker. **c**, The closed KvAP structure is based on the paddle depth and orientation in **a** (red), and adjusting the S5 and S6 helices of KvAP to the positions in KcsA, a closed K⁺ channel. **d**, The opened KvAP structure is based on the paddle depth and orientation in **b** (red), and the pore of KvAP.

In moving from their closed to their opened position, the voltage-sensor paddles' centre of mass translates approximately 20 Å (assuming a membrane thickness of 35 Å) through the membrane from inside to out, and the paddles tilt from a somewhat horizontal to a more vertical orientation. Arginines 117, 120, 123 and 126, the first four arginines on S4 (Fig. 1a), are distributed along the paddles. In the closed conformation, arginines 126,

直的取向靠近膜的外表面，如图所示（图 5b）。

图 5. 关闭和开放构象期间电压感受桨在膜内的位置，以及与孔道开放结合的假设。**a** 和 **b** 分别表示关闭和开放状态时桨的位置，是基于生物素–抗生物素的连接以及借助 Fabs 结合进行的结构和功能测定。如图 3 中显示电压感受桨为一个带有彩色编码侧链的蓝绿色带。灰色侧链显示桨上的 4 个精氨酸残基，(b) 中的绿色带为晶体中一个结合的 Fab 的局部结构。水平实线显示外侧和内侧膜表面，虚线表明由生物素及其接头决定的距膜表面 10 Å 的距离。**c**，关闭的 KvAP 结构是基于 **a**(红色) 中桨的深度和位置，并调整 KvAP 的 S5 和 S6 螺旋到 KcsA 中位置，使通道关闭。**d**，开放的 KvAP 结构基于 **b**(红色) 中桨的深度和方向，以及 KvAP 孔道。

在它们从关闭位置移动到开放位置的过程中，电压感受桨的质量中心从内到外穿过膜移动大约 20 Å（假设膜厚度为 35 Å），而桨从相对水平向更加垂直的方向倾斜。S4 上位于 117 位、120 位、123 位和 126 位的前 4 个精氨酸（图 1a）沿桨分布。在关闭的构象中，126 位、123 位，也许还有 120 位的精氨酸可将带正电荷的胍基延

123 and perhaps 120 can probably extend their positively charged guanidinium group to the internal lipid head group layer, whereas arginine 117 is near the internal side but still within the membrane. In the opened conformation, arginines 117, 120 and probably 123 can extend to the external solution or lipid head group layer, whereas 126 is near the external side but still within the membrane. The near-complete transfer of these four arginine residues across the membrane (in each of the four subunits) is compatible with the total gating charge in the *Shaker* K$^+$ channel of 12–14 electrons (3.0–3.5 electrons per subunit)[15-17], and with the demonstration that each of these four arginine residues carries approximately one electron charge unit[16,17].

A positional aspect of the voltage-sensor paddles not constrained by these experiments is whether they lie tangential to the channel's outer surface or whether they point in a radial direction away from it. The flexible S3 loops and S4–S5 linkers probably do not constrain the paddles much. However, we have two reasons for thinking that the paddles are positioned tangentially, which is the way they are positioned in Fig. 5c. First, the paddles are oriented tangentially in the crystal structure of the full channel; and second, the crystal structure of the isolated voltage sensor shows interesting salt-bridge interactions between S4 and S2, and between S3a and S2 (ref. 4). A tangential orientation would favour salt-bridge interactions between arginine residues on the voltage-sensor paddles and acidic residues on the S2 and S3a helices. Studies by Papazian and co-workers on the *Shaker* K$^+$ channel indeed suggest that salt-bridge pairs are important, and that they might exchange as the paddles move between their closed and opened positions on the outer perimeter of the channel[18-20].

To a first approximation, we describe the voltage-sensor paddles as hydrophobic cations that carry gating charges through the lipid bilayer. Ionic interactions between S4 arginines and S2 and S3 acidic residues probably assist the gating charge movement, and the presence of a polar, sometimes acidic loop between S3b and S4 in certain voltage-dependent K$^+$ channels (for example, the *Shaker* K$^+$ channel[21]) raises interesting questions about the structure of the lipid–water interface above the paddles when they are in their closed channel position. However, there is no escaping the basic finding that the paddles are located at the protein–lipid interface, and move while contacting the lipid membrane. Given that the paddles move through a lipid environment, it is interesting to ask why the basic residues on the voltage-sensor paddles are nearly always arginine and not lysine? One reason is that arginine (p$K_a \approx$ 12.5 in water) will nearly always move through the membrane with a protonated, charged side chain, whereas lysine (p$K_a \approx$ 10.5 in water) will sometimes be unprotonated. Another reason may be that arginine can easily participate in multiple hydrogen bonds (perhaps with acidic side chains) in a spatially directed way. Yet a third possible reason is that it might be energetically less costly to transfer from water to lipid the diffuse positive charge on a guanidinium group (arginine) than the more focused charge on an amino group (lysine). Studies of the transfer of hydrophobic peptides from water to octanol by White and co-workers[22] provide evidence for this idea by showing that the charged lysine side chain is energetically more costly in this assay than the charged arginine by about 1.0 kcal mol^{-1}. Given that four voltage-sensor paddles must move through the membrane to open the pore,

伸至内侧的脂质头部基团，而 117 位精氨酸接近内侧但仍然在膜内。在开放的构象中，117 位、120 位，或许还有 123 位的精氨酸可以延伸至外侧溶液或脂质头部基团层，而 126 位精氨酸接近外侧但仍然在膜内。这 4 个精氨酸残基跨膜接近完全的转移（在 4 个亚基中的每一个内）与 12~14 个电子的 Shaker K⁺ 通道的总门控电荷（每个亚基 3.0~3.5 个电子）相一致 [15-17]，并证明了每组 4 个精氨酸残基搬运了约 1 个电荷单位 [16,17]。

不受这些实验限制的电压感受桨要么位于通道外表面的切面上，要么指向一个远离通道外表面的径向方向。柔性的 S3 无规卷曲和 S4-S5 接头可能不太限制桨的位置。但是，我们有两个理由认为桨是切向定位的，它们的定位方式见图 5c。首先，在通道的完整晶体结构中桨是切向定位的；其次，独立的电压感受器的晶体结构显示了 S2 与 S4 之间和 S3a 与 S2 之间存在有趣的盐桥相互作用（参考文献 4）。切线方向将有利于电压感受桨上的精氨酸残基和 S2 与 S3a 螺旋上的酸性残基之间的盐桥相互作用。帕帕济安及其同事们对 Shaker K⁺ 通道的研究表明盐桥对确实具有重要意义，当桨在关闭和开放位置间运动时，它们可能在通道外口周围发生交换 [18-20]。

我们已经描述了电压感受器桨作为疏水阳离子可携带门控电荷通过脂质双层。S4 精氨酸与 S2 和 S3 上酸性残基之间的离子相互作用可能协助门控电荷的运动并产生极性，有时候，在某些电压依赖性 K⁺ 通道（例如，Shaker K⁺ 通道 [21]）中的 S3b 和 S4 之间的酸性环带来当通道在关闭位置时桨上方脂-水界面结构的有趣问题。然而，无法回避的基本结果是，即桨位于蛋白质-脂质界面，且随着脂质膜移动。已知桨是在脂质环境中移动，有趣的是，为什么电压感受桨上的碱性残基几乎总是精氨酸而不是赖氨酸？ 一个原因是，精氨酸（在水中 $pK_a \approx 12.5$）几乎总是带有一个质子化的、带电的侧链进行跨膜运动，而赖氨酸（在水中 $pK_a \approx 10.5$）有时是非质子化的。另外一个原因可能是精氨酸易于在空间定向上形成多个氢键（也许是与酸性侧链）。第三个可能的原因是，从水向脂质转移在胍基（精氨酸）上分散的正电荷比转移氨基（赖氨酸）上更集中的电荷耗费较少的能量。怀特及其同事 [22] 对疏水多肽从水向辛醇转移的研究为这一想法提供了证据，他们的研究显示带电赖氨酸侧链在这一实验中比带电精氨酸耗费的能量大约多 $1.0 \text{ kcal} \cdot \text{mol}^{-1}$。鉴于 4 个电压感受桨必须通过膜内运动才能打开孔道，我们推测从进化的角度讲更偏向于精氨酸而非赖氨酸。在这方面，有趣的是，最近发现机械敏感性通道 MscS 的结构在其跨膜区段有两个碱性氨基酸，

we might expect there to be a strong evolutionary bias in favour of arginine over lysine. In this regard, it is interesting that the recent structure of MscS, a mechanosensitive channel, has two basic amino acids in its transmembrane segments that are arginine[23]. MscS is not gated by voltage *per se*, but its mechanical force-induced opening can be modulated by voltage[24], and the candidate residues that are proposed to underlie voltage modulation are arginine, not lysine[23].

On the basis of the KvAP crystal structure[4], the deduced positions of its voltage-sensor paddles in the functioning channel (Fig. 5a, b), and previous studies of opened and closed K⁺ channels[25,26], we propose a model for how membrane voltage gates the pore (Fig. 5c, d). This is a working model to envision how the electromechanical coupling process might occur, and it will need to be revised as more data are obtained. In the closed conformation (Fig. 5c), the positively charged voltage-sensor paddles (red) are near the intracellular membrane surface, held there by the large electric field (mean value $> 10^7$ V m^{-1}) imposed by the negative resting membrane voltage. In this conformation, the S5 and S6 (outer and inner) helices are arranged as they are in KcsA, a closed K⁺ channel[25]; favourable packing interactions between the inner helices have been proposed to help to stabilize the closed conformation[27]. In response to depolarization, the voltage-sensor paddles move across the membrane to their external position, which exerts a force on the S4–S5 linker, pulling the S5 helices away from the pore axis (Fig. 5d). The crystal structure of KvAP shows that the S5 helices form a cuff outside the S6 helices, and suggests that when the S5 cuff is expanded, the S6 helices follow, opening the pore[4].

Although previous mutational studies of voltage-dependent gating have been interpreted in the context of the conventional models, many of the data are consistent with the structural model presented here, and indeed help to constrain it. For example, second-site suppressor mutations in the *Shaker* K⁺ channel suggest that certain salt bridges probably break and reform as the voltage-sensor paddles move[20]. In addition to four S4 arginine residues, a component of the gating charge in *Shaker* was shown to come from an S2 acidic residue (glutamate 293, corresponding to aspartate 72 in KvAP)[16], implying that S2 might change its position in the membrane as the voltage-sensor paddles move; the loose attachment of S2 to the pore in the KvAP crystal structure certainly would allow this to happen. Disulphide cross-linking of S4 to the turret loop between S5 and the pore helix[28], and of two S4 segments within a tetramer to each other[29] (an observation that was very difficult to understand in the context of conventional models), are in agreement with the mobile voltage-sensor paddles in Fig. 5c, d. The accessibility of thiol-reactive compounds to cysteine residues introduced into the *Shaker* K⁺ channel S4 (refs 30–32), and the ability of histidine residues to shuttle protons across the membrane[33], are in reasonable agreement with our data on voltage-sensor paddle movements. However, our structural and mechanistic interpretation, summarized in Fig. 5, differs fundamentally from past models of voltage-dependent gating. This new picture is based on the elucidation of the voltage-sensor paddle structure, its flexible attachments and disposition relative to the pore, and the paddles' positions in the membrane when the channel is closed and opened.

均是精氨酸 [23]。MscS 不受电压本身门控，而它由机械外力诱导的开放可被电压调节 [24]，并且认为产生电压调节的候补残基是精氨酸而不是赖氨酸 [23]。

基于 KvAP 晶体结构 [4]、推导的电压感受桨在功能通道中的位置（图 5a 和 b）和以往对开放和关闭 K⁺ 通道的研究 [25,26]，我们提出了一个膜电压如何门控孔道的模型（图 5c 和 d）。即一个如何产生电–机械耦联的工作模式的假想模型，该模型在获得更多的数据时需要做修正。在关闭构象下（图 5c），带正电荷的电压感受桨（红色）接近细胞内膜表面，在这附近由于负的静息膜电位而存在较大电场（平均值 > 10^7 V·m⁻¹）。在此构象中，S5 和 S6（外和内）螺旋的排列与它们在 KcsA（一个关闭的 K⁺ 通道）中一致 [25]；推测内螺旋间的相互作用有利于稳定关闭构象 [27]。当发生去极化反应时，电压感受桨跨膜移动到其位于膜外的位置上，也对 S4–S5 连接施加力量，拉动 S5 螺旋远离孔轴（图 5d）。KvAP 晶体结构表明，S5 螺旋在 S6 螺旋外形成一个袖口，并推测当 S5 袖口扩大时，S6 螺旋跟随其后，打开孔道 [4]。

虽然已进行的电压依赖性门控的突变研究已经解释了本文介绍的模型，许多数据与这里呈现的结构模型是一致的，并且确实有助于修正它。例如，Shaker K⁺ 通道中第二位点抑制突变表明，当电压感受桨运动时某些盐桥可能断裂或重组 [20]。除了 4 个 S4 精氨酸残基以外，Shaker 中门控电荷的一个组成被证明来自 S2 上的一个酸性残基（293 位谷氨酸，对应于 KvAP 的 72 位天门冬氨酸）[16]，这意味着当电压感受桨移动时 S2 可能改变其在膜中的位置；在 KvAP 晶体结构中 S2 松散连接到孔上将允许这种情况发生。二硫键将 S4 交联到 S5 和孔区螺旋之间的塔形无规卷曲上 [28]，并将四聚体内的 2 个 S4 片段相互交联 [29]（这种现象在传统模型背景下很难理解），这种二硫交联与图 5c 和 d 中可移动的电压感受桨一致。巯基化合物与 Shaker K⁺ 通道 S4 的半胱氨酸残基的可结合性（参考文献 30～32），以及组氨酸残基跨膜穿梭运送质子的能力 [33]，与我们关于电压感受桨移动的数据相当一致。然而，我们关于结构和机械运动的解释（归纳在图 5 中）本质上不同于过去的电压依赖性门控模型。这幅新图是以电压感受桨的结构阐明、它与孔道的柔性连接及与孔道功能的关系，以及当通道关闭和开放时桨在膜中的位置这三点为前提的。

Conclusion

Here and in an accompanying paper[4], we have shown that (1) the gating charges are carried on voltage-sensor paddles, which are helix–turn–helix structures attached to the channel through flexible S3 loops and S4–S5 linkers; (2) the paddles are located at the channel's outer perimeter and move within the lipid membrane; (3) the S2 helices lie beside the pore and contain acidic amino acids that could help to stabilize positive charges on the paddles as they move across the membrane; (4) the total displacement of the voltage-sensor paddles is approximately 20 Å perpendicular to the membrane; and (5) the large displacement of the paddles could open the pore by pulling on the S4–S5 linker. We conclude that the voltage sensor operates by an extraordinarily simple principle based on hydrophobic cations attached to levers, which enables the membrane electric field to perform mechanical work to open and close the ion-conduction pore.

Methods

Biotinylation

All biotinylation studies were carried out using a KvAP channel in which the single endogenous cysteine was mutated to serine (C247S). This mutant showed no detectable electrophysiological differences when compared to wild-type KvAP. Single cysteine mutations were then added to the voltage-sensor paddle (positions 101 to 127) using the QuickChange method (Stratagene) and confirmed by sequencing the entire gene. Mutant channels were expressed and purified by the same protocol as wild-type KvAP channels[5], except that before gel filtration, mutant KvAP channels were incubated with 10 mM DTT for 1 h. Immediately after gel filtration, mutant channels (at 0.5–1.0 mg ml⁻¹) were incubated with 500 μM PEO-iodoacetylbiotin (Pierce) for 2–3 h at room temperature, and then either reconstituted into lipid vesicles for electrophysiological analysis, or purified away from the excess biotin reagent on a desalting column, complexed with avidin (Pierce) and run on an SDS gel to assess the extent of biotinylation.

Electrophysiology

Fabs (6E1 and 33H1) and VSTX1 were purified as described in the companion paper[4] and used in electrophysiological assays. Electrophysiological studies of wild-type and biotinylated KvAP channels were carried out as described[5]. To measure inhibition, Fabs (~500 nM), VSTX1 (30 nM) or avidin (40 μg ml⁻¹) were added to wild-type and/or cysteine-mutant, biotinylated channels reconstituted into lipid membranes, and studied using various voltage protocols.

(**423**, 42-48; 2003)

结　论

在本文及一篇相关论文[4]中，我们已经表明：(1)在电压感受桨上携带有门控电荷，它们通过灵活的 S3 无规卷曲和 S4-S5 接头连接到通道上的螺旋-转角-螺旋结构；(2)桨位于通道的外围并在脂质膜内移动；(3)S2 螺旋位于孔道旁边并含有酸性氨基酸，当桨跨膜移动时，这些酸性氨基酸可能有助于稳定桨上的正电荷；(4)电压感受桨垂直于膜的总位移约 20 Å；(5)桨的较大位移可以通过拉动 S4-S5 接头打开孔道。我们总结如下：电压传感器的操作是基于一个非常简单的将疏水阳离子连接到杠杆上的原理，使得膜电场转为机械操作来打开和关闭离子导通孔。

方　法

生物素化

所有的生物素化研究都是在 KvAP 通道上进行的，在 KvAP 通道中单个内源性半胱氨酸被突变为丝氨酸(C247S)。与野生型 KvAP 相比，这个突变体没有可检测到的电生理方面的差异。使用 QuickChange 法(Stratagene 公司)，将电压感受桨上的单个半胱氨酸(101 位至 127 位)突变，并通过全基因测序验证突变。采用与野生型 KvAP 通道相同的方法表达和纯化了突变通道[5]，与野生型不同的是，在凝胶过滤前，突变的 KvAP 通道需先与 10 mM DTT(二硫苏糖醇)温育 1 h。凝胶过滤后，突变的通道(0.5～1.0 mg·ml^{-1})立即与 500 μM PEO-碘代乙酰生物素(皮尔斯公司)在室温下温育 2～3 h，然后将突变通道重建到脂质膜上进行电生理分析，或者用脱盐柱纯化以除去过量的生物素试剂，与抗生物素蛋白(皮尔斯公司)结合并通过 SDS 凝胶电泳评估生物素化的程度。

电生理学

如本文的相关论文中[4]所描述，Fabs(6E1 和 33H1)以及 VSTX1 被纯化并用于电生理实验。野生型和生物素化 KvAP 通道的电生理研究按描述的方法进行[5]。为检测抑制情况，Fabs(约 500 nM)，VSTX1(30 nM)或抗生物素蛋白(40 μg·ml^{-1})被加到野生型和(或)半胱氨酸突变体的生物素标记的通道上，通道重建在脂质膜中，并利用各种电压刺激方式对它们进行研究。

(李梅 翻译；王晓良 审稿)

Youxing Jiang*, Vanessa Ruta, Jiayun Chen, Alice Lee & Roderick MacKinnon
Howard Hughes Medical Institute, Laboratory of Molecular Neurobiology and Biophysics, Rockefeller University, 1230 York Avenue, New York, New York 10021, USA
* Present address: University of Texas Southwestern Medical Center, Department of Physiology, 5323 Harry Hines Blvd, Dallas, Texas 75390-9040, USA

Received 19 February; accepted 11 March 2003; doi: 10.1038/nature01581.

References:

1. Sigworth, F. J. Voltage gating of ion channels. *Q. Rev. Biophys.* **27**, 1-40 (1994).

2. Armstrong, C. M. & Bezanilla, F. Charge movement associated with the opening and closing of the activation gates of the Na⁺ channels. *J. Gen. Physiol.* **63**, 533-552 (1974).

3. Bezanilla, F. The voltage sensor in voltage-dependent ion channels. *Physiol. Rev.* **80**, 555-592 (2000).

4. Jiang, Y. *et al.* X-ray structure of a voltage-dependent K⁺ channel. *Nature* **423**, 33-41 (2003).

5. Ruta, V., Jiang, Y., Lee, A., Chen, J. & MacKinnon, R. Functional analysis of an archeabacterial voltage-dependent K⁺ channel. *Nature* **422**, 180-185; advance online publication, 2 March 2003 (doi:10.1038/nature01473).

6. Swartz, K. J. & MacKinnon, R. Mapping the receptor site for hanatoxin, a gating modifier of voltage-dependent K⁺ channels. *Neuron* **18**, 675-682 (1997).

7. Slatin, S. L., Qiu, X. Q., Jakes, K. S. & Finkelstein, A. Identification of a translocated protein segment in a voltage-dependent channel. *Nature* **371**, 158-161 (1994).

8. Qiu, X. Q., Jakes, K. S., Finkelstein, A. & Slatin, S. L. Site-specific biotinylation of colicin Ia. A probe for protein conformation in the membrane. *J. Biol. Chem.* **269**, 7483-7488 (1994).

9. Qiu, X. Q., Jakes, K. S., Kienker, P. K., Finkelstein, A. & Slatin, S. L. Major transmembrane movement associated with colicin Ia channel gating. *J. Gen. Physiol.* **107**, 313-328 (1996).

10. Pugliese, L., Coda, A., Malcovati, M. & Bolognesi, M. Three-dimensional structure of the tetragonal crystal form of egg-white avidin in its functional complex with biotin at 2.7 Å resolution. *J. Mol. Biol.* **231**, 698-710 (1993).

11. Zagotta, W. N., Hoshi, T., Dittman, J. & Aldrich, R. W. Shaker potassium channel gating. II. Transitions in the activation pathway. *J. Gen. Physiol.* **103**, 279-319 (1994).

12. Zagotta, W. N., Hoshi, T. & Aldrich, R. W. Shaker potassium channel gating. III. Evaluation of kinetic models for activation. *J. Gen. Physiol.* **103**, 321-362 (1994).

13. Schoppa, N. E. & Sigworth, F. J. Activation of Shaker potassium channels. III. An activation gating model for wild-type and V2 mutant channels. *J. Gen. Physiol.* **111**, 313-342 (1998).

14. Cole, K. S. & Moore, J. W. Potassium ion current in the squid giant axon: dynamic characteristic. *Biophys. J.* **1**, 1-14 (1960).

15. Schoppa, N. E., McCormack, K., Tanouye, M. A. & Sigworth, F. J. The size of gating charge in wild-type and mutant Shaker potassium channels. *Science* **255**, 1712-1715 (1992).

16. Seoh, S. A., Sigg, D., Papazian, D. M. & Bezanilla, F. Voltage-sensing residues in the S2 and S4 segments of the Shaker K⁺ channel. *Neuron* **16**, 1159-1167 (1996).

17. Aggarwal, S. K. & Mackinnon, R. Contribution of the S4 segment to gating charge in the Shaker K⁺ channel. *Neuron* **16**, 1169-1177 (1996).

18. Papazian, D. M. *et al.* Electrostatic interactions of S4 voltage sensor in Shaker K⁺ channel. *Neuron* **14**, 1293-1301 (1995).

19. Tiwari-Woodruff, S. K., Lin, M. A., Schulteis, C. T. & Papazian, D. M. Voltage-dependent structural interactions in the Shaker K⁺ channel. *J. Gen. Physiol.* **115**, 123-138 (2000).

20. Papazian, D. M., Silverman, W. R., Lin, M. C., Tiwari-Woodruff, S. K. & Tang, C. Y. Structural organization of the voltage sensor in voltage-dependent potassium channels. *Novartis Found. Symp.* **245**, 178-190 (2002).

21. Gonzalez, C., Rosenman, E., Bezanilla, F., Alvarez, O. & Latorre, R. Periodic perturbations in Shaker K⁺ channel gating kinetics by deletions in the S3-S4 linker. *Proc. Natl Acad. Sci. USA* **98**, 9617-9623 (2001).

22. Wimley, W. C., Creamer, T. P. & White, S. H. Solvation energies of amino acid side chains and backbone in a family of host-guest pentapeptides. *Biochemistry* **35**, 5109-5124 (1996).

23. Bass, R. B., Strop, P., Barclay, M. & Rees, D. C. Crystal structure of *Escherichia coli* MscS, a voltage-modulated and mechanosensitive channel. *Science* **298**, 1582-1587 (2002).

24. Martinac, B., Buechner, M., Delcour, A. H., Adler, J. & Kung, C. Pressure-sensitive ion channel in *Escherichia coli*. *Proc. Natl Acad. Sci. USA* **84**, 2297-2301 (1987).

25. Doyle, D. A. *et al.* The structure of the potassium channel: molecular basis of K⁺ conduction and selectivity. *Science* **280**, 69-77 (1998).

26. Jiang, Y. *et al.* The open pore conformation of potassium channels. *Nature* **417**, 523-526 (2002).

27. Yifrach, O. & MacKinnon, R. Energetics of pore opening in a voltage-gated K⁺ channel. *Cell* **111**, 231-239 (2002).

28. Laine, M. *et al.* Structural interactions between voltage sensor and pore in the Shaker K⁺ channels. *Biophys. J.* **82**, 231a (2002).

29. Aziz, Q. H., Partridge, C. J., Munsey, T. S. & Sivaprasadarao, A. Depolarization induces intersubunit cross-linking in a S4 cysteine mutant of the Shaker potassium channel. *J. Biol. Chem.* **277**, 42719-42725 (2002).

30. Larsson, H. P., Baker, O. S., Dhillon, D. S. & Isacoff, E. Y. Transmembrane movement of the Shaker K⁺ channel S4. *Neuron* **16**, 387-397 (1996).

292

31. Yusaf, S. P., Wray, D. & Sivaprasadarao, A. Measurement of the movement of the S4 segment during the activation of a voltage-gated potassium channel. *Pflugers Arch.* **433**, 91-97 (1996).

32. Baker, O. S., Larsson, H. P., Mannuzzu, L. M. & Isacoff, E. Y. Three transmembrane conformations and sequence-dependent displacement of the S4 domain in Shaker K⁺ channel gating. *Neuron* **20**, 1283-1294 (1998).

33. Starace, D. M., Stefani, E. & Bezanilla, F. Voltage-dependent proton transport by the voltage sensor of the Shaker K⁺ channel. *Neuron* **19**, 1319-1327 (1997).

Acknowledgements. We thank D. Gadsby and O. Andersen for helpful discussions and advice on the manuscript. This work was supported in part by a grant from the National Institutes of Health (NIH) to R.M. V.R. is supported by a National Science Foundation Graduate Student Research Fellowship, and R.M. is an Investigator in the Howard Hughes Medical Institute.

Competing interests statement. The authors declare that they have no competing financial interests.

Correspondence and requests for materials should be addressed to R.M. (mackinn@rockvax.rockefeller.edu).

The International HapMap Project

The International HapMap Consortium[*]

Editor's Note

This paper describes the International HapMap Project, a large international collaborative effort to identify and catalog the common patterns of human DNA sequence variation. By making the information freely available, the project aimed to help researchers identify genes related to health, disease and responses to drugs and environmental factors. Here, they describe the strategy and key components of the project, including the genotyping of over a million sequence variants, their frequencies and degrees of association, in DNA samples from populations rooted in parts of Africa, Asia and Europe. The Project, officially launched in 2002, successfully published the completed Haplotype Map in 2005, then a more detailed second-generation map in 2007.

The goal of the International HapMap Project is to determine the common patterns of DNA sequence variation in the human genome and to make this information freely available in the public domain. An international consortium is developing a map of these patterns across the genome by determining the genotypes of one million or more sequence variants, their frequencies and the degree of association between them, in DNA samples from populations with ancestry from parts of Africa, Asia and Europe. The HapMap will allow the discovery of sequence variants that affect common disease, will facilitate development of diagnostic tools, and will enhance our ability to choose targets for therapeutic intervention.

COMMON diseases such as cardiovascular disease, cancer, obesity, diabetes, psychiatric illnesses and inflammatory diseases are caused by combinations of multiple genetic and environmental factors[1]. Discovering these genetic factors will provide fundamental new insights into the pathogenesis, diagnosis and treatment of human disease. Searches for causative variants in chromosome regions identified by linkage analysis have been highly successful for many rare single-gene disorders. By contrast, linkage studies have been much less successful in locating genetic variants that affect common complex diseases, as each variant individually contributes only modestly to disease risk[2,3]. A complementary approach to identifying these specific genetic risk factors is to search for an association between a specific variant and a disease, by comparing a group of affected individuals with a group of unaffected controls[4]. In the absence of strong natural selection, there is likely to be a broad spectrum of frequency of such variants, many of which are likely to be common in the population. A number

---

[*] A full list of participants and affiliations is given in the original paper.

国际人类基因组单体型图计划

国际人类基因组单体型图协作组[*]

编者按

本文描述了国际人类基因组单体型图计划，这是一个大型的国际合作项目，旨在识别和编目人类 DNA 序列变异的常见模式。该计划通过免费提供这些信息，帮助研究人员识别与健康、疾病以及对药物和环境因素产生响应的相关基因。本文中，他们描述了该计划的策略和关键组成部分，包括从部分非洲、亚洲和欧洲地区提供的 DNA 样本中对 100 多万个序列变异进行基因分型以及它们的频率和关联程度。该计划划于 2002 年正式启动，2005 年成功发布了完整的单体型图谱，2007 年又发布了更详细的第二代图谱。

国际人类基因组单体型图计划的目标是确定人类基因组中 DNA 序列变异的共同模式，并将这些资料免费向公众开放。一个国际协作组将通过来自部分非洲、亚洲和欧洲族群的 DNA 样本，确定 100 万或更多序列变异的基因型以及它们的频率和它们之间的相关程度，从而绘制整个基因组的模式图谱。HapMap 将支持我们发现影响常见疾病的序列变异，促进疾病诊断工具的发展，并且提高我们选择治疗干预靶标的能力。

常见的疾病如心血管疾病、癌症、肥胖、糖尿病，精神疾病和炎症性疾病，是由多种基因和环境因素的组合共同造成的[1]。发现这些遗传因素将为研究人类疾病的发病机理、诊断和治疗提供重要的新见解。对许多罕见的单基因疾病来说，通过连锁分析的方法鉴定染色体区域中的致病变异已经非常成功了。相比之下，通过连锁分析寻找影响常见复杂疾病的遗传变异却不怎么成功，因为每个单独的变异只会增加轻微的疾病风险[2,3]。通过比较一组病例和正常对照来寻找具体某个遗传变异和某一种疾病间的关联，是确定这些具体遗传风险因素的一个补充方法[4]。缺乏强大的自然选择时，这种变异的频率范围可能是广泛的，其中许多变异可能是群体中常见的。经过一些侧重于候选基因、与疾病连锁的区域或更大范围的关联研究，人

---

* 协作组的参与者及所属单位的名单请参见原文。

of association studies, focused on candidate genes, regions of linkage to a disease or more large-scale surveys, have already led to the discovery of genetic risk factors for common diseases. Examples include type 1 diabetes (human leukocyte antigen (HLA[5]), insulin[6] and *CTLA4* (ref. 7)), Alzheimer's disease (*APOE*)[8], deep vein thrombosis (factor V)[9], inflammatory bowel disease (*NOD2* (refs 10, 11) and also 5q31 (ref. 12)), hypertriglyceridaemia (*APOAV*)[13], type 2 diabetes (*PPARG*)[14,15], schizophrenia (neuregulin 1)[16], asthma (*ADAM33*)[17], stroke (*PDE4D*)[18] and myocardial infarction (*LTA*)[19].

One approach to doing association studies involves testing each putative causal variant for correlation with the disease (the "direct" approach)[2]. To search the entire genome for disease associations would entail the substantial expense of whole-genome sequencing of numerous patient samples to identify the candidate variants[3]. At present, this approach is limited to sequencing the functional parts of candidate genes (selected on the basis of a previous functional or genetic hypothesis) for potential disease-associated candidate variants. An alternative approach (the "indirect" approach) has been proposed[20], whereby a set of sequence variants in the genome could serve as genetic markers to detect association between a particular genomic region and the disease, whether or not the markers themselves had functional effects. The search for the causative variants could then be limited to the regions showing association with the disease.

Two insights from human population genetics suggest that the indirect approach is able to capture most human sequence variation, with greater efficiency than the direct approach. First, ~90% of sequence variation among individuals is due to common variants[21]. Second, most of these originally arose from single historical mutation events, and are therefore associated with nearby variants that were present on the ancestral chromosome on which the mutation occurred. These associations make the indirect approach feasible to study variants in candidate genes, chromosome regions or across the whole genome. Prior knowledge of putative functional variants is not required. Instead, the approach uses information from a relatively small set of variants that capture most of the common patterns of variation in the genome, so that any region or gene can be tested for association with a particular disease, with a high likelihood that such an association will be detectable if it exists.

The aim of the International HapMap Project is to determine the common patterns of DNA sequence variation in the human genome, by characterizing sequence variants, their frequencies, and correlations between them, in DNA samples from populations with ancestry from parts of Africa, Asia and Europe. The project will thus provide tools that will allow the indirect association approach to be applied readily to any functional candidate gene in the genome, to any region suggested by family-based linkage analysis, or ultimately to the whole genome for scans for disease risk factors.

Common variants responsible for disease risk will be most readily approached by this strategy, but not all predisposing variants are common. However, it should be noted that even a relatively uncommon disease-associated variant can potentially be discovered using this approach. Reflecting its historical origins, the uncommon variant will be travelling on

们已经发现了一些常见疾病的遗传风险因素。例如 1 型糖尿病（人类白细胞抗原（HLA[5]），胰岛素[6] 和 CTLA4（参考文献 7）），阿尔茨海默病（APOE）[8]，深静脉血栓症（V 因子）[9]，炎症性肠病（NOD2（参考文献 10 和 11）和 5q31（参考文献 12）），高甘油三酯血症（APOAV）[13]，2 型糖尿病（PPARG）[14,15]，精神分裂症（神经调节蛋白1）[16]，哮喘（ADAM33）[17]，中风（PDE4D）[18] 和心肌梗死（LTA）[19]。

进行关联研究的一个方法是测试每个潜在致病变异与疾病的相关性（"直接"方法）[2]。寻找整个基因组中的疾病相关变异，则需要对众多患者样本开展全基因组测序来确定候选变异，这需要投入大量费用[3]。目前，这种做法仅限于对候选基因的功能部分（基于前期的功能或遗传假说进行选择）进行测序以寻找潜在的疾病相关候选变异。人们已提出了另一种方法（"间接"方法）[20]，利用基因组内一些序列变异作为遗传标签，来检测特定基因组区域和疾病之间的关联，无论这些标签本身是否有功能效应。这样一来，就可以限制在与疾病相关的区域寻找致病变异了。

来自人类群体遗传学的两个观点表明，间接方法能捕获绝大多数的人类序列变异，比直接方法的效率更高。首先，个体间约 90% 序列变异是由常见变异组成的[21]。其次，这些变异中大多数最初产生于单一的历史突变事件，因此，与出现在突变发生的祖先染色体上的邻近变异有关联。这些关联使间接方法易于研究候选基因、染色体区域或整个基因组内的变异。这不需要与假定功能变异相关的先验知识。相反，这个方法用相对较小的一组变异信息来涵盖基因组中绝大多数变异的常见模式，因此可以检测任何基因组区域或基因与特定疾病的关联性，如果存在此种关联，被检测到的可能性很高。

国际人类基因组单体型图计划的目的是通过描述部分非洲、亚洲和欧洲族群的DNA 样本序列变异、序列变异的频率和它们之间的相关性等特征，确定人类基因组中 DNA 序列变异的常见模式。因此该计划将提供工具，使间接关联方法适用于基因组中任何功能候选基因、家族型连锁分析提示的任何区域或最终应用于寻找疾病危险因素的全基因组扫描。

与疾病风险关联的常见变异通过这一策略很容易找到，但并非所有致病变异都是常见的。但是，应该指出的是，即使是相对罕见的疾病，相关变异也可能通过这种方法被发现。罕见的变异将在携带邻近序列变异特有模式的染色体上移动，反映

a chromosome that carries a characteristic pattern of nearby sequence variants. In a group of people affected by a disease, the rare variant will be enriched in frequency compared with its frequency in a group of unaffected controls. This observation, for example, was of considerable assistance in the identification of the genes responsible for cystic fibrosis[22] and diastrophic dysplasia[23], after linkage had pointed to the general chromosomal region.

Below we provide a brief description of human sequence variation, and then describe the strategy and key components of the project. These include the choice of samples and populations for study, the process of community engagement or public consultation, selection of single-nucleotide polymorphisms (SNPs), genotyping, data release and analysis.

Human DNA Sequence Variation

Any two copies of the human genome differ from one another by approximately 0.1% of nucleotide sites (that is, one variant per 1,000 bases on average)[24-27]. The most common type of variant, a SNP, is a difference between chromosomes in the base present at a particular site in the DNA sequence (Fig. 1a). For example, some chromosomes in a population may have a C at that site (the "C allele"), whereas others have a T (the "T allele"). It has been estimated that, in the world's human population, about 10 million sites (that is, one variant per 300 bases on average) vary such that both alleles are observed at a frequency of $\geq 1\%$, and that these 10 million common SNPs constitute 90% of the variation in the population[21,28]. The remaining 10% is due to a vast array of variants that are each rare in the population. The presence of particular SNP alleles in an individual is determined by testing ("genotyping") a genomic DNA sample.

Nearly every variable site results from a single historical mutational event as the mutation rate is very low (of the order of 10^{-8} per site per generation) relative to the number of generations since the most recent common ancestor of any two humans (of the order of 10^4 generations). For this reason, each new allele is initially associated with the other alleles that happened to be present on the particular chromosomal background on which it arose. The specific set of alleles observed on a single chromosome, or part of a chromosome, is called a haplotype (Fig. 1b). New haplotypes are formed by additional mutations, or by recombination when the maternal and paternal chromosomes exchange corresponding segments of DNA, resulting in a chromosome that is a mosaic of the two parental haplotypes[29].

The coinheritance of SNP alleles on these haplotypes leads to associations between these alleles in the population (known as linkage disequilibrium, LD). Because the likelihood of recombination between two SNPs increases with the distance between them, on average such associations between SNPs decline with distance. Many empirical studies have shown highly significant levels of LD, and often strong associations between nearby SNPs, in the human genome[30-34]. These strong associations mean that in many chromosome regions there are only a few haplotypes, and these account for most of the variation among people

其历史起源。相比于不受影响的对照组，罕见变异将会显著富集于受某种疾病影响的人群中。在连锁分析已经显示大致染色体易感区域之后，这个发现对鉴定如引起囊性纤维症[22] 和畸形发育不良[23] 的基因具有相当大的帮助。

下面我们将简要说明人类序列变异，然后描述这个项目的策略和关键组成部分。其中包括选择研究的样本和群体，社会参与或公共咨询的过程，单核苷酸多态性（SNP）的选择，基因分型，数据的公布和分析。

人类 DNA 序列变异

任何两份人类基因组具有大约 0.1%的核苷酸位点差异（即，平均每 1,000 个碱基有一个变异）[24-27]。最常见的变异类型——单核苷酸多态性（SNP），是染色体间 DNA 序列特定位点的碱基差异（图 1a）。例如，在某一群体中，有些染色体在某个位点可能有一个 C（"C 等位基因"），而其他染色体有一个 T（"T 等位基因"）。据估计，在世界人群中，约 1,000 万位点（即，平均每 300 个碱基有一个变异）在两个等位基因的变异频率 ≥1%，并且这 1,000 万常见的 SNP 贡献了种群变异的 90%[21,28]。其余 10%是群体中各种各样的罕见变异。个体中存在特定 SNP 等位基因是通过检测（"基因分型"）一个基因组 DNA 样本确定的。

相对于任何两个人最近的共同祖先之后的世代数（大约 10^4 代），几乎每个来自单一历史突变事件的可变异位点的突变率都是非常低的（每代每个位点大约 10^{-8}）。出于这个原因，每一个新的等位基因最初都是与它所在的特定染色体背景上的恰好存在的其他等位基因相联系。在单一染色体上或染色体的一部分上观察到的一套具体的等位基因，称为一个单体型（图 1b）。或者额外突变或者母本和父本染色体交换相应 DNA 片段的重组，形成了新的单体型，产生了双方父母单体型嵌合的染色体[29]。

这些单体型上的 SNP 等位基因的共同继承导致群体中这些等位基因间的相互关联（称为连锁不平衡，LD）。因为两个 SNP 间重组的可能性随它们之间距离的增加而增加，因此平均来说，SNP 之间的这种关联会随距离的增加而减少。许多实证研究表明在人类基因组中存在高显著性水平的 LD，而且相邻的 SNP 通常具有显著关联[30-34]。这些紧密关联意味着在许多染色体区域中只有少数单体型，而它们代表了

in those regions[31,35,36].

Fig. 1. SNPs, haplotypes and tag SNPs. **a**, SNPs. Shown is a short stretch of DNA from four versions of the same chromosome region in different people. Most of the DNA sequence is identical in these chromosomes, but three bases are shown where variation occurs. Each SNP has two possible alleles; the first SNP in panel **a** has the alleles C and T. **b**, Haplotypes. A haplotype is made up of a particular combination of alleles at nearby SNPs. Shown here are the observed genotypes for 20 SNPs that extend across 6,000 bases of DNA. Only the variable bases are shown, including the three SNPs that are shown in panel **a**. For this region, most of the chromosomes in a population survey turn out to have haplotypes 1–4. **c**, Tag SNPs. Genotyping just the three tag SNPs out of the 20 SNPs is sufficient to identify these four haplotypes uniquely. For instance, if a particular chromosome has the pattern A–T–C at these three tag SNPs, this pattern matches the pattern determined for haplotype 1. Note that many chromosomes carry the common haplotypes in the population.

The strong associations between SNPs in a region have a practical value: genotyping only a few, carefully chosen SNPs in the region will provide enough information to predict much of the information about the remainder of the common SNPs in that region. As a result, only a few of these "tag" SNPs are required to identify each of the common haplotypes in a region[35,37-39] (Fig. 1c).

As the extent of association between nearby markers varies dramatically across the genome[30-32,34,35,40], it is not efficient to use SNPs selected at random or evenly spaced in the genome sequence. Instead, the patterns of association must be empirically determined for efficient selection of tag SNPs. On the basis of empirical studies, it has been estimated that most of the information about genetic variation represented by the 10 million common SNPs in the population could be provided by genotyping 200,000 to 1,000,000 tag SNPs across the genome[31,36,38,39]. Thus, a substantial reduction in the amount of genotyping can be obtained with little loss of information, by using knowledge of the LD present in the genome.

这些区域人群间的大多数变异[31,35,36]。

图 1. SNP，单体型和标签 SNP。**a**，SNP。所示的是不同人的同一染色体区域四个版本的一小段 DNA。在这些染色体中大多数 DNA 序列是相同的，但显示了三个发生变异的碱基。每个 SNP 有两个可能的等位基因；第一个 SNP 在 **a** 图中有等位基因 C 和 T。**b**，单体型。单体型是由邻近 SNP 的等位基因的特定组合构成的。此处显示的是观察到的跨越 6,000 个 DNA 碱基的 20 个 SNP 的基因型。只显示变异的碱基，包括 **a** 图中显示的 3 个 SNP。对此区域，调查群体中大多数染色体有单体型 1~4。**c**，标签 SNP。只对 20 个 SNP 中的三个标签 SNP 进行基因分型就足以确定这四个独特的单体型。例如，如果某一特定染色体在这三个标签 SNP 上有 A–T–C 模式，这种模式匹配由单体型 1 确定的模式。请注意，群体中许多染色体携带共同的单体型。

　　一个区域内 SNP 之间的紧密关联有着实际的意义：只对该区域内少数、精心挑选的 SNP 进行基因分型将提供足够的信息来预测那个区域剩余的常见 SNP 的大量信息。因此，只需要少量这种"标签"SNP，就可以确定一个区域内的每个常见单体型[35,37-39]（图 1c）。

　　因为基因组内邻近标记间的关联程度变化显著[30-32,34,35,40]，用随机选择或基因组序列间均匀分隔的 SNP 都不是很有效。相反，相互关联的模式必须凭实验确定，以选择更为有效的标签 SNP。在实验研究的基础上，我们估计群体中 1,000 万常见 SNP 所代表的大部分遗传变异信息，可以通过对基因组内的 200,000 至 1,000,000 标签 SNP 进行基因分型来提供[31,36,38,39]。因此，运用基因组中 LD 的知识，基因分型的数量大幅度减少而得到的信息几乎没有损失。

For common SNPs, which tend to be older than rare SNPs, the patterns of LD largely reflect historical recombination and demographic events[41]. Some recombination events occur repeatedly at "hotspots"[30,42]. The result of these processes is that current chromosomes are mosaics of ancestral chromosome regions[29]. This explains the observations that haplotypes and patterns of LD are shared by apparently unrelated chromosomes within a population and generally among populations[43].

These observations are the conceptual and empirical foundation for developing a haplotype map of the human genome, the "HapMap". This map will describe the common patterns of variation, including associations between SNPs, and will include the tag SNPs selected to most efficiently and comprehensively capture this information.

The International HapMap Consortium

An initial meeting to discuss the scientific and ethical issues associated with developing a human haplotype map was held in Washington DC on 18–19 July 2001 (http://www.genome.gov/10001665). Groups were organized to consider the ethical issues, to develop the scientific plan and to choose the populations to include. The International HapMap Project (http://www.hapmap.org/) was then formally initiated with a meeting in Washington DC on 27–29 October 2002 (http://www.genome.gov/10005336). The participating groups and funding sources are listed in Table 1.

Table 1. Groups participating in the International HapMap Project

Country	Research Group	Institution	Role	Per cent genome	Chromosomes	Funding agency
Japan	Yusuke Nakamura	RIKEN, Univ. of Tokyo	Genotyping: Third Wave	25.1%	5, 11, 14, 15, 16, 17, 19	Japanese MEXT
	Ichiro Matsuda	Health Science Univ. of Hokkaido, Eubios Ethics Inst., Shinshu Univ.	Public consultation, Samples			
United Kingdom	David Bentley	Sanger Inst.	Genotyping: Illumina	24.0%	1, 6, 10, 13, 20	Wellcome Trust
	Peter Donnelly	Univ. of Oxford	Analysis			TSC, US NIH
	Lon Cardon	Univ. of Oxford	Analysis			Wellcome Trust, TSC, US NIH
Canada	Thomas Hudson	McGill Univ. and Génome Québec Innovation Centre	Genotyping: Illumina	10.0%	2, 4p	Genome Canada, Génome Québec

常见的 SNP 往往比罕见的 SNP 更古老，其 LD 的模式基本上可以反映历史重组和人口事件[41]。一些重组事件在"热点区"反复发生[30,42]。这些过程的结果是：现在的染色体是祖先染色体区域的嵌合体[29]。这解释了单体型和 LD 的模式被某一群体内显然不相关的染色体或群体之间共享这一观察结果[43]。

这些观察是开发人类基因组单体型图"HapMap"的概念和经验基础。这个图谱将介绍常见的变异模式，包括 SNP 间的关联，未来还将包括用于最有效和全面捕获这些遗传信息的标签 SNP。

国际 HapMap 协作组

最初的讨论关于开发人类单体型图的科学和伦理问题的会议是 2001 年 7 月 18日至 19 日在华盛顿举行的(http://www.genome.gov/10001665)。协作组被组织起来考虑道德问题，制定科学计划，并选择包括的人群。之后国际 HapMap 计划(http://www.hapmap.org/) 于 2002 年 10 月 27 日至 29 日在华盛顿会议上正式启动(http://www.genome.gov/10005336)。参加的团体和资金来源列于表 1。

表 1. 参与国际人类基因组单体型图计划的团队

国家	研究团队	机构	任务	基因组百分数	染色体	资助机构
日本	中村佑辅	日本理化学研究所，东京大学	基因型分型：Third Wave 公司	25.1%	5, 11, 14, 15, 16, 17, 19	日本文部科学省
	松田一郎	北海道医疗大学，生物伦理研究所，信州大学	公众咨询，样本			
英国	戴维·本特利	桑格尔研究所	基因型分型：Illumina 公司	24.0%	1, 6, 10, 13, 20	维康基金会
	彼得·唐纳利	牛津大学	分析			SNP 协作组，美国国立卫生研究院
	朗·卡登	牛津大学	分析			维康基金会，SNP 协作组，美国国立卫生研究院
加拿大	托马斯·哈德森	麦吉尔大学和魁北克基因组创新中心	基因型分型：Illumina 公司	10.0%	2, 4p	加拿大基因组，魁北克基因组

Continued

Country	Research Group		Institution	Role	Per cent genome		Chromosomes	Funding agency
China	Huanming Yang The Chinese HapMap Consortium	Changqing Zeng	Beijing Genomics Inst., Chinese National Human Genome Center at Beijing	Genotyping: PerkinElmer and Sequenom	4.8%	10%	3, 8p, 21	Chinese MOST, Chinese Academy of Sciences, Natural Science Foundation of China, Hong Kong Innovation and Technology Commission, University Grants Committee of Hong Kong
		Wei Huang	Chinese National Human Genome Centre at Shanghai, Inst. of Biomedical Sciences (Taiwan)	Genotyping: Illumina	3.2%			
		Lap-Chee Tsui	Univ. of Hong Kong, Hong Kong Univ. of Sci. & Tech., Chinese Univ. of Hong Kong	Genotyping: Sequenom	2.0%			
	Houcan Zhang		Beijing Normal Univ.	Community engagement				Chinese MOST
	Changqing Zeng		Beijing Genomics Inst.	Samples				
United State	Mark Chee		Illumina	Genotyping: Illumina	15.5%	30.9%	8q, 9, 18q, 22, X	US NIH
	David Altshuler		Whitehead Inst.	Genotyping: Sequenom and Illumina	9.1%		4q, 7q, 18p, Y	
				Analysis				
	Richard Gibbs		Baylor College of Medicine, ParAllele	Genotyping: ParAllele	4.4%		12	
	Pui-Yan Kwok		UCSF, Washington Univ.	Genotyping: PerkinElmer	1.9%		7p	
	Aravinda Chakravarti		Johns Hopkins Univ.	Analysis				
	Mark Leppert		Univ. of Utah	Community engagement Samples				W. M. Keck Foundation, Delores Dore Eccles Foundation, US NIH
Nigeria	Charles Rotimi		Howard Univ., Univ. of Ibadan	Community engagement Samples				US NIH
	Lincoln Stein		Cold Spring Harbor Lab., New York	Data coordination centre				TSC

DNA Samples and Populations

Human populations are the products of numerous social, historical and demographic processes. As a result, no populations are typical, special or sharply bounded[44,45]. As

国家	研究团队		机构	任务	基因组百分数	染色体	资助机构
中国	杨焕明 中国人类基因组单体型图协作组	曾长青	北京基因组研究所，国家人类基因组北方研究中心	基因型分型：PerkinElmer 公司和 Sequenom 公司	4.8%	3, 8p, 21	中国科技部，中国科学院，国家自然科学基金，香港创新科技署，香港大学教育资助委员会
		黄薇	国家人类基因组南方研究中心，生物医学科学研究所（台湾）	基因型分型：Illumina 公司	3.2%		
		徐立之	香港大学，香港科技大学，香港中文大学	基因型分型：Sequenom 公司	2.0%	10%	
	张厚粲		北京师范大学	社会参与			中国科技部
	曾长青		北京基因组研究所	样本			
美国	陈马克（音译）		Illumina 公司	基因型分型：Illumina 公司	15.5%	8q, 9, 18q, 22, X	美国国立卫生研究院
	戴维·阿特舒勒		怀特黑德研究所	基因型分型：Sequenom 公司和 Illumina 公司	9.1%	4q, 7q, 18p, Y	
				分析			
	理查德·吉布斯		贝勒医学院，ParAllele 公司	基因型分型：ParAllele 公司	4.4%	12	
	郭沛恩		加州大学旧金山分校，华盛顿大学	基因型分型：PerkinElmer 公司	1.9%	30.9%	7p
	阿拉温达·查克拉瓦蒂		约翰斯·霍普金斯大学	分析			
	马克·莱珀特		犹他大学	社会参与，样本			凯克基金会，德洛丽丝·多尔·埃克尔斯基金会，美国国立卫生研究院
尼日利亚	查尔斯·罗蒂米		霍华德大学，伊巴丹大学	社会参与，样本			美国国立卫生研究院
	林肯·斯坦		纽约冷泉港实验室	数据协调中心			SNP 协作组

DNA 样本和群体

人类群体是许多社会、历史和人口学过程的产物。因此，没有哪个人群是典型的、特殊的或有明显界限的 [44,45]，因为最常见的变异模式可以在任一人群中找到 [46]，

most common patterns of variation can be found in any population[46], no one population is essential for inclusion in the HapMap. Nonetheless, we decided to include several populations from different ancestral geographic locations to ensure that the HapMap would include most of the common variation and some of the less common variation in different populations, and to allow examination of various hypotheses about patterns of LD.

Studies of allele frequency distributions suggest that ancestral geography is a reasonable basis for sampling human populations[44,47,48]. Pilot studies using samples from the Yoruba, Japanese, Chinese and individuals with ancestry from Northern and Western Europe have shown substantial similarity in their haplotype patterns, although the frequencies of haplotypes often differ[31,44]. Given these scientific findings, coupled with consideration of ethical, social and cultural issues, these populations were approached for inclusion in the HapMap through a process of community engagement or consultation (see Box 1).

Box 1. Community engagement, public consultation and individual consent

As no personally identifiable information will be linked to the samples, the risk that an individual will be harmed by a breach of privacy, or by discrimination based on studies that use the HapMap, is minimal. However, because tag SNPs for future disease studies will be chosen on the basis of haplotype frequencies in the populations included in the HapMap, the data will be identified as coming from one of the four populations involved, and it will be possible to make comparisons between the populations. As a result, the use of population identifiers may create risks of discrimination or stigmatization, as might occur if a higher frequency of a disease-associated variant were to be found in a group and this information were then overgeneralized to all or most of its members[64]. It is possible that there are other culturally specific risks that may not be evident to outsiders[65]. To identify and address these group risks, a process of community engagement, or public consultation, was undertaken to confer with members of the populations being approached for sample donation about the implications of their participation in the project[66,67]. The goal was to give people in the localities where donors were recruited the opportunity to have input into the informed consent and sample collection processes, and into such issues as how the populations from which the samples were collected would be named. Community engagement is not a perfect process, but it is an effort to involve potential donors in a more extended consideration of the implications of a research project before being asked to take part in it[68]. Community engagement and individual informed consent were conducted under the auspices of local governments and ethics committees, taking into account local ethical standards and international ethical guidelines. As in any cross-cultural endeavour, the form and outcome of the processes varied from one population to another. A Community Advisory Group is being set up for each community to serve as a continuing liaison with the sample repository, to ensure that future uses of the samples are consistent with the uses described in the informed consent documents. A more detailed article discussing ethical, social and cultural issues relevant to the project, and describing the processes used to engage donor populations in identifying and evaluating these issues, is in preparation.

没有哪个人群是必须列入 HapMap 的。尽管如此，我们依旧决定将几个位于不同祖先地理位置的群体列入其中，以确保 HapMap 可以包括大多数常见变异和不同群体中的一些不太常见的变异，并允许检查各种关于 LD 模式的假说。

对等位基因频率分布的研究表明，祖先地理是选取人群样本的一个合理的依据[44,47,48]。对约鲁巴、日本和中国样本以及对北欧和西欧后裔个体的先导研究表明，虽然单体型的频率常常不同，但其单体型模式有很大相似性[31,44]。鉴于这些科学成果，加上对道德、社会和文化问题的考虑，通过社会参与或咨询后，这些群体被列入了 HapMap 中（见框 1）。

框 1. 社会参与、公众咨询及个人同意

由于个人身份信息不会与样本相联系，侵犯个人隐私或基于利用 HapMap 进行研究而受到的歧视的风险非常小。然而，因为未来用于疾病研究的标记 SNP 将在 HapMap 群体单体型频率的基础上选择，这些数据将被认为是来自四个群体中的某一个，而且将有可能在群体间进行比较。因此，使用群体标识可能产生歧视或侮辱的风险，如果在一个组中发现某种疾病有关的变异频率较高，然后泛化过渡到所有或大部分成员中，就会产生这种风险[64]。还有可能存在其他对外不明显的文化特异的风险[65]。为查明并解决这些风险，将通过社会参与或公共咨询来与样本捐助群体的成员协商参与此计划的意义[66,67]。该计划的目标是让居住在招募捐助者地方的人们有机会加入知情同意和样本收集过程，并参与这些问题的讨论，如收集样本的群体将如何被命名。社会参与不是一个完美的过程，但它努力让潜在的捐助者在被要求参加这个计划前更广泛会考虑该计划研究的意义[68]。社会参与和个人知情同意是在地方政府和道德委员会的帮助下实施的，并考虑了当地的道德标准和国际道德准则。正如在任何跨越文化中的努力一样，这个过程的形式和结果在不同群体间是变化的。正在建立的社区咨询团体充当了使每个社区与样本资源库保持持续联系的角色，确保今后样本的用途与知情同意书中所描述的用途一致。目前正在编写一篇更详细的文章，该文章讨论了有关此项目的伦理、社会和文化问题，并说明招募捐助群体参与确定和评价这些问题的过程。

The HapMap developed with samples from these four large populations will include a substantial amount of the genetic variation found in all populations throughout the world. The goal of the HapMap is medical, and the common patterns of variation identified by the project will be useful to identify genes that contribute to disease and drug response in many other populations. Samples from several other populations are being collected for studies that will examine how similar their haplotype patterns are to those in the HapMap. If the patterns found are very different, samples from some of these populations may be genotyped on a large scale to make the HapMap more applicable to them. Further follow-up studies in other populations, small and large, are likely to be undertaken by scientists in many nations for common disease gene discovery.

The project will study a total of 270 DNA samples: 90 samples (see Supplementary Information, part 1) from a US Utah population with Northern and Western European ancestry (samples collected in 1980 by the Centre d'Etude du Polymorphisme Humain (CEPH)[49] and used for other human genetic maps, 30 trios of two parents and an adult child), and new samples collected from 90 Yoruba people in Ibadan, Nigeria (30 trios), 45 unrelated Japanese in Tokyo, Japan, and 45 unrelated Han Chinese in Beijing, China. All donors gave specific consent for their inclusion in the project. Population membership was determined in ways appropriate for each culture: for the Yoruba by asking the donor whether all four grandparents were Yoruba, for the Han Chinese by asking the donor whether at least three of four grandparents were Han Chinese, and for the Japanese by self-identification. The CEPH samples are available from the non-profit Coriell Institute of Medical Research (http://locus.umdnj.edu/nigms/); cell lines and DNA from the new samples will be available from Coriell in early 2004 for future studies with research protocols approved by appropriate ethics committees. It is anticipated that other researchers will genotype additional SNPs in these samples in the future, and that these data will continuously improve the HapMap.

These samples will have population and sex identifiers without information that could link them to individual donors. As the goal of the project is solely to identify patterns of genetic variation, no medical or other phenotypic information will be included. About 50% more samples were collected than will be used, so that inclusion of a sample from any particular donor cannot be known.

Samples of 45 unrelated individuals should be sufficient to find 99% of haplotypes with a frequency of 5% or greater in a population. Studies of LD can use random individual samples, trios or larger pedigrees; each design has advantages (ease of sampling) and disadvantages (decreasing efficiency with increasing numbers of related individuals). Analysis of existing data and computer simulations suggested that unrelated individuals and trios have considerable power for estimating local LD patterns. The trios will provide useful information on the accuracy of the genotyping platforms being used for the project.

用这四大群体的样本开发的 HapMap 将包括世界各地所有人群中发现的大量的遗传变异。HapMap 计划的目标是医疗，通过此计划确定的共同变异模式可用于鉴定在其他许多人群中对疾病和药物响应的基因。其他几个群体的样本正在收集以用于检测它们的单体型模式与 HapMap 中的有多大相似性。如果发现模式有很大的不同，将对它们中的某些群体样本进行更大规模的基因分型，以使 HapMap 更适用于它们。许多国家的科学家为了发现常见的疾病基因，可能会对其他小型和大型群体进行后续研究。

这个项目将总共研究 270 份 DNA 样本：90 份（见补充资料，第 1 部分）来自祖先是北欧和西欧的美国犹他州居民的样本（样本是由人类多态性研究中心（CEPH）于 1980 年采集的 [49]，并用于其他人类的遗传图谱，30 个由父母双方和一个成年孩子组成的三体家系），以及从以下来源收集到的新的样本：90 个尼日利亚伊巴丹的约鲁巴人（30 个三体家系）、45 个互不相关的来自日本东京的日本人和 45 个互不相关的来自中国北京的汉族人。所有捐助者都同意加入该计划，通过与各自背景相符的方式确定群体成员资格：对约鲁巴人，询问捐助者他们的四个祖父母是否都是约鲁巴人；对汉族人，询问捐助者他们的四个祖父母是否至少有三个是汉族人；对日本人只是询问祖先是否来自日本。人类多态性研究中心的样本来自非营利机构科里尔医学研究所（http://locus.umdnj.edu/nigms/）。2004 年，研究协议经相应的伦理委员会批准后，科里尔研究所将为进一步的研究提供新样本的细胞系和 DNA。预计，今后其他研究人员将对这些样本中更多的 SNP 进行基因型分析，这些数据将不断改善 HapMap。

这些样本有群体和性别标识而无捐助者个人标识。正如这一计划的目的仅仅是确定遗传变异的模式，不包含医疗或其他表型信息。收集的样本超过 50% 未被采用，因此并不能知道列入的样本来自哪个捐助者。

从 45 个无关的个体样本中应当足以找到群体中 99% 的、频率大于 5% 的单体型。LD 研究可以使用随机个体样本、三体家系或较大的家系；每个设计都有优势（方便抽样）和缺点（随着亲缘个体数目的增加而效率降低）。分析现有的数据和计算机模拟表明，无血缘关系的个体和三体家系对估计 LD 模式有相当强的能力。三体家系将对用于此计划的基因分型平台的准确性提供有益的信息。

Choice of SNPs

A high density of SNPs is needed to describe adequately the genetic variation across the entire genome. When the project started, the average density of markers in the public database dbSNP (http://www.ncbi.nlm.nih.gov/SNP/)[50] was approximately one every kilobase (2.8 million SNPs) but, given their variable distribution, many regions had a lower density of SNPs.

Further SNPs were obtained by random shotgun sequencing from whole-genome and whole-chromosome (flow-sorted) libraries[51], using methods developed for the initial human SNP map[52], and also by collaboration with Perlegen Sciences[36] and through the purchase of sequence traces from Applied Biosystems[53] for SNP detection (see Supplementary Information, part 2). One useful result of this search for more SNPs is the confirmation of SNPs found previously. SNPs for which each allele has been seen independently in two or more samples ("double-hit" SNPs) have a higher average minor allele frequency than do "single-hit" SNPs[28]. This leads to substantial savings in assay development. On 4 November 2003, the number of SNPs (with a unique genomic position) in dbSNP (build 118) was 5.7 million, and the number of double-hit SNPs was over 2 million. By February of 2004, 6.8 million SNPs (with a unique genomic position) are expected to be in dbSNP and available for the project, including 2.7 million double-hit SNPs.

As the extent of LD and haplotypes varies by 100-fold across the genome[30-32,34,35], a hierarchical genotyping strategy has been adopted. In an initial round of genotyping, the project aims to genotype successfully 600,000 SNPs spaced at approximately 5-kilobase intervals and each with a minor allele frequency of at least 5%, in the 270 DNA samples. Priority is being given to previously validated SNPs, double-hit SNPs and SNPs causing amino-acid changes (as these may alter protein function). When these genotyping data are produced (by mid-2004; see below for details of data release), they will be analysed for associations between neighbouring SNPs. Additional SNPs will then be genotyped in the same DNA samples at a higher density only in regions where the associations are weak. Further rounds of analysis and genotyping will be carried out as required. It is expected that more than one million SNPs will be genotyped overall. This hierarchical strategy will permit regions of the genome with the least LD to be characterized at densities of up to one SNP per kilobase, maximizing the characterization of regions with associations only over short distances.

Genotyping

Each genotyping centre is responsible for genotyping all the samples for all the selected SNPs on the chromosome regions allocated (Table 1). Among the centres, a total of five high-throughput genotyping technologies are being used, which will provide an opportunity to compare their accuracy, success rate, throughput and cost. Access to several platforms is

SNP 的 选 择

充分描述全基因组的遗传变异需要高密度的 SNP。当这个计划开始时，公共数据库 dbSNP(http://www.ncbi.nlm.nih.gov/SNP/)[50] 中的平均标记密度为大约每千碱基中有一个 SNP(280 万个 SNP)，但鉴于其分布不同，许多区域的 SNP 密度比较低。

使用最初为人类 SNP 图谱开发的方法[52]，通过对全基因组和整个染色体（流式分离）文库[51]随机鸟枪法测序得到更多的 SNP，通过与 Perlegen Sciences[36] 合作并从 Applied Biosystems 购买序列示踪剂[53] 来检测 SNP(见补充资料，第 2 部分)也可得到更多的 SNP。通过上述方法搜索更多 SNP 得到的一个有用的结果是对以前发现的 SNP 进行确认。当 SNP 的每个等位基因在两个或多个样本中分别被发现时（"两次发现"SNP），这些 SNP 比"单次发现"的 SNP 具有更高的平均最小等位基因型频率[28]，这在研发分析中节省了大笔开支。2003 年 11 月 4 日，dbSNP(118 版本) 中的 SNP(每个具有独特的基因组位置) 的数目是 570 万，而"两次发现"SNP 已经超过 200 万。到 2004 年 2 月，预计 dbSNP 有 680 万 SNP(每个具有独特的基因组位置) 可用于此计划，其中包括 270 万"两次发现"SNP。

因为 LD 和单体型在基因组内有着 100 倍的变化范围[30-32,34,35]，因此已采取分级基因分型策略。在最初一轮的基因分型中，该计划的目标是在 270 个 DNA 样本中，对间隔为大约 5 kb 的 600,000 个 SNP 成功进行基因分型，并且每一个 SNP 的最小等位基因型频率至少达到 5%。优先考虑先前确定的 SNP、"两次发现"SNP 及造成氨基酸变化的 SNP(因为这些可能会改变蛋白质的功能)。当得到这些基因分型数据后(截至 2004 年中期；发布的详细数据见下文)，将分析相邻 SNP 间的关联性。其余的 SNP 将在相同的 DNA 样本中以高密度方式对相关性很弱的区域进行基因分型，这需要进一步进行几轮分析和基因分型。预计总共进行基因分型的 SNP 超过 100 万。这一分级战略将允许对 LD 密度最小的基因组区域以高达每千碱基一个 SNP 的密度基因分型，最大限度地确定仅有短距离联系的区域。

基 因 分 型

每个基因分型中心负责对所有的样本中分配的染色体区域内全部选定的 SNP 进行基因分型(表 1)。在这些中心内，一共使用了 5 个高通量基因分型技术，用来比较其准确性、成功率、通量和成本。可以使用几个平台是这个计划的优势，因为一

an advantage for the project, as a SNP assay that fails on one platform may be developed successfully using another method in order to fill a gap in the HapMap. All platforms will be evaluated using a common set of performance criteria to ensure that the quality of data produced for the project meets a uniformly high standard.

Genotype quality is being assessed in three ways. First, at the beginning of the project, all centres were assigned the same randomly selected set of 1,500 SNPs for assay development and genotyping in the 90 CEPH DNA samples being used for the project. Genotyping centres produced data that were on average more than 99.2% complete and more than 99.5% accurate (as compared to the consensus of at least two other platforms). Second, every genotyping experiment includes samples for internal quality checks, with each 96-well plate containing duplicates of five different samples, and one blank. In addition, the data from trios provide a check for consistent mendelian inheritance of SNP alleles. For all the populations, the data from the unrelated samples provide a check that the SNPs are in Hardy–Weinberg equilibrium (a test of genetic mating patterns). Although a small proportion of SNPs may fail these checks for biological reasons, they more typically fail if a genotyping platform makes consistent errors, such as undercalling heterozygotes. Third, a sample of SNP genotypes deposited by each centre will be selected at random and re-genotyped by other centres. These stringent third-party evaluations of quality will ensure the completeness and reliability of the data produced by the project.

Data Release

The project is committed to rapid and complete data release, and to ensuring that project data remain freely available in the public domain at no cost to users. The project follows the data-release principles of a "community resource project" (http://www.wellcome. ac.uk/en/1/awtpubrepdat.html).

All data on new SNPs, assay conditions, and allele and genotype frequencies will be released rapidly into the public domain on the internet at the HapMap Data Coordination Center (DCC) (http://www.hapmap.org/) and deposited in dbSNP. Individual genotype and haplotype data initially will be made available at the DCC under a short-term "click-wrap" licence agreement. This strategy has been adopted to ensure that data from the project cannot be incorporated into any restrictive patents, and will thus remain freely available in the long term. The only condition for data access is that users must agree not to restrict use of the data by others and to share the data only with others who have agreed to the same condition. When haplotypes are defined in a region, then the individual genotypes, haplotypes and tag SNPs in that region will be publicly released to dbSNP, where there are no licensing conditions. Project participants have agreed that their own laboratories will access the data through the DCC and under the click-wrap licence, ensuring that all scientists have equal access to the data for research.

The consortium believes that SNP, genotype and haplotype data in the absence of specific

个 SNP 分析在一个平台失败，可以用其他方法成功地开展以填补 HapMap 的缺口。所有平台将使用一套共同的性能标准评价，以确保为此计划产生的数据质量符合一致的高标准。

基因分型质量有三种方法进行评估。首先，在计划开始时，所有的中心分配同一套随机挑选的 1,500 个 SNP 进行实验开发和对用于该计划的 90 个 CEPH DNA 样本进行基因分型。分型中心产生数据的完整性和准确性平均分别超过 99.2% 和 99.5%（相对于至少有两个其他平台的一致性）。其次，每个基因分型实验包括样本的内部质量检查，每 96 孔板含有五个不同样本的重复和一个空白对照。此外，三体家系数据检查 SNP 等位基因符合孟德尔遗传。对于所有群体，无血缘关系的样本数据检查 SNP 的哈迪–温伯格平衡（一个遗传交配模式测试）。虽然因为生物学原因，一小部分 SNP 在这些检查中可能会失败，但如果一个基因分型平台产生一致的错误，它们可能会出现更典型的失败，例如复杂杂合子。第三，每个中心存放的 SNP 基因型的样本将随机抽样并由其他中心重新基因分型。这些严格的第三方质量评价将确保这个计划产生的数据的完整性和可靠性。

数 据 公 布

该计划致力于迅速和完全发布数据，并确保此计划的数据免费向公众开放。该计划遵循"公众资源计划"的数据发布原则（http://www.wellcome.ac.uk/en/1/awtpubrepdat.html）。

关于新 SNP、实验条件、等位基因和基因型频率的所有数据将迅速公布在位于 HapMap 数据协调中心（DCC）（http://www.hapmap.org/）的公共领域并储存在 dbSNP 中。个体基因型和单体型数据最初将在短期"点击许可"协议下由 DCC 提供。采用这一策略以确保该计划的数据不被纳入任何限制性专利中，因此将继续长期免费提供。数据存取唯一的条件是，用户必须同意不限制其他人使用数据并且仅与其他已同意相同条件的用户共享。当单体型在一个区域被确定后，同一区域的单个基因型、单体型和标签 SNP 将公开发布到 dbSNP 上，没有任何附加条款。该计划的参与者已同意自己的实验室也将在"点击许可"协议下通过 DCC 获得数据，以确保所有科学家有平等机会获得数据进行研究。

协作组认为，没有具体效用的 SNP、基因型和单体型数据，并不适于申请专

utility do not constitute appropriately patentable inventions. Specific utility would involve, for example, finding an association of a SNP or haplotype with a medically important phenotype such as a disease risk or drug response. The project does not include any phenotype association studies. However, the data-release policy does not block users from filing for appropriate intellectual property on such associations, as long as any ensuing patent is not used to prevent others' access to the HapMap data.

Data Analysis

The project will apply existing and new methods for analysis and display of the data. LD between pairs of markers will be calculated using standard measures such as D' (ref. 54), r^2 (refs 55, 56) and others. Various methods are being evaluated to define regions of high LD and haplotypes along chromosomes. Existing methods include "sliding window" LD profiles[57,58], LD unit maps[59], haplotype blocks[31,35] and estimates of meiotic recombination rates along chromosomes[35,60-62]. After analysis of the LD in the first phase of the project, regions in which there is little or no LD will be identified and ranked for further SNP selection and genotyping. Methods to select optimal collections of tag SNPs will be developed and evaluated (see above). The project will thus provide views of the data and tag SNPs that will be useful to the research community. As all data and analysis methods will be made available, other researchers will also be able to analyse the data and improve the analysis methods.

To assist optimization of SNP selection and analysis of LD and haplotypes, a pilot study is underway to produce a dense set of genotypes across large genomic regions. Ten 500-kilobase regions of the genome (see Supplementary Information, part 3) will be sequenced in 48 unrelated HapMap DNA samples (16 CEPH (currently being sequenced), 16 Yoruba, 8 Japanese and 8 Han Chinese). All SNPs identified, as well any additional SNPs in the public databases, will be genotyped in all of the 270 HapMap DNA samples, and the genotype data will be released following the guidelines described above. This study will provide dense genotype data for developing methods for SNP selection and for assessing the completeness of the information extracted, to guide the later stages of genotyping.

When the HapMap is used to examine large genomic regions, the problem of multiple comparisons will arise from testing tens to hundreds of thousands of SNPs and haplotypes for disease associations. This will lead to difficulty in separating true from false-positive results. Thus, new statistical methods, replication studies and functional analyses of variants will be important to confirm the findings and identify the functionally important SNPs.

Conclusion

The goal of the International HapMap Project is to develop a research tool that will help investigators across the globe to discover the genetic factors that contribute to susceptibility

利。具体的效用应涉及如找到一个 SNP 或单体型与医学重要的表型如疾病风险或药物反应的关联。该计划不包括任何表型关联研究。但是，数据发布政策并不阻止用户对这些关联申请适当的知识产权，只要任何随后的专利不被用于防止他人使用 HapMap 数据。

数 据 分 析

该计划将采用现有的和新的方法来分析和显示数据。成对标记间的 LD 将使用如 D'（参考文献 54）和 r^2（参考文献 55 和 56）等标准的措施计算。各种方法正在接受评估以确定高 LD 区域和沿染色体的各个单体型。现有的方法包括"滑动窗口"LD 描绘 [57,58]，LD 单位图 [59]，单体型区块 [31,35] 和沿染色体估计减数分裂重组率 [35,60-62]。经过该计划第一阶段 LD 分析，只有很少或没有 LD 的区域将被确定和分级用于进一步 SNP 选择和基因分型。选择最佳的收集标签 SNP 的方法将被制定和评估（见上文）。因此，该计划将提供对数据和标签 SNP 的看法，这些看法将对研究团体有帮助。所有数据和分析方法将被公开，其他研究人员也可以分析数据，提高分析方法。

为帮助优化 SNP 选择和 LD、单体型分析，我们正在开展一个先导研究对一些大片段的基因组区域进行致密的基因分型。基因组的 10 个 500-kb 区域（见补充资料，第 3 部分）将在 48 个无血缘关系的 HapMap DNA 样本（16 个 CEPH（目前正在测序）、16 个约鲁巴人、8 个日本人和 8 个中国汉族人）中测序。所有确定的 SNP 以及公共数据库中任何更多的 SNP，将在所有的 270 份 HapMap DNA 样本中进行基因分型，并且基因型数据都将按照上文所述的准则发布。这项研究将为开发 SNP 选择方法和评估提取数据的完整性提供密集的基因型数据，以对后期基因分型进行指导。

用 HapMap 来研究大的基因组区域，检测成千上万 SNP 和单体型与疾病的关联时将产生多重比较的问题。这将导致难以从假阳性结果中分离出真正阳性的结果。因此，新的统计方法、验证研究和功能分析对确认发现和鉴定具有重要功能的 SNP 很重要。

结 论

国际 HapMap 计划的目标是建立一个研究工具，这将有助于在全球范围内调查发现有助于探索疾病的遗传易感因素、对抗疾病的保护方法和药物反应情况。

to disease, to protection against illness and to drug response. The HapMap will provide an important shortcut to carry out candidate-gene, linkage-based and genome-wide association studies, transforming an unfeasible strategy into a practical one. In its scope and potential consequences, the International HapMap Project has much in common with the Human Genome Project, which sequenced the human genome[63]. Both projects have been scientifically ambitious and technologically demanding, have involved intense international collaboration, have been dedicated to the rapid release of data into the public domain, and promise to have profound implications for our understanding of human biology and human health. Whereas the sequencing project covered the entire genome, including the 99.9% of the genome where we are all the same, the HapMap will characterize the common patterns within the 0.1% where we differ from each other.

For the full potential of the HapMap to be realized, several things must occur. The technology for genotyping must become more cost efficient, and the analysis methods must be improved. Pilot studies with other populations must be completed to confirm that the HapMap is generally applicable, with consideration given to expanding the HapMap if needed so that all major world populations can derive the greatest benefit. To use the tools created by the HapMap, later projects must establish carefully phenotyped sets of affected and unaffected individuals for many common diseases in a way that preserves confidentiality but retains detailed clinical and environmental exposure data. Longitudinal cohort studies of hundreds of thousands of individuals will also be invaluable for assessing the genetic and environmental contributions to disease.

Careful and sustained attention must also be paid to the ethical issues that will be raised by the HapMap and the studies that will use it. By consulting members of donor populations about the consent process and the implications of population-specific findings before sample collection, the project has helped to advance the ethical standard for international population genetics research. Future population genetics projects will continue to refine this approach. It will be an ongoing challenge to avoid misinterpretations or misuses of results from studies that use the HapMap. Researchers using the HapMap should present their findings in ways that avoid stigmatizing groups, conveying an impression of genetic determinism, or attaching incorrect levels of biological significance to largely social constructs such as race.

The HapMap holds much promise as a powerful new tool for discovery—to enhance our understanding of the hereditary factors involved in health and disease. Realizing its full benefits will involve the close partnership of basic science researchers, population geneticists, epidemiologists, clinicians, social scientists, ethicists and the public.

(**426**, 789-796; 2003)

doi:10.1038/nature02168.

HapMap 将提供一个实现候选基因、连锁和全基因组关联研究的捷径，将一个不可行战略变为实际。在适用范围和潜在后果方面，国际 HapMap 计划与为人类基因组测序 [63] 的人类基因组计划在很多方面有相同之处。这两个项目都有远大的科学雄心并对技术要求很高，涉及广泛的国际合作，一直致力于向公众领域迅速发布数据，承诺将对人类生物学和人类健康的理解产生深刻的影响。测序项目涵盖了整个基因组，包括人类 99.9% 的相同基因组，而 HapMap 计划将确定人类互不相同的 0.1% 的常见模式。

为充分发挥 HapMap 计划的潜力，有几件事情必须考虑。基因分型技术必须更具成本效益，分析方法必须加以改进。关于其他群体的先导研究必须完成以确认 HapMap 计划是普遍适用的，如果需要的话，HapMap 计划可以考虑扩大以使全球所有主要的群体能够获得最大的利益。如果要使用 HapMap 项目所创造的工具，后来的研究必须仔细建立许多受常见疾病影响和不受影响的个体的表型集合。这些集合除了详细的临床及环境暴露数据，其他都处于机密状态。纵向研究几十万个个体对评估疾病的遗传和环境因素将有重大意义。

由 HapMap 和使用 HapMap 进行的研究引发的道德问题需得到认真持续的关注。通过在样本采集前与捐助群体成员就是否同意这个过程以及种群特异性发现的意义进行商议，该项目帮助推动了国际人口遗传学研究的道德标准，未来群体遗传学项目将继续完善这一做法。这将是一项持续的挑战，以避免误解或误用 HapMap 的研究结果。研究人员利用 HapMap 呈现其研究结果时应避免污蔑某一种群，或传达遗传决定论的思想，或将生物意义与大的社会建构如种族联系在一起。

HapMap 项目很有希望成为强大的新搜索工具，以提高我们对涉及健康和疾病的遗传因素的理解。充分发挥它的作用将涉及基础科学的研究人员、群体遗传学家、流行病学家、临床医生、社会科学家、伦理学家和公众的紧密合作。

(李梅 翻译；常江 审稿)

References:

1. King, R. A., Rotter, J. I. & Motulsky, A. G. *The Genetic Basis of Common Diseases* Vol. 20 (eds Motulsky, A. G., Harper, P. S., Scriver, C. & Bobrow, M.) (Oxford Univ. Press, Oxford, 1992).

2. Risch, N. J. Searching for genetic determinants in the new millennium. *Nature* **405**, 847-856 (2000).

3. Botstein, D. & Risch, N. Discovering genotypes underlying human phenotypes: past successes for mendelian disease, future approaches for complex disease. *Nature Genet.* **33** (Suppl.), 228-237 (2003).

4. Risch, N. & Merikangas, K. The future of genetic studies of complex human diseases. *Science* **273**, 1516-1517 (1996).

5. Dorman, J. S., LaPorte, R. E., Stone, R. A. & Trucco, M. Worldwide differences in the incidence of type I diabetes are associated with amino acid variation at position 57 of the HLA-DQ β chain. *Proc. Natl Acad. Sci. USA* **87**, 7370-7374 (1990).

6. Bell, G. I., Horita, S. & Karam, J. H. A polymorphic locus near the human insulin gene is associated with insulin-dependent diabetes mellitus. *Diabetes* **33**, 176-183 (1984).

7. Nisticò, L. *et al.* The *CTLA-4* gene region of chromosome 2q33 is linked to, and associated with, type 1 diabetes. *Hum. Mol. Genet.* **5**, 1075-1080 (1996).

8. Strittmatter, W. J. & Roses, A. D. Apolipoprotein E and Alzheimer's disease. *Annu. Rev. Neurosci.* 19, 53-77 (1996).

9. Dahlbäck, B. Resistance to activated protein C caused by the factor V R^{506}Q mutation is a common risk factor for venous thrombosis. *Thromb. Haemost.* **78**, 483-488 (1997).

10. Hugot, J. P. *et al.* Association of NOD2 leucine-rich repeat variants with susceptibility to Crohn's disease. *Nature* **411**, 599-603 (2001).

11. Ogura, Y. *et al.* A frameshift mutation in NOD2 associated with susceptibility to Crohn's disease. *Nature* **411**, 603-606 (2001).

12. Rioux, J. D. *et al.* Genetic variation in the 5q31 cytokine gene cluster confers susceptibility to Crohn disease. *Nature Genet.* **29**, 223-228 (2001).

13. Pennacchio, L. A. *et al.* An apolipoprotein influencing triglycerides in humans and mice revealed by comparative sequencing. *Science* **294**, 169-173 (2001).

14. Deeb, S. S. *et al.* A Pro12Ala substitution in PPARγ2 associated with decreased receptor activity, lower body mass index and improved insulin sensitivity. *Nature Genet.* **20**, 284-287 (1998).

15. Altshuler, D. *et al.* The common PPARγ Pro12Ala polymorphism is associated with decreased risk of type 2 diabetes. *Nature Genet.* **26**, 76-80 (2000).

16. Stefansson, H. *et al.* Neuregulin 1 and susceptibility to schizophrenia. *Am. J. Hum. Genet.* **71**, 877-892 (2002).

17. Van Eerdewegh, P. *et al.* Association of the *ADAM33* gene with asthma and bronchial hyperresponsiveness. *Nature* **418**, 426-430 (2002).

18. Gretarsdottir, S. *et al.* The gene encoding phosphodiesterase 4D confers risk of ischemic stroke. *Nature Genet.* **35**, 131-138 (2003).

19. Ozaki, K. *et al.* Functional SNPs in the lymphotoxin-α gene that are associated with susceptibility to myocardial infarction. *Nature Genet.* **32**, 650-654 (2002).

20. Collins, F. S., Guyer, M. S. & Chakravarti, A. Variations on a theme: cataloging human DNA sequence variation. *Science* **278**, 1580-1581 (1997).

21. Kruglyak, L. & Nickerson, D. A. Variation is the spice of life. *Nature Genet.* **27**, 234-236 (2001).

22. Kerem, B. *et al.* Identification of the cystic fibrosis gene: genetic analysis. *Science* **245**, 1073-1080 (1989).

23. Hästbacka, J. *et al.* Linkage disequilibrium mapping in isolated founder populations: diastrophic dysplasia in Finland. *Nature Genet.* **2**, 204-211 (1992).

24. Li, W. H. & Sadler, L. A. Low nucleotide diversity in man. *Genetics* **129**, 513-523 (1991).

25. Wang, D. G. *et al.* Large-scale identification, mapping, and genotyping of single-nucleotide polymorphisms in the human genome. *Science* **280**, 1077-1082 (1998).

26. Cargill, M. *et al.* Characterization of single-nucleotide polymorphisms in coding regions of human genes. *Nature Genet.* **22**, 231-238 (1999).

27. Halushka, M. K. *et al.* Patterns of single-nucleotide polymorphisms in candidate genes for blood-pressure homeostasis. *Nature Genet.* **22**, 239-247 (1999).

28. Reich, D. E., Gabriel, S. B. & Altshuler, D. Quality and completeness of SNP databases. *Nature Genet.* **33**, 457-458 (2003).

29. Pääbo, S. The mosaic that is our genome. *Nature* **421**, 409-412 (2003).

30. Jeffreys, A. J., Kauppi, L. & Neumann, R. Intensely punctate meiotic recombination in the class II region of the major histocompatibility complex. *Nature Genet.* **29**, 217-222 (2001).

31. Gabriel, S. B. *et al.* The structure of haplotype blocks in the human genome. *Science* **296**, 2225-2229 (2002).

32. Reich, D. E. *et al.* Linkage disequilibrium in the human genome. *Nature* **411**, 199-204 (2001).

33. Abecasis, G. R. *et al.* Extent and distribution of linkage disequilibrium in three genomic regions. *Am. J. Hum. Genet.* **68**, 191-197 (2001).

34. Dawson, E. *et al.* A first-generation linkage disequilibrium map of human chromosome 22. *Nature* **418**, 544-548 (2002).

35. Daly, M. J., Rioux, J. D., Schaffner, S. F., Hudson, T. J. & Lander, E. S. High-resolution haplotype structure in the human genome. *Nature Genet.* **29**, 229-232 (2001).

36. Patil, N. *et al.* Blocks of limited haplotype diversity revealed by high-resolution scanning of human chromosome 21. *Science* **294**, 1719-1723 (2001).

37. Johnson, G. C. L. *et al.* Haplotype tagging for the identification of common disease genes. *Nature Genet.* **29**, 233-237 (2001).

38. Carlson, C. S. *et al.* Additional SNPs and linkage-disequilibrium analyses are necessary for whole-genome association studies in humans. *Nature Genet.* **33**, 518-521 (2003).

39. Goldstein, D. B., Ahmadi, K. R., Weale, M. E. & Wood, N. W. Genome scans and candidate gene approaches in the study of common diseases and variable drug responses. *Trends Genet.* **19**, 615-622 (2003).

40. Taillon-Miller, P. *et al.* Juxtaposed regions of extensive and minimal linkage disequilibrium in human Xq25 and Xq28. *Nature Genet.* **25**, 324-328 (2000).

41. Chakravarti, A. Population genetics—making sense out of sequence. *Nature Genet.* **21**, 56-60 (1999).

42. Chakravarti, A. *et al.* Nonuniform recombination within the human β-globin gene cluster. *Am. J. Hum. Genet.* **36**, 1239-1258 (1984).

43. Tishkoff, S. A. *et al.* Global patterns of linkage disequilibrium at the CD4 locus and modern human origins. *Science* **271**, 1380-1387 (1996).

44. Cavalli-Sforza, L. L., Menozzi, P. & Piazza, A. *The History and Geography of Human Genes* (Princeton Univ. Press, Princeton, 1994).

45. Foster, M. W. & Sharp, R. R. Race, ethnicity, and genomics: social classifications as proxies of biological heterogeneity. *Genome Res.* **12**, 844-850 (2002).

46. Barbujani, G., Magagni, A., Minch, E. & Cavalli-Sforza, L. L. An apportionment of human DNA diversity. *Proc. Natl Acad. Sci. USA* **94**, 4516-4519 (1997).

47. Rosenberg, N. A. *et al.* Genetic structure of human populations. *Science* **298**, 2381-2385 (2002).

48. Jorde, L. B. *et al.* Microsatellite diversity and the demographic history of modern humans. *Proc. Natl Acad. Sci. USA* **94**, 3100-3103 (1997).

49. Dausset, J. *et al.* Centre d'Etude du Polymorphisme Humain (CEPH): collaborative genetic mapping of the human genome. *Genomics* **6**, 575-577 (1990).

50. Sherry, S. T. *et al.* dbSNP: the NCBI database of genetic variation. *Nucleic Acids Res.* **29**, 308-311 (2001).

51. Ning, Z., Cox, A. J. & Mullikin, J. C. SSAHA: a fast search method for large DNA databases. *Genome Res.* **11**, 1725-1729 (2001).

52. The International SNP Working Group. A map of human genome sequence variation containing 1.42 million single nucleotide polymorphisms. *Nature* **409**, 928-933 (2001).

53. Venter, J. C. *et al.* The sequence of the human genome. *Science* **291**, 1304-1351 (2001).

54. Lewontin, R. C. The interaction of selection and linkage. I. General considerations: heterotic models. *Genetics* **49**, 49-67 (1964).

55. Hill, W. G. & Robertson, A. Linkage disequilibrium in finite populations. *Theor. Appl. Genet.* **38**, 226-231 (1968).

56. Ohta, T. & Kimura, M. Linkage disequilibrium due to random genetic drift. *Genet. Res.* **13**, 47-55 (1969).

57. Dawson, K. J. The decay of linkage disequilibrium under random union of gametes: how to calculate Bennett's principal components. *Theor. Popul. Biol.* **58**, 1-20 (2000).

58. Langley, C. H. & Crow, J. F. The direction of linkage disequilibrium. *Genetics* **78**, 937-941 (1974).

59. Maniatis, N. *et al.* The first linkage disequilibrium (LD) maps: delineation of hot and cold blocks by diplotype analysis. *Proc. Natl Acad. Sci. USA* **99**, 2228-2233 (2002).

60. Hudson, R. R. Estimating the recombination parameter of a finite population model without selection. *Genet. Res.* **50**, 245-250 (1987).

61. Fearnhead, P. & Donnelly, P. Estimating recombination rates from population genetic data. *Genetics* **159**, 1299-1318 (2001).

62. McVean, G., Awadalla, P. & Fearnhead, P. A coalescent-based method for detecting and estimating recombination from gene sequences. *Genetics* **160**, 1231-1241 (2002).

63. International Human Genome Sequencing Consortium. Initial sequencing and analysis of the human genome. *Nature* **409**, 860-921 (2001).

64. Clayton, E. W. The complex relationship of genetics, groups, and health: what it means for public health. *J. Law Med. Ethics* **30**, 290-297 (2002).

65. Foster, M. W. & Sharp, R. R. Genetic research and culturally specific risks: one size does not fit all. *Trends Genet.* **16**, 93-95 (2000).

66. Sharp, R. R. & Foster, M. W. Involving study populations in the review of genetic research. *J. Law Med. Ethics* **28**, 41-51 (2000).

67. Marshall, P. A. & Rotimi, C. Ethical challenges in community-based research. *Am. J. Med. Sci.* **322**, 241-245 (2001).

68. Juengst, E. T. Commentary: what "community review" can and cannot do. *J. Law Med. Ethics* **28**, 52-54 (2000).

Supplementary Information accompanies the paper on www.nature.com/nature.

Acknowledgements. We thank many people who contributed to this project: J. Beck, C. Beiswanger, D. Coppock, J. Mintzer and L. Toji at the Coriell Institute for Medical Research for transforming the samples, distributing the DNA and cell lines, and storing the samples for use in future research; J. Greenberg and R. Anderson of the NIH National Institute of General Medical Sciences (NIGMS) for providing funding and support for cell-line transformation and storage in the NIGMS Human Genetic Cell Repository at the Coriell Institute; K. Wakui at Shinshu University for assistance in transforming the Japanese cell lines; N. Carter and D. Willey at the Wellcome Trust Sanger Institute for flow sorting the chromosomes and for library construction, respectively; M. Deschesnes and B. Godard for assistance at the University of Montréal; C. Darmond-Zwaig, J. Olivier and S. Roumy at McGill University and Génome Québec Innovation Centre; C. Allred, B. Gillman, E. Kloss and M. Rieder for help in implementing data flow protocols; S. Olson for work on the website explanations; S. Adeniyi-Jones, D. Burgess, W. Burke, T. Citrin, A. Clark, D. Cowhig, P. Epps, K. Hofman, A. Holt, E. Juengst, B. Keats, J. Levin, R. Myers, A. Obuoforibo, F. Romero, C. Tamura and A. Williamson for providing advice on the project to NIH; A. Peck and J. Witonsky of the National Human Genome Research Institute (NHGRI) for help with project management; E. DeHaut-Combs and S. Saylor of NHGRI for staff support; M. Gray for organizing phone calls and meetings; the people of Tokyo, Japan, the Yoruba people of Ibadan, Nigeria, and the community at Beijing Normal University, who participated in public consultations and community engagements; and the people in these communities who were generous in donating their blood samples. This work was supported in part by Genome Canada, Génome Québec, the Chinese Ministry of Science and Technology, the Chinese Academy of Sciences, the Natural Science Foundation of China, the Hong Kong Innovation and Technology Commission, the University Grants Committee of Hong Kong, the Japanese Ministry of Education, Culture, Sports, Science and Technology, the Wellcome Trust, the SNP Consortium, the US National Institutes of Health (FIC, NCI, NCRR, NEI, NHGRI, NIA, NIAAA, NIAID, NIAMS, NIBIB, NIDA, NIDCD, NIDCR, NIDDK, NIEHS, NIGMS, NIMH, NINDS, OD), the W.M. Keck Foundation and the Delores Dore Eccles Foundation.

Competing interests statement. The authors declare that they have no competing financial interests.

Correspondence and requests for materials should be addressed to D.B. (drb@sanger.ac.uk) or M.F. (fost1848@msmailhub.oulan.ou.edu).

A Correlation between the Cosmic Microwave Background and Large-scale Structure in the Universe

S. Boughn and R. Crittenden

Editor's Note

The ripples in the cosmic microwave background radiation are relics of the seeds from which the large-scale structure of the Universe grew. If this is so, hot spots in this radiation should correspond to concentrations of galaxies, and cold spots to voids. This paper by Stephen Boughn and Robert Crittenden reports the first observation of such a correlation. X-rays from hot gas inside clusters of galaxies turn out to be correlated with fluctuations in the backgrounds. The distribution of galaxies that are bright radio sources is also correlated with the fluctuations. The authors point out that the correlation supports the idea that dark energy, which drives the acceleration of cosmic expansion, has left an imprint on large-scale structure.

Observations of distant supernovae and the fluctuations in the cosmic microwave background (CMB) indicate that the expansion of the Universe may be accelerating[1] under the action of a "cosmological constant" or some other form of "dark energy". This dark energy now appears to dominate the Universe and not only alters its expansion rate, but also affects the evolution of fluctuations in the density of matter, slowing down the gravitational collapse of material (into, for example, clusters of galaxies) in recent times. Additional fluctuations in the temperature of CMB photons are induced as they pass through large-scale structures[2] and these fluctuations are necessarily correlated with the distribution of relatively nearby matter[3]. Here we report the detection of correlations between recent CMB data[4] and two probes of large-scale structure: the X-ray background[5] and the distribution of radio galaxies[6]. These correlations are consistent with those predicted by dark energy, indicating that we are seeing the imprint of dark energy on the growth of structure in the Universe.

IN the standard model of the origin of structure, most of the fluctuations in the CMB were imprinted as the photons last scattered off free electrons, when the universe was just 400,000 years old (at a redshift of $z \approx 1,100$). However, once the dark energy (or the spatial curvature[7]) becomes important dynamically ($z \approx 1$), additional fluctuations are induced in the CMB photons by what is known as the integrated Sachs–Wolfe (ISW) effect[2]. The gravitational potentials of large, diffuse concentrations and rarefactions of matter begin to evolve, causing the energy of photons passing through them to change by an amount that depends on the depth of the potentials. The amplitude of these ISW fluctuations tends to

宇宙微波背景和大尺度结构的相关

博夫恩，克里滕登

编者按

宇宙微波背景辐射中的波纹是"种子"的遗迹，宇宙的大尺度结构便是从这些"种子"发育而成。如果真如上所言，这种辐射中的热斑应该对应于星系的聚集，而冷斑则对应巨洞。本文作者史蒂夫·博夫恩和罗伯特·克里滕登首次报道了这种相关性。来自星系团内的热气体的 X 射线与背景中的扰动相关。作为亮射电源的星系的分布也与扰动相关。作者指出，这种相关性支持以下观点：驱动宇宙膨胀加速的暗能量在大尺度结构上留下了印记。

对遥远的超新星和宇宙微波背景辐射 (CMB) 涨落的观测表明，宇宙很可能在"宇宙学常数"或者某种其他形式的暗能量作用下加速膨胀 [1]。暗能量在当前宇宙中占主导地位，它不仅改变了宇宙的膨胀速率，也影响了物质密度扰动的演化，减慢了物质的引力塌缩 (例如星系团的生成过程)。宇宙微波背景辐射温度的额外涨落来自于 CMB 光子穿越大尺度结构时所受到的扰动 [2]，因此这些涨落必然与所对应区域邻近物质的分布相关 [3]。在这里我们报道最近的 CMB 数据 [4] 和两种大尺度结构的观测结果 (X 射线背景 [5] 和射电星系分布 [6]) 之间的相关性。这些相关性与暗能量的预言相符，表明我们在宇宙结构演化的过程中观测到了暗能量的印记。

在结构起源的标准模型中，大部分 CMB 涨落都带有光子被自由电子最后一次散射时的特征，此刻宇宙只有 400,000 年的历史 (红移大约为 1,100)。但是一旦暗能量 (或者空间曲率 [7]) 逐渐变得重要 (红移大约为 1)，累计萨克斯-沃尔夫效应 (ISW) 将会在 CMB 中引入额外的扰动 [2]。由于大量聚集和稀薄的弥散物质的引力势随时间开始演化，穿过引力势阱的光子能量发生变化，这个变化量取决于势阱的深度。除了在很大的尺度上以外，ISW 的扰动幅度要比源自最后散射的扰动小得多。然而

be small compared to the fluctuations originating at the epoch of last scattering except on very large scales. However, as ISW fluctuations were created more locally, it is expected that the CMB fluctuations should be partially correlated with galaxies, which serve as tracers of the large-scale matter distribution.

Detecting the relatively weak ISW effect requires correlating the CMB with the distribution of galaxies spread over a large fraction of the observable Universe. This necessitates a survey of galaxies covering much of the sky, out to distances of many billions of light years ($z \approx 1$). Focus thus has been on luminous active galaxies, which are believed to trace the mass distribution on large scales. Although active galaxies emit at a wide range of frequencies, the most useful maps are in the hard X-rays (2–10 keV), where they dominate the X-ray sky, and in the radio, where the number counts are dominated by sources at $z \lesssim 1$. The full sky map of the intensity of the hard X-ray background made by the HEAO-1 satellite[5] and a map of the number density of radio sources provided by the NRAO VLA sky survey (NVSS)[6] are two of the best maps in which to look for this effect. To predict the expected level of the ISW effect in these two surveys, it is essential to know both the inherent clustering of the sources and their distribution in redshift. The former can be determined from previous studies of the X-ray and radio auto-correlation functions[8,9] and the latter can be estimated from deep, pointed surveys[10,11].

Previous attempts at correlating the CMB with both the HEAO-1 and the NVSS maps have yielded only upper limits[8,9,12]. Here we repeat these analyses using the much improved CMB maps recently provided by the WMAP satellite mission[4]. We have compared two different CMB maps generated from this data (the "internal linear combination" map[13], and the "cleaned" map of ref. 14) with the HEAO and NVSS maps. The dominant "noise" in the maps is due to the fluctuations in the CMB itself and is well characterized, while the instrument noise is negligible on the angular scales relevant to the present analysis. To reduce possible contamination by emission from our Milky Way Galaxy as well as from other nearby radio sources, these maps were masked with the most aggressive foreground template provided by the WMAP team[13]. The X-ray map was similarly masked and was corrected for several large-scale systematics including a linear drift of the detectors[9]. Finally, the NVSS catalogue was corrected for a systematic variation of source counts with declination[8]. The sky coverage was 68% for the CMB maps, 56% for the NVSS map, and 33% for the X-ray map. The reduced coverage of the X-ray map was the result of its low resolution (3°) and a larger number of foreground sources. Significantly, however, our results do not depend on the corrections or the level of masking of the maps.

A standard measure of the correspondence of two data sets is the cross-correlation function, CCF(θ). It represents the extent to which the two measures of the sky separated by an angle θ are correlated. Figures 1 and 2 show the CCFs of the WMAP data with the X-ray and radio surveys. The results using the "internal linear combination" and "cleaned" CMB maps were entirely consistent with each other, and we plot the averages of the results for the two maps. Four hundred Monte Carlo simulations of the CMB sky were also cross-correlated with the actual X-ray and radio maps. The r.m.s. values of these trials are

ISW 扰动是在局部空间产生的，CMB 涨落应与星系分布部分相关，故可以以此探测大尺度上的物质分布。

探测相对较弱的 ISW 效应要求研究 CMB 与占可观测宇宙中较大部分的星系分布的相关性。这需要星系巡天具有大比例的天空覆盖，且巡天深度延伸至几十亿光年的距离（红移为 1 左右）。因此巡天目标集中在明亮的活动星系，这被认为可以很好地示踪大尺度的质量分布。虽然活动星系在很宽的波段内都有辐射，但是最有效的成图在硬 X 射线波段（2～10 keV），它主导了 X 射线天空，同时在射电波段，射电源计数由红移 ≤1 的源所主导。HEAO-1 卫星所作的亮硬 X 射线背景强度全天图 [5] 和 NRAO VLA 巡天（NVSS）所作的射电源数密度巡天图为寻找 ISW 效应提供了最好的图像。为了预测在这两个巡天中 ISW 效应所期望达到的水平，清楚这些源内在的成团性和它们随红移的分布是至关重要的。成团性可由过去已有的对 X 射线和射电源的自相关函数 [8,9] 的研究中得到，分布则可由深度指向巡天 [10,11] 来估计。

过去将 CMB 与 HEAO-1、NVSS 天图做交叉相关的尝试仅得到了相关的上限 [8,9,12]。在这里我们用 WMAP 卫星计划 [4] 最近提供的有显著改进的 CMB 图重复这种相关分析。我们将从 WMAP 得到的两种不同的 CMB 图（"内在线性组合"图 [13] 和"净化"图 [14]）与 HEAO 和 NVSS 的天图相比较。图中"噪声"的主要成分来自 CMB 自身的涨落，其特征能够被很好地描述，而在要分析的角尺度上仪器噪声则可以忽略。为了减少来自银河系和其他附近射电源的辐射污染，这些图均按 WMAP 团队所提供的最苛刻的前景模板进行了掩模 [13]。X 射线图也进行了类似的掩模，同时还修正了几个大尺度上类似探测器线性漂移的系统误差 [9]。最后，NVSS 星表也修正了源计数偏差引起的系统误差 [8]。CMB 图覆盖了整个天空的 68%，NVSS 图覆盖了 56%，X 射线图只覆盖了 33%。X 射线图的覆盖率偏低是因为较低的分辨率（3度）和大量的前景源。尽管如此，我们的结果与修正或对图像的掩模程度明显地关系不大。

度量两个数据集合相关性的标准方法是求交叉相关函数 $CCF(\theta)$。它表征了角间距为 θ 的两个方向之间的空间相关性。图 1 与图 2 表示 WMAP 分别与 X 射线巡天图和射电巡天图之间的交叉相关函数。用 CMB 的"内在线性组合"图和"洁化"图得到的结果是完全符合的；我们还绘出了这两种图结果的平均。通过四百次蒙特卡洛方法模拟得到的 CMB 图被用于与实际的 X 射线巡天图和射电巡天图做交叉相关。

taken as the errors for each bin and these are highly correlated owing to the large-scale structure in the maps. For comparison, the uncertainties were also estimated from the data themselves by rotating the maps with respect to each other, and the errors determined in this way were very similar to those found using the simulated maps. The significance of the detection of the ISW effect is estimated by fitting the amplitude of the theoretical profile to the data. For the X-ray/CMB CCF, the correlations are detected at a confidence level (CL) of 99.9%, that is, a 3.0σ detection. The radio/CMB CCF is detected at a 99.4% CL, or a 2.5σ detection. These confidence limits are consistent with the number of times the CCF(θ) of the Monte Carlo trials exceed the values of the measured CCF(θ).

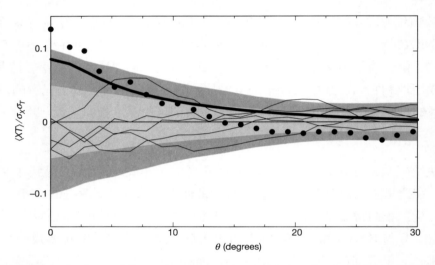

Fig. 1. The X-ray background fluctuations are correlated with the microwave sky at a higher level than would be expected by chance. Here we plot the cross correlation (filled circles) between the X-ray intensity (X) measured by HEAO-A1 and the CMB temperature fluctuations (T) measured by WMAP. We normalize by the r.m.s. levels of the two maps (σ_x and σ_T, respectively), which makes it independent of any linear biasing of the survey. To give an idea of the level of accidental correlations, the shaded areas show the 1σ and 2σ regions derived from simulated, uncorrelated CMB maps with the same power spectrum as the WMAP data. The thin solid lines show the results for five such Monte Carlo simulations, and we see that the signals in neighbouring bins are highly correlated for a given realization. The signal-to-noise ratio is greatest at smaller angular separations, even though the error is amplified because fewer pairs of pixels contribute to the correlation. For $\theta = 0°$, 1.3° and 2.6°, the Monte Carlo trials exceed the amplitude of the actual X-ray/CMB correlation only 0.3%, 0.8% and 0.3% of the time, respectively. The bold line shows theoretical predictions for the ISW effect in a cosmological-constant-dominated Universe, using the best-fit WMAP model for scale-invariant fluctuations[19] (dark energy fraction $\Omega_\Lambda = 0.73$, Hubble constant $H_0 = 100\,h$ km s^{-1} Mpc^{-1} with $h = 0.72$, matter density $\Omega_m h^2 = 0.14$ and baryon density $\Omega_b h^2 = 0.024$). At larger angular separations, the observed correlations appear to fall faster than predicted by theory, but the low signal-to-noise ratio makes it difficult to say whether this is a real effect.

这些试验的均方根被认为是每一个数据间隔的误差，由于天图存在的大尺度结构，它们是高度相关的。作为比较，不确定性可以通过天图本身的相对旋转由对原始数据的分析获得，它所给出的误差与通过使用模拟图得到的误差非常接近。ISW 效应探测的显著性可以通过理论轮廓的大小和实际数据的拟合来估计。对于 CMB 与 X 射线巡天之间的交叉相关函数，探测的置信水平为 99.9%（即 3σ 探测）；对于 CMB 与射电巡天之间的交叉相关函数，探测的置信水平为 99.4%（即 2.5σ 探测）。这些置信限与大量蒙特卡洛试验得出的交叉相关函数是一致的。

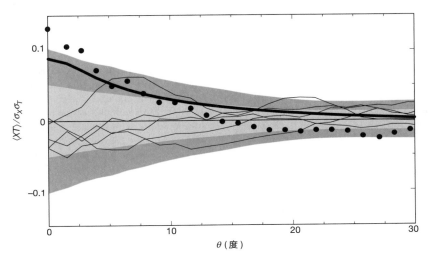

图 1. X 射线背景扰动与微波背景的相关性高于偶然事件的概率，这里我们给出了 HEAO–A1 测得的 X 射线强度（X）和 WMAP 观测的微波背景辐射温度扰动（T）的交叉相关（实心圆）。我们用两个图的均方根水平（σ_X 和 σ_T）做归一化，使得它与巡天的线性偏袒无关。为了了解偶然事件导致相关的可能性，阴影区域显示与 WMAP 具有相同功率谱且统计无关的 CMB 模拟图给出的 1σ 和 2σ 区域。细实线显示了 5 个这样的蒙特卡罗模拟，我们注意到，临近数据区间的信号与给定的模拟实现高度相关。尽管贡献相关性的像素较少而使误差被放大，这个信噪比在小角间距下还是最大的。对 $\theta = 1$ 度、1.3 度和 2.6 度，蒙特卡罗的结果只超过真实 X 射线/CMB 相关的 0.3%、0.8% 和 0.3%。图中粗线显示在宇宙学常数主导的宇宙中 ISW 效应的理论预测，它采用了尺度不变扰动的 WMAP 最佳拟合模型 [19]（暗物质分数 $\Omega_\Lambda = 0.73$，哈勃常数 $H_0 = 100h$ km · s^{-1} · Mpc^{-1}，$h = 0.72$，物质密度 $\Omega_m h^2 = 0.14$，重子密度 $\Omega_b h^2 = 0.024$）。对更大的角间距，观测到的相关性看上去比理论预言的相对性下降得更快，但是信噪比很低，因此很难说这是否是真实的结果。

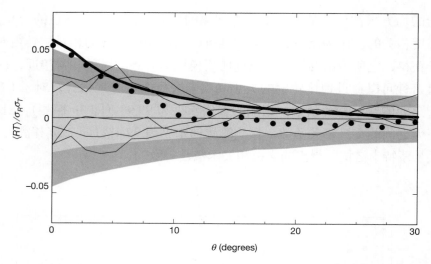

Fig. 2. The distribution of radio galaxies is correlated with the microwave sky. Here we plot the correlation (filled circles) between the NVSS radio galaxy number counts (R) and the WMAP temperature maps (T). The other curves are as in Fig. 1. The Monte Carlo trials exceed the amplitude of the actual radio/CMB correlation in the lowest three bins 1.2%, 1.9% and 3.4% of the time, respectively. Again, there is good agreement with the theoretical predictions, with the signal again falling off somewhat faster than predicted at larger angles. The lower amplitude compared to the X-ray result is due to the higher resolution of the radio map, which increases the radio r.m.s. (σ_R) without significantly increasing the cross-correlation. The consistency of the NVSS and X-ray CCFs suggests that the signal is not the result of unknown systematics in either the X-ray or the NVSS map. It is possible that microwave emission from the radio/X-ray sources themselves could result in the positive correlation of the maps. However, extrapolations of the frequency spectra of the radio galaxies indicate that the microwave emission is much smaller than the observed signal[8]. In addition, the clustering of radio sources is on a much smaller angular scale than the apparent signals, so any such contamination would appear only at $\theta \approx 0°$ and not at larger angles.

The theoretical curves for the ISW effect also are shown in Figs 1 and 2, and fall off with angular separation similarly to the observed correlations. For these calculations, we have assumed that the fluctuations in matter density, $\delta\rho$, are traced directly by the fluctuations in the number density of the sources. That is, $\delta N/N = b\delta\rho/\rho$ where the bias factor, b, is assumed to be constant and its value is derived from the auto-correlation function of the X-ray or radio sources. The predictions assume a scale-invariant primordial spectrum and the best-fit cosmology determined from WMAP. Although the derived bias factors depend on precisely how the sources are assumed to be distributed in redshift, the expected cross-correlation is only weakly dependent on this or on the possible evolution of the bias factor with redshift. Detailed considerations for calculating the amplitude of the ISW effect can be found elsewhere[3,12].

It is important to consider what else might be contributing to the observed correlation. Unmasked foreground sources are not a major contaminant, because the observed correlations do not change when the Galactic cuts are varied nor when the aggressiveness of the masking is changed. In fact, the amplitudes of the CCFs are essentially unchanged when no masking at all is applied to the CMB maps. Also, because the results from analysing

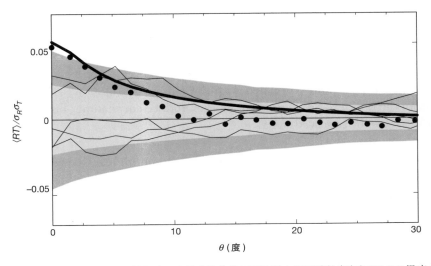

图 2. 射电星系的分布与微波背景的相关。这里我们绘出 NVSS 射电星系计数 (R) 和 WMAP 温度 (T) 的相关图(用实心圆表示)。其他曲线的含义与图 1 相同。蒙特卡罗试验中超过实际射电/CMB 相关的幅度在最低的三个区间分别为 1.2%、1.9%、3.4%。这与理论预言再一次保持一致,而在大角度处信号衰减速度再次快于预言。其幅度比 X 射线低是由于射电图更高的分辨率增加了射电的均方根 (σ_R),而没有显著增加交叉相关。NVSS 和 X 射线交叉相关函数的一致暗示了信号不是来自 X 射线或者 NVSS 图像中未知的系统误差,而来自射电或者 X 射线源的微波辐射可能导致图像的正相关。尽管如此,射电星系的频谱外推指出这种微波辐射远小于观测结果 [8]。而且,射电源的成团性发生在比视信号小得多的角度上,因此所有这种污染应该出现在 $\theta \approx 0°$ 而非更大的角度。

ISW 效应的理论曲线同时在图 1 和图 2 中给出,它与观测所得的相关类似,随着角间隔增大而衰减。在这些计算中,我们已经假设物质密度扰动 ($\delta\rho$) 可直接由辐射源的数密度扰动所示踪。即 $\delta N/N = b\delta\rho/\rho$,假设偏袒因子 b 为常数且它的值可通过 X 射线或者射电源的自相关函数得出。预测过程中假设了尺度不变的原初功率谱以及由 WMAP 数据的最优拟合得到的宇宙学。虽然由此得到的偏袒因子 b 严格依赖于对源的红移分布的假设,但对期望的交叉相关函数而言,其对红移分布的依赖性比较弱,对偏袒因子 b 可能的红移演化的依赖性也不强。对 ISW 效应幅度计算的详细讨论容易在其他文献中找到 [3,12]。

还有一点非常重要,即要考虑是否还有其他过程对观测到的相关有贡献。未掩模的前景源不是主要的污染,因为当改变银河系扣除方式,或者改变前述的严格掩模处理,观察到的相关性都不会改变。实际上,即使完全不对 CMB 做任何掩模处理,交叉相关函数的幅度都不会有本质的改变。同时,因为对不同半球的巡天图的

the different hemispheres of the maps separately are consistent, it is unlikely that a small number of diffuse foreground sources is responsible for the signal. Fluctuations caused by the Sunyaev–Zeldovich effect—the scattering of CMB photons as they travel through the ionized intergalactic medium of rich clusters of galaxies—are expected to contribute at smaller angles and be anti-correlated with the matter distribution[15]. Finally, microwave emission from the radio/X-ray sources could also produce correlations, but on much smaller angular scales than the observed signal.

The correlated signal evident in the figures is large enough to have been seen in our previous analyses using a COBE satellite combination map[8,9], albeit with a smaller signal-to-noise ratio because of that map's significant instrument noise and low angular resolution. However, we found no evidence for a correlation in the COBE analysis. When the differences in angular resolution are taken into account, the WMAP and COBE maps are consistent given COBE's large instrumental noise ($\sim 70 \, \mu K$ per pixel)[4]. The difference between the observed cross-correlations implies that a small part (r.m.s. $\approx 1–2$ mK) of the (COBE-WMAP) difference map is anti-correlated with the X-ray and radio maps. This is an unlikely occurrence (1 in 100) if the COBE instrument noise model is correct. There are known systematics in the COBE data[16] above this level, but the large instrument noise makes it difficult to ascertain whether this is the origin of the problem. In any case, the source of the discrepancy almost certainly lies with the COBE data, which contain much larger noise and systematic effects than the WMAP data. Thus, we believe the WMAP correlations presented here are robust. Further discussion of this and other issues are available as Supplementary Information.

The confidence levels that we quote (99.9% and 99.4%) are not primarily limited by experimental error, but by the fact that we can only observe a finite region of the Universe. We find it significant that both signals are consistent with the theoretical predictions with no free parameters. However, it should be emphasized that these two measurements are by no means independent. Both of them use the same CMB maps and, furthermore, the X-ray background is highly correlated with the NVSS radio sources[17]. If the distribution of sources of one of the maps by chance coincided with the fluctuations of the CMB, one would expect the other map also to be correlated with the CMB to some degree. The coincidence of the expected amplitudes of the two signals is encouraging but by no means definitive. On the other hand, the detection of the ISW-type signal in both CCFs gives a strong indication that they are not due to unknown systematic effects in the maps. The radio and X-ray data were gathered by quite distinct methods, and it would be surprising if unknown systematics in the two maps were correlated in any way. We will present more detailed analysis of these issues elsewhere.

We conclude that we have observed the ISW effect. If so, these observations offer the first direct glimpse into the production of CMB fluctuations, and provide important, independent confirmation of the new standard cosmological model: an accelerating universe, dominated by dark energy. It should be pointed out that measurements of the power spectrum of CMB fluctuations do not show evidence of increased power on large

分析得到的结果是一致的，因此很难想象这些相关的信号是由少量的弥散前景源所导致的。苏尼阿耶夫–泽尔多维奇效应（CMB 光子在穿越富星系团中的电离星系际介质时发生的散射）引起的扰动应该贡献在小角度上，并且与物质分布反相关 [15]。最后，射电源和 X 射线源发射的微波辐射也可能产生相关，但其发生的角尺度比观测信号要小得多。

图中给出的相关信号的证据已经足够大到即使使用宇宙背景探测器（COBE）卫星组合图也应该在我们前述的分析中被观察到 [8,9]，尽管由于图像显著的仪器噪声和低角分辨率，信号的信噪比会比较低。但是我们并没有在对 COBE 的分析中发现存在相关性的证据。当考虑 WMAP 和 COBE 的角分辨率不同，以及在 COBE 具有较大仪器噪声（约 70 μK 每像素）[4] 的情况下，COBE 和 WMAP 的图像是一致的。观测到交叉相关的差别意味着，在 COBE 与 WMAP 的图像差中的一小部分（均方根约为 1~2 μK）存在与 X 射线图和射电图的反相关。如果 COBE 的仪器噪声的模型是正确的，上述情况不大可能发生（发生概率为 1/100）。虽然已知在 COBE 的数据中系统误差高于这个水平，但仪器噪声过大让我们很难确定这是否是问题的根源。无论如何，这个不一致的来源都被认为来自 COBE 数据自身 [16]，因为它包含的噪声和系统性效应比 WMAP 数据要大得多。因此，我们相信 WMAP 的相关性是稳健的。进一步的讨论和更多的问题详见补充材料。

我们报道的置信度（99.9% 和 99.4%）并非主要受限于试验误差，而是由于我们只能观测到宇宙的有限区域。重要的是，理论预言并不需要加入自由参数就能和两种信号很好地吻合。但应该强调，这两种方法并不完全独立。因为两者都使用了相同的 CMB 图，并且 X 射线背景与 NVSS 射电源 [17] 高度相关。如果某一种图的源分布偶然地与 CMB 的扰动相符，那么另一种图也会在某种程度上与 CMB 相关。虽然两个信号的期望幅度的一致性令人振奋，但还不是确定性的结果。另一方面，在两个交叉相关函数中都观测到 ISW 型的信号，强烈地表明这并非由图中未知的系统误差所引起的。射电数据和 X 射线数据是用非常不同的方法所采集的，如果两种巡天图中某种未知的系统误差存在关联，那将是令人惊奇的。我们会在其他论文中给出对这一问题的细致分析。

我们的结论是我们已观测到 ISW 效应。如果确实如此，这是第一次直接观测到 CMB 涨落的产生，也为新标准宇宙学模型——一个加速膨胀的、暗能量占主导的宇宙提供了重要的、独立的支持。应该指出的是，CMB 扰动功率谱的测量并没有如 ISW 效应所预言的那样在大的角尺度上（$\theta > 20°$）上升，而是可能存在扰动功

angular scales ($\theta > 20°$) as predicted by the ISW effect, but rather indicate that there may be power missing[4]. Although this deficit is only at the 2σ level, it is intriguing, and may be telling us something about the formation of the very largest structures in the Universe. The consequences of the ISW effect reported here are primarily on intermediate angular scales, and are not in direct conflict with the power deficit on larger angular scales. Finally, we note that the WMAP-NVSS results have recently been independently analysed by the WMAP team, who find a similar level of correlation[18].

(**427**, 45-47; 2004)

Stephen Boughn[1] **& Robert Crittenden**[2]
[1] Department of Astronomy, Haverford College, Haverford, Pennsylvania 19041, USA
[2] Institute of Cosmology and Gravitation, University of Portsmouth, Portsmouth PO1 2EG, UK

Received 15 April; accepted 8 October 2003; doi:10.1038/nature02139.

References:

1. Bahcall, N., Ostriker, J. P., Perlmutter, S. & Steinhardt, P. The cosmic triangle: Revealing the state of the universe. *Science* **284**, 1481-1488 (1999).

2. Sachs, R. K. & Wolfe, A. M. Perturbations of a cosmological model and angular variations of the microwave background. *Astrophys. J.* **147**, 73-90 (1967).

3. Crittenden, R. & Turok, N. Looking for a cosmological constant with the Rees-Sciama effect. *Phys. Rev. Lett.* **76**, 575-578 (1996).

4. Bennett, C. L. *et al.* First year *Wilkinson Microwave Anisotropy Probe* observations: Preliminary maps and basic results. *Astrophys. J. Suppl.* **148**, 1-27 (2003).

5. Boldt, E. The cosmic X-ray background. *Phys. Rep.* **146**, 215-257 (1987).

6. Condon, J. *et al.* The NRAO VLA sky survey. *Astron. J.* **115**, 1693-1716 (1998).

7. Kinkhabwala, A. & Kamionkowski, M. New constraint on open cold-dark-matter models. *Phys. Rev. Lett.* **82**, 4172-4175 (1999).

8. Boughn, S. & Crittenden, R. Cross correlation of the CMB with radio sources: Constraints on an accelerating universe. *Phys. Rev. Lett.* **88**, 021302 (2002).

9. Boughn, S., Crittenden, R. & Koehrsen, G. The large scale structure of the X-ray background and its cosmological implications. *Astrophys. J.* **580**, 672-684 (2002).

10. Cowie, L. L., Barger, A. J., Bautz, M. W., Brandt, W. N. & Garmire, G. P. The redshift evolution of the 2-8 keV X-ray luminosity function. *Astrophys. J.* **584**, 57-60 (2003).

11. Dunlop, J. S. & Peacock, J. A. The redshift cut-off in the luminosity function of radio galaxies and quasars. *Mon. Not. R. Astron. Soc.* **247**, 19-42 (1990).

12. Boughn, S., Crittenden, R. & Turok, N. Correlations between the cosmic X-ray and microwave backgrounds: Constraints on a cosmological constant. *New Astron.* **3**, 275-291 (1998).

13. Bennett, C. L. *et al.* First year *Wilkinson Microwave Anisotropy Probe* observations: Foreground emission. *Astrophys. J. Suppl.* **148**, 97-117 (2003).

14. Tegmark, M., de Oliveira-Costa, A. & Hamilton, A. A high resolution foreground cleaned CMB map from WMAP. Preprint at ⟨http://xxx.lanl.gov/astro-ph/0302496⟩ (2003).

15. Peiris, H. V. & Spergel, D. N. Cross-correlating the Sloan Digital Sky Survey with the microwave sky. *Astrophys. J.* **540**, 605-613 (2000).

16. Kogut, A. *et al.* Calibration and systematic error analysis for the COBE DMR 4 year sky maps. *Astrophys. J.* **470**, 653-673 (1996).

17. Boughn, S. Cross-correlation of the 2-10 keV X-ray background with radio sources: Constraining the large-scale structure of the X-ray background. *Astrophys. J.* **499**, 533-541 (1998).

18. Nolta, M.R. *et al.* First year *Wilkinson Microwave Anisotropy Probe* observations: Dark energy induced correlation with radio sources. Preprint at ⟨http://xxx.lanl.gov/astro-ph/0305907⟩ (2003).

19. Spergel, D. N. *et al.* First year *Wilkinson Microwave Anisotropy Probe* observations: Determination of cosmological parameters. *Astrophys. J. Suppl.* **148**, 175-194 (2003).

Supplementary Information accompanies the paper on www.nature.com/nature.

Acknowledgements. We are grateful to M. Nolta, L. Page and the rest of the WMAP team, as well as to N. Turok, B. Partridge and B. Bassett, for useful conversations. R.C. acknowledges financial support from a PPARC fellowship.

Competing interests statement. The authors declare that they have no competing financial interests.

Correspondence and requests for materials should be addressed to R.C. (Robert.Crittenden@port.ac.uk).

率丢失 [4]。虽然亏损的置信水平只有 2σ，但这一现象却十分神秘，这也许告诉了我们一些宇宙中非常大的结构形成的信息。这里对 ISW 效应所下的结论主要在中等角尺度上，并不与更大角尺度上的扰动功率丢失相矛盾。最后，WMAP 团队最近也对 WMAP–NVSS 结果做了独立的分析，他们也发现了类似水平的相关性 [18]。

（周杰 翻译；冯珑珑 审稿）

Mice Cloned from Olfactory Sensory Neurons

K. Eggan *et al.*

Editor's Note

By 2004, various mammals including sheep and mice had been cloned by injecting donor DNA into enucleated eggs. But in this paper, American cell biologist Rudolf Jaenisch and colleagues use donor DNA taken from mature olfactory neurons to generate fertile mouse clones by the process of nuclear transfer. The study demonstrates that DNA taken from a specialised cell that has stopped dividing can re-enter the cell cycle and be reprogrammed to an embryonic-like state after nuclear transfer. The cloned mice possessed the full range of organized, odorant receptor genes that were indistinguishable from those of normal mice, suggesting that selection of a particular receptor gene in a mature olfactory neuron does not cause irreversible changes in DNA.

Cloning by nuclear transplantation has been successfully carried out in various mammals, including mice. Until now mice have not been cloned from post-mitotic cells such as neurons. Here, we have generated fertile mouse clones derived by transferring the nuclei of post-mitotic, olfactory sensory neurons into oocytes. These results indicate that the genome of a post-mitotic, terminally differentiated neuron can re-enter the cell cycle and be reprogrammed to a state of totipotency after nuclear transfer. Moreover, the pattern of odorant receptor gene expression and the organization of odorant receptor genes in cloned mice was indistinguishable from wild-type animals, indicating that irreversible changes to the DNA of olfactory neurons do not accompany receptor gene choice.

THE chromosome is a dynamic structure that undergoes complex changes that underlie the development and differentiated function of an organism. Alterations in chromosome structure include variation in the complement of regulatory proteins, covalent modifications in chromatin proteins or DNA, and in rare instances, DNA rearrangements[1]. The extent to which such chromosomal changes are reversible can be discerned by cloning experiments involving nuclear transfer. Thus far, cloning experiments using nuclei from post-mitotic cells that have irreversibly exited the cell cycle as part of their programme of differentiation have not generated viable embryos or mice[2,3]. These observations have led to the suggestion that post-mitotic cells might be refractory to epigenetic reprogramming or alternatively might have acquired changes in their DNA that could limit their developmental potential[4,5].

Directed DNA rearrangements are rarely observed as part of a normal differentiation programme and, in vertebrates, they have been described only for the generation of the diverse repertoire of antibodies and T-cell receptors[6-8]. Several observations have suggested

从嗅觉神经元克隆小鼠

编者按

截至 2004 年，包括绵羊和小鼠在内的多种哺乳动物已通过将供体 DNA 注射到去核卵细胞中被成功克隆。但在本文中，美国细胞生物学家鲁道夫·耶尼施及其同事使用从成熟嗅觉神经元中提取的供体 DNA 通过核移植获得可育的克隆小鼠。该研究表明，从已经停止分裂的特化细胞中提取的 DNA 可以重新进入细胞周期，并在核移植后重编程为胚胎样状态。克隆小鼠具有与正常小鼠无法区分的全系列有组织的气味受体基因，这表明在成熟的嗅觉神经元中选择特定的受体基因不会引起 DNA 的不可逆变化。

通过细胞核移植进行的克隆已成功地在包括小鼠在内的多种哺乳动物中进行。到目前为止，还没有报道称可以利用有丝分裂后的细胞（如神经元）克隆小鼠。在这里，我们通过将有丝分裂后的嗅觉神经元的细胞核转移到卵母细胞中，成功获得可育克隆小鼠。这些结果表明，有丝分裂后终末分化的神经元基因组可以重新进入细胞周期，并在核移植后重编程产生全能性。此外，克隆小鼠的气味受体基因表达模式和气味受体基因的组构与野生型动物没有显著区别，这表明嗅觉神经元 DNA 的不可逆变化不随受体基因的选择同时出现。

染色体是一种动态结构，经历复杂的变化，是生物发育和分化功能的基础。染色体结构的变化包括调节蛋白的结合，染色质蛋白或 DNA 中的共价修饰，以及在极少数情况下发生的 DNA 重排[1]。染色体变化的可逆程度可以通过涉及核移植的克隆实验确定。有丝分裂后的细胞不可逆地退出细胞周期，这是其分化程序的一部分。迄今为止，使用这种细胞的细胞核进行克隆实验，尚未获得存活的胚胎或小鼠[2,3]。这些观察结果表明，有丝分裂后的细胞可能难以进行表观遗传重编程，或者后天获得的 DNA 变化可能会限制其发育潜力[4,5]。

定向 DNA 重排很少作为正常分化过程的一部分被观察到，而在脊椎动物中，它们被描述成只发生在产生抗体和 T 细胞受体多样性过程中[6-8]。一些观察结果表

that post-mitotic neurons may also use irreversible DNA alterations to generate diversity. First, a population of neurons undergoes apoptosis in mice bearing mutations in the double-strand-break DNA-repair enzymes, which are also required for DNA rearrangements in lymphocytes[9,10]. Second, cortical neurons exhibit a higher incidence of aneuploidy than other cell types, although the functional significance of these changes is unknown[11,12]. These observations and the inability to clone mice from neuronal nuclei have led to models in which the DNA of post-mitotic neurons might undergo rearrangements to supply additional genetic diversity that may enhance neural function[4,5,13-15].

One particularly clear example of neuronal diversity is provided by the olfactory sensory epithelium. In the mouse, each of the 2,000,000 cells in the olfactory epithelium expresses only one of about 1,500 odorant receptor genes, such that the functional identity of a neuron is defined by the nature of the receptor it expresses[16]. Thus, the sensory epithelium consists of at least 1,500 neuronal types. The pattern of receptor expression is apparently random within one of four zones in the epithelium, suggesting that the choice of receptor gene may be stochastic[17,18]. One mechanism to permit the stochastic choice of a single receptor could involve DNA rearrangements[19,20].

Here we report the generation of fertile mouse clones by transferring the nuclei of post-mitotic olfactory neurons into enucleated oocytes. Thus, a post-mitotic nucleus can re-enter the cell cycle and be reprogrammed to totipotency. The DNA of mice derived from sensory neurons reveals no evidence for rearrangements of the expressed olfactory receptor gene. The pattern of receptor expression in these mice was indistinguishable from that of wild-type animals, indicating that irreversible changes in DNA do not accompany olfactory receptor gene choice.

Genetic Marking of Olfactory Sensory Neurons

Less than 1% of nuclear transfers result in the production of an embryonic stem (ES) cell line or live animal[1]. It is therefore difficult to identify with certainty the origin of the donor nucleus that contributed to the generation of a particular cloned animal[2]. This problem is particularly apparent in the olfactory epithelium, which contains mature sensory neurons intermingled with stem cells, neural progenitors and support cells. Therefore, we generated mice in which the endogenous olfactory marker protein (OMP) promoter drives simultaneous expression of OMP and Cre recombinase by inserting an internal ribosome entry site (IRES)-Cre cassette 3′ of the OMP stop codon. OMP is expressed only in mature olfactory sensory neurons (OSNs). When OMP–IRES-Cre mice are crossed to a reporter mouse strain (Z/EG), Cre expression catalyses the excision of a transcriptional stop sequence and results in green fluorescent protein (GFP) expression solely in mature OSNs (Fig. 1a and Methods). Transfer of marked OSN nuclei into oocytes should generate embryos in which every cell expresses GFP, as the Z/EG reporter uses the ubiquitous actin promoter.

明，有丝分裂后的神经元也可以利用不可逆的 DNA 变化来产生多样性。首先，一群神经元在带有双链断裂 DNA 修复酶突变的小鼠中经历细胞凋亡，该酶是淋巴细胞中 DNA 重排所必需的 [9,10]。其次，尽管这些变化的功能意义尚不清楚，但皮质神经元表现出比其他细胞类型更高的非整倍性发生率 [11,12]。这些观察结果和无法从神经元核中克隆小鼠的事实，促使新的模式被提出：有丝分裂后的神经元的 DNA 可经历重排以提供额外的遗传多样性来增强神经功能 [4,5,13-15]。

嗅觉上皮提供了一个特别清楚的神经元多样性的例子。在小鼠嗅觉上皮中约有 2,000,000 个细胞，每一个细胞仅表达大约 1,500 个气味受体基因中的一种，因而神经元的功能由所表达受体的性质决定 [16]。因此，感觉上皮由至少 1,500 种神经元类型组成。在上皮的四个区域中的某个区域内，受体表达的模式显然是随机的，这表明受体基因的选择可能是随机的 [17,18]。一种允许随机选择单一受体的机制可能涉及 DNA 重排 [19,20]。

在这里，我们报道通过将有丝分裂后的嗅觉神经元的细胞核移植到去核卵母细胞中产生的可育克隆小鼠。因此，有丝分裂后的细胞核可以重新进入细胞周期并被重编程和获得全能性。源自感觉神经元的小鼠 DNA 并未显示出其表达的嗅觉受体基因重排的证据。这些小鼠中受体表达的模式与野生型动物无法区分，表明 DNA 的不可逆变化不伴随嗅觉受体基因选择。

嗅觉神经元的遗传标记

只有不到 1% 的细胞核移植可以产生胚胎干细胞系或活体动物 [1]。因此很难确定克隆动物来源于哪个供体核 [2]。这个问题在嗅上皮中特别明显，嗅上皮含有成熟的感觉神经元，它们与干细胞、神经祖细胞和支持细胞混合在一起。因此，我们建立了一种小鼠模型，其中在内源性嗅觉标记蛋白（OMP）终止密码子的 3′ 后端插入了内部核糖体进入位点（IRES）-Cre 盒。这样 OMP 启动子同时驱动 OMP 和 Cre 重组酶的表达。OMP 仅在成熟的嗅觉神经元（OSN）中表达。当 OMP–IRES-Cre 小鼠与报告小鼠品系（Z/EG）杂交时，Cre 的表达催化了转录终止序列的切除，并导致仅在成熟 OSN 中表达绿色荧光蛋白（GFP）（图 1a 和方法）。将标记的 OSN 核转移到卵母细胞应该可以产生胚胎，并且因为 Z/EG 报告基因使用普遍存在的肌动蛋白启动子，胚胎中每个细胞都表达 GFP。

Fig. 1. Genetically marking post-mitotic OSNs. **a**, Donor animals carry one OMP–IRES-Cre allele and one copy of the Z/EG Cre reporter transgene. Cre expression in OSNs catalyses excision of the β-geo/stop cassette, resulting in selective GFP expression and genetic marking of mature OSNs. Thus, GFP⁺ neurons could be selectively chosen for nuclear transfer. **b**, Schematic diagram of the approximate laminar distribution of cell types in the mouse olfactory epithelium. **c–f**, Three-colour immunofluorescence staining. Blue, nuclear marker TOTO-3; green, GFP protein fluorescence (**c**, **d**) or antibody to GFP protein (**e**, **f**); red, antibodies to Cre recombinase (**c**), progenitor-specific marker MASH-1 (**d**), markers of dividing cells, BrdU (**e**) and Ki67 (**f**).

In mice bearing the OMP–IRES-Cre allele and the Z/EG reporter gene, GFP expression was observed only in the most mature OSNs. Sections through the entire olfactory epithelium of several adult mice revealed GFP expression in the regions that contain mature OSNs (Fig. 1b–f). Cell counts revealed no GFP⁺ cells in either the basal cell layers, where immature progenitors and stem cells reside, or in the apical support cell layer (0 of 835 GFP⁺ cells)[21,22]. Double immunostaining for GFP and Cre protein revealed that all GFP⁺ cells with visible nuclei also expressed Cre recombinase (599 of 599) (Fig. 1c). In addition, none of the MASH-1⁺ basal cell precursors of OSNs expressed GFP (0 of 350 MASH-1⁺ cells) (Fig. 1d). These results showed that GFP expression was restricted to mature sensory neurons.

We confirmed that the GFP⁺ mature OSNs were post-mitotic by injecting mice with 5-bromodeoxyuridine (BrdU) and staining the olfactory epithelium with anti-BrdU and GFP antibodies (Fig. 1e). BrdU incorporation was observed in the more basal GFP-negative layers as well as in rare support cells in the apical layers. Examination of more than 3,000 GFP⁺ cells never revealed a GFP⁺ BrdU⁺ cell. In a separate experiment, labelling with an antibody specific to Ki67, a protein restricted to the nuclei of dividing cells, revealed no staining coincident with GFP[23,24] (Fig. 1f). These data show that GFP⁺ cells in the olfactory epithelium of donor animals are mature post-mitotic OSNs.

图 1. 有丝分裂后 OSN 的遗传标记。**a**，供体动物携带一个 OMP–IRES-Cre 等位基因和一个 Z/EG Cre 报道转基因拷贝。OSN 中 Cre 的表达催化 β-geo/终止盒的切除，导致选择性 GFP 表达和成熟 OSN 的遗传标记。因此，可以选择性地使用 GFP⁺ 神经元进行核转移。**b**，小鼠嗅上皮各细胞类型近似层状分布的示意图。**c ~ f**，三色免疫荧光染色。蓝色，核标记物 TOTO-3；绿色，GFP 蛋白荧光（**c**、**d**）或 GFP 蛋白抗体（**e**、**f**）；红色，Cre 重组酶的抗体（**c**），祖细胞特异性标记物 MASH-1（**d**），分裂细胞标记物 BrdU（**e**）和 Ki67（**f**）。

　　在携带 OMP–IRES-Cre 等位基因和 Z/EG 报告基因的小鼠中，仅在最成熟的 OSN 中观察到 GFP 表达。数只成年小鼠的整个嗅上皮切片显示，GFP 在含有成熟 OSN 的区域中表达（图 1b ~ 1f）。细胞计数显示，无论是存在未成熟祖细胞和干细胞的基底细胞层，抑或顶端支持细胞层中均没有 GFP⁺ 细胞（835 个细胞中 GFP⁺ 细胞有 0 个）[21,22]。对 GFP 和 Cre 蛋白的双重免疫染色显示，所有具有可见核的 GFP⁺ 细胞均表达 Cre 重组酶（599/599）（图 1c）。此外，OSN 的 MASH-1⁺ 基底细胞前体均未表达 GFP（350 个 MASH-1⁺ 细胞中 GFP⁺ 细胞有 0 个）（图 1d）。这些结果表明 GFP 表达仅限于成熟的感觉神经元。

　　我们通过向小鼠注射 5–溴脱氧尿苷（BrdU）并用抗 BrdU 抗体和 GFP 抗体染色嗅上皮，来证实 GFP⁺ 的成熟 OSN 是经过有丝分裂的（图 1e）。在较多的 GFP 阴性基底细胞和较少的顶层支撑细胞中也观察到 BrdU 整合。检查 3,000 多个 GFP⁺ 细胞，并未发现一个 GFP⁺ BrdU⁺ 细胞。在另一个实验中，用仅使分裂细胞核显色的 Ki67 特异性抗体标记细胞，显示没有 GFP⁺ Ki67⁺ 细胞（图 1f）[23,24]。这些数据显示供体动物嗅上皮中的 GFP⁺ 细胞是成熟的有丝分裂后的 OSN。

Cloning Mice from Neuronal Nuclei

We asked whether the nucleus of a post-mitotic OSN could re-enter the cell cycle and direct preimplantation development. We dissociated the olfactory epithelium and picked GFP-expressing OSNs for nuclear transfer into enucleated oocytes (Fig. 2a)[25-29]. Of the 352 embryos generated, 48 (14%) developed to the blastocyst stage (Table 1). All blastocysts expressed GFP, demonstrating that they were derived from the mature OSN donor nuclei (Fig. 2b). We confirmed that Cre expression in the OSNs caused constitutive GFP expression after nuclear transfer by generating blastocysts with GFP-negative cells from the donor mice. As expected, none of these blastocysts expressed GFP, demonstrating that Cre is not aberrantly expressed as a result of nuclear transfer or subsequent cloning procedures.

Fig. 2. Mice derived from OSN nuclei. **a**, Strategy to generate cloned ES cell lines and OSN-derived mice by tetraploid complementation with cloned ES cells. **b**, **c**, Bright-field and fluorescence images of nuclear

通过神经元细胞的核移植克隆小鼠

我们探究有丝分裂后 OSN 的细胞核是否可以重新进入细胞周期并指导胚胎植入前发育。我们裂解了嗅上皮组织，并选择了表达 GFP 的 OSN，将其核移植到去核卵母细胞中（图 2a）[25-29]。在产生的 352 个胚胎中，48 个（14%）发育到囊胚期（表 1）。所有囊胚均表达 GFP，证明它们来自成熟的 OSN 供体细胞核（图 2b）。我们通过对来自供体的 GFP 阴性细胞进行核移植产生囊胚验证了组成型 GFP 表达是由 OSN 中的 Cre 表达所致。正如预期的那样，这些囊胚中没有一个表达 GFP，这表明 Cre 不会因核移植或随后的克隆程序而异常表达。

图 2. 源自 OSN 细胞核的小鼠。**a**，获得克隆 ES 细胞系和通过四倍体补偿法获得 OSN 衍生小鼠的方法。**b**、**c**，由 OSN 细胞核产生的核移植囊胚（**b**）和 OSN3 衍生 ES 细胞（**c**）的明场和荧光图像。**d**，通过

transfer blastocysts (**b**) and OSN3 ES cells (**c**) produced from OSN nuclei. **d**, A P0.5 mouse produced by tetraploid complementation with OSN3 ES cells (top) and a P0.5 C57/B6 control (bottom). **e–h**, *In situ* hybridization on the olfactory epithelium of mice wholly derived from OSN3 ES cells with probes for odorant receptors P2 (**e**), M50 (**f**), I7 (**g**) and M71 (**h**). **i**, **j**, Contribution of GFP⁺ OSN2 ES cells to the olfactory epithelium (**i**) and olfactory bulb (**j**) of chimaeras generated by injecting OSN2 ES cells into diploid blastocysts. Several representative glomeruli are demarcated with asterisks.

Table 1. Production of ES cell lines and mice by nuclear transfer

Donor cells	Oocytes surviving (% injected)	Oocytes activated (% surviving)	Two-cell embryos to oviduct (% oocytes activated)	Blastocysts (% oocytes activated)	ES cell lines (% oocytes activated)	Alive at term (% into oviduct)
OSNs	508 (88)	352 (69)	—	48 (14)	3 (1)	—
P2 OSNs	261 (95)	141 (54)	—	18 (13)	2 (1)	—
P2SN1 ES	50 (95)	38 (76)	14 (37)	—	—	1 (7)
P2SN2 ES	47 (90)	37 (79)	18 (49)	—	—	1 (6)

The 48 GFP⁺ blastocysts were used to generate ES cell lines and three gave rise to colonies that resembled ES cells (OSN1–3). All three lines expressed GFP, and Southern blotting confirmed the predicted genomic rearrangement at the Z/EG locus (Fig. 2c and data not shown). When the OSN2 and OSN3 ES cells were injected into diploid blastocysts, they contributed extensively to all tissues of the resulting chimaeras, including the germ line (Fig. 2i, j and data not shown).

We injected these cloned ES cells into tetraploid blastocysts to perform the most stringent test of their developmental potency (Table 2). Tetraploid embryo complementation generates an "ES-fetus" in which all embryonic lineages are derived from the injected ES cells, whereas the extraembryonic lineages develop from the host blastocyst[29,30]. Both OSN2 and OSN3 ES cells gave rise to embryos of embryonic day (E) 19.5 that expressed GFP ubiquitously (Table 2 and Fig. 2d). Mice derived from OSN3 survived to adulthood, were fertile and were overtly normal. Histological examination of serial sections through their brains revealed no obvious abnormalities (data not shown). These results indicate that the genome of a post-mitotic, terminally differentiated neuron can be reprogrammed after nuclear transfer and direct the development of all embryonic lineages.

Table 2. Mice produced from sensory neurons by tetraploid embryo complementation

ES cell line	Receptor expressed	Tetraploid blastocysts injected	Mice alive at term (% injected)	Breathing normally (% injected)	Cross-fostered	Survival to maturity (% fostered)
OSN1	?	137	0	0	0	0
OSN2	?	160	1 (1)	0	0	0
OSN3	?	273	49 (18)	29 (11)	21	17 (81)
P2SN1	P2	89	16 (18)	16 (100)	13	12 (92)
P2SN2	P2	151	31 (21)	28 (90)	28	22 (78)

OSN3 ES 细胞利用四倍体补偿法产生的 P0.5 小鼠(上图)和 P0.5 C57/B6 对照小鼠(下图)。**e～h**,用针对气味受体 P2(**e**)、M50(**f**)、I7(**g**)和 M71(**h**)的探针,在完全来自 OSN3 衍生 ES 细胞的小鼠嗅上皮进行原位杂交的结果。**i**、**j**,GFP+ OSN2 衍生 ES 细胞对通过将其注射到二倍体囊胚中获得的嵌合体小鼠嗅上皮(**i**)和嗅球(**j**)的贡献。几个代表性的嗅小球用星号标出。

表 1. 通过核移植获得 ES 细胞系和小鼠的情况

供体细胞	存活卵母细胞数(% 占总注射数百分比)	激活卵母细胞数(% 占总存活数百分比)	进入输卵管的双细胞胚胎数(% 占总激活卵母细胞数百分比)	囊胚数(% 占总激活卵母细胞数百分比)	ES 细胞系数(% 占总激活卵母细胞数百分比)	实验过程中存活(% 占总进入输卵管胚胎数百分比)
OSNs	508 (88)	352 (69)	—	48 (14)	3 (1)	—
P2 OSNs	261 (95)	141 (54)	—	18 (13)	2 (1)	—
P2SN1 ES	50 (95)	38 (76)	14 (37)	—	—	1 (7)
P2SN2 ES	47 (90)	37 (79)	18 (49)	—	—	1 (6)

48 个 GFP+ 囊胚用于获得 ES 细胞系,其中 3 个产生类似 ES 细胞的集落(OSN1～OSN3)。所有三个品系都表达 GFP,Southern 印迹证实了之前预测的在 Z/EG 基因座处发生的基因组重排(图 2c,未显示数据)。当将 OSN2 和 OSN3 ES 细胞注射到二倍体囊胚中时,它们对所得嵌合体的所有组织(包括生殖细胞系)产生了广泛嵌合(图 2i、2j,未显示数据)。

我们将这些克隆的 ES 细胞注射到四倍体囊胚中,以对其发育潜力进行最严格的测试(表 2)。四倍体胚胎补偿法获得"ES 胎儿",其中所有胚胎细胞谱系来自注射的 ES 细胞,而胚外细胞谱系来自宿主囊胚[29,30]。OSN2 和 OSN3 的 ES 细胞均获得可长至 19.5 天的胚胎,其细胞普遍表达 GFP(表 2 和图 2d)。源自 OSN3 的小鼠存活至成年,可育并且明显正常。大脑连续切片的组织学检查显示没有明显的异常(数据未显示)。这些结果表明,有丝分裂后终末分化的神经元的基因组可以在核移植后重编程,并指导所有胚胎细胞谱系的发育。

表 2. 感觉神经元通过四倍胚胎互补法获得小鼠的情况

ES 细胞系	受体表达	四倍体囊胚注射数	实验过程中小鼠存活数(% 占总注射数百分比)	正常呼吸的小鼠数(% 占总注射数百分比)	交叉抚育小鼠数	存活至性成熟小鼠数(% 占交叉抚育百分比)
OSN1	?	137	0	0	0	0
OSN2	?	160	1 (1)	0	0	0
OSN3	?	273	49 (18)	29 (11)	21	17 (81)
P2SN1	P2	89	16 (18)	16 (100)	13	12 (92)
P2SN2	P2	151	31 (21)	28 (90)	28	22 (78)

Odorant Receptor Expression in Cloned Mice

We examined the patterns of receptor gene expression in the olfactory epithelium of the cloned mice generated by tetraploid complementation. If irreversible genetic rearrangements are required for receptor choice we might expect an altered profile of receptor expression in animals cloned from an OSN. In the simplest model, a rearrangement involving one receptor gene might persist in all neurons such that all neurons will express the same receptor. This scenario was observed in mice derived from a B-cell nucleus, in which all B cells expressed the same immunoglobulin gene[28]. We therefore asked whether sensory neurons from cloned mice express a single receptor or a repertoire of receptor genes. We performed *in situ* hybridization on the olfactory epithelium of mice derived from OSN3 ES cells using probes specific for seven different odorant receptors (Fig. 2e–h and data not shown). The pattern of expression of all seven receptors was indistinguishable from control mice, excluding a simple model of gene rearrangement that would result in the expression of a single receptor gene in all OSNs.

As a neuron expresses a receptor from only one of the two alleles, it remained possible that a rearranged receptor gene expressed in the donor nucleus would be expressed in only half of the sensory neurons. We therefore analysed the repertoire of receptors expressed by polymerase chain reaction with reverse transcription (RT–PCR) to determine whether a single receptor transcript was enriched in the epithelium of OSN-derived mice. RNA from the olfactory epithelium of cloned animals was used in RT–PCR reactions with degenerate primers that recognize conserved motifs present in the majority of odorant receptors. Forty-four PCR products were cloned and restriction digest analysis indicated that they encoded 38 different receptors. Sequence analysis of 20 of these PCR clones revealed that they encoded 20 different receptors, which were located in seven clusters on six different chromosomes. This suggests that a single odorant receptor did not predominate in the olfactory epithelium of mice derived from OSN nuclei.

One additional assay for the diversity of odorant receptor expression is based on the observation that neurons expressing a given receptor, although randomly distributed within a zone of the epithelium, converge on two spatially invariant loci or glomeruli in the olfactory bulb[18,31]. If half of the OSNs from cloned mice expressed the same receptor, then their axonal projections should preferentially innervate a small set of glomeruli. Analysis of the olfactory bulb of chimaeric mice produced with OSN2 ES cells revealed that the OSN2-derived GFP+ cells innervated most, if not all glomeruli, with no glomerulus receiving predominant input (Fig. 2i, j). These results show that the sensory neurons of mice cloned from an OSN that had expressed a single receptor can express a large repertoire of odorant receptor genes.

克隆小鼠中的气味受体表达

我们检查了由四倍体补偿法获得的克隆小鼠的嗅上皮中受体基因表达的模式。如果受体选择需要不可逆的基因重排，我们可能会从 OSN 克隆的动物中发现受体表达的改变。在最简单的模型中，涉及一个受体基因的重排可能在所有神经元中持续存在，使得所有神经元都表达相同的受体。在源自 B 细胞核的小鼠中观察到这种情况；在这些小鼠中，所有 B 细胞表达相同的免疫球蛋白基因[28]。因此，我们想知道克隆小鼠的感觉神经元是表达单一受体还是表达受体基因库。我们使用对七种不同气味受体特异的探针对源自 OSN3 的 ES 细胞的小鼠的嗅上皮进行原位杂交（图 2e～2h，未显示数据）。所有七种受体的表达模式与对照小鼠无法区分，而基因重排的简单模型将导致所有 OSN 中表达单一受体基因，因此排除了这种简单模型。

由于神经元仅从两个等位基因中选择一个表达受体，因此在供体细胞核中表达的重排受体基因仍然可能仅在一半感觉神经元中表达。因此，我们通过逆转录聚合酶链反应（RT–PCR）分析了表达的受体库，以确定单个受体转录物是否富集在 OSN 衍生小鼠的上皮细胞中。来自克隆动物嗅上皮的 RNA 用于 RT–PCR 反应，其中简并引物识别大多数气味受体中存在的保守基序。克隆得到 44 种 PCR 产物，限制性消化分析表明它们编码了 38 种不同的受体。对这些 PCR 克隆中的 20 个进行序列分析，发现它们编码了 20 种不同的受体，这些受体位于 6 个不同染色体上的 7 个簇中。这表明源自 OSN 核的小鼠的嗅上皮，并非只表达单一气味受体。

气味受体表达多样性的另一种测定是基于以下观察：表达给定受体的神经元虽然随机分布在上皮特定区域内，但会富集在嗅球中两个空间位置不变的基因座或嗅小球上[18,31]。如果来自克隆小鼠的 OSN 中有一半表达相同的受体，那么它们的轴突投射应该优先支配一小组嗅小球。对 OSN2 的 ES 细胞衍生的嵌合小鼠的嗅球分析显示，OSN2 衍生的 GFP+ 细胞支配绝大多数嗅小球，没有嗅小球接受（单一受体对应的）优先支配（图 2i、2j）。这些结果表明，由表达单一受体的 OSN 克隆获得的小鼠，其感觉神经元可以表达大量的气味受体基因。

Mice Cloned from Neurons Expressing the P2 Receptor

The previous experiments suggest that irreversible rearrangements are not required for receptor gene expression. Because these experiments did not allow the prospective identification of the receptor gene expressed by the donor OSN nucleus, we were unable to examine its pattern of expression or its DNA sequence in the cloned mice. Neurons that express the P2 odorant receptor were marked by introducing an IRES directing the translation of GFP into the 3′ untranslated region of the P2 gene (P2–IRES-GFP)[32]. These mice were crossed with strains carrying both the OMP–IRES-Cre alteration and a reporter allele in which the *Rosa26* promoter is separated from a weak GFP gene by a LoxP-flanked transcriptional terminator[33] (Fig. 3a). Mice carrying the P2–IRES-GFP, OMP–IRES-Cre and *Rosa26*–LoxP-Stop-LoxP–weak GFP reporter genes exhibited intense GFP fluorescence in the approximately 0.1% of the OSNs that expressed the P2–IRES-GFP allele, whereas all other neurons appeared dark (Fig. 3b). *Rosa26*-driven GFP was present in mature OSNs, but the GFP signal was too weak to be detected by direct fluorescence. No green cells were observed in animals that contained only the OMP–IRES-Cre and *Rosa26*–LoxP-Stop-LoxP–weak GFP genes (Fig. 3c). Evidence for Cre-mediated excision of the transcription terminator and the resulting expression of weak GFP in mature OSNs was detected by amplifying the signal with GFP antibodies (data not shown).

Fluorescent cells expressing the P2–IRES-GFP allele were picked and their nuclei were injected into enucleated oocytes (Fig. 3d). Eighteen blastocysts developed from 141 reconstructed oocytes generating two ES cell lines: P2SN1 and P2SN2 (Table 1). PCR analysis revealed Cre-mediated excision at the *Rosa26* locus in both cell lines, indicating their origin from cloned nuclei of post-mitotic OSNs (Supplementary Fig. 1). Tetraploid embryos injected with P2SN1 and P2SN2 cells resulted in the birth of multiple viable pups that survived to adulthood (Table 2). These mice exhibited no gross anatomic or behavioural abnormalities and were fertile. PCR analyses of non-neuronal tissues revealed recombination at the *Rosa26* reporter allele, indicating that the cloned mice were derived from mature OMP⁺ OSNs (data not shown). In addition, we detected the weak *Rosa26*-driven GFP expression by *in situ* hybridization in both the olfactory epithelium and non-neuronal tissues, demonstrating genetic activation of the reporter (Fig. 3g, h and data not shown).

The expression pattern of P2–IRES-GFP in clones was indistinguishable from that of control donor animals. Approximately 0.1% of the neurons expressed GFP at a high level within zone II of the epithelium (Fig. 3e). The GFP-expressing neurons projected axons to one medial and one lateral glomerulus in the olfactory bulb (Fig. 3f). Moreover, the P2–IRES-GFP allele was expressed at a frequency approximately equal to that of the unmodified P2 allele. *In situ* hybridization was performed on sections through the olfactory epithelium with RNA probes specific to GFP- and P2-coding sequences (Fig. 3g–j). The number of GFP-expressing cells in one section was roughly 50% of the number of P2-expressing cells found in neighbouring sections ($45 \pm 14\%$, s.d.), revealing no preference

由表达 P2 受体的神经元克隆小鼠

先前的实验表明，受体基因表达并不需要不可逆的重排。因为这些实验不允许对供体 OSN 细胞核表达的受体基因进行前瞻性鉴定，所以我们无法检查克隆小鼠中的受体表达模式或其 DNA 序列。表达 P2 气味受体的神经元通过在 P2 基因的 3′ 非翻译区插入 IRES 来标记，该 IRES 可以指导 GFP 翻译（P2–IRES-GFP）[32]。将这些小鼠与同时携带 OMP–IRES-Cre 变异并报告等位基因的小鼠杂交，该报告基因中 *Rosa26* 启动子和弱 GFP 基因通过 LoxP 中间的转录终止子分开 [33]（图 3a）。携带 P2-IRES-GFP，OMP–IRES-Cre 和 *Rosa26*–LoxP-Stop-LoxP– 弱 GFP 报告基因的小鼠在表达 P2–IRES-GFP 等位基因的 OSN 中大约有 0.1% 表现出强烈的 GFP 荧光，而其他所有神经元都很暗不发荧光（图 3b）。*Rosa26* 驱动的 GFP 存在于成熟的 OSN 中，但 GFP 信号太弱而不能通过直接荧光检测到。在仅含有 OMP–IRES-Cre 和 *Rosa26*–LoxP-Stop-LoxP– 弱 GFP 基因的动物中未观察到绿色细胞（图 3c）。用 GFP 抗体扩增信号来检测 Cre 介导的转录终止子切除，及其导致的成熟 OSN 中弱 GFP 表达（数据未显示）。

挑选表达 P2–IRES-GFP 等位基因的荧光细胞，并将它们的细胞核注射到去核卵母细胞中（图 3d）。从 141 个重建的卵母细胞发育出 18 个囊胚，产生了两个 ES 细胞系：P2SN1 和 P2SN2（表 1）。PCR 分析显示两种细胞系中均出现 Cre 介导的 *Rosa26* 基因座处的切除，表明它们来自有丝分裂后 OSN 的克隆核（补充图 1）。注射 P2SN1 和 P2SN2 细胞到四倍体囊胚获得存活至成年的多个活幼崽（表 2）。这些小鼠没有表现出严重的解剖学异常或行为异常，且可育。非神经元组织的 PCR 分析揭示了 *Rosa26* 报告等位基因的重组，表明克隆的小鼠源自成熟的 OMP⁺ OSN（数据未显示）。此外，我们通过嗅上皮和非神经组织中的原位杂交检测到弱 *Rosa26* 驱动的 GFP 表达，证明了报告基因的遗传激活（图 3g、3h，未显示数据）。

克隆中 P2–IRES-GFP 的表达模式与对照供体动物的表达模式不可区分。大约 0.1% 的神经元在上皮区 II 内以高水平表达 GFP（图 3e）。表达 GFP 的神经元将轴突投射到嗅球中的一个内侧嗅小球和一个旁侧嗅小球（图 3f）。此外，P2–IRES-GFP 等位基因的表达频率大约等于未修饰的 P2 等位基因的表达频率。使用对 GFP 和 P2 编码序列特异的 RNA 探针对嗅上皮切片进行原位杂交（图 3g ~ 3j）。在一个切片中表达 GFP 的细胞数量大约是在相邻切片中发现的表达 P2 的细胞数量的 50%（45%±14%，标准差），表明 P2–IRES-GFP 等位基因并不优先表达。此外，用对另

for the expression of the P2–IRES-GFP allele. Furthermore, *in situ* hybridization with probes specific to six additional olfactory receptors revealed similar expression patterns in control and cloned mice (Fig. 3k, l and data not shown).

Fig. 3. Mice produced from OSNs expressing the P2 odorant receptor. **a**, Strategy to label P2 sensory neurons with GFP and genetically mark mature OSNs. **b**, **c**, Immunofluorescence staining with nuclear marker TOTO-3 (blue), GFP fluorescence (green) and antibodies to Cre recombinase (red) of the olfactory epithelium of donor animals heterozygous for the P2–IRES-GFP, OMP–IRES-Cre and *Rosa26*–LoxP-Stop-LoxP–weak GFP alleles (**b**) or of control animals heterozygous for the OMP–IRES-Cre and *Rosa26*–LoxP-Stop-LoxP–weak GFP alleles (**c**). **d**, Bright-field and fluorescence merged image of picking a P2–IRES-GFP⁺ neuron from the dissociated olfactory epithelium of a donor for nuclear transfer. **e**, **f**, GFP fluorescence (green) and TOTO-3⁺ nuclei (blue) visualized in sections of the olfactory epithelium (**e**) and olfactory bulb (**f**) of an animal generated by tetraploid complementation with P2SN1 ES cells. **g**–**l**, *In situ* hybridization on olfactory epithelium sections derived entirely from P2SN2 ES cells (**g**, **i**, **k**) and a wild-type control (**h**, **j**, **l**) with probes for GFP (**g**, **h**), P2 receptor (**i**, **j**) and I7 receptor (**k**, **l**).

We also performed Southern blotting, PCR and genome sequencing to examine the organization of the P2–IRES-GFP allele in the chromosome of cloned mice in an effort to detect potential DNA rearrangement events. If choice of a single receptor gene involved gene conversion into a single active locus, cells expressing the P2–IRES-GFP allele might contain a second copy of this allele at the active locus. Southern blotting to distinguish

外六种气味受体特异的探针进行的原位杂交揭示了对照和克隆小鼠中相似的受体表达模式(图 3k、3l，未显示数据)。

图 3. 由表达 P2 气味受体的 OSN 获得的小鼠。**a**，用 GFP 标记 P2 感觉神经元和遗传标记成熟 OSN 的方法。**b**、**c**，用核标记物 TOTO-3(蓝色)、GFP 荧光(绿色)和 Cre 重组酶抗体(红色)对嗅上皮进行免疫荧光染色。嗅上皮分别来自携带 P2–IRES–GFP、OMP–IRES–Cre 和 *Rosa26*–LoxP-Stop-LoxP– 弱 GFP 等位基因的杂合供体动物(**b**)和携带 OMP–IRES-Cre 和 *Rosa26*–LoxP-Stop-LoxP– 弱 GFP 等位基因的杂合对照动物(**c**)。**d**，从供体裂解的嗅上皮细胞中挑选 P2–IRES–GFP+ 神经元进行核移植的明场和荧光合并图像。**e**、**f**，GFP 荧光(绿色)和 TOTO-3+ 细胞核(蓝色)在通过 P2SN1 ES 细胞与四倍体囊胚补偿得到的动物嗅上皮(**e**)和嗅球(**f**)切片中可视化。**g~l**，对完全来源于 P2SN2 ES 细胞的嗅上皮切片(**g**、**i**、**k**)和野生型对照切片(**h**、**j**、**l**)进行原位杂交，探针为 GFP(**g**、**h**)、P2 受体(**i**、**j**)和 I7 受体(**k**、**l**)。

我们还进行了 Southern 印迹、PCR 和基因组测序，以检查克隆小鼠染色体中 P2–IRES-GFP 等位基因的组构，来检测潜在的 DNA 重排事件。如果单个受体基因的选择涉及基因转变成单个活性基因座，则表达 P2–IRES-GFP 等位基因的细胞可能在活性基因座处含有该等位基因的第二个拷贝。用于区分修饰的克隆小鼠 P2–IRES-the modified P2–IRES-GFP allele from the unmodified endogenous P2 allele in DNA from control and cloned mice revealed only two bands of equal intensity, suggesting that gene conversion into an active locus does not accompany olfactory receptor gene choice (Supplementary Fig. S2). In addition, Southern blot analyses using multiple DNA probes to examine the organization of about 60 kilobases (kb) of DNA 5' and 3' of the P2 coding sequence failed to detect any differences between donor, control and cloned animals (Supplementary Fig. S3). Sequencing of 10 kb 3' of the P2 coding sequence showed that the P2–IRES-GFP allele was identical in donor, control and cloned mice (data not shown). These results suggest that irreversible changes in DNA do not accompany choice of the P2 odorant receptor gene.

Totipotency of Neuronal Nuclei

The two-step cloning procedure used to produce mice from neuronal nuclei generates mice in which the neuronally derived ES cells give rise to all embryonic tissues, whereas cells from the tetraploid host blastocyst contribute to the embryonic trophectoderm[30]. Thus, neither this work nor the cloning of lymphocytes via an ES cell intermediate[28] demonstrated the totipotency of a nucleus from a terminally differentiated cell[34]. To demonstrate totipotency of mature OSN nuclei, we transplanted nuclei from P2SN1 and P2SN2 ES cells into enucleated oocytes[29]. The resulting embryos were cultured for 24 h and transferred to pseudopregnant recipients (Table 1). Upon caesarean section of the recipients, we recovered full-term pups from both the P2SN1 and P2SN2 cell lines. These pups had enlarged placentas (P2SN1, 0.35 g; P2SN2, 0.40 g) but displayed no overt anatomical or behavioural abnormalities, were fertile and survived to adulthood, consistent with previous cloning experiments[29]. These observations demonstrate that nuclei of terminally differentiated olfactory neurons can be reprogrammed to totipotency, directing development of both embryonic and extraembryonic lineages.

Discussion

We have asked whether the nucleus of a post-mitotic olfactory sensory neuron can re-enter the cell cycle and undergo reprogramming to direct development of a mouse. ES cell lines were generated from OSN nuclei at frequencies similar to those obtained with differentiated lymphoid cells that can be induced to proliferate under physiological conditions[2]. Thus the mechanisms that lead to the cell-cycle exit and irreversible mitotic arrest that accompany neural differentiation do not result from irreversible epigenetic or genetic events that would interfere with nuclear totipotency.

The differentiation of neurons requires that neural progenitors exit the cell cycle before a restriction point late in G1. This decision is governed by a complex balance of cell-cycle regulators and proneural genes that drive cells into G0 and prevent them from progressing beyond the restriction point[35]. Although most cells that enter G0 can re-enter the cycle on

GFP 等位基因与来自对照小鼠 DNA 中未修饰的内源性 P2 等位基因的 Southern 印迹仅显示两条相等强度的条带，表明基因转变为活性基因座不伴随气味受体基因的选择（补充图 S2）。此外，使用多个 DNA 探针对 P2 编码序列 5′ 和 3′ 端约 60 千碱基 (kb) 的 DNA 进行 Southern 印迹分析，未能检测到供体、对照和克隆动物之间的任何差异（补充图 S3）。对 P2 编码序列 3′ 端的 10 kb 进行测序，显示 P2–IRES-GFP 等位基因在供体、对照和克隆小鼠中是相同的（数据未显示）。这些结果表明 DNA 的不可逆变化不伴随 P2 气味受体基因的选择。

神经元细胞核的全能性

使用两步克隆法从神经元细胞核获得的小鼠中，神经元衍生的 ES 细胞发育为所有胚胎组织，而来自四倍体宿主囊胚的细胞发育成滋养外胚层 [30]。因此，这一工作和通过 ES 细胞中间体克隆淋巴细胞 [28] 都不能证明来自终末分化细胞的细胞核具有全能性 [34]。为了证明成熟 OSN 细胞核的全能性，我们将 P2SN1 和 P2SN2 衍生 ES 细胞的细胞核移植到去核卵母细胞中 [29]。将得到的胚胎培养 24 小时并转移到假孕雌鼠中（表 1）。在对雌鼠进行剖宫产后，我们获得了来源于 P2SN1 和 P2SN2 细胞系的足月幼崽。这些幼仔具有大于常态的胎盘（P2SN1，0.35 g；P2SN2，0.40 g），但没有显示出明显的解剖学异常或行为异常，具有生育能力并存活至成年期，与先前的克隆实验结果一致 [29]。这些观察结果表明，终末分化的嗅觉神经元的细胞核可以重编程恢复全能性，指导胚胎和胚胎外细胞系的发育。

讨　　论

我们提出疑问，有丝分裂后嗅觉神经元的细胞核是否可以重新进入细胞周期并进行重编程以指导小鼠的发育。ES 细胞系由 OSN 细胞核产生，该过程的频率与用分化的淋巴细胞获得 ES 细胞系的频率相似，后者可在生理条件下可诱导增殖 [2]。因此，伴随着神经分化，导致细胞周期退出和不可逆有丝分裂停滞的机制不是由不可逆的表观遗传或遗传事件引起的，尽管这些事件会干扰核的全能性。

神经元的分化需要神经祖细胞在 G1 晚期的限制点之前退出细胞周期。这一行为受细胞周期调节因子和原神经基因的复杂平衡调控，原神经基因使细胞进入 G0 并阻止它们越过限制点 [35]。虽然大多数进入 G0 的细胞可以在适当的刺激下重新进

appropriate stimulation, neurons normally undergo an irreversible mitotic arrest. Whatever mechanisms keep neurons in a post-mitotic state, our experiments demonstrate that they can be overcome in the environment of the egg.

The nervous system contains a diverse array of neural cell types and this diversity is reflected by distinct patterns of gene expression in different neurons. The regulation of gene expression by DNA rearrangements is rare but this mechanism has nonetheless been suggested to explain the diversity inherent in complex nervous systems[36]. DNA recombination events provide *Saccharomyces cerevisiae*, trypanosomes and lymphocytes with a mechanism to stochastically express one member of a set of genes that modulate cellular interactions with the environment. One attractive feature shared by gene rearrangements in trypanosomes and lymphocytes is that gene choice by recombination is a random event. Cells that undergo correct or successful rearrangements are then afforded a selective survival advantage. The stochastic rearrangement of one gene from a gene family and subsequent selection could also provide a mechanism to generate the vast diversity of neuronal cell types. In this manner, neurons with subtly different genotypes would exhibit the array of neuronal phenotypes required for a functioning nervous system.

The olfactory sensory epithelium provides a clear example of neuronal diversity, and it has been suggested that this diversity is generated by stochastic DNA rearrangement events[19,20]. However, efforts to examine the DNA of OSNs expressing a given receptor have been seriously hampered by the inability to obtain homogeneous populations of neurons or clonal cell lines in which each cell expresses the same receptor. We have addressed this problem by generating cloned ES cell lines and mice derived from the nuclei of olfactory sensory neurons expressing the P2 receptor. Analyses of the sequence and organization of the DNA surrounding the expressed P2 allele from cloned ES cells and mice revealed no evidence for either gene conversion or local transpositions at the P2 locus. These results concur with fluorescence *in situ* hybridization studies showing that gene conversion into an active locus is an unlikely mechanism for odorant receptor expression[37]. In addition, the pattern of receptor gene expression in the sensory epithelium of cloned mice was wild type; multiple odorant receptor genes are expressed without preference for the P2 allele expressed in the donor nucleus.

These data demonstrate that the mechanism responsible for the choice of a single odorant receptor gene does not involve irreversible changes in DNA. More dynamic, reversible recombination events might accompany odorant receptor gene choice, but this is unlikely given the current data. Our results, in combination with experiments showing that the expression of various odorant receptor transgenes is influenced by proximal sequence elements, are consistent with epigenetic models of odorant receptor choice[37-42]. In a broader context, the generation of fertile cloned mice that are anatomically and behaviourally indistinguishable from wild-type mice indicates that olfactory sensory neurons do not undergo other irreversible DNA rearrangements that would interfere with either the development or function of the nervous system during adult life.

入细胞周期，但神经元通常会发生不可逆的有丝分裂停滞。无论使神经元保持在有丝分裂后的状态的机制是什么，我们的实验证明神经元可以在卵细胞的环境中重新进入细胞周期。

　　神经系统包含多种神经细胞类型，这种多样性通过不同神经元中不同的基因表达模式反映出来。通过 DNA 重排调节基因表达是罕见的，但这种机制仍被建议用于解释复杂神经系统固有的多样性[36]。DNA 重组能够使酿酒酵母、锥虫和淋巴细胞随机表达调节细胞与环境相互作用的一组基因中的一个。锥虫和淋巴细胞中基因重排共有一个明显特征，即通过重组导致的基因选择是随机事件。之后，经历正确或成功重排的细胞具有选择性存活优势。来自基因家族的一个基因的随机重排和随后的选择也可以提供产生大量多样的神经元细胞类型的机制。以这种方式，具有微妙不同基因型的神经元将表现出功能性神经系统所需的多种神经元表型。

　　嗅觉上皮提供了一个神经元多样性的明显例子，并且已经表明这种多样性是由随机 DNA 重排事件造成的[19,20]。然而，由于无法获得其中每个细胞表达相同受体的均质神经元群或克隆细胞系，所以一直难以对表达给定受体的 OSN 的 DNA 进行检测。我们通过用表达 P2 受体的嗅觉神经元细胞核获得克隆的 ES 细胞系和小鼠来解决这个问题。对来自克隆的 ES 细胞和小鼠的表达的 P2 等位基因周围的 DNA 的序列和组构的分析显示，在 P2 基因座处没有发生基因转变或局部转座。这些结果与荧光原位杂交研究一致，表明基因转变为活性基因座不太可能是气味受体表达的机制[37]。此外，克隆小鼠感觉上皮细胞中受体基因表达的模式为野生型；表达多种气味受体基因而并不优先表达在供体细胞核中表达的 P2 等位基因。

　　这些数据表明，负责选择单一气味受体基因的机制不涉及 DNA 的不可逆变化。更活跃的、可逆的重组事件可能伴随气味受体基因选择，但鉴于目前的数据，这也不太可能。我们的结果与表明各种气味受体转基因的表达受近端序列元件影响的实验相结合，与气味受体选择的表观遗传模型一致[37-42]。在更广泛的背景下，能够产生在解剖学上和行为上与野生型小鼠无显著区别的可育克隆小鼠表明，嗅觉神经元不经历其他干扰神经系统发育或者成年期功能的不可逆的 DNA 重排。

Methods

Preparation of donor neurons

Olfactory epithelia were dissected in L15 medium (Gibco) at 4 °C, then chopped into small pieces and incubated with type IV collagenase at 1 μg ml^{-1} at 37 °C for 15 min with occasional vigorous shaking. The collagenase digestion was stopped by addition of DMEM plus 10% FBS. Cells were spun down and resuspended in trituration medium (PBS plus 30% glucose plus 10% FBS plus penicillin/streptomycin) and triturated with several widths of pipette tips to produce single cell suspensions. Cells were pelleted and resuspended in L15/10% FBS before picking.

ES cell lines and tetraploid embryo complementation

Production of ES cell lines from nuclear transfer embryos was exactly as described[28], and generation of mice by tetraploid embryo complementation was exactly as described[29].

Generation of cloned embryos and mice

Production of cloned embryos by nuclear transfer was essentially as described[25,29] except that only GFP$^+$ cells from the two donor populations, as identified by epifluorescence, were picked and used for nuclear transfer.

In situ hybridization and immunohistochemistry

Animals were killed by approved methods and tissues of interest were either fresh frozen in OCT or fixed for 2–12 h in 4% PFA/1 × PBS, then washed and equilibrated in 30% sucrose before freezing. Frozen sections (from 20–30 μm) were placed on slides and standard immunohistochemistry and digoxigenin-labelled probe *in situ* hybridization protocols were used[32]. We used the following antibodies: rabbit anti-GFP antibody (Molecular Probes), rabbit anti-Cre recombinase antibody (Novagen), goat anti-Ki67 antibody (Santa Cruz Biotechnology), rat anti-BrdU antibody (abcam) and rabbit anti-MASH-1 antibody (a gift of J. Johnson).

BrdU labelling and visualization

Mice were injected intraperitoneally with a 5 mg ml^{-1} solution of BrdU in PBS every 2 h for 12 h. Each mouse received BrdU at 100 μg g^{-1} body weight for each injection. Two hours after the last injection mice were killed and tissues were fixed for 2 h in 4% PFA and PBS, washed and sucrose protected, and frozen. To permit simultaneous visualization of BrdU and GFP, sections were first stained with anti-GFP antibody then fixed in 4% PFA/PBS for 15 min, then washed, treated with

方　法

供体神经元的制备

将嗅上皮于 4℃ L15 培养基（Gibco）中裂解，然后切成小块并与 1μg/ml 的 IV 型胶原酶在 37℃ 下孵育 15 分钟，偶尔剧烈摇动。通过加入含有 10% FBS 的 DMEM 终止胶原酶消化。将细胞离心并重悬于研磨培养基（PBS 加 30% 葡萄糖加 10% FBS 加青霉素/链霉素）中，并用不同口径的移液管尖端研磨以获得单细胞悬浮液。收集前将细胞沉淀并重新悬浮于 L15/10% FBS 中。

ES 细胞系和四倍体胚胎补偿法

来自核移植胚胎的 ES 细胞系的获得完全如之前文献描述 [28]，且通过四倍体胚胎补偿获得小鼠的步骤也完全如之前文献描述 [29]。

克隆胚胎和小鼠的获得

通过核移植产生克隆胚胎基本如文献描述 [25,29]，唯一不同点是仅有来自两个供体群的 GFP+ 细胞通过荧光挑选出来，并用于核移植。

原位杂交和免疫组织化学法

通过经批准的方法处死动物，目标组织放于 OCT 中尽快冷冻，或于 4% PFA/1×PBS 中固定 2~12 小时，然后洗涤并在冷冻前于 30% 蔗糖中平衡。将冷冻切片（20~30 μm 厚）置于载玻片上，并进行标准免疫组织染色和用地高辛标记的探针进行原位杂交 [32]。我们使用以下抗体：兔抗 GFP 抗体（Molecular Probes），兔抗 Cre 重组酶抗体（Novagen），山羊抗 Ki67 抗体（Santa Cruz Biotechnology），大鼠抗 BrdU 抗体（abcam）和兔抗 MASH-1 抗体（来自 J.Johnson 的礼物）。

BrdU 标记和可视化

每 2 小时向小鼠腹膜内注射 5 mg/ml 的 BrdU PBS 溶液，持续进行 12 小时。每次注射时，每只小鼠接受 100 μg/g 体重的 BrdU。在最后一次注射后 2 小时，处死小鼠并将组织在 4% PFA 和 PBS 中固定 2 小时，洗涤并用蔗糖保护，之后冷冻。为了同时观察 BrdU 和 GFP，首先用抗 GFP 抗体对切片染色，然后在 4% PFA/PBS 中固定 15 分钟，之后洗涤，用

4 M HCl/0.1% Triton X-100 for 10 min, washed and stained with rat anti-BrdU followed by the appropriate secondary antibodies.

Gene targeting and generation of donor mouse lines

The OMP–IRES-Cre mouse line was generated as described previously except that the Cre recombinase gene sequence was inserted in place of the tTA sequence[32]. An IRES directing the translation of Cre recombinase was introduced into the 3′ untranslated region of the OMP locus by homologous recombination in ES cells. Transgenic mice were generated and crossed with a strain bearing the Z/EG reporter transgene. The *Rosa26*–LoxP-Stop-LoxP–GFP line was generated as described previously except that the GFP sequence replaced the CFP and YFP sequences in the *Rosa26* cassette[33].

Southern blotting, PCR and RT–PCR

Southern blots and PCR screening of ES cells and tails used standard methods[43]. RT–PCR was performed on RNA isolated from mouse olfactory turbinates that had been frozen in Trizol (Invitrogen), and then treated as per the manufacturer's protocol. RNA was reverse transcribed using the Superscript II kit (Invitrogen) and complementary DNA was subjected to PCR using standard conditions.

(**428**, 44-49; 2004)

Kevin Eggan[1]*[†], Kristin Baldwin[2]*, Michael Tackett[1], Joseph Osborne[2][†], Joseph Gogos[2], Andrew Chess[1], Richard Axel[2] & Rudolf Jaenisch[1]

[1] Whitehead Institute for Biomedical Research and Department of Biology, Massachusetts Institute of Technology, 9 Cambridge Center, Cambridge, Massachusetts 02142, USA

[2] Department of Biochemistry and Molecular Biophysics, Howard Hughes Medical Institute, College of Physicians and Surgeons, Columbia University, 701 West 168th Street, New York, New York 10032, USA

* These authors contributed equally to this work

[†] Present addresses: Department of Physiology and Cellular Biophysics, College of Physicians and Surgeons, Columbia University, 630 West 168th Street, New York, New York 10032, USA (J.O.); Department of Molecular and Cellular Biology, Harvard University, 7 Divinity Avenue, Cambridge, Massachusetts 02138, USA (K.E.)

Received 13 November 2003; accepted 14 January 2004; doi:10.1038/nature02375.
Published online 15 February 2004.

References:

1. Rideout, W. M., Eggan, K. & Jaenisch, R. Nuclear cloning and epigenetic reprogramming of the genome. *Science* **293**, 1093-1098 (2001).

2. Hochedlinger, K. & Jaenisch, R. Nuclear transplantation: lessons from frogs and mice. *Curr. Opin. Cell Biol.* **14**, 741-748 (2002).

3. Gurdon, J. B. & Byrne, J. A. The first half-century of nuclear transplantation. *Proc. Natl Acad. Sci. USA* **100**, 8048-8052 (2003).

4. Osada, T., Kusakabe, H., Akutsu, H., Yagi, T. & Yanagimachi, R. Adult murine neurons: their chromatin and chromosome changes and failure to support embryonic development as revealed by nuclear transfer. *Cytogenet. Genome Res.* **97**, 7-12 (2002).

5. Yamazaki, Y. *et al.* Assessment of the developmental totipotency of neural cells in the cerebral cortex of mouse embryo by nuclear transfer. *Proc. Natl Acad. Sci. USA* **98**, 14022-14026 (2001).

4 M HCl/0.1% Triton X-100 处理 10 分钟，再次洗涤并用大鼠抗 BrdU 染色，然后用适当的二抗染色。

基因靶向和供体小鼠系的获得

除了插入 Cre 重组酶基因序列以代替 tTA 序列 [32]，OMP–IRES-Cre 小鼠系的获得方法如前所述。通过 ES 细胞中的同源重组，将指导 Cre 重组酶翻译的 IRES 引入 OMP 基因座的 3′ 非翻译区。获得转基因小鼠，并与携带 Z/EG 报告转基因的小鼠杂交。获得 Rosa26–LoxP-Stop-LoxP–GFP 系小鼠，除用 GFP 序列替换 Rosa26 盒中的 CFP 和 YFP 序列外其余步骤均已在文献中描述 [33]。

Southern 印迹、PCR 和 RT–PCR

对 ES 细胞和小鼠尾部进行的 Southern 印迹和 PCR 筛选均使用标准方法 [43]。对从 Trizol (Invitrogen) 中冷冻的小鼠嗅鼻甲中分离的 RNA 进行 RT–PCR，然后按照试剂制造商的方案进行处理。使用 Superscript II 试剂盒 (Invitrogen) 逆转录 RNA，并使用标准条件对互补 DNA 进行 PCR。

（任奕 翻译；王宇 审稿）

6. Chien, Y. H., Gascoigne, N. R., Kavaler, J., Lee, N. E. & Davis, M. M. Somatic recombination in a murine T-cell receptor gene. *Nature* **309**, 322-326 (1984).

7. Hozumi, N. & Tonegawa, S. Evidence for somatic rearrangement of immunoglobulin genes coding for variable and constant regions. *Proc. Natl Acad. Sci. USA* **73**, 3628-3632 (1976).

8. Brack, C., Hirama, M., Lenhard-Schuller, R. & Tonegawa, S. A complete immunoglobulin gene is created by somatic recombination. *Cell* **15**, 1-14 (1978).

9. Gao, Y. *et al.* A critical role for DNA end-joining proteins in both lymphogenesis and neurogenesis. *Cell* **95**, 891-902 (1998).

10. Frank, K. M. *et al.* Late embryonic lethality and impaired V(D)J recombination in mice lacking DNA ligase IV. *Nature* **396**, 173-177 (1998).

11. Rehen, S. K. *et al.* Chromosomal variation in neurons of the developing and adult mammalian nervous system. *Proc. Natl Acad. Sci. USA* **98**, 13361-13366 (2001).

12. Kaushal, D. *et al.* Alteration of gene expression by chromosome loss in the postnatal mouse brain. *J. Neurosci.* **23**, 5599-5606 (2003).

13. Chun, J. & Schatz, D. G. Rearranging views on neurogenesis: neuronal death in the absence of DNA end-joining proteins. *Neuron* **22**, 7-10 (1999).

14. Chun, J. Selected comparison of immune and nervous system development. *Adv. Immunol.* **77**, 297-322 (2001).

15. Yagi, T. Diversity of the cadherin-related neuronal receptor/protocadherin family and possible DNA rearrangement in the brain. *Genes Cells* **8**, 1-8 (2003).

16. Zhang, X. & Firestein, S. The olfactory receptor gene superfamily of the mouse. *Nature Neurosci.* **5**, 124-133 (2002).

17. Ressler, K. J., Sullivan, S. L. & Buck, L. B. A zonal organization of odorant receptor gene expression in the olfactory epithelium. *Cell* **73**, 597-609 (1993).

18. Vassar, R., Ngai, J. & Axel, R. Spatial segregation of odorant receptor expression in the mammalian olfactory epithelium. *Cell* **74**, 309-318 (1993).

19. Buck, L. & Axel, R. A novel multigene family may encode odorant receptors: a molecular basis for odor recognition. *Cell* **65**, 175-187 (1991).

20. Kratz, E., Dugas, J. C. & Ngai, J. Odorant receptor gene regulation: implications from genomic organization. *Trends Genet.* **18**, 29-34 (2002).

21. Goldstein, B. J. & Schwob, J. E. Analysis of the globose basal cell compartment in rat olfactory epithelium using GBC-1, a new monoclonal antibody against globose basal cells. *J. Neurosci.* **16**, 4005-4016 (1996).

22. Holbrook, E. H., Szumowski, K. E. & Schwob, J. E. An immunochemical, ultrastructural, and developmental characterization of the horizontal basal cells of rat olfactory epithelium. *J. Comp. Neurol.* **363**, 129-146 (1995).

23. Ohta, Y. & Ichimura, K. Proliferation markers, proliferating cell nuclear antigen, Ki67, 5-bromo-2′-deoxyuridine, and cyclin D1 in mouse olfactory epithelium. *Ann. Otol. Rhinol. Laryngol.* **109**, 1046-1048 (2000).

24. Gerdes, J. *et al.* Cell cycle analysis of a cell proliferation-associated human nuclear antigen defined by the monoclonal antibody Ki-67. *J. Immunol.* **133**, 1710-1715 (1984).

25. Wakayama, T., Perry, A. C., Zuccotti, M., Johnson, K. R. & Yanagimachi, R. Full-term development of mice from enucleated oocytes injected with cumulus cell nuclei. *Nature* **394**, 369-374 (1998).

26. Wakayama, T., Rodriguez, I., Perry, A. C., Yanagimachi, R. & Mombaerts, P. Mice cloned from embryonic stem cells. *Proc. Natl Acad. Sci. USA* **96**, 14984-14989 (1999).

27. Rideout, W. M. *et al.* Generation of mice from wild-type and targeted ES cells by nuclear cloning. *Nature Genet.* **24**, 109-110 (2000).

28. Hochedlinger, K. & Jaenisch, R. Monoclonal mice generated by nuclear transfer from mature B and T donor cells. *Nature* **415**, 1035-1038 (2002).

29. Eggan, K. *et al.* Hybrid vigor, fetal overgrowth, and viability of mice derived by nuclear cloning and tetraploid embryo complementation. *Proc. Natl Acad. Sci. USA* **98**, 6209-6214 (2001).

30. Nagy, A. *et al.* Embryonic stem cells alone are able to support fetal development in the mouse. *Development* **110**, 815-821 (1990).

31. Wang, F., Nemes, A., Mendelsohn, M. & Axel, R. Odorant receptors govern the formation of a precise topographic map. *Cell* **93**, 47-60 (1998).

32. Gogos, J. A., Osborne, J., Nemes, A., Mendelsohn, M. & Axel, R. Genetic ablation and restoration of the olfactory topographic map. *Cell* **103**, 609-620 (2000).

33. Srinivas, S. *et al.* Cre reporter strains produced by targeted insertion of EYFP and ECFP into the ROSA26 locus. *BMC Dev. Biol.* **1**, 4 (2001).

34. Rossant, J. A monoclonal mouse? *Nature* **415**, 967-969 (2002).

35. Ohnuma, S. & Harris, W. A. Neurogenesis and the cell cycle. *Neuron* **40**, 199-208 (2003).

36. Edelman, G. M. *Neural Darwinism* (Basic Books, New York, NY, 1987).

37. Ishii, T. *et al.* Monoallelic expression of the odourant receptor gene and axonal projection of olfactory sensory neurones. *Genes Cells* **6**, 71-78 (2001).

38. Serizawa, S. *et al.* Negative feedback regulation ensures the one receptor-one olfactory neuron rule in mouse. *Science* **302**, 2088-2094 (2003).

39. Serizawa, S. *et al.* Mutually exclusive expression of odorant receptor transgenes. *Nature Neurosci.* **3**, 687-693 (2000).

40. Ebrahimi, F. A., Edmondson, J., Rothstein, R. & Chess, A. YAC transgene-mediated olfactory receptor gene choice. *Dev. Dyn.* **217**, 225-231 (2000).

41. Qasba, P. & Reed, R. R. Tissue and zonal-specific expression of an olfactory receptor transgene. *J. Neurosci.* **18**, 227-236 (1998).

42. Vassalli, A., Rothman, A., Feinstein, P., Zapotocky, M. & Mombaerts, P. Minigenes impart odorant receptor-specific axon guidance in the olfactory bulb. *Neuron* **35**, 681-696 (2002).

43. Sambrook, J., Fritsch, E. F. & Maniatis, T. *Molecular Cloning: a Laboratory Manual* 2nd edn (Cold Spring Harbor Laboratory Press, Cold Spring Harbor, NY, 1989).

Supplementary Information accompanies the paper on www.nature.com/nature.

Acknowledgements. We thank L. Moring, A. Nemes, M. Mendelsohn, J. Loring, J. Dausman, A. Meissner and K. Hochedlinger for assistance during the course of these experiments; T. Cutforth, J. de Nooij, T. Jessell and J. Johnson for sharing reagents necessary for our experiments; and members of the Jaenisch, Axel and Chess laboratories for discussion and assistance during the course of these experiments, especially F. A. Ebrahimi, M. Rios, W. M. R. Rideout, L. Jackson-Grusby and B. Shykind. This research was sponsored by NIH grants to R.J., R.A., A.C. and M.T.. K.B. is an Associate and R.A. is an Investigator of the Howard Hughes Medical

Institute. K.E. is a Junior Fellow in the Harvard Society of Fellows.

Competing interests statement. The authors declare that they have no competing financial interests.

Correspondence and requests for materials should be addressed to R.J. (jaenisch@wi.mit.edu) or A.C. (achess@wi.mit.edu).

A Precision Measurement of the Mass of the Top Quark

DØ Collaboration[*]

Editor's Note

Although the standard model of particle physics is extremely successful, it does not in itself explain the masses of subatomic particles. Instead, they are hypothesized to arise from the interactions of particles with the so-called Higgs boson. Here an international team called the D0 collaboration, working at the Tevatron supercollider at Fermilab in Illinois, report a high-precision measurement of the mass of the top quark, which helps to constrain the range of allowable masses for the Higgs boson. The results suggest that it is more massive than was previously thought, so that more energy will be required to make it. The Higgs boson was finally observed in the Large Hadron Collider at CERN in Geneva in 2012. Its mass is lighter than was expected.

The standard model of particle physics contains parameters—such as particle masses—whose origins are still unknown and which cannot be predicted, but whose values are constrained through their interactions. In particular, the masses of the top quark (M_t) and W boson (M_W)[1] constrain the mass of the long-hypothesized, but thus far not observed, Higgs boson. A precise measurement of M_t can therefore indicate where to look for the Higgs, and indeed whether the hypothesis of a standard model Higgs is consistent with experimental data. As top quarks are produced in pairs and decay in only about 10^{-24} s into various final states, reconstructing their masses from their decay products is very challenging. Here we report a technique that extracts more information from each top-quark event and yields a greatly improved precision (of ± 5.3 GeV/c^2) when compared to previous measurements[2]. When our new result is combined with our published measurement in a complementary decay mode[3] and with the only other measurements available[2], the new world average for M_t becomes[4] 178.0 ± 4.3 GeV/c^2. As a result, the most likely Higgs mass increases from the experimentally excluded[5] value[6] of 96 to 117 GeV/c^2, which is beyond current experimental sensitivity. The upper limit on the Higgs mass at the 95% confidence level is raised from 219 to 251 GeV/c^2.

THE discovery of the top quark in 1995 served as one of the major confirmations of the validity of the standard model (SM)[7,8]. Of its many parameters, the mass of the top quark, in particular, reflects some of the most crucial aspects of the SM. This is because, in principle, the top quark is point-like and should be massless; yet, through

* A full list of participants and affiliations is given in the original paper.

顶夸克质量的精确测量

DØ 项目合作组 [*]

编者按

尽管粒子物理的标准模型是非常成功的，但模型本身解释不了亚原子粒子的质量问题，亚原子粒子的质量被假定来源于粒子与所谓的希格斯玻色子之间的相互作用。本文中，一个名为 D0 合作组的国际团队通过伊利诺伊州费米实验室的万亿电子伏特加速器 (Tevatron) 得到了顶夸克质量的精确测定，由此有助于限定希格斯玻色子允许质量的范围。结果表明，希格斯玻色子的质量比之前预期的要大，因而需要更大的能量才能产生希格斯玻色子。2012 年，位于瑞士日内瓦的欧洲核子研究组织 (CERN) 的大型强子对撞机终于观测到希格斯玻色子，但其质量比预期的要轻。

粒子物理标准模型包含了像粒子质量这一类的参数，这类参数起源不清，无法预言，但是其量值可以通过它们之间的相互作用来限定。特别是一直被预言存在但是从未被观测到的希格斯玻色子的质量，可以由顶夸克的质量 (M_t) 和 W 玻色子的质量 (M_W) [1] 进行限定。因而，M_t 的精确测量可以更好地指导我们寻找希格斯子，甚至可验证标准模型预言的希格斯子是否与实验数据相符。由于顶夸克成对产生，并在 10^{-24} 秒后就衰变为各种末态，通过衰变的产物来重建其质量是非常困难的。本文提出的技术可以从每一个顶夸克对事例中获取更多信息并得到比之前测量值 [2] 更高的精度 ($\pm 5.3 \text{ GeV}/c^2$)。我们最新的结果结合之前发表的互补衰变模式（全轻衰变模式）的测量值 [3] 和目前其余已知的结果 [2]，得到的新的全球 M_t 平均值是 $178.0 \pm 4.3 \text{ GeV}/c^2$ [4]。由此，最有可能的希格斯子质量的值从已经被实验 [5,6] 排除的 $96 \text{ GeV}/c^2$ 提高到 $117 \text{ GeV}/c^2$，这比当前的实验灵敏度要高。在 95% 置信水平，希格斯子的质量上限从 $219 \text{ GeV}/c^2$ 提高到 $251 \text{ GeV}/c^2$。

1995 年顶夸克的发现是对标准模型 (SM) 的重要支持之一 [7,8]。在众多参数中，顶夸克的质量尤其反映了标准模型的一些根本特征。这是因为本质上顶夸克是一个无质量的点粒子，然而通过与预言的希格斯场的相互作用，顶夸克获得的物理质量大致相当于一个金原子核质量。这个质量如此之大，使得顶夸克（和 W 玻色子一起）

---

[*] 合作组的参与者及所属单位的名单请参见原文。

its interactions with the hypothesized Higgs field, the physical mass of the top quark appears to be about the mass of a gold nucleus. Because it is so heavy, the top quark (along with the W boson) provides an unusually sensitive tool for investigating the Higgs field. M_W is known to a precision of 0.05%, while the uncertainty on M_t is at the 3% level[1]. Improvements in both measurements are required to restrict further the allowed range of mass for the Higgs; however, given the large uncertainty in M_t, an improvement in its precision is particularly important. As has been pointed out recently[9,10], a potential problem for the SM is that, on the basis of the currently accepted value for M_t, the most likely value of the Higgs mass[6] lies in a range that has already been excluded by experiment[5]. Precise knowledge of the Higgs mass is crucial for our understanding of the SM and any possible new physics beyond it. For example, in a large class of supersymmetric models (theoretically preferred solutions to the deficiencies of the SM), the Higgs mass has to be less than about 135 GeV/c^2. Although, unlike the SM, supersymmetry predicts more than one Higgs boson, the properties of the lightest one are expected to be essentially the same as those for the SM Higgs boson. Thus, if the SM-like Higgs is heavier than about 135 GeV/c^2, it would disfavour a large class of supersymmetric models. In addition, some of the current limits on supersymmetric particles from LEP[11] are extremely sensitive to M_t. In fact, for M_t greater than 179 GeV/c^2, the bounds on one of the major supersymmetry parameters, $\tan\beta$, which relates the properties of the SM-like Higgs boson and its heavier partners, would disappear completely[12]. Hence, in addition to the impact on searches for the Higgs boson, other important consequences call for improved precision on M_t, and this goal is the main subject of this paper.

The DØ experiment at the Fermilab Tevatron has studied a sample of $t\bar{t}$ events produced in proton–antiproton ($p\bar{p}$) interactions[13]. The total energy of 1.8 TeV released in a head-on collision of a 900-GeV p and a 900-GeV $\bar{p}$ is almost as large as the rest energy of ten gold nuclei. Each top (antitop) quark decays almost immediately into a bottom $b(\bar{b})$ quark and a $W^+ (W^-)$ boson, and we have reexamined those events in which one of the W bosons decays into a charged lepton (electron or muon) and a neutrino, and the other W into a quark and an antiquark (see Fig. 1). These events and their selection criteria are identical to those used to extract the mass of the top quark in our previous publication, and correspond to an integrated luminosity of 125 events per pb. (That is, given the production cross-section of the $t\bar{t}$ in $p\bar{p}$ collisions at 1.8 TeV of 5.7 pb, as measured by DØ[14], these data correspond to approximately 700 produced $t\bar{t}$ pairs, a fraction of which is fully detected in various possible decay modes. Approximately 30% of these correspond to the lepton + jets topology categorized in Fig. 2, where "jet" refers to products of the fragmentation of a quark into a collimated group of particles that are emitted along the quark's original direction.) The main background processes correspond to multijet production (20%), where one of the jets is reconstructed incorrectly as a lepton, and the W + jets production with leptonic W decays (80%), which has the same topology as the $t\bar{t}$ signal.

成为一个超常灵敏的研究希格斯场的手段。M_W 的测量值仅有 0.05% 的不确定度，而 M_t 的测量值有 3% 的不确定度 [1]。要进一步缩小希格斯子质量的可能范围，需要改进这两个量值的精确度。但因为 M_t 的测量值不确定度大，所以对其精度的改进就格外地重要。正如最近 [9,10] 已指出的，标准模型的一个潜在问题在于，根据当前公认的 M_t 测量值，最有可能的希格斯子质量 [6] 落在已被实验排除的区间 [5]。准确地认识希格斯子的质量，对于我们理解标准模型或者标准模型以外的其他可能的新物理理论，都是非常重要的。比如说，在一大类超对称模型中（解决标准模型缺陷的首选理论），希格斯子质量必须小于约 135 GeV/c^2。和标准模型不同的是，超对称性预言的希格斯子不止一个，但是其中最轻的那一个的性质基本上与标准模型中的希格斯玻色子相同。因此，如果类标准模型希格斯玻色子的质量超过 135 GeV/c^2，这一大类超对称模型就不再被看好。另外，从大型正负电子对撞机 (LEP) [11] 得到的一些超对称粒子当前的限制对 M_t 非常敏感。实际上，当 M_t 大于 179 GeV/c^2 时，一个联系类标准模型希格斯玻色子及其更重的伴子的主要的超对称参数 ($\tan\beta$) 的限制将完全消失 [12]。除了对希格斯玻色子的寻找有影响，改进 M_t 的测量精度还有其他重要意义，这个目标也是本文的主要研究问题。

    DØ 项目在费米实验室的万亿电子伏特加速器 (Tevatron) 上研究了用质子–反质子 ($p\bar{p}$) 对撞产生的顶夸克–反顶夸克 ($t\bar{t}$) 事例 [13]。900 GeV 的质子 (p) 和 900 GeV 的反质子 ($\bar{p}$) 对撞释放了 1.8 TeV 的总能量，几乎相当于十个金原子核的静止质量。每个顶 (反顶) 夸克几乎立即衰变为一个底 (反底) 夸克 b($\bar{b}$) 和一个 W^+(W^-) 玻色子。我们重新检查了那些一个 W 玻色子衰变为一个带电轻子 (电子或者 μ 子) 和一个中微子，而另一个 W 玻色子衰变为一个夸克和一个反夸克的事例 (图 1)。挑选这些事例所用选择条件及实验数据样本与我们之前发表的获取顶夸克质量的工作中所用的选择条件和数据样本相同，即对应每 pb 有 125 个事例积分亮度的实验数据。(就是说，与 DØ 实验中测得的结果 [14] 一致，假定 $p\bar{p}$ 对撞中的 $t\bar{t}$ 在能量为 1.8 TeV 时产生截面为 5.7 皮靶，这些数据大概对应于 700 个 $t\bar{t}$ 对，其中只有部分通过各种可能的衰变模式检测到了。大概有 30% $t\bar{t}$ 衰变模式对应于图 2 归类的轻子 + 喷注拓扑，其中"喷注"这个词表示夸克分裂产生的成群粒子沿夸克原来的方向平行前进)。主要的背景过程包括多喷注产生 (20%，其中的一个喷注被错误地重建为轻子) 和与 $t\bar{t}$ 信号有相同拓扑结构的轻子型 W 衰变的 W+ 喷注产生 (80%)。

Fig. 1. Feynman diagrams for $t\bar{t}$ production in $p\bar{p}$ collisions, with subsequent decays into an electron, neutrino, and quarks. Quark–antiquark production (**a**) is dominant, but gluon fusion (**b**) contributes ~10% to the cross-section. This particular final state ($ev u\bar{d}b\bar{b}$) is one of the channels used in the analysis.

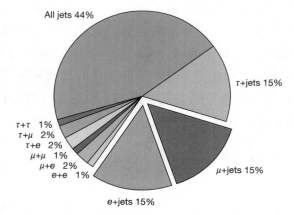

Fig. 2. Relative importance of various $t\bar{t}$ decay modes. The "lepton+jets" channel used in this analysis corresponds to the two offset slices of the pie-chart and amounts to 30% of all the $t\bar{t}$ decays

The previous DØ measurement of M_t in this lepton + jets channel is $M_t = 173.3 \pm 5.6$ (stat) ± 5.5 (syst) GeV/c^2, and is based on 91 candidate events. Information pertaining to the older analysis and the DØ detector can be found elsewhere[13,15].

The new method of M_t measurement is similar to one suggested previously (ref. 16 and references therein, and ref. 17) for $t\bar{t}$ dilepton decay channels (where both W bosons decay leptonically), and used in previous mass analyses of dilepton events[3], and akin to an approach suggested for the measurement of the mass of the W boson at LEP[18-20]. The critical differences from previous analyses in the lepton + jets decay channel lie in: (1) the assignment of more weight to events that are well measured or more likely to correspond to $t\bar{t}$ signal, and (2) the handling of the combinations of final-state objects (lepton, jets and imbalance in transverse momentum, the latter being a signature for an undetected neutrino) and their identification with top-quark decay products in an event (such as from ambiguity in choosing jets that correspond to b or $\bar{b}$ quarks from the decays of the t and $\bar{t}$ quarks). Also, because leading-order matrix elements were used to calculate the event weights, only events with exactly four jets are kept in this analysis, resulting in a candidate sample of 71 events. Although we are left with fewer events, the new method for extracting M_t provides

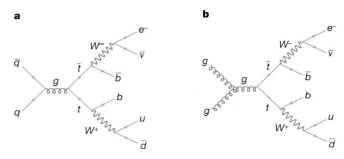

图 1. $p\bar{p}$(正反质子)对撞中 $t\bar{t}$(正反顶夸克)产生的费曼图。产生的顶夸克随即衰变为一个电子、中微子和数个夸克。(a) 图所示的夸克–反夸克产生过程是主要的，(b) 图中的胶子聚变过程贡献大约 10% 的截面。这个末态 $(ev u\bar{d}b\bar{b})$ 是分析中用到的通道之一。

图 2. 各个 $t\bar{t}$ 衰变模式的比例。本分析中用到的"轻子 + 喷注"衰变道对应于扇面图中分割出的两片，总共占 $t\bar{t}$ 衰变的 30%。

以前在通过轻子 + 喷注衰变道测量 M_t 值的 DØ 实验中，根据 91 个候选事例得到的量值是 $M_t = 173.3 \pm 5.6$(统计不确定度) ± 5.5(系统不确定度) GeV/c^2。以前的分析以及 DØ 探测器的相关信息可以在相关文献 [13,15] 中找到。

测量 M_t 的新方法类似于之前文献(参考文献 16 以及其中引用的文献，参考文献 17) 提出的关于 $t\bar{t}$ 双轻子衰变道(其中两个 W 玻色子的衰变都是轻子型的)中的测量方法，该方法曾被应用于之前双轻子事例的质量分析 [3]，与之前建议的在 LEP 上测量 W 玻色子质量的方法也是相似的 [18-20]。轻子 + 喷注衰变道的分析与之前的分析关键的不同之处在于：(1) 测量得比较精确的事例或者更可能对应于 $t\bar{t}$ 信号的事例这点被赋予了更大的权重，(2) 对末态产物(轻子、喷注和不平衡的横向动量，最后一项表明了一个未探测到的中微子的存在)的各种组合的处理以及在事例中用顶夸克衰变产物对它们的确证(比如解决喷注是对应于 t 夸克衰变中的 b 夸克还是 $\bar{t}$ 夸克衰变中的 $\bar{b}$ 夸克的不确定性问题)。另外，由于使用领头阶矩阵元计算事例权重，分析中只保留了恰好有 4 个喷注的事例，这样得到的候选样本有 71 个事例。虽然事例数

substantial improvement in both statistical and systematic uncertainties.

We calculate as a function of M_t the differential probability that the measured variables in any event correspond to signal. The maximum of the product of these individual event probabilities provides the best estimate of M_t in the data sample. The impact of biases from imperfections in the detector and event-reconstruction algorithms is taken into account in two ways. Geometric acceptance, trigger efficiencies, event selection, and so on enter through a multiplicative acceptance function that is independent of M_t. Because the angular directions of all the objects in the event, as well as the electron momentum, are measured with high precision, their measured values are used directly in the calculation of the probability that any event corresponds to $t\bar{t}$ or background production. The known momentum resolution is used to account for uncertainties in measurements of jet energies and muon momenta.

As in the previous analysis[13], momentum conservation in γ+jet events is used to check that the energies of jets in the experiment agree with Monte Carlo (MC) simulations. This calibration has an uncertainty $\delta E = (0.025E+0.5\ \text{GeV})$. Consequently, all jet energies in our sample are rescaled by $\pm\delta E$, the analysis redone, and half of the difference in the two rescaled results for M_t ($\delta M_t = 3.3\ \text{GeV}/c^2$) is taken as a systematic uncertainty from this source. All other contributions to systematic uncertainty: MC modelling of signal ($\delta M_t = 1.1\ \text{GeV}/c^2$) and background ($\delta M_t = 1.0\ \text{GeV}/c^2$), effect of calorimeter noise and event pile-up ($\delta M_t = 1.3\ \text{GeV}/c^2$), and other corrections from M_t extraction ($\delta M_t = 0.6\ \text{GeV}/c^2$) are much smaller, and discussed in detail elsewhere[21,22]. It should be noted that the new mass measurement method provides a significant (about 40%, from ± 5.5 to $\pm 3.9\ \text{GeV}/c^2$) reduction in systematic uncertainty, which is ultimately dominated by the measurement of jet energies. For details on the new analysis, see the Methods.

The final result is $M_t = 180.1 \pm 3.6\ (\text{stat}) \pm 3.9\ (\text{syst})\ \text{GeV}/c^2$. The improvement in statistical uncertainty over our previous measurement is equivalent to collecting a factor of 2.4 as much data. Combining the statistical and systematic uncertainties in quadrature, we obtain $M_t = 180.1 \pm 5.3\ \text{GeV}/c^2$, which is consistent with our previous measurement in the same channel (at about 1.4 standard deviations), and has a precision comparable to all previous M_t measurements combined[1].

The new measurement can be combined with that obtained for the dilepton sample that was also collected at DØ during run I (ref. 3) ($M_t = 168.4 \pm 12.3\ (\text{stat}) \pm 3.6\ (\text{syst})\ \text{GeV}/c^2$), to yield the new DØ average for the mass of the top quark:

$$M_t = 179.0 \pm 5.1\ \text{GeV}/c^2 \tag{1}$$

Combining this with measurements from the CDF experiment[2] provides a new "world average" (based on all measurements available) for the mass of the top quark[4]:

$$M_t = 178.0 \pm 4.3\ \text{GeV}/c^2 \tag{2}$$

少了，但是提取 M_t 的新方法在统计不确定度和系统不确定度上都有实质性的改进。

我们计算了以 M_t 及事例观测量作为变量的函数，并将该函数对应为信号的微分概率。这些独立事例概率的最大乘积提供了数据样本中 M_t 的最佳估计值。我们从两个方面考虑了探测器和事例重建算法的不完美引起的偏差影响。几何接收率、触发效率、事例选择等被包含在一个不依赖 M_t 的多元接收函数中。由于事例中所有对象的角度方向和电子动量的测量精度都很高，它们的测量值被直接用来计算任何对应于 $t\bar{t}$ 事例或者背景事例的产生概率。使用已知的动量分辨率来解释测量喷注能量和 μ 子动量时的不确定度。

和以前的分析[13]一样，γ+ 喷注事例中的动量守恒被用来检查喷注的能量是否与蒙特卡罗（MC）模拟结果相符合。这个校准的不确定度 $\delta E = (0.025E+0.5\,\mathrm{GeV})$。因此，我们的样本中所有喷注能量都以 $\pm\delta E$ 重新标度，两次重新标度和分析后的 $M_t(\delta M_t = 3.3\,\mathrm{GeV}/c^2)$ 结果之差的一半被作为喷注能量测量不确定度引起的系统性不确定度。对系统不确定度有贡献的其他因素包括：信号和背景的蒙特卡罗建模（$\delta M_t = 1.1\,\mathrm{GeV}/c^2$ 和 $\delta M_t = 1.0\,\mathrm{GeV}/c^2$），量能器噪声和事例堆积的影响（$\delta M_t = 1.3\,\mathrm{GeV}/c^2$）以及其他源于 M_t 提取的修正（$\delta M_t = 0.6\,\mathrm{GeV}/c^2$）。以上这些因素的贡献要小得多，有另文[21,22]具体讨论。这里需要指出，新的质量测量方法明显减小了主要由测量喷注能量导致的系统不确定度（减小了约 40%，从 $\pm5.5\,\mathrm{GeV}/c^2$ 减到 $\pm3.9\,\mathrm{GeV}/c^2$）。关于新分析方法的细节，请参看本文后面的**方法**。

最后的结果是 $M_t = 180.1 \pm 3.6$（统计误差）± 3.9（系统误差）GeV/c^2。和之前的测量结果比较，新方法在统计不确定度上的改进相当于将数据量增加至原来的 2.4 倍。将统计和系统不确定度求均方根，我们得到 $M_t = 180.1 \pm 5.3\,\mathrm{GeV}/c^2$，这与我们之前在相同衰变道的测量结果相符（在大约 1.4 个标准差偏离下），与之前所有的 M_t 测量的联合精度相当[1]。

将新的测量结果与通过第 I 轮 DØ 实验（参考文献 3）中搜集到的双轻子样本得到的结果（$M_t = 168.4 \pm 12.3$（统计误差）± 3.6（系统误差）GeV/c^2）相结合，得出顶夸克质量的新的 DØ 平均：

$$M_t = 179.0 \pm 5.1\,\mathrm{GeV}/c^2 \tag{1}$$

把这一结果和 CDF 实验的测量结果[2]进一步结合起来，得到以我们最近的结果为主导的顶夸克质量新的"全球平均"（基于目前所有已知的测量结果）[4]：

$$M_t = 178.0 \pm 4.3\,\mathrm{GeV}/c^2 \tag{2}$$

dominated by our new measurement. This new world average shifts the best-fit value of the expected Higgs mass from 96 GeV/c^2 to 117 GeV/c^2 (see Fig. 3), which is now outside the experimentally excluded region, yet accessible in the current run of the Tevatron and at future runs at the Large Hadron Collider (LHC), at present under construction at CERN. (The upper limit on the Higgs mass at the 95% confidence level changes from 219 GeV/c^2 to 251 GeV/c^2.) Figure 3 shows the effect of using only the new DØ top mass for fits to the Higgs mass, and indicates a best value of 123 GeV/c^2 and the upper limit of 277 GeV/c^2 at the 95% confidence level. It should be noted that the horizontal scale in Fig. 3 is logarithmic, and the limits on the Higgs boson mass are therefore asymmetric.

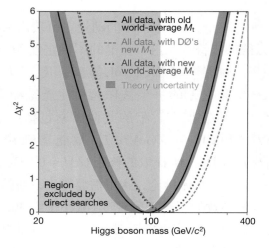

Fig. 3. Current experimental constraints on the mass of the Higgs boson. The χ^2 for a global fit to electroweak data[6] is shown as a function of the Higgs mass. The solid line corresponds to the result for the previous world-averaged $M_t = 174.3 \pm 5.1$ GeV/c^2, with the blue band indicating the impact of theoretical uncertainty. The dotted line shows the result for the new world-average M_t of 178.0 ± 4.3 GeV/c^2, whereas the dashed line corresponds to using only the new DØ average of 179.0 ± 5.1 GeV/c^2. The yellow-shaded area on the left indicates the region of Higgs masses excluded by experiment (> 114.4 GeV/c^2 at the 95% confidence level[5]). The improved M_t measurement shifts the most likely value of the Higgs mass above the experimentally excluded range.

The new method is already being applied to data being collected by the CDF and DØ experiments at the new run of the Fermilab Tevatron and should provide even higher precision on the determination of M_t, equivalent to more than a doubling of the data sample, relative to using the conventional method. An ultimate precision of about 2 GeV/c^2 on the mass of the top quark is expected to be reached in several years of Tevatron operation. Further improvement may eventually come from the LHC.

Methods

The probability density as a function of M_t can be written as a convolution of the calculable cross-

这个新的全球平均将预言的希格斯子质量的最佳拟合值从 96 GeV/c^2 提高到 117 GeV/c^2（见图 3），现在这个值已经落在了实验排除的区间之外，但可以在 Tevatron 上目前正运行的实验中以及 CERN 目前正在建设的大型强子对撞机（LHC）上将开展的实验中达到。（在 95% 置信度水平下，希格斯子质量的上限值从 219 GeV/c^2 变为 251 GeV/c^2）。图 3 显示如果只采用最新的 DØ 顶夸克质量来拟合希格斯子质量，获得的最佳的结果为 123 GeV/c^2，在 95% 置信度水平下最佳上限值为 277 GeV/c^2。注意图 3 中水平坐标是对数尺度，因而希格斯玻色子质量的上下限值是不对称的。

图 3. 当前实验得出的对希格斯玻色子质量的限定。图中显示电弱数据 [6] 全局拟合的 χ^2 值随希格斯子质量的变化。实线对应于之前的全球平均 $M_t = 174.3 \pm 5.1$ GeV/c^2 的结果，蓝色带状区域表示理论不确定度的影响。点线表示新的全球平均 $M_t = 178.0 \pm 4.3$ GeV/c^2 的结果，短横线对应只采用 DØ 实验新平均值 179.0 ± 5.1 GeV/c^2 的结果。左边黄色阴影区域表示实验排除的希格斯质量范围（> 114.4 GeV/c^2，95% 置信水平下 [5]）。改进后的 M_t 测量值使得最有可能的希格斯子质量移至实验排除的区间之外。

新方法已经被用来处理费米实验室 Tevatron 上新一轮 CDF 实验和 DØ 实验中所收集到的数据，以期得到更精确的 M_t 值，以达到相当于常规方法两倍多数据样本的精度。可以预期经过未来几年在 Tevatron 上的实验，顶夸克质量的精度最终能够达到 2 GeV/c^2。而更进一步的精度提升最终将有赖于 LHC 的投入使用。

方　　法

作为 M_t 函数的概率密度可以表示为可计算的截面与所有来自测量分辨率的效应的

section and any effects from measurement resolution

$$P(x, M_t) = \frac{1}{\sigma(M_t)} \int d\sigma(y, M_t) dq_1 dq_2 f(q_1) f(q_2) W(y, x)$$

(3)

where $W(y, x)$, our general transfer function, is the normalized probability for the measured set of variables x to arise from a set of nascent (partonic) variables y, $d\sigma(y, M_t)$ is the partonic theoretical differential cross-section, $f(q)$ are parton distribution functions that reflect the probability of finding any specific interacting quark (antiquark) with momentum q within the proton (antiproton), and $\sigma(M_t)$ is the total cross-section for producing $t\bar{t}$. The integral in equation (3) sums over all possible parton states, leading to what is observed in the detector.

The acceptance of the detector is given in terms of a function $A(x)$ that relates the probability $P_m(x, M_t)$ of measuring the observed variables x to their production probability $P(x, M_t)$: $P_m(x, M_t) = A(x)P(x, M_t)$. Effects from energy resolution, and so on are taken into account in the transfer function $W(y, x)$. The integrations in equation (3) over the eleven well-measured variables (three components of charged-lepton momentum and eight jet angles) and the four equations of energy-momentum conservation leave five integrals that must be performed to obtain the probability that any event represents $t\bar{t}$ (or background) production for some specified value of M_t.

The probability for a $t\bar{t}$ interpretation can be written as:

$$P_{t\bar{t}} = \frac{1}{12\sigma_{t\bar{t}}} \int d^5\Omega \sum_{\text{perm.,}\nu} |M_{t\bar{t}}|^2 \frac{f(q_1)f(q_2)}{|q_1||q_2|} \Phi_6 W_{\text{jets}}(E_{\text{part}}, E_{\text{jet}})$$

where Ω represent a set of five integration variables, $M_{t\bar{t}}$ is the leading-order matrix element for $t\bar{t}$ production[23,24], $f(q_1)$ and $f(q_2)$ are the CTEQ4M parton distribution functions for the incident quarks[25], Φ_6 is the phase-space factor for the six-object final state, and the sum is over all 12 permutations of the jets and all possible neutrino solutions. $W_{\text{jets}}(E_{\text{part}}, E_{\text{jet}})$ corresponds to a function that maps parton-level energies E_{part} to energies measured in the detector E_{jet} and is based on MC studies. A similar expression, using a matrix element for W+jets production (the dominant background source) that is independent of M_t, is used to calculate the probability for a background interpretation, P_{bkg}.

Studies of samples of HERWIG (ref. 26; we used version 5.1) MC events indicate that the new method is capable of providing almost a factor-of-two reduction in the statistical uncertainty on the extracted M_t. These studies also reveal that there is a systematic shift in the extracted M_t that depends on the amount of background there is in the data. To minimize this effect, a selection is introduced, based on the probability that an event represents background. The specific value of the P_{bkg} cut-off is based on MC studies carried out before applying the method to data, and, for $M_t = 175$ GeV/c^2, retains 71% of the signal and 30% of the background. A total of 22 data events out of our 71 candidates pass this selection.

The final likelihood as a function of M_t is written as:

卷积

$$P(x, M_t) = \frac{1}{\sigma(M_t)} \int d\sigma(y, M_t) dq_1 dq_2 f(q_1) f(q_2) W(y, x) \tag{3}$$

其中广义传递函数 $W(y, x)$ 表示从一组部分子水平的变量 y 中产生探测器水平变量 x 的归一化概率；$d\sigma(y, M_t)$ 是部分子水平的理论微分截面；$f(q)$ 是部分子的分布函数，表示质子（反质子）内发现处于特定相互作用中、动量为 q 的夸克（反夸克）的概率，$\sigma(M_t)$ 是产生 $t\bar{t}$ 的总截面。式（3）中的积分要对所有可能的部分子态进行求和，从而得到探测器水平的观测结果。

探测器的接受特性由函数 $A(x)$ 表达。这个函数将观测到的探测器水平变量 x 的概率 $P_m(x, M_t)$ 与其产生概率 $P(x, M_t)$ 联系起来：$P_m(x, M_t) = A(x)P(x, M_t)$。能量分辨率等效应包含在传递函数 $W(y, x)$ 中。式（3）中对 11 个精确测量的变量（带电轻子动量的 3 个分量以及 8 个喷注角度）的积分，加上四个能量–动量守恒关系，使得要完成 5 次积分才能得到特定 M_t 质量值下任何可代表 $t\bar{t}$（或者背景）产生事例的概率。

$t\bar{t}$ 事例判读的概率可以表示为

$$P_{t\bar{t}} = \frac{1}{12\sigma_{t\bar{t}}} \int d^5\Omega \sum_{\text{perm.},\nu} |M_{t\bar{t}}|^2 \frac{f(q_1)f(q_2)}{|q_1||q_2|} \Phi_6 W_{\text{jets}}(E_{\text{part}}, E_{\text{jet}})$$

其中 Ω 代表一组积分变量（5 个），对于 $t\bar{t}$ 产生事例，$M_{t\bar{t}}$ 是其领头阶矩阵元[23,24]。$f(q_1)$ 和 $f(q_2)$ 是入射夸克的 CTEQ4M 部分子分布函数[25]，Φ_6 是 6 体末态的相空间因子，求和运算针对喷注的全部 12 种排列和所有可能的中微子解进行。$W_{\text{jets}}(E_{\text{part}}, E_{\text{jet}})$ 对应于一个基于蒙特卡罗模拟研究的、将部分子水平的能量 E_{part} 映射到探测器测量到的能量 E_{jet} 的函数。利用一个不依赖 M_t 的 W+喷注产生（主要的背景来源）的矩阵元，一个类似表达式被用来计算背景判读概率 P_{bkg}。

对 HERWIG（参考文献 26，我们用的是 5.1 版本）蒙特卡罗事例样本的研究表明，新方法能够使得到的 M_t 统计不确定度降低将近一半。这些研究也揭示，获取的 M_t 值存在一个系统漂移，这一漂移依赖于数据中的背景数目。为了尽量减小这一效应，我们根据一个事例代表背景的概率引入了一个遴选程序。应用本方法处理数据之前，根据蒙特卡罗模拟，确定了具体的 P_{bkg} 截断值。对于 $M_t = 175\ \text{GeV}/c^2$，71% 的信号和 30% 的背景都得到保留。71 个候选事例中，有 22 个通过了遴选。

最终作为 M_t 函数的似然函数表达式如下：

$$\ln L(M_t) = \sum_{i=1}^{n} \ln[c_1 P_{t\bar{t}}(x_i, M_t) + c_2 P_{\text{bkg}}(x_i)] - N \int A(x)[c_1 P_{t\bar{t}}(x, M_t) + c_2 P_{\text{bkg}}(x)]dx$$

The integration is performed using MC methods. The best value of M_t (when L is at its maximum L_{max}) represents the most likely mass of the top quark in the final N-event sample, and the parameters c_i reflect the amounts of signal and background. MC studies show that there is a downward shift of 0.5 GeV/c^2 in the extracted mass, and this correction is applied to the result. Reasonable changes in the cut-off on P_{bkg} do not have a significant impact on M_t.

Figure 4 shows the value of $L(M_t)/L_{\text{max}}$ as a function of M_t for the 22 events that pass all selection criteria, after correction for the 0.5 GeV/c^2 bias in mass. The likelihood is maximized with respect to the parameters c_i at each mass point. The gaussian fit in the figure yields $M_t = 180.1$ GeV/c^2, with a statistical uncertainty of $\delta M_t = 3.6$ GeV/c^2. The systematic uncertainty, dominated by the measurement of jet energies, as discussed above, amounts to $\delta M_t = 3.9$ GeV/c^2. When added in quadrature to the statistical uncertainty from the fit, it yields the overall uncertainty on the new M_t measurement of ± 5.3 GeV/c^2.

Fig. 4. Determination of the mass of the top quark using the maximum-likelihood method. The points represent the likelihood of the fit used to extract M_t divided by it maximum value, as a function of M_t (after a correction for a -0.5 GeV/c^2 mass bias, see text). The solid line shows a gaussian fit to the points. The maximum likelihood corresponds to a mass of 180.1 GeV/c^2, which is the new DØ measurement of M_t in the lepton+jets channel. The shaded band corresponds to the range of ± 1 standard deviation, and indicates the ± 3.6 GeV/c^2 statistical uncertainty of the fit.

(**429**, 638-642; 2004)

Received 23 January; accepted 21 April 2004; doi:10.1038/nature02589.

References:

1. Hagiwara, K. *et al.* Review of particle physics. *Phys. Rev. D* **66**, 010001 (2002).

2. Affolder, T. *et al.* (CDF Collaboration). Measurement of the top quark mass with the Collider Detector at Fermilab. *Phys. Rev. D* **63**, 032003 (2001).

3. Abbott, B. *et al.* (DØ Collaboration). Measurement of the top quark mass in the dilepton channel. *Phys. Rev. D* **60**, 052001 (1999).

4. The CDF Collaboration, the DØ Collaboration, and the TEVATRON Electro-Weak Working Group. Combination of CDF and DØ Results on the Top-Quark Mass. Preprint at http://www.arXiv.org/hep-ex/0404010 (2004).

5. Barate, R. *et al.* (ALEPH Collaboration, DELPHI Collaboration, L3 Collaboration, OPAL Collaboration, and LEP Working Group for Higgs boson searches). Search for the standard model Higgs boson at LEP. *Phys. Lett. B* **565**, 61-75 (2003).

6. The LEP Collaborations ALEPH, DELPHI, L3, and OPAL, the LEP Electroweak Working Group, and the SLD Heavy Flavour Group. A combination of preliminary electroweak measurements and constraints on the standard model. Preprint at http://www.arXiv.org/hep-ex/0312023 (2003).

7. Abe, F. *et al.* (CDF Collaboration). Observation of top quark production in $p\bar{p}$ collisions with the Collider Detector at Fermilab. *Phys. Rev. Lett.* **74**, 2626-2631 (1995).

$$\ln L(M_t) = \sum_{i=1}^{n} \ln[c_1 P_{t\bar{t}}(x_i, M_t) + c_2 P_{bkg}(x_i)] - N \int A(x)[c_1 P_{t\bar{t}}(x, M_t) + c_2 P_{bkg}(x)]dx$$

积分运算是通过蒙特卡罗方法完成的。M_t 的最佳值（当 L 等于其最大值 L_{max}）代表了最终的 N 事例样本中最有可能的顶夸克质量值，参数 c_i 反映信号和背景的数量。蒙特卡罗模拟研究表明获取的质量值有一个向下的 $0.5\,\mathrm{GeV}/c^2$ 的漂移，由此我们对结果进行了修正。在合理范围内 P_{bkg} 截断值的变动对 M_t 没有显著的影响。

图 4 显示了进行 $0.5\,\mathrm{GeV}/c^2$ 的质量偏差的修正之后，通过所有遴选标准的 22 个事例的 $L(M_t)/L_{max}$ 比值随 M_t 的变化。在图中每一个质量数据点，对参数 c_i 取最大似然。图中所示数据的高斯拟合得到 $M_t = 180.1\,\mathrm{GeV}/c^2$，统计不确定度 $\delta M_t = 3.6\,\mathrm{GeV}/c^2$。如上文所述，系统不确定度主要受喷注能量的测量的影响，大小为 $\delta M_t = 3.9\,\mathrm{GeV}/c^2$。系统不确定度与拟合得到的统计不确定度求均方根，得到新的 M_t 测量值的总不确定度为 $\pm 5.3\,\mathrm{GeV}/c^2$。

图 4. 用最大似然法确定顶夸克的质量。数据点表示用以获取 M_t 的拟合的似然值与其最大值的比，该比是 M_t 的函数（已进行 $0.5\,\mathrm{GeV}/c^2$ 的质量偏差的修正，见正文）。实线表示对数据点的高斯拟合结果。最大似然值对应质量为 $180.1\,\mathrm{GeV}/c^2$，这也是新的轻子 + 喷注衰变道中 M_t 的 DØ 实验测定值。带颜色的区域对应正负一个标准差区间，表示 $\pm 3.6\,\mathrm{GeV}/c^2$ 的拟合统计不确定度。

（何钧 翻译；曹庆宏 审稿）

8. Abachi, S. *et al.* (DØ Collaboration). Observation of the top quark. *Phys. Rev. Lett.* **74**, 2632-2637 (1995).

9. Ellis, J. The 115 GeV Higgs odyssey. *Comments Nucl. Part. Phys. A* **2**, 89-103 (2002).

10. Chanowitz, M. S. Electroweak data and the Higgs boson mass: a case for new physics. *Phys. Rev. D* **66**, 073002 (2002).

11. The LEP Collaborations ALEPH, DELPHI, L3 & OPAL, the LEP Higgs Working Group. Searches for the neutral Higgs bosons of the MSSM: preliminary combined results using LEP data collected at energies up to 209 GeV. Preprint at http://www.arXiv.org/hep-ex/0107030 (2001).

12. Degrassi, G., Heinemeyer, S., Hollik, W., Slavich, P. & Weiglein, G. Towards high-precision predictions for the MSSM Higgs sector. *Eur. Phys. J. C* **28**, 133-143 (2003).

13. Abbott, B. *et al.* (DØ Collaboration). Direct measurement of the top quark mass by the DØ collaboration. *Phys. Rev. D* **58**, 052001 (1998).

14. Abazov, V. M. *et al.* (DØ Collaboration). $t\bar{t}$ production cross section in $p\bar{p}$ collisions at $\sqrt{s} = 1.8$ TeV. *Phys. Rev. D* **67**, 012004 (2003).

15. Abachi, S. *et al.* (DØ Collaboration). The DØ detector. *Nucl. Instrum. Methods A* **338**, 185-253 (1994).

16. Dalitz, R. H. & Goldstein, G. R. Test of analysis method for top–antitop production and decay events. *Proc. R. Soc. Lond. A* **445**, 2803-2834 (1999).

17. Kondo, K. *et al.* Dynamical likelihood method for reconstruction of events with missing momentum. 3: Analysis of a CDF high p_{T} $e\mu$ event as $t\bar{t}$ production. *J. Phys. Soc. Jpn* **62**, 1177-1182(1993).

18. Berends, F. A., Papadopoulos, C. G. & Pittau, R. On the determination of M_{w} and TGCs in W-pair production using the best measured kinematical variables. *Phys. Lett. B* **417**, 385-389 (1998).

19. Abreu, P. *et al.* (DELPHI Collaboration). Measurement of the W pair cross-section and of the W Mass in $e^{+}e^{-}$ interactions at 172 GeV. *Eur. Phys. J. C* **2**, 581-595 (1998).

20. Juste, A. Measurement of the W mass in $e^{+}e^{-}$ annihilation PhD thesis, 1-160, Univ. Autonoma de Barcelona (1998).

21. Estrada, J. Maximal use of kinematic information for extracting the top quark mass in single-lepton $t\bar{t}$ events PhD thesis, 1-132, Univ. Rochester (2001).

22. Canelli, F. Helicity of the W boson in single-lepton $t\bar{t}$ events PhD thesis. 1-241, Univ. Rochester (2003).

23. Mahlon, G. & Parke, S. Angular correlations in top quark pair production and decay at hadron colliders. *Phys. Rev. D* **53**, 4886-4896 (1996).

24. Mahlon, G. & Parke, S. Maximizing spin correlations in top quark pair production at the Tevatron. *Phys. Lett. B* **411**, 173-179 (1997).

25. Lai, H. L. *et al.* (CTEQ Collaboration). Global QCD analysis and the CTEQ parton distributions. *Phys. Rev. D* **51**, 4763-4782 (1995).

26. Marchesini, G. *et al.* HERWIG: a Monte Carlo event generator for simulating hadron emission reactions with interfering gluons. *Comput. Phys. Commun.* **67**, 465-508 (1992).

Acknowledgements. We are grateful to our colleagues A. Quadt and M. Mulders for reading of the manuscript and comments. We thank the staffs at Fermilab and collaborating institutions, and acknowledge support from the Department of Energy and National Science Foundation (USA), Commissariat à L'Energie Atomique and CNRS/Institut National de Physique Nucléaire et de Physique des Particules (France), Ministry for Science and Technology and Ministry for Atomic Energy (Russia), CAPES, CNPq and FAPERJ (Brazil), Departments of Atomic Energy and Science and Education (India), Colciencias (Colombia), CONACyT (Mexico), Ministry of Education and KOSEF (Korea), CONICET and UBACyT (Argentina), The Foundation for Fundamental Research on Matter (The Netherlands), PPARC (UK), Ministry of Education (Czech Republic), the A. P. Sloan Foundation, and the Research Corporation.

Authors' contributions. We wish to note the great number of contributions made by the late Harry Melanson to the DØ experiment, through his steady and inspirational leadership of the physics, reconstruction and algorithm efforts.

Competing interests statement. The authors declare that they have no competing financial interests.

Correspondence and requests for materials should be addressed to J. Estrada (estrada@fnal.gov).

Genetic Evidence Supports Demic Diffusion of Han Culture

B. Wen *et al.*

Editor's Note

Long-established disciplines situated between the natural sciences and the humanities, such as linguistics, anthropology and archaeology, have been transformed in the past several decades by the availability of genetic data for large numbers of people. The distribution of genes in a population encodes a historical record of cultural movements, interactions and relationships, which can be used to test theories about the dissemination of culture, language and traditions. In this paper by geneticist Li Jin and coworkers, genetic profiles of more than 1,000 individuals in China are used to examine alternative theories of how the Han culture came to be dominant throughout China. One possibility is that the culture was spread by migration (demic diffusion); another is that it happened by cultural exchange without mass movement of people. The Han people of the north are genetically distinct from those of the south, but the results show that southern Han are more closely related to northern Han than they are to southern ethnic minorities, especially through paternal descent—supporting the demic model, driven mostly by migration of northern males. This migration happened largely in three waves within the first and early second millennium, during the Western Jin, Tang and Song dynasties.

The spread of culture and language in human populations is explained by two alternative models: the demic diffusion model, which involves mass movement of people; and the cultural diffusion model, which refers to cultural impact between populations and involves limited genetic exchange between them[1]. The mechanism of the peopling of Europe has long been debated, a key issue being whether the diffusion of agriculture and language from the Near East was concomitant with a large movement of farmers[1-3]. Here we show, by systematically analysing Y-chromosome and mitochondrial DNA variation in Han populations, that the pattern of the southward expansion of Han culture is consistent with the demic diffusion model, and that males played a larger role than females in this expansion. The Han people, who all share the same culture and language, exceed 1.16 billion (2000 census), and are by far the largest ethnic group in the world. The expansion process of Han culture is thus of great interest to researchers in many fields.

ACCORDING to the historical records, the Hans were descended from the ancient Huaxia tribes of northern China, and the Han culture (that is, the language and its associated cultures) expanded into southern China—the region originally inhabited by the southern natives, including those speaking Daic, Austro-Asiatic and Hmong-

遗传学证据支持汉文化的扩散源于人口扩张

文波等

编者按

在过去的数十年间，科学家获得了大量的人群遗传数据，也因此改变了处在自然科学与人文科学之间的一批学科，诸如语言学、人类学和考古学。一个群体中基因的分布，记录着文化变革、互动和源流关系的历史，可以用来验证关于文化、语言和传统传播的各种假说。遗传学家金力及合作者在这篇论文中，利用中国一千多个个体的遗传学数据，验证了汉文化如何在中国成为主流的两种假说。一种可能性是移民传播了文化（人口扩张说）；也有可能只是文化交流而没有大规模的人口移动。从遗传学看，北方的汉族人群与南方的显然有差异，但是结果却显示：南方汉族人群更接近北方汉族人群，而不是接近南方少数民族，特别是在父系血缘中。这支持了人口扩张说，主要是北方男性移民传播了文化。这种迁移大量发生于公元后第一个千年，以及第二个千年早期，有西晋、唐代和宋代三次高潮。

语言和文化在人群间的扩散有两种不同的模式：一种是人口扩张、人群迁徙模式；另一种是文化传播模式，人群之间有文化传播，而基因交流却很有限 [1]。同一语系的欧洲人群的形成机制争议颇多，争论的焦点在于来自近东的农业文明和语言的扩散是否伴随着大量的农业人口的迁移 [1-3]。本文中，通过对汉族群体的 Y 染色体和线粒体 DNA 多态性系统地进行分析，我们发现汉文化向南扩散的格局符合人口扩张模式，而且在扩张过程中男性占主导地位。汉族有着共同的文化和语言，人口超过了十一亿六千万（2000 年人口统计），无疑是全世界人口最多的民族。因此汉文化的扩散过程广受各领域研究者的关注。

史载汉族源于古代中国北方的华夏部族，在过去的两千多年间，汉文化（汉语和相关的文化传统）扩散到了中国南方，而中国南方原住民族则是说侗台语、南亚

Mien languages—in the past two millennia[4,5]. Studies on classical genetic markers and microsatellites show that the Han people, like East Asians, are divided into two genetically differentiated groups, northern Han and southern Han[6,8], separated approximately by the Yangtze river[9]. Differences between these groups in terms of dialect and customs have also been noted[10]. Such observations seem to support a mechanism involving primarily cultural diffusion and assimilation (the cultural diffusion model) in Han expansion towards the south. However, the substantial sharing of Y-chromosome and mitochondrial lineages between the two groups[11,12] and the historical records describing the expansion of Han people[5] contradict the cultural diffusion model hypothesis of Han expansion. In this study, we aim to examine the alternative hypothesis; that is, that substantial population movements occurred during the expansion of Han culture (the demic diffusion model).

To test this hypothesis, we compared the genetic profiles of southern Hans with their two parental population groups: northern Hans and southern natives, which include the samples of Daic, Hmong-Mien and Austro-Asiatic speaking populations currently residing in China, and in some cases its neighbouring countries. Genetic variation in both the non-recombining region of the Y chromosome (NRY) and mitochondrial DNA (mtDNA)[13-16] were surveyed in 28 Han populations from most of the provinces in China (see Fig. 1 and Supplementary Table 1 for details).

Fig. 1. Geographic distribution of sampled populations. Shown are the three waves of north-to-south migrations according to historical record. The identifications of populations are given in Supplementary Table 1. Populations 1–14 are northern Hans, and 15–28 are southern Hans. The solid, dashed and dotted arrows refer to the first, second and third waves of migrations, respectively. The first wave involving 0.9

语和苗瑶语的人群[4,5]。经典遗传标记和微卫星位点研究显示，汉族和其他东亚人群一样都可以以长江为界[9]分为两个遗传亚群：北方汉族和南方汉族[6,8]。两个亚群之间的方言和习俗差异也很显著[10]。这些现象看似支持文化传播模式，即汉族向南扩张主要是文化传播和同化的结果。然而，两个亚群之间有着许多共同的Y染色体和线粒体类型[11,12]，历史记载的汉族移民史[5]也与汉族的文化传播模式假说相矛盾。本研究对这两种假说进行了检验，证实汉文化的扩散中的确发生了大规模的人群迁徙（人口扩张模式）。

为了验证这些假说，我们把南方汉族的遗传结构与两个亲本群体作比较，其一是北方汉族，其二是南方原住民族，即现居于中国境内和若干邻国的侗台语、苗瑶语和南亚语群体。我们分析了中国汉族 28 个群体的 Y 染色体非重组区（NRY）和线粒体 DNA(mtDNA) 遗传多态[13-16]，这些样本覆盖了中国绝大部分的省份（详见图 1 和补充信息表 1）。

图 1. 调查群体的地理分布。图中标出了历史记载中自北而南的三次迁徙浪潮。各群体的详细信息见补充信息表 1。群体 1～14 是北方汉族，15～28 是南方汉族。实线、短划线和虚线箭头依次表示三次迁徙浪潮。第一次发生于西晋时期（公元 265～316 年），迁徙人口约 90 万（大约是当时南方人口的

million (approximately one-sixth of the southern population at that time) occurred during the Western Jin Dynasty (AD 265–316); the second migration, more extensive than the first, took place during the Tang Dynasty (AD 618–907); and the third wave, including, ~5 million immigrants, occurred during the Southern Song Dynasty (AD 1127–1279).

On the paternal side, southern Hans and northern Hans share similar frequencies of Y-chromosome haplogroups (Supplementary Table 2), which are characterized by two haplogroups carrying the M122-C mutations (O3-M122 and O3e-M134) that are prevalent in almost all Han populations studied (mean and range: 53.8%, 37–71%; 54.2%, 35–74%, for northern and southern Hans, respectively). Haplogroups carrying M119-C (O1* and O1b) and/or M95-T (O2a* and O2a1) (following the nomenclature of the Y Chromosome Consortium) which are prevalent in southern natives, are more frequent in southern Hans (19%, 3–42%) than in northern Hans (5%, 1–10%). In addition, haplogroups O1b-M110, O2a1-M88 and O3d-M7, which are prevalent in southern natives[17], were only observed in some southern Hans (4% on average), but not in northern Hans. Therefore, the contribution of southern natives in southern Hans is limited, if we assume that the frequency distribution of Y lineages in southern natives represents that before the expansion of Han culture that started 2,000 yr ago[5]. The results of analysis of molecular variance (AMOVA) further indicate that northern Hans and southern Hans are not significantly different in their Y haplogroups ($F_{ST} = 0.006$, $P > 0.05$), demonstrating that southern Hans bear a high resemblance to northern Hans in their male lineages.

On the maternal side, however, the mtDNA haplogroup distribution showed substantial differentiation between northern Hans and southern Hans (Supplementary Table 3). The overall frequencies of the northern East Asian-dominating haplogroups (A, C, D, G, M8a, Y and Z) are much higher in northern Hans (55%, 49–64%) than are those in southern Hans (36%, 19–52%). In contrast, the frequency of the haplogroups that are dominant lineages (B, F, R9a, R9b and N9a) in southern natives[12,14,18] is much higher in southern (55%, 36–72%) than it is in northern Hans (33%, 18–42%). Northern and southern Hans are significantly different in their mtDNA lineages ($F_{ST} = 0.006$, $P < 10^{-5}$). Although the F_{ST} values between northern and southern Hans are similar for mtDNA and the Y chromosome, F_{ST} accounts for 56% of the total among-population variation for mtDNA but only accounts for 18% for the Y chromosome.

A principal component analysis is consistent with the observation based on the distribution of the haplogroups in Han populations. For the NRY, almost all Han populations cluster together in the upper right-hand part of Fig. 2a. Northern Hans and southern natives are separated by the second principal component (PC2) and southern Hans' PC2 values lie between northern Hans and southern natives but are much closer to northern Hans (northern Han, 0.58 ± 0.01; southern Han, 0.46 ± 0.03; southern native, -0.32 ± 0.05), implying that the southern Hans are paternally similar to northern Hans, with limited influence from southern natives. In contrast, for mtDNA, northern Hans and southern natives are distinctly separated by PC2 (Fig. 2b), and southern Hans are located between them but are closer to southern natives (northern Han, 0.56 ± 0.02; southern Han, 0.09 ± 0.06; southern native,

六分之一）；第二次发生于唐代（公元 618~907 年），规模比第一次大得多；第三次发生于南宋（公元 1127~1279 年），迁徙人口近 500 万。

父系方面，南方汉族与北方汉族的 Y 染色体单倍群频率分布非常相近（见补充信息表 2），尤其是具有 M122-C 突变的单倍群（O3-M122 和 O3e-M134）普遍存在于我们研究的汉族群体中（北方汉族在 37%~71% 之间，平均 53.8%；南方汉族在 35%~74% 之间，平均 54.2%）。南方原住民族中普遍出现的单倍群 M119-C(O1* 和 O1b) 和（或）M95-T(O2a* 和 O2a1)（遵循 Y 染色体委员会的命名法）在南方汉族中的频率（3%~42%，平均 19%）高于北方汉族（1%~10%，平均 5%）。而且，南方原住民族中普遍存在的单倍群 O1b-M110、O2a1-M88 和 O3d-M7[17]，在南方汉族中低频存在（平均 4%），而北方汉族中却没观察到。如果我们假定在起始于两千多年前的汉文化扩散[5] 之前南方原住民族的 Y 类型频率与现在基本一致的话，南方汉族中南方原住民族的成分应该是不多的。分子方差分析（AMOVA）进一步显示北方汉族和南方汉族的 Y 染色体单倍群频率分布没有显著差异（$F_{ST} = 0.006$，$P > 0.05$），说明南方汉族在父系上与北方汉族非常相似。

母系方面，北方汉族与南方汉族的 mtDNA 单倍群分布非常不同（补充信息表 3）。东亚北部的主要单倍群(A，C，D，G，M8a，Y，Z) 在北方汉族中的频率（49%~64%，平均 55%）比在南方汉族中（19%~52%，平均 36%）高得多。另一方面，南方原住民族的主要单倍群(B，F，R9a，R9b，N9a)[12,14,18] 在南方汉族中的频率（36%~72%，平均 55%）要比在北方汉族中（18%~42%，平均 33%）高得多。mtDNA 类型的分布在南北汉族之间有极显著差异（$F_{ST} = 0.006$，$P < 10^{-5}$）。虽然南北汉族之间 mtDNA 和 Y 染色体的 F_{ST} 值相近，但 mtDNA 的南北差异 F_{ST} 值占群体间总方差的 56%，而 Y 染色体仅仅占 18%。

用汉族群体的单倍群频率数据所做的主成分分析与以上结果相一致。对 NRY 的分析发现，几乎所有的汉族群体都聚在图 2a 的右上方。北方汉族和南方原住民族在第 2 主成分上分离，南方汉族的第 2 主成分值处于北方汉族和南方原住民族之间，但是更接近于北方汉族（北方汉族 0.58±0.01；南方汉族 0.46±0.03；南方原住民族 −0.32±0.05），这表明南方汉族在父系上与北方汉族相近，受到南方原住民族的影响很小。就 mtDNA 而言，北方汉族和南方原住民族仍然被第 2 主成分分开（图 2b），南方汉族也在两者之间但稍微接近南方原住民族（北方汉族 0.56±0.02；南方汉族 0.09±0.06；南方原住民族 −0.23±0.04），表明南方汉族的女性基因库比男性

-0.23 ± 0.04), indicating a much more substantial admixture in southern Hans' female gene pool than in its male counterpart.

Fig. 2. Principal component plot. **a**, **b**, Plots are of Y-chromosome (**a**) and mtDNA (**b**) haplogroup frequency. Population groups: H-M, Hmong-Mien; DAC, Daic; A-A, Austro-Asiatic; SH, southern Han; NH, northern Han.

The relative contribution of the two parental populations (northern Hans and southern natives) in southern Hans was estimated by two different statistics[19,20], which are less biased than other statistics for single-locus data[21] (Table 1). The estimations of the admixture coefficient (M, proportion of northern Han contribution) from the two methods are highly consistent (for the Y chromosome, $r = 0.922$, $P < 0.01$; for mtDNA, $r = 0.970$, $P < 0.01$). For the Y chromosome, all southern Hans showed a high proportion of northern Han contribution (M_{BE}: 0.82 ± 0.14, range from 0.54 to 1; M_{RH}: 0.82 ± 0.12, range from 0.61 to 0.97) (see refs 20 and 19 for definitions of M_{BE} and M_{RH}, respectively) indicating that males from the northern Hans are the primary contributor to the gene pool of the southern

380

基因库有更多的混合成分。

图 2. 主成分散点图。**a** 为 Y 染色体单倍群散点图，**b** 为 mtDNA 单倍群散点图。群体标记：▲北方汉族，△南方汉族，＋侗台语民族，×南亚语民族，＊苗瑶语民族。

我们进一步用两种不同的统计方法[19,20]来估计两个亲本（北方汉族和南方原住民）对南方汉族基因库的相对贡献（表 1），这两个统计量用于单位点分析时比其他的方法更为准确[21]。两种方法得到的混合系数估计值（M，北方汉族的贡献比例）高度一致（Y 染色体，$r = 0.922$，$P < 0.01$；mtDNA，$r = 0.970$，$P < 0.01$）。就 Y 染色体而言，所有的南方汉族都包含很高比例的北方汉族混合比率（M_{BE}:0.82±0.14，范围 0.54～1；M_{RH}:0.82±0.12，范围 0.61～0.97）（M_{BE} 和 M_{RH} 的定义分别见参考文献 20 和 19），这表明南方汉族男性基因库的主要贡献成分来自北方汉族。相反，南

Hans. In contrast, northern Hans and southern natives contributed almost equally to the southern Hans' mtDNA gene pool (M_{BE}: 0.56 ± 0.24 [0.15, 0.95]; M_{RH}: 0.50 ± 0.26 [0.07, 0.91]). The contribution of northern Hans to southern Hans is significantly higher in the paternal lineage than in the maternal lineage collectively (t-test, $P < 0.01$) or individually (11 out of 13 populations for M_{BE}, and 13 out of 13 populations for M_{RH}: $P < 0.01$, assuming a null binomial distribution with equal male and female contributions), indicating a strong sex-biased population admixture in southern Hans. The proportions of northern Han contribution (M) in southern Hans showed a clinal geographic pattern, which decreases from north to south. The Ms in southern Hans are positively correlated with latitude ($r^2 = 0.569$, $P < 0.01$) for mtDNA, but are not significant for the Y chromosome ($r^2 = 0.072$, $P > 0.05$), because the difference of Ms in the paternal lineage among southern Hans is too small to create a statistically significant trend.

Table 1. Northern Han admixture proportion in southern Hans

Population	Y Chromosome		mtDNA	
	M_{BE} (± s.e.m)	M_{RH}	M_{BE} (± s.e.m)	M_{RH}
Anhui	0.868 ± 0.119	0.929	0.816 ± 0.214	0.755
Fujian	1	0.966	0.341 ± 0.206	0.248
Guangdong1	0.677 ± 0.121	0.669	0.149 ± 0.181	0.068
Guangdong2	ND	ND	0.298 ± 0.247	0.312
Guangxi	0.543 ± 0.174	0.608	0.451 ± 0.263	0.249
Hubei	0.981 ± 0.122	0.949	0.946 ± 0.261	0.907
Hunan	0.732 ± 0.219	0.657	0.565 ± 0.297	0.490
Jiangsu	0.789 ± 0.078	0.821	0.811 ± 0.177	0.786
Jiangxi	0.804 ± 0.113	0.829	0.374 ± 0.343	0.424
Shanghai	0.819 ± 0.087	0.902	0.845 ± 0.179	0.833
Sichuan	0.750 ± 0.118	0.713	0.509 ± 0.166	0.498
Yunnan1	1	0.915	0.376 ± 0.221	0.245
Yunnan2	0.935 ± 0.088	0.924	0.733 ± 0.192	0.645
Zhejiang	0.751 ± 0.084	0.763	0.631 ± 0.180	0.540
Average	0.819	0.819	0.560	0.500

M_{BE} and M_{RH} refer to the statistics described in refs 20 and 19, respectively. The standard error of M_{BE} was obtained by bootstrap with 1,000 replications. The proportions of contribution from northern Hans were estimated using northern Hans and southern natives as the parental populations of the southern Hans. It was assumed that the allele frequency in the southern natives remained unchanged before and after the admixture, which started about 2,000 yr ago, and the genetic exchange between northern Hans and southern natives has been limited. In fact, the gene flow from northern Hans to southern natives has been larger than that from southern natives to northern Hans; therefore, the level of admixture presented in this table is underestimated and is without proper adjustment. The demic expansion of Han would have been more pronounced than was observed in this study.

We provide two lines of evidence supporting the demic diffusion hypothesis for the expansion of Han culture. First, almost all Han populations bear a high resemblance in

方汉族的 mtDNA 基因库中北方汉族和南方原住民族的贡献比例几乎相等（M_{BE}：0.56 ± 0.24 [0.15, 0.95]；M_{RH}：0.50 ± 0.26 [0.07, 0.91]）。总体上北方汉族对南方汉族的遗传贡献父系比母系高得多（t 检验，$P<0.01$）；各群体分别看也是这样：绝大部分南方汉族群体中北方汉族的贡献在父系上大于母系（M_{BE}，11/13，M_{RH}，13/13，$P<0.01$，零假设为男女的贡献相等为二项分布），这表明南方汉族的群体混合过程有很强的性别偏向。南方汉族中北方汉族贡献的比例（M）呈现出由北向南递减的梯度地理格局。南方汉族 mtDNA 的 M 值与纬度正相关（$r^2=0.569$，$P<0.01$），但 Y 染色体的相关性不显著（$r^2=0.072$，$P>0.05$），因为南方汉族父系的 M 值差异太小，不足以导致统计上的显著性。

表 1. 南方汉族中的北方汉族混合比例

群体	Y 染色体		线粒体 DNA	
	M_{BE}（$\pm$ s.e.m）	M_{RH}	M_{BE}（$\pm$ s.e.m）	M_{RH}
安徽	0.868 ± 0.119	0.929	0.816 ± 0.214	0.755
福建	1	0.966	0.341 ± 0.206	0.248
广东 1	0.677 ± 0.121	0.669	0.149 ± 0.181	0.068
广东 2	ND	ND	0.298 ± 0.247	0.312
广西	0.543 ± 0.174	0.608	0.451 ± 0.263	0.249
湖北	0.981 ± 0.122	0.949	0.946 ± 0.261	0.907
湖南	0.732 ± 0.219	0.657	0.565 ± 0.297	0.490
江苏	0.789 ± 0.078	0.821	0.811 ± 0.177	0.786
江西	0.804 ± 0.113	0.829	0.374 ± 0.343	0.424
上海	0.819 ± 0.087	0.902	0.845 ± 0.179	0.833
四川	0.750 ± 0.118	0.713	0.509 ± 0.166	0.498
云南 1	1	0.915	0.376 ± 0.221	0.245
云南 2	0.935 ± 0.088	0.924	0.733 ± 0.192	0.645
浙江	0.751 ± 0.084	0.763	0.631 ± 0.180	0.540
平均	0.819	0.819	0.560	0.500

M_{BE} 和 M_{RH} 分别为参考文献 20 和 19 所描述的统计量。M_{BE} 的标准误差通过 1,000 次自展获得。把南方原住民族和北方汉族作为南方汉族的亲本群体估计北方汉族的遗传贡献比例，假定 2,000 多年前开始的混合过程前后南方原住民族的等位基因频率基本不变，并且北方汉族和南方原始民族之间的遗传交流不多。实际上，从北方汉族到南方原住民族的基因流动比反向的流动大得多，所以表中的估计值在没有适当调整前是低估的。因而汉族实际的人口扩张程度应该大于本项研究得出的数值。

综上所述，我们提出了两项证据支持汉文化扩散的人口扩张假说。首先，几乎所有的汉族群体的 Y 染色体单倍群分布都极为相似，Y 染色体主成分分析也把几

Y-chromosome haplogroup distribution, and the result of principal component analysis indicated that almost all Han populations form a tight cluster in their Y chromosome. Second, the estimated contribution of northern Hans to southern Hans is substantial in both paternal and maternal lineages and a geographic cline exists for mtDNA. It is noteworthy that the expansion process was dominated by males, as is shown by a greater contribution to the Y-chromosome than the mtDNA from northern Hans to southern Hans. A sex-biased admixture pattern was also observed in Tibeto-Burman-speaking populations[22].

According to the historical records, there were continuous southward movements of Han people due to warfare and famine in the north, as illustrated by three waves of large-scale migrations (Fig. 1). Aside from these three waves, other smaller southward migrations also occurred during almost all periods in the past two millennia. Our genetic observation is thus in line with the historical accounts. The massive movement of the northern immigrants led to a change in genetic makeup in southern China, and resulted in the demographic expansion of Han people as well as their culture. Except for these massive population movements, gene flow between northern Hans, southern Hans and southern natives also contributed to the admixture which shaped the genetic profile of the extant populations.

Methods

Samples

Blood samples of 871 unrelated anonymous individuals from 17 Han populations were collected across China. Genomic DNA was extracted by the phenol-chloroform method. By integrating the additional data obtained from the literatures on the Y chromosome and on mtDNA variation, the final sample sizes for analysis expanded to 1,289 individuals (23 Han populations) for the Y chromosome and 1,119 individuals (23 Han populations) for mtDNA. These samples encompass most of the provinces in China (Fig. 1 and Supplementary Table 1).

Genetic markers

Thirteen bi-allelic Y-chromosome markers, YAP, M15, M130, M89, M9, M122, M134, M119, M110, M95, M88, M45 and M120 were typed by polymerase chain reaction-restriction-fragment length polymorphism methods[11]. These markers are highly informative in East Asians[23] and define 13 haplogroups following the Y Chromosome Consortium nomenclature[24].

The HVS-1 of mtDNA and eight coding region variations, 9-bp deletion, 10397 *Alu*I, 5176 *Alu*I, 4831 *Hha*I, 13259 *Hinc*II, 663 *Hae*III, 12406 *Hpa*I and 9820 *Hinf*I were sequenced and genotyped as in our previous report[22]. Both the HVS-1 motif and the coding region variations were used to infer haplogroups following the phylogeny of East Asian mtDNAs[18].

乎所有的汉族群体都集合成一个紧密的聚类。其二，北方汉族对南方汉族的遗传贡献无论父系方面还是母系方面都是可观的，在线粒体 DNA 分布上也存在地理梯度。北方汉族对南方汉族的遗传贡献在父系（Y 染色体）上远大于母系（mtDNA），表明这一扩张过程中汉族男性处于主导地位。性别偏向的混合格局也同样存在于藏缅语人群中 [22]。

据历史记载，受北方战乱和饥荒的影响，汉人不断南迁，图 1 中画出了三次大规模移民的浪潮。在两千多年间，除了这三次大潮，各个时期几乎都有小规模的南迁。所以，我们的遗传研究也与历史记载相吻合。大量的北方移民改变了中国南方的遗传构成，而汉族人口扩张的同时也带动了汉文化的扩散。除了大规模的人群迁徙，北方汉族、南方汉族和南方原住民族之间的基因交流造成的族群混合也在很大程度上改变了中国人群的遗传结构。

方　　法

样本

采集中国各地的 17 个汉族群体 871 个随机不相关个体的血样。用酚–氯仿法抽提基因组 DNA。结合文献报道的 Y 染色体和 mtDNA 多态性数据，总共分析的样本量是：Y 染色体 23 个群体 1,289 人，mtDNA23 个群体 1,119 人。这些样本涉及了中国的大部分省份（图 1 和补充信息表 1）。

遗传标记

通过聚合酶链式反应–限制性片段长度多态性方法 [11] 分型 Y 染色体上的 13 个双等位标记：YAP，M15，M130，M89，M9，M122，M134，M119，M110，M95，M88，M45，M120。根据 Y 染色体委员会的命名系统 [24]，这些标记构成 13 个单倍群，在东亚人群中具有较高的信息量 [23]。

mtDNA 上，对高变 1 区进行测序，对编码区 8 个多态位点（9-bp 缺失，10397 *Alu*I，5176 *Alu*I，4831 *Hha*I，13259 *Hinc*II，663 *Hae*III，12406 *Hpa*I，9820 *Hinf* I）做了分型，有关方法已有报道 [22]。根据东亚 mtDNA 系统树 [18]，用高变 1 区突变结构和编码区多态性构建单倍群。

Data analysis

Population relationship was investigated by principal component analysis, which was conducted using mtDNA and Y-chromosome haplogroup frequencies and SPSS10.0 software (SPSS Inc.). The genetic difference between northern and southern Hans was tested by AMOVA[25], using ARLEQUIN software[26]. ADMIX 2.0 (ref. 27) and LEADMIX[21] software were used to estimate the level of admixture of the northern Hans and southern natives in the southern Han populations, using two different statistics[19,20]. The selection of parental populations is critical for appropriate estimation of admixture proportion[28,29] and we were careful to minimize bias by using large data sets across East Asia. In this analysis, the average haplogroup frequencies (for Y-chromosome or mtDNA markers, respectively) of northern Hans (arithmetic mean of 10 northern Hans) were taken for the northern parental population. The frequency of southern natives was estimated by the average of three groups including Austro-Asiatic (NRY, 6 populations; mtDNA, 5 populations), Daic (NRY, 22 populations; mtDNA, 11 populations) and Hmong-Mien (NRY, 18 populations; mtDNA, 14 populations). The geographic pattern of Han populations was revealed by the linear regression analysis of admixture proportion against the latitudes of samples[1,3].

(**431**, 302-305, 2004)

Bo Wen[1,2], Hui Li[1], Daru Lu[1], Xiufeng Song[1], Feng Zhang[1], Yungang He[1], Feng Li[1], Yang Gao[1], Xianyun Mao[1], Liang Zhang[1], Ji Qian[1], Jingze Tan[1], Jianzhong Jin[1], Wei Huang[2], Ranjan Deka[3], Bing Su[1,3,4], Ranajit Chakraborty[3] & Li Jin[1,3]

[1] State Key Laboratory of Genetic Engineering and Center for Anthropological Studies, School of Life Sciences and Morgan-Tan International Center for Life Sciences, Fudan University, Shanghai 200433, China

[2] Chinese National Human Genome Center, Shanghai 201203, China

[3] Center for Genome Information, Department of Environmental Health, University of Cincinnati, Cincinnati, Ohio 45267, USA

[4] Key Laboratory of Cellular and Molecular Evolution, Kunming Institute of Zoology, the Chinese Academy of Sciences, Kunming 650223, China

Received 28 April; accepted 20 July, 2004; doi: 10.1038/nature02878.

References:

1. Cavalli-Sforza, L. L., Menozzi, P. & Piazza, A. *The History and Geography of Human Genes* (Princeton Univ. Press, Princeton, 1994).

2. Sokal, R., Oden, N. L. & Wilson, C. Genetic evidence for the spread of agriculture in Europe by demic diffusion. *Nature* **351**, 143-145 (1991).

3. Chikhi, L. *et al.* Y genetic data support the Neolithic demic diffusion model. *Proc. Natl Acad. Sci. USA* **99**, 11008-11013 (2002).

4. Fei, X. T. *The Pattern of Diversity in Unity of the Chinese Nation* (Central Univ. for Nationalities Press, Beijing, 1999).

5. Ge, J. X., Wu, S. D. & Chao, S. J. *Zhongguo yimin shi (The Migration History of China)* (Fujian People's Publishing House, Fuzhou, China, 1997).

6. Zhao, T. M. & Lee, T. D. Gm and Km allotypes in 74 Chinese populations: a hypothesis of the origin of the Chinese nation. *Hum. Genet.* **83**, 101-110 (1989).

7. Du, R. F., Xiao, C. J. & Cavalli-Sforza, L. L. Genetic distances calculated on gene frequencies of 38 loci. *Sci. China* **40**, 613 (1997).

8. Chu, J. Y. *et al.* Genetic relationship of populations in China. *Proc. Natl Acad. Sci. USA* **95**, 11763-11768 (1998).

9. Xiao, C. J. *et al.* Principal component analysis of gene frequencies of Chinese populations. *Sci. China* **43**, 472-481 (2000).

10. Xu, Y. T. A brief study on the origin of Han nationality. *J. Centr. Univ. Natl* **30**, 59-64 (2003).

11. Su, B. *et al.* Y chromosome haplotypes reveal prehistorical migrations to the Himalayas. *Hum. Genet.* **107**, 582-590 (2000).

12. Yao, Y. G. *et al.* Phylogeographic differentiation of mitochondrial DNA in Han Chinese. *Am. J. Hum. Genet.* **70**, 635-651 (2002).

13. Cavalli-Sforza, L. L. & Feldman, M. W. The application of molecular genetic approaches to the study of human evolution. *Nature Genet.* **33**, 266-275 (2003).

14. Wallace, D. C., Brown, M. D. & Lott, M. T. Nucleotide mitochondrial DNA variation in human evolution and disease. *Gene* **238**, 211-230 (1999).

15. Underhill, P. A. *et al.* Y chromosome sequence variation and the history of human populations. *Nature Genet.* **26**, 358-361 (2000).

数据分析

根据 mtDNA 和 Y 染色体单倍群频率，用 SPSS10.0 软件（SPSS 公司）作主成分分析，研究群体间关系。南北汉族的遗传差异用 ARLEQUIN 软件[26] 做 AMOVA 检验[25]。南方汉族中北方汉族和南方原住民族的混合比例估计用两种不同的统计方法[19,20]：ADMIX 2.0[27] 和 LEADMIX[21] 软件。亲本群体的选择对混合比例的适当估计很重要[28,29]，我们通过扩大东亚的参考数据来减小偏差。分析中，10 个北方汉族群体的各单倍群频率（Y 染色体和 mtNDA 标记分别分析）的算术平均作为北方亲本群体。南方原住民族的频率是三个族群的平均：侗台语群（NRY，22 群体；mtNDA，11 群体），南亚语群（NRY，6 群体；mtNDA，5 群体），苗瑶语群（NRY，18 群体；mtNDA，14 群体）。通过样本的混合比例与纬度[1,3] 的线性回归分析揭示汉族群体的地理格局。

（李辉 翻译；徐文堪 审稿）

16. Jobling, M. A. & Tyler-Smith, C. The human Y chromosome: an evolutionary marker comes of age. *Nature Rev. Genet.* **4**, 598-612 (2003).

17. Su, B. *et al.* Y-chromosome evidence for a northward migration of modern humans into eastern Asia during the last ice age. *Am. J. Hum. Genet.* **65**, 1718-1724 (1999).

18. Kivisild, T. *et al.* The emerging limbs and twigs of the East Asian mtDNA tree. *Mol. Biol. Evol.* **19**, 1737-1751 (2002).

19. Roberts, D. F. & Hiorns, R. W. Methods of analysis of the genetic composition of a hybrid population. *Hum. Biol.* **37**, 38-43 (1965).

20. Bertorelle, G. & Excoffier, L. Inferring admixture proportions from molecular data. *Mol. Biol. Evol.* **15**, 1298-1311 (1998).

21. Wang, J. Maximum-likelihood estimation of admixture proportions from genetic data. *Genetics* **164**, 747-765 (2003).

22. Wen, B. *et al.* Analyses of genetic structure of Tibeto-Burman populations revealed a gender-biased admixture in southern Tibeto-Burmans. *Am. J. Hum. Genet.* **74**, 856-865 (2004).

23. Jin, L. & Su, B. Natives or immigrants: modern human origin in East Asia. *Nature Rev. Genet.* **1**, 126-133 (2000).

24. The Y Chromosome Consortium, A nomenclature system for the tree of human Y-chromosomal binary haplogroups. *Genome Res.* **12**, 339-348 (2002).

25. Excoffier, L., Smouse, P. E. & Quattro, J. M. Analysis of molecular variance inferred from metric distances among DNA haplotypes: application to human mitochondrial DNA restriction data. *Genetics* **131**, 479-491 (1992).

26. Schneider, S., *et al.* Arlequin: Ver. 2.000. A software for population genetic analysis. (Genetics and Biometry Laboratory, Univ. of Geneva, Geneva, 2000).

27. Dupanloup, I. & Bertorelle, G. Inferring admixture proportions from molecular data: extension to any number of parental populations. *Mol. Biol. Evol.* **18**, 672-675 (2001).

28. Chakraborty, R. Gene admixture in human populations: Models and predictions. *Yb. Phys. Anthropol.* **29**, 1-43 (1986).

29. Sans, M. *et al.* Unequal contributions of male and female gene pools from parental populations in the African descendants of the city of Melo, Uruguay. *Am. J. Phys. Anthropol.* **118**, 33-44 (2002).

Supplementary Information accompanies the paper on www.nature.com/nature.

Acknowledgements. We thank all of the donors for making this work possible. The data collection was supported by NSFC and STCSM to Fudan and a NSF grant to L.J. L.J., R.D. and R.C. are supported by NIH.

Competing interests statement. The authors declare that they have no competing financial interests.

Correspondence and requests for materials should be addressed to L.J. (lijin@fudan.edu.cn or li.jin@uc.edu). The mtDNA HVS-1 sequences of 711 individuals from 15 Han populations were submitted to GenBank with accession numbers AY594701–AY595411.

A New Small-bodied Hominin from the Late Pleistocene of Flores, Indonesia

P. Brown *et al.*

Editor's Note

When archaeologist Michael Morwood set out to trace how early modern humans got to Australia, the last thing he and his colleagues expected to unearth in Liang Bua cave on Flores was a creature out of folk-tale. But that's what they discovered. "The Hobbit": a human-like creature that stood barely a metre tall, had a very small brain and a body reminiscent of hominids that lived in Africa, three or more million years ago—but which survived until at least 18,000 years ago. *Homo floresiensis* challenged conventional wisdom about the adaptability of the human form, as well as the assumption that *Homo sapiens* reigned alone on Earth. The sensation created by this strangest of fossil humans has yet to fade.

Currently, it is widely accepted that only one hominin genus, *Homo*, was present in Pleistocene Asia, represented by two species, *Homo erectus* and *Homo sapiens*. Both species are characterized by greater brain size, increased body height and smaller teeth relative to Pliocene *Australopithecus* in Africa. Here we report the discovery, from the Late Pleistocene of Flores, Indonesia, of an adult hominin with stature and endocranial volume approximating 1 m and 380 cm^3, respectively—equal to the smallest-known australopithecines. The combination of primitive and derived features assigns this hominin to a new species, *Homo floresiensis*. The most likely explanation for its existence on Flores is long-term isolation, with subsequent endemic dwarfing, of an ancestral *H. erectus* population. Importantly, *H. floresiensis* shows that the genus *Homo* is morphologically more varied and flexible in its adaptive responses than previously thought.

THE LB1 skeleton was recovered in September 2003 during archaeological excavation at Liang Bua, Flores[1]. Most of the skeletal elements for LB1 were found in a small area, approximately 500 cm^2, with parts of the skeleton still articulated and the tibiae flexed under the femora. Orientation of the skeleton in relation to site stratigraphy suggests that the body had moved slightly down slope before being covered with sediment. The skeleton is extremely fragile and not fossilized or covered with calcium carbonate. Recovered elements include a fairly complete cranium and mandible, right leg and left innominate. Bones of the left leg, hands and feet are less complete, while the vertebral column, sacrum, scapulae, clavicles and ribs are only represented by fragments. The position of the skeleton suggests that the arms are still in the wall of the excavation, and may be recovered in the future. Tooth eruption, epiphyseal union and tooth wear indicate an adult, and pelvic

印度尼西亚弗洛勒斯晚更新世一身材矮小人族新成员

布朗等

编者按

当考古学家迈克尔·莫伍德开始研究早期现代人是如何到达澳大利亚的时候，他和他的同事们最不希望在弗洛勒斯的利昂布阿洞穴发现的是一种民间传说中的生物，但这就是他们的发现。"霍比特人"：这是一种类似人类的生物，身高只有一米，大脑非常小，身体让人想起300万年前或更早以前生活在非洲的原始人，但这种原始人至少存活到18,000年前。弗洛勒斯人挑战了关于人类形态适应性的传统观点，也挑战了智人独自统治地球的假设。这种由最奇怪的人类化石产生的轰动还没有消退。

目前，人们普遍认为，更新世人族在亚洲仅存在一个属，即人属，以直立人和智人两个物种为代表。相对于非洲上新世的南方古猿属，这两个种的特征是脑容量更大，身高更高，牙齿更小。在此我们报道，在印度尼西亚弗洛勒斯岛晚更新世发现的一个人族成员成年个体化石，其身高和颅腔容量分别约为1米和380立方厘米，相当于已知最小的南方古猿。其原始与衍生特征的组合，将这一人族成员定为一个新的物种——弗洛勒斯人。对其为何存在于弗洛勒斯岛上，最可能的解释是一个祖先直立人种群的长期隔离，并在随后出现了地方性的矮化。重要的是，弗洛勒斯人显示出人属在形态上的适应性反应比以前所想象的更多样化，也更灵活。

LB1骨架是2003年9月在弗洛勒斯岛的利昂布阿进行考古挖掘期间出土的[1]。LB1的大部分骨骼部位都是在大约500平方厘米的一个很小的区域内被发现的，骨架不少部位仍然互相关节，胫骨弯曲在股骨下方。骨架方位与遗址地层的相对关系表明躯体在被沉积物掩埋之前，沿坡轻微向下移动了一些。骨骼非常脆弱，没有石化，也未被碳酸钙覆盖。出土的部位包括相当完整的颅骨与下颌骨，右腿和左髋骨。左腿、手和脚的骨头的完整性稍差，而脊柱、荐椎、两侧肩胛骨、两侧锁骨和肋骨仅有一些碎片保存。骨架的姿态表明其手臂还埋在发掘探方的侧壁里，将来可能会被发现。牙齿的萌发状况、骨骺的愈合程度及牙齿的磨损程度表明这是一个成年个

anatomy strongly supports the skeleton being that of a female. On the basis of its unique combination of primitive and derived features we assign this skeleton to a new species, *Homo floresiensis*.

Description of *Homo floresiensis*

Order Primates Linnaeus, 1758

Suborder Anthropoidea Mivart, 1864

Superfamily Hominoidea Gray, 1825

Family Hominidae Gray, 1825

Tribe Hominini Gray, 1825

Genus *Homo* Linnaeus, 1758

Homo floresiensis sp. nov.

Etymology. Recognizing that this species has only been identified on the island of Flores, and a prolonged period of isolation may have resulted in the evolution of an island endemic form.

Holotype. LB1 partial adult skeleton excavated in September 2003. Recovered skeletal elements include the cranium and mandible, femora, tibiae, fibulae and patellae, partial pelvis, incomplete hands and feet, and fragments of vertebrae, sacrum, ribs, scapulae and clavicles. The repository is the Centre for Archaeology, Jakarta, Indonesia.

Referred material. LB2 isolated left mandibular P_3. The repository is the Centre for Archaeology, Jakarta, Indonesia.

Localities. Liang Bua is a limestone cave on Flores, in eastern Indonesia. The cave is located 14 km north of Ruteng, the provincial capital of Manggarai Province, at an altitude of 500 m above sea level and 25 km from the north coast. It occurs at the base of a limestone hill, on the southern edge of the Wae Racang river valley. The type locality is at 08° 31′ 50.4″ south latitude 120° 26′ 36.9″ east longitude.

Horizon. The type specimen LB1 was found at a depth of 5.9 m in Sector VII of the excavation at Liang Bua. It is associated with calibrated accelerator mass spectrometry (AMS) dates of approximately 18 kyr and bracketed by luminescence dates of 35 ± 4 kyr and 14 ± 2 kyr. The referred isolated left P_3 (LB2) was recovered just below a discomformity

体，骨盆的解剖学结构特征有力地支持这是一个女性个体的骨架。根据其原始与衍生特征的独特组合，我们将这具骨架定为一新种——弗洛勒斯人。

弗洛勒斯人的描述

灵长目　Primates Linnaeus，1758

类人猿亚目　Anthropoidea Mivart，1864

人猿超科　Hominoidea Gray，1825

人科　Hominidae Gray，1825

人族　Hominini Gray，1825

人属　*Homo* Linnaeus，1758

弗洛勒斯人（新种）*Homo floresiensis* sp. nov.

词源　考虑到该种仅发现于弗洛勒斯岛，并且可能由于长期的隔离才造成了一个岛屿特有类型的演化。

正型标本　2003 年 9 月发掘出土的不完整成年个体骨架 LB1。出土的骨骼部位包括颅骨与下颌骨，两侧股骨，胫骨，腓骨和髌骨，不完整骨盆，不完全的双手和双脚，以及椎体、荐椎、肋骨、两侧肩胛骨和两侧锁骨的碎片。存放在印度尼西亚雅加达考古中心。

归入材料　LB2 游离左下第 3 前臼齿。存放在印度尼西亚雅加达考古中心。

产地　利昂布阿是印度尼西亚东部弗洛勒斯岛上的一个石灰岩洞穴。该洞穴位于芒加莱省会城市鲁滕以北 14 千米处，其海拔 500 米，距北海岸 25 千米。它位于威拉肯河谷南缘的石灰岩山丘底部。模式产地位于南纬 08°31′50.4″ 东经 120°26′36.9″。

层位　模式标本 LB1 发现于利昂布阿发掘 VII 区 5.9 米深处。与其直接相关的校准加速器质谱法（AMS）测定年代大约为 18,000 年，释光法把年代限定在 35,000±4,000 年与 14,000±2,000 年之间。归入材料中的游离左下第 3 前臼齿（LB2）发现于 IV 区 4.7 米处不整合面正下方，其年代限定范围在流石 U 系测定年代

at 4.7 m in Sector IV, and bracketed by a U-series date of 37.7 ± 0.2 kyr on flowstone, and 20 cm above an electron-spin resonance (ESR)/U-series date of 74^{+14}_{-12} kyr on a *Stegodon* molar.

Diagnosis. Small-bodied bipedal hominin with endocranial volume and stature (body height) similar to, or smaller than, *Australopithecus afarensis*. Lacks masticatory adaptations present in *Australopithecus* and *Paranthropus*, with substantially reduced facial height and prognathism, smaller postcanine teeth, and posteriorly orientated infraorbital region. Cranial base flexed. Prominent maxillary canine juga form prominent pillars, laterally separated from nasal aperture. Petrous pyramid smooth, tubular and with low relief, styloid process absent, and without vaginal crest. Superior cranial vault bone thicker than *Australopithecus* and similar to *H. erectus* and *H. sapiens*. Supraorbital torus arches over each orbit and does not form a flat bar as in Javan *H. erectus*. Mandibular P₃ with relatively large occlusal surface area, with prominent protoconid and broad talonid, and either bifurcated roots or a mesiodistally compressed Tomes root. Mandibular P₄ also with Tomes root. First and second molar teeth of similar size. Mandibular coronoid process higher than condyle, and the ramus has a posterior orientation. Mandibular symphysis without chin and with a posterior inclination of the symphysial axis. Posteriorly inclined alveolar planum with superior and inferior transverse tori. Ilium with marked lateral flare. Femur neck long relative to head diameter, the shaft circular and without pilaster, and there is a high bicondylar angle. Long axis of tibia curved and the midshaft has an oval cross-section.

Description and Comparison of the Cranial and Postcranial Elements

Apart from the right zygomatic arch, the cranium is free of substantial distortion (Figs 1 and 2). Unfortunately, the bregmatic region, right frontal, supraorbital, nasal and subnasal regions were damaged when the skeleton was discovered. To repair post-mortem pressure cracks, and stabilize the vault, the calvarium was dismantled and cleaned endocranially before reconstruction. With the exception of the squamous suture, most of the cranial vault sutures are difficult to locate and this problem persists in computed tomography (CT) scans. As a result it is not possible to locate most of the standard craniometric landmarks with great precision.

$37,700 \pm 200$ 年以及 20 厘米之上的一个剑齿象臼齿电子自旋共振（ESR）/U 系测定年代 $74,000^{+14,000}_{-12,000}$ 年之间。

特征　身材矮小两足行走的人族成员，其颅腔容积和身材（身高）相当于或小于南方古猿阿法种。缺少南方古猿与傍人所表现出的咀嚼适应性变化，面部高度与凸颌程度明显降低，犬后齿较小，眶下区朝后。颅底角度收缩。突出的上犬齿隆突呈突出柱状，在侧面与鼻孔分离。岩锥平滑、呈管状且凸出程度低，茎突缺失，且没有茎突鞘脊。上部颅顶骨厚于南方古猿而与直立人及智人相当。眶上圆枕在每一个眼眶上呈拱形，且不像爪哇直立人那样呈水平条状。下第 3 前臼齿有相对较大的咀嚼面表面积，下原尖突出，下跟座宽阔，而且牙根或者完全分叉或者为前后压扁的托姆斯式齿根。下第 4 前臼齿也具有托姆斯式齿根。第一和第二臼齿大小相当。颌骨冠状突高于髁突，且上升支向后倾。下颌联合部没有颏，联合部轴线向后倾斜。齿槽面向后倾斜，并且有上下圆枕。髂骨具明显侧向展开。股骨颈部相对于股骨头直径相对显长，骨干截面呈圆形且没有粗线嵴发育，双髁角角度大。胫骨长轴弯曲且骨干中部的横截面为椭圆形。

颅骨与颅后骨骼部位的描述与对比

除了右侧颧弓，颅骨基本没有变形（图 1、图 2）。不幸的是，骨架发现时，其前囟区、右侧额骨、眶上、鼻骨及鼻下区域被损坏。为了修复死后遭受压力产生的裂缝、稳固穹隆，在重建前拆开了颅顶穹隆并从颅内进行了清理。除鳞骨骨缝以外，大部分颅骨穹隆骨缝难以定位，这一问题在计算机断层扫描（CT）中也存在。因此大多数标准颅骨测量标志点都不可能高精度定位。

Fig. 1. The LB1 cranium and mandible in lateral and three-quarter views, and cranium in frontal, posterior, superior and inferior views. Scale bar, 1 cm.

The LB1 cranial vault is long and low. In comparison with adult *H. erectus* (including

图 1. LB1 颅骨与下颌骨的侧视图与四分之三视图。颅骨的正视、后视、顶视及底视图。比例尺, 1 厘米。

LB1 颅骨穹隆长而低。与成年直立人（包括被归属为匠人与格鲁吉亚人的标本）

specimens referred to as *Homo ergaster* and *Homo georgicus*) and *H. sapiens* the calvarium of LB1 is extremely small. Indices of cranial shape closely follow the pattern in *H. erectus* (Supplementary Table 1). For instance, maximum cranial breadth is in the inflated supramastoid region, and the vault is broad relative to its height. In posterior view the parietal contour is similar to *H. erectus* but with reduced cranial height[2,3]. Internal examination of the neurocranium, directly and with CT scan data, indicates that the brain of LB1 had a flattened platycephalic shape, with greatest breadth across the temporal lobes and reduced parietal lobe development compared with *H. sapiens*. The cranial base angle (basion–sella–foramen caecum) of 130° is relatively flexed in comparison with both *H. sapiens* (mean 137°–138° (refs 4, 5)) and Indonesian *H. erectus* (Sambungmacan 4 141° (ref. 6)). Other small-brained hominins, for instance STS 5 *Australopithecus africanus*, have the primitive less-flexed condition.

Fig. 2. Rendered three-dimensional and individual midsagittal CT section views of the LB1 cranium and mandible. Scale bar, 1 cm.

The endocranial volume, measured with mustard seed, is 380 cm³, well below the previously accepted range for the genus *Homo*[7] and equal to the minimum estimates for *Australopithecus*[8]. The endocranial volume, relative to an indicator of body height (maximum femur length 280 mm), is outside the recorded hominin normal range (Fig. 3). Medially, laterally and basally, the cranial vault bone is thick and lies within the range of *H. erectus* and *H. sapiens*[9,10] (Supplementary Table 1 and Fig. 2). Reconstruction of the cranial vault, and CT scans, indicated that for most of the cranial vault the relative thickness of the tabular bone and diploë are similar to the normal range in *H. erectus* and *H. sapiens*. In common with *H. erectus* the vault in LB1 is relatively thickened posteriorly and in areas of pneumatization in the lateral cranial base. Thickened vault bone in LB1, relative to that in *Australopithecus* and early *Homo*[2], results in a substantially reduced endocranial volume in comparison to Plio-Pleistocene hominins with similar external vault dimensions.

及智人相比，LB1 的颅骨穹隆部极小。颅骨形状指数非常符合直立人的模式（补充表 1）。例如，颅骨宽度最大在膨胀的乳突上方区域，穹隆相对于其高度更显宽阔。在后视图中，顶骨轮廓与直立人相似，但是颅骨高度减小 [2,3]。对脑颅内部的直接观察与 CT 扫描数据观察表明 LB1 的大脑具有变平了的扁头形状，最大宽度横过颞叶；与智人相比，顶叶发育减弱。颅底角（颅底点–蝶鞍点–孔盲）为 130°，它与智人（平均为 137°～138°（参考文献 4、5））及印度尼西亚直立人（萨姆伯戈默卡 4 141°（参考文献 6））相比，相对屈曲。其他脑容量小的人族成员，例如，STS 5 南方古猿非洲种，拥有屈曲程度较低的原始状态。

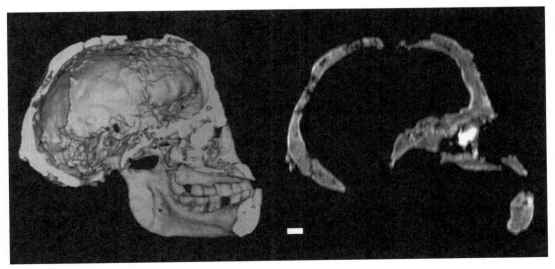

图 2. LB1 颅骨与下颌骨渲染三维视图与单个正中矢状面 CT 截面视图。比例尺，1 厘米。

用芥菜籽来测量的颅腔容积是 380 立方厘米，远低于以前公认的人属 [7] 的范围，而与南方古猿 [8] 的最小估计值相当。相对于身高指标（最大股骨长度 280 毫米），颅腔容积位于已知人族成员的正常范围之外（图 3）。颅骨穹隆部骨骼在中间、侧面及底部都厚且在直立人与智人 [9,10] 的范围之内（补充表 1 和图 2）。颅骨穹隆的重建及 CT 扫描表明，对于颅骨穹隆的大部分来讲，板状骨与板障骨的相对厚度与直立人及智人的正常范围相当。与直立人相同，在 LB1 穹隆后部与颅底侧面气腔区域相对变厚。相对于南方古猿和早期人属成员 [2]，LB1 增厚的穹隆骨骼，导致与外部穹隆尺寸相似的上新世–更新世人族成员相比，颅腔容积大幅减少。

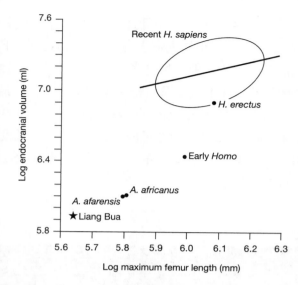

Fig. 3. Relationship between endocranial volume and femur length in LB1, *A. afarensis*, *A. africanus*, early *Homo* sp., *H. erectus* and modern *H. sapiens*. Modern human data, with least squares regression line and 95% confidence ellipse, from a global sample of 155 individuals collected by P.B. Details of the hominin samples are in the Supplementary Information.

The occipital of LB1 is strongly flexed, with an occipital curvature angle of 101° (Supplementary Information), and the length of the nuchal plane dominates over the occipital segment. The occipital torus forms a low extended mound, the occipital protuberance is not particularly prominent compared with Indonesian *H. erectus* and there is a shallow supratoral sulcus. The endinion is positioned 12 mm inferior to the inion, which is within the range of *H. erectus* and *Australopithecus*[10]. Compared with *Australopithecus* and early *Homo*[2] the foramen magnum is narrow (21 mm) relative to its length (28 mm), and mastoid processes are thickened mediolaterally and are relatively deep (20.5 mm). In common with Asian, and some African, *H. erectus* a deep fissure separates the mastoid process from the petrous crest of the tympanic[10,11]. Bilaterally there is a recess between the tympanic plate and the entoglenoid pyramid. These two traits are not seen in modern humans, and show varied levels of development in Asian and African *H. erectus* and Pliocene hominins[10]. The depth and breadth of the glenoid fossae and angulation of the articular eminence are within the range of variation in *H. sapiens*. The inferior surface of the petrous pyramid has numerous similarities with Zhoukoudian *H. erectus*[12], with a smooth tubular external surface as in chimpanzees, and a constricted foramen lacerum. Styloid processes and vaginal crests are not present.

The temporal lines approach to within 33 mm of the coronal suture and have a marked posterior extension. There are no raised angular tori as is common in *H. erectus*[10] and some terminal Pleistocene Australians, and no evidence of parietal keeling. Posteriorly there is some asymmetrical obelionic flattening and CT scans indicate that the parietals reduce in thickness in this slightly depressed area (Fig. 2). A principal component analysis (PCA) of five cranial vault measurements separates LB1, STS5 (*A. africanus*) and KNM-ER 1813

图 3. 在 LB1、南方古猿阿法种、南方古猿非洲种、早期人属未定种、直立人及现代智人中，颅腔容积与股骨长度之间的关系。现代人类的数据带有最小二乘回归线与 95% 置信椭圆，来自布朗收集的全球 155 个个体样本。人族成员样本的详细情况见补充信息。

    LB1 的枕骨强烈向下屈曲，枕骨弯曲角 101°（补充信息），而且项平面长度占了枕节的大部分。枕骨圆枕形成了一个较低的延伸小丘，与印度尼西亚直立人相比，枕骨隆突不是特别突出，并且有一浅上圆枕沟。枕内点位置低于枕外隆凸点 12 毫米，在直立人与南方古猿的范围之内 [10]。与南方古猿及早期人属成员 [2] 相比，枕骨大孔相对于其长度（28 毫米）显狭窄（21 毫米），乳突由中线向侧面增厚，相对较深（20.5 毫米）。与亚洲和某些非洲直立人相同，有一条很深的裂缝将乳突与鼓室的岩骨脊分开 [10,11]。在鼓板与内颞颌关节锥之间有一两侧凹陷。这两个特征在现代人中是看不到的，显示出亚洲及非洲直立人和上新世人族成员的多样的发育水平 [10]。关节窝的深度和宽度以及关节隆起的角度在智人的变异范围之内。岩锥的下表面与周口店直立人 [12] 有许多相似之处，拥有黑猩猩那样光滑管状的外表面，以及收缩的破裂孔。无茎突与茎突鞘脊突。

    颞线与冠状缝相交的位置，距离冠状缝起点在 33 毫米之内，且颞线有明显的向后延伸。不具有直立人 [10] 与一些更新世末尾的澳大利亚人中常见的升高的角圆枕，也没有顶骨矢状隆起的证据。在后方矢状缝的顶骨孔之间区域有一不对称变平，CT 扫描表明顶骨在这个稍微凹陷的区域厚度减少（图 2）。5 个颅骨穹隆测量值的主成分分析（PCA），将 LB1、STS5（南方古猿非洲种）与 KNM-ER 1813（早期人属成员）

(early *Homo*) from other hominin calvaria in size and shape. Shape, particularly height and breadth relationships, placed LB1 closest to ER-3883, ER-3733 and Sangiran 2 *H. erectus* (Supplementary Fig. 1).

The face of LB1 lacks most of the masticatory adaptations evident in *Australopithecus* and its overall morphology is similar to members of the genus *Homo*[2,3]. In comparison with *Australopithecus*, tooth dimensions and the alveolar segment of the maxillae are greatly reduced, as are facial height and prognathism. The facial skeleton is dominated by pronounced canine juga, which form prominent pillars lateral to the nasal aperture. However, these are distinct from the anterior pillars adjacent to the nasal aperture in *A. africanus*[2,3]. The infraorbital fossae are deep with large infraorbital foramina, the orbits have a particularly arched superior border and a volume of 15.5 cm^3 (ref. 13). On the better preserved right-hand side, the supraorbital torus arches over the orbit and does not form a straight bar, with bulbous laterally projecting trigones, as in Indonesian *H. erectus*[11]. The preserved section of the right torus only extends medially slightly past mid-orbit, and the morphology of the glabella region and medial torus is unknown. In facial view the zygo-maxillary region is medially deep relative to facial height, and the inferior border of the malars are angled at 55° relative to the coronal plane. In lateral view the infraorbital region is orientated posteriorly as in other members of the genus *Homo*, rather than the more vertical orientation in *A. africanus*[2,3]. The root of the maxillary zygomatic process is centred above the first molar, and the incisive canal is relatively large and has an anterior location, contrasting with African and Javan *H. erectus*. In lateral view, curvature of the frontal squama is more similar to African early *Homo* and Dmanisi *H. ergaster*[3,14] than it is to the Javan hominins. The frontal squama is separated from the supraorbital torus by a supraorbital sulcus. In the middle third of the frontal there is a slight sagittal keel, extending into the remains of a low, broad prebregmatic eminence. On the midfrontal squama there is a circular healed lesion, probably the remains of a depressed fracture, which is about 15 mm across.

The mandible is complete, apart from some damage to the right condyle (Fig. 4) and combines features present in a variety of Pliocene and Pleistocene hominins. Post-mortem breaks through the corpus at the right P_3 and M_2, and the left canine have resulted in some lateral distortion of the right ramus. There is a strong Curve of Spee. The ramus root inserts on the corpus above the lateral prominence, and in lateral aspect obscures the distal M_3. The ramus is broadest inferiorly, slopes slightly posteriorly and is thickened medio-laterally, and the coronoid process is higher than the condyle. The right condyle has a maximum breadth of 18 mm. There is a narrow and shallow extramolar sulcus and moderate lateral prominence. The anterior portion of the corpus is rounded and bulbous and without a chin. In the posterior symphyseal region the alveolar planum inclines postero-inferiorly, there is a moderate superior torus, deep and broad digastric fossa, and the inferior transverse torus is low and rounded rather than shelf-like (Fig. 4). There is a strong posterior angulation of the symphyseal axis, and the overall morphology of the symphysis is very similar to LH4 *A. afarensis* and unlike Zhoukoudian and Sangiran *H. erectus*. There are bilaterally double mental foramina, with the posterior foramina smaller and located more inferiorly. Double

在大小与形状上与其他人族成员颅顶分开。形状，特别是高度和宽度之间的关系，把 LB1 放到最靠近 ER-3883、ER-3733 及桑吉兰 2 直立人的位置（补充图 1）。

LB1 面部缺少绝大多数南方古猿中明显的与咀嚼相关的适应特征，且其总体形态与人属成员相似 [2,3]。与南方古猿对比，其牙齿大小与上颌骨的齿槽部分都明显减小，面部高度和凸颌程度也是同样的情况。犬齿隆凸突出，在面部骨骼上非常显著，在鼻孔侧面形成突出圆柱。然而，这与南方古猿非洲种中邻近鼻孔的前部圆柱截然不同 [2,3]。眶下窝深，眶下孔大，眼窝具有一个特别拱曲的上缘，其容积为 15.5 立方厘米（参考文献 13）。在保存较好的右侧，眶上圆枕在眼眶上成拱形，并不是形成平直条状，具有向侧面突出的球状三角区，正如印度尼西亚直立人中那样 [11]。保存的圆枕右侧仅向中间延伸稍微超过眼眶中部，眉间区与中间圆枕形态未知。在正视图中，颧骨上颌骨区域，相对于面高，至面部中线的深度显大，颧骨下缘相对于冠状面所成角度为 55°。侧视图中，眶下区域朝向后方，如人属其他成员一样，而不像南方古猿非洲种那样朝向更加垂直 [2,3]。上颌骨颧突根部以第一臼齿上方为中心，门齿管相当大且位置靠前，与非洲和爪哇直立人不同。在侧面图中，额骨鳞部的弯曲程度较爪哇人族成员与非洲的早期人属与德马尼西匠人 [3,14] 更接近。一眶上沟把额骨鳞部与眶上圆枕分开。在额骨中部三分之一，有一轻微矢状隆起，延伸成为低而宽阔的前囟前部隆起的残留。在中额骨鳞部，有一圆形已愈合的损伤，可能是凹陷骨折的痕迹，大约 15 毫米宽。

下颌骨完整，仅右侧髁突部分损坏（图 4），且复合了多种上新世与更新世人族成员的特征。右下第 3 前臼齿和第 2 臼齿以及左犬齿处的死后破裂贯穿了下颌体，使得右侧上升枝有些侧向变形。下颌齿列表现出强烈的施佩曲线。上升枝根部在侧面下颌突之上嵌入下颌体，从侧面遮挡下第 3 臼齿远中部。上升枝下部最宽，向后稍有倾斜，中侧向变厚，冠状突高于髁突。右侧髁突最大宽度 18 毫米。外臼齿沟窄而浅，下颌突中等程度发育。下颌体前部浑圆肥硕且没有颏。在下颌联合后部区域，齿槽面向后向下倾斜，上圆枕中等程度发育，二腹肌窝深且宽阔，下圆枕低而圆，不呈搁架状（图 4）。下颌联合轴线有一个强烈向后的角度，下颌联合的总体形态与 LH4 南方古猿阿法种很相似，而与周口店及桑吉兰直立人不相像。在两侧都有两个颏孔，后一个孔较小，位置更靠下。双颏孔在印度尼西亚直立人 [15] 中普遍存在。而

mental foramina are common in Indonesian *H. erectus*[15]. While the mandibular dental arch is narrow anteriorly, and long relative to its breadth, the axis of P_3–M_3 is laterally convex rather than straight (Fig. 4).

Fig. 4. Right lateral and occlusal views of the LB1 mandible, sagittal profile of the symphysis, occlusal view of the mandibular dentition and occlusal views of the mandibular premolars. Scale bars, 1 cm.

The right P_4 is absent and the alveolus completely fused, the left P_4 was lost after death, and CT scans indicate that the maxillary right M^3 was congenitally absent. The relatively small and conical alveolus for the missing left M^3 suggests that it had a much smaller crown than M^1 and M^2. Size, spacing and angulation of the maxillary incisor alveoli, and absence of a mesial facet on the canines suggest that incisor I^2 was much smaller than I^1, and there may have been a diastema. Occlusal wear has removed details of cusp and fissure morphology from most of the maxillary and mandibular teeth. The canines have worn down to a relatively flat surface and there would have been an edge-to-edge bite anteriorly.

下颌骨齿弓前面窄，相对于宽度显得长，下第 3 前臼齿至第 3 臼齿轴线向侧面凸出而不是直的（图 4）。

图 4. LB1 下颌骨的右侧视图与咀嚼面视图、联合部矢状面轮廓、下齿列咀嚼面视图及下前臼齿咀嚼面视图。比例尺，1 厘米。

右下第 4 前臼齿缺失且齿槽完全合并，左下第 4 前臼齿为死后丢失，CT 扫描显示右上第 3 臼齿先天缺失。丢失的左上第 3 臼齿齿槽相对小且呈圆锥形，这表明其齿冠要远小于上第 1 臼齿和上第 2 臼齿。上门齿齿槽的大小、间距和角度，以及犬齿近中接触面缺失表明，上第 2 门牙比上第 1 门牙小得多，并且可能存在齿隙。上下颌牙齿咀嚼面的磨耗已经把大部分上下颌牙齿上的齿尖及裂隙形态的细节都磨掉了。犬齿已经磨耗到一个相当平坦的平面，在牙齿前部可能曾有边缘对边缘的咬合。

Interproximal wear is pronounced and in combination with the loss of crown height means that mesio-distal crown dimensions convey little phylogenetic information. With the exception of P_3 the size and morphology of the mandibular teeth follow the pattern in *H. erectus* and *H. sapiens* (Fig. 5, Supplementary Table 2). There is not a great deal of difference between the size of the molar teeth in each quadrant, and the size sequence for both mandibular and maxillary teeth is $M1 \geqslant M2 > M3$. Using the megadontial quotient as a measure of relative tooth size[16], and substituting P_3 crown area for the missing P_4s, LB1 is megadont (1.8) relative to *H. sapiens* (0.9) and *H. ergaster* (0.9), but not *H. habilis* (1.9) (ref. 8) (Supplementary Information). The P_3s have a relatively great occlusal surface area (molariform) and when unworn had a prominent protoconid and broad talonid. Both P_3s have bifurcated roots and the alveolus for the left P_4 indicates a mesiodistally compressed, broad Tomes' root. A larger, less worn, isolated left P_3 from the deposit (LB2) has a more triangular occlusal outline, and a Tomes' root (Supplementary Fig. 2). Mandibular P_3s and P_4s with similar crown and root morphology have been recorded for *Australopithecus* and early *Homo*[17,18], and some Indonesian *H. erectus* mandibular premolars also have bifurcated or Tomes' roots[15]. Unusually, both maxillary P^4s are rotated parallel to the tooth row, a trait that seems to be unrecorded in any other hominin. Maxillary canines and P^3s have long roots and very prominent juga. The P^3 juga are emphasized by the rotation of the adjacent P^4 roots.

Fig. 5. Mean buccolingual tooth crown breadths for mandibular teeth in *A. afarensis* (filled circles), *A. africanus* (open circles), early *Homo* sp. (open squares), modern *H. sapiens* (filled squares), LB1 (filled stars) and LB2 (open stars). There are no mandibular P_4s preserved for LB1. Data for *Australopithecus* and early *Homo* are from ref. 49. Modern human data from a global sample of 1,199 individuals collected by P.B.

The pelvic girdle is represented by a right innominate, with damage to the iliac crest and pubic region, and fragments of the sacrum and left innominate. The right innominate, which is undistorted, has a broad greater sciatic notch suggesting that LB1 is a female (Fig. 6). In common with all bipedal hominins, the iliac blade is relatively short and wide[19]; however, the ischial spine is not particularly pronounced. Compared with modern humans the LB1

齿间磨耗显著，加上齿冠高度的磨损，意味着齿冠近远中尺寸所含有的系统发育信息很少。除了下第3前臼齿，下颌牙齿的大小和形态遵循直立人与智人的模式（图5和补充表2）。在每个四分之一齿枝上，臼齿的大小没有很大差别，上下颌臼齿的大小次序是 M1 ≥ M2 > M3。如果以牙齿巨大系数作为牙齿相对尺寸的量度[16]，用下第3前臼齿齿冠面积替代失去的下第4前臼齿，相对于智人（0.9）与匠人（0.9），LB1 属于牙齿巨大（1.8），但相对于能人（1.9）则不是如此（参考文献8）（补充信息）。下第3前臼齿拥有相对大的咀嚼面表面积（臼齿形），未磨耗时下原尖突出，下跟座宽阔。两侧下第3前臼齿均拥有二分叉齿根，左下第4前臼齿的齿槽孔表明其拥有近远中向压扁且宽阔的托姆斯式齿根。1枚来自沉积物的更大且磨耗程度较低的左下第3前臼齿（LB2）拥有更趋于三角形的咀嚼面轮廓和托姆斯式齿根（补充图2）。下颌第3和第4前臼齿具有相似的齿根和齿冠形态，这在南方古猿与早期人属中已有记载[17,18]，而且一些印度尼西亚直立人下颌前臼齿也有二分叉或托姆斯式齿根[15]。不同寻常的是，两侧的上颌上第4前臼齿均旋转并平行于齿列，这个特征似乎在任何其他人族成员中都没有记载过。上颌犬齿与上第3前臼齿牙根长且隆凸十分突出。上第3前臼齿隆凸由于相邻上第4前臼齿齿根的旋转而显加强。

图5. 南方古猿阿法种（实心圆）、南方古猿非洲种（空心圆）、早期人属（空心正方形）、现代智人（实心正方形）、LB1（实心五角形）及 LB2（空心五角形）的下颌牙齿齿冠颊舌向的平均宽度。LB1 的两侧下第4前臼齿未保存。南方古猿与早期人属数据来自参考文献49。现代人类数据来自布朗收集的一个包括1,199个个体的全球样本。

腰带部分保存了髂嵴与耻骨区域破损的右侧髋骨和骶骨及左侧髋骨碎片。右侧髋骨，未变形，坐骨大切迹宽阔，表明 LB1 为一女性（图6）。和所有两足直立行走的人族成员一样，髂骨刃相对短而宽[19]；不过，坐骨棘不是特别明显。与现代人相

ilium has marked lateral flare, and the blade would have projected more laterally from the body, relative to the plane of the acetabulum. The left acetabulum is of circular shape, and has a maximum width of 36 mm.

Fig. 6. Comparison of the left innominate from LB1 with a modern adult female *H. sapiens*. Lateral (external), and medial and lateral views of maximum iliac breadth. The pubic region of LB1 is not preserved and the iliac crest is incomplete. Scale bar, 1 cm.

Apart from damage to the lateral condyle and distal shaft, the right femur is complete and undistorted (Fig. 7). The overall anatomy of the femur is most consistent with the broad range of variation in *H. sapiens*, with some departures that may be the result of the allometric effects of very small body size. The femur shaft is relatively straight, and areas of muscle attachment, including the linea aspera, are not well developed. In contrast with some examples of Asian and African *H. erectus*, the femora do not have reduced medullary canals[20]. On the proximal end, the lesser trochanter is extremely prominent and the strong development of the intertrochanteric crest is similar to *H. sapiens* rather than the flattened intertrochanteric area in *Australopithecus* and *H. erectus* (KNM-ER 1481A, KNM-WT 15000). The biomechanical neck length is 55.5 mm and the neck is long relative to the femoral head diameter (31.5 mm), as is common to both *Australopithecus* and early *Homo*[19]. The neck–head junction is 31.5 mm long, with a shaft–neck angle of 130°, and the femur neck is compressed anteroposteriorly (Fig. 7). Several indices of femoral size and shape, for example the relationship between femoral head size and midshaft circumference (66 mm), and femur

比，LB1 髂骨侧面显著变宽，这表明，相对于髋臼平面，髂骨刃会向身体侧面凸出更多。左侧髋臼呈圆形，最大宽 36 毫米。

图 6. LB1 左侧髋骨与一现代女性智人的对比。髂骨最大宽度侧（外）视图、内侧视图及侧视图。LB1 的耻骨区域未保存，且髂嵴不完整。比例尺，1 厘米。

除了外侧髁突和远端骨干有破损，右侧股骨完整且未变形（图 7）。股骨的整体解剖学特征与智人宽泛变异范围是最为一致的，一些偏差可能是由体型矮小的异速生长效应导致。股骨干相对较直，包括股骨粗线在内的肌肉附着区不很发育。与亚洲及非洲直立人的一些例子不同，其两侧股骨没有减弱的髓腔[20]。在近中末端，小转子极其突出，转子间嵴的强烈发育类似于智人，而与南方古猿属和直立人（KNM-ER 1481A，KNM-WT 15000）的平坦的转子间区不同。股骨颈的生物力学长度为55.5 毫米，且相对于股骨头直径（31.5 毫米）显长，这在南方古猿属及早期人属中也普遍存在[19]。股骨颈–股骨头联合处长 31.5 毫米，股骨干–股骨颈成 130°角，股骨颈前后压缩（图 7）。股骨大小与形状的几个指标，例如股骨头大小和股骨干中部周长（66 毫米）间及股骨长度和转子下方骨干大小间的关系[21]，都落入黑猩猩与南方古猿的变异范围之内。股骨干没有粗线嵴，其横截面呈圆形，骨干中部横截面面积

length and sub-trochanteric shaft size[21], fall within the chimpanzee and australopithecine range of variation. The femur shaft does not have a pilaster, is circular in cross-section, and has cross-sectional areas of 370 mm^2 at the midshaft and 359 mm^2 at the midneck. It is therefore slightly more robust than the best-preserved small-bodied hominin femur of similar length (AL288-1; ref. 21). Distally there is a relatively high bicondylar angle of 14°, which overlaps with that found in *Australopithecus*[22].

Fig. 7. Anterior and posterior views of the LB1 right femur and tibia, with cross-sections of the femur neck and midshaft, and tibia midshaft. The anterior surfaces of the medial and lateral condyles of the femur are not preserved. With the exception of the medial malleolus, the tibia is complete and undistorted. Scale bar, 1 cm.

The right tibia is complete apart from the tip of the medial malleolus (Fig. 7). Its most distinctive feature, apart from its small size (estimated maximum length 235 mm, bicondylar breadth 51.5 mm) and the slight curvature in the long axis, is a shaft that is oval in cross-section (midshaft 347 mm^2), without a sharp anterior border, and relatively thickened medio-laterally in the distal half. The relationship between the midshaft circumference and the length of the tibia is in the chimpanzee range of variation and distinct from *Homo*[21].

Additional evidence of a small-bodied adult hominin is provided by an unassociated left radius shaft, without the articular ends, from an older section of the deposit (74–95 kyr). The estimated maximum length of this radius when complete is approximately 210 mm. Although the arms of LB1 have not been recovered, the dimensions of this radius are compatible with a hominin of LB1 proportions.

Although there is considerable interspecific variation, stature has been shown to have phylogenetic and adaptive significance among hominins[23]. Broadly speaking, *Australopithecus*

为 370 平方毫米，股骨颈中部横截面面积为 359 平方毫米。因此，它比保存最完好且具有相似长度的身材矮小的人族成员的股骨略显更加粗壮（AL288-1；参考文献21）。在远端双髁角相对显大，为 14°，与南方古猿属重叠[22]。

图 7. LB1 右侧股骨和胫骨的前视图与后视图，及股骨颈、股骨干与胫骨干的横截面。股骨的中髁突与侧髁突前方未保存。除了内踝，胫骨完整且未变形。比例尺，1 厘米。

除了内踝末端破损，右胫骨完整（图 7）。除了其尺寸较小（估计最大长为 235毫米，双髁宽为 51.5 毫米）以及长轴微弯外，它最与众不同的特征是其骨干的横截面呈椭圆形（骨干中部横截面面积为 347 平方毫米），无明显的前嵴，远端半部的内–侧向加厚。骨干中部周长和胫骨长度之间的关系在黑猩猩的变异范围之内，而与人属截然不同[21]。

另外一根采自更老堆积物（74,000 ~ 95,000 年）且与之不相关的缺失关节部位的左侧桡骨骨干，为身材矮小的成年人族成员提供了附加的证据。该桡骨完整状态下推测最大长度约为 210 毫米。虽然 LB1 的双臂还没有被发现，但该桡骨的尺寸与LB1 这一人族成员的比例一致。

虽然种间变异相当大，但身高已经在人族之中被证明具有系统发育和适应方面

and the earliest members of the genus *Homo* are shorter than *H. erectus* and more recent hominins[8]. The maximum femur length of LB1 (280 mm) is just below the smallest recorded for *A. afarensis* (AL-288-1, 281 mm[24]) and equal to the smallest estimate for the OH 62 *H. habilis* femur (280–404 mm)[21]. Applying stature estimation formulae developed from human pygmies[25] gives a stature estimate of 106 cm for LB1 (Supplementary Information). This is likely to be an overestimation owing to LB1's relatively small cranial height.

A stature estimate for LB1 of 106 cm gives a body mass of 16 to 28.7 kg, and a femur cross-sectional area of 525 mm^2 gives a mass of 36 kg (Supplementary Information). The brain mass for LB1, calculated from its volume[26], is 433.2 g; this gives an encephalization quotient (EQ)[27] range of 2.5–4.6, which compares with 5.8–8.1 for *H. sapiens*, 3.3–4.4 for *H. erectus/ergaster* and 3.6–4.3 for *H. habilis*, and overlaps with the australopithecine range of variation[28,29]. If LB1 shared the lean and relatively narrow body shape typical of Old World tropical modern humans then the smallest body weight estimate, based on Jamaican school children data[19], is probably most appropriate. This would support the higher EQ estimate and place LB1 within the *Homo* range of variation. Although neurological organization is at least as important as EQ in determining behavioural complexity, these data are consistent with *H. floresiensis* being the Pleistocene toolmaker at Liang Bua.

Origins and Evolution

The LB1 skeleton was recovered from Flores, an island of 14,000 km^2 east of the Wallace Line, in Indonesia. It combines extremely small stature and an endocranial volume in the early australopithecine range, with a unique mosaic of primitive and derived traits in the cranium, mandible and postcranial skeleton. Both its geographic location and comparatively recent date suggest models that differ to those for more expected geological contexts, such as Pliocene eastern Africa. Among modern humans, populations of extremely small average stature were historically found in predominantly rainforest habitat in the equatorial zone of Africa, Asia and Melanesia[30,31]. Explanations for the small body size of these people generally focus on the thermoregulatory advantages for life in a hot and humid forest, either through evaporative cooling[32] or reduced rates of internal heat production[30]. For African pygmies, smaller body size is the result of reduced levels of insulin-like growth factor 1 (IGF-1) throughout the growth period[33], or reduced receptivity to IGF-1 (ref. 34). Although adult stature is reduced, cranio-facial proportions remain within the range of adjacent larger-bodied populations, as does brain size[35,36]. The combination of small stature and brain size in LB1 is not consistent with IGF-related postnatal growth retardation. Similarly, neither pituitary dwarfism, nor primordial microcephalic dwarfism (PMD) in modern humans replicates the skeletal features present in LB1 (refs 37–40).

Other mechanisms must have been responsible for the small body size of these hominins, with insular dwarfing being the strongest candidate. Although small body size was an attribute of Pliocene australopithecines, the facial and dental characteristics of LB1 link it with larger-bodied Pleistocene *Homo*. In this instance, body size is not a direct expression

的意义[23]。宽泛地讲，南方古猿属与人属最早成员矮于直立人与更晚的人族成员[8]。LB1 的股骨最大长度（280 毫米）刚好低于南方古猿阿法种（AL-288-1，281 毫米[24]）的最小记录值，而等于 OH 62 能人股骨长度（280 ~ 404 毫米）的最小估计值[21]。应用基于俾格米人[25]开发的身高估算公式，估算出 LB1 身高为 106 厘米（补充信息）。由于 LB1 的颅骨高度相对较小，这一身高可能是过高估值。

根据 LB1 106 厘米的身高估值，得出其体重为 16 至 28.7 千克，而根据股骨横截面面积为 525 平方毫米，得出体重为 36 千克（补充信息）。根据 LB1 的脑容量来计算[26]，其大脑重量为 433.2 克，从而得到脑系数（EQ）[27]的范围为 2.5 ~ 4.6，而智人为 5.8 ~ 8.1，直立人/匠人为 3.3 ~ 4.4，能人为 3.6 ~ 4.3，与南方古猿的变异范围重叠[28,29]。如果 LB1 享有旧世界热带现代人典型的清瘦和相对狭窄的体型，那么，基于牙买加入学儿童的数据[19]，体重的最小估值或许是最适当的。这会支持较高的 EQ 估值，而把 LB1 置于人属变异范围之内。虽然在决定行为的复杂性上，神经结构至少也与 EQ 一样重要，但这些数据与利昂布阿的弗洛勒斯人是更新世工具制造者是一致的。

起源与演化

LB1 骨架发现于印度尼西亚华莱士线以东方圆 14,000 平方千米的弗洛勒斯岛。它兼具落入早期南方古猿范围的极其矮小的身材和颅内容积，及在颅骨、下颌骨和颅后骨骼中独特的原始和衍生特征的镶嵌。其地理位置和相当晚的年代都表明了与更加期望的地质背景（如上新世非洲东部）不同的模型。在现代人中，平均身高极其矮小的种群在历史时期主要发现于非洲赤道地区、亚洲及美拉尼西亚的热带雨林栖息地[30,31]。对这些人体型小的解释，一般聚焦于在炎热潮湿的森林里生活的热调节优势，无论是通过蒸发降温[32]还是降低体内热量产生的速度[30]。对非洲俾格米人而言，体型较小是由于在整个生长期类胰岛素生长因子 1（IGF-1）分泌水平的降低[33]，或对 IGF-1 的接受能力的降低（参考文献 34）。虽然成年身高降低，但像大脑大小一样，其颅–面比例仍然保持在邻近大体型种群的范围之内[35,36]。LB1 中身材矮小与脑容量小兼备，与 IGF 相关的后天发育延缓不一致。同样，现代人中无论是垂体性侏儒症还是先天性小头侏儒症（PMD）都不能再现 LB1 中出现的骨骼特征（参考文献 37 ~ 40）。

一定是其他机制造成了这些人族成员的身材矮小，而岛屿侏儒化是最佳候选。虽然体型小是上新世南方古猿的特性，但 LB1 的面部与牙齿的特征将其与体型较

of phylogeny. The location of these small hominins on Flores makes it far more likely that they are the end product of a long period of evolution on a comparatively small island, where environmental conditions placed small body size at a selective advantage. Insular dwarfing, in response to the specific ecological conditions that are found on some small islands, is well documented for animals larger than a rabbit[41,42]. Explanations of the island rule have primarily focused on resource availability, reduced levels of interspecific competition within relatively impoverished faunal communities and absence of predators. It has been argued that, in the absence of agriculture, tropical rainforests offer a very limited supply of calories for hominins[43]. Under these conditions selection should favour the reduced energy requirements of smaller individuals. Although the details of the Pleistocene palaeoenvironment on Flores are still being documented, it is clear that until the arrival of Mesolithic humans the faunal suit was relatively impoverished, and the only large predators were the Komodo dragon and another larger varanid. Dwarfing in LB1 may have been the end product of selection for small body size in a low calorific environment, either after isolation on Flores, or another insular environment in southeastern Asia.

Anatomical and physiological changes associated with insular dwarfing can be extensive, with dramatic modification of sensory systems and brain size[44], and certainly exceed what might be predicted by the allometric effects of body size reduction alone. Evidence of insular dwarfing in extinct lineages, or the evolution of island endemic forms, is most often provided by the fossil record. Whereas there is archaeological evidence of hominins being on Flores by approximately 840 kyr[45], there is no associated hominin skeletal material, and the currently limited evidence from Liang Bua is restricted to the Late Pleistocene. The first hominin immigrants may have had a similar body size to *H. erectus* and early *Homo*[21,46], with subsequent dwarfing; or, an unknown small-bodied and small-brained hominin may have arrived on Flores from the Sunda Shelf.

Discussion

When considered as a whole, the cranial and postcranial skeleton of LB1 combines a mosaic of primitive, unique and derived features not recorded for any other hominin. Although LB1 has the small endocranial volume and stature evident in early australopithecines, it does not have the great postcanine tooth size, deep and prognathic facial skeleton, and masticatory adaptations common to members of this genus[2,47]. Instead, the facial and dental proportions, postcranial anatomy consistent with human-like obligate bipedalism[48], and a masticatory apparatus most similar in relative size and function to modern humans[48] all support assignment to the genus *Homo*—as does the inferred phylogenetic history, which includes endemic dwarfing of *H. erectus*. For these reasons, we argue that LB1 is best placed in this genus and have named it accordingly.

On a related point, the survival of *H. floresiensis* into the Late Pleistocene shows that the genus *Homo* is morphologically more varied and flexible in its adaptive responses than is generally recognized. It is possible that the evolutionary history of *H. floresiensis* is unique,

大的更新世人属联系起来。在这种情况下，体型大小不是系统发育的直接表现。弗洛勒斯岛上这些矮小人族成员的发现位置，使其更有可能是在一个相对较小的岛屿上经过长期演化的最终产物，那里的环境条件使得小体型更具有选择优势。岛屿侏儒化，作为对一些小岛上特殊生态条件的响应，在比兔子大的动物中有很详细的记载[41,42]。对岛屿规则的解释主要聚焦于资源的可获得性、相对贫困的动物群落中种间竞争的减少以及捕食者的消失。有人提出，在农业出现前，热带雨林提供给人族成员的卡路里十分有限[43]。在这样的条件下，选择应该偏向于能量需求降低的较矮小个体。虽然弗洛勒斯的更新世古环境资料正处于记载中，但很明显，在中石器时代人类到来前，整个动物群还比较单薄，唯一的大型捕食者是科莫多巨蜥和另一种体型较大的巨蜥。无论是在弗洛勒斯岛上被隔离后，还是在东南亚的另一个孤立环境中，LB1 的侏儒化可能是在低卡路里环境下选择偏向小体型的最终产物。

与岛屿侏儒化相关的解剖学和生理学变化非常之多，伴随对感觉系统和大脑尺寸的改变[44]，并且肯定超过了仅由身体体型减小的异速生长效应所能预测出的程度。已经绝灭的谱系中岛屿侏儒化，或岛屿特有类型的演化的证据，最常由化石记录提供。虽然有考古证据表明，人族成员在弗洛勒斯岛上大约有 840,000 年了[45]，但并没有相关的人族成员的骨骼材料，而现在来自利昂布阿的有限证据仅限于晚更新世。第一批人族成员移民可能有类似于直立人和早期人属成员的身体大小[21,46]，但随后矮化；或者，一种未知的身材矮小、脑容量小的人族成员从巽他大陆架来到了弗洛勒斯。

讨　论

当作为一个整体来看时，LB1 颅骨和颅后骨骼兼具原始和独特的衍生特征的镶嵌，这些衍生特征在其他任何人族成员中都没有记载过。虽然 LB1 像早期南方古猿那样颅内容积及身高小，但其没有硕大的犬后齿尺寸、深而前突的面部骨骼以及这一属的成员所共有的咀嚼适应特征[2,47]。相反，面部和牙齿的比例、颅后骨骼的解剖特征与似人的习惯性两足行走一致[48]，而且其咀嚼器官与现代人在相对大小与功能上最相似[48]，这一切都支持将其归入人属，包括直立人的地方性矮化在内的系统发育史同样支持将其归入人属。基于这些原因，我们认为 LB1 最适合放在这个属，并因此而给她命名。

关于另外相关的一点，弗洛勒斯人能幸存下来延续到晚更新世，显示了人属在其适应性响应中，形态上比人们一般认为的更加多样化和灵活。弗洛勒斯人的演化历史可能是独一无二的，但我们认为更有可能的情况是，随着人属走出非洲，该属

but we consider it more likely that, following the dispersal of *Homo* out of Africa, there arose much greater variation in the morphological attributes of this genus than has hitherto been documented. We anticipate further discoveries of highly endemic, hominin species in locations similarly affected by long-term genetic isolation, including other Wallacean islands.

(**431**, 1055-1061; 2004)

P. Brown[1], T. Sutikna[2], M. J. Morwood[1], R. P. Soejono[2], Jatmiko[2], E. Wayhu Saptomo[2] & Rokus Awe Due[2]
[1] Archaeology & Palaeoanthropology, School of Human & Environmental Studies, University of New England, Armidale, New South Wales 2351, Australia
[2] Indonesian Centre for Archaeology, Jl. Raya Condet Pejaten No. 4, Jakarta 12001, Indonesia

Received 3 March; accepted 8 September 2004.

References:

1. Morwood, M. J. *et al.* Archaeology and age of a new hominin from Flores in eastern Indonesia. *Nature* doi:10.1038/nature02956 **431**, 1087-1091 (2004).

2. Wood, B. A. *Koobi Fora Research Project, Vol. 4: Hominid Cranial Remains* (Clarendon, Oxford, 1991).

3. Vekua, A. K. *et al.* A new skull of early *Homo* from Dmanisi, Georgia. *Science* **297**, 85-89 (2002).

4. Spoor, C. F. Basicranial architecture and relative brain size of STS 5 (*Australopithecus africanus*) and other Plio-Pleistocene hominids. *S. Afr. J. Sci.* **93**, 182-186 (1997).

5. Lieberman, D., Ross, C. F. & Ravosa, M. J. The primate cranial base: ontogeny, function, and integration. *Yearb. Phys. Anthropol.* **43**, 117-169 (2000).

6. Baba, H. *et al. Homo erectus* calvarium from the Pleistocene of Java. *Science* **299**, 1384-1388 (2003).

7. Tobias, P. V. *The Skulls, Endocasts and Teeth of* Homo habilis (Cambridge Univ. Press, Cambridge, 1991).

8. McHenry, H. M. & Coffing, K. E. *Australopithecus* to *Homo*: Transformations of body and mind. *Annu. Rev. Anthropol.* **29**, 125-166 (2000).

9. Brown, P. Vault thickness in Asian *Homo erectus* and modern *Homo sapiens*. *Courier Forschungs-Institut Senckenberg* **171**, 33-46 (1994).

10. Bräuer, G. & Mbua, E. *Homo erectus* features used in cladistics and their variability in Asian and African hominids. *J. Hum. Evol.* **22**, 79-108 (1992).

11. Santa Luca, A. P. *The Ngandong Fossil Hominids* (Department of Anthropology Yale Univ., New Haven, 1980).

12. Weidenreich, F. The skull of *Sinanthropus pekinensis*: a comparative study of a primitive hominid skull. *Palaeontol. Sin.* **D10**, 1-485 (1943).

13. Brown, P. & Maeda, T. Post-Pleistocene diachronic change in East Asian facial skeletons: the size, shape and volume of the orbits. *Anthropol. Sci.* **112**, 29-40 (2004).

14. Gabunia, L. K. *et al.* Earliest Pleistocene hominid cranial remains from Dmanisi, Republic of Georgia: taxonomy, geological setting, and age. *Science* **288**, 1019-1025 (2000).

15. Kaifu, Y. *et al.* Taxonomic affinities and evolutionary history of the Early Pleistocene hominids of Java: dento-gnathic evidence. *Am. J. Phys. Anthropol.* (in the press).

16. McHenry, H. M. in *Evolutionary History of the "Robust" Australopithecines* (ed. Grine, F. E.) 133-148 (Aldine de Gruyter, New York, 1988).

17. Wood, B. A. & Uytterschaut, H. Analysis of the dental morphology of the Plio-Pleistocene hominids. III. Mandibular premolar crowns. *J. Anat.* **154**, 121-156 (1987).

18. Wood, B. A., Abbott, S. A. & Uytterschaut, H. Analysis of the dental morphology of Plio-Pleistocene hominids. IV. Mandibular postcanine root morphology. *J. Anat.* **156**, 107-139 (1988).

19. Aiello, A. & Dean, C. *An Introduction to Human Evolutionary Anatomy* (Academic, London, 1990).

20. Kennedy, G. E. Some aspects of femoral morphology in *Homo erectus*. *J. Hum. Evol.* **12**, 587-616 (1983).

21. Haeusler, M. & McHenry, H. M. Body proportions of *Homo habilis* reviewed. *J. Hum. Evol.* **46**, 433-465 (2004).

22. Stern, J. T. J. & Susman, R. L. The locomotor anatomy of *Australopithecus afarensis*. *Am. J. Phys. Anthropol.* **60**, 279-317 (1983).

23. Ruff, C. B. Morphological adaptation to climate in modern and fossil hominids. *Yearb. Phys. Anthropol.* **37**, 65-107 (1994).

24. Jungers, W. L. Lucy's limbs: skeletal allometry and locomotion in *Australopithecus afarensis*. *Nature* **297**, 676-678 (1982).

25. Jungers, W. L. Lucy's length: stature reconstruction in *Australopithecus afarensis* (A.L.288–1) with implications for other small-bodied hominids. *Am. J. Phys. Anthropol.* **76**, 227-231 (1988).

26. Count, E. W. Brain and body weight in man: their antecedants in growth and evolution. *Ann. NY Acad. Sci.* **46**, 993-1101 (1947).

27. Martin, R. D. Relative brain size and basal metabolic rate in terrestrial vertebrates. *Nature* **293**, 57-60 (1981).

28. Jerison, H. J. *Evolution of the Brain and Intelligence* (Academic, New York, 1973).

29. McHenry, H. M. in *The Primate Fossil Record* (ed. Hartwig, C. H.) 401-406 (Cambridge Univ. Press, Cambridge, 2002).

30. Cavalli-Sforza, L. L. (ed.) *African Pygmies* (Academic, Orlando, 1986).

31. Shea, B. T. & Bailey, R. C. Allometry and adaptation of body proportions and stature in African Pygmies. *Am. J. Phys. Anthropol.* **100**, 311-340 (1996).

32. Roberts, D. F. *Climate and Human Variability* (Cummings Publishing Co., Menlo Park, 1978).

的形态特性产生了比截止目前已记载的更多的变异。我们预期会有更多高度特化的人族成员物种在同样受到长期遗传隔离的地方被发现，包括其他华莱士区的岛屿。

（田晓阳 翻译；张颖奇 审稿）

33. Merimee, T. J., Zapf, J., Hewlett, B. & Cavalli-Sforza, L. L. Insulin-like growth factors in pygmies. *N. Engl. J. Med.* **15**, 906-911 (1987).

34. Geffner, M. E., Bersch, N., Bailey, R. C. & Golde, D. W. Insulin-like growth factor I resistance in immortalized T cell lines from African Efe Pygmies. *J. Clin. Endocrinol. Metab.* **80**, 3732-3738 (1995).

35. Hiernaux, J. *The People of Africa* (Charles Scribner's Sons, New York, 1974).

36. Beals, K. L., Smith, C. L. & Dodd, S. M. Brain size, cranial morphology, climate and time machines. *Current Anthropology* **25**, 301-330 (1984).

37. Rimoin, D. L., Merimee, T. J. & McKusick, V. A. Growth-hormone deficiency in man: an isolated, recessively inherited defect. *Science* **152**, 1635-1637 (1966).

38. Jaffe, H. L. *Metabolic, Degenerative and Inflammatory Disease of Bones and Joints* (Lea and Febiger, Philadelphia, 1972).

39. Seckel, H. P. G. *Bird-Headed Dwarfs* (Karger, Basel, 1960).

40. Jeffery, N. & Berkovitz, B. K. B. Morphometric appraisal of the skull of Caroline Crachami, the Sicilian "Dwarf" 1815?–1824: A contribution to the study of primordial microcephalic dwarfism. *Am. J. Med. Genet.* **11**, 260-270 (2002).

41. Sondaar, P. Y. in *Major Patterns in Vertebrate Evolution* (eds Hecht, M. K., Goody, P. C. & Hecht, B. M.) 671-707 (Plenum, New York, 1977).

42. Lomolino, M. V. Body size of *mammals* on islands: The island rule re-examined. *Am. Nat.* **125**, 310-316 (1985).

43. Bailey, R. C. & Headland, T. The tropical rainforest: Is it a productive habitat for human foragers? *Hum. Ecol.* **19**, 261-285 (1991).

44. Köhler, M. & Moyà-Solà, S. Reduction of brain and sense organs in the fossil insular bovid *Myotragus. Brain Behav. Evol.* **63**, 125-140 (2004).

45. Morwood, M. J., O'Sullivan, P. B., Aziz, F. & Raza, A. Fission-track ages of stone tools and fossils on the east Indonesian island of Flores. *Nature* **392**, 173-176 (1998).

46. Walker, A. C. & Leakey, R. (eds) *The Nariokotome* Homo erectus *skeleton* (Harvard Univ. Press, Cambridge, 1993).

47. Rak, Y. The *Australopithecine Face* (Academic, New York, 1983).

48. Wood, B. A. & Collard, M. The human genus. *Science* **284**, 65-71 (1999).

49. Johanson, D. C. & White, T. D. A systematic assessment of early African Hominids. *Science* **202**, 321-330 (1979).

Supplementary Information accompanies the paper on www.nature.com/nature.

Acknowledgements. We would like to thank F. Spoor and L. Aiello for data and discussion. Comments by F. Spoor and D. Lieberman greatly improved aspects of the original manuscript. Conversation with S. Collier, C. Groves, T. White and P. Grave helped clarify some issues. CTscans were produced by CT-Scan KSU, Medical Diagnostic Nusantara, Jakarta. S. Wasisto completed complex section drawings and assisted with the excavation of Sector VII. The 2003 excavations at Liang Bua, undertaken under Indonesian Centre for Archaeology Permit Number 1178/SB/PUS/ BD/24.VI/2003, were funded by a Discovery Grant to M.J.M. from the Australian Research Council. UNE Faculty of Arts, and M. Macklin, helped fund the manufacture of stereolithographic models of LB1.

Authors contributions. P.B. reconstructed the LB1 cranium and was responsible for researching and writing this article, with M.J.M. T.S. directed many aspects of the Liang Bua excavations, including the recovery of the hominin skeleton. M.J.M. and R.P.S. are Principal Investigators and Institutional Counterparts in the ARC project, as well as Co-Directors of the Liang Bua excavations. E.W.S. and Jatmiko assisted T.S., and had prime responsibility for the work in Sector VII. R.A.D. did all of the initial faunal identifications at Liang Bua, including hominin material, and helped clean and conserve it.

Competing interests statement. The authors declare that they have no competing financial interests.

Correspondence and requests for materials should be addressed to P.B. (pbrown3@pobox.une.edu.au).

Unusual Activity of the Sun during Recent Decades Compared to the Previous 11,000 Years

S. K. Solanki *et al.*

Editor's Note

In the debate over whether human activities are the main cause of global warming during the past century, one of the main arguments for this trend being instead of natural origin is that it might be due to enhanced solar activity—the Sun giving out more heat. That idea is examined in this paper, in which the authors reconstruct solar activity over the past 11,400 years (since the last ice age ended) by using levels of atmospheric carbon-14 as a proxy. ^{14}C is produced by cosmic rays impinging on the atmosphere—a process affected by changes in solar activity—and its accumulation in tree rings provided an annual, dateable record over many millennia. The authors conclude that there has been exceptional solar activity over the past 70 years, but that this does not suffice to explain recent global warming.

Direct observations of sunspot numbers are available for the past four centuries[1,2], but longer time series are required, for example, for the identification of a possible solar influence on climate and for testing models of the solar dynamo. Here we report a reconstruction of the sunspot number covering the past 11,400 years, based on dendrochronologically dated radiocarbon concentrations. We combine physics-based models for each of the processes connecting the radiocarbon concentration with sunspot number. According to our reconstruction, the level of solar activity during the past 70 years is exceptional, and the previous period of equally high activity occurred more than 8,000 years ago. We find that during the past 11,400 years the Sun spent only of the order of 10% of the time at a similarly high level of magnetic activity and almost all of the earlier high-activity periods were shorter than the present episode. Although the rarity of the current episode of high average sunspot numbers may indicate that the Sun has contributed to the unusual climate change during the twentieth century, we point out that solar variability is unlikely to have been the dominant cause of the strong warming during the past three decades[3].

SUNSPOTS—strong concentrations of magnetic flux at the solar surface—are the longest-studied direct tracers of solar activity. Regular telescopic observations are available after AD 1610. In addition to the roughly 11-year solar cycle, the number of sunspots, formalized in the group sunspot number[1] (GSN), exhibits prominent fluctuations on longer timescales. Notable are an extended period in the seventeenth century called the Maunder minimum, during which practically no sunspots were present[2], and the period of high solar activity since about AD 1940 with average sunspot numbers above 70.

最近几十年太阳活动的异动：
与过去的 11,000 年相比

索兰基等

编者按

在关于人类活动是否是上个世纪全球变暖主因的辩论中，认为变暖乃是自然发生一派的一个主要观点是说太阳活动的加强导致了这种趋势——即太阳释放了更多的热量。本文作者检验了上述观点，他们利用大气中碳–14 活度作为代用指标，重建了过去 11,400 年（即从末次冰期结束时开始）的太阳活动。碳–14 由宇宙射线与大气层中的物质碰撞而产生，这一过程会受到太阳活动变化的影响，而碳–14 则会在树木年轮中积累，进而提供了年度的、可用于定年的千年纪记录。作者的结论是，尽管最近 70 年太阳活动出现异常，但这不足以解释近年来全球变暖的现象。

太阳黑子数目的直接观测数据只包含过去四个世纪[1,2]，但我们需要更长时间序列的数据以完成特定的研究。譬如，识别太阳活动对气候可能的影响以及检验太阳发电机模型都需要长序列的太阳活动数据。这里，我们基于树轮年代学所确定的放射性碳元素丰度，重建了过去 11,400 年的太阳黑子数目。我们将每个基于物理学的过程模型进行了整合，这些模型将放射性碳元素丰度与太阳黑子联系起来。根据我们的重建结果，过去 70 年太阳活动比较异常，而上一次太阳有如此高的活动性要追溯到 8,000 多年前。我们发现在过去的 11,400 年里，太阳只有 10% 的时间处在相似的磁场活动水平上，而且几乎所有早期的高活动性时段都短于当今阶段。需要指出的是，尽管当前高平均太阳黑子数目可能说明太阳对于二十世纪不寻常的气候变化存在影响，但太阳的变化不太可能是过去三十年间全球剧烈变暖的主导因素[3]。

太阳黑子——太阳表面磁场流量的强聚集区——是太阳活动的直接示踪物中被研究最久的一种。早在公元 1610 年就开始了利用常规望远镜对其的观测。除了大致上为 11 年的太阳周期，太阳黑子的数目，即正式文献中所谓的"太阳黑子团数"（GSN）[1]，在长时间尺度下具有显著地波动。延续到十七世纪的"蒙德极小期"尤为明显，在此期间几乎没有任何太阳黑子出现[2]；而在大约始于 1940 年的高太阳活动期当中，平均太阳黑子数目在 70 个以上。

A physical approach to reconstruction of the sunspot number back in time is based on archival proxies, such as the concentration of the cosmogenic isotopes ^{14}C in tree rings[4-6] or ^{10}Be in ice cores[7,8]. This approach has recently been strengthened by the development of physics-based models describing each link in the chain of processes connecting the concentration of cosmogenic isotopes with the sunspot number[9-12]. This advance allowed a reconstruction of the sunspot number since AD 850 based on ^{10}Be records from Antarctica and Greenland[13,14]. The current period of high solar activity is unique within this interval, but the covered time span is too short to judge just how unusual the current state of solar activity is.

Here we present a reconstruction of the sunspot number covering the Holocene epoch, the modern period of relatively warm climate that superseded the glacial period about 11,000 years ago. The reconstruction is based on Δ^{14}C, the ^{14}C activity in the atmosphere[15] obtained from high-precision ^{14}C analyses on decadal samples of mid-latitude tree-ring chronologies. The data set has been created in an international collaboration of dendrochronologists and radiocarbon laboratories[16]. The absolutely and precisely dated original data set used for the sunspot number reconstruction is represented by the black line in Fig. 1. Starting at a level 15% higher than the reference level of AD 1950, the atmospheric ^{14}C shows a long-term trend (indicated by the red line), which is mainly the result of changes in the intensity of the geomagnetic dipole field before and during the Holocene epoch. The fluctuations on shorter timescales predominantly result from variations of the ^{14}C production rate due to heliomagnetic variability, which modulates the cosmic ray flux.

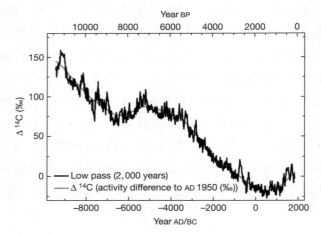

Fig. 1. Atmospheric radiocarbon level Δ^{14}C (expressed as deviation, in ‰, from the AD 1950 standard level[15]) derived from mostly decadal samples of absolutely dated tree-ring chronologies (INTCAL98 data set)[16]. The Δ^{14}C measurement precision is generally 2–3‰, although in the earlier part of the time series it can reach up to 4–5‰. The INTCAL98 data for times earlier than 11,400 BP are not directly employed for the reconstruction because of larger errors and uncertainties in the carbon cycle acting at that time. See Supplementary Information for more information on the data set, initial conditions used for the reconstruction, and error estimates. The long-term decline (indicated by the red curve) is caused by a reduction in ^{14}C production rate due mainly to an increase in the geomagnetic shielding of the cosmic ray flux. The short-term fluctuations (duration one to two centuries) reflect changes of the production rate due to solar variability. Years BC are shown negative here and in other figures.

重建太阳黑子的数目，物理方法是利用档案代用指标，譬如树木年轮中宇宙成因同位素 ^{14}C[4-6] 或冰芯中的 ^{10}Be。近来，这种方法借助于物理学模型的发展而得以强化，模型描述了宇宙成因同位素丰度与太阳黑子数目之间联系的每一环节。这一最新进展，使得利用南极和格陵兰 ^{10}Be 记录来重建自公元 850 年以来的太阳黑子数目成为可能 [13,14]。当前的高太阳活动期在此区间内是独一无二的，但由于涵盖的时间太短，尚不足以对现阶段的异常程度做出判断。

这里，我们重建了涵盖整个全新世及 11,000 年前由冰期更替为气候温暖的现代时期之后的太阳黑子数目。重建工作基于 Δ^{14}C，大气中的 ^{14}C 活度是基于中纬度树木年轮几十年的样本的高精度分析而获得的 [15]。所用的数据集是多个树轮年代学和放射性碳实验室间国际合作的成果 [16]。用于太阳黑子数重建且具有被绝对而精确定年的原始数据在图 1 用黑色实线表示。以公元 950 年的数据为参照点，起始数据与之相比高出 15%，且大气中的 ^{14}C 表现出一种长期的变化趋势（以红线标出），这主要是地磁偶极场在全新世之前和期间的强度变化的结果。更短时间的波动主要是太阳磁场变化引起宇宙射线通量的变化，进而对 ^{14}C 的产生速率产生影响的结果。

图 1. 基于具有绝对年代的树木年轮的十年际样本（INTCAL98 数据集）[16] 获得的大气放射性碳水平 Δ^{14}C（以相对公元 1950 年标准水平的偏差表示，单位为千分之一 [15]）。尽管早期 Δ^{14}C 时间序列的误差部分会达到 4‰ ~ 5‰，但总体为 2‰ ~ 3‰。早于 11,400 BP 的 INTCAL98 数据不被直接用于重建，因为当时的碳循环存在较大的误差与不确定性。更多关于数据、重建初始条件，以及误差估计的信息参见补充信息。长时间尺度的下降趋势（图中红色曲线）是 ^{14}C 产率下降的结果，主要是地磁场对宇宙射线屏蔽增强造成的。短期的波动（为期 1~2 个世纪）反映了 ^{14}C 产率随太阳活动的变化。图中公元前（BC）在数轴上记为负数。

The atmospheric ^{14}C level may also be affected by changes in the partition of carbon between the major reservoirs, that is, deep ocean, ocean mixed layer, biosphere and atmosphere. Variations in ocean circulation[17] could influence ^{14}C via a variable uptake of CO_2 into the ocean or by the exchange of ^{14}C-depleted carbon from the deep ocean, but, owing to the rather small ^{14}C gradients among the reservoirs, strong changes in these processes need to be invoked. For the Holocene, there is no evidence of considerable oceanic variability, so we can assume that the short- and mid-term fluctuations of ^{14}C predominantly reflect solar variability. This is supported by the strong similarity of the fluctuations of ^{10}Be in polar ice cores compared to ^{14}C, despite their completely different geochemical history[18-20].

We first determine the ^{14}C production rate in the Earth's atmosphere following Usoskin and Kromer[21]. They used two distinct methods, which take into account carbon cycle effects in different ways. Both methods give similar results when applied to the tree-ring Δ^{14}C data set described above. For the current reconstruction we use the average of the ^{14}C production rate deduced using both techniques. In accordance with the decadal sampling of the ^{14}C data we reconstruct the 10-year averaged sunspot number. Because the Δ^{14}C data are contaminated by extensive burning of ^{14}C-free fossil fuel since the late nineteenth century[22] and later by atmospheric nuclear bomb tests, we use ^{14}C data before AD 1900 only and take the historical sunspot number record for the most recent period.

From the ^{14}C production rate we obtain the sunspot number in multiple steps, each substantiated by a physics-based model. A model describing the transport and modulation of galactic cosmic rays within the heliosphere[11] is inverted to find the cosmic ray flux corresponding to the determined ^{14}C production rate. The transport of galactic cosmic rays in the heliosphere is affected by the Sun's open magnetic flux, that is, the fraction of the Sun's total magnetic flux that reaches out into interplanetary space[12]. The open flux is linked with the sunspot number by inverting a model describing the evolution of the open magnetic flux for given sunspot number[9,10]. All adjustable parameters entering this chain of models were fixed using independent data prior to the current reconstruction, so that no free parameter remains when reconstructing the sunspot number from ^{14}C data (see Supplementary Table S1). This reconstruction method was previously applied to ^{10}Be data from Greenland and Antarctica. Only the first step changes when using Δ^{14}C instead of ^{10}Be data to reconstruct the sunspot number. Hence, possible errors and uncertainties in the later steps are similar to those studied in our earlier papers[13,14].

Applying our reconstruction method to Δ^{14}C, we first determine the sunspot number since AD 850 in order to compare these values with the historical record of GSNs since 1610 and with the reconstruction on the basis of ^{10}Be data[14]. Figure 2 shows that the reconstructed average sunspot number from Δ^{14}C is remarkably similar to the 10-year averaged GSN series (correlation coefficient $0.925^{+0.02}_{-0.03}$ with a false alarm probability $< 10^{-6}$). The difference between the reconstructed and measured sunspot number is nearly gaussian with a standard deviation of 5.8, which is smaller than the theoretical estimate of the reconstructed sunspot number uncertainty (about 8 for the last millennium, see Supplementary Information),

大气 ^{14}C 水平可能也会受到 ^{14}C 主要碳库——深海、海洋混合层、生物圈、大气圈——之间碳配比变化的影响。洋流的变化 [17] 可能会通过改变海洋吸收的 CO_2，或者通过与深海 ^{14}C 贫化的碳之间的交换来影响 ^{14}C。但是，由于不同碳库间的 ^{14}C 梯度非常的小，需要考虑上述过程中的剧烈变化。对于全新世来说，没有海洋碳库剧烈变化的明显证据。因此，我们可以假设 ^{14}C 短期和中期变化主要反映了太阳活动的变化。上述假设得到了极地冰芯 ^{10}Be 与 ^{14}C 对比分析结果的支持。尽管具有不同的地球化学历史，但两者的波动变化极为相似 [18-20]。

我们根据乌索斯金和克罗默的方法，首先来确定地球大气中 ^{14}C 的产生速率 [21]。他们采用了两种不同的办法，即以不同的方式考虑了碳循环的影响。将两者应用于前述树木年轮的 Δ^{14}C 数据集时，两种方法给出了相似的结果。对当前生产速率的重建工作，我们采用了两种方法所得结果的平均值。与 ^{14}C 十年期采样一致，我们重建了十年平均的太阳黑子数。因为 Δ^{14}C 数据受到 19 世纪晚期大量的无 ^{14}C 化石燃料燃烧及后期大气核弹试验的污染 [22]，我们仅采用公元 1900 年以前的数据，对于最近的一段时期，我们只使用历史记录的太阳黑子数数据。

从 ^{14}C 的产生速率，我们分多步得到了太阳黑子数目，每一步都有物理模型证实。利用限定太阳风层内宇宙射线的传输和调节模型 [11] 的反演，来寻找已确定 ^{14}C 产率对应的宇宙射线通量。太阳风层内宇宙射线的传输受太阳开放磁通量的影响。开放通量是指太阳总磁通量中到达行星际空间的组分 [12]。通过给定太阳黑子数目下的开放磁通量演化模型的反演，将开放通量与太阳黑子的数目联系起来 [9,10]。所有进入模型链的可变参数都用以前重建工作的独立数据来确定，所以在利用 ^{14}C 数据重建太阳黑子数目时已经没有自由参数（见补充表格 S1）。这种重建方法曾被用于格陵兰和南极 ^{10}Be 的数据重建。在用 Δ^{14}C 数据取代 ^{10}Be 数据重建太阳黑子数时，仅第一步发生了改变。因此，后续步骤中可能出现的误差和不确定性都与我们先前的研究相似 [13,14]。

将我们的重建方法应用于 Δ^{14}C。为了将这些值与自 1610 年以来 GSN 的历史记录和基于 ^{10}Be 数据的重建结果进行对比 [14]，我们首先确定了自公元 850 年至今的太阳黑子数目。图 2 表明由 Δ^{14}C 重建的平均黑子数目与 10 年平均的 GNS 序列十分相似（相关系数 $0.925^{+0.02}_{-0.03}$，误报可能性 $< 10^{-6}$）。重建数据和观测到的黑子数目的误差基本符合标准差为 5.8 的高斯分布，这个标准差小于重建黑子数目的理论估计（对于上个千年大约为 8，见参考信息），这表明了后者的保守特性。基于 ^{10}Be 重建的两个

indicating the conservative nature of the latter. Two ^{10}Be-based sunspot number reconstructions are plotted in Fig. 2, which correspond to extreme assumptions about the geographic area of ^{10}Be production relevant for its deposition in polar ice. The local polar production model (green curve) provides an upper limit to the sunspot number[14], while the global production model (magenta dashed curve) gives a lower limit[13]. The sunspot number time series obtained from Δ^{14}C lies between the two ^{10}Be-based curves, and for the period after AD 1200 is closer to the ^{10}Be-based reconstruction under the assumption of global production.

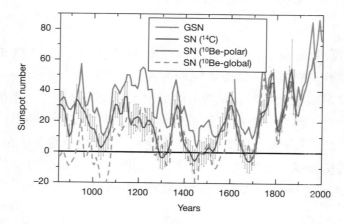

Fig. 2. Comparison between directly measured sunspot number (SN) and SN reconstructed from different cosmogenic isotopes. Plotted are SN reconstructed from Δ^{14}C (blue), the 10-year averaged group sunspot number[1] (GSN, red) since 1610 and the SN reconstruction[14] from ^{10}Be under the two extreme assumptions of local (green) and global (magenta, dashed) production, respectively. The slightly negative values of the reconstructed SN during the grand minima are an artefact; they are compatible with SN = 0 within the uncertainty of these reconstructions as indicated by the error bars. Δ^{14}C is connected with the ^{14}C production rate via a carbon cycle model[21]. The connection between the ^{14}C production rate, R, and the cosmic ray flux is given by $R = \int_{\theta=0}^{\pi} \int_{P_C(\theta,M)}^{\infty} X(P, \Phi)Y(P)\mathrm{d}P\sin\theta\mathrm{d}\theta$, where θ is the colatitude relative to the geomagnetic dipole axis, and $P_C(\theta, M)$ is the local cosmic ray rigidity cutoff (which depends on θ and the virtual geomagnetic dipole moment, M)[23]. $X(P, \Phi)$ is the differential cosmic ray rigidity spectrum near Earth, Φ is the modulation strength describing the average rigidity losses of cosmic rays inside the heliosphere, $Y(P)$ is the differential yield function[24] of ^{14}C, and P is the rigidity of the primary cosmic rays. For studies of long-term changes of the cosmic ray flux, the parameter Φ alone adequately describes the modulation of the cosmic ray spectrum $X(P)$[11,24]. The two most abundant cosmic ray species, protons and α-particles, are taken into account in the model[13]. The cosmic ray transport model relates R to Φ, which in turn depends on the Sun's open magnetic flux[12]. The open flux is linked with the magnetic flux in sunspots (and thus with the SN) via the source term in a system of differential equations[9,10]. The value of R is obtained from Δ^{14}C and M is known for the whole interval of interest[25,26], so that Φ can be obtained from the inversion of the equation given above. Error bars depict the 68% confidence interval for the reconstructed SN, which takes into account both random and systematic uncertainties (see Supplementary Information).

Figure 3a shows the reconstruction based on the 11,400-year set of Δ^{14}C data. Clearly, the level of activity has remained variable, with episodes of particularly low numbers of sunspots (grand minima) distributed over the whole record. Episodes of high activity are also present. These are mostly concentrated in the earliest three millennia (before 6000

黑子数目序列见图 2，它们对应于对极地冰中与 ^{10}Be 沉积有关的产率的地理区域的极端假设。局地极地产生模型（绿色曲线）为太阳黑子数提供了上限，而全球产生模型（品红色曲线）则提供了下限。基于 Δ^{14}C 重建的太阳黑子时间序列介于基于 ^{10}Be 重建的两条曲线之间。对于公元 1200 年之后的时期来说，该曲线要更靠近于 ^{10}Be 全球产生模型下的重建。

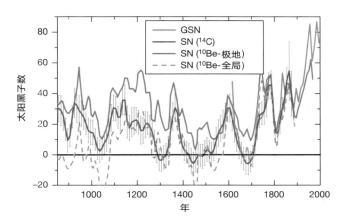

图 2. 直接测量获得的太阳黑子数（SN）与基于宇宙成因同位素重建的太阳黑子数的比较。图中 SN 分别通过以下数据重建：Δ^{14}C（蓝色）、1610 年来十年期平均太阳黑子群数 [1]（GSN，红色），以及在两个极端假设条件（局域，绿色实线；全局，洋红色虚线）下的 ^{10}Be[14]。在大的极小期 SN 的偏负数值是人为造成的，在重建的误差范围内（图中误差棒所示）SN 近似为零。Δ^{14}C 通过碳循环模型与 ^{14}C 的产率联系起来 [21]，而 ^{14}C 的生成率（R）与宇宙射线通量之间的关系式为：$R = \int_{\theta=0}^{\pi} \int_{0}^{\infty} P_C(\theta,M) X(P,\Phi) Y(P) \mathrm{d}P \sin\theta \mathrm{d}\theta$，其中 θ 是相对于地磁偶极子轴的磁余纬，$P_C(\theta,M)$ 是局域宇宙射线刚性截止（值取决于 θ 以及虚拟地磁偶极子矩 M）[23]。$X(P,\Phi)$ 是靠近地球处宇宙射线刚性谱的微分，Φ 是调制强度，用来限定太阳风层内宇宙射线的平均刚性损失，$Y(P)$ 是 ^{14}C 产率函数的微分，P 是原始宇宙射线的刚性。对于宇宙射线通量变化的长期研究，只利用参数 Φ 就足以描述宇宙射线谱的调制 $X(P)$[11,24]。模型也考虑了两种最丰富的宇宙射线，即质子和 α 粒子 [13]。宇宙射线传输模型将 R 和 Φ 相联系，它们转而依赖于太阳开放磁场通量 [12]。在太阳黑子中，开放通量通过系统微分方程组中的源项与磁通量联系起来（因而也与 SN 相关联）[9,10]。R 的值由 Δ^{14}C 获得，M 在整个研究时段是已知的 [25,26]，故 Φ 可以通过上面给出的方程反演得到。误差棒表示考虑了随机和系统误差的重建 SN 的 68% 置信区间（详见补充信息）。

图 3a 显示了基于 11,400 年 Δ^{14}C 数据集的太阳黑子重建情况。显然，活动水平持续变化，太阳黑子数很少的时期（长极小期）在整个记录中都有分布。高活动性的时期也有，主要集中在最早的三个千年（公元前 6000 年之前），这些时期也表现为

BC), which also exhibit a high average sunspot number (35.6 compared to 25.6 after 6000 BC). During the last eight millennia, the episode with the highest average sunspot number is the ongoing one that started about 60 years ago. The sunspot number averaged over the whole period is 28.7 with a standard deviation of 16.2. The average number of 75 since 1940 thus lies 2.85 standard deviations above this long-term average.

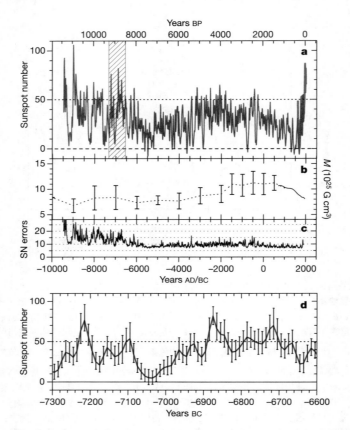

Fig. 3. Reconstructed sunspot number and its uncertainty for the whole interval of time considered. **a**, 10-year averaged SN reconstructed from Δ^{14}C data since 9500 BC (blue curve) and 10-year averaged group sunspot number[1] (GSN) obtained from telescopic observations since 1610 (red curve). The horizontal dotted line marks the threshold above which we consider the Sun to be exceptionally active. It corresponds to 1.3 standard deviations above the mean. **b**, Evolution of the virtual geomagnetic dipole moment[26] with error bars that take into account the scatter between different palaeomagnetic reconstructions. (The error bars give the s.d. in the reconstructed virtual geomagnetic dipole moment.) The geomagnetic field data of ref. 25 are given by the dotted line. **c**, Uncertainty in the reconstructed SN. It includes errors introduced at each step of the reconstruction process. The largest sources of random errors are the uncertainty in the knowledge of the geomagnetic dipole moment and in the ^{14}C production rate. We also consider systematic errors—for example, due to uncertainties in the ^{14}C production rate prior to the considered period of time. A discussion of how these uncertainties are estimated is given in Supplementary Information. Clearly, the uncertainties are sufficiently small that they do not affect the presence or absence of grand minima or of episodes of high activity, except in already marginal cases. **d**, A detail from the full time series of reconstructed SN with expanded temporal scale. The chosen interval (corresponding to the shaded part of **a**) exhibits three episodes of high solar activity and a grand minimum. The error bars indicate the total uncertainty, σ, in the reconstruction. (They depict the 68% confidence interval for the reconstructed SN,

高平均太阳黑子数目（35.6 个，而公元前 6000 年之后仅为 25.6 个）。在过去的八个千年之中，具有最高平均太阳黑子数目的时期就是开始于 60 年前且当前还在进行的时段。太阳黑子数目在整个时期的平均值是 28.7 个，标准差为 16.2。而自 1940 年以来的平均数达 75，高于 2.85 个标准差的平均变化。

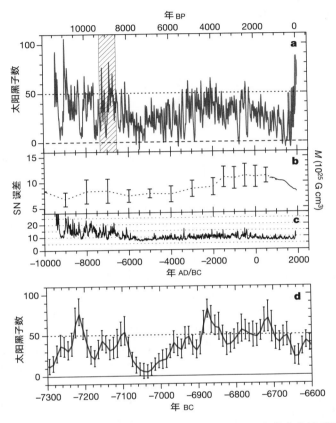

图 3. 重建的太阳黑子数与整个研究时段的不确定性。**a.** 公元前 9500 年以来基于 $\Delta^{14}C$ 数据重建的 10 年平均 SN（蓝色曲线）和由 1610 年来望远镜观测数据获得的 10 年平均太阳黑子群数（GSN）[1]（红色曲线）。水平虚线表示我们认为太阳活动异常活跃的阈值，其对应了平均值之上 1.3 个标准差。**b.** 虚拟地磁偶极矩的演化[26]，其中误差棒考虑了不同的古地磁重建之间的离散（误差棒给出了重建虚拟地磁偶极矩的标准差）。来自文献 25 的地磁场数据用虚线表示。**c.** 重建太阳黑子数的不确定性，包括了重建过程中每一步的误差。最大的随机误差源是对于地磁偶极矩和对研究期之前的 ^{14}C 产率了解不足。我们也考虑了系统误差，如早于研究时段的 ^{14}C 产率的不确定性。关于误差估计的详细内容参见补充信息。显然，这些不确定性因素较小，除了边际情况，不足以影响大的极小期和高活动性事件的出现和缺失。**d.** 时间尺度扩展到整个时段的 SN 序列细节图。选取时段（对应于图 **a** 的阴影部分）展示了三个高太阳活动事件和一个大的极小期。误差棒指示重建过程中总误差 σ（包括随机误差和系统误差的 68% 置信区间，详见补充信息）。两个最强的极大值分别位于高活动性阈值（50）的 2.1σ 和 3.0σ 处。因而，与这些误差相关的统计波动导致误差的概率分别为 3% 和 0.2%。整个高活动期（比如持续 50 年）是由统计波动引起的误差的概率相当小。

which takes into account both random and systematic uncertainties (see Supplementary Information).) The two strongest maxima lie 2.1σ and 3.0σ, respectively, above the high-activity threshold of 50. Hence the probability that they are due to statistical fluctuations related to these errors is 3% and 0.2%, respectively. The probability that a whole episode of high activity (lasting, say, 50 years) is due to a statistical fluctuation is significantly smaller.

A major uncertainty in the reconstructed sunspot number is related to the evolution of the geomagnetic field, which is represented in Fig. 3b. A weaker geomagnetic field leads to an increased cosmic ray flux impinging on the terrestrial atmosphere and thus to a higher ^{14}C production rate, mimicking a lower value of sunspot number if not properly taken into account. The uncertainties in the reconstructed sunspot numbers are discussed in Supplementary Information and enter into Fig. 3c, where the sum of the random and systematic uncertainties affecting the reconstruction is given. For the whole time interval, the mean uncertainty of the reconstructed sunspot number is about 10.

In Fig. 3d we show a sub-interval of 700 years duration from our reconstruction, which exhibits three prominent periods of high sunspot number (average values exceeding 50) and a grand minimum. Within the 95% confidence interval, the Sun spent in total between 780 and 1,060 years in a high-activity state (sunspot number > 50), which corresponds to 6.9–9.3% of the total duration of our reconstruction. The most probable values are 950 years and 8.3%, respectively. Although the rarity of the current episode of high average sunspot number may be taken as an indication that the Sun has contributed to the unusual degree of climate change during the twentieth century, we stress that solar variability is unlikely to be the prime cause of the strong warming during the last three decades[3]. In ref. 3, reconstructions of solar total and spectral irradiance as well as of cosmic ray flux were compared with surface temperature records covering approximately 150 years. It was shown that even under the extreme assumption that the Sun was responsible for all the global warming prior to 1970, at the most 30% of the strong warming since then can be of solar origin.

There are 31 periods during which the 10-year averaged sunspot number consistently exceeds a level of 50. The average length of such episodes is about 30 years, the longest being 90 years (around 9000 BC). The distribution of the durations of such episodes is given in Fig. 4a. The number of high-activity periods decreases exponentially with increasing duration. The current level of high solar activity has now already lasted close to 65 years and is marked by the arrow on the figure. This implies that not only is the current state of solar activity unusually high, but also this high level of activity has lasted unusually long. Assuming the previous episodes of high activity to be typical, we can estimate the probability with which the solar activity level will remain above a sunspot number of 50 over the next decades. The result is given in Fig. 4b, which shows that there is only a probability of $8\%^{+3\%}_{-4\%}$ that the current high-activity episode will last another 50 years (and thus reach a total duration of 115 years), while the probability that it will continue until the end of the twenty-first century is below 1%.

430

在重建黑子数目的过程中，一个主要的不确定性因素与地磁场的演化相关，见图 3b。较弱的地磁场导致射入地球大气中的宇宙射线流通量增加，^{14}C 产率增高。如果无法对这一影响进行正确处理，其产生的结果与低太阳黑子产生的结果类似。关于重建黑子数目过程中的不确定性的讨论见补充信息以及图 3c。在图中，我们给出了重建的随机以及系统误差总和。对整个时间区间而言，太阳黑子数目重建的平均误差大约为 10。

图 3d 是我们重建结果中为期 700 年的一个子区间，上面展示了三个明显的高太阳黑子数时期（平均值超过 50）和一个大的极小期。在 95% 置信区间内，太阳高活动期（太阳黑子数 > 50）持续时间在 780 到 1,060 年之间，对应于总重建时间的 6.9% ~ 9.3%。最有可能的时间跨度为 950 年，占总重建时间的 8.3%。尽管当代罕见的高平均太阳黑子数或许可以作为太阳对二十世纪异常气候变化影响的标示，但我们仍要强调太阳活动的变化不可能是最近三十年气候强烈变暖的主要原因 [3]。参考文献 3 重建了过去 150 年来的太阳总辐照度和光谱辐照度，以及宇宙射线通量，并与地表温度记录进行对比。结果显示，即使在最极端的假设下，即太阳对 1970 年前所有的全球变暖现象皆有影响，最多也只有 30% 的强气候变暖源于太阳活动。

太阳黑子数十年平均值持续高于 50 的有 31 个时段，这些时段的平均长度大约为 30 年，最长达 90 年（约在公元前 9000 年）。这些事件的持续时间分布见图 4a。随持续时间的增加，高活跃度时段的数量呈指数下降。现今的高太阳活动已经持续了将近 65 年，在图中以箭头标示。这说明不仅当下太阳活动异常活跃，而且持续时间也异常长。假设过去的高活跃事件具有代表性，我们可以估计未来数十年太阳黑子数保持大于 50 的概率。结果见图 4b，太阳现有高活动水平再持续 50 年（持续总时间达到 115 年）的概率只有 $8\%^{+3\%}_{-4\%}$，而持续到二十一世纪末的概率小于 1%。

Fig. 4. Distribution of the duration of episodes of high solar activity and the probability that the current episode will reach a given duration. **a**, Histogram of the distribution function of the duration of episodes of high solar activity during which the 10-year averaged SN exceeds 50. Some bins have been enlarged in order to improve the statistics; in such cases the average number per bin is given. The vertical error bars correspond to $\sqrt{N}$, where N is the number of events combined in one data point. The length of the current period of high activity is marked by the arrow. The solid line is a least-squares exponential fit to the plotted points. The dashed and dotted lines represent exponential fits to the distributions obtained from extreme SN reconstructions including the influence of random and systematic errors as given in Fig. 3 (see also the discussion in Supplementary Information). **b**, The probability of the total duration of a state of high activity (SN level exceeding 50). For the current episode, which started in AD 1940 (~65 years ago), the start of the diagram corresponds to the year AD 2015. Each curve is based upon the corresponding fit shown in **a**. The probability (for the reference curve) that the high activity continues for another 5 decades for a total duration of 115 years is only 8%.

(**431**, 1084-1087, 2004)

图 4. 高太阳活动持续时间的分布与当代事件达到给定时长的概率。**a.** 10 年平均 SN 超过 50 的高太阳活动事件持续时间分布函数的直方图。有些组被放大以方便统计，在这些情况下，给出的是每组的平均数。垂直误差棒对应于 $\sqrt{N}$，其中 N 代表组合成一个数据点的事件数目。当代高活动期的长度在图中用箭头标示。实线代表基于标出点并利用最小二乘法指数拟合的曲线。虚线和点线表示基于极端 SN 重建分布（包括随机和系统误差的影响，见图 3）的指数拟合（参见补充信息中的讨论）。**b.** 高活动性（SN 水平高于 50）总持续时间的概率。当今时段始于 1940 年，即大约 65 年前，图中开始于 2015 年。每条曲线都是基于图 **a** 所示对应状态的拟合。未来高活动性再持续 50 年，总时长达 115 年的概率仅为 8%。

（汪浩 翻译；许冰 审稿）

433

S. K. Solanki[1], **I. G. Usoskin**[2], **B. Kromer**[3], **M. Schüssler**[1] **& J. Beer**[4]

[1] Max-Planck-Institut für Sonnensystemforschung (formerly the Max-Planck-Institut für Aeronomie), 37191 Katlenburg-Lindau, Germany

[2] Sodankylä Geophysical Observatory (Oulu unit), University of Oulu, 90014 Oulu, Finland

[3] Heidelberger Akademie der Wissenschaften, Institut für Umweltphysik, Neuenheimer Feld 229, 69120 Heidelberg, Germany

[4] Department of Surface Waters, EAWAG, 8600 Dübendorf, Switzerland

Received 20 February; accepted 1 September 2004; doi 10.1038/nature02995.

References:

1. Hoyt, D. V. & Schatten, K. H. Group sunspot numbers: A new solar activity reconstruction. *Sol. Phys.* **179**, 189-219 (1998).

2. Eddy, J. A. The Maunder minimum. *Science* **192**, 1189-1202 (1976).

3. Solanki, S. K. & Krivova, N. Can solar variability explain global warming since 1970? *J. Geophys. Res.* **108**, doi: 10.1029/2002JA009753 (2003).

4. Stuiver, M. & Braziunas, T. F. Atmospheric ^{14}C and century-scale solar oscillations. *Nature* **338**, 405-408 (1989).

5. Stuiver, M. & Braziunas, T. F. Sun, ocean, climate and atmospheric $^{14}CO_2$: an evaluation of causal and spectral relationships. *Holocene* **3**, 289-305 (1993).

6. Damon, P. E. & Sonett, C. P. in *The Sun in Time* (eds Sonnet, C. P., Giampapa, M. S. & Matthews, M. S.) 360-388 (Univ. Arizona, Tucson, 1991).

7. Beer, J. *et al.* Use of ^{10}Be in polar ice to trace the 11-year cycle of solar activity. *Nature* **347**, 164-166 (1990).

8. Beer, J. Long-term indirect indices of solar variability. *Space Sci. Rev.* **94**, 53-66 (2000).

9. Solanki, S. K., Schüssler, M. & Fligge, M. Evolution of the Sun's large-scale magnetic field since the Maunder minimum. *Nature* **408**, 445-447 (2000).

10. Solanki, S. K., Schüssler, M. & Fligge, M. Secular variation of the Sun's magnetic flux. *Astron. Astrophys.* **383**, 706-712 (2002).

11. Usoskin, I. G., Alanko, K., Mursula, K. & Kovaltsov, G. A. Heliospheric modulation strength during the neutron monitor era. *Sol. Phys.* **207**, 389-399 (2002).

12. Usoskin, I. G., Mursula, K., Solanki, S. K., Schüssler, M. & Kovaltsov, G. A. A physical reconstruction of cosmic ray intensity since 1610. *J. Geophys. Res.* **107**, doi:10.1029/2002JA009343 (2002).

13. Usoskin, I. G., Mursula, K., Solanki, S. K., Schüssler, M. & Alanko, K. Reconstruction of solar activity for the last millenium using ^{10}Be data. *Astron. Astrophys.* **413**, 745-751 (2004).

14. Usoskin, I. G., Solanki, S. K., Schüssler, M., Mursula, K. & Alanko, K. A millenium scale sunspot number reconstruction: evidence for an unusually active Sun since the 1940s. *Phys. Rev. Lett.* **91**, 211101 (2003).

15. Stuiver, M. & Pollach, P. Discussion: reporting of ^{14}C data. *Radiocarbon* **19**, 355-363 (1977).

16. Stuiver, M. *et al.* INTCAL98 Radiocarbon age calibration. *Radiocarbon* **40**, 1041-1083 (1998).

17. Broecker, W. S. An unstable superconveyor. *Nature* **367**, 414-415 (1994).

18. Bond, G. *et al.* Persistent solar influence on North Atlantic surface circulation during the Holocene. *Science* **294**, 2130-2136 (2001).

19. Muscheler, R., Beer, J. & Kromer, B. *Solar Variability as an Input to the Earth's Environment* 305-316 (ESA SP-535, European Space Agency, Noordwijk, 2003).

20. Bard, E., Raisbeck, G. M., Yiou, F. & Jouzel, J. Solar modulation of cosmogenic nuclide production over the last millennium: comparison between ^{14}C and ^{10}Be records. *Earth Planet. Sci. Lett.* **150**, 453-462 (1997).

21. Usoskin, I. G. & Kromer, B. Reconstruction of the ^{14}C production rate from measured relative abundance. *Radiocarbon* (in the press).

22. Suess, H. E. Radiocarbon content in modern wood. *Science* **122**, 415-417 (1955).

23. Elsasser, W., Ney, E. P. & Winckler, J. R. Cosmic-ray intensity and geomagnetism. *Nature* **178**, 1226-1227 (1956).

24. Castagnoli, G. & Lal, D. Solar modulation effects in terrestrial production of carbon-14. *Radiocarbon* **22**, 133-158 (1980).

25. Hongre, L., Hulot, G. & Khokhlov, A. An analysis of the geomagnetic field over the past 2000 years. *Phys. Earth Planet. Inter.* **106**, 311-335 (1998).

26. Yang, S., Odah, H. & Shaw, J. Variations in the geomagnetic dipole moment over the last 12000 years. *Geophys. J. Int.* **140**, 158-162 (2000).

Supplementary Information accompanies the paper on www.nature.com/nature.

Competing interests statement. The authors declare that they have no competing financial interests.

Correspondence and requests for materials should be addressed to S.K.S. (solanki@mps.mpg.de).

434

Tomographic Imaging of Molecular Orbitals

J. Itatani *et al.*

Editor's Note

In molecules, the electron orbitals of the constituent atoms are considered to overlap and reconfigure into molecular orbitals that determine the molecule's structure and chemical behaviour. The shape and nature of these molecular orbitals can be calculated from quantum theory, but they have been largely treated as a mere mathematical formalism that permits a quantum description of the chemical bond. Here, however, David Villeneuve in Canada and his coworkers show that molecular orbitals can actually be imaged in a slice-wise tomographic fashion by looking at the way the electron clouds of molecules interact with extremely short pulses of laser light. They present a map of the quantum-mechanical wavefunction for a molecular orbital of the nitrogen molecule.

Single-electron wavefunctions, or orbitals, are the mathematical constructs used to describe the multi-electron wavefunction of molecules. Because the highest-lying orbitals are responsible for chemical properties, they are of particular interest. To observe these orbitals change as bonds are formed and broken is to observe the essence of chemistry. Yet single orbitals are difficult to observe experimentally, and until now, this has been impossible on the timescale of chemical reactions. Here we demonstrate that the full three-dimensional structure of a single orbital can be imaged by a seemingly unlikely technique, using high harmonics generated from intense femtosecond laser pulses focused on aligned molecules. Applying this approach to a series of molecular alignments, we accomplish a tomographic reconstruction of the highest occupied molecular orbital of N_2. The method also allows us to follow the attosecond dynamics of an electron wave packet.

THE electrons that make up molecules are organized by energy in orbitals[1,2]. Although total electron density in molecules is routinely measured by X-ray diffraction or electron scattering, only two methods are able to "see" the highest occupied molecular orbitals (HOMOs)—electron momentum spectroscopy and scanning tunnelling microscopy. Electron momentum spectroscopy[3] is an $(e, 2e)$ scattering technique that can determine the radially averaged density of the outermost valence electrons. Scanning tunnelling microscopy[4] gives the electron density, distorted by surface states. We show that high harmonic emission from molecules[5-11] allows the three-dimensional shape of the highest electronic orbital to be measured, including the relative phase of components of the wavefunction. Our results may be compared with predictions of the various models that are used to describe many-electron systems[12], such as the Hartree-Fock, the Kohn-Sham and the Dyson approaches.

分子轨道的层析成像

板谷治郎 等

编者按

在分子中，大家认为构成原子的电子轨道通过重叠和重新组合成为分子轨道，这种分子轨道可决定其分子结构及化学行为。通过量子论可以估算出这些分子轨道的形状和性质，但是，在很大程度上，它们只不过被视为数学形式体系，该数学形式可以量子化地描述化学键。然而，加拿大的戴维·维尔纳夫和他的合作者们在本文中表明，通过观察分子的电子云与激光的极短脉冲之间相互作用的方式，证明了分子轨道实际上可以以切片层析的方式成像。他们提供了一张氮分子的分子轨道的量子力学波函数的图像。

单电子波函数（或称轨道）是用来描述分子的多电子波函数的数学构造。由于最外层轨道决定分子的化学性质，因而值得我们格外关注。观察这些轨道在化学键形成和断裂时的变化就是观察化学反应的本质。不过单轨道很难用实验方法加以观测，而且到目前为止，在化学反应的时间尺度上是不可能做到这种观测的。我们要在本文中说明的是，单一轨道的完整三维结构可以通过一种看似不大可能的技术来成像，即采用高次谐波，它是通过高强度的飞秒激光脉冲聚焦于排列的分子而产生的。将这种方法应用于一系列分子排列，我们实现了对于 N_2 中最高占据分子轨道的层析重建。这种方法还使我们得以探索一个电子波包的阿秒动力学。

构成分子的电子依其能量而分列于轨道之中[1,2]。尽管分子中总的电子密度可用 X 射线衍射或电子散射等常规的方式测得，但只有两种方法能够"看到"最高占据分子轨道（HOMOs）——电子动量谱学和扫描隧道显微镜。电子动量谱学[3] 是一种 $(e, 2e)$ 散射技术，它能测定最外层价电子的径向平均密度。扫描隧道显微镜[4] 则给出被表面状态扭曲的电子密度。我们要说明的是，来自分子的高次谐波发射[5-11] 使我们得以测定最外层电子轨道的三维形状，包括波函数分量的相对相位。可以将我们的结果与用来描述多电子体系的各种模型[12]——例如哈特里–福克、科恩–沙姆以及戴森方法——的预测结果加以比较。

If we can measure orbitals with femtosecond laser technology, we can also observe orbital changes occurring on the timescale of chemical reactions. The next challenge will be to measure attosecond bound-state electron dynamics. We show that imaging orbitals can be extended to imaging coherent electron motion in atoms or molecules. Quantum mechanically, electron motion is described by a coherent superposition of electronic states. This is the closest that quantum mechanics allows to imaging the "Bohr orbital motion" of electrons.

Tomographic imaging of a molecular orbital is achieved in three crucial steps. (1) Alignment of the molecular axis in the laboratory frame. (2) Selective ionization of the orbital. (3) Projection of the state onto a coherent set of plane waves.

Alignment of Gas-phase Molecules

Computed tomography refers to the technology of retrieving sectional images of an object, such as a human body, from a series of one-dimensional projections[13]. For a projection direction fixed in the laboratory frame, the object must be rotated. Thus, we begin by discussing how molecules can be aligned[14].

A relatively intense, non-resonant laser pulse induces a Stark shift of the ground state of molecules that depends on the angle of the molecular axis to the laser polarization[15]. It has been demonstrated that gas-phase molecules can be aligned adiabatically[16], aligned in three dimensions[17] or oriented[18]. We use non-adiabatic alignment[19,20]. It results in field-free alignment of linear molecules well after the aligning pulse has terminated. A 60-fs laser pulse produces a rotational wave packet in N_2. This wave packet periodically rephases, giving periods when the molecular axes are aligned in space. The probe pulse coincides with the first half-revival at 4.1 ps (ref. 20). The degree of angular alignment is good enough to see a difference in the harmonic spectra for a 5° rotation of the alignment direction.

High Harmonic Generation from Molecules

High harmonics are produced by ionizing atoms or molecules. We choose to operate in the tunnel ionization regime[21] because the rate of tunnel ionization depends exponentially on the ionization potential. Hence the orbital with the lowest ionization potential (the HOMO in an unexcited molecule) is preferentially selected. This is the second requirement for tomographic imaging of a single molecular orbital.

The third requirement for tomography is that we can take a series of projected images of the molecular orbital. For this we record high harmonic emission generated from the molecule itself. High harmonics have been extensively studied from atoms, whereas harmonics from molecules have been studied with isotropic distributions[5,6] or with weak alignment[7]. It has

如果能够用飞秒激光技术测定轨道，那么我们也能观测到在化学反应时间尺度上发生的轨道变化。下一个挑战将会是测定阿秒束缚态电子动力学。我们将会说明，轨道成像技术的适用范围可以扩展至原子或分子中相干电子运动的成像。在量子力学中，电子运动是用电子态的相干叠加来描述的，就量子力学所允许的意义而言，这是最接近于电子"玻尔轨道运动"的成像。

分子轨道的层析成像是通过三个重要的步骤来实现的。(1) 在实验室坐标系中分子轴的排列。(2) 轨道的选择性电离。(3) 该状态在一组相干平面波上的投影。

气相分子的排列

计算机层析成像术指的是从物体（诸如人体）的一系列一维投影中恢复剖视图像的技术 [13]。对于实验室坐标系中的一个固定的投影方向，必然需要将该物体旋转。因此，我们从分子可以被如何排列 [14] 开始讨论。

一个相当强度的且非共振的激光脉冲会激发分子基态的斯塔克位移，该位移取决于分子轴与激光偏振方向之间的夹角 [15]。实验已经证明，气相分子可以在绝热的条件下排列 [16]，即在三维空间中排列 [17] 或者定向排列 [18]。我们使用非绝热的排列 [19,20]。这导致线性脉冲结束后线型分子在无外场的作用下实现排列。一个 60 fs 激光脉冲在 N_2 中产生了一个旋转的波包。这个波包周期性地重现，使分子轴在空间中排列时呈现周期性。探测脉冲的作用时间与位于 4.1 ps 的前半个重现相一致（参考文献 20）。角度排列的程度足够好，使得当分子的排列方向旋转了 5° 以后就可以从谐波谱中观察到它们的差别了。

分子高次谐波的产生

通过电离原子或分子可以产生高次谐波。我们选择在隧道电离区域 [21] 进行操作，因为隧道电离速率以指数方式随电离势而变化。因此，具有最低电离势的轨道（未激发分子中的 HOMO）便是优选的。这是一个单分子轨道层析成像所需的第二个条件。

层析需要的第三个条件是，我们能够获得一系列分子轨道的投影图像。为此我们记录下分子自身所产生的高次谐波发射。源于原子的高次谐波已被人们广泛地研究，而源于分子的谐波则是通过各向同性分布 [5,6] 或弱的排列 [7] 进行研究。采用实

been observed[8-11] both experimentally and numerically, that harmonic emission from aligned molecules is sensitive to both the alignment angle and to the spatial structure of the electronic wavefunction. These observations provide the basis for our analysis.

High harmonic generation is understood using the three-step quasi-static model[22]—(1) tunnel ionization by an intense low-frequency laser field, (2) acceleration of the free electron, and (3) re-collision. Tunnel ionization coherently transfers a part of the bound-state electron wavefunction to the continuum. Once free, the strong laser field dominates the motion of the continuum electron wave packet. First it propagates away from the molecule (Fig. 1a) and is then driven back after the field reverses its direction. Figure 1b shows the re-colliding wave packet expanding laterally. By the time of re-collision, the electron wave packet has a typical transverse $1/e$ width of 9 Å for 800-nm laser fields[23,24]. Because the wave packet is much larger than the size of small molecules (typically ~1 Å, shown by the lines in Fig. 1b), the molecule sees essentially a plane electron wave re-colliding. We will see that the planar nature of the re-collision electron allows us to experimentally retrieve a one-dimensional projection of the ground-state wavefunction.

Fig. 1. Illustration of the tunnel ionization process from an aligned molecule. **a,** The orange line on the potential surface is an isopotential contour slightly above the energy level of the bound state at the peak of the field amplitude. The opening of the contour shows the saddle point region where the bound-state

验方法和数值方法进行的研究 [8-11] 均表明，源于排列分子的谐波发射对于排列角度和电子波函数的空间结构都很敏感。这些结果为我们的分析提供了研究的基础。

利用三步准静态模型 [22] 可以理解高次谐波生成——（1）利用强低频激光场进行隧道电离，（2）自由电子的加速，（3）再碰撞。隧道电离以相干方式将一部分束缚态电子波函数转化成连续态。一旦不受约束，强激光场控制连续电子波包的运动。它先是从分子传播开去（如图 1a 所示），接着在场反转方向后返回。图 1b 显示了再碰撞波包横向扩展。再碰撞时，800 nm 激光场条件下电子波包的一个典型的横向 $1/e$ 宽度为 9 Å[23,24]。因为波包的尺寸比小分子（典型情况约为 1 Å，如图 1b 中直线所示）要大得多，所以在分子看来实际上是一个平面电子波的再碰撞。我们将会看到，再碰撞电子的平面属性使我们得以通过实验恢复基态波函数的一维投影。

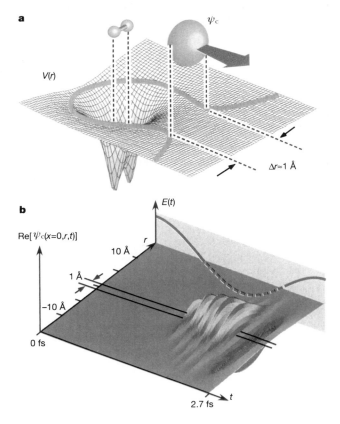

图 1. 排列分子隧道电离过程的图示。**a**，势能面上的橙色线是略高于电场振幅峰值处束缚态能级的等势线。等势线的开口部分显示鞍点区域，束缚态电子波函数会从这里隧穿为连续态。电子波包 ψ_c 的横向伸展是由鞍点区域的宽度 Δr 决定的，后者取决于分子取向。在连续态中传播时，波包会根据不确定性

electron wavefunction will tunnel through to the continuum. The lateral spread of the electron wave packet ψ_c is determined by the width of the saddle point region Δr that depends on the molecular alignment. The wave packet expands in the lateral direction during propagation in the continuum because of the initial momentum spread Δp given by the uncertainty principle, $\Delta p \approx h/\Delta r$. **b,** Illustration of the re-colliding wave packet seen by a molecule (the real part of the wave packet $\mathrm{Re}[\psi_c(x = 0, t)]$ is shown). The kinetic energy at the time of re-collision is taken from the classical trajectory, and determines the instantaneous frequency of the wave packet as seen by the molecule. The lateral spread is calculated by the free expansion of a gaussian wave packet with an initial $1/e$ full width of 1 Å.

The laser field shears the initial continuum wave packet in such a way that the low kinetic energy (long de Broglie wavelength) part of the wave packet re-collides first. Over the next half laser period, it chirps to high kinetic energy (short wavelength) and then back to low energy[25]. In our experiment, the highest-energy electron has a wavelength of ~1.5 Å. This wavelength is related to the high harmonic cut-off. The broad range of electron wavelengths allows us to experimentally retrieve the spatial shape of the bound-state wavefunction.

Figure 2 illustrates the final step in the harmonic generation process. Figure 2a shows a bound-state wavefunction, ψ_g. A fraction of the electron wavefunction tunnels from this orbital. The re-colliding electron wave packet, ψ_c, shown as a plane wave in Fig. 2b, overlaps the remaining portion of the initial wavefunction. The coherent addition of the two wavefunctions induces a dipole, seen as the asymmetric localization of electron density in Fig. 2c. The induced dipole oscillates as the continuum wavefunction propagates. It is this oscillating dipole that emits high harmonic radiation. The instantaneous frequency of the oscillating dipole is related to the electron kinetic energy by $\hbar\omega = E_k$ (refs 22, 25). In other words, the electron wave packet and the emitted photons are related by energy conservation, and are mutually coherent. We do not use the more usual expression[22], $\hbar\omega = E_k + I_p$, where I_p is the ionization potential and E_k is the instantaneous kinetic energy of the electron in the continuum at the time of re-collision calculated for a delta function potential, because here we are concerned with the electron kinetic energy seen by the bound-state electron wavefunction.

原理 $\Delta p \approx h/\Delta r$，由于初始动量的伸展 Δp 而发生横向扩展。**b**，一个分子的再碰撞波包的图示（所示为波包的实部 $\mathrm{Re}[\psi_c(x=0,t)]$）。再碰撞时刻的动能是根据经典轨迹得到的，它决定了分子"看到"的波包瞬时频率。横向扩展是利用具有 1 Å 初始 $1/e$ 全宽的高斯波包的自由展开而计算出来的。

激光场以特定的方式剪切初始连续波包，以使波包的低动能（长的德布罗意波长）部分首先发生再碰撞。在下面的半个激光周期中，高动能的部分继而发生再碰撞，接着再变回低能[25]。在我们的实验中，最高能量的电子具有约为 1.5 Å 的波长。该波长与高次谐波的截止区有关。电子波长的宽广范围使我们能够通过实验恢复束缚态波函数的空间形状。

图 2 描绘了谐波生成过程中的最后一步。图 2a 显示了束缚态波函数 ψ_g。电子波函数的一部分从这一轨道隧穿。图 2b 显示为平面波的再碰撞电子波包 ψ_c 与初始波函数的剩余部分重叠。两个波函数的相干叠加产生一个偶极，看起来如同图 2c 中电子密度的不对称分布。当连续波函数传播时，诱发偶极振荡。正是这个振荡偶极发射出高次谐波辐射。振荡偶极的瞬时频率与电子动能的关系是 $\hbar\omega = E_k$（参考文献 22 和 25）。换句话说，电子波包和发射的光子通过能量守恒而联系起来，因而是彼此相干的。我们没有使用更常见的表达式[22]，$\hbar\omega = E_k + I_p$，式中 I_p 为电离势，E_k 为连续态中再碰撞时刻的电子瞬时动能，是对于 δ 函数势能计算得到的；因为在本文中我们所考虑的是束缚态电子波函数所观察到的电子动能。

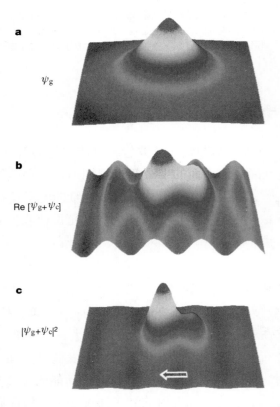

Fig. 2. Illustration of a dipole induced by the superposition of a ground-state wavefunction ψ_g and a re-colliding plane wave packet ψ_c. **a**, Bound-state wavefunction (for example, H atom, 1 s). **b**, The real part of the superposition of the bound-state wavefunction ψ_g and the continuum plane wave ψ_c. **c**, The total electron density distribution $|\psi_g + \psi_c|^2$. The superposition of the two wavefunctions induces a dipole $d(t)$ as shown by the red arrow. As the wave packet propagates, the induced dipole oscillates back and forth and leads to the emission of harmonics.

Formally, we are measuring the transition dipole moment from the highest occupied state to a set of continuum wavefunctions. Mathematically, the harmonic spectrum from a single atom or molecule is given by the Fourier transform of the dipole acceleration[26]. We relate the dipole acceleration spectrum to the dipole moment using the slowly varying envelope approximation (see Methods section). The spectral intensity (I) and phase of harmonics (ϕ) at frequency ω can respectively be written as $I(\omega) \propto \omega^4 |d(\omega)|^2$ and $\phi(\omega) = \arg[d(\omega)]$, where the transition dipole moment in the spectral domain is $\mathbf{d}(\omega) = a[k(\omega)] \int \psi_g(\mathbf{r})(e\mathbf{r}) \exp[ik(\omega)x] d\mathbf{r}$. Here the electron wave packet seen by the molecule is expanded in a superposition of plane waves as $\psi_c = \int a(k) \exp[ik(\omega)x] dk$, $k(\omega)$ is the wavenumber (momentum) of the electron corresponding to harmonic frequency ω, and $a[k(\omega)]$ is its complex amplitude[25]. A similar approach was taken by Sanpera *et al.*[27], who divided the electron wavefunction into bound and continuum parts and modelled the continuum part as a gaussian wave packet. Provided that $a[k(\omega)]$ is known, then measuring the harmonic spectrum—its amplitude, phase and polarization—is equivalent to measuring this integral, evaluated for different $k(\omega)$. This is an experimental determination of the one-dimensional spatial

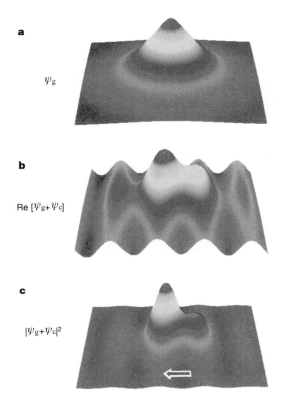

图 2. 由基态波函数 ψ_g 与再碰撞平面波包 ψ_c 间叠加而诱导出的偶极的图像。**a**，束缚态波函数（例如 H 原子的 $1s$ 轨道）。**b**，束缚态波函数 ψ_g 与连续平面波 ψ_c 叠加的实部。**c**，总电子密度分布 $|\psi_g+\psi_c|^2$。两个波函数的叠加诱导出一个偶极 $d(t)$，如图中红色箭头所示。随着波包的传播，诱导偶极来回振动从而导致谐波发射。

从形式上来讲，我们将要测定从最高占据态到一组连续波函数的跃迁偶极矩。用数学语言来讲，单个原子或分子的谐波谱是通过偶极加速度的傅里叶变换而给出的 [26]。我们利用缓变包络近似（参见介绍方法的小节）将偶极加速度谱和偶极矩联系起来。光谱强度 (I) 与频率为 ω 的谐波相位 (ϕ) 可以分别写成 $I(\omega) \propto \omega^4|d(\omega)|^2$ 和 $\phi(\omega) = \arg[d(\omega)]$，式中光谱域中的跃迁偶极矩为 $\mathbf{d}(\omega) = a[k(\omega)] \int \psi_g(\mathbf{r})(e\mathbf{r})\exp[ik(\omega)x]d\mathbf{r}$。这里，分子所"看到"的电子波包扩展为平面波的叠加，$\psi_c = \int a(k)\exp[ik(\omega)x]dk$，式中 $k(\omega)$ 为对应于谐波频率 ω 的电子波数（动量），$a[k(\omega)]$ 则是其复振幅 [25]。桑佩拉等人 [27] 使用了一种类似的方法，将电子波函数划分成束缚态部分和连续态部分，并将连续态部分按照高斯波包来建模。假设 $a[k(\omega)]$ 为已知的，那么测定谐波谱——它的振幅、相位和偏振——就等价于测定对于不同 $k(\omega)$ 值

Fourier transform of $\mathbf{r}\psi_g(\mathbf{r})$.

Experimentally, we concentrate on a specific molecule, N_2. High harmonics are generated with a 30-fs, 2×10^{14} W cm^{-2}, 800-nm, horizontally polarized probe pulse in a $\sim 10^{17}$ cm^{-3} molecular gas jet described in the Methods section. The molecular alignment axis is rotated relative to the polarization of the probe pulse.

The probe pulse intensity was kept as low as possible to avoid saturation or depletion of the ground state. The molecular beam thickness was less than 1 mm and the laser focus was before the beam—conditions that minimize phase mismatch and select only the short electron trajectories[28].

Figure 3 shows the intensities of each harmonic as the laser polarization is rotated from 0 to 90° (in steps of 5°) with respect to the molecular axis. The intensity contrast between 0 and 90° exceeds an order of magnitude for some harmonics. We use these data to reconstruct the molecular orbital of N_2. Also shown is the spectrum from the reference atom, argon, recorded under conditions identical to those for the nitrogen.

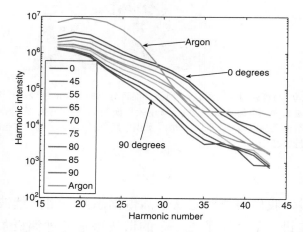

Fig. 3. High harmonic spectra were recorded for N_2 molecules aligned at 19 different angles between 0 and 90° relative to the polarization axis of the laser. For clarity, only some of the angles have been plotted above. The high harmonic spectrum from argon is also shown; argon is used as the reference atom. Clearly the spectra depend on both the alignment angle and shape of the molecular orbital.

Calibrating the Continuum Wave Packet

As discussed above, the harmonic spectrum is an experimental evaluation of the dipole, $\mathbf{d}(\omega)$. If we could evaluate the plane-wave amplitude $a[k(\omega)]$ independently, then our measurement would determine $\int \psi_g(\mathbf{r})(e\mathbf{r})\exp[ik(\omega)x]\,d\mathbf{r}$—that is, the spatial Fourier components of $\mathbf{r}\psi_g(\mathbf{r})$. One way to do this is to perform the same experiment with a reference atom.

的积分。这是对于 $\mathbf{r}\psi_g(\mathbf{r})$ 的一维空间傅里叶变换的一种实验测定方法。

在实验方面，我们重点关注一种特定的分子，N_2。在下面方法的小节中我们会谈到，利用分子密度约为 $10^{17}\,\text{cm}^{-3}$ 的气体喷嘴，30 fs、$2\times10^{14}\,\text{W}\cdot\text{cm}^{-2}$、800 nm、水平偏振的探测脉冲，可以产生高次谐波。分子的排列轴相对于探测脉冲的偏振方向旋转。

探测脉冲强度保持尽可能低以免基态饱和或耗散。分子束粗细小于 1 mm，并且激光要在分子束前面聚焦——这些条件能使相位失配最小化从而只选取电子短轨道[28]。

图 3 显示了随着激光偏振方向相对于分子轴从 0° 到 90° 旋转（步长为 5°）时每个谐波的强度。对于 0° 和 90° 之间的某些谐波，强度对比超出一个数量级。我们利用这些数据来重建 N_2 的分子轨道。同时显示出来的还有参考原子氩的光谱，这是在与氮相同的条件下记录的。

图 3. 在相对于激光偏振轴呈 0° 到 90° 之间的 19 个不同的指定夹角处记录的 N_2 分子的高次谐波谱。为清晰起见，上面只画出了某些角度的情况。同时显示的还有氩的高次谐波谱；氩用作参照原子。很明显，光谱同时决定于所排列的角度和分子轨道的形状。

校准连续波包

如同上面已讨论过的，谐波谱是偶极 $\mathbf{d}(\omega)$ 的实验估算值。如果我们能够独立地估算出平面波振幅 $a[k(\omega)]$ 的数值，那么我们的测量结果就能确定 $\int\psi_g(\mathbf{r})(e\mathbf{r})\exp[ik(\omega)x]\mathrm{d}\mathbf{r}$，也就是 $\mathbf{r}\psi_g(\mathbf{r})$ 的空间傅里叶分量。做到这一点的一种方法，就是用参考原子进行同样的实验。

Argon is very similar to N_2 in its response to strong laser fields, having nearly the same ionization potential and intensity-dependent ionization probability[6]. This is confirmed by the dependence of the instantaneous ionization rates[29] for atoms, and for different orientations of N_2 (ref. 30). That means that the first, critical, step in the three-step high harmonic generation process is the same. Because the laser field dominates wave packet motion in the direction of the laser field, the second step, which determines the chirp of the re-colliding wave packets seen by Ar or N_2, will be the same. Thus, $a[k(\omega)]$ will be the same.

The continuum wave packet will also be similar for Ar and N_2. The narrow saddle point through which the electron tunnels acts as a spatial filter that removes much of the structure of the orbital from the continuum wave packet. This can be seen in numerical simulations[31]. By measuring the ellipticity dependence of the high harmonic signal[24] produced by N_2 and argon, we confirmed that the lateral spread of the wave packets is similar. The ionization rate of N_2 is angle-dependent[30,32], but is readily measured from the ion yield, and varies only by 25% for N_2 (ref. 33). This variation is almost cancelled by the angular dependence of the wave-packet spread in the lateral direction[23]. Thus we use the harmonic spectrum from argon to determine $|a[k(\omega)]|$ without including the angular dependence of tunnel ionization rate and wave-packet spread in the continuum.

Tomographic Reconstruction of the Orbital

We have shown that (1) tunnel ionization, owing to its nonlinearity, is extremely selective[29,30]. In N_2, it ionizes only the highest electronic state—the HOMO. And (2), the harmonic spectra contain a range of spatial Fourier components of the shape of this single orbital. We have recorded the harmonic spectra at a series of angles between the molecular axis and the re-colliding electron. We now show that we can invert this information to obtain the shape of the orbital.

The Fourier slice theorem[13] proves that the Fourier transform of a projection P_θ is equal to a cut at angle θ through the two-dimensional Fourier transform F of the object. This is the basis of computed tomography based on the inverse Radon transform. Our dipole is the Fourier transform of a projection of the wavefunction, and so can be inverted.

We describe the mathematical details of the tomographic reconstruction in the Methods section. This procedure can reconstruct orbital shapes with symmetries such as σ_g, π_g and π_u, using harmonics 17–51 of an 800-nm laser field and 25 angles from 0° to 180° (fewer angles are needed for symmetric molecules).

A complete inversion of a general orbital requires knowledge of the relative phase and amplitude of each harmonic for two orthogonal polarizations. Although we measured only the amplitude (the phase of each harmonic can be directly measured[28]) the relative phase of the harmonics is known from first principles. As with any classical or quantum resonance,

氩与 N_2 在强激光场的作用非常相似,具有几乎相同的电离势和依赖于强度的电离概率 [6]。瞬时电离速率 [29] 对于原子以及 N_2 不同取向的依赖性确证了这一点(参考文献 30)。这意味着,在分三步进行的高次谐波生成过程中,第一步(关键的步骤)是相同的。由于激光场主导着波包在激光场方向上的运动,因此第二个步骤——它决定了 Ar 或 N_2 所"看"到的再碰撞波包的啁啾——也会是相同的。于是, $a[k(\omega)]$ 就应该相同。

Ar 和 N_2 的连续波包同样会是相似的。电子隧穿所经的狭窄的鞍点起到空间滤波器的作用,从连续波包中移除了大部分的轨道结构。在许多数值模拟中可以看到这一点 [31]。通过测定 N_2 和 Ar 产生的高次谐波信号对于椭偏率的依赖性 [24],我们证实了波包的横向伸展是类似的。虽然 N_2 的电离速率是依赖于角度的 [30,32],但是很容易利用离子产量测得,而且对于 N_2 只变化了 25%(参考文献 33)。横向上的伸展的波包的角度依赖性基本上消除了这一差异 [23]。因此我们可以利用来自氩的谐波谱来确定 $|a[k(\omega)]|$,而不必考虑隧道电离速率和连续态中的波包伸展对于角度的依赖性。

轨道的层析成像重建

我们已经表明:(1)隧道电离,由于其非线性,是极具有选择性的 [29,30]。对于 N_2,它只电离最高电子态——HOMO。(2)谐波谱中包含这一单个轨道形状的一部分空间傅里叶分量。我们已经在分子轴与再碰撞电子之间的一系列角度处记录了谐波谱。现在,我们来展示能够将这一信息逆推以得知轨道的形状。

傅里叶切片定理 [13] 证明,投影 P_θ 的傅里叶变换等于物体的二维傅里叶变换 F 在角度 θ 处的切片。这是基于逆向拉东变换的计算机层析成像术的基础。我们的偶极是波函数投影的傅里叶变换,因而可以被逆推出来。

我们在关于方法的小节中描述层析重建方法的细节。利用 800 nm 激光场的 $17\sim51$ 阶谐波,以及从 $0°$ 到 $180°$ 中的 25 个角度(对称分子需要更少的角度),这个过程能够重建具有诸如 σ_g、π_g 和 π_u 等对称性的轨道形状。

对于一个一般轨道的全反演,需要了解对于两个正交偏振的每一个谐波的相对相位和振幅。尽管我们仅仅测定了振幅(每一个谐波的相位可以被直接测得 [28]),但是利用第一性原理即可知道谐波的相对相位。如同具有任何经典的或量子共振的时

a phase jump of π occurs as the driving (electron) frequency moves across resonance. Calculations by Hay *et al.*[9] show minimum harmonic signal and a π phase jump at the 25th harmonic for $0°$ when the re-collision electron wavelength resonates with the projected molecular dimension. We assume a phase jump of π where the measured dipole of N_2 goes through a minimum, corresponding to a change of sign of the dipole. This occurs at the 25th harmonic.

The reconstructed molecular orbital of N_2 is shown in Fig. 4a, based upon the 19 projections. It can be compared with the *ab initio* orbital calculation of the N_2 $2p$ σ_g orbital. Note that the recovered wavefunction has both positive and negative lobes, so it is not the square of the wavefunction, but the wavefunction itself, up to an arbitrary phase.

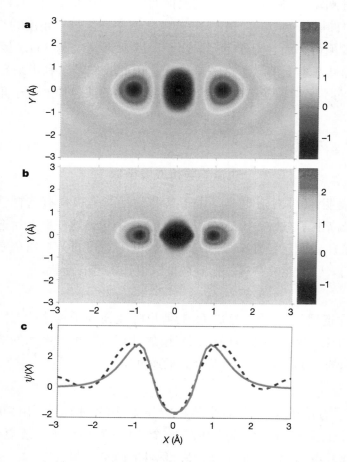

Fig. 4. Molecular orbital wavefunction of N_2. **a**, Reconstructed wavefunction of the HOMO of N_2. The reconstruction is from a tomographic inversion of the high harmonic spectra taken at 19 projection angles. Both positive and negative values are present, so this is a wavefunction, not the square of the wavefunction, up to an arbitrary phase. **b**, The shape of the N_2 $2p$ σ_g orbital from an ab initio calculation. The colour scales are the same for both images. **c**, Cuts along the internuclear axis for the reconstructed (dashed) and *ab initio* (solid) wavefunctions.

候一样，π 的相位阶跃随驱动（电子）频率穿过共振而发生。通过海等人的计算 [9] 表明，当再碰撞电子波长与分子尺度的投影发生共振时，对于 0° 的第 25 阶谐波处有极小谐波信号和 π 相位阶跃。我们假定 π 相位阶跃——此时所测得的 N_2 偶极经历极小值——对应于偶极符号的变化。它在第 25 阶谐波处发生。

图 4a 中显示了基于 19 个投影重建的 N_2 的分子轨道。可以将它与第一性原理轨道计算所得的 N_2 的 $2p$ σ_g 轨道相比较。需要我们注意的是重新获得的波函数兼有正负的两片，因此它不是波函数的平方而是波函数本身，相对于任意相位。

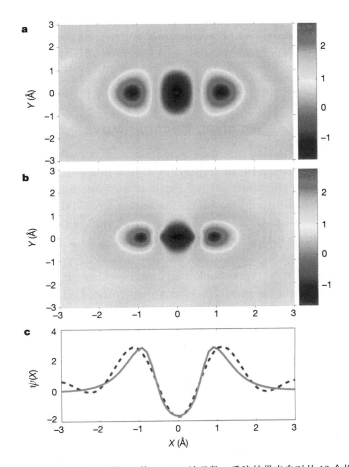

图 4. N_2 的分子轨道波函数。**a**，重建的 N_2 的 HOMO 波函数。重建结果来自对从 19 个投影角度取得的高次谐波谱的层析成像反演。相对于任意相位，正值和负值都包括在内，因此这是一个波函数而不是波函数的平方。**b**，利用第一性原理计算得到的 N_2 的 $2p$ σ_g 轨道形状。两幅图像的彩色标度是一样的。**c**，重建的（短划线）和第一性原理计算的（实线）波函数沿核间轴的截面。

451

Our orbital reconstruction method is similar to medical tomography. However, we image a single orbital among many orbitals. The coherence of the re-collision provides this specificity. Of all the occupied or unoccupied states of the molecule, the re-colliding electron wave packet is only coherent with the state from which it tunnelled (or, as we will show below, with any other coherently related state). Measurable high harmonic emission requires a macroscopic number of ionizing molecules, so only the coherent emission interferes constructively and is observed experimentally. This coherent filtering is conceptually similar to the homodyne detection technique and is naturally implemented in harmonic generation.

Tomographic approaches have previously been used for molecular measurements, but in a very different way[34,35]. Although tomographic reconstruction algorithms are used, they are based on "rotations" in the position–momentum phase-space distributions, not physical rotations of an object. These techniques yield the one-dimensional Wigner distribution $W(x,p)$ of the phase-space density of a vibrating[34] or dissociating[35] molecule. In contrast, we measure the actual three-dimensional wavefunction of a single electron orbital of a molecule.

Watching Electrons Move

So far, we have shown that we can take a snapshot of a molecular orbital using 30-fs laser pulses. Thus, in a pump-probe experiment, it is possible to image (probe) changes to molecular orbitals on the timescale of nuclear motion (the femtosecond timescale). However, electronic motion can be much faster. Can orbital imaging be extended to measuring electronic wave packets? We now show that the motion of this electronic wave packet can indeed be mapped to the harmonic spectrum.

It may seem that measuring wave-packet dynamics contradicts our assertion that the coherence of high harmonic generation selects a single orbital. However, an electronic wave packet is a coherent superposition of electronic states. Therefore, all states forming the wave packet are coherent with the returning electron provided it tunnelled from one or more of the states. They all contribute to the induced dipole that emits harmonics, even though only the highest-energy state contributed to the ionization. Therefore the relative intensity of each harmonic will depend on the relative phases between these electronic states.

To demonstrate how the bound-state wave-packet motion appears in harmonic spectra, we use the one-dimensional time-dependent Schrödinger equation to simulate an electron in a diatomic potential in the presence of an intense laser field. The field is chosen at a wavelength of 1.6 μm and duration of 8 fs to induce a single re-collision. To form a fast-moving bound-state wave packet, two electronic states with energy difference of $\Delta E = 9.5$ eV are equally populated before the arrival of the laser pulse. This energy difference corresponds to wave-packet motion with a period of 435 as. By varying the initial phase of the two states, we perform a numerical pump–probe measurement of the wave-packet motion.

我们的轨道重建方法与医学中的层析成像相类似。然而，我们描绘的是很多轨道中的一个。再碰撞的相干性提供了这种特征。在分子所有占据态或未占据态中，再碰撞电子波包都只与它隧穿时所来自的那个态相干（或者，如同我们下面将要说明的那样，与任意其他相关态相干）。可观测的高次谐波发射需要大量的电离分子，因此只有相干发射才能有效地干涉从而能用实验方法观测到。从概念上说，这种相干滤波类似于零差检测技术，因而能够自然地被应用于谐波产生中。

以前曾将层析成像方法用于分子测量，不过是以一种极为不同的方式 [34,35]。尽管使用了层析成像的重建算法，但是它们所依据的是位置–动量相空间分布中的"旋转"，而不是物体的物理旋转。这些技术产生出一个振动分子 [34] 或离解分子 [35] 的相空间密度的一维维格纳分布 $W(x, p)$。与之相比，我们测得的是一个分子中单独一个电子轨道的实际的三维波函数。

观看电子运动

目前为止，实验表明，我们能够利用 30 fs 激光脉冲获得一个分子的快照。因此，在一次泵浦–探测实验中，有可能在核运动的时间尺度上（飞秒时间尺度）描绘（探测）出分子轨道的变化。然而，电子运动可能还要快很多。轨道成像能够扩展以观测电子波包吗？现在，我们来说明这种电子波包的运动确实能够映射到谐波谱上。

看来有可能的是，对波包动力学的观测与我们的下列断言相矛盾：高次谐波生成的相干性选择了单一轨道。然而，一个电子波包是电子态的相干叠加。因此，如果该电子从一个或多个态进行隧穿的话，那么构成波包的所有态都是与该返回电子相干的。虽然只有最高能量态才对电离有贡献，但所有态都对发射谐波的诱导偶极有贡献。因此，每一个谐波的相对强度都会依赖于这些电子态之间的相对相位。

为了说明束缚态波包的运动如何出现在谐波谱中，我们利用一维含时薛定谔方程来模拟在有强激光场存在时双原子势场中的一个电子。选取该场波长为 1.6 μm，持续时间为 8 fs，以诱导出单独一次再碰撞。为形成一个快速运动的束缚态波包，要在激光脉冲到达之前等量地占据在能量差为 $\Delta E = 9.5$ eV 的两个电子态。这一能量差对应于具有 435 as 周期的波包运动。通过改变两种态的初始相位，我们对波包运动进行了数值的泵浦–探测测量。

Figure 5 shows the calculated harmonic spectrum versus the initial phase of the two states. The structure in the harmonic spectrum synchronizes with the bound-state wave-packet motion. Both the modulation in the single time delay spectrum and the movement of the modulation in the pump–probe spectrum measure wave-packet dynamics.

Fig. 5. A one-dimensional Schrödinger calculation shows that attosecond electronic wave-packet motion is resolved in the high harmonic spectra. The bottom curve shows a spectrum at a particular pump–probe delay time; the minima are due to interference caused by the wave-packet motion. The top picture shows the spectra at a range of time delays, showing that the minima move with pump–probe time delay. The simulation populated the ground and first excited state (9.5 eV above ground) of a model atom to create an electronic wave packet.

Promises and Challenges

Our experimental condition—N_2 illuminated by an 800-nm pulse at an intensity of 2×10^{14} W cm^{-2}—is not special. Ionization intensities of $\sim 10^{14}$ W cm^{-2} are typical for small- to intermediate-sized molecules[36]. For these laser parameters a re-collision electron has a wavelength of 1–2 Å—the correct range for measuring orbital structure. Thus, it appears feasible to extend tomography to many other molecules, provided there is a general method for determining $a[k(\omega)]$. This seems very promising. The phase dependence of the ionization rate determines $a[k(\omega)]$ up to a global constant describing the total ionization probability. Theories of time-dependent ionization of atoms[29] and small molecules[30] shows that the phase-dependent ionization rate is determined mainly by the ionization potential. If this remains true for more-complex molecules, then a reference atom (or molecule) can always be found to experimentally determine $a[k(\omega)]$. If a reference atom is not possible then $a[k(\omega)]$ can be characterized experimentally through the ellipticity dependence of the harmonics[24], and by directly measuring the electron spectrum in elliptically or circularly polarized light.

图 5 显示出计算所得的谐波谱与两种态初始相位的关系。谐波谱的结构与束缚态波包同步运动。单时间延迟光谱中的调制和泵浦–探测光谱中调制的运动都量度了波包动力学。

图 5. 一维的薛定谔计算显示阿秒电子波包运动在高次谐波谱中是可分辨的。底部的曲线显示出特定的泵浦–探测延迟时间时的光谱；极小值源于波包运动所导致的干涉。顶部的图像显示出一个时间延迟范围内的光谱，表明极小值会随着泵浦–探测时间延迟的改变而运动。模拟构造了一个模型原子的基态和第一激发态 (高于基态 9.5 eV) 以制造出一个电子波包。

前景与挑战

我们的实验条件——用强度为 2×10^{14} W·cm^{-2} 的 800 nm 脉冲照射 N_2——并不是特定的。约为 10^{14} W·cm^{-2} 的激光诱发的电离强度对于小型和中型分子来说是典型的 [36]。对于上述这些激光参数而言，再碰撞电子具有 1～2 Å 的波长，这是测定轨道结构的合理范围。因此，假定存在一种确定 $a[k(\omega)]$ 的通用方法，那么将层析方法拓展用于很多其他分子看来是可行的。这似乎是大有前景的。电离速率的相位依赖性决定了 $a[k(\omega)]$ 是一个描述总电离概率的全局常数。原子 [29] 和小分子 [30] 含时电离理论指出，相位相关电离速率主要是由电离势决定的。如果这一点对于更复杂的分子仍然是正确的话，那么就总可以找到一个参考原子 (或分子) 以便用实验方法测定 $a[k(\omega)]$。如果不存在参考原子的话，那么借助于谐波对椭偏率的依赖性 [24]，并且通过在椭圆或圆偏振光中直接测定电子光谱，也能够用实验方法来表征 $a[k(\omega)]$。

But does the strong electric field of the laser modify the orbital? In small molecules the modification is small, because the re-colliding electron returns near the zero-crossing of the optical field. However, it may not be small in large molecules whose bound electrons can move more freely: that is, where the molecular polarizability is larger. Thus, it may be necessary to "shield" the orbital from the intense field. One method of shielding is to exploit traditional spectroscopy. A state, first excited by resonant light, can provide the continuum electron needed for tomography as long as it remains coherent with the ground state. Because the excited state will ionize much more easily than the ground state, tomography can be performed at field strengths in which the ground-state wavefunction is unperturbed. (Longer laser wavelengths will be required to keep the electron kinetic energy high in order to maintain sufficient spatial resolution.) Exploiting excited states has two additional advantages. First, the direction of the transition moment selects the alignment of those molecules that will ultimately ionize. Second, any orbital that is optically accessible can be imaged, not just the HOMO.

The ability of harmonics to measure the three-dimensional structure of orbitals is most important for molecular dynamics. It should be possible to observe an orbital while it changes its symmetry as a result of a curve-crossing, or to observe a chemical bond being broken—the very foundations of chemistry. With our wave-packet approach to align molecules, the only restriction is that the molecular dynamics must be faster than the duration of a rotational revival. To observe electronic rearrangement during chemical dynamics we would need to add an additional pulse to our pulse sequence[37]. Its function would be to induce dynamics. The first pulse aligns the molecule; the second one initiates the vibrational (or electronic) dynamics that we wish to study; and the final pulse would produce the harmonic radiation that could probe the evolution of the wavefunction.

Methods

Experimental details

For all measurements, we used a pulsed gas jet with a density of $\sim 10^{17}$ cm^{-3} in the interaction region. The laser beams were focused ~ 1 mm below the orifice of the gas nozzle. The intensity of the pump pulse was set at $\sim 4 \times 10^{13}$ W cm^{-2}. This intensity is below the ionization threshold, where no ions are detected by a d.c.-biased electrode placed near the gas jet, and no harmonic emission is detected. The intensity of the probe pulse was estimated to be $\sim 2 \times 10^{14}$ W cm^{-2} from the cut-off of high harmonics. This laser intensity is well below the saturation of ionization and harmonic generation, ensuring that high harmonics are emitted mostly at the peak of the laser pulse without depleting the ground state.

Tomographic procedure

The angular frequency ω of the radiated extreme-ultraviolet field, and the wavenumber k

但是，激光的强电场是否会改变轨道？在小分子中，这种改变是较小的，因为再碰撞电子在光场过零点附近返回。然而，在大分子中，这种改变就可能不小了，因为大分子的束缚电子能够更为自由地运动，也就是说，分子的极化性更大了。于是，就必然需要对轨道"屏蔽"强场。一种屏蔽方法是开发传统的光谱学。一个态在最初被共振光激发后，只要它保持与基态相干，那么就能够为层析方法提供连续电子。由于激发态会比基态更容易电离，因此在基态波函数未受扰动的场强中能够使用层析方法（需要较长的激光波长来维持电子的高动能，以保证充分的空间分辨率）。对激发态的利用还有两个附加优点：第一，跃迁偶极矩的方向选择了最终将要电离的那些分子的排列。第二，任一光学意义上可接触的轨道都能成像，而不仅仅是 HOMO。

谐波的这种检测轨道三维结构的能力对于分子动力学而言是极为重要的。通过这个可能观测到一个轨道由于曲线交叉而改变其对称性，或者观测到一个化学键正在断裂——化学的基础所在。使用我们的波包方法排列分子时，唯一的限制是，分子动力学必须要比旋转复原的时间更快。要观测到化学动力学过程中的电子重排，需要在我们的脉冲序列中增添一个附加的脉冲[37]。它的功能是诱导动力学过程。第一个脉冲将分子排列；第二个脉冲引发我们希望研究的振动（或电子）动力学过程；而最后一个脉冲则产生谐波辐射，此谐波辐射能够检测出波函数的演化。

方　　法

实验细节

在所有的观测中，我们使用了在相互作用区域中密度约为 10^{17} cm^{-3} 的脉动式气体喷嘴。在气体喷嘴口的下方，激光束聚焦至约 1 mm。泵浦脉冲的强度设置约为 4×10^{13} W·cm^{-2}。这一强度低于电离阈值，此处置于气体喷嘴附近的直流偏压电极没有检测到任何离子，也没有检测到任何谐波发射。通过高次谐波的截止位置，估计探测脉冲的强度约为 2×10^{14} W·cm^{-2}。这一激光强度大大低于电离和谐波产生的饱和值，以确保高次谐波几乎都是在激光脉冲峰值处发射的，没有基态耗散。

层析过程

辐射出的极紫外场的角频率 ω，以及对应于在再碰撞时刻生成它的电子波的波数 k，通

corresponding to the electron wave that produced it at the time of recollision, are related by $k(\omega) = (2\omega)^{1/2}$ in atomic units. The transition dipole moment between the orbital wavefunction and the continuum electron is $\mathbf{d}(\omega;\theta) = \; < \psi(\mathbf{r};\theta) \,|\, \mathbf{r} \,|\, \exp[ik(\omega)x] > $. This is a complex vector, and $\psi(\mathbf{r};\theta)$ represents the orbital wavefunction rotated by Euler angle θ. Assuming perfect phase-matching, the extreme-ultraviolet signal that is emitted is given as $S(\omega;\theta) = N^2(\theta) \; \omega^4 |a[k(\omega)]\mathbf{d}(\omega;\theta)|^2$. Here $a[k(\omega)]$ is the complex amplitude of component k of the continuum wave packet, and $N(\theta)$ is the number of ions produced.

The value of $a[k(\omega)]$ is determined experimentally by recording $S(\omega)$ for a reference argon atom whose orbital $(2p_x)$, and hence $d(\omega)$, is known. Hence, $a[k(\omega)] = \omega^{-2}[S_{\mathrm{ref}}(\omega)]^{1/2} \, [\,|<\psi_{\mathrm{ref}}|r|k>|^2]^{-1/2}$. This calibration not only characterizes the continuum wave packet, it also includes experimental factors such as detector efficiency.

Then $S(\omega;\theta)$ is recorded for an unknown molecule, yielding its transition dipole moment $d(\omega;\theta)$. The definition of $d(\omega;\theta)$ is a spatial Fourier transform of the orbital in the x direction. We apply the Fourier slice theorem[13] to do the inversion, with one important modification. The Fourier transform contains the factor $\mathbf{r}$, which, being defined in the laboratory frame, does not rotate with the molecular frame, θ.

The tomographic inversion requires two intermediate functions,

$$f_x(x, y) = \sum_\theta \sum_\omega [d_x(\omega;\theta)\cos\theta + d_y(\omega;\theta)\sin\theta]\exp[ik(\omega)(x\cos\theta + y\sin\theta)]$$

$$f_y(x, y) = \sum_\theta \sum_\omega [-d_x(\omega;\theta)\sin\theta + d_y(\omega;\theta)\cos\theta]\exp[ik(\omega)(x\cos\theta + y\sin\theta)]$$

Then the wavefunction is given as:

$$\psi(x, y) = \mathrm{Re}(f_x/x + f_y/y).$$

We must also include the angle dependence of the ionization rate to normalize each spectrum. The ionization rate is known for simple molecules such as N_2 (refs 30, 32) but can be measured at the same time as the harmonic spectrum is being recorded[33] simply by measuring the total ion yield, $N(\theta)$.

(**432**, 867-871; 2004)

J. Itatani[1,2], J. Levesque[1,3], D. Zeidler[1], Hiromichi Niikura[1,4], H. Pépin[3], J. C. Kieffer[3], P. B. Corkum[1] & D. M. Villeneuve[1]
[1] National Research Council of Canada, 100 Sussex Drive, Ottawa, Ontario K1A 0R6, Canada
[2] University of Ottawa, 150 Louis Pasteur, Ottawa, Ontario K1N 6N5, Canada
[3] INRS- Energie et Materiaux, 1650 boulevard Lionel-Boulet, CP 1020, Varennes, Québec J3X 1S2, Canada
[4] PRESTO, Japan Science and Technology Agency, 4-1-8 Honcho Kawaguchi Saitama, 332-0012, Japan

Received 8 June; accepted 9 November 2004; doi:10.1038/nature03183.

References:
1. Mulliken, R. S. Electronic structures of polyatomic molecules and valence. II. General considerations. *Phys. Rev.* **41**, 49-71 (1932).

过用原子单位表示的 $k(\omega) = (2\omega)^{1/2}$ 联系起来。轨道波函数与连续电子之间的跃迁偶极矩为 $\mathbf{d}(\omega;\theta) = <\psi(\mathbf{r};\theta)|\mathbf{r}|\exp[ik(\omega)x]>$。这是一个复向量，$\psi(\mathbf{r};\theta)$ 表示旋转了欧拉角 θ 的轨道波函数。假定相位匹配是完美的，则所发射的极紫外信号由 $S(\omega;\theta) = N^2(\theta)\omega^4|a[k(\omega)]\mathbf{d}(\omega;\theta)|^2$ 给出。这里，$a[k(\omega)]$ 是连续波包中成分 k 的复振幅，而 $N(\theta)$ 则是所产生的离子数。

通过记录参考原子氩的 $S(\omega)$——氩原子的轨道 $(2p_x)$ 以及 $d(\omega)$ 是已知的——可以用实验方法测定 $a[k(\omega)]$ 的数值。因此，$a[k(\omega)] = \omega^{-2}[S_{\text{ref}}(\omega)]^{1/2}[|<\psi_{\text{ref}}|r|k>|^2]^{-1/2}$。这一校准不仅表征了连续波包，而且包含了诸如检测器效率等实验因素。

接着对于一种未知分子记录其 $S(\omega;\theta)$，得出跃迁偶极矩 $d(\omega;\theta)$。$d(\omega;\theta)$ 界定为轨道 x 方向上的空间傅里叶变换。我们利用傅里叶切片定理 [13] 来进行逆变换，并进行了一个重要的修正。傅里叶变换包含因子 $\mathbf{r}$，它是在实验室坐标系中定义的，不随着分子结构 θ 旋转。

层析逆变换需要两个中间函数，

$$f_x(x, y) = \sum_\theta \sum_\omega [d_x(\omega;\theta)\cos\theta + d_y(\omega;\theta)\sin\theta]\exp[ik(\omega)(x\cos\theta + y\sin\theta)]$$

$$f_y(x, y) = \sum_\theta \sum_\omega [-d_x(\omega;\theta)\sin\theta + d_y(\omega;\theta)\cos\theta]\exp[ik(\omega)(x\cos\theta + y\sin\theta)]$$

接着波函数由下式给出：

$$\psi(x, y) = \text{Re}(f_x/x + f_y/y)$$

我们还必须考虑电离速率的角度依赖性以将每一谱图归一化。诸如 N_2 等简单分子的电离速率是已知的（参考文献 30 和 32），但是也可以在记录谐波谱 [33] 的同时，简单地通过测量总的离子产量 $N(\theta)$ 而得到。

（王耀杨 翻译；陆培祥 审稿）

2. Linus, C. P. *The Nature of the Chemical Bond and the Structure of Molecules and Crystals* (Cornell Univ. Press, Ithaca, New York, 1960).

3. Brion, C. E., Cooper, G., Zheng, Y., Litvinyuk, I. V. & McCarthy, I. E. Imaging of orbital electron densities by electron momentum spectroscopy—a chemical interpretation of the binary (e, 2e) reaction. *Chem. Phys.* **270**, 13-30 (2001).

4. Binning, G., Rohrer, H., Gerber, Ch. & Weibel, E. Surface studies by scanning tunneling microscopy. *Phys. Rev. Lett.* **49**, 57-61 (1982).

5. Sakai, H. & Miyazaki, K. High-order harmonic generation in nitrogen molecules with subpicosecond visible dye-laser pulses. *Appl. Phys. B* **61**, 493-498 (1995).

6. Liang, Y., Augst, A., Chin, S. L., Beaudoin, Y. & Chaker, M. High harmonic generation in atomic and diatomic molecular gases using intense picosecond laser pulses—a comparison. *J. Phys. B* **27**, 5119-5130 (1994).

7. Velotta, R., Hay, N., Manson, M. B., Castillejo, M. & Marangos, J. P. High-order harmonic generation in aligned molecules. *Phys. Rev. Lett.* **87**, 183901 (2001).

8. de Nalda, R. *et al.* Role of orbital symmetry in high-order harmonic generation from aligned molecules. *Phys. Rev. A* **69**, 031804(R) (2004).

9. Hay, N. *et al.* Investigations of electron wave-packet dynamics and high-order harmonic generation in laser-aligned molecules. *J. Mod. Opt.* **50**, 561-571 (2003).

10. Hay, N. *et al.* High-order harmonic generation in laser-aligned molecules. *Phys. Rev. A* **65**, 053805 (2002).

11. Lein, M., Corso, P. P., Marangos, J. P. & Knight, P. L. Orientation dependence of high-order harmonic generation in molecules. *Phys. Rev. A* **67**, 023819 (2003).

12. Parr, R. G. & Yang, W. *Density-functional Theory of Atoms and Molecules* (Oxford Univ. Press, New York, 1989).

13. Kak, A. C. & Slaney, M. *Principles of Computerized Tomographic Imaging* (Society for Industrial and Applied Mathematics, New York, 2001).

14. Stapelfeldt, H. & Seideman, T. Aligning molecules with strong laser pulses. *Rev. Mod. Phys.* **75**, 543-557 (2003).

15. Stapelfeldt, H., Sakai, H., Constant, E. & Corkum, P. B. Deflection of neutral molecules using the nonresonant dipole force. *Phys. Rev. Lett.* **79**, 2787-2790 (1997).

16. Sakai, H. *et al.* Controlling the alignment of neutral molecules by a strong laser field. *J. Chem. Phys.* **110**, 10235-10238 (1999).

17. Larsen, J. J., Hald, K., Bjerre, N. & Stapelfeldt, H. Three dimensional alignment of molecules using elliptically polarized laser fields, *Phys. Rev. Lett.* **85**, 2470-2473 (2000).

18. Sakai, H., Minemoto, S., Nanjo, H., Tanji, H. & Suzuki, T. Controlling the orientation of polar molecules with combined electrostatic and pulsed nonresonant laser fields. *Phys. Rev. Lett.* **90**, 083001 (2003).

19. Rosca-Pruna, F. & Vrakking, M. J. J. Experimental observation of revival structures in picosecond laser-induced alignment of I_2. *Phys. Rev. Lett.* **87**, 153902 (2001).

20. Dooley, P. W. *et al.* Direct imaging of rotational wave-packet dynamics of diatomic molecules. *Phys. Rev. A* **68**, 023406 (2003).

21. Delone, N. B. & Krainov, V. P. *Multiphoton Processes in Atoms* (Springer, Heidelberg, 2000).

22. Corkum, P. B. Plasma perspective on strong-field multiphoton ionization. *Phys. Rev. Lett.* **71**, 1994-1997 (1993).

23. Niikura, H. *et al.* Sub-laser-cycle electron pulses for probing molecular dynamics. *Nature* **417**, 917-922 (2002).

24. Dietrich, P., Burnett, N. H., Ivanov, M. & Corkum, P. B. High-harmonic generation and correlated two-electron multiphoton ionization with elliptically polarized light. *Phys. Rev. A* **50**, R3585-R3588 (1994).

25. Lewenstein, M., Balcou, Ph., Ivanov, M. Yu., L'Huillier, A. & Corkum, P. B. Theory of high-harmonic generation by low-frequency laser fields. *Phys. Rev. A.* **49**, 2117-2132 (1994).

26. Burnett, K., Reed, V. C., Cooper, J. & Knight, P. L. Calculation of the background emitted during high-harmonic generation. *Phys. Rev. A* **45**, 3347-3349 (1992).

27. Sanpera, A. *et al.* Can harmonic generation cause non-sequential ionization? *J. Phys. B* **31**, L841-L848 (1998).

28. Mairesse, Y. *et al.* Attosecond synchronization of high-harmonic soft x-rays. *Science* **302**, 1540-1543 (2003).

29. Yudin, G. & Ivanov, M. Yu. Nonadiabatic tunnel ionization: Looking inside a laser cycle. *Phys. Rev. A* **64**, 013409 (2001).

30. Tong, X. M., Zhao, Z. X. & Lin, C. D. Theory of molecular tunneling ionization. *Phys. Rev. A* **66**, 033402 (2002).

31. Spanner, M., Smirnova, O., Corkum, P. B. & Ivanov, M. Yu. Reading diffraction images in strong field ionization of diatomic molecules. *J. Phys. B* **37**, L243-L250 (2004).

32. Otobe, T., Yabana, K. & Iwata, J.-I. First-principles calculations for the tunnel ionization rate of atoms and molecules. *Phys. Rev. A* **69**, 053404 (2004).

33. Litvinyuk, I. V. *et al.* Alignment-dependent strong field ionization of molecules. *Phys. Rev. Lett.* **90**, 233003 (2003).

34. Dunn, T. J., Walmsley, I. A. & Mukamel, S. Experimental determination of the quantum mechanical state of a molecular vibrational mode using fluorescence tomography. *Phys. Rev. Lett.* **74**, 884-887 (1995).

35. Skovsen, E., Stapelfeldt, H., Juhl, S. & Mølmer, K. Quantum state tomography of dissociating molecules. *Phys. Rev. Lett.* **91**, 090406 (2003).

36. Hankin, S. M., Villeneuve, D. M., Corkum, P. B., & Rayner, D. M. Nonlinear ionization of organic molecules in high intensity laser fields. *Phys. Rev. Lett.* **84**, 5082-5085 (2000).

37. Lee, K. F. *et al.* Two-pulse alignment of molecules. *J. Phys. B* **37**, L43-L48 (2004).

Acknowledgements. In addition to the NRC, we acknowledge financial support from the National Science and Engineering Research Council, Photonic Research Ontario, the Canadian Institute for Photonic Innovation, the Alexander von Humboldt-Stiftung and the Japan Society for the Promotion of Science. We thank M. Yu. Ivanov, M. Spanner, J. P. Marangos, M. Lein, P. H. Bucksbaum, I. A. Walmsley, D. Jonas, J. Tse and J. G. Underwood for discussions.

Competing interests statement. The authors declare that they have no competing financial interests.

Correspondence and requests for materials should be addressed to D.M.V. (david.villeneuve@nrc.ca).

Stratigraphic Placement and Age of Modern Humans from Kibish, Ethiopia

I. McDougall *et al.*

Editor's Note

Where did our own species come from, and when? Fossils discovered in 1967 in the Kibish Formation in southern Ethiopia yielded hominid skull remains identifiable as anatomically modern humans, but their antiquity had been much debated. Geochronologists McDougall and colleagues sought to settle the matter with accurate argon-argon dates on volcanic layers in the Formation, together with work on the history of the Omo river valley compared with that of the Nile. The final date—195,000 years old, plus or minus 5,000—made the Omo Kibish hominids the oldest examples of *Homo sapiens* from anywhere in the world. Ethiopia was the birthplace of humankind, as it had been for so many other species in the wider human family.

In 1967 the Kibish Formation in southern Ethiopia yielded hominid cranial remains identified as early anatomically modern humans, assigned to *Homo sapiens*[1-4]. However, the provenance and age of the fossils have been much debated[5,6]. Here we confirm that the Omo I and Omo II hominid fossils are from similar stratigraphic levels in Member I of the Kibish Formation, despite the view that Omo I is more modern in appearance than Omo II[1-3]. ^{40}Ar/^{39}Ar ages on feldspar crystals from pumice clasts within a tuff in Member I below the hominid levels place an older limit of 198 ± 14 kyr (weighted mean age 196 ± 2 kyr) on the hominids. A younger age limit of 104 ± 7 kyr is provided by feldspars from pumice clasts in a Member III tuff. Geological evidence indicates rapid deposition of each member of the Kibish Formation. Isotopic ages on the Kibish Formation correspond to ages of Mediterranean sapropels, which reflect increased flow of the Nile River, and necessarily increased flow of the Omo River. Thus the ^{40}Ar/^{39}Ar age measurements, together with the sapropel correlations, indicate that the hominid fossils have an age close to the older limit. Our preferred estimate of the age of the Kibish hominids is 195 ± 5 kyr, making them the earliest well-dated anatomically modern humans yet described.

THE principal outcrops of the Kibish Formation are along the Omo River where it skirts the Nkalabong Range (Fig. 1), with the highest outcrops close in elevation to that of the watershed between the Omo and the Nile rivers[7,8]. Former hydrographic links are apparent from Nilotic fauna in the Turkana Basin sequence[8-10].

来自埃塞俄比亚基比什的现代人的
地层位置和年代

麦克杜格尔等

编者按

我们自己的物种从何而来，何时而来？1967 年，科学家在埃塞俄比亚南部的基比
什组中发现了古人类头骨化石，这些化石被认为是解剖学意义上的早期现代人，被
归入智人这一类群。但这些化石的出土地点和年代一直备受争议。地质年表学家麦
克杜格尔及其同事们试图用地层中火山层的氩精确年代，以及奥莫河谷与尼罗河的
历史对比来解决这个问题。最终的年代——19.5 万±0.5 万年——使得奥莫基比什
古人类成为目前发现的世界上最古老的智人。埃塞俄比亚是人类的诞生地，同人类
大家庭中许多其他物种一样。

1967 年，在埃塞俄比亚南部的基比什组挖掘出来了古人类头盖骨遗迹，该头
盖骨被鉴定为解剖学上的早期现代人，被划分到了智人 [1-4]。然而，这些化石的出
土地点和年代却饱受争议 [5,6]。尽管有观点认为奥莫 I 号化石的形态比奥莫 II 号更
加接近现代 [1-3]，但是我们确证了奥莫 I 号和奥莫 II 号古人类化石是来自于基比什
组 I 段的相似层位。人们采集了古人类化石出土层位下方的 I 段的凝灰岩内的浮石
碎屑，从中得到的长石晶体确定了 $^{40}Ar/^{39}Ar$ 年代，将古人类化石的年代下限确定在
198±14 kyr(kyr 为千年)（加权均值年代为 196±2 kyr）。III 段凝灰岩内的浮石碎屑
中的长石则提供了古人类化石的年代上限，为 104±7 kyr。地质学证据表明基比什
组的每一段都经历了快速的沉积作用。基比什组的同位素年龄与地中海腐泥的年代
一致，这反映了尼罗河流量的增加，以及由此引起的奥莫河流量的必然增加。因此
$^{40}Ar/^{39}Ar$ 方法得出的年代值，以及它与地中海腐泥形成时间的相关关系，共同暗示
了古人类化石的年代接近于上述测年结果的下限。我们更倾向于估计基比什古人类
的年代约为 195±5 kyr，这样他们就成为迄今描述过的最早的可以清楚追溯到其年
代的解剖学上的现代人。

基比什组的主要露头地是沿着奥莫河一带，那里位于纳卡拉邦山脉的边缘（图
1），其中位置最高的露头，在海拔上接近奥莫河与尼罗河的分水岭 [7,8]。在图尔卡纳
盆地的沉积序列里，出现了尼罗河动物群，显然，从前这两条河流有十分接近的水
文关系 [8-10]。

Fig. 1. Map showing the distribution of the Kibish Formation (shaded) in the lower Omo Valley, southern Ethiopia, after Davidson[29]. Inset on lower left, locations of Omo I, Omo II, measured sections, and dated samples.

The Kibish Formation (about 100 m thick) consists of flat-lying, tectonically undisturbed, unconsolidated sediments deposited mainly in deltaic environments over brief periods. It comprises the youngest exposed sedimentary sequence in the Omo Basin, and lies disconformably upon the Nkalabong Formation[11,12] or on the underlying Mursi Formation[12]. Strata are composed principally of claystone and siltstone, with subordinate fine sandstone, conglomerate and tuffs (Fig. 2).

图 1. 埃塞俄比亚南部下奥莫河谷的基比什组（阴影部分）的分布地图（戴维森指定的[29]）。左下方的插图
表示的是奥莫 I 号和奥莫 II 号的位置、测量的剖面以及确定年代的样本。

　　基比什组（约 100 米厚）主要由短时间内堆积在三角洲环境的平整且未受到干扰
的、松散的沉积物组成。其包含奥莫盆地最晚近的暴露沉积序列，以不整合的方式
位于纳卡拉邦组之上[11,12] 或在下方的穆尔斯组上[12]。地层主要由黏土岩和粉砂岩构
成，附着有细砂岩、砾岩和凝灰岩（图 2）。

Fig. 2. Composite stratigraphy of the Kibish Formation. Member I was measured near the type section at Makul; Member II was measured near Harpoon Hill, and Members III and IV were measured along Camp Road (see Fig. 1 for locations).

Butzer *et al.*[13] and Butzer[14] divided the Kibish Formation into Members I to IV on the basis of disconformities with up to 30 m relief (Fig. 2). The members record discrete times of deposition when the northern margin of Lake Turkana and the Omo delta lay about 100 km north of their current positions. As the higher lake levels reflect significantly higher precipitation in the region, such periods should be recognizable at least regionally, and perhaps globally.

图 2. 基比什组的复合地层学。经测量，I 段位于马库拉的典型剖面附近，II 段位于哈尔普丘陵附近，III 段和 IV 段沿着营路测量的（具体位置见图 1）。

　　布策等人[13] 和布策[14] 根据基比什组高达 30 米的地层不整合现象，将其划分成了 I 到 IV 段（图 2）。在那时，图尔卡纳湖的北部边界和奥莫三角洲，在它们现在位置的北边 100 千米，基比什组的四个段精确记录了那时沉积过程的不连续时间。由于湖泊水位的升高反映了该地区降水的显著增加，所以至少在区域上，甚至在全球范围内，都应该可以辨别出这些时期。

Member I (26 m thick; Fig. 2) was deposited disconformably on the Nkalabong Formation in a deltaic environment. Small (less than 30 mm) rounded pumice clasts occur in an impure tuff in Member I, 7 m below the base of Member II. This tuff lies near, but probably slightly below, the levels from which Omo I and Omo II were derived. Glass shards from the tuff are very similar in composition to the glass from three pumice clasts enclosed in the tuff (Supplementary Table 1), indicating a common origin. Further, this composition is distinct from the glass composition of any other tuff in the Kibish Formation. Member II, about 28 m thick, was deposited on a topographic surface developed on Member I with at least 19 m of relief. Member II contains two discrete sequences, separated by an internal disconformity, designated Members IIa and IIb on Fig. 2. Member II was incised by as much as 25 m before the deposition of Member III[11,14], which begins with thin siltstone and claystone beds that drape topography. These beds, averaging about 3 cm thick, fine upward internally, and represent annual flooding. Thus, deposition of the lower part of Member III may record less than 1 kyr. A tuff 3.5–12 m thick, 18 m above the base of Member III, locally contains pumice clasts with alkali feldspar phenocrysts. Glass of the pumices normally differs compositionally from the glass of the tuff (Supplementary Table 1). However, one pumice sample yielded two contrasting sets of analyses: one corresponding to the tuff, the other to the dominant pumices. The youngest unit of the Kibish Formation, Member IV, was deposited on the underlying sediments after up to 30 m of dissection. Member IV comprises at most 21 m of strata deposited between about 9.5 and 3.3 kyr ago, on the basis of ^{14}C dating of mollusc shell[7,14,15].

Omo I was found at Kamoya's Hominid Site (KHS; 5° 24.15′ N, 35° 55.81′ E), which was identified from contemporary photographs, from evidence of the 1967 excavations and by additional hominid bone material conjoining the 1967 finds[16]. The hominid fossils were recovered from a siltstone 2.4 m below the base of Member II[14]. Thus, Omo I derives from near the top of Member I. Butzer et al.[13] reported a ^{230}Th/^{234}U date of 130 ± 5 kyr on Etheria from essentially the same level as the hominid, but they and others have questioned the reliability of the age[5,6].

Omo II was found on the surface at PHS (Paul's Hominid Site), which Butzer[14] mapped about 2.6 km northwest of KHS. A map drawn at the time by Paul Abell (discoverer of Omo II), together with contemporary photographs of the site supplied by K.W. Butzer, have positively identified PHS at 5° 24.55′ N, 35° 54.07′ E, about 3.3 km west by north of KHS (Fig. 1). Although PHS was mislocated on the published map, Butzer's[14] stratigraphic description at the site is correct. The base of Member II lies about 3 m above the approximate level from which Omo II was recovered. The basal tuff of Member II is of unique composition, and correlates from KHS to PHS (Supplementary Table 1).

Ages on alkali feldspars separated from pumice clasts from tuffs in Members I and III reflect the time of their eruption, and provide maximum and minimum ages for the hominid fossils, respectively. ^{40}Ar/^{39}Ar results are summarized in Table 1, with details listed in Supplementary Tables 2–4.

468

I 段（26 米厚；图 2）是在三角洲环境中不整合地沉积在纳卡拉邦组上的。小型（不足 30 毫米）的圆形浮岩出现于 I 段的掺杂的凝灰岩中，位于 II 段基底之下 7 米处。这种凝灰岩位于奥莫 I 号和奥莫 II 号的层位附近，但可能略低于该水平。凝灰岩中的玻璃碎片与凝灰岩中附着的三种浮岩碎屑的玻璃在构成上非常相似（附表 1），这暗示着它们具有共同的来源。此外，这种成分与基比什组的其他凝灰岩中的玻璃成分都不一样。II 段约有 28 米厚，沉积在一个 I 段上发展起来的表面上，具有至少 19 米的起伏地势。II 段内部有一个不整合面，将这段地层分成了两部分，图 2 中将它们指定为 IIa 和 IIb 段。III 段的沉积过程是从覆盖地形的薄的粉砂岩和黏土岩床开始的，但在沉积开始之前，II 段被侵入了 25 米之多[11,14]。这些平均约 3 厘米厚的河床，内部向上部位的颗粒都很精细，代表了每年一次的洪灾。因此，III 段的下半部分的沉积岩，记录的时代可能少于 1,000 年。一层 3.5 米到 12 米厚的凝灰岩，位于 III 段的基底之上 18 米处，局部含有浮岩碎屑和碱性长石斑晶。浮岩的玻璃质通常与凝灰岩玻璃质在成分上有所不同（附表 1），但是，对一例浮岩样本的分析，产生了两个截然不同的结果，一套对应凝灰岩，另一套则对应于占优势的浮岩。基比什组中最年轻的单元——IV 段是在高达 30 米的不连续层之后沉积在下面的沉积物上的。根据软体动物外壳进行的 ^{14}C 年代测定发现，IV 段沉积形成的时代为 9,500 年到 3,300 年前，地层厚度约为 21 米[7,14,15]。

奥莫 I 号是在卡莫亚古人类遗址（KHS；北纬 5°24.15′，东经 35°55.81′）发现的，可以根据 1967 年挖掘的证据结合 1967 年发现的其他古人类化石以及同时期的照片上鉴别出来[16]。古人类化石从 II 段的基底之下的 2.4 米处的粉砂岩处发掘出来[14]。因此，奥莫 I 号出土位置接近 I 段的顶部。布策等[13] 使用 $^{230}Th/^{234}U$ 测年法，测定了一例与古人类化石来自同一层位的艾特利亚人的年代为 130±5 kyr，但是他们和其他人都对这一年代的可靠性表示质疑[5,6]。

奥莫 II 号发现于保罗古人类遗址（PHS）的地表，根据布策[14] 的标记，这一地点位于 KHS 西北约 2.6 千米处。根据保罗·埃布尔（奥莫 II 号的发现者）当时绘制的地图与布策提供的同一时期的照片，最终确定 PHS 位于 KHS 北部约 3.3 千米处，地理坐标为北纬 5°24.55′ 东经 35°54.07′（图 1）。尽管在已发表的地图上将 PHS 的位置搞错了，但是布策[14] 对该遗址进行的地层学描述是正确的。II 段的基底在奥莫 II 号出土位置之上约 3 米处。II 段的基底凝灰岩具有独特的成分，从 KHS 到 PHS 都与其具有相关性（附表 1）。

从 I 段和 III 段的凝灰岩中的浮岩碎屑分离得到的碱性长石的年代反映了它们爆发的时间，并且分别提供了古人类化石的最大和最小年代。$^{40}Ar/^{39}Ar$ 的结果在表 1 中进行了总结，详细情况在附表 2～4 中列出。

Table 1. Summary of $^{40}Ar/^{39}Ar$ alkali feldspar laser fusion ages from pumice clasts in tuffs of the Kibish area, Turkana Basin, Ethiopia

Sample no.	Tuff	Locality	Irradiation	n	n used	Simple mean age (kyr)	Weighted mean age (kyr)	Isochron age (kyr)	MSWD	$(^{40}Ar/^{39}Ar)_i$
						Kibish Formation, Member III				
99-275A	Member III	0.4 km SSE of KHS	ANU58/L10	10	10	105.4 ± 5.0	106.0 ± 1.6	108.0 ± 3.1	1.03	292.2 ± 4.1
99-275C	Member III	0.4 km SSE of KHS	ANU58/L1	13	11	107.5 ± 7.1	105.4 ± 1.8	101.1 ± 8.4	2.04	303.6 ± 13.8
99-274A	Member III	0.5 km SE of KHS	ANU58/L6	13	13	98.1 ± 5.3	98.2 ± 1.1	97.4 ± 2.2	2.47	298.9 ± 6.8
99-274B	Member III	0.5 km SE of KHS	ANU58/L7	14	13	105.0 ± 8.3	109.6 ± 1.3	110.2 ± 4.4	3.27	292.9 ± 16.2
						Kibish Formation, Member I, near Omo II site, just west of Omo River, Nakaa'kire, 5° 24.6′N, 35° 54.5′E				
99-273A	Member I	Nakaa'kire	ANU58/L3	9	9	319.8 ± 18.6	315.3 ± 3.6	318.2 ± 16.6	3.55	287.3 ± 41.5
99-273B	Member I	Nakaa'kire	ANU58/L4	8	7	220.8 ± 13.3	210.9 ± 2.1	209.6 ± 2.0	0.55	301.4 ± 3.1
02-01A	Member I	Nakaa'kire	ANU98/L9	16	16	204.2 ± 14.9	205.3 ± 2.2	194.1 ± 5.4	2.66	315.8 ± 7.3
02-01B	Member I	Nakaa'kire	ANU98/L10	15	14	194.7 ± 10.8	191.5 ± 1.9	184.9 ± 3.8	2.13	304.0 ± 3.5
02-01C	Member I	Nakaa'kire	ANU98/L3	14	14	195.6 ± 15.0	192.7 ± 2.3	192.5 ± 6.7	3.85	295.7 ± 5.8

^{40}K decay constant $\lambda = 5.543 \times 10^{-10}$ yr^{-1}. Fluence monitor: Fish Canyon Tuff sanidine 92-176 of reference age 28.1 Myr. Samples 99-275A and 99-275C (laboratory sample numbers at ANU) = KIB99-47 (field sample number); 99-274A and 99-274B = KIB99-41; 99-273A and 99-273B = KIB99-19. Results with errors are means ± s.d. MSWD, mean square of weighted deviates.

The five pumice clasts measured from Member I yielded three different ages (Table 1), with at least the oldest age interpreted as evidence for reworking of that particular pumice clast. Nine analyses on 99-273A gave a mean age of 320 ± 19 kyr. Seven analyses on 99-273B yielded a mean age of 221 ± 13 kyr after rejecting one outlier (269 ± 18 kyr). Single feldspar crystals from 02-01B yielded a mean age of 195 ± 11 kyr ($n = 14$), forming a concordant data set after one rejection (333 ± 6 kyr). Multiple crystals ($n \leqslant 3$) were analysed in 12 of 16 measurements for 02-01A, and in 8 of 14 analyses for 02-01C ($n \leqslant 4$). No ages were rejected on 02-01A, whose mean age is 204 ± 15 kyr, or on 02-01C, whose mean age is 196 ± 15 kyr. It is probable that these latter three pumice clasts are products of the same volcanic eruption, as shown by their concordant ages and similar mean K/Ca ratios. When combined, all 44 analyses provide an arithmetic mean age of 198 ± 14 kyr and a weighted mean age of 195.8 ± 1.6 kyr. The mean age calculated for pumice 99-273B is statistically older than the ages determined on the three pumice clasts 02-01, so that 99-273B might also be a reworked pumice clast. Clearly, the age of deposition of a tuff must be younger than the youngest igneous component found within it. Thus, this tuffaceous level of Member I of the Kibish Formation was deposited after 196 kyr ago, on the basis of the mean age determined on the three 02-01 pumice clasts.

表 1. 对埃塞俄比亚图尔卡纳盆地基比什地区的凝灰岩中的
浮岩碎屑进行的 $^{40}Ar/^{39}Ar$ 碱性长石激光聚变测年概况

样品编号	凝灰岩	产地	放射	取样量	实际使用数目	简单平均年代 (kyr)	加权平均年代 (kyr)	等龄线法年代 (kyr)	加权均方差	$(^{40}Ar/^{39}Ar)_i$
基比什组，III 段										
99-275A	III 段	KHS 东南偏南 0.4 千米处	ANU58/L10	10	10	105.4±5.0	106.0±1.6	108.0±3.1	1.03	292.2±4.1
99-275C	III 段	KHS 东南偏南 0.4 千米处	ANU58/L1	13	11	107.5±7.1	105.4±1.8	101.1±8.4	2.04	303.6±13.8
99-274A	III 段	KHS 东南 0.5 千米处	ANU58/L6	13	13	98.1±5.3	98.2±1.1	97.4±2.2	2.47	298.9±6.8
99-274B	III 段	KHS 东南 0.5 千米处	ANU58/L7	14	13	105.0±8.3	109.6±1.3	110.2±4.4	3.27	292.9±16.2
基比什组，I 段，靠近奥莫 II 遗址，就在奥莫河以西，Nakaa'kire，5°24.6′N, 35°54.5′E										
99-273A	I 段	Nakaa'kire	ANU58/L3	9	9	319.8±18.6	315.3±3.6	318.2±16.6	3.55	287.3±41.5
99-273B	I 段	Nakaa'kire	ANU58/L4	8	7	220.8±13.3	210.9±2.1	209.6±2.0	0.55	301.4±3.1
02-01A	I 段	Nakaa'kire	ANU98/L9	16	16	204.2±14.9	205.3±2.2	194.1±5.4	2.66	315.8±7.3
02-01B	I 段	Nakaa'kire	ANU98/L10	15	14	194.7±10.8	191.5±1.9	184.9±3.8	2.13	304.0±3.5
02-01C	I 段	Nakaa'kire	ANU98/L3	14	14	195.6±15.0	192.7±2.3	192.5±6.7	3.85	295.7±5.8

^{40}K 衰变常数 $\lambda = 5.543 \times 10^{-10}$ yr^{-1}。流量监测器：参考年代为 2,810 万年的菲什峡谷凝灰岩透长石 92-176。样本 99-275A 和 99-275C（ANU 的实验室样本编号）= KIB99-47（野外样本编号）；99-274A 和 99-274B = KIB99-41；99-273A 和 99-273B = KIB99-19。结果与误差用平均值 ± 标准差表示。

对 I 段得到的五份浮岩碎屑的测年产生了三个不同的结果（表 1），至少最古老的年代被解读为这一例浮岩碎屑曾经被搬运的证据。对 99-273A 进行的九项分析给出的平均年代为 320±19 kyr。对 99-273B 进行的七项分析在排除一个离群值（269±18 kyr）之后，测得的平均年代为 221±13 kyr。来自 02-01B 的唯一长石晶体测得的平均年代为 195±11 kyr（$n = 14$），在剔除一个离群值（333±6 kyr）之后，形成了一套整合的数据集。对 02-01A 的 16 个测量值中的 12 个进行了多晶体（$n \leqslant 3$）分析，对 02-01C（$n \leqslant 4$）的 14 个测量值中的 8 个进行了分析。得到的 02-01A 的所有年代数值中没有离群值，其平均年代为 204±15 kyr，02-01C 的也没有离群值，其平均年代为 196±15 kyr。有可能后面这三种浮岩碎屑是同一次火山喷发的产物，正如它们的一致年代和相似的平均 K/Ca 比例反映的一样。综合分析，所有 44 个结果提供的算术平均年代是 198±14 kyr，加权平均年代是 195.8±1.6 kyr。统计学上看，浮岩 99-273B 计算出来的平均年代比三种 02-01 浮岩碎屑确定的年代更古老，所以 99-273B 可能也是一种二次搬运的浮岩碎屑。显然，凝灰岩层的年代肯定比其中最年轻的火成组分更年轻。因此，根据这三种 02-01 浮岩碎屑确定的平均年代，基比什组 I 段的凝灰岩层是在 196 kyr 之后沉积下来的。

Feldspars from four pumice clasts from the Member III tuff were analysed. Two were *in situ* (99-275A, C), and two (99-274A, B) had weathered out of the same unit about 150 m farther east (Fig. 1). Ages on 99-275A range from 98.0 ± 7.7 kyr to 114.6 ± 4.3 kyr. Five single-crystal measurements have an arithmetic mean age of 105.5 ± 7.0 kyr, identical to five measurements on groups of two or three crystals (mean age 105.4 ± 2.7 kyr), indicating a homogeneous population. The overall mean age is 105.4 ± 5.0 kyr, with a weighted mean age of 106.0 ± 1.6 kyr. Eleven analyses on sample 99-275C yield a mean age of 107.5 ± 7.1 kyr and a weighted mean of 105.4 ± 1.8 kyr, after rejection of two outliers (142.1 ± 3.3 and 128.8 ± 8.3 kyr). Concordant results from 99-274A on seven single crystals and six pairs of crystals gave an overall arithmetic mean age of 98.1 ± 5.3 kyr. The companion clast 99-274B gave a mean age of 105.0 ± 8.3 kyr, after elimination of one outlier (Supplementary Table 4). Again these results reflect a single age population, as shown by the similar mean ages of the individual pumices, and the overlapping average K/Ca ratios. Combining all these results (except outliers), the overall arithmetic mean age is 103.7 ± 7.4 kyr ($n = 47$) and the weighted mean age is 103.7 ± 0.9 kyr. Thus, the depositional age must be equal to or younger than 104 kyr, providing evidence that Members I and II of the Kibish Formation are older than 104 kyr.

Each of the members of the Kibish Formation was deposited during intervals when Lake Turkana was at a much higher level than at present, and Member II has an internal disconformity. The upper part of Member I was being deposited at or after 196 kyr ago, and the upper part of Member III was being deposited at or after 104 kyr ago; ^{14}C ages on Member IV correspond to deposition between 9.5 and 3.3 kyr ago. These ages are remarkably similar to ages of Mediterranean sapropels S7, S4 and S1. Sapropels S1–S7 have the following estimated ages: 195 kyr (S7), 172 kyr (S6), 124 kyr (S5), 102 kyr (S4), 81 kyr (S3), 55 kyr (S2) and 8 kyr (S1)[17]. In many cases sapropels are related to a greatly increased flow of the Nile River into the Mediterranean Sea as a consequence of intensification of the African monsoon[18], recorded in more negative $\delta^{18}O$ in planktonic foraminifera. As the Omo River shares a divide with the Blue Nile and with tributaries of the White Nile, the Nile and the Omo must be affected similarly. As noted, deposition of each of the members of the Kibish Formation was probably very rapid. Thus, the close correspondence between the ages of Member I (196 kyr) and of sapropel S7 (195 kyr), of Member III (104 kyr) and of sapropel S4 (102 kyr), and of Member IV (3.3–9.5 kyr) and of sapropel S1 (8 kyr) is probably causally related. Sapropel S2 (55 kyr) is absent from or poorly represented in many Mediterranean sedimentary cores and has a very small $\delta^{18}O$ residual; thus, it is not surprising that no deposits of this age have been identified in the Kibish Formation. Sapropel S6, deposited during a European glacial period[19], might also be absent from the Kibish Formation, because it too has a small $\delta^{18}O$ anomaly. The two parts of Member II may be accommodated by sapropels S5 and S6, or they may correspond to the two phases identified in sapropel S5 (119–124 kyr), which are separated by 700–900 yr (ref. 20). This link between sapropel formation in the Mediterranean and very high levels of Lake Turkana is a particularly notable finding. In contrast, S3 is very well represented in many Mediterranean sedimentary cores and is therefore expected to be recorded in the Kibish Formation, but has not been recognized. Given the large expanse of the plain in the

对来自 III 段凝灰岩的四例浮岩碎屑中的长石进行了分析。两例是在原位 (99-275A，C) 采集的，另外两例 (99-274A，B) 也来自同一地层单元，但它们被风化搬运到了东部约 150 米远的地方 (图 1)。99-275A 的年代从 98.0 ± 7.7 kyr 到 114.6 ± 4.3 kyr 不等。五个单晶体测量结果的算术平均值是 105.5 ± 7.0 kyr，与两三种晶体一组的五个结果是一致的 (均值为 105.4 ± 2.7 kyr)，显示它们是同一群体。总平均年代为 105.4 ± 5.0 kyr，加权平均年代为 106.0 ± 1.6 kyr。对样本 99-275C 进行的十一项分析在剔除掉两个离群值 (142.1 ± 3.3 和 128.8 ± 8.3 kyr) 之后产生的平均年代为 107.5 ± 7.1 kyr，加权均值为 105.4 ± 1.8 kyr。对 99-274A 进行的七种单晶体和六对晶体分析得到的一致结果给出的总算术平均值是 98.1 ± 5.3 kyr。在剔除掉一个离群值后，伴随碎屑 99-274B 给出的平均年代为 105.0 ± 8.3 kyr (附表 4)。这些结果再次反映了这些样本来源于同一次沉积，另外，单个浮岩样本有相似的平均年代，它们的 K/Ca 比值和滑动平均 K/Ca 比所表明的一样。将所有这些结果 (除了离群值) 综合起来，总算术平均年代为 103.7 ± 7.4 kyr ($n = 47$)，加权平均年代为 103.7 ± 0.9 kyr。因此，沉积年代必须等于或小于 104 kyr，这为基比什组的 I 段和 II 段的年代要早于 104 kyr 提供了证据。

基比什组的每个地层段都是在图尔卡纳湖处于比现在更高的水位上的间隔期间沉积下来的，II 段地层具有内部不整合性。I 段地层的上半部分是在 196 kyr 前或晚些时候沉积下来的，III 段的上半部分是在 104 kyr 前或晚些时候沉积下来的；IV 段的 ^{14}C 年代分析表明其对应的沉积作用发生于距今 9.5 kyr 到 3.3 kyr 前。这些年代与地中海腐泥 S7、S4 和 S1 阶段年代非常相似。腐泥 S1 ~ S7 的估计年代如下：195 kyr(S7)、172 kyr(S6)、124 kyr(S5)、102 kyr(S4)、81 kyr(S3)、55 kyr(S2) 和 8 kyr(S1)[17]。浮游有孔虫中 $\delta^{18}O$ 的负值显示非洲季风的加剧，尼罗河流入地中海的水量大幅增加，很多情况下这与腐泥形成有关[18]。由于奥莫河与青尼罗河以及白尼罗河支流共有分水岭，所以尼罗河和奥莫河也必然会受到相似的影响。如前所述，基比什组的各成员层的沉积作用可能非常迅速。因此，I 段地层 (196 kyr) 和腐泥 S7 (195 kyr) 的年代之间、III 段地层 (104 kyr) 和腐泥 S4 (102 kyr) 的年代之间、IV 段地层 (3.3 ~ 9.5 kyr) 和腐泥 S1 (8 kyr) 的年代之间可能是有因果关系的。腐泥 S2 层 (55 kyr) 在许多地中海沉积物岩芯中都不存在或者含量很少，$\delta^{18}O$ 残值也很小；因此，在基比什组没有测定出该年代的堆积物也不足为奇。腐泥 S6 是在欧洲冰期[19]堆积下来的，可能在基比什组也不存在，因为它也有一个小的 $\delta^{18}O$ 异常。II 段地层存在两个不同的部分，二者可能对应腐泥层 S5 和 S6，或者它们可能对应于腐泥 S5 层 (119 ~ 124 kyr) 所代表的两个时期，即被 700 ~ 900 年分开的两个时期 (参考文献 20)。地中海的腐泥地层和图尔卡纳湖的高水位之间的这种联系是一项非常值得注意的发现。相反，很多地中海沉积物岩芯中都能发现 S3 腐泥层，因此也希望基比什组

region underlain by the Kibish Formation, it is quite possible that deposits correlative with sapropel S3 are present but are not exposed in the immediate Kibish region that we have studied.

Our palaeontological and stratigraphic studies support the original report[14] that Omo I and Omo II are derived from comparable stratigraphic levels within Member I of the Kibish Formation despite their morphological differences[1-3,21,22]. Morphological diversity among fossil hominids from the Middle and Late Pleistocene of Africa is of major importance in understanding the tempo and mode of modern human origins[21,23].

^{40}Ar/^{39}Ar dating of feldspars from tuffs in Member I and Member III of the Kibish Formation shows that its hominid fossils are younger than 195.8 ± 1.6 kyr and older than 103.7 ± 0.9 kyr. Direct isotopic dating of volcanic eruptions recorded in the Kibish Formation does not enable us to place narrower limits on the age. However, the suggested correlations of Member IIa and Member IIb with either the two identified phases of sapropel S5 or sapropels S6 and S5, respectively, indicate that deposition of Member I of the Kibish Formation occurred earlier than about 125 kyr ago or earlier than 172 kyr ago. The geological evidence for rapid deposition of Member I and the remarkably close correspondence of the isotopic ages on the youngest pumice clasts in the tuff of Member I at 196 kyr with the estimated age of sapropel S7 is regarded as strongly supporting the view that Member I was deposited close to 196 ± 2 kyr ago. On this basis we suggest that hominid fossils Omo I and Omo II are relatively securely dated to 195 ± 5 kyr old, somewhat older than the age of between 154 and 160 kyr assigned to the hominid fossils from Herto, Ethiopia[24], making Omo I and Omo II the oldest anatomically modern human fossils yet recovered.

Methods

Age measurements

Alkali feldspar crystals were separated from pumice clasts and cleaned ultrasonically in 7% HF for 5–10 min to remove adhering volcanic glass and surface alteration. Although separations were performed on the coarsest crystals present, in several cases crystals were less than 1 mm, with masses less than 0.8 mg. In such cases several crystals were used for each analysis (see Supplementary Tables 2–4).

Samples were irradiated in facilities X33 or X34 of the High Flux Australian Reactor (Lucas Heights, Sydney, Australia) for 6 h as described in ref. 25. Cadmium shielding 0.2 mm thick was used to reduce the $(^{40}$Ar/^{39}Ar$)_K$ correction factor, which was measured by analysis of zero-aged synthetic potassium silicate glass co-irradiated with the unknowns. This correction is particularly important because of the young age of the samples, so interpolated values for each sample are given in the Supplementary Tables 2–4. The fluence monitor employed was sanidine 92-176, separated from the Fish Canyon Tuff, with a reference age of 28.1 Myr (ref. 26).

能够有相应的记录，但尚未得到确认。鉴于该地区位于基比什组之下的平原如此之大，与腐泥 S3 相关的堆积物非常可能存在，只是在我们研究过的基比什地区周围没有暴露出来而已。

尽管奥莫 I 号和奥莫 II 号古人类化石存在形态学差异 [1-3,21,22]，但我们的古生物和地层学研究支持原先的报道 [14]，即奥莫 I 号和奥莫 II 号化石都来自基比什组的 I 段地层，其出土层位比较接近。来自非洲中、晚更新世时期的古人类化石之间存在的形态学多样性，对于理解现代人起源的进度和模式具有非常重要的意义 [21,23]。

对基比什组的 I 段和 III 段地层中的凝灰岩里的长石进行 $^{40}Ar/^{39}Ar$ 年代测定，表明古人类化石的年代区间为 195.8±1.6 kyr 至 103.7±0.9 kyr。对基比什组所记录的火山爆发的同位素直接测年并不能帮助我们将年代范围缩小。然而，IIa 组和 IIb 组分别与地中海腐泥 S5 或腐泥 S6 和 S5 两个已知时期的相关性表明，基比什组的 I 段地层的堆积作用发生的年代早于约 125 kyr 前，或者早于 172 kyr 前。地质学证据表明，I 段存在着快速堆积作用，另外，I 段地层的凝灰岩中的最晚的浮岩碎屑的同位素年代（196 kyr）与腐泥 S7 的年代的非常密切的对应性强烈支持了如下观点，即 I 段是在接近 196±2 kyr 前堆积起来的。以此为基础，我们认为奥莫 I 和奥莫 II 的古人类化石比较肯定的年代是 195±5 kyr，比埃塞俄比亚赫托 [24] 的古人类（154 kyr 至 160 kyr）的年代早一些，因此奥莫 I 和奥莫 II 也成为迄今挖掘出来的年代最古老的解剖学上的现代人化石。

方　　法

年代测定

碱性长石晶体是从浮岩碎屑中分离出来的，然后用 7% 的氢氟酸超声波洗涤 5 至 10 分钟以去除黏附的火山玻璃和表面蚀变。尽管是在目前最粗糙的晶体上进行分离操作的，但是有些情况下，晶体还不足 1 毫米，质量也不到 0.8 毫克。这些情况下，每个分析都要使用几种晶体（见附表 2~4）。

样本使用澳大利亚高通量反应器（卢卡斯高地，悉尼，澳大利亚）的 X33 或 X34 仪器照射 6 小时，具体方法见参考文献 25 中的描述。用 0.2 毫米厚的镉屏蔽减小 $(^{40}Ar/^{39}Ar)_K$ 校正因子，该因子通过分析与未知因素共同照射的年代为零的合成硅酸钾玻璃来进行测定。由于样本的年代较近，所以这一修正就格外重要，附表 2~4 中给出了按照此法得到的每个样本的内插值。采用的流量监控器是透长石 92-176，是从菲什峡谷凝灰岩上分离下来的，其参考年代为 2,810 万年（参考文献 26）。

After irradiation, feldspar crystals were loaded into wells in a copper sample tray, installed in the vacuum system and baked overnight. Samples were fused with a focused argon-ion laser beam with up to 10 W of power. After purification of the gases released during fusion, the argon was analysed isotopically in a VG3600 mass spectrometer, using a Daly collector. The overall sensitivity of the system was about 2.5×10^{-17} mol mV^{-1}. Mass discrimination was monitored through regular measurements of atmospheric argon. The irradiation parameter, J, for each unknown was derived by interpolation from the measurements made on the fluence monitor crystals, with at least five analyses per level; the precision generally was in the range 0.3–0.75%, standard deviation of the population. Calcium correction factors[27] used in all calculations were $({}^{36}\mathrm{Ar}/{}^{37}\mathrm{Ar})_{Ca} = 3.49 \times 10^{-4}$ and $({}^{39}\mathrm{Ar}/{}^{37}\mathrm{Ar})_{Ca} = 7.86 \times 10^{-4}$.

Data handling

In calculating the arithmetic mean age for each pumice clast, any result more than two standard deviations from the initial mean of each sample was rejected iteratively until no further outliers were identified. No more than two measurements were rejected in any group of analyses, and no results were rejected for about half the groups. The error quoted in Table 1 is the standard deviation of the population, but because uncertainties on individual ages are variable, a weighted mean age and error is also given, weighting each age by the inverse of the variance. Differences in these mean ages are small (Table 1), but the error of the weighted mean age is usually much lower. In addition, data from each pumice clast, after exclusion of outliers, were plotted in an isotope correlation diagram ($^{36}\mathrm{Ar}/{}^{40}\mathrm{Ar}$ versus $^{39}\mathrm{Ar}/{}^{40}\mathrm{Ar}$), using the York[28] procedure. The derived ages are quite close to the mean ages (Table 1), and the calculated trapped argon composition generally has the atmospheric argon ratio of 295.5, within uncertainty.

(**433**, 733-736; 2005)

Ian McDougall[1], Francis H. Brown[2] & John G. Fleagle[3]

[1] Research School of Earth Sciences, Australian National University, Canberra, ACT 0200, Australia

[2] Department of Geology and Geophysics, University of Utah, Salt Lake City, Utah 84112, USA

[3] Department of Anatomical Science, Stony Brook University, Stony Brook, New York 11794, USA

Received 22 September; accepted 8 December 2004; doi:10.1038/nature03258.

References:

1. Day, M. H. Omo human skeletal remains. *Nature* **222**, 1135-1138 (1969).

2. Day, M. H. & Stringer, C. B. in *Congrès International de Paléontologie Humaine I, Nice* Vol. 2, 814-846 (Colloque International du CNRS, 1982).

3. Day, M. H. & Stringer, C. B. Les restes crâniens d'Omo-Kibish et leur classification à l'intérieur du genre *Homo. Anthropologie* **95**, 573-594 (1991).

4. Day, M. H., Twist, M. H. C. & Ward, S. Les vestiges post-crâniens d'Omo I (Kibish). *Anthropologie* **95**, 595-610 (1991).

5. Howell, F. C. in *Evolution of African Mammals* (eds Maglio, V. J. & Cooke, H. B. S.) 154-248 (Harvard Univ. Press, Cambridge, Massachusetts, 1978).

6. Smith, F. H., Falsetti, A. B. & Donnelly, S. M. Modern human origins. *Yb Phys. Anthropol.* **32**, 35-68 (1989).

7. Butzer, K. W., Isaac, G. Ll., Richardson, J. L. & Washbourn-Kamau, C. Radiocarbon dating of East African lake levels. *Science* **175**, 1069-1076 (1972).

8. Fuchs, V. E. The geological history of the Lake Rudolf Basin, Kenya Colony. *Phil. Trans. R. Soc. Lond. B* **229**, 219-274 (1939).

9. Arambourg, C. *Mission Scientifique de l'Omo 1932–1933. Geologie–Anthropologie–Paleontologie* (Muséum National d'Histoire Naturelle, Paris, 1935-1947).

10. Butzer, K. W. The Lower Omo Basin: Geology, fauna and hominids of Plio-Pleistocene formations. *Naturwissenschaften* **58**, 7-16 (1971).

照射之后，将长石晶体加样到一个铜质样品托盘的加样孔中，安装到真空系统后烘烤过夜。使用聚焦氩离子激光束以高达 10 W 的功率使样本熔化。对熔化期间释放出来的气体进行纯化后，使用戴利收集器在 VG3600 质谱仪中对氩进行同位素分析。该系统的综合灵敏度约为 $2.5 \times 10^{-17}\,\mathrm{mol \cdot mV^{-1}}$。质量甄别通过大气中的氩的常规含量进行监控。每个未知的照射参数 J 都是通过在流量监控晶体上进行的测量得到的插入值派生出来的，每个水平至少进行五次分析；通常的精确性范围是 0.3% ~ 0.75%，群体的标准差。在所有计算中使用的钙修正因子[27]都是 $(^{36}\mathrm{Ar}/^{37}\mathrm{Ar})_{Ca} = 3.49 \times 10^{-4}$ 和 $(^{39}\mathrm{Ar}/^{37}\mathrm{Ar})_{Ca} = 7.86 \times 10^{-4}$。

数据处理

在计算每种浮岩碎屑的算术平均年代时，每个样本的最初均值中存在两个以上标准差的任何结果都被反复检查剔除掉了，直到不再出现离群值为止。任何一组分析中，都没有剔除掉两个以上的测量值，而且约有一半的组中都没有剔除掉任何结果。表 1 中引用的误差是群体的标准差，但是由于个体年代的不确定性是不同的，所以给出了加权平均年代和误差，即对变异反向的每个年代进行了加权。这些平均年代的差异很小（表 1），但是加权平均年代的误差通常更低。此外，每种浮岩碎屑的数据在剔除掉离群值之后，都使用 York[28] 程序在同位素相关性表格（$^{36}\mathrm{Ar}/^{40}\mathrm{Ar}$ 对 $^{39}\mathrm{Ar}/^{40}\mathrm{Ar}$）中绘图。派生的年代与平均年代非常接近（表 1），而计算出来的捕获氩成分一般具有大气中的氩比值——295.5，属误差之内。

（刘皓芳 翻译；潘雷 审稿）

11. Butzer, K. W. in *Earliest Man and Environments in the Lake Rudolf Basin* (eds Coppens, Y., Howell, F. C., Isaac, G. Ll. & Leakey, R. E. F.) 12-23 (Univ. of Chicago Press, Chicago, 1976).

12. Butzer, K. W. & Thurber, D. L. Some late Cenozoic sedimentary formations of the Lower Omo Basin. *Nature* **222**, 1138-1143 (1969).

13. Butzer, K. W., Brown, F. H. & Thurber, D. L. Horizontal sediments of the lower Omo Valley: the Kibish Formation. *Quaternaria* **11**, 15-29 (1969).

14. Butzer, K. W. Geological interpretation of two Pleistocene hominid sites in the Lower Omo Basin. *Nature* **222**, 1133-1135 (1969).

15. Owen, R. B., Barthelme, J. W., Renaut, R. W. & Vincens, A. Palaeolimnology and archaeology of Holocene deposits north-east of Lake Turkana, Kenya. *Nature* **298**, 523-529 (1982).

16. Fleagle, J. *et al.* The Omo I partial skeleton from the Kibish Formation. *Am. J. Phys. Anthropol. Suppl.* **36**, 95 (2003).

17. Lourens, L. J. *et al.* Evaluation of the Plio-Pleistocene astronomical timescale. *Paleoceanography* **11**, 391-413 (1996).

18. Rossignol-Strick, M., Nesteroff, W., Olive, P. & Vergnaud-Grazzini, C. After the deluge: Mediterranean stagnation and sapropel formation. *Nature* **295**, 05-110 (1982).

19. Rossignol-Strick, M. & Paterne, M. A synthetic pollen record of the eastern Mediterranean sapropels of the last 1 Ma: implications for the time-scale and formation of sapropels. *Mar. Geol.* **153**, 221-237 (1999).

20. Rohling, E. J. *et al.* African monsoon variability during the previous interglacial maximum. *Earth Planet. Sci. Lett.* **202**, 61-75 (2002).

21. Haile-Selassie, Y., Asfaw, B. & White, T. D. Hominid cranial remains from Upper Pleistocene deposits at Aduma, Middle Awash, Ethiopia. *Am. J. Phys. Anthropol.* **123**, 1-10 (2004).

22. Rightmire, G. P. in *The Origins of Modern Humans: A World Survey of the Fossil Evidence* (eds Smith, F. H. & Spencer, F.) 295-325 (Alan R. Liss, New York, 1984).

23. Howell, F. C. in *Origins of Anatomically Modern Humans* (eds Nitecki, M. H. & Nitecki, D. V.) 253-319 (Plenum, New York, 1994).

24. Clark, J. D. *et al.* Stratigraphic, chronological and behavioural contexts of Pleistocene *Homo sapiens* from Middle Awash, Ethiopia. *Nature* **423**, 747-752 (2003).

25. McDougall, I. & Feibel, C. S. Numerical age control for the Miocene–Pliocene succession at Lothagam, a hominoid-bearing sequence in the northern Kenya Rift. *J. Geol. Soc. Lond.* **156**, 731-745 (1999).

26. Spell, T. L. & McDougall, I. Characterization and calibration of $^{40}Ar/^{39}Ar$ dating standards. *Chem. Geol.* **198**, 189-211 (2003).

27. Spell, T. L., McDougall, I. & Doulgeris, A. P. The Cerro Toledo Rhyolite, Jemez Volcanic Field, New Mexico: $^{40}Ar/^{39}Ar$ geochronology of eruptions between two caldera-forming events. *Bull. Geol. Soc. Am.* **108**, 1549-1566 (1996).

28. York, D. Least squares fitting of a straight line with correlated errors. *Earth Planet. Sci. Lett.* **5**, 320-324 (1969).

29. Davidson, A. *The Omo River Project* (Bulletin 2, Ethiopian Institute of Geological Surveys, Addis Ababa, 1983).

Supplementary Information accompanies the paper on www.nature.com/nature.

Acknowledgements. We thank J. Mya, R. Maier and X. Zhang for technical support for the geochronology; participants in the Kibish expeditions between 1999 and 2003, including Z. Assefa, J. Shea, S. Yirga, J. Trapani and especially C. Feibel, B. Passey and C. Fuller for their geological contributions; and R. Leakey, K. Butzer and especially P. Abell for providing us with information and documents about the 1967 expedition to the Kibish area. We thank the Government of Ethiopia, the Ministry of Youth, Sports and Culture, the Authority for Research and Conservation of Cultural Heritage, and the National Museum of Ethiopia for permission to study the Kibish Formation. Support was provided by the National Science Foundation, the Leakey Foundation, the National Geographic Society and the Australian National University. Neutron irradiations were facilitated by the Australian Institute of Nuclear Science and Engineering and the Australian Nuclear Science and Technology Organization.

Competing interests statement. The authors declare that they have no competing financial interests.

Correspondence and requests for materials should be addressed to I.McD (ian.mcdougall@anu.edu.au).

The DNA Sequence of the Human X Chromosome

M. T. Ross *et al.*

The enigmatic X chromosome reveals its genetic secrets in this paper detailing its DNA sequence. Female mammals carry two X chromosomes, whist males carry one X and one Y. Geneticist Mark Ross and colleagues determined the sequence of over 99% of the gene-containing region of the human X chromosome. The data reveal how X and Y chromosomes evolved from a pair of regular chromosomes around 300 million years ago. It also suggests that nearly 10% of the chromosome's 1,098 genes belong to a group that is upregulated in testicular and other cancers, and links a particular type of repetitive sequence with X-inactivation—the process that silences one of the two copies of the X chromosome in females to avoid a double dose of X chromosome genes.

The human X chromosome has a unique biology that was shaped by its evolution as the sex chromosome shared by males and females. We have determined 99.3% of the euchromatic sequence of the X chromosome. Our analysis illustrates the autosomal origin of the mammalian sex chromosomes, the stepwise process that led to the progressive loss of recombination between X and Y, and the extent of subsequent degradation of the Y chromosome. LINE1 repeat elements cover one-third of the X chromosome, with a distribution that is consistent with their proposed role as way stations in the process of X-chromosome inactivation. We found 1,098 genes in the sequence, of which 99 encode proteins expressed in testis and in various tumour types. A disproportionately high number of mendelian diseases are documented for the X chromosome. Of this number, 168 have been explained by mutations in 113 X-linked genes, which in many cases were characterized with the aid of the DNA sequence.

T HE X chromosome has many features that are unique in the human genome. Females inherit an X chromosome from each parent, but males inherit a single, maternal X chromosome. Gene expression on one of the female X chromosomes is silenced early in development by the process of X-chromosome inactivation (XCI), and this chromosome remains inactive in somatic tissues thereafter. In the female germ line, the inactive chromosome is reactivated and undergoes meiotic recombination with the second X chromosome. The male X chromosome fails to recombine along virtually its entire length during meiosis: instead, recombination is restricted to short regions at the tips of the X chromosome arms that recombine with equivalent segments on the Y chromosome.

人类 X 染色体的 DNA 序列

罗斯等

编者按

这篇论文通过详细介绍神秘的 X 染色体的 DNA 序列，揭示了它的遗传秘密。雌性哺乳动物有两条 X 染色体，雄性哺乳动物有一条 X 染色体和一条 Y 染色体。遗传学家马克·罗斯和他的同事们确定了人类 X 染色体中 99% 以上基因区域的序列，这些数据揭示了大约 3 亿年前 X 和 Y 染色体是如何从一对普通染色体进化而来的。它也表明染色体的 1,098 个基因的近 10% 属于一个群体，该群体调节睾丸和其他癌症；并且将一个特定类型的重复序列与 X 染色体失活联系起来，这个过程使得女性当中一个 X 染色体的两个副本之一沉默，来避免 X 染色体基因剂量加倍。

人类 X 染色体有一种独特的生物学特性，这种特性是由其进化形成的，即男性和女性共有的性染色体。我们已经确定了 X 染色体上 99.3% 的常染色质序列。我们的分析表明了哺乳动物性染色体起源于常染色体，X 和 Y 之间重组逐渐丢失的过程，以及 Y 染色体随后的退化程度。LINE1 重复元件占 X 染色体的三分之一，其分布与它们在 X 染色体失活过程中作为中转站的作用一致。我们在这个序列中发现了 1,098 个基因，其中有 99 个编码在睾丸和各种肿瘤类型中表达的蛋白质。X 染色体记录了大量不成比例的孟德尔病。在这一数字中，有 168 个可以用 113 个 X 连锁基因的突变解释，这些突变在许多情况下是借助 DNA 序列来表征的。

X 染色体上有许多人类基因组中独特的特征。女性从父母双方各继承一条 X 染色体，但男性只继承一条母亲的 X 染色体。其中一条女性 X 染色体的基因表达在发育早期被 X 染色体失活（XCI）过程所抑制，此后该染色体在身体组织中仍旧保持失活。在女性生殖系中，失活的染色体被重新激活，经过减数分裂后与第二条 X 染色体进行重组。在减数分裂过程中，男性的 X 染色体不能沿着其整个长度进行重组，相反，重组仅限于与 Y 染色体上的等值段进行重组的 X 染色体臂端的短区域。这些区域内的基因在性染色体间共享，因此它们的行为被称为"假常染色体"。X 染色体

481

Genes inside these regions are shared between the sex chromosomes, and their behaviour is therefore described as "pseudoautosomal". Genes outside these regions of the X chromosome are strictly X-linked, and the vast majority are present in a single copy in the male genome.

The unique properties of the X chromosome are a consequence of the evolution of sex chromosomes in mammals. The sex chromosomes have evolved from a pair of autosomes within the last 300 million years (Myr)[1]. In the process, the original, functional elements have been conserved on the X chromosome, but the Y chromosome has lost almost all traces of the ancestral autosome, including the genes that were once shared with the X chromosome. The hemizygosity of males for almost all X chromosome genes exposes recessive phenotypes, thus accounting for the large number of diseases that have been associated with the X chromosome[2]. The characteristic pattern of X-linked inheritance (affected males and no male-to-male transmission) was recognized by the eighteenth century for some cases of haemophilia, and gave impetus in the 1980s to the earliest successes in positional cloning— of the genes for chronic granulomatous disease[3] and Duchenne muscular dystrophy[4]. For females, the major consequence of the loss of genes from the Y chromosome is XCI, which equalizes the dosage of X-linked gene products between the sexes.

The biological consequences of sex chromosome evolution account for the intense interest in the human X chromosome in recent decades. However, evolutionary processes are likely to have shaped the behaviour and structure of the X chromosome in many other ways, influencing features such as repeat content, mutation rate, gene content and haplotype structure. The availability of the finished sequence of the human X chromosome, described here, now allows us to explore its evolution and unique properties at a new level.

The X Chromosome Sequence

We constructed a map of the X chromosome using predominantly P1-artificial chromosome (PAC) and bacterial artificial chromosome (BAC) clones (Supplementary Table 1), which were assembled into contigs using restriction-enzyme fingerprinting and integrated with earlier maps using sequence-tagged site (STS) content analysis[5]. Gaps were closed by targeted screening of clone libraries in bacteria or yeast, and by assessing BAC and fosmid end-sequence data for evidence of spanning clones. Fourteen euchromatic gaps remain intractable, despite using libraries with a combined 80-fold chromosome coverage. Five of these gaps are within the 2.7 megabase (Mb) pseudoautosomal region at the tip of the chromosome short arm (PAR1). This is reminiscent of the situation in other human sub-telomeric regions[6], and might reflect cloning difficulties in an area with a high content of (G+C) nucleotides and minisatellite repeats.

We selected 1,832 clones from the map for shotgun sequencing and directed finishing using established procedures[7]. Finished sequences were estimated to be more than 99.99% accurate by independent assessment[8]. The sequence of the X chromosome has been

上这些区域外的基因是严格的 X 连锁的，并且绝大多数都存在于男性基因组的单拷贝中。

X 染色体独特的特性是哺乳动物性染色体进化的结果。性染色体在过去的 3 亿年内从一对常染色体进化而来 [1]。在这个过程中，原有的功能元件保留在 X 染色体上，而 Y 染色体已经失去了几乎所有祖先常染色体的痕迹，包括曾经与 X 染色体共享的基因。男性的半杂合性使几乎所有 X 染色体上的基因暴露隐性表型，从而产生大量 X 染色体连锁的疾病 [2]。X 连锁遗传的特征模式（影响男性，没有男性之间的传递）因十八世纪血友病的一些案例而被识别出，并推动了 20 世纪 80 年代定位克隆的初步成功——对慢性肉芽肿病 [3] 和进行性假肥大性肌营养不良 [4] 的克隆。对女性来说，Y 染色体基因丢失的主要后果是 XCI，它可以使 X 连锁基因产物在两性之间的剂量均衡。

性染色体进化的生物学影响解释了近几十年人们为什么对人类 X 染色体有如此强烈的兴趣。然而，进化过程可能以许多其他方式塑造了 X 染色体的行为和结构，影响如重复序列的含量、突变率、基因含量和单体型结构等特征。这里所描述的已经完成的人类 X 染色体序列让我们在一个新的水平上探索其进化和特性。

X 染色体序列

我们主要通过限制性内切酶指纹法将 P1 人工染色体（PAC）和细菌人工染色体（BAC）克隆（补充表 1）组装成重叠群，并使用序列标签位点（STS）含量分析与早先图谱整合，构建了一个 X 染色体图谱 [5]。通过有针对性的筛选细菌或酵母菌克隆文库，并通过评估 BAC 和 F 黏粒末端序列数据来寻找跨域克隆的证据，以封闭缺口。即使使用了染色体覆盖率达 80 倍的文库，仍有 14 个常染色质缺口无法解决。其中五个缺口在染色体短臂末端 2.7 Mb 的假常染色体区域（PAR1）。这使人想起在人类其他亚端粒区域的情况 [6]，并可能反映在（G+C）核苷酸和小卫星重复含量高的区域的克隆难度。

我们从图谱中选择 1,832 个克隆进行鸟枪法测序并用已建立的程序进行定向指导 [7]。通过独立评价，完成的序列准确率超过 99.99% [8]。该 X 染色体的序列是

assembled from the individual clone sequences and comprises 16 contigs. These extend into the telomeric (TTAGGG)n repeat arrays at the ends of the chromosome arms, and include both pseudoautosomal regions (PARs). The data were frozen for the analyses described below, at which point we had determined 150,396,262 base pairs (bp) of sequence (Supplementary Table 2). Subsequently, we obtained a further 609,664 bp of sequence. The 14 euchromatic gaps are estimated to have a combined size of less than 1 Mb (see Methods and Supplementary Table 2), and the sequence therefore covers at least 99.3% of the X chromosome euchromatin. There is also a single heterochromatic gap corresponding to the polymorphic 3.0 (± 0.4) Mb array[9] of alpha satellite DNA at the centromere. On this basis, we conclude that the X chromosome is approximately 155 Mb in length.

The coverage and quality of the finished sequence have been assessed using independent data. All markers from the deCODE genetic map[10] are found in the sequence and the concordance of marker orders is excellent with only one discrepancy. DXS6807 is the most distal Xp marker on the deCODE map (4.39 cM), but in the sequence this marker is proximal to three others with genetic locations of 9–11 cM on the deCODE map. Out of 788 X chromosomal RefSeq[11] messenger RNAs that were assessed, 783 were found completely in the sequence, and parts of four others are also present (T. Furey, personal communication). The missing segments of *GTPBP6*, *CRLF2*, *DHRSX* and *FGF16* lie within gaps 1, 4, 5 and 10, respectively, and the *GAGE3* gene is in gap 7 (Supplementary Table 2). The sequence assembly was assessed using fosmid end-sequence pairs that match the X chromosome sequence. The orientation and separation of end-pairs of more than 17,000 fosmids were consistent with the sequence assembly. In two cases, sequences had been misassembled owing to long and highly similar repeats. There were six instances of large deletions in sequenced clones, which were resolved by determining fosmid sequences through the deleted regions. Finally, there were two cases of apparent length variation between the reference sequence and the DNA used for the fosmid library.

Features of the X Chromosome Sequence

The annotated sequence of the X chromosome is presented in Supplementary Fig. 1, and updates are contained in the Vertebrate Genome Annotation (VEGA) database (http://vega.sanger.ac.uk/Homo_sapiens/). The distribution of a number of sequence features on the chromosome is shown in Fig. 1 (Editorial note: this figure was originally included as a foldout insert. For details, see *Nature*'s web site). Analysis of the sequence reveals a gene-poor chromosome that is highly enriched in interspersed repeats and has a low (G+C) content (39%) compared with the genome average (41%).

Fig. 1. Features of the X chromosome sequence. **a**, X chromosome ideogram according to Francke[65]. **b**, Evolutionary domains of the X chromosome: the X-added region (XAR), the X-conserved region (XCR; dotted region in proximal Xp does not appear to be part of the XCR), the pseudoautosomal region PAR1, and evolutionary strata S5–S1. **c**, Sequence scale in intervals of 1 Mb. Note that correlation between cytogenetic band positions and physical distance is imprecise, owing to varying levels of condensation of different Giemsa bands. **d**, (G+C) content of 100-kb sequence windows. **e**, Number of genes in 1-Mb

由单个克隆序列组装而成，包括 16 个重叠群。它们延伸到染色体臂末端的端粒（TTAGGG）n 重复序列，并包括两个假常染色体区域（PAR）。这些数据被冻结用于下述分析，在此，我们已确定 150,396,262 bp 的序列（补充表 2）。随后，我们进一步获得了长度为 609,664 bp 的序列。估计 14 个常染色质缺口合并大小小于 1 Mb（见方法和补充表 2），因此，该序列至少覆盖 99.3% 的 X 染色体常染色质。还有一个异染色质缺口对应着丝粒上 α 卫星 DNA 的多态性 3.0（±0.4）Mb 阵列[9]。在此基础上，我们得出结论：X 染色体长度大约 155 Mb。

　　我们用独立的数据对已经完成序列的覆盖度和质量进行了评估，在序列中发现了 deCODE 遗传图谱[10] 的所有标记，并且标记顺序一致性很高，只有一个除外。DXS6807 是 deCODE 图上最远端 Xp 标记（4.39 cM），但在序列中这个标记与其他三个在 deCODE 图上遗传位置距离 9～11 cM 的标记最接近。我们评估了 788 个 X 染色体的信使 RNA 的参考序列[11]，其中 783 个在序列中被完全发现，其他 4 个也部分出现在序列中（富里，个人交流）。GTPBP6、CRLF2、DHRSX 和 FGF16 丢失的片段分别位于缺口 1、4、5 和 10，GAGE3 基因在缺口 7 中（补充表 2）。序列组装使用匹配 X 染色体序列的 F 黏粒末端序列对进行评估。超过 1.7 万 F 黏粒的末端对方向和间距与序列组装一致。序列长度长且高度相似的重复序列导致有两例组装错误。在测序的克隆中有六个大的缺失实例，这些实例已通过确定缺失区域的 F 黏粒序列来解决。最后，有两例在参考序列和用于 F 黏粒文库的 DNA 之间有明显的长度差异。

X 染色体序列的特征

　　X 染色体的注解序列见补充图 1，在脊椎动物基因组注释（VEGA）数据库（http://vega.sanger.ac.uk/Homo_sapiens/）里进行更新。此染色体上若干序列特征的分布如图 1（编者注：在原文中，本图是一个折叠插入图，更多细节请看《自然》官网）所示。序列分析揭示了一个基因贫乏的染色体，其高度富集散在重复序列，与基因组的平均水平（41%）相比（G+C）含量（39%）较低。

图 1. X 染色体序列特征。a，根据弗兰克的 X 染色体表意图[65]。b，X 染色体进化域：X 增加区（XAR），X 保守区（XCR；Xp 近端虚线区域不属于 XCR），假常染色体区域 PAR1 和进化层 S5～S1。c，序列刻度间隔为 1 Mb。请注意，由于不同吉姆萨带缩合程度不同，细胞遗传学带位置和物理距离间的相关性并不精确，d，100 kb 序列窗口的（G+C）含量。e，1 Mb 序列窗口中的基因数量（不包括假基因）。f～k，100 kb 窗口的序列被散在重复序列部分覆盖：L1 重复（f），L1 重复亚族 L1M（g）、L1 重复

sequence windows (pseudogenes not included). **f–k**, Fractional coverage of 100-kb sequence windows by interspersed repeats: L1 repeats (**f**), L1M subfamilies of L1 repeats (**g**), L1P subfamilies of L1 repeats (**h**), *Alu* repeats (**i**), L2 repeats (**j**), MIR repeats (**k**). Vertical grey lines in **d–k** represent gaps in the euchromatic sequence of the chromosome. Grey bar centred at approximately 60 Mb shows the position of the centromere. **l**, A selection of landmark genes on the chromosome. *OPN* refers to the three opsin genes in the reference sequence, which are organized as follows: cen-*OPN1LW-OPN1MW-OPN1MW*-tel. **m**, Genes that escape from X-chromosome inactivation as previously identified[48]. **n**, Cancer-testis antigen genes, belonging to the *MAGE* (light green), *GAGE* (dark green), *SSX* (magenta), *SPANX* (orange) or other (grey) CT gene families. For the genes in **l–n**, arrows indicate the direction of transcription.

Genes

Based on a manual assessment of all publicly available human expressed sequences and genes from other organisms, we have annotated 1,098 genes (7.1 genes per Mb) across four different categories (see Methods): known genes (699), novel coding sequences (132), novel transcripts (166), and putative transcripts (101). We have also identified 700 pseudogenes in the sequence (4.6 pseudogenes per Mb), of which 644 are classified as processed and 56 as non-processed. The gene density (excluding pseudogenes) on the X chromosome is among the lowest for the chromosomes that have been annotated to date. This might simply reflect a low gene density on the ancestral autosomes. Alternatively, selection may have favoured transposition of particular classes of gene from the X chromosome to the autosomes during mammalian evolution. These could include developmental genes for which the protein products are required in double dose in males (or in females after XCI has occurred), or genes for which mutation in male somatic tissues is lethal.

Physical characteristics of the genes and pseudogenes are summarized in Supplementary Table 3. Exons of the 1,098 genes account for only 1.7% of the X chromosome sequence. On the basis of the lengths of these gene loci, 33% of the chromosome is transcribed. This is considerably below the recent estimates for chromosomes 6 (ref. 12), 9 (ref. 6), 10 (ref. 13) and 13 (ref. 14), to which the equivalent gene annotation procedure was applied (Supplementary Table 4), and is a reflection not just of low gene density on chromosome X but also of low gene length. For example, mean gene length is 49 kilobases (kb) on chromosome X compared with 57 kb on chromosome 13. Nevertheless, the X chromosome contains the largest known gene in the human genome, the dystrophin (*DMD*) locus in Xp21.1, which spans 2,220,223 bp. Consistent with its low gene density, the frequency of predicted CpG islands on the X chromosome is only 5.25 per Mb, which is exactly half of the estimated genome average[7]. There is an association with a CpG island for 49% of the known genes, the category for which the most complete gene structures are expected in the current annotation.

We identified evolutionarily conserved regions (ECRs) by comparing the X chromosome sequence to the genomes of mouse, rat, zebrafish and the pufferfishes *Tetraodon nigroviridis* and *Fugu rubripes* (Supplementary Table 5). There are 4,493 ECRs that are conserved between the X chromosome and all of the other species. Of these, 4,393 overlap with

亚族 L1P(**h**)、*Alu* 重复(**i**)、L2 重复(**j**)、MIR 重复(**k**)。**d ~ k** 中的垂直灰线代表染色体常染色质序列中的缺口。集中在大约 60 Mb 处的灰色条块代表着丝粒的位置。**l**，染色体上标志性基因的选择。*OPN* 是指参考序列中的三个视蛋白基因，排列如下：着丝粒 -*OPN1LW-OPN1MW-OPN1MW*- 端粒。**m**，如前所述，从 X 染色体失活中逃逸的基因 [48]。**n**，癌/睾丸抗原基因，属于 *MAGE*(浅绿色)、*GAGE*(深绿色)、*SSX*(品红色)、*SPANX*(橙色)或其他(灰色)CT 基因家族。对于 **l ~ n** 中的基因，箭头指示转录的方向。

基　因

在人工评估所有已公布的人类表达序列和其他生物基因的基础上，我们已注释了四个不同类别的 1,098 个基因(每 Mb 有 7.1 个基因)(见方法)：已知基因(699)、新的编码序列(132)、新转录本(166)、假定转录本(101)。我们还在序列中确定了 700 个假基因(每 Mb 有 4.6 个假基因)，其中 644 个为已加工的基因，56 个为未加工的基因。X 染色体上的基因密度(不包括假基因)是迄今为止已注释的染色体中最低的。这可能只是反映了祖先染色体上的低基因密度。或者，在哺乳动物进化中选择可能有利于从 X 染色体向常染色转移某些类别的基因。这些基因可能包括男性(或 XCI 发生后的女性)需要双倍剂量的蛋白质产物发育基因，或男性体细胞组织中突变致死的基因。

补充表 3 总结了这些基因和假基因的物理特性。1,098 个基因的外显子只占 X 染色体序列的 1.7%。根据这些基因座的长度，有 33% 的染色体被转录。这大大低于最近采用等效的基因注释程序(补充表 4)对染色体 6(参考文献 12)、9(参考文献 6)、10(参考文献 13)和 13(参考文献 14)的估计，不仅是 X 染色体上低基因密度的反映，同时也是低基因长度的反映。例如，X 染色体上平均基因长度为 49 千碱基(kb)，相比之下 13 号染色体上的为 57 kb。然而，X 染色体包含人类基因组中已知最大的基因——在 Xp21.1 上的肌萎缩蛋白基因座 *DMD*，它跨越 2,220,223 个碱基对。与其低基因密度相符的是，预测 X 染色体上每 Mb 只有 5.25 个 CpG 岛，这正好是基因组平均估计值的一半 [7]。在已知基因中有 49% 与 CpG 岛相关，预计在目前的注释中这类基因结构最完整。

我们通过将 X 染色体序列与小鼠、大鼠、斑马鱼、黑青斑河鲀和红鳍东方鲀的基因组序列进行比较，确定了进化上的保守区域(ECR)(补充表 5)。在 X 染色体和所有其他物种间有 4,493 ECR 是保守的。其中，4,393 个与 4,373 个已注释的外显子

4,373 annotated exons. The remaining 100 ECRs are most likely to be unannotated exons, although some could be highly conserved control or structural elements. From these data we conclude that we have annotated at least 97.8% of the protein-coding exons on the X chromosome ($[4,373/(4,373 + 100)] \times 100$).

Non-coding RNA Genes

The gene set described above includes non-coding RNA (ncRNA) genes only when there is supporting evidence of expression from complementary DNA or expressed-sequence-tag (EST) sources. Using a complementary approach, we analysed the X chromosome sequence using the Rfam[15] database of structural RNA alignments, and predicted 173 ncRNA genes and/or pseudogenes (Supplementary Fig. 1 and Supplementary Table 6). These are physically separate from the genes described in the preceding section and are not included in the total gene count, owing to the difficulty in discriminating between genes and pseudogenes for these ncRNA predictions. Using tRNAscan-SE[16], we predicted only two transfer RNA genes on the X chromosome (Supplementary Table 6), out of the several hundred predicted in the human genome[7]. Thirteen microRNAs from the microRNA registry[17] have also been mapped onto the sequence (Supplementary Table 7).

The most prominent of the ncRNA genes on the X chromosome is *XIST* (X (inactive)-specific transcript)[18], which is critical for XCI. The *XIST* locus spans 32,103 bp in Xq13, and its untranslated transcript coats and transcriptionally silences one X chromosome in *cis*. The RefSeq[11] transcript of *XIST* is an RNA of 19,275 bases, which includes the largest exon on the chromosome (exon 1: 11,372 bp). There is also evidence for shorter *XIST* transcripts generated by alternative splicing, particularly in the 3′ region of the gene[19]. In the mouse, *Tsix* is antisense to *Xist*[20], and its transcript (or the process of its transcription) is believed to repress the accumulation of *Xist* RNA. There is evidence for transcription antisense to *XIST* in human[21,22], but we have been unable to annotate the human *TSIX* gene as there are no corresponding expressed sequences in the public databases, and because there is a lack of primary sequence conservation between the human and mouse regions. In the human sequence, two other ncRNA genes are annotated in the 400 kb region distal to *XIST*, which are orthologues of the mouse genes described previously as *Jpx* and *Ftx* (ref. 23). In the mouse, *Xist*, *Jpx* and *Ftx* are located within a smaller area of approximately 200 kb[23].

The Cancer-testis Antigen Genes

On assessing the predicted proteome of the X chromosome for Pfam[24] domains, our most prominent finding was the presence of the MAGE domain (IPR002190) in 32 genes (Supplementary Table 8). In comparison, only four other MAGE genes are reported in the rest of the genome: *MAGEF1* on chromosome 3, and *MAGEL2*, *NDN* and *NDNL2* on chromosome 15. The *MAGE* gene products are members of the cancer-testis (CT) antigen group, which are characterized by their expression in a number of cancer types, while their

重叠。其余 100 个 ECR 最可能是未注释的外显子，尽管有一些可能是高度保守的控制元件或结构元件。从这些数据中我们得出结论：我们至少已经注释了 X 染色体 97.8% 的编码蛋白质的外显子（[4,373/(4,373+100)]×100）。

非编码 RNA 基因

上文所述基因集合只有存在互补 DNA 表达或表达序列标签（EST）表达的支持性证据时才包含非编码 RNA（ncRNA）基因。利用互补性方法，我们用 Rfam[15] 数据库的结构 RNA 比对分析了 X 染色体序列，并预测了 173 个 ncRNA 基因和（或）假基因（补充图 1 和补充表 6）。由于这些 ncRNA 预测难以区分基因和假基因，因此它们与前面章节所描述的基因有实质区别，不包括在基因总数中。使用 tRNAscan-SE[16]，我们预测 X 染色体上只有两个转移 RNA 基因（补充表 6），而在人类基因组中预测有几百个 [7]。13 个来自微 RNA 注册表的微 RNA[17] 也绘制在了序列中（补充表 7）。

X 染色体上最明显的 ncRNA 基因是 *XIST*（X（失活）特异转录本）[18]，它对 X 染色体失活至关重要。*XIST* 基因座在 Xq13 中跨越 32,103 bp，其未翻译的转录本覆盖并转录沉默一条 X 染色体。*XIST* 的 RefSeq[11] 转录本是一个包含 19,275 个碱基的 RNA，它包括此染色体上最大的外显子（外显子 1：11,372 bp）。还有证据表明较短的 *XIST* 转录本通过可变剪接产生，特别是在基因 3′ 区 [19]。在小鼠中，*Tsix* 与 *Xist*[20] 是反义的，其转录本（或转录过程）被认为抑制 *Xist* RNA 的积累。有证据证明转录本与人类 *XIST* 是反义的 [21,22]，由于在公共数据库中没有相应的表达序列，且人类和小鼠序列区域缺乏基本的保守性，因此我们无法对人类 *TSIX* 基因进行注释。在人类序列中，其他两个注释的 ncRNA 基因在 *XIST* 远端 400 kb 区域，它们是之前描述的小鼠 *Jpx* 和 *Ftx* 基因的直系同源基因（参考文献 23）。在小鼠中，*Xist*、*Jpx* 和 *Ftx* 都位于一个大约 200 kb 的小区域内 [23]。

癌/睾丸抗原基因

在评估预测 X 染色体蛋白质组的 Pfam[24] 结构域时，我们最突出的发现是在 32 个基因中存在 MAGE 抗原结构域（IPR002190）（补充表 8）。相比之下，在剩余基因组中只报道了另外四个 MAGE 基因：3 号染色体上的 *MAGEF1* 和 15 号染色体上的 *MAGEL2*、*NDN* 和 *NDNL2*。*MAGE* 基因产物是癌/睾丸（CT）抗原组的成员，其特点是在大量癌症类型中表达，而它们在正常组织中的表达仅在或主要是在睾丸中。这

expression in normal tissues is solely or predominantly in testis. This expression profile has led to the suggestion that the CT antigens are potential targets for tumour immunotherapy. A recent report listed 84 CT antigen genes for the human genome[25]. The X chromosome gene set we describe above contains 99 CT antigen genes and includes novel members of the *MAGE*, *GAGE*, *SSX*, *LAGE*, *CSAGE* and *NXF* families (Supplementary Table 9). Assessment of the most recent RefSeq[11] information shows that this set does not include two known *MAGE* genes (*MAGEA5* and *MAGEA7*) and seven *GAGE* genes (*GAGE3–7*, *7B* and *8*), which are expected to lie in gaps 14 and 7, respectively (Supplementary Table 2). Furthermore, gaps 6 and 9 are also within regions of CT antigen gene duplication. Therefore, we predict that approximately 10% of the genes on the X chromosome are of the CT antigen type.

Conclusive data on the normal functions of the CT antigens, or their involvement in disease conditions, are very limited. However, the remarkable enrichment for CT antigen genes on the X chromosome relative to the rest of the genome might be indicative of a male advantage associated with these genes. Recessive alleles that are beneficial to males are expected to become fixed more rapidly on the X chromosome than on an autosome[26]. If these alleles are detrimental to females, their expression could become restricted to male tissues as they rise to fixation. Both the concentration of the CT antigen genes on the X chromosome and their expression profiles are consistent with this model of male benefit. The CT antigen genes on the X chromosome are also notable for the expansion of various gene families by duplication. This degree of duplication is perhaps an indication of selection in males for increased copy number. In this context, it is of interest that the *MAGE* family has independently expanded on the X chromosome in both the human and mouse lineages[27].

Repetitive Sequences

Interspersed repeats account for 56% of the euchromatic X chromosome sequence, compared with a genome average of 45% (Supplementary Table 10). Within this, the *Alu* family of short interspersed nuclear elements (SINEs) is below average, in keeping with the gene-poor nature of the chromosome. Conversely, long terminal repeat (LTR) retroposon coverage is above average; but the most remarkable enrichment is for long interspersed nuclear elements (LINEs) of the L1 family, which account for 29% of the X chromosome sequence compared to a genome average of only 17%. The possible significance of this enrichment for XCI is discussed later.

Applying the criterion of at least 90% sequence identity over at least 5 kb (ref. 28), we estimate that intrachromosomal segmental duplications account for 2.59% of the X chromosome (Supplementary Table 11 and Supplementary Fig. 2). In contrast, interchromosomal segmental duplications indicated by sequence matches to the autosomes account for a very small fraction (0.24%) of the X chromosome (Supplementary Table 12). Six gaps in the X chromosome map are either flanked by or contained within

种基因表达谱表明 CT 抗原是肿瘤免疫治疗的潜在靶标。最近的一份报告列出了人类基因组中 84 个 CT 抗原基因 [25]。上述 X 染色体基因集包含 99 个 CT 抗原基因，包括 *MAGE*、*GAGE*、*SSX*、*LAGE*、*CSAGE* 和 *NXF* 家族的新成员（补充表 9）。对最新 RefSeq[11] 信息的评估表明，这个集合不包括两个已知 *MAGE* 基因（*MAGEA5* 和 *MAGEA7*）和 7 个 *GAGE* 基因（*GAGE3 ~ 7，7B* 和 *8*），预计分别位于缺口 14 和 7（补充表 2）。此外，缺口 6 和 9 也在 CT 抗原基因复制区域内。因此，我们预测，X 染色体上大约 10% 的基因是 CT 抗原类型。

关于 CT 抗原的正常功能，或它们在疾病中的作用的结论性数据非常有限。然而，相比于基因组的其他部分，X 染色体上的 CT 抗原基因显著富集可能表明男性优势与这些基因相关。预计对男性有益的隐性等位基因在 X 染色体上比在常染色体上固定得更快 [26]。如果这些等位基因对女性有害，当它们上升到固定状态时表达可能会局限于男性组织。CT 抗原基因在 X 染色体上的浓度和它们的基因表达谱都符合男性受益模式。X 染色体上的 CT 抗原基因也通过复制显著扩大了各种基因家族。复制的程度可能是男性选择增加拷贝数量的标志。在此背景下，有意思的是，在人类和小鼠的谱系中，*MAGE* 家族都独立地扩展到了 X 染色体上 [27]。

重复序列

散在重复序列占 X 染色体常染色质序列的 56%，而基因组的平均水平为 45%（补充表 10）。在这个范围内，*Alu* 家族短散在重复序列（SINE）低于平均水平，这与染色体的基因贫乏性质一致。相反，长末端重复序列（LTR）逆转座子覆盖率高于平均水平；L1 家族长散在重复序列（LINE）很多，占 X 染色体序列的 29%，而基因组平均水平只有 17%。稍后将讨论富含 XCI 可能的意义。

应用在至少 5 kb 上至少 90% 以上序列同源这一标准（参考文献 28），我们估计，染色体内片段性重复占 X 染色体的 2.59%（补充表 11 和补充图 2）。与此相反，染色体间片段重复的序列与常染色体的匹配只占 X 染色体很小一部分（0.24%）（补充表 12）。X 染色体图上六个缺口或在染色体内重复片段的两侧或包含在其中（见补充表

intrachromosomally-duplicated segments (gaps 2, 3, 6, 7, 9 and 14 in Supplementary Table 2), which might produce instability of clones or otherwise confound mapping progress. The intrachromosomal duplicates are striking in their proximity. Apart from the two segments containing *SSX* gene copies, which are separated by 4.5 Mb, only six of 229 matches are separated by more than 1 Mb. Among these duplications are well-described cases that are associated with genomic disorders[29]. In Xp22.32, deletions of the steroid sulphatase (*STS*) gene, causing X-linked ichthyosis (Online Mendelian Inheritance in Man (OMIM)[2] entry number 308100), result from recombination between flanking duplications that contain copies of the *VCX* gene. Also, some instances of Hunter syndrome (OMIM 309900), red-green colour blindness (OMIM 303800), Emery-Dreifuss muscular dystrophy (OMIM 310300), incontinentia pigmenti (OMIM 308300) and haemophilia A (OMIM 306700) result from rearrangements involving duplicated sequences in Xq28. In haemophilia A, mutations are frequently the result of inversions between a sequence in intron 22 of the *F8* gene and one of two more distally located copies. A novel finding from our analysis of the X chromosome reference sequence is that the two distal copies are in opposite orientations. Therefore, a large deletion involving *F8* and several more distal genes could be an alternative to the inversion rearrangement. A deletion consistent with this prediction has been reported in a family in which carrier females are affected by a high spontaneous-abortion rate in pregnancy[30].

The X Chromosome Centromere

The X chromosome sequence extends from both arms into centromeric, higher-order repeat sequences, which are known to be associated functionally with the X centromere[31-33]. The most proximal 494 kb and 360 kb of the Xp and Xq sequences, respectively, consist of extensive regions of satellite DNA, adjacent to euchromatin of the chromosome arms that is exceptionally high in L1 content (Fig. 2). The satellite region on Xp contains small amounts of other satellite families[31], whereas that on Xq consists entirely of alpha satellite. Similar to all other human chromosome arms that have been examined[33,34], these transition regions consist of monomeric alpha satellite that is not associated with centromere function. Both the Xp and Xq contigs reported here, though, extend more proximally and reach into highly homogeneous, higher-order repeat alpha satellite (DXZ1). Critically, the Xp and Xq contig copies of the DXZ1 repeat are themselves 98–100% identical in sequence, and are oriented in the same direction along the chromosome (Fig. 2). On this basis, the two contigs reach the "end" of each chromosome arm and thus also reach the centromeric locus from either side. This represents a logical endpoint for efforts to complete the sequence of chromosome arms in the human genome, and the first demonstration of this endpoint is provided by the X chromosome sequence.

2 中的缺口 2、3、6、7、9 和 14），这可能会导致克隆的不稳定或混淆绘图过程。染色体内的重复惊人的接近。除了两个含有 *SSX* 基因拷贝的片段被 4.5 Mb 分开，229个匹配中只有 6 个匹配之间的距离大于 1 Mb。在这些重复中有与基因组无序相联系的并且充分描述的病例[29]。在 Xp22.32 中，类固醇硫酸酯酶（*STS*）基因缺失导致了 X 连锁鱼鳞病（在线人类孟德尔遗传数据库（OMIM）[2] 索引号 308100），这是由包含 *VCX* 基因拷贝的侧翼重复间的重组造成的。还有一些列子：亨特综合征（OMIM 309900），红绿色盲（OMIM 303800），埃德二氏肌营养不良症（OMIM 310300），色素失调症（OMIM 308300）和血友病 A（OMIM 306700）都是 Xq28 重复序列重排的结果。在血友病 A 中，突变通常是在 *F8* 基因内含子 22 中的序列和两个以上远端拷贝中的一个之间倒位的结果。从对 X 染色体参考序列的分析中我们有了一个新发现：这两个远端的拷贝方向相反。因此，涉及 *F8* 和多个远端基因的大片段缺失可能是反向重排的替代方法。符合这一预测的缺失已在一个妊娠期有高自然流产率的女性携带者家族中报道过[30]。

X 染色体着丝粒

X 染色体序列从两个臂向着丝粒延伸，分布了许多功能上与 X 着丝粒有联系的高度有序的重复序列[31-33]。Xp 序列近端的 494 kb 和 Xq 序列近端的 360 kb，由广泛的卫星 DNA 区域组成，毗邻 L1 含量非常高的由常染色质组成的染色体臂（见图2）。Xp 上卫星区域包含少量其他卫星家族[31]，而 Xq 上的卫星区域包含全部的 α 卫星。与所有其他已检测的人类染色体臂相似[33,34]，这些过渡区域包括与着丝粒功能无关的单体 α 卫星。但这里报道的 Xp 和 Xq 重叠群以更接近的方式延伸并成为了高度均匀的、更高阶重复的 α 卫星（DXZ1）。更为重要的是，DXZ1 重复的 Xp 和 Xq 重叠序列本身序列一致性达 98% ~ 100%，并且沿染色体的方向相同（见图2）。在此基础上，这两个重叠群到达各自染色体臂的"末端"，从而也从两侧到达着丝粒基因座。这代表了努力完成人类基因组染色体臂序列的一个合乎逻辑的终点，而这个终点是由 X 染色体序列证实的。

Fig. 2. Xp and Xq pericentromeric contigs extend into the X-chromosome-specific higher-order alpha satellite, DXZ1. The pericentromeric region of the X chromosome is shown as a truncated ideogram. Self-self alignments of proximal sequences from each arm are illustrated by dotter plots below the ideogram. On each plot, the junction between the arm sequence and the arm-specific satellite region is marked by a red arrow, and the junction between the arm-specific satellite region and the X-chromosome-specific alpha satellite array (DXZ1) is marked with a blue arrow. Approximately 594 kb of sequence were analysed from Xp, including ~21 kb of DXZ1 sequence. The ~454 kb of sequence analysed from Xq included ~44 kb of DXZ1 sequence. In each case, ~100 kb of arm sequence were included. The highly repetitive structure of pericentromeric satellites is in stark contrast to the near absence of repetitive structure in the arm sequences, despite an unusually high density of LINE repeats in these regions. Gaps in the dark satellite regions occur where interspersed elements (LINEs, SINEs and LTRs) interrupt the satellite sequences. In the Array Sequences dotter plot, the most proximal ~21 kb of the Xp sequence is joined to the most proximal ~44 kb of the Xq sequence. The periodic nature of the centromeric, higher-order alpha satellite array is evident. Black horizontal lines on the plot reveal near identity of sequences spaced at ~2 kb intervals. This DXZ1 sample represents ~65 kb of the 3 ($\pm$0.4) Mb alpha satellite array. The regions outlined in blue are self-self alignments ("Xp DXZ1" and "Xq DXZ1"), and the remaining rectangular region of the plot is an alignment of Xp versus Xq DXZ1, which reveals the close relationship between DXZ1 sequences from each arm.

Single-nucleotide Polymorphisms

A total of 153,146 candidate single-nucleotide polymorphisms (SNPs) have been mapped onto the X chromosome sequence and are displayed in the VEGA database. These include 901 SNPs that result in non-synonymous changes in protein-coding regions, and are therefore candidate functional protein variants. The heterozygosity level on the X chromosome is known to be well below that of the autosomes, and this difference can be explained partly or entirely by population genetic factors[35]. Included in the mapped

图 2. Xp 和 Xq 着丝粒周边重叠群延伸到 X 染色体特异高阶 α 卫星 DXZ1。X 染色体着丝粒周边区域显示为一个截断表意图。每个臂近端序列自身比对通过表意图下方的带点小块说明。每个小块上，臂序列和臂特异卫星区域间的连接点用红色箭头标记，臂特异卫星区域和 X 染色体特异 α 卫星阵列（DXZ1）的连接点用蓝色箭头标记。从 Xp 中分析了大约 594 kb 的序列，其中包括 ~21 kb 的 DXZ1 序列。从 Xq 中分析了 ~454 kb 的序列，包括 ~44 kb 的 DXZ1 序列。在每一种情况下，都包括 ~100 kb 的臂序列。着丝粒周边卫星序列的高度重复结构与臂序列中几乎没有重复结构形成鲜明对照，尽管这些区域 LINE 重复的密度非常高。黑色卫星区域的缺口发生在散在元件（LINE、SINE 和 LTR）中断卫星序列的地方。在阵列的序列带点小块中，Xp 序列最近端 ~21 kb 与 Xq 序列最近端 ~44 kb 相连接。着丝粒恒定，高阶 α 卫星阵列的周期性是显而易见的。小块上的黑色水平线显示间隔为 ~2 kb 的序列几乎是一致的。这个 DXZ1 样本代表 3(±0.4) Mb 阿尔法卫星阵列的 ~65 kb。蓝色轮廓区域是自身比对（"Xp DXZ1" 和 "Xq DXZ1"），小块的其余矩形区域是 Xp 与 Xq 的 DXZ1 的比对，它揭示了每个臂的 DXZ1 序列间密切的关系。

单核苷酸多态性

共有 153,146 个候选单核苷酸多态性（SNP）绘制到 X 染色体序列并显示在 VEGA 数据库中。其中包括导致蛋白质编码区域非同义改变的 901 个 SNP，因此，是候选功能蛋白变异。X 染色体上的杂合水平远低于常染色体，这种差异可以部分或者全部由群体遗传因素解释[35]。被绘制到图谱里的 62,334 个 SNP 是通过将流式

SNPs are 62,334 that were identified by alignment of flow-sorted X chromosome shotgun sequence reads to the X chromosome reference sequence. Using comparable sequence data for chromosome 20, we calculated that the heterozygosity level on the X chromosome is approximately 57% of that observed for the autosome.

Evolution of the Human X Chromosome

Males of the three mammalian groups—Eutheria ("placental" mammals), Metatheria (marsupials) and Prototheria (egg-laying mammals)—have X and Y sex chromosomes. Ohno proposed in 1967 that the mammalian sex chromosomes evolved from an autosome pair following their recruitment into a chromosomal system for sex determination[1]. A barrier to recombination developed between these "proto" sex chromosomes, isolating the sex-determining regions and eventually spreading throughout the two homologues. In the absence of recombination, the accumulation of mutation events subsequently led to the degeneration of the Y chromosome. The sex chromosomes of birds are not homologous to those of the mammals. The sex chromosome system of birds evolved independently during the last 300 Myr, giving rise to homogametic (ZZ) male birds and heterogametic (ZW) female birds, in contrast to the mammalian system of XY males and XX females.

The autosomal origin of the mammalian sex chromosomes is vividly illustrated by alignment of the human X and chicken whole genome sequences (Fig. 3a). Orthologues of some human X chromosome genes were previously mapped to chicken chromosomes 1q13-q21 and 4p11-p14 (ref. 36). Using genomic sequence alignment, we identified approximately 30 regions of homology that together cover most of human Xq and are confined to a single section of approximately 20 Mb at the end of chicken chromosome 4p (Fig. 3a). In contrast, most of the short arm (Xp11.3–pter), including the pseudoautosomal region PAR1, matches a single block of chicken chromosome 1q. No clear picture emerges regarding the origin of the remainder of the short arm (Xcen–p11.3). We were unable to detect large regions of conserved synteny using sequence alignment, and genes from this region have orthologues on several chicken autosomes, including chromosomes 12, 1 and 4 (ref. 37). This region is also characterized by the expansion of several families of CT antigen genes (Fig. 1), which have no readily detectable orthologues in chicken. The present analysis supports the notion of a mammalian "X-conserved region" (XCR)[38], which includes the long arm and is descended from the proto-X chromosome. It also supports a separate, large addition ("X-added region" or XAR[38]) to the established X chromosome by translocation from a second autosome, which occurred in the eutherian mammals before their radiation (~105 Myr ago). In contrast to earlier hypotheses, however, it appears that much of the proximal short arm (Xcen–p11.3) should no longer be considered part of an XCR.

X 染色体鸟枪序列数据与 X 染色体参考序列比对后确定的。比较 20 号染色体的序列数据后，我们计算出 X 染色体的杂合水平大约是常染色体的 57%。

人类 X 染色体的进化

三个哺乳动物群体——真兽次亚纲（有"胎盘"的哺乳动物），后兽次亚纲（有袋的哺乳动物）和原兽亚纲（产卵哺乳动物），它们的雄性体内含有 X 和 Y 性染色体。1967 年大野提出哺乳动物性染色体是从一对常染色体进化而来的，它们进入染色体系统之后用来决定性别[1]。这些"原始"性染色体之间形成了重组障碍，分离出决定性别的区域并最终在这两个同源物中传播。如果没有重组，随后的基因突变事件积累导致 Y 染色体退化。鸟的性染色体与哺乳动物的性染色体没有同源性。鸟类性染色体在过去的 3 亿年独立进化，从而形成同型配子(ZZ)的雄鸟和异型配子(ZW)的雌鸟，与哺乳动物系统的 XY 雄性和 XX 雌性相反。

人类 X 染色体和鸡全基因组序列的比对，生动地说明哺乳动物性染色体起源于常染色体（图 3a）。人类的一些 X 染色体基因直系同源物以前被绘制到鸡染色体 1q13-q21 和 4p11-p14 中（参考文献 36）。利用基因组序列比对，我们确定了大约 30 个覆盖了人类 Xq 大部分的同源区域，这些区域都限制在鸡染色体 4p 末端大约 20 Mb 的单一区域内（图 3a）。相比之下，短臂(Xp11.3-pter)的大部分区域，包括假常染色体区域 PARl，与鸡染色体 1q 的单一区块相匹配。关于短臂(Xcen-p11.3)剩余部分的起源没有清楚的图片展示。我们用序列比对无法检测到大的同线性保守区域，并且这些区域的基因在鸡的一些常染色体上有直系同源物，这些常染色体包括 12 号、1 号和 4 号染色体（参考文献 37）。这一区域还表现出若干 CT 抗原基因家族（图 1）扩展的特点，而这在鸡中并没有检测到同源物。这个分析支持哺乳动物"X 保守区"(XCR)的概念[38]，X 保守区包括长臂，它是从原始 X 染色体留下来的。它还支持从第二个常染色体易位到已有的 X 染色体上从而形成的独立的、大型增加片段（"X 补充区域"或 XAR[38]）的概念，这发生在真兽类哺乳动物适应辐射前（~ 1 亿 500 万年前）。但是，与早期假设相反，好像大部分的近端短臂(Xcen-p11.3)不应该被认为是 XCR 的一部分。

Fig. 3. Homologies between the human X chromosome and chicken autosomes. **a**, Plot of BLASTZ sequence alignments between the X chromosome and chicken chromosomes 1 (red) and 4 (blue). Grey bar centred at approximately 60 Mb shows the position of the X centromere. Only the relevant section of each chicken chromosome is shown (see Mb scale at left for chromosome 1 and at right for chromosome 4). A schematic interpretation of the homologies shows the XAR and XCR as red and blue bars, respectively (see Fig. 1). Homologies at the ends of the XAR are indicated with arrows and are expanded in **b**. **b**, (Top) Genes at the ends of the human XAR. Genes from distal Xp (magenta arrow in **a**) are in magenta and genes from Xp11.3 (black arrow in **a**) are shown in black. (Bottom) Arrangement of the orthologous genes on chicken chromosome 1. A hypothetical ring chromosome, with the equivalent gene order to that observed in the chicken, is indicated by the curved, dotted red line. Recombination between one end of the established X chromosome and the ring chromosome at the arrowed position could, in a single step, have added the XAR and created the gene order observed on the human X chromosome.

The precise location of genes that demarcate the XAR suggests a possible mechanism for the addition. The annotated genes at the extreme ends of the 47 Mb XAR are *PLCXD1* (cU136G2.1 in Supplementary Fig. 1) near Xpter, and *RGN* in Xp11.3. We also found an unprocessed *RGN* pseudogene (*RGN2P*) at Xpter, distal to *PLCXD1*. The orthologues for these three loci are adjacent on chicken chromosome 1, in the order (tel)–*RGN*– *RGN2*–*PLCXD1*–(cen) (Fig. 3b). The generation of these two different gene orders from a common ancestral sequence would require a minimum of two rearrangements as well as the translocation that added the XAR. A more parsimonious model suggested by these data, however, is that the XAR was acquired by recombination between the X chromosome and a ring chromosome in which the ancestral *PLCXD1*, *RGN* and *RGN2* sequences were neighbours (Fig. 3b).

In order to examine more recent patterns of evolution, we compared the human X chromosome with other mammalian sequences. We saw nine major blocks of sequence homology between

498

图 3. 人类 X 染色体和鸡常染色体的同源性。**a**，X 染色体和鸡 1 号（红色）和 4 号（蓝色）染色体间 BLASTZ 序列比对。集中在约 60 Mb 的灰色条块显示的是 X 染色体着丝粒的位置。鸡的每条染色体只显示有关的片段（1 号染色体看左边的 Mb 比例尺，4 号染色体看右边的 Mb 比例尺）。一个解释同源性的示意图分别显示了红色条 XAR 和蓝色条 XCR（见图 1）。XAR 末端的同源性用箭头指示，并在 **b** 中扩大显示。**b**，（上）人 XAR 末端的基因。Xp 远端的基因（**a** 中品红色箭头）是品红色，Xp11.3 的基因（**a** 中黑色箭头）显示为黑色。（下）鸡的 1 号染色体上直系同源基因的排列。由弯曲的红色虚线表示的一个假设的环状染色体，其基因顺序与在鸡染色体中观察到的一致。已建立的 X 染色体一端与箭头所指位置的环状染色体之间的重组可以一步完成 XAR 的添加，重组还能创建在人类 X 染色体上观察到的基因顺序。

　　划分 XAR 的基因的确切位置表明序列增加的可能机制。在 47 Mb XAR 末端的注释基因是接近 Xpter 的 *PLCXD1*（cU136G2.1 见补充图 1）以及在 Xp11.3 中的 *RGN*。我们还在 *PLCXD1* 远端的 Xpter 上发现一个未处理的 *RGN* 假基因（*RGN2P*）。这三个基因座的直系同源物在鸡的 1 号染色体上相邻，顺序为（端粒）–*RGN*–*RGN2*–*PLCXD1*–（着丝粒）（图 3b）。从一个共同祖先的序列产生这两个不同的基因顺序最少需要两个重排，以及增加 XAR 的易位。然而，这些数据暗示了一个更为简洁的模型，即 XAR 是通过 X 染色体与祖先 *PLCXD1*、*RGN* 和 *RGN2* 序列相邻的环状染色体重组获得的（图 3b）。

　　为了研究更近期的进化模式，我们将人类 X 染色体与其他哺乳动物序列进行了比对。我们发现人类和小鼠 X 染色体之间有 9 个主要的序列同源性区块，人类与

human and mouse X chromosomes, and eleven between human and rat (Fig. 4). The homology blocks occupy almost the entirety of each X chromosome, confirming the remarkable degree of conserved synteny of this chromosome within the eutherian mammalian lineage. This is consistent with Ohno's law, which predicts that the establishment of a dosage compensation mechanism had a stabilizing effect on the gene content of the mammalian X chromosome[1]. On the long arm, just two blocks of homology account for the entire alignment of the human and corresponding mouse sequences, but the mouse homologous regions are punctuated with three additional segments, each containing long and very similar repeats (arrowed in Fig. 4). Alignment of human Xq with the rat sequence reveals four discrete homology blocks; the greater fragmentation compared with the mouse alignment would be explained by a minimum of two rearrangements, one in each of the two mouse–human homology blocks, specifically on the rat lineage. The mouse-specific repeat segments are not detected in the current version of the rat genome sequence. On the short arm of the human X chromosome, seven major blocks of homology with each rodent account for most of the human sequence (Fig. 4). Using the dog as an outgroup, we established that the human and dog X chromosome sequences are essentially collinear (K. Lindblad-Toh, personal communication). Therefore, all of the rearrangements indicated in Fig. 4 occurred in the rodent lineage, and the human X chromosome appears to have been remarkably stable in its organization since the radiation of eutherian mammals. This is consistent with the recent prediction, derived from a comparison of human, rodent and chicken chromosomes, that the human X chromosome is identical to the putative ancestral (eutherian) mammalian X chromosome[39].

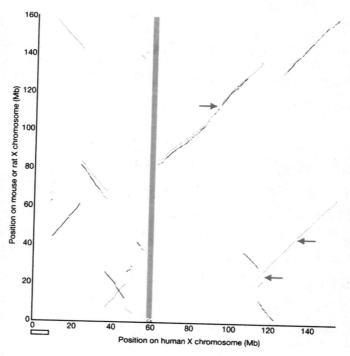

Fig. 4. Conservation of the X chromosome in eutherian mammals. Plot of BLASTZ sequence alignments between the human X chromosome and the mouse (red) and rat (blue) X chromosomes. The rodent

大鼠之间有 11 个（图 4）。这些同源区块几乎占据整个 X 染色体，证实了这条染色体在真兽类哺乳动物谱系内具有显著的保守同线性。这与大野的定律一致，该定律预测剂量补偿机制的建立对哺乳动物 X 染色体的基因含量有稳定作用[1]。在染色体长臂上，人类和小鼠相应序列整体比对后只有两个同源性区块，但小鼠同源区域被另外三个额外的片段隔开，每个片段包含长的、非常相似的重复序列（图 4 中箭头所示）。人类 Xq 与大鼠序列比对揭示四个分离的同源区块；与小鼠比对相比，将通过至少两个重排来解释更大的片段化，即在两个鼠–人同源性区块中分别有一个重排，特别是在大鼠谱系中。小鼠特异性重复片段在目前的大鼠基因组序列中未检测到。人类 X 染色体短臂上与每个啮齿动物同源的 7 个主要区块占了人类序列的大部分（图 4）。使用狗作为外类群，我们确定人和狗 X 染色体的 DNA 序列本质上是共线性的（林德布拉德–托，个人交流）。因此，图 4 所显示的所有重排发生在啮齿动物谱系中，从真兽类哺乳动物适应辐射以来，人类 X 染色体在其系统内似乎非常稳定。这与最近比较人类、啮齿动物和鸡染色体得出的预测一致，即人类 X 染色体与假定哺乳动物祖先（真兽类）X 染色体一致[39]。

图 4. 在真兽类哺乳动物中 X 染色体的保守性。人类 X 染色体与小鼠（红色）和大鼠（蓝色）X 染色体之间 BLASTZ 序列比对图。啮齿类动物的染色体着丝粒是向下的。箭头指示的区域在小鼠序列中是长度

chromosomes are oriented with their centromeres pointing downwards. Regions indicated with arrows are long, highly similar repeats in the mouse sequence that are absent from the human and rat sequences. These repeats were apparently collapsed in an earlier analysed version of the mouse sequence, which also had a large inversion with respect to the mouse assembly used here (NCBI32)[66]. The NCBI32 assembly has a gap from 0–3 Mb, which explains the absence of homology to the human X sequence in this part of the plot. The open horizontal bar shows the terminal section of human Xp, which is not conserved on the rodent X chromosomes.

The most notable difference we found between the human and rodent X chromosomes is the existence of 9 Mb of sequence at the tip of the human short arm (including human PAR1) that is apparently missing from the rodent X chromosomes (Fig. 4). There are 34 known and novel protein-coding genes in this segment of the human X chromosome (Supplementary Fig. 1), enabling us to investigate how this difference arose. A comprehensive database search of the rodent genome sequences revealed convincing orthologues for only thirteen of these genes in rat and five in mouse. Most of the rat orthologues are located in two groups on chromosome 12, and the only genes for which X-linked orthologues could be found in both rodents were *PRKX* and *STS*. In contrast, we found 24 of these 34 genes on chicken chromosome 1, and the order of these genes is perfectly conserved between the two genomes. Therefore, we conclude that this large terminal segment was present in the XAR and was subsequently removed from the X chromosome in a common murid ancestor of mouse and rat. The relative paucity of rodent ECRs in this segment of the X chromosome sequence (Supplementary Fig. 1) suggests that much of the region may be absent altogether from the genomes of *Mus musculus* and *Rattus norvegicus*.

Comparison of the Human X and Y Chromosomes

The evolutionary process has eradicated most traces of the ancestral relationship between the human X and Y chromosomes. At the cytogenetic level, the Y chromosome has a large and variably sized heterochromatic block and is considerably smaller than the X chromosome, and the euchromatic part of the X chromosome is six times longer than that of Y. Few genes on human chromosome X have an active counterpart on the Y chromosome, and the majority of these are contained in regions where XY homology is of relatively recent origin.

A detailed comparison of the human X and Y chromosome sequences reveals the extent of Y chromosome decay in non-recombining regions. All of the large homologous blocks visible in Fig. 5 (and represented schematically in Fig. 6) are descended from material that was added to the established sex chromosomes. The tip of the short arm of the X and Y chromosomes comprises the 2.7 Mb pseudoautosomal region PAR1. Homology between the X and Y chromosomes in PAR1 is maintained by an obligatory recombination in male meiosis; gene loci in this region are present in two copies in both males and females and are not subject to dosage compensation by XCI. At the tip of the long arm of X and Y is a second pseudoautosomal region, the 330 kb PAR2, which was created by duplication

很长且高度相似的重复序列，在人类和大鼠序列中缺失。这些重复序列在较早分析版本的小鼠序列中显然是塌陷的，该版本的小鼠序列与此处使用的小鼠序列（NCBI32）[66] 相比也有较大的不同。NCBI32 序列有一个 0～3 Mb 的缺口，这就解释了在图的这一部分中缺少与人类 X 序列的同源性。空心的横杠显示人类 Xp 末端部分，它在啮齿动物 X 染色体上并不保守。

我们在人类和啮齿动物的 X 染色体间发现的最显著的差异是人类染色体短臂末端（包括人类 PAR1）存在的 9 Mb 序列在啮齿动物 X 染色体中明显缺失（图 4）。在人类 X 染色体的这一段序列中，有 34 个已知的、新的蛋白编码基因（补充图 1），使我们能够研究这种差异是如何产生的。对啮齿动物基因组序列数据库进行全面搜索显示，大鼠中只有 13 个基因有高可信度直系同源物，而小鼠只有 5 个。大多数大鼠直系同源物位于 12 号染色体的两个组上，在两种啮齿动物中发现的 X 连锁同源基因只有 PRKX 和 STS。相比之下，我们在鸡的 1 号染色体上发现了这 34 个基因中的 24 个，并且这些基因的顺序在两个基因组间非常保守。因此，我们得出这样的结论：这个大型末端序列曾出现在 XAR 中，后来从小鼠和大鼠共同的鼠科祖先的 X 染色体中被移除。啮齿动物 ECR 在 X 染色体序列的这一段相对缺失（补充图 1）表明，该区域的大部分序列可能在小家鼠和褐家鼠的基因组中共同缺失。

比较人类 X 和 Y 染色体

进化过程已消除人类 X 染色体和 Y 染色体之间祖先关系的大部分痕迹。在细胞遗传学水平上，Y 染色体有一个大的大小可变的异染色质块，但这个异染色质块比 X 染色体小得多，X 染色体常染色质部分是 Y 的 6 倍。人类 X 染色体上很少有基因在 Y 染色体上有活跃的对应基因，其中大多数包含在 XY 同源性起源较晚的区域。

对人类 X 染色体和 Y 染色体序列的详细比较揭示了 Y 染色体在非重组区域衰减的程度。在图 5 中可看到的所有大型同源区块（并在图 6 中示意出）都来自于增加到既定的性染色体的物质。X 染色体和 Y 染色体短臂末端包含 2.7 Mb 的假常染色体区域 PAR1。PAR1 中的 X 染色体和 Y 染色体之间的同源性是通过雄性减数分裂中必要的重组来维持的；这个区域的基因座在男性和女性中都有两个拷贝，不受 XCI 的剂量补偿影响。在 X 染色体和 Y 染色体长臂末端是第二个假常染色体区域，即 330 kb 的 PAR2，它是自人类和黑猩猩谱系分化以来，通过复制从 X 到 Y 的物质

of material from X to Y since the divergence of human and chimpanzee lineages[40]. Some genes in PAR2 are subject to XCI, presumably reflecting their status on the X chromosome before the duplication event. Outside the PARs, homologies between the X and Y chromosomes are in non-recombining regions, predominantly in other parts of the XAR, together with a large "X-transposed region" (XTR)[41] in Xq21.3 and Yp11.2–p11.3 (see below). It is thought that the XAR originally formed a large pseudoautosomal region with an equivalent YAR, which is now largely eroded. At a gross level, the homology between the XAR and YAR is continuous for 6 Mb proximal to the pseudoautosomal boundary on the X (PABX), but is considerably more fragmented on the Y chromosome (Figs 5b and 6). Beyond this, the remaining 38.5 Mb of the XAR detects few other remnants of the YAR. Homologies are mostly in small islands around genes with functional orthologues on both sex chromosomes (for example, *AMELX/AMELY*, *ZFX/ZFY*, see Table 1).

Fig. 5. Limited homology between the human sex chromosomes illustrates the extent of Y chromosome erosion in non-recombining regions. **a**, BLASTN alignments (length ⩾ 80 bp, sequence identity ⩾ 70%) between the finished sequences of the X and Y chromosomes. The centromere positions are represented by grey bars. The analysed Y chromosome sequence ends at the large, heterochromatic segment on Yq, which is indicated by the black bar on the truncated Y chromosome ideogram. **b**, Major blocks of homology remaining between the XAR and the YAR. Expansion of the BLASTN plot from 0–12 Mb on the X chromosome and 0–20 Mb on the Y chromosome. On the X chromosome, the major homologies lie in the terminal 8.5 Mb of Xp: PAR1 (magenta line) and numbered blocks 1–10. Lesser homologies 11 and 12 contain the *TBL1X/TBL1Y* and *AMELX/AMELY* genes, respectively. **c**, The XTR region in detail (88–93 Mb on X and 2.8–6.8 Mb on Y). Black arrows show large segments deleted from the Y chromosome

产生的[40]。PAR2 中有些基因受 XCI 影响，这很可能反映了它们在复制事件之前在 X 染色体上的状态。PAR 以外，X 染色体和 Y 染色体之间的同源性在非重组区域，主要位于 XAR 的其他区域，以及在 Xq21.3 和 Yp11.2–p11.3 中的大型"X 转置区"（XTR）[41]（见下文）。我们认为，XAR 最初形成与 YAR 等同的大型假常染色体区域，现在 YAR 在很大程度上消退了。总的来说，XAR 和 YAR 之间的同源性有 X 假常染色体边界近端（PABX）的连续 6 Mb，但在 Y 染色体上是相当多的分散片段（图 5b 和 6）。除此之外，XAR 其余的 38.5 Mb 检测到其他几个残余的 YAR。同源性大多在两条性染色体上有功能性直系同源物的基因周围（例如，*AMELX*/*AMELY*、*ZFX*/*ZFY*，见表 1）。

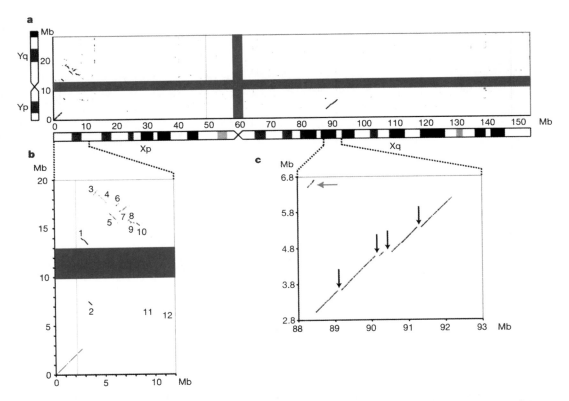

图 5. 人类性染色体之间有限的同源性说明 Y 染色体在非重组区域消退的程度。**a**，X 染色体和 Y 染色体完成的序列之间 BLASTN 比对（长度 ≥ 80 bp，序列一致性 ≥ 70%）。灰色条框指示着丝粒的位置。所分析的 Y 染色体序列末端在 Yq 上大的异染色质片段处，通过图上截断 Y 染色体的黑色条块表示。**b**，XAR 和 YAR 之间主要同源性区块。X 染色体上从 0 ~ 12 Mb，Y 染色体从 0 ~ 20 Mb 的 BLASTN 扩展图。在 X 染色体上，主要的同源性位于 8.5 Mb 的 Xp 末端：PAR1（品红色线）和编号区块 1 ~ 10。较小的同源性片段 11 和 12 分别包含 *TBL1X*/*TBL1Y* 和 *AMELX*/*AMELY* 基因。**c**，XTR 区域详细信息（在 X 染色体上 88 ~ 93 Mb 和在 Y 染色体上 2.8 ~ 6.8 Mb）。黑色箭头显示从 XTR 的 Y 染色体拷贝中删除的大片段。品红色箭头表示通过 Y 染色体臂内倒位后从 XTR 剩余部分分离出的短片段。人类群体中

copy of the XTR. The magenta arrow indicates the short segment that is separated from the rest of the XTR by a paracentric inversion on the Y chromosome. An independent inversion polymorphism on Yp in human populations encompasses this small segment. The position and orientation of the segment shows that the Y chromosome reference sequence is of the less common, derived Y chromosome.

Fig. 6. Schematic representation of major homologies between the human sex chromosomes. The entire X and Y chromosomes are shown using the same scale on the left and right sides of the figure, respectively. The major heterochromatic region on Yq is indicated by the pale grey box proximal to PAR2. Expanded sections of X and Y are shown in the centre of the figure. Homologies coloured in the figure are either part of the XAR (PAR1 and blocks 1–12), or were duplicated from the X chromosome to the Y chromosome since the divergence of human and chimpanzee lineages (XTR and PAR2). The numbering of XAR-YAR blocks follows that in Fig. 5b. Blocks inverted on the Y chromosome relative to the X chromosome are assigned red, negative numbers.

Yp 上的一个独立的倒位多态现象包括这个小片段。这个片段的位置和方向表明，Y 染色体参考序列是不太常见的衍生 Y 染色体。

图 6. 人类性染色体之间主要的同源性示意图。整个 X 染色体和 Y 染色体分别以相同的比例显示在图左侧和右侧。Yq 上主要的异染色质区域用接近 PAR2 的浅灰色框指示。图中央显示了 X 和 Y 的展开部分。图中着色的同源物或者是 XAR 的一部分（PAR1 和 1～12 区块），或者是自人类和黑猩猩谱系分化以来（XTR 和 PAR2）从 X 染色体到 Y 染色体的物质所复制的。XAR-YAR 的编号按照图 5b 所示。Y 染色体相对 X 染色体反转的区块用红色负数标记。

507

Table 1. Homologous genes on the human X and Y chromosomes

Region	Distance from Xpter (Mb)	X gene*	Y gene	Distance from Ypter (Mb)†	XY homology block‡
Pseudoautosomal region PAR1 (XAR)	0.15	cU136G2.1 (*PLCXD1*)	cU136G2.1 (*PLCXD1*)	0.15	PAR1
	0.17	cU136G2.2 (*GTPBP6*)	cU136G2.2 (*GTPBP6*)	0.17	PAR1
	0.25	cM56G10.2§	cM56G10.2§	0.25	PAR1
	0.29	cM56G10.1 (*PPP2R3B*)	cM56G10.1 (*PPP2R3B*)	0.29	PAR1
	0.57	*SHOX*	*SHOX*	0.57	PAR1
	0.92	bA309M23.1§	bA309M23.1§	0.92	PAR1
	1.31	*CRLF2*	*CRLF2*	1.31	PAR1
	1.38	*CSF2RA*	*CSF2RA*	1.38	PAR1
	1.52	*IL3RA*	*IL3RA*	1.52	PAR1
	1.55	*SLC25A6*	*SLC25A6*	1.55	PAR1
	1.56	bA261P4.5§	bA261P4.5§	1.56	PAR1
	1.57	bA261P4.6 (*CXYorf2*)	bA261P4.6 (*CXYorf2*)	1.57	PAR1
	1.59	*ASMTL*	*ASMTL*	1.59	PAR1
	1.66	bA261P4.4 (*P2RY8*)	bA261P4.4 (*P2RY8*)	1.66	PAR1
	1.76	*DXYS155E* (*CXYorf3*)	*DXYS155E* (*CXYorf3*)	1.76	PAR1
	1.79	*ASMT*	*ASMT*	1.79	PAR1
	1.79	bB297E16.3§	bB297E16.3§	1.79	PAR1
	1.91	bB297E16.4§	bB297E16.4§	1.91	PAR1
	1.93	bB297E16.5§	bB297E16.5§	1.93	PAR1
	2.37	*DHRSX*	*DHRSX*	2.37	PAR1
	2.41	*ALTE* (*ZBED1*)	*ALTE* (*ZBED1*)	2.41	PAR1
	2.54	Em:AC097314.2§	Em:AC097314.2§	2.54	PAR1
	2.53	Em:AC097314.3§	Em:AC097314.3§	2.53	PAR1
	2.63	*CD99*	*CD99*	2.63	PAR1
X-added region (XAR)	3.57	*PRKX*	*PRKY*	7.23	2
	5.81	*NLGN4X*	*NLGN4Y*	15.23	5
	6.31	Em:AC108684.1 (*VCX3A*)	*VCY, VCY1B*	14.54, 14.6	6
	7.62	*VCX*	*VCY, VCY1B*	14.54, 14.6	9
	7.95	Em:AC097626.1 (*VCX2*)	*VCY, VCY1B*	14.54, 14.6	10
	8.24	Em:AC006062.2 (*VCX3B*)	*VCY, VCY1B*	14.54, 14.6	10
	9.37	*TBL1X*	*TBL1Y*	6.97	11
	11.07	*AMELX*	*AMELY*	6.78	12
	12.75	*TMSB4X*	*TMSB4Y*	14.25	

表 1. 人类 X 和 Y 染色体上的同源基因

区域	与 Xpter 的距离 (Mb)	X 基因 *	Y 基因	与 Ypter 的距离 (Mb)†	XY 同源性 区块 ‡
	0.15	cU136G2.1 (*PLCXD1*)	cU136G2.1 (*PLCXD1*)	0.15	PAR1
	0.17	cU136G2.2 (*GTPBP6*)	cU136G2.2 (*GTPBP6*)	0.17	PAR1
	0.25	cM56G10.2§	cM56G10.2§	0.25	PAR1
	0.29	cM56G10.1 (*PPP2R3B*)	cM56G10.1 (*PPP2R3B*)	0.29	PAR1
	0.57	*SHOX*	*SHOX*	0.57	PAR1
	0.92	bA309M23.1§	bA309M23.1§	0.92	PAR1
	1.31	*CRLF2*	*CRLF2*	1.31	PAR1
	1.38	*CSF2RA*	*CSF2RA*	1.38	PAR1
	1.52	*IL3RA*	*IL3RA*	1.52	PAR1
	1.55	*SLC25A6*	*SLC25A6*	1.55	PAR1
	1.56	bA261P4.5§	bA261P4.5§	1.56	PAR1
假常染色体区 PAR1 (XAR)	1.57	bA261P4.6 (*CXYorf2*)	bA261P4.6 (*CXYorf2*)	1.57	PAR1
	1.59	*ASMTL*	*ASMTL*	1.59	PAR1
	1.66	bA261P4.4 (*P2RY8*)	bA261P4.4 (*P2RY8*)	1.66	PAR1
	1.76	*DXYS155E* (*CXYorf3*)	*DXYS155E* (*CXYorf3*)	1.76	PAR1
	1.79	*ASMT*	*ASMT*	1.79	PAR1
	1.79	bB297E16.3§	bB297E16.3§	1.79	PAR1
	1.91	bB297E16.4§	bB297E16.4§	1.91	PAR1
	1.93	bB297E16.5§	bB297E16.5§	1.93	PAR1
	2.37	*DHRSX*	*DHRSX*	2.37	PAR1
	2.41	*ALTE* (*ZBED1*)	*ALTE* (*ZBED1*)	2.41	PAR1
	2.54	Em:AC097314.2§	Em:AC097314.2§	2.54	PAR1
	2.53	Em:AC097314.3§	Em:AC097314.3§	2.53	PAR1
	2.63	*CD99*	*CD99*	2.63	PAR1
	3.57	*PRKX*	*PRKY*	7.23	2
	5.81	*NLGN4X*	*NLGN4Y*	15.23	5
	6.31	Em:AC108684.1 (*VCX3A*)	*VCY*, *VCY1B*	14.54, 14.6	6
	7.62	*VCX*	*VCY*, *VCY1B*	14.54, 14.6	9
X 增加区 (XAR)	7.95	Em:AC097626.1 (*VCX2*)	*VCY*, *VCY1B*	14.54, 14.6	10
	8.24	Em:AC006062.2 (*VCX3B*)	*VCY*, *VCY1B*	14.54, 14.6	10
	9.37	*TBL1X*	*TBL1Y*	6.97	11
	11.07	*AMELX*	*AMELY*	6.78	12
	12.75	*TMSB4X*	*TMSB4Y*	14.25	

Continued

Region	Distance from Xpter (Mb)	X gene*	Y gene	Distance from Ypter (Mb)†	XY homology block‡
X-added region (XAR)	16.59	CXorf15	CYorf15A, CYorf15B	20.13, 20.15	
	19.91	EIF1AX	EIF1AY	21.08	
	23.96	ZFX	ZFY	2.87	
	40.78	USP9X	USP9Y	13.33	
	40.96	DDX3X	DDX3Y	13.46	
	44.61	UTX	UTY	13.91	
X-conserved region (XCR)	53.00	dJ290F12.2 (TSPYL2)	TSPY (~35)	9.50	
	53.12	SMCX	SMCY	20.27	
	71.27	RPS4X	RPS4Y1, RPS4Y2	2.77, 21.27	
X-transposed region (XTR)	88.50	bB348B13.2§	n/a	2.96	XTR
	88.99	TGIF2LX	TGIF2LY	3.49	XTR
	91.26	PCDH11X	PCDH11Y	5.28	XTR
X-conserved region (XCR)	135.68	RNMX (RBMX)	RBMY (6)	22.02, 22.04, 22.37, 22.41, 22.66, 22.85	
	139.31	SOX3	SRY	2.70	
	148.38	Em:AC016940.3 (HSFX2)§	HSFY1, HSFY2	19.3, 19.12	
	148.56	Em:AC016939.4 (HSFX1)§	HSFY1, HSFY2	19.3, 19.12	
Pseudoautosomal region PAR2	154.57	SPRY3	SPRY3	57.44	PAR2
	154.71	SYBL1	SYBL1	57.58	PAR2
	154.81	IL9R	IL9R	57.67	PAR2
	154.81	Em:AJ271736.5§	Em:AJ271736.5§	57.69	PAR2
	154.82	Em:AJ271736.6 (FAM39A)§	Em:AJ271736.6 (FAM39A)§	57.69	PAR2

Pseudogenes are not included in the table.

* Gene names as shown in Supplementary Fig. 1. HUGO name is in parentheses when the two names differ. Em, EMBL entry.

† Distances refer to Y chromosome sequence assembly NCBI35. Where multiple Y chromosome orthologues exist, the locations of all copies are shown on the Y chromosome. The exception is TSPY, which has ~35 copies in an array centred at approximately 9.5 Mb on the Y chromosome[41].

‡ Major homology blocks as shown in Figs 5 and 6.

§ Novel cases of X genes with Y homologues assigned to these categories.

The XTR arose by duplication of material from X to Y since the divergence of the human and chimpanzee lineages[42]. The duplicated region spans 3.91 Mb on X, but the corresponding region is only 3.38 Mb on the Y chromosome (Fig. 5c). We have aligned the entire X and Y copies of this region. Excluding insertions and deletions, sequence identity between the copies is 98.78%. We estimate that the transposition event occurred

区域	与 Xpter 的距离 (Mb)	X 基因 *	Y 基因	与 Ypter 的距离 (Mb)†	XY 同源性区块‡
X 增加区 (XAR)	16.59	CXorf15	CYorf15A, CYorf15B	20.13, 20.15	
	19.91	EIF1AX	EIF1AY	21.08	
	23.96	ZFX	ZFY	2.87	
	40.78	USP9X	USP9Y	13.33	
	40.96	DDX3X	DDX3Y	13.46	
	44.61	UTX	UTY	13.91	
X 保守区 (XCR)	53.00	dJ290F12.2 (TSPYL2)	TSPY (~35)	9.50	
	53.12	SMCX	SMCY	20.27	
	71.27	RPS4X	RPS4Y1, RPS4Y2	2.77, 21.27	
X 转置区 (XTR)	88.50	bB348B13.2§	n/a	2.96	XTR
	88.99	TGIF2LX	TGIF2LY	3.49	XTR
	91.26	PCDH11X	PCDH11Y	5.28	XTR
X 保守区 (XCR)	135.68	RNMX (RBMX)	RBMY (6)	22.02, 22.04, 22.37, 22.41, 22.66, 22.85	
	139.31	SOX3	SRY	2.70	
	148.38	Em:AC016940.3 (HSFX2)§	HSFY1, HSFY2	19.3, 19.12	
	148.56	Em:AC016939.4 (HSFX1)§	HSFY1, HSFY2	19.3, 19.12	
假常染色体区 PAR2	154.57	SPRY3	SPRY3	57.44	PAR2
	154.71	SYBL1	SYBL1	57.58	PAR2
	154.81	IL9R	IL9R	57.67	PAR2
	154.81	Em:AJ271736.5§	Em:AJ271736.5§	57.69	PAR2
	154.82	Em:AJ271736.6 (FAM39A)§	Em:AJ271736.6 (FAM39A)§	57.69	PAR2

假基因不列入表中。

* 基因名称显示在补充图 1 中。当两个名字不同时，HUGO 用括号括起来。Em，EMBL 索取号。

† 距离参考 Y 染色体序列组装 NCBI35。存在多个 Y 染色体直系同源物，所有拷贝的位置显示在 Y 染色体上。唯一的例外是 TSPY，它在 Y 染色体上有 ~35 个拷贝，位于以 9.5 Mb 为中心的阵列中 [41]。

‡ 主要同源区块如图 5 和图 6 所示。

§ 与 Y 染色体同源的 X 基因的新实例纳入这些类别。

自人类和黑猩猩谱系分化以来，XTR 通过从 X 染色体到 Y 染色体的物质复制产生 [42]。复制区域横跨 X 染色体上的 3.91 Mb，但相应的区域在 Y 染色体上只有 3.38 Mb(图 5c)。我们比对了这一区域整个 X 和 Y 拷贝。不包括插入和缺失，拷贝之间序列一致性达到 98.78%。我们估计，转座事件发生在大约 470 万年前(补充讨

approximately 4.7 Myr ago (Supplementary Discussion 1), which is close to the suggested date of the speciation event that led to humans and chimpanzees, assumed here to be 6 Myr ago. The sequence alignment demonstrates the substantial changes to the XTR on the Y chromosome since the transposition. An inversion is known to have separated a 200-kb section from the rest of the XTR[43] (Fig. 5c). Also, the main block of homology is 540 kb shorter on Y than X, owing in particular to the absence of four large regions from the Y chromosome (Fig. 5c). The detection of these sequences at the expected positions on the chimpanzee X chromosome confirms that they were deleted from the Y chromosome after the transposition.

We found that only 54 of the 1,098 genes annotated on the X chromosome have functional homologues on the Y chromosome (Table 1). We obtained direct evidence for 24 genes in PAR1. Twenty-three of them are annotated (Supplementary Fig. 1), and the location of the 5′ end of *CRLF2* indicates that the rest of this gene is in gap 4 of the human X sequence (see the VEGA database). On the basis of the excellent conservation of synteny between human PAR1 and the chicken sequence, we infer that a stromal antigen gene (orthologue of chicken Ensembl gene ENSGALG00000016716) lies in gap 1 (see Fig. 3b). As the annotated putative transcript cM56G10.2 might represent the 3′ end of this gene, we conclude that PAR1 contains at least 24 genes. Together with the five annotated genes in PAR2, 29 genes lie entirely within the recombining regions of the sex chromosomes. Additionally, the *XG* locus spans the boundary between PAR1 and X-specific DNA, but has been disrupted by rearrangement on the Y chromosome.

Outside the XY-recombining regions of the X chromosome, we observed 25 genes that have functional homologues on the Y chromosome (Table 1). Fifteen of these are within the XAR, and a further three genes are shared by the X and Y copies of the XTR. The seven other XY gene pairs are believed to have descended from the proto-sex chromosomes. Only five cases have been described previously[44,45]: the X chromosome genes are *SOX3*, *SMCX*, *RPS4X*, *RBMX* and *TSPYL2*, which are located on the long arm and proximal short arm (Table 1). The two additional cases we report here involve heat-shock transcription factor genes, designated *HSFX1* and *HSFX2*. They are assigned to the category of XCR genes on the basis of a high degree of divergence from their Y chromosome homologues and their location distal to *SOX3* within the XCR. *HSFX1* and *HSFX2* lie within the separate copies of a palindromic repeat in Xq28 and are identical to each other. By analogy, their Y chromosome homologues (*HSFY1* and *HSFY2*) lie within the arms of a Y chromosome palindrome, the similarity of which is thought to be maintained by gene conversion[41].

On the basis of this and previously published information[41], we can conclude that approximately 15 protein-coding genes on the Y chromosome have no detectable X chromosome homologue.

论 1)，这与人类和黑猩猩物种分化的日期接近，分化时间假设是 600 万年前。序列比对显示，自转座以来，Y 染色体上的 XTR 发生了实质性的变化。已知的倒位将一个 200 kb 的片段从 XTR 其余的部分分离出来[43]（图 5c）。此外，Y 染色体上的主要同源性区块比 X 染色体的短 540 kb，尤其是因为 Y 染色体缺失了四个大型区域（图 5c）。对黑猩猩 X 染色体上预期位置序列的检测证实，它们是在转座后从 Y 染色体上删除的。

我们发现，X 染色体注释的 1,098 个基因中只有 54 个在 Y 染色体上有功能同源基因（表 1）。我们在 PAR1 中获得了 24 个基因的直接证据。其中 23 个是有注释的（补充图 1），*CRLF2* 的 5′ 端的位置表明该基因的其余部分在人类 X 染色体序列缺口 4 中（见 VEGA 数据库）。根据人类 PAR1 和鸡序列间良好的同线性保守关系，我们推断，一个基质抗原基因（鸡 Ensembl 基因 ENSGALG00000016716 的直系同源物）位于缺口 1 中（见图 3b）。因为注释的假定转录本 cM56G10.2 可能代表这个基因的 3′ 末端，我们推断 PAR1 至少包含 24 个基因。连同 PAR2 中 5 个注释基因，29 个基因完全在性染色体重组区域内部。此外，*XG* 基因座跨越 PAR1 和 X 特异性 DNA 边界，但被 Y 染色体上的重排打乱。

在 X 染色体上 XY 重组区域之外，我们观察到 25 个基因在 Y 染色体上有功能同源基因（表 1）。其中 15 个基因在 XAR 内，另外三个基因由 XTR 的 X 和 Y 拷贝共享，其他 7 个 XY 基因对被认为是原始性染色体的后代。这其中只有 5 个实例是之前报道过的[44,45]：在 X 染色体上的基因是 *SOX3*、*SMCX*、*RPS4X*、*RBMX* 和 *TSPYL2*，它们位于长臂和近端短臂上（表 1）。这里我们报道另外两个涉及热激转录因子基因的实例，这两个基因分别为 *HSFX1* 和 *HSFX2*。根据它们的 Y 染色体同源物与 XCR 远端 *SOX3* 位置的高度分化，我们将其归为 XCR 基因。*HSFX1* 和 *HSFX2* 位于 Xq28 一个回文重复的单独拷贝中并且完全一样。通过类推，其 Y 染色体同源物（*HSFY1* 和 *HSFY2*）位于 Y 染色体回文臂内，其相似性被认为是通过基因转变来维持的[41]。

基于此信息以及以前公布的信息[41]，我们可以得出结论，Y 染色体上大约 15 个蛋白编码基因没有可检测的 X 染色体同源物。

The Progressive Loss of XY Recombination

The barrier to recombination between the proto-X and Y chromosomes initially encompassed the sex-determining locus on the Y (*SRY*) and possibly other loci affecting male fitness. It is proposed that rearrangement of the Y chromosome led to the development of this barrier. Thereafter, successive rearrangements that encompassed parts of the pseudoautosomal region resulted in segments of Y-linked DNA that could no longer recombine and consequently degenerated over time. Evidence for the role of Y-specific (as opposed to X-specific) rearrangement in this phenomenon is most clearly illustrated by our analysis of the XAR, which shows very little rearrangement between human and avian lineages (Fig. 3a).

In a previous study[46], four broad physical and evolutionary regions were defined on the X chromosome. The X chromosome genes within a given region all showed a similar level of divergence from their Y chromosome counterparts. However, between regions, levels of divergence were very different, presumably reflecting the stepwise loss of recombination between the X and Y chromosomes.

The physical order of the four regions on the X chromosome was seen to parallel their evolutionary ages, and therefore the chromosome was described as having four "evolutionary strata"[46]. In general, gene pairs were found to be less divergent moving through the strata from Xqter to Xpter. The first two strata (S1 and S2) encompass the long arm and proximal short arm, respectively, and were defined by the genes that survive from the proto-sex chromosomes. Gene pairs were found to be increasingly similar moving through strata 3 and 4, which occupy the proximal and distal sections of the XAR, respectively.

We re-evaluated XY homology in S4 and S3 using finished, genomic sequences from the two chromosomes. For S4 in particular, substantial blocks of homology exist between the chromosomes (blocks 1–10 in Fig. 5b and Fig. 6). Aligning the X and Y chromosome sequences across this region, we observed a bipartite organization, with markedly greater XY identity in the distal 1.0 Mb compared with the proximal 4.5 Mb (Fig. 7a). On this basis, the distal portion containing the *GYG2, ARSD, ARSE, ARSF, ADLICAN* and *PRKX* genes can be redefined as a new, fifth stratum, S5 (Figs 1 and 7a). A most parsimonious series of inversions, from the current arrangement of homologous blocks on X to that on Y, is consistent with the proposed strata (Fig. 7b). These data refine the picture of loss of XY recombination during evolution, which occurred by migration of the PABX in a stepwise manner distally through the XAR. The available evidence now suggests that there have been at least four PABX positions within the XAR, which are at the S2/S3, S3/S4 and S4/S5 boundaries (~47 Mb, ~8.5 Mb and ~4 Mb from Xpter, respectively), and at the current position (2.7 Mb from Xpter). We estimate that the two most recent PABX movements, which created first S4 and then S5, occurred 38–44 Myr ago and 29–32 Myr ago, respectively (Supplementary Discussion 2).

514

XY 重组逐步丧失

原始 X 染色体和 Y 染色体之间重组的障碍最初包括 Y 染色体上的性别决定基因（*SRY*）和其他可能影响男性适合度的基因座。有人提出 Y 染色体的重排导致了这一障碍的发展。之后，包括部分假常染色体区域的连续重排导致 Y 连锁的 DNA 片段不能再重组，因此随着时间的推移这些片段逐渐退化。我们对 XAR 的分析清楚地说明了 Y 染色体特异性（与 X 特异性相反）重排在这一现象中所起的作用。XAR 显示人类和鸟类谱系之间几乎没有重排（图 3a）。

在先前的研究中 [46]，在 X 染色体上定义了四个广泛的物理和进化区域。给定区域内 X 染色体基因都表现出与 Y 染色体对应物相似程度的分化。然而，在不同的区域之间，分化程度有很大的不同，这大概反映了 X 和 Y 染色体间重组的逐步丧失。

可以看出 X 染色体上四个区域的物理顺序与它们的进化年龄平行，因此，染色体被描述为有四个"进化阶段"[46]。一般情况下，在从 Xqter 到 Xpter 的基因阶段中，基因对的差异很小。前两个阶段（S1 和 S2）分别包含长臂和近端短臂，这两个阶段通过原始性染色体存留下来的基因确定。位于 XAR 近端和远端的基因对在第 3 阶段和第 4 阶段越来越相似。

我们使用来自两条染色体的完整基因组序列重新评估了 S4 和 S3 中的 XY 同源性。尤其是 S4，大量同源区块存在于染色体之间（在图 5b 和图 6 中的区块 1 ~ 10）。比对这一区域的 X 染色体和 Y 染色体序列，我们观察到了一个由两部分构成的组织。与近端 4.5 Mb 相比，远端 1.0 Mb 的 XY 特性更显著（图 7a）。在此基础上，我们将包含 *GYG2*、*ARSD*、*ARSE*、*ARSF*、*ADLICAN* 和 *PRKX* 基因的远端部分重新定义为一个新的第五阶段——S5（图 1 和 7a）。从目前的 X 染色体上同源区块的排列，到 Y 染色体上同源区块的排列这一系列最简约的倒位与之前提出的阶段一致（图 7b）。这些数据完善了进化过程中 XY 重组缺失的图像，这种缺失是由 PABX 在远端通过 XAR 的逐步迁移造成的。现有的证据表明，在 XAR 内至少有四个 PABX 位置，分别位于 S2/S3、S3/S4 和 S4/S5 边界（分别位于 Xpter 的 ~47 Mb，~8.5 Mb 和 ~4 Mb）和当前位置（位于 Xpter 的 2.7 Mb）。我们估计最近的两次 PABX 运动，先产生了 S4，之后产生了 S5，分别发生在 3,800 万 ~ 4,400 万年前和 2,900 万 ~ 3,200 万年前（补充讨论 2）。

Fig. 7. Evidence for a fifth evolutionary stratum on the X chromosome. **a**, Sequence identity between the X and Y homology blocks 1–12 (see Figs 5b and 6) plotted in 5-kb windows. The scale shows the total amount of sequence aligned, excluding insertions and deletions (see Methods). A 10-kb spacer is placed between each consecutive block of homology. Segments of the plot are coloured according to the system used in Figs 6 and 7b. On the basis of this plot, a new evolutionary stratum S5 is defined, which includes homology blocks 1 and 2. **b**, A most parsimonious series of inversion events from the arrangement of homology blocks 1–12 on the X chromosome (top) to the Y chromosome (bottom), calculated using GRIMM[64]. The grey boxes show the suggested extents of former pseudoautosomal regions within the distal part of the XAR, and the magenta box (bottom row) shows the position of the current pseudoautosomal region. This inversion sequence provides independent support for the proposed pseudoautosomal boundary movements and evolutionary strata. It was previously suggested that *AMELX* (in block 12) is in S4 (ref. 46), or possibly at the boundary between S3 and S4 (ref. 67). However, the more distal location of block 11, which contains *TBL1X* (an S3 gene[46]), is not consistent with these suggestions. The two regions of increased sequence identity within block 10 contain the *VCX2* and *VCX3B* genes on the X chromosome and the *VCY1B* and *VCY* genes on the Y chromosome. This gene family might have arisen *de novo* in the simian lineage[68], which could account for the unusual characteristics of this part of the alignment.

In addition to the varied degree of XY sequence identity within S3, S4, S5 and PAR1, we found marked differences in their sequence composition, which were presumably also caused by the loss of recombination in each region during evolution. Specifically, we observed that L1, L2 and mammalian interspersed repeat (MIR) coverage decrease with each more distal stratum and PAR1 (Table 2 and Fig. 1), but (G+C) levels and *Alu* repeat content increase abruptly at the boundary between S4 and S5 (Table 2 and Fig. 8); variations in the incidence of different *Alu* subfamilies (Y, S and J) also contribute to the

516

图 7. X 染色体上第五个进化阶段的证据。**a**，在 5 kb 窗口中绘制的 X 染色体和 Y 染色体同源性区块 1 ~ 12 的序列一致性（见图 5b 和 6）。该比例显示序列比对的总量，但不包括插入和缺失（见方法）。在每个同源性连续区块之间有 10 kb 的间隔。根据图 6 和 7b 中用的系统对每个片段着色。在此划分的基础上，我们确定了一个新的进化阶段 S5，包括同源块 1 和 2。**b**，用 GRIMM 计算，X 染色体（上）到 Y 染色体（下）同源区块 1 ~ 12 排列的一系列最简约的倒位事件[64]。灰色框显示 XAR 远端部分内之前的假常染色体区域的建议范围，品红色方块（下排）表明目前的假常染色体区域的位置。倒位序列为假常染色体边界运动和进化阶段的观点提供了独立的支持。早前有人提出，*AMELX*（在区块 12）位于 S4 中（参考文献 46），也可能位于 S3 和 S4 间的边界（参考文献 67）。然而，包含 *TBL1X*（一个 S3 基因[46]）的区块 11 的较远端的位置与这些观点不符。区块 10 内序列一致性增加的两个区域包含 X 染色体上的 *VCX2* 和 *VCX3B* 基因以及 Y 染色体上的 *VCY1B* 和 *VCY* 基因。这一基因家族可能是在类人猿谱系中新产生的[68]，这可以解释这部分排列的不寻常特征。

　　除了 S3、S4、S5 和 PAR1 内 XY 序列同源程度不同外，我们还发现它们的序列组成存在显著差异，这也可能是进化时每个区域内重组缺失造成的。具体来说，我们观察到 L1、L2 和哺乳动物散在重复（MIR）覆盖度随每个更远端阶段和 PAR1 减少（表 2 和图 1），但（G+C）水平和 *Alu* 重复含量在 S4 和 S5 边界突然增加（表 2 和图 8）；不同 *Alu* 亚家族（Y、S 和 J）发病率的变化促成了每个阶段和 PAR1 的不同

distinct character of each stratum and PAR1 (Supplementary Table 13). The compositional differences between S4 and S5 provide additional support for the subdivision of the original stratum 4 (Fig. 8).

Table 2. Sequence characteristics of evolutionary domains of the X chromosome

Region	(G+C) (%)	L1 (%)	L1P (%)	L1M (%)	Alu (%)	L2 (%)	MIR+MIR3 (%)
X chromosome	39.46	28.87	13.39	15.21	8.23	2.98	2.07
XAR	39.87	17.89	6.60	11.23	10.28	2.63	1.76
XCR	39.28	33.50	16.38	16.97	7.28	3.12	2.19
PAR1	48.11	6.97	2.64	4.38	28.88	0.24	0.21
S5	42.86	8.89	4.36	4.59	18.72	0.66	0.31
S4	38.87	11.10	4.31	6.80	8.60	1.59	0.95
S3	39.46	19.55	7.14	12.34	9.24	2.94	1.98

See Supplementary Table 13 for additional repeat element data.

Fig. 8. Sequence compositional changes in the distal evolutionary strata of the X chromosome. Shown are the positions of SINE and LINE repeats and (G+C) content within PAR1, S5 and the distal half of S4. The percentage of Alu, L1 and (G+C) are shown for each region (including the whole of S4). There is an abrupt increase in Alu repeat levels and (G+C) content from S4 to S5. The five euchromatic gaps in PAR1 are shown as light brown bars. Pale blue bars represent clones for which the sequences were unfinished at the time of the sequence assembly.

X-chromosome Inactivation

XCI in mammals achieves dosage compensation between males and females for X-linked gene products. Inactivation of one X chromosome occurs early in female development and is initiated from the X-inactivation centre (XIC). The *XIST* transcript is expressed initially on both X chromosomes, but later the transcript from the chromosome that is destined for inactivation becomes more stable than the other. Finally, the transcript is expressed only from the inactive X chromosome (X_i). Coating with the *XIST* transcript is the earliest of many chromatin modifications on X_i.

XCI was first proposed based partly on the study of X: autosome translocations in female mice[47]. Studies of derivative chromosomes containing inactivated X chromosome segments

特性（补充表 13）。S4 和 S5 之间的成分差异为原始阶段 4 的细分提供了额外的支持（图 8）。

表 2. X 染色体进化区域的序列特征

区域	(G+C) (%)	L1 (%)	L1P (%)	L1M (%)	Alu (%)	L2 (%)	MIR+MIR3 (%)
X 染色体	39.46	28.87	13.39	15.21	8.23	2.98	2.07
XAR	39.87	17.89	6.60	11.23	10.28	2.63	1.76
XCR	39.28	33.50	16.38	16.97	7.28	3.12	2.19
PAR1	48.11	6.97	2.64	4.38	28.88	0.24	0.21
S5	42.86	8.89	4.36	4.59	18.72	0.66	0.31
S4	38.87	11.10	4.31	6.80	8.60	1.59	0.95
S3	39.46	19.55	7.14	12.34	9.24	2.94	1.98

其他重复元件数据见补充表 13。

图 8. 在 X 染色体进化最远阶段序列成分变化。图中所示的是 SINE 和 LINE 重复的位置以及 PAR1、S5 和 S4 远端一半的（G+C）含量。每个区域显示了 Alu、L1 和（G+C）的百分比（包括整个 S4）。Alu 重复水平和（G+C）含量从 S4 到 S5 突然增加。PAR1 中五个常染色质缺口显示为浅褐色方框。淡蓝色方框代表序列组装时未完成序列的克隆。

X 染色体失活

在哺乳动物中，XCI 实现了雄性与雌性之间 X 连锁基因产物的剂量补偿效应。一条 X 染色体失活发生在雌性发育早期，而且是从 X 失活中心（XIC）开始。XIST 转录本最初在两条 X 染色体上都有表达，但后来在注定要失活的染色体上的转录本变得比另一条更稳定。最后，转录本只在失活的 X 染色体（Xi）上表达。在 Xi 上的许多染色质修饰中，包覆 XIST 转录本是最早的。

XCI 的首次提出部分是基于对 X 染色体的研究：雌性老鼠中常染色体易位[47]。我们通过对含有失活 X 染色体片段的衍生染色体进行研究后得出结论，失活可以跨

later concluded that the inactivation could spread across the translocation boundary to the autosomal segment, but that inactivation of this segment was incomplete. More recently, it has become clear that more than 15% of the genes on the human X chromosome, including many without functional equivalents on the Y, escape from XCI, as presented in detail elsewhere[48]. The majority of the genes that escape XCI lie within the distal regions of the XAR (Fig. 1): all genes studied in PAR1, S5 and S4 were found to escape from XCI, but there is a lower proportion of escapees in S3, and very few examples in the XCR[48]. This observation correlates with our picture of X chromosome evolution: XCI follows Y chromosome attrition[49], which is less advanced in the distal strata of the XAR.

Inefficient inactivation of the autosomal segment in X_i: autosome translocations led to the proposal that "way stations" on the X chromosome boost the spread of XCI. According to this model, way stations are present throughout the genome but are enriched on the X chromosome, particularly in the region of the XIC[50]. Lyon suggested that L1 elements are good candidates for acting as way stations on account of their enrichment on the mammalian X chromosome[51]. We observe a distribution of L1 elements on the chromosome that is consistent with both the way station and the Lyon hypotheses (Fig. 1 and Table 2). The coverage of L1 repeats is very high in the XCR, especially around the XIC. As noted previously[52], this enrichment in L1 levels is accounted for particularly by elements that were active more recently in mammalian evolution[53] (L1P in Fig. 1). In the XAR, L1 coverage is close to autosome levels, whereas L1 levels are particularly low in the distal evolutionary strata of the XAR, where genes consistently escape inactivation. The *XIST* locus itself lies in a 60 kb region that is virtually devoid of L1 elements, whereas L1 levels are extremely high in the adjacent regions. Based on their distributions, other interspersed repeats are not strong candidates for way stations. For example, although L2 and MIR elements are reduced in S4, S5 and particularly PAR1 relative to the rest of the chromosome, their overall levels on the X chromosome are not enriched relative to the autosomes but are slightly reduced. Furthermore, L2 and MIR levels are low in the region distal to the XIC. These characteristics do not preclude an involvement in XCI, but are not consistent with a role as way stations.

The possible causal relationship of L1 elements to the spread of XCI remains a subject of debate. Some studies have reported significant associations between L1 coverage and inactivation[52], and others have refuted this[54]. Our observations on regional differences in composition emphasize that such studies should compare active and inactivated genes (or domains) from the same evolutionary stratum, in order to avoid correlations that are unrelated to XCI.

Medical Genetics and the X Chromosome Sequence

The X chromosome holds a unique place in the history of medical genetics. Ascertainment of X-linked diseases is enhanced by the relative ease of recognizing this mode of inheritance. More important, however, is the fact that a disproportionately large number of

越易位边界扩散到常染色体片段中，但该片段失活尚不完全。最近，人们已经清楚地看到：人类 X 染色体上超过 15% 的基因，包括许多在 Y 染色体上没有功能等同物的基因，没有发生 XCI，这在其他地方也有详细说明[48]。大多数没发生 XCI 的基因位于 XAR 远端区域（图 1）：在 PAR1、S5 和 S4 中研究的所有基因都没发生 XCI，但 S3 中没发生 XCI 的比例很低，在 XCR 中实例也很少[48]。这一观察结果与我们的 X 染色体进化情况有关：XCI 发生在 Y 染色体削弱之后[49]，而 Y 染色体的削弱在 XAR 较远的阶段几乎不发生。

X_i 中常染色体片段低效失活：常染色体易位导致提出 X 染色体上的"中转站"促进 XCI 的扩散这一观点。根据这一模型，中转站出现在整个基因组中，但在 X 染色体上富集，特别是在 XIC 区域[50]。莱昂认为由于 L1 元件在哺乳动物 X 染色体上富集，所以它是作为中转站的理想选择[51]。我们观察到 L1 元件在染色体上的分布符合中转站和莱昂假设（图 1 和表 2）。在 XCR 中，L1 重复的覆盖率非常高，特别是 XIC 周围。正如之前所述[52]，最近在哺乳动物进化中活跃的元件解释了 L1 水平的富集[53]（图 1 中的 L1P）。在 XAR 中，L1 覆盖率接近常染色体水平，而 L1 水平在 XAR 远端进化阶段特别低，在该阶段基因始终没有发生 XCI。*XIST* 基因座本身位于一个实际上缺少 L1 元件的 60 kb 区域，而在邻近区域 L1 水平极其高。根据它们的分布，其他散在重复中没有强有力的中转站候选。例如，虽然 L2 和 MIR 元件在 S4、S5，尤其是 PAR1 中相对于染色体的其余部分有所减少，但它们在 X 染色体上的总体水平相对于常染色体并没有富集，而是略有降低。此外，L2 和 MIR 水平在 XIC 远端较低。这些特征不排除参与 XCI，但不符合中转站的功能。

L1 元件与 XCI 扩展可能的因果关系仍然是一个有争议的话题。一些研究报告了 L1 的覆盖率和失活之间的显著联系[52]，而另一些研究则反驳了这一说法[54]。我们经过对区域组成差异的观察后，强调了这种研究应比较同一进化阶段的活性和失活基因（或域），以避免与 XCI 无关的相关性。

医学遗传学和 X 染色体序列

X 染色体在医学遗传学历史上占有独特的地位。识别这种遗传模式相对容易，于是增强了对 X 连锁疾病的确定。然而更重要的是，实际上大量的疾病条件都与 X 染色体有关，因为任何在 Y 染色体上没有活性对应物的基因，其隐性突变的表型结

disease conditions have been associated with the X chromosome because the phenotypic consequence of a recessive mutation is revealed directly in males for any gene that has no active counterpart on the Y chromosome. Thus, although the X chromosome contains only 4% of all human genes, almost 10% of diseases with a mendelian pattern of inheritance have been assigned to the X chromosome (307 out of 3,199; information obtained from OMIM[2]). These two aspects of the medical genetics of the X chromosome have greatly stimulated progress in the positional cloning of many genes associated with human disease. To date, the molecular basis for 168 X-linked phenotypes has been determined, and the X chromosome sequence has aided this process for 43 of them, by providing positional candidate genes or a reference sequence for comparison to patient samples (Supplementary Table 14).

Identifying genes involved in rare conditions yields important biological insights. For example, discovery of mutations in the *SH2D1A* gene[55] (involved in X-linked lymphoproliferative disease (XLP, OMIM 308240)) led to identification of a new mediator of signal transduction between T and NK cells, and a novel family of proteins involved in the regulation of the immune response. Mental retardation is one of the most common problems in clinical genetics, and affects significantly more males than females. To date, 16 genes from the X chromosome have been associated with cases of non-syndromic X-linked mental retardation (NS-XLMR), in which mental retardation is the only phenotypic feature. These genes encode a range of protein types, and some are also involved in syndromic forms of mental retardation. For example, the *ARX* gene encodes an aristaless-related homeobox transcription factor and is linked to NS-XLMR cases, as well as to syndromic mental retardation associated with epilepsy (infantile spasm syndrome, ISSX, OMIM 308350) or with dystonic hand movements (Partington syndrome, PRTS, OMIM 309510)[56]. The *MECP2* gene, which encodes a methyl-CpG-binding protein, was initially linked to cases of Rett syndrome in girls[57] (RTT, OMIM 312750) but was later also seen to be mutated in males or females with NS-XLMR[58]. The molecular defect has been determined in only a minority of families affected by NS-XLMR, which has led to speculation that there could be as many as 100 genes on the X chromosome that are associated with NS-XLMR[59]. Discovering the genes for these and other rare, monogenic disorders is of critical value in extending our understanding of fundamental new processes in human biology, and the annotated X chromosome will further facilitate this process.

Concluding Remarks

The completion of the X chromosome sequencing project is an essential component of the goal of obtaining a high-quality, annotated human genome sequence for use in studies of gene function, sequence variation, disease and evolution. It also means that for the first time, we now have the finished sex chromosome sequences of an organism. The study of these sequences gives a greater insight into mammalian sex chromosome evolution and its consequences. As these analyses are extended to other genomes, we will gain a greater appreciation of the different evolutionary forces that shape sex chromosome and autosome

果直接在男性中显示。因此，尽管 X 染色体只含有 4% 的人类基因，但几乎 10% 的孟德尔遗传模式的疾病与 X 染色体有关（3,199 种疾病中有 307 种；信息从 OMIM[2] 获得）。X 染色体的医学遗传学的这两个方面极大地促进了与人类疾病相关的许多基因定位克隆的发展。迄今为止，我们已经确定了 168 个 X 连锁表型的分子基础，通过为患者样本的比较提供位置候选基因或参考序列，X 染色体序列为其中 43 个的分子基础的确定提供了帮助（补充表 14）。

识别罕见情况下涉及的基因可以获得重要的生物学见解。例如，*SH2D1A* 基因突变的发现 [55]（涉及 X 连锁淋巴组织增生性疾病（XLP，OMIM 308240））使得我们在 T 细胞和 NK 细胞之间鉴定出一个新的信号转导调节物，以及一个涉及免疫反应调节的新的蛋白家族。精神发育迟缓是临床遗传学最常见问题之一，并且它对男性的影响比对女性的大。迄今为止，已有 16 个来自 X 染色体的基因与非综合征 X 连锁智力低下（NS-XLMR）病例相关，其中智力低下是唯一的表型特征。这些基因编码一系列蛋白类型，其中一些基因还与精神发育迟缓的综合征形式有关。例如，*ARX* 基因编码一个无芒样同源框转录因子，并与 NS-XLMR 病例以及与癫痫（婴儿痉挛综合征，ISSX，OMIM 308350）或手部运动异常（帕廷顿综合征，PRTS，OMIM 309510）有关的精神发育迟缓的综合征相关 [56]。编码甲基化 CpG 结合蛋白的 *MECP2* 基因，最初与女孩中的雷特综合征的病例有关 [57]（RTT，OMIM 312750），但后来也被发现在患有 NS-XLMR 的男性或女性中发生突变 [58]。这种分子缺陷只在少数受 NS-XLMR 影响的家族中被发现，人们推测 X 染色体上可能有多达 100 个基因与 NS-XLMR 相关 [59]。发现上述基因和其他罕见的单基因疾病对于扩展我们对人类生物学新的基本过程的理解具有重要价值，而标注的 X 染色体将进一步促进这一过程。

结 束 语

X 染色体测序项目的完成是获得用于基因功能、序列变异、疾病和进化研究的高质量、带注释的人类基因组序列的重要组成部分。这也意味着，我们第一次拥有了一个有机体的已完成的性染色体序列。对这些序列的研究使我们对哺乳动物性染色体进化及其结果有了更深入的了解。当这些分析扩大到其他基因组时，我们将对形成性染色体和常染色体的不同进化力量有更深入的了解。非常重要的是研究突变过程速率的差异，并考虑不同寻常的雄性重组模式对这些过程的影响。显然，这种

evolution. It will be important to study differences in the rates of mutational processes, and to consider the influence of the unusual pattern of male recombination on these processes. Clearly, this analysis should not be restricted to a consideration of mammalian sex chromosomes, and it will be of great interest to make comparisons with non-mammalian systems that arose independently in evolution.

Methods

The approach used to establish a bacterial clone map of the X chromosome has been previously described[5]. 13,264 clones were identified using 4,363 STS markers derived from published genetic or physical maps, from shotgun sequencing of flow-sorted X chromosomes, or from end-sequences of clones at contig ends. Clones were assembled into contigs using restriction-enzyme fingerprinting, and were integrated with the Washington University Genome Sequencing Center whole genome BAC map[60] in order to identify additional clones. Nine euchromatic gaps were measured using fluorescent *in situ* hybridization of clones to extended DNA fibres, and a tenth gap was estimated on the basis of end-sequence data from spanning, unstable BAC clones (Supplementary Table 2). On the basis of pulsed-field gel electrophoresis experiments, we expect the sizes of the other four euchromatic gaps to have a combined size of less than 400 kb.

Finished sequences of individual clones were determined using procedures described in ref. 7. For the analyses described above, the sequence was frozen in March 2004, at which point 150,396,262 bp of sequence had been determined from a minimal tiling path of 1,832 clones (1,616 sequence accessions). This sequence is available at http://www.sanger.ac.uk/HGP/ChrX/, and its annotation is represented in Supplementary Fig. 1. Updates to the sequence and annotation can be obtained from the VEGA database.

Manual annotation of gene structures has been described elsewhere[14], and used guidelines agreed at the human annotation workshop (HAWK; http://www.sanger.ac.uk/HGP/havana/hawk.shtml). Genes were assigned to one of four groups: (1) known genes that are identical to human cDNAs or protein sequences and have a RefSeq RNA (and RefSeq protein, if the gene encodes a protein); (2) novel coding sequences, which have an open reading frame (ORF) and are identical to spliced ESTs, or have similarity to other genes/proteins (any species); (3) novel transcripts, which are similar to novel coding sequences, except that no ORF can be determined with confidence; and (4) putative transcripts, which are identical to splicing human ESTs but have no ORF. Gene symbols were approved by the HUGO Gene Nomenclature Committee wherever possible. Predicted protein translations were analysed for Pfam domains using InterProScan (http://www.ebi.ac.uk/InterProScan/). CpG islands were predicted using the program GpG (G. Micklem, personal communication).

Interspersed repeats were identified and classified using RepeatMasker (http://repeatmasker.genome. washington.edu). In order to search for segmental duplications, WU-BLASTN (http://blast.wustl. edu) was used to align the current X chromosome sequence to itself or to the NCBI34 autosome assemblies. Duplicated blocks at least 5 kb in length were defined as described in ref. 28.

分析不应局限于对哺乳动物性染色体的考虑，将哺乳动物系统与在进化中独立产生的非哺乳动物系统进行比较将是非常有趣的。

方　　法

建立 X 染色体细菌克隆图谱的方法以前已描述过 [5]。13,264 个克隆通过 4,363 个 STS 标记被鉴定出来，这些 STS 标记来自已发表的遗传或物理图谱、流式 X 染色体鸟枪法测序、重叠群末端克隆的末端序列。用限制酶指纹法将克隆组装到重叠群，并与华盛顿大学基因组测序中心全基因组 BAC 图谱 [60] 进行整合，用以确定其他的克隆。使用荧光原位杂交克隆来测量 9 条常染色体缺口以扩展 DNA 纤维，基于不稳定 BAC 克隆末端序列数据，我们对第十个缺口进行了评估（补充表 2）。根据脉冲场凝胶电泳实验，我们预计其他四个常染色体缺口的合并大小小于 400 kb。

使用参考文献 7 中描述的步骤确定单个克隆的完成序列。在上述的分析中，该序列在 2004 年 3 月被冻结，那时从 1,832 个克隆的最小叠瓦式中确定了 150,396,262 bp 的序列（1,616 个序列登入册）。该序列可在 http://www.sanger.ac.uk/HGP/ChrX/ 获得，其注解如补充图 1 所示。更新的序列和注解可从 VEGA 数据库获取。

人工注释基因结构在其他地方也有描述 [14]，并且使用的准则经过了人类注解研讨会的同意（HAWK；http://www.sanger.ac.uk/HGP/havana/hawk.shtml）。基因被分为四组：(1) 与人类 cDNA 或蛋白质序列一致且具有 RNA 参考序列（以及蛋白质参考序列，如果该基因编码了一种蛋白质）的已知基因；(2) 有开放阅读框且与剪切表达序列标签一致或与其他基因/蛋白（任何物种）相似的新编码序列；(3) 与新编码序列一致的新转录本，但排除了确定没有开放阅读框的情况；(4) 与剪切人类表达序列标签一致但没有开放阅读框的假定转录本。基因符号尽可能由 HUGO 基因命名委员会批准。用 InterProScan 分析 Pfam 域的预测蛋白翻译（http://www.ebi.ac.uk/InterProScan/）。使用 CpG 程序分析 CpG 岛（米克勒姆，个人交流）。

使用 RepeatMasker（http://repeatmasker.genome.washington.edu）对散在重复序列进行识别和分类。为了寻找片段重复，我们使用 WU-BLASTN（http://blast.wustl.edu）将当前的 X 染色体序列与自身或与 NCBI34 常染色体组进行比对。如参考文献 28 所述，确定的重复区块长度至少有 5 kb。

SNPs (dbSNP release 119) were mapped onto the X chromosome sequence using first SSAHA[61] and then Cross-match (http://www.phrap.org/phredphrapconsed.html).

Comparative analysis

The genome assemblies used for comparative analyses were: *Gallus gallus* WASHUC1 (Washington University Genome Sequencing Center, http://www.genome.wustl.edu/projects/chicken), *Rattus norvegicus* RGSC3.1 (Rat Genome Sequencing Consortium http://www.hgsc.bcm.tmc.edu/projects/rat/), *Mus musculus* NCBI32 (Mouse Genome Sequencing Consortium, http://www.ncbi.nlm.nih.gov/genome/seq/NCBIContigInfo.html), *Danio rerio* version 3 (Sanger Institute, http://www.sanger.ac.uk/Projects/D_rerio), *T. nigroviridis* version 6 (Genoscope and the Broad Institute, http://www.genoscope.cns.fr/externe/tetraodon/Ressource.html), and *F. rubripes* version 2 (International Fugu Genome Consortium, http://www.fugu-sg.org/project/info.html). ECRs between the X chromosome and the rodent and fish genomes were obtained as described elsewhere[13]. In order to visualize regions of conserved synteny, the X chromosome sequence was aligned to the chicken and rodent genome sequences using BLASTZ (with default parameters), and matches were plotted by chromosome position. Matches to the rodent genomes were filtered to include only those with a sequence identity of at least 70% to the human sequence. The Ensembl database (http://www.ensembl.org) was used to search for orthologous gene pairs between the X chromosome and the other three genomes.

Genomic sequence homologies between the X and Y chromosomes were identified by aligning the two finished chromosome sequences using WU-BLASTN, and then filtering the alignments to include only those of at least 70% sequence identity and 80 bp length. In order to calculate the sequence identity between large, XY-homologous regions, a global alignment of unmasked sequence was generated using LAGAN[62]. Gapped regions, which result from insertions or deletions, were removed from the alignment, and then the nucleotide sequence identity was calculated for the remainder. Sequence identity plots were produced by parsing the LAGAN output into VISTA[63]. GRIMM[64] was used to calculate a most parsimonious series of inversions that would account for differences in homology block order and orientation between the X and Y chromosomes. Homologous protein-coding gene pairs between the X and Y chromosomes were identified by TBLASTN searching with the coding sequences of annotated coding genes on the Y chromosome against the X chromosome genomic sequence.

(**434**, 325-337; 2005)

Mark T. Ross[1], Darren V. Grafham[1], Alison J. Coffey[1], Steven Scherer[2], Kirsten McLay[1], Donna Muzny[2], Matthias Platzer[3], Gareth R. Howell[1], Christine Burrows[1], Christine P. Bird[1], Adam Frankish[1], Frances L. Lovell[1], Kevin L. Howe[1], Jennifer L. Ashurst[1], Robert S. Fulton[4], Ralf Sudbrak[5,6], Gaiping Wen[3], Matthew C. Jones[1], Matthew E. Hurles[1], T. Daniel Andrews[1], Carol E. Scott[1], Stephen Searle[1], Juliane Ramser[7], Adam Whittaker[1], Rebecca Deadman[1], Nigel P. Carter[1], Sarah E. Hunt[1], Rui Chen[2], Andrew Cree[2], Preethi Gunaratne[2], Paul Havlak[2], Anne Hodgson[2], Michael L. Metzker[2], Stephen Richards[2], Graham Scott[2], David Steffen[2], Erica Sodergren[2], David A. Wheeler[2], Kim C. Worley[2], Rachael Ainscough[1], Kerrie D. Ambrose[1], M. Ali Ansari-Lari[2], Swaroop Aradhya[2], Robert I. S. Ashwell[1], Anne K. Babbage[1], Claire L. Bagguley[1], Andrea Ballabio[2], Ruby Banerjee[1], Gary E. Barker[1], Karen F. Barlow[1], Ian P. Barrett[1], Karen N. Bates[1], David M. Beare[1],

首先使用 SSAHA[61] 将 SNP(dbSNP 发布版 119)映射到 X 染色体序列上，然后进行交叉匹配(http://www.phrap.org/phredphrapconsed.html)。

对比分析

用于比较分析的基因组组合是：原鸡 WASHUC1(华盛顿大学基因组测序中心，http://www.genome.wustl.edu/project/chicken)，褐家鼠 RGSC3.1(大鼠基因组测序协作组 http://www.hgsc.bcm.tmc.edu/projects/rat/)，小家鼠 NCBI32(小鼠基因组测序协作组，http://www.ncbi.nlm.nih.gov/genome/seq/NCBIContigInfo.html)，斑马鱼第 3 版(桑格研究所，http://www.sanger.ac.uk/Project/D_rerio)，黑青斑河鲀第 6 版 (Genoscope 和布罗德研究所，http://www.genoscope.cns.fr/externe/tetraodon/Ressource.html) 和红鳍东方鲀第 2 版(国际河豚基因协作组 http://www.fugu-sg.org/project/info.html)。X 染色体与啮齿动物和鱼类基因组之间的 ECR 如其他地方所述[13]。为了可视化保守的同源区域，X 染色体序列使用 BLASTZ(默认参数)与鸡和啮齿类动物基因组序列进行比对，并通过染色体位置绘制匹配。与啮齿动物基因组匹配的基因经过筛选，只包括那些至少与人类序列一致性达 70% 的基因。使用 Ensembl 数据库(http://www.ensembl.org) 来寻找 X 染色体和其他三个基因组间直系同源基因对。

通过用 WU-BLASTN 对两个已完成的染色体序列进行比对，确定了 X 染色体和 Y 染色体间的基因组序列同源性，然后对比对结果进行筛选，只包含序列一致性不低于 70%、长度不小于 80 bp 的染色体序列。为了计算大的 XY 同源性区域间的序列一致性，使用 LAGAN[62] 生成了未掩蔽全序列比对。将插入或删除导致的缺口区域从比对中移除，然后计算剩余序列的核苷酸序列一致性。通过将 LAGAN 输出解析为 VISTA[63] 来生成序列标识图。用 GRIMM[64] 计算出一系列最简单的逆序序列，这些逆序序列可以解释 X 染色体和 Y 染色体在同源块顺序和方向上的差异。利用带注释的编码序列进行 TBLASTN 搜索，确定 X 染色体和 Y 染色体之间的同源蛋白编码基因对。

(李梅 翻译；胡松年 审稿)

Helen Beasley[1], Oliver Beasley[1], Alfred Beck[5], Graeme Bethel[1], Karin Blechschmidt[3], Nicola Brady[1], Sarah Bray-Allen[1], Anne M. Bridgeman[1], Andrew J. Brown[1], Mary J. Brown[2], David Bonnin[2], Elspeth A. Bruford[8], Christian Buhay[2], Paula Burch[2], Deborah Burford[1], Joanne Burgess[1], Wayne Burrill[1], John Burton[1], Jackie M. Bye[1], Carol Carder[1], Laura Carrel[9], Joseph Chako[2], Joanne C. Chapman[1], Dean Chavez[2], Ellson Chen[10], Guan Chen[2], Yuan Chen[11], Zhijian Chen[2], Craig Chinault[2], Alfredo Ciccodicola[12], Sue Y. Clark[1], Graham Clarke[1], Chris M. Clee[1], Sheila Clegg[1], Kerstin Clerc-Blankenburg[2], Karen Clifford[1], Vicky Cobley[1], Charlotte G. Cole[1], Jen S. Conquer[1], Nicole Corby[1], Richard E. Connor[1], Robert David[2], Joy Davies[1], Clay Davis[2], John Davis[1], Oliver Delgado[2], Denise DeShazo[2], Pawandeep Dhami[1], Yan Ding[2], Huyen Dinh[2], Steve Dodsworth[1], Heather Draper[2], Shannon Dugan-Rocha[2], Andrew Dunham[1], Matthew Dunn[1], K. James Durbin[2], Ireena Dutta[1], Tamsin Eades[1], Matthew Ellwood[1], Alexandra Emery-Cohen[2], Helen Errington[1], Kathryn L. Evans[13], Louisa Faulkner[1], Fiona Francis[14], John Frankland[1], Audrey E. Fraser[1], Petra Galgoczy[3], James Gilbert[1], Rachel Gill[2], Gernot Glöckner[3], Simon G. Gregory[1], Susan Gribble[1], Coline Griffiths[1], Russell Grocock[1], Yanghong Gu[2], Rhian Gwilliam[1], Cerissa Hamilton[2], Elizabeth A. Hart[1], Alicia Hawes[2], Paul D. Heath[1], Katja Heitmann[5], Steffen Hennig[5], Judith Hernandez[2], Bernd Hinzmann[3], Sarah Ho[1], Michael Hoffs[1], Phillip J. Howden[1], Elizabeth J. Huckle[1], Jennifer Hume[2], Paul J. Hunt[1], Adrienne R. Hunt[1], Judith Isherwood[1], Leni Jacob[2], David Johnson[1], Sally Jones[2], Pieter J. de Jong[15], Shirin S. Joseph[1], Stephen Keenan[1], Susan Kelly[2], Joanne K. Kershaw[1], Ziad Khan[2], Petra Kioschis[16], Sven Klages[5], Andrew J. Knights[1], Anna Kosiura[5], Christie Kovar-Smith[2], Gavin K. Laird[1], Cordelia Langford[1], Stephanie Lawlor[1], Margaret Leversha[1], Lora Lewis[2], Wen Liu[2], Christine Lloyd[1], David M. Lloyd[1], Hermela Loulseged[2], Jane E. Loveland[1], Jamieson D. Lovell[1], Ryan Lozado[2], Jing Lu[2], Rachael Lyne[1], Jie Ma[2], Manjula Maheshwari[2], Lucy H. Matthews[1], Jennifer McDowall[1], Stuart McLaren[1], Amanda McMurray[1], Patrick Meidl[1], Thomas Meitinger[17], Sarah Milne[1], George Miner[2], Shailesh L. Mistry[1], Margaret Morgan[2], Sidney Morris[2], Ines Müller[5,18], James C. Mullikin[19], Ngoc Nguyen[2], Gabriele Nordsiek[3], Gerald Nyakatura[3], Christopher N. O'Dell[1], Geoffery Okwuonu[2], Sophie Palmer[1], Richard Pandian[1], David Parker[2], Julia Parrish[2], Shiran Pasternak[2], Dina Patel[1], Alex V. Pearce[1], Danita M. Pearson[1], Sarah E. Pelan[1], Lesette Perez[2], Keith M. Porter[1], Yvonne Ramsey[1], Kathrin Reichwald[3], Susan Rhodes[1], Kerry A. Ridler[1], David Schlessinger[20], Mary G. Schueler[19], Harminder K. Sehra[1], Charles Shaw-Smith[1], Hua Shen[2], Elizabeth M. Sheridan[1], Ratna Shownkeen[1], Carl D. Skuce[1], Michelle L. Smith[1], Elizabeth C. Sotheran[1], Helen E. Steingruber[1], Charles A. Steward[1], Roy Storey[1], R. Mark Swann[1], David Swarbreck[1], Paul E. Tabor[2], Stefan Taudien[3], Tineace Taylor[2], Brian Teague[2], Karen Thomas[1], Andrea Thorpe[1], Kirsten Timms[2], Alan Tracey[1], Steve Trevanion[1], Anthony C. Tromans[1], Michele d'Urso[12], Daniel Verduzco[2], Donna Villasana[2], Lenee Waldron[2], Melanie Wall[1], Qiaoyan Wang[2], James Warren[2], Georgina L. Warry[1], Xuehong Wei[2], Anthony West[1], Siobhan L. Whitehead[1], Mathew N. Whiteley[1], Jane E. Wilkinson[1], David L. Willey[1], Gabrielle Williams[2], Leanne Williams[1], Angela Williamson[2], Helen Williamson[1], Laurens Wilming[1], Rebecca L. Woodmansey[1], Paul W. Wray[1], Jennifer Yen[2], Jingkun Zhang[2], Jianling Zhou[2], Huda Zoghbi[2], Sara Zorilla[2], David Buck[1], Richard Reinhardt[5], Annemarie Poustka[16], André Rosenthal[3], Hans Lehrach[5], Alfons Meindl[7], Patrick J. Minx[4], LaDeana W. Hillier[4], Huntington F. Willard[21], Richard K. Wilson[4], Robert H. Waterston[4], Catherine M. Rice[1], Mark Vaudin[1], Alan Coulson[1], David L. Nelson[2], George Weinstock[2], John E. Sulston[1], Richard Durbin[1], Tim Hubbard[1], Richard A. Gibbs[2], Stephan Beck[1], Jane Rogers[1] & David R. Bentley[1]

[1] The Wellcome Trust Sanger Institute, Wellcome Trust Genome Campus, Hinxton, Cambridge CB10 1SA, UK

[2] Baylor College of Medicine Human Genome Sequencing Center, Department of Molecular and Human Genetics, One Baylor Plaza, Houston, Texas 77030, USA

[3] Genomanalyse, Institut für Molekulare Biotechnologie, Beutenbergstr. 11, 07745 Jena, Germany

[4] Washington University Genome Sequencing Center, Box 8501, 4444 Forest Park Avenue, St. Louis, Missouri 63108, USA

[5] Max Planck Institute for Molecular Genetics, Ihnestrasse 73, 14195 Berlin, Germany

[6] Institute for Clinical Molecular Biology, Christian-Albrechts-University, 24105 Kiel, Germany

[7] Medizinische Genetik, Ludwig-Maximilian-Universität, Goethestr. 29, 80336 München, Germany

[8] HUGO Gene Nomenclature Committee, The Galton Laboratory, Department of Biology, University College London, Wolfson House, 4 Stephenson Way, London NW1 2HE, UK

[9] Department of Biochemistry and Molecular Biology, Pennsylvania State College of Medicine, Hershey, Pennsylvania 17033, USA

[10] Advanced Center for Genetic Technology, PE-Applied Biosystems, Foster City, California 94404, USA

[11] European Bioinformatics Institute, Wellcome Trust Genome Campus, Hinxton, Cambridge CB10 1SD, UK

[12] Institute of Genetics and Biophysics, Adriano Buzzati-Traverso, Via Marconi 12, 80100 Naples, Italy

[13] Medical Genetics Section, University of Edinburgh, Western General Hospital, Edinburgh EH4 2XU, UK

[14] Laboratoire de Génétique et de Physiopathologie des Retards Mentaux, Institut Cochin. Inserm U567, Université Paris V., 24 rue du Faubourg Saint Jacques, 75014 Paris, France

[15] BACPAC Resources, Children's Hospital Oakland Research Institute, 747 52nd Street, Oakland, California 94609, USA

[16] Molekulare Genomanalyse, Deutsches Krebsforschungszentrum, Im Neuenheimer Feld 580, 69120 Heidelberg, Germany

[17] Institute of Human Genetics, GSF National Research Center for Environment and Health, Ingolstädter Landstr. 1, 85764 Neuherberg, Germany

[18] RZPD Resource Center for Genome Research, 14059 Berlin, Germany

[19] National Human Genome Research Institute, National Institutes of Health, Bethesda, Maryland 20892, USA

[20] Laboratory of Genetics, National Institute on Aging, 333 Cassell Drive, Baltimore, Maryland 21224, USA

[21] Institute for Genome Sciences & Policy, Duke University, Durham, North Carolina 27708, USA

Received 1 February; accepted 7 February 2005; doi:10.1038/nature03440.

References:

1. Ohno, S. *Sex Chromosomes and Sex-linked Genes* (Springer, Berlin, 1967).

2. McKusick-Nathans Institute for Genetic Medicine, Johns Hopkins University and National Center for Biotechnology Information, National Library of Medicine. *OMIM: Online Mendelian Inheritance in Man*. 〈http://www.ncbi.nlm.nih.gov/omim/〉 (2000).

3. Royer-Pokora, B. *et al.* Cloning the gene for an inherited human disorder—chronic granulomatous disease—on the basis of its chromosomal location. *Nature* **322**, 32-38 (1986).

4. Monaco, A. P. *et al.* Isolation of candidate cDNAs for portions of the Duchenne muscular dystrophy gene. *Nature* **323**, 646-650 (1986).

5. Bentley, D. R. *et al.* The physical maps for sequencing human chromosomes 1, 6, 9, 10, 13, 20 and X. *Nature* **409**, 942-943 (2001).

6. Humphray, S. J. *et al.* DNA sequence and analysis of human chromosome 9. *Nature* **429**, 369-374 (2004).

7. International Human Genome Sequencing Consortium. Initial sequencing and analysis of the human genome. *Nature* **409**, 860-921 (2001).

8. Schmutz, J. *et al.* Quality assessment of the human genome sequence. *Nature* **429**, 365-368 (2004).

9. Mahtani, M. M. & Willard, H. F. Physical and genetic mapping of the human X chromosome centromere: repression of recombination. *Genome Res.* **8**, 100-110 (1998).

10. Kong, A. *et al.* A high-resolution recombination map of the human genome. *Nature Genet.* **31**, 241-247 (2002).

11. Pruitt, K. D., Katz, K. S., Sicotte, H. & Maglott, D. R. Introducing RefSeq and LocusLink: curated human genome resources at the NCBI. *Trends Genet.* **16**, 44-47 (2000).

12. Mungall, A. J. *et al.* The DNA sequence and analysis of human chromosome 6. *Nature* **425**, 805-811 (2003).

13. Deloukas, P. *et al.* The DNA sequence and comparative analysis of human chromosome 10. *Nature* 429, 375-381 (2004).

14. Dunham, A. *et al.* The DNA sequence and analysis of human chromosome 13. *Nature* **428**, 522-528 (2004).

15. Griffiths-Jones, S., Bateman, A., Marshall, M., Khanna, A. & Eddy, S. R. Rfam: an RNA family database. *Nucleic Acids Res.* **31**, 439-441 (2003).

16. Lowe, T. M. & Eddy, S. R. tRNAscan-SE: a program for improved detection of transfer RNA genes in genomic sequence. *Nucleic Acids Res.* **25**, 955-964 (1997).

17. Griffiths-Jones, S. The microRNA Registry. *Nucleic Acids Res.* **32** (Database issue), D109-111 (2004).

18. Brown, C. J. *et al.* A gene from the region of the human X inactivation centre is expressed exclusively from the inactive X chromosome. *Nature* 349, 38-44 (1991).

19. Brown, C. J. *et al.* The human XIST gene: analysis of a 17 kb inactive X-specific RNA that contains conserved repeats and is highly localized within the nucleus. *Cell* **71**, 527-542 (1992).

20. Lee, J. T., Davidow, L. S. & Warshawsky, D. Tsix, a gene antisense to Xist at the X-inactivation centre. *Nature Genet.* **21**, 400-404 (1999).

21. Migeon, B. R., Chowdhury, A. K., Dunston, J. A. & McIntosh, I. Identification of TSIX, encoding an RNA antisense to human XIST, reveals differences from its murine counterpart: implications for X inactivation. *Am. J. Hum. Genet.* **69**, 951-960 (2001).

22. Chow, J. C., Hall, L. L., Clemson, C. M., Lawrence, J. B. & Brown, C. J. Characterization of expression at the human XIST locus in somatic, embryonal carcinoma, and transgenic cell lines. *Genomics* **82**, 309-322 (2003).

23. Chureau, C. *et al.* Comparative sequence analysis of the X-inactivation center region in mouse, human, and bovine. *Genome Res.* **12**, 894-908 (2002).

24. Bateman, A. *et al.* The Pfam protein families database. *Nucleic Acids Res.* **32** (Database issue), D138-141 (2004).

25. Scanlan, M. J., Simpson, A. J. & Old, L. J. The cancer/testis genes: review, standardization, and commentary. *Cancer Immun.* [online] **4**, 1 (2004).

26. Hurst, L. D. Evolutionary genomics: Sex and the X. *Nature* **411**, 149-150 (2001).

27. Chomez, P. *et al.* An overview of the MAGE gene family with the identification of all human members of the family. *Cancer Res.* **61**, 5544-5551 (2001).

28. Cheung, J. *et al.* Genome-wide detection of segmental duplications and potential assembly errors in the human genome sequence. *Genome Biol.* **4**, R25 (2003).

29. Stankiewicz, P. & Lupski, J. R. Genome architecture, rearrangements and genomic disorders. *Trends Genet.* **18**, 74-82 (2002).

30. Pegoraro, E. *et al.* Familial skewed X inactivation: a molecular trait associated with high spontaneous- abortion rate maps to Xq28. *Am. J. Hum. Genet.* **61**, 160-170 (1997).

31. Schueler, M. G., Higgins, A. W., Rudd, M. K., Gustashaw, K. & Willard, H. F. Genomic and genetic definition of a functional human centromere. *Science* **294**, 109-115 (2001).

32. Spence, J. M. *et al.* Co-localization of centromere activity, proteins and topoisomerase II within a subdomain of the major human X alpha-satellite array. *EMBO J.* **21**, 5269-5280 (2002).

33. Rudd, M. K. & Willard, H. F. Analysis of the centromeric regions of the human genome assembly. *Trends Genet.* **20**, 529-533 (2004).

34. She, X. *et al.* The structure and evolution of centromeric transition regions within the human genome. *Nature* **430**, 857-864 (2004).

35. The International SNP Map Working Group. A map of human genome sequence variation containing 1.42 million single nucleotide polymorphisms. *Nature* **409**, 928-933 (2001).

36. Schmid, M. *et al.* First report on chicken genes and chromosomes 2000. *Cytogenet. Cell Genet.* **90**, 169-218 (2000).

37. Kohn, M., Kehrer-Sawatzki, H., Vogel, W., Graves, J. A. & Hameister, H. Wide genome comparisons reveal the origins of the human X chromosome. *Trends Genet.* **20**, 598-603 (2004).

38. Graves, J. A. The origin and function of the mammalian Y chromosome and Y-borne genes—an evolving understanding. *Bioessays* **17**, 311-320 (1995).

39. Hillier, L. W. *et al.* Sequence and comparative analysis of the chicken genome provide unique perspectives on vertebrate evolution. *Nature* **432**, 695-716 (2004).

40. Freije, D., Helms, C., Watson, M. S. & Donis-Keller, H. Identification of a second pseudoautosomal region near the Xq and Yq telomeres. *Science* **258**, 1784-1787 (1992).

41. Skaletsky, H. *et al.* The male-specific region of the human Y chromosome is a mosaic of discrete sequence classes. *Nature* **423**, 825-837 (2003).

42. Page, D. C., Harper, M. E., Love, J. & Botstein, D. Occurrence of a transposition from the X-chromosome long arm to the Y-chromosome short arm during human evolution. *Nature* **311**, 119-123 (1984).

43. Sargent, C. A. *et al.* The sequence organization of Yp/proximal Xq homologous regions of the human sex chromosomes is highly conserved. *Genomics* **32**, 200-209 (1996).

44. Toder, R., Wakefield, M. J. & Graves, J. A. The minimal mammalian Y chromosome - the marsupial Y as a model system. *Cytogenet. Cell Genet.* **91**, 285-292 (2000).

45. Delbridge, M. L. *et al.* TSPY, the candidate gonadoblastoma gene on the human Y chromosome, has a widely expressed homologue on the X - implications for Y chromosome evolution. *Chromosome Res.* **12**, 345-356 (2004).

46. Lahn, B. T. & Page, D. C. Four evolutionary strata on the human X chromosome. *Science* **286**, 964-967 (1999).

47. Lyon, M. F. Gene action in the X-chromosome of the mouse (*Mus musculus* L.). *Nature* **190**, 372-373 (1961).

48. Carrel, L. & Willard, H. F. X-inactivation profile reveals extensive variability in X-linked gene expression in females. *Nature* doi:10.1038/nature03479 (this issue).

49. Jegalian, K. & Page, D. C. A proposed path by which genes common to mammalian X and Y chromosomes evolve to become X inactivated. *Nature* **394**, 776-780 (1998).

50. Gartler, S. M. & Riggs, A. D. Mammalian X-chromosome inactivation. *Annu. Rev. Genet.* **17**, 155-190 (1983).

51. Lyon, M. F. X-chromosome inactivation: a repeat hypothesis. *Cytogenet. Cell Genet.* **80**, 133-137 (1998).

52. Bailey, J. A., Carrel, L., Chakravarti, A. & Eichler, E. E. Molecular evidence for a relationship between LINE-1 elements and X chromosome inactivation: the Lyon repeat hypothesis. *Proc. Natl Acad. Sci. USA* **97**, 6634-6639 (2000).

53. Smit, A. F., Toth, G., Riggs, A. D. & Jurka, J. Ancestral, mammalian-wide subfamilies of LINE-1 repetitive sequences. *J. Mol. Biol.* **246**, 401-417 (1995).

54. Ke, X. & Collins, A. CpG islands in human X-inactivation. *Ann. Hum. Genet.* **67**, 242-249 (2003).

55. Coffey, A. J. *et al.* Host response to EBV infection in X-linked lymphoproliferative disease results from mutations in an SH2-domain encoding gene. *Nature Genet.* **20**, 129-135 (1998).

56. Stromme, P. *et al.* Mutations in the human ortholog of *Aristaless* cause X-linked mental retardation and epilepsy. *Nature Genet.* **30**, 441-445 (2002).

57. Amir, R. E. *et al.* Rett syndrome is caused by mutations in X-linked MECP2, encoding methyl-CpG-binding protein 2. *Nature Genet.* **23**, 185-188 (1999).

58. Orrico, A. *et al.* MECP2 mutation in male patients with non-specific X-linked mental retardation. *FEBS Lett.* **481**, 285-288 (2000).

59. Ropers, H. H. *et al.* Nonsyndromic X-linked mental retardation: where are the missing mutations? *Trends Genet.* **19**, 316-320 (2003).

60. The International Human Genome Mapping Consortium. A physical map of the human genome. *Nature* **409**, 934-941 (2001).

61. Ning, Z., Cox, A. J. & Mullikin, J. C. SSAHA: a fast search method for large DNA databases. *Genome Res.* **11**, 1725-1729 (2001).

62. Brudno, M. *et al.* LAGAN and Multi-LAGAN: efficient tools for large-scale multiple alignment of genomic DNA. *Genome Res.* **13**, 721-731 (2003).

63. Frazer, K. A., Pachter, L., Poliakov, A., Rubin, E. M. & Dubchak, I. VISTA: computational tools for comparative genomics. *Nucleic Acids Res.* **32**, W273–W279 (2004).

64. Bourque, G. & Pevzner, P. A. Genome-scale evolution: reconstructing gene orders in the ancestral species. *Genome Res.* **12**, 26-36 (2002).

65. Francke, U. Digitized and differentially shaded human chromosome ideograms for genomic applications. *Cytogenet. Cell Genet.* **65**, 206-218 (1994).

66. Gibbs, R. A. *et al.* Genome sequence of the Brown Norway rat yields insights into mammalian evolution. *Nature* **428**, 493-521 (2004).

67. Iwase, M. *et al.* The amelogenin loci span an ancient pseudoautosomal boundary in diverse mammalian species. *Proc. Natl Acad. Sci. USA* **100**, 5258-5263 (2003).

68. Lahn, B. T. & Page, D. C. A human sex-chromosomal gene family expressed in male germ cells and encoding variably charged proteins. *Hum. Mol. Genet.* **9**, 311-319 (2000).

Supplementary Information accompanies the paper on www.nature.com/nature.

Acknowledgements. We thank the Washington University Genome Sequencing Center for access to chicken and chimpanzee genome sequence data before publication; the Broad Institute for access to dog and chimpanzee genome sequence data before publication, for *T. nigroviridis* genome data, and for fosmid end-sequence data and clones; members of the Sanger Institute zebrafish genome project; the mouse, rat and *F. rubripes* sequencing consortia; Genoscope for *T. nigroviridis* genome data; the Ensembl, UCSC, EMBL and GenBank database groups; G. Schuler for information on sequence overlaps; T. Furey for information on RefSeq RNA coverage; D. Jaffe for data on fosmid end-sequence matches; D. Vetrie, E. Kendall, D. Stephan, J. Trent, A. P. Monaco, J. Chelly, D. Thiselton, A. Hardcastle, G. Rappold and the Resource Centre of the German Human Genome Project (RZPD) for the provision of clones and mapping data; the HUGO Gene Nomenclature

Committee (S. Povey (chair), M. W. Wright, M. J. Lush, R. C. Lovering, V. K. Khodiyar, H. M. Wain and C. C. Talbot Jr) for assigning official gene symbols; C. Rees for assistance with the manuscript; C. Tyler-Smith for critical reading of the manuscript; and the Wellcome Trust, the NHGRI, and the Ministry of Education and Research (Germany) for financial support.

Competing interests statement. The authors declare that they have no competing financial interests.

Correspondence and requests for materials should be addressed to M.T.R. (mtr@sanger.ac.uk). All DNA sequences reported in this study have been deposited in the EMBL or GenBank databases, and accession numbers are given in Supplementary Fig. 1.

Infrared Radiation from an Extrasolar Planet

D. Deming *et al.*

Editors's Note

Many of the planets that have been found outside our solar system are "hot Jupiters", with masses similar to that of Jupiter and orbiting very close to their parent stars. Some of these planets' orbits are aligned such that the planet periodically crosses the face of the star (from our perspective) and is then eclipsed by it. Here Drake Deming and colleagues report infrared observations of the planet HD 209458b while it was neither crossing nor eclipsed, so that light from the planet contributed to the total light from the system. By subtracting the light when the planet was in eclipse, they were able for the first time to detect light coming directly from the atmosphere of an extrasolar planet.

A class of extrasolar giant planets—the so-called "hot Jupiters" (ref. 1)—orbit within 0.05 AU of their primary stars (1 AU is the Sun–Earth distance). These planets should be hot and so emit detectable infrared radiation[2]. The planet HD 209458b (refs 3, 4) is an ideal candidate for the detection and characterization of this infrared light because it is eclipsed by the star. This planet has an anomalously large radius (1.35 times that of Jupiter[5]), which may be the result of ongoing tidal dissipation[6], but this explanation requires a non-zero orbital eccentricity (~0.03; refs 6, 7), maintained by interaction with a hypothetical second planet. Here we report detection of infrared (24 μm) radiation from HD 209458b, by observing the decrement in flux during secondary eclipse, when the planet passes behind the star. The planet's 24-μm flux is 55 ± 10 μJy (1σ), with a brightness temperature of $1{,}130 \pm 150$ K, confirming the predicted heating by stellar irradiation[2,8]. The secondary eclipse occurs at the midpoint between transits of the planet in front of the star (to within ± 7 min, 1σ), which means that a dynamically significant orbital eccentricity is unlikely.

OPERATING cryogenically in a thermally stable space environment, the Spitzer Space Telescope[9] has sufficient sensitivity to detect hot Jupiters at their predicted infrared flux levels[8]. We observed the secondary eclipse (hereafter referred to as "the eclipse") of HD 209458b with the 24-μm channel of the Multiband Imaging Photometer for Spitzer (MIPS)[10]. Our photometric time series observations began on 6 December 2004 at 21:29 UTC (Coordinated Universal Time), and ended at approximately 03:23 UTC on 7 December 2004 (5 h 54 min duration). We analyse 1,696 of the 1,728 10-s exposures so acquired, rejecting 32 images having obvious flaws. The Supplementary Information contains a sample image, together with information on the noise properties of the data.

来自一颗系外行星的红外辐射

戴明等

编者按

太阳系外已经发现的行星中，大部分都是"热木星"。它们的质量和木星相近，并以非常近的距离围绕它们的主星公转。从我们的视角来看，这些行星当中的一部分有着"对齐"的公转轨道，这种"对齐"使得它们会周期性地先从主星面前经过，接着被主星所遮掩。本文中，德雷克·戴明和他的同事们报告了他们对行星 HD 209458b 在既没有经过恒星表面，也没有被恒星所遮掩时进行的红外观测。这时，来自该系统的所有光线中有一部分是行星所贡献的。通过扣除行星在被主星遮掩时的光线，他们第一次得以探测到直接来自一颗系外行星大气层的光线。

所谓的"热木星"[1]，是一类太阳系外巨行星。它们在距离主星 0.05 个天文单位的范围内（1 个天文单位指的是太阳到地球的平均距离）围绕主星公转。由于靠近主星，这些行星的温度较高，所以可以发出可探测的红外辐射[2]。行星 HD 209458b[3,4] 因为会被其主星所遮掩，所以是探测并刻画这种红外辐射的理想候选体。这颗行星的半径较大，略显反常，是木星的 1.35 倍[5]。这可能是正在发生的潮汐耗散作用的结果[6]，但是这种解释需要假设存在第二颗行星，以使 HD 209458b 始终保持非零的轨道偏心率（约 0.03[6,7]）。这里我们报告通过观测行星经过恒星背面（即次食）时流量降低的程度而探测到的来自 HD 209458b 的红外辐射（24 微米）。这颗行星的 24 微米流量为 55 ± 10 μJy (1σ)，表面亮温度为 $1,130 \pm 150$ K。这确认了预测存在的由恒星辐射所产生的加热[2,8]。行星在经过恒星表面的时候会产生凌星现象。由于次食恰好发生在两次凌星的中间时刻（正负偏差在 7 分钟以内，1σ），这就意味着该行星不太可能有一个在动力学上显著的轨道偏心率。

在热稳定的太空环境中低温运行的斯皮策空间望远镜[9]，它的精度足够在理论预测的红外流量水平对热木星进行探测[8]。我们利用斯皮策多波段成像光度计（MIPS）[10] 的 24 微米通道，对 HD 209458b 的次食进行了观测。我们的测光时序观测开始于 2004 年 12 月 6 日 UTC 时间（协调世界时）21:29，大致结束于 2004 年 12 月 7 日 UTC 时间 03:23（持续时间 5 小时 54 分钟）。在观测获得的 1,728 张 10 秒曝光图片中，我们舍弃 32 张有明显缺陷的图片，并对剩下的 1,696 张进行研究。补充信息中包含了一张示例图片，并附上了与数据噪声属性相关的信息。

533

We first verify that circumstellar dust does not contribute significantly to the stellar flux. Summing each stellar image over a 13×13 pixel synthetic aperture (33×33 arcsec), we multiply the average sum by 1.15 to account for the far wings of the point spread function (PSF)[11], deriving a flux of 21.17 ± 0.11 mJy. The temperature of the star is close to 6,000 K (ref. 12). At a distance of 47 pc (ref. 13), a model atmosphere[14] predicts a flux of 22 mJy, agreeing with our observed flux to within an estimated ~2 mJy error in absolute calibration. We conclude that the observed flux is dominated by photospheric emission, in agreement with a large Spitzer study of planet-bearing stars at this wavelength[11].

Our time series analysis is optimized for high relative precision. We extract the intensity of the star from each image using optimal photometry with a spatial weighting function[15]. Selecting the Tiny Tim[16] synthetic MIPS PSF for a 5,000-K source at 24 μm, we spline-interpolate it to 0.01 pixel spacing, rebin it to the data resolution, and centre it on the stellar image. The best centring is judged by a least-squares fit to the star, fitting to within the noise level. The best-centred PSF becomes the weighting function in deriving the stellar photometric intensity. We subtract the average background over each image before applying the weights. MIPS data includes per-pixel error estimates[17], which we use in the optimal photometry and to compute errors for each photometric point. The optimal algorithm[15] predicts the signal-to-noise ratio (SNR) for each photometric point, and these average to 119. Our data are divided into 14 blocks, defined by pre-determined raster positions of the star on the detector. To check our SNR, we compute the internal scatter within each block. This gives SNR in the range from 95 to 120 (averaging 111), in excellent agreement with the optimal algorithm. For each point we use the most conservative possible error: either the scatter within that block or the algorithm estimate, whichever is greater. We search for correlations between the photometric intensities and small fluctuations in stellar position, but find none. We also perform simple aperture photometry on the images, and this independent procedure confirms our results, but with 60% greater errors.

The performance of MIPS at 24 μm is known to be excellent[18]. Only one instrument quirk affects our photometry. The MIPS observing sequence obtains periodic bias images, which reset the detector. Images following resets have lower overall intensities (by ~0.1–1%), which recover in later images. The change is common to all pixels in the detector, and we remove it by dividing the stellar intensities by the average zodiacal background in each image. We thereby remove variations in instrument/detector response, both known and unknown. The best available zodiacal model[19] predicts a background increase of 0.18% during the ~6 h

我们首先确认了星周尘对恒星流量没有明显贡献。利用一个大小为 13×13 像素的合成孔径（33×33 角秒），我们在每一张恒星图像上进行求和。考虑到点扩散函数（PSF）线翼远端的贡献，我们又对和的平均值乘以系数 1.15[11]，最终得到其流量为 21.17 ± 0.11 mJy。这颗恒星的温度接近 6,000 K[12]，在 47 pc[13] 的距离上，利用大气模型[14] 估计的流量为 22 mJy。这个值与我们观测到的流量相吻合，差别在绝对定标时对误差的估计（约为 2 mJy）以内。由此我们得出结论，观测到的流量中光球层发射占主导。在此波长上，该结论与一个利用斯皮策望远镜对带有行星的恒星所进行的大型研究相吻合[11]。

我们的时序分析对高相对精度进行了优化。在从每幅图像中抽取恒星强度的过程中，我们利用了带有空间权重函数的优化测光算法[15]。我们选择了利用 Tiny Tim 软件包[16] 合成 MIPS 点扩散函数，并将源的温度设定为 5,000 K，波长设定为 24 微米。接着，我们在将该点扩散函数样条插值至 0.01 像素的间距，并在重新合并至数据分辨率精度后，将其中心与恒星图像对齐。中心对齐的最好结果是由对恒星的最小二乘拟合来判定的，拟合程度为噪声范围以内。中心对齐最好的点扩散函数成为在计算恒星测光强度过程中的权重函数。在利用权重以前，我们从每幅图像中都扣除了背景平均值。MIPS 数据中包含了每个像素的误差估计[17]，我们在优化测光算法和计算每个测光数据点的误差中都使用了这些误差估计。我们使用的优化算法[15] 可以估计每个测光数据点的信噪比（SNR），它们的平均值为 119。我们的数据被分为 14 个区块，它们是利用恒星在传感器上预定的光栅位置来确定的。为了检验我们的信噪比，我们在每个区块的内部计算了内部的弥散。计算结果给出的信噪比范围为 95 到 120（平均值为 111），与优化算法给出的结果很好地吻合。在每一个测光点的误差选择上，我们采用了最为保守的方法：选择该点所在的区块内的弥散值和算法给出的误差估计中偏大的结果。在测光强度和细微的恒星位置波动之间，我们也没有找到相关性。我们在恒星图像上还使用了简单的孔径测光法来提取恒星强度。这种方法与前述方法之间是相互独立的，它也确认了我们得出的结果，但是得出的误差却高出 60%。

众所周知，MIPS 在 24 微米处的性能非常优秀[18]，只有一处与仪器相关的问题影响测光精度。MIPS 在观测过程中，会周期性地拍摄偏置图像。该过程会重置传感器。传感器在重置过程后所拍摄的图像在总体强度上会有所偏小（约 0.1～1%），但会随着拍摄过程而逐渐恢复。该变化过程在传感器所有像素上都有体现，因此我们对其改正的方法为在每一幅图像上用得到的恒星强度除以平均黄道背景。由此，我们移除了仪器/设备上已知和未知的变化。在可用的黄道模型中，最好的模型[19] 在

of our photometry. Because the star will not share this increase, we remove a 0.18% linear baseline from the stellar photometry. Note that the eclipse involves both a decrease and increase in flux, and its detection is insensitive to monotonic linear baseline effects.

To detect weak signals reliably requires investigating the nature of the errors. We find that shot noise in the zodiacal background is the dominant source of error; systematic effects are undetectable after normalizing any individual pixel to the total zodiacal background. All of our results are based on analysis of the 1,696 individual photometric measurements versus heliocentric phase from a recent ephemeris[20] (Fig. 1a). We propagate the individual errors (not shown on Fig. 1a) through a transit curve fit to calculate the error on the eclipse depth. Because about half of the 1,696 points are out of eclipse, and half are in eclipse, and the SNR ≈ 111 per point, the error on the eclipse depth should be $\sim 0.009 \times 2^{0.5}/848^{0.5} = 0.044\%$ of the stellar continuum. Model atmospheres for hot Jupiters[2,8,21-24] predict eclipse depths in the range from 0.2–0.4% of the stellar continuum, so we anticipate a detection of 4–9σ significance. The eclipse is difficult to discern by eye on Fig. 1a, because the observed depth (0.26%) is a factor of 4 below the scatter of individual points. We use the known period (3.524 days) and radii[5] to fit an eclipse curve to the Fig. 1a data, varying only the eclipse depth, and constraining the central phase to 0.5. This fit detects the eclipse at a depth of $0.26\% \pm 0.046\%$, with a reduced χ^2 of 0.963, denoting a good fit. Note that the 5.6σ significance applies to the aggregate result, not to individual points. The eclipse is more readily seen by eye on Fig. 1b, which presents binned data and the best-fit eclipse curve. The data are divided into many bins, so the aggregate 5.6σ significance is much less for a single bin (SNR ≈ 1 per point). Nevertheless, the dip in flux due to the eclipse is apparent, and the observed duration is approximately as expected. As a check, we use a control photometric sequence (Fig. 1b) to eliminate false positive detection of the eclipse due to instrument effects. We also plot the distribution of points in intensity for both the in-eclipse and out-of-eclipse phase intervals (Fig. 1c). This shows that the entire distribution shifts as expected with the eclipse, providing additional discrimination against a false positive detection.

我们约 6 小时的测光观测中所预测的背景强度升高 0.18%。由于恒星本身并不受这种增加的影响，所以我们在恒星测光中移除了一条 0.18% 的线性基线。需要指出的是，次食过程既包含了流量下降的过程也包含了流量上升的过程，而探测次食现象并不受单调的线性基线影响。

探究误差的本质在可靠地探测较弱信号的过程中是必需的。我们发现黄道背景中的散粒噪声是误差的最主要来源；把所有像素以黄道背景总和为标准进行归一化后，来源于系统误差的影响均无法探测到。我们所有的结果都是从 1,696 张独立测光观测中获得的。这些测光观测对应于该系统最近的一个星历测定工作所得出的日心相位 [20]（图 1a）。为了计算次食时掩食深度的误差，我们通过拟合凌星曲线来传递每个测光数据点的误差（误差并没有在图 1a 中标注）。因为在 1,696 个数据点中，次食内和次食外的点各占一半左右，并且每个点的信噪比约为 111，所以次食时的掩食深度误差应为恒星连续谱的 $\sim 0.009 \times 2^{0.5}/848^{0.5} = 0.044\%$。热木星的大气模型 [2,8,21-24] 对次食时的掩食深度的预计范围为恒星连续谱的 $0.2 \sim 0.4\%$，所以我们估计本次探测的显著程度应在 $4 \sim 9\sigma$ 之间。由于观测到的次食深度（0.26%）仅为单独数据点的弥散程度的 1/4 左右，在图 1a 上很难用肉眼识别出次食的形状。我们使用已知的周期（3.524 天）和半径 [5] 在图 1a 的数据上进行次食曲线的拟合。拟合过程中，我们将相位中心固定至 0.5，只调整次食的掩食深度。该拟合结果较好，探测到的次食深度为 0.26%±0.046%，约化 χ^2 为 0.963。需要指出的是，5.6σ 的显著程度适用于累计的结果，并不适用于单独的数据点。图 1b 展示了合并以后的数据和最佳拟合的次食曲线，在图 1b 上更容易用肉眼观测到次食。因为数据点被分隔至很多个区间中，所以累计的 5.6σ 显著程度对每一个单独的区间要小很多（每个点信噪比约为 1）。尽管如此，由次食所造成的流量下降是明显的，而且观测到的次食时长也与预期基本相符。作为检查手段，我们使用了一个对照测光序列（图 1b）来消除由于可能的仪器效应所造成的次食假阳性探测。我们还按照强度区间，画出了次食相位内和次食相位外的数据点的分布（图 1c）。该图展示了整个分布会根据次食相位的不同而移动，这是与预期相吻合的，也提供了探测到的次食并非假阳性结果的额外证据。

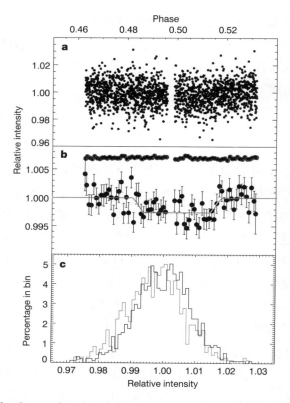

Fig. 1. Observations showing our detection of the secondary eclipse in HD 209458. **a**, Relative intensities versus heliocentric phase (scale at top) for all 1,696 data points. The phase is corrected for light travel time at the orbital position of the telescope. Error bars are suppressed for clarity. The gap in the data near phase 0.497 is due to a pause for telescope overhead activity. The secondary eclipse is present, but is a factor of ~4 below the ~1% noise level of a single measurement. **b**, Intensities from **a**, averaged in bins of phase width 0.001 (scale at top), with 1σ error bars computed by statistical combination from the errors of individual points. The red line is the best-fit secondary eclipse curve (depth = 0.26%), constrained to a central phase of 0.5. The points in blue are a control sequence, summing intensities over a 10×10-pixel region of the detector, to beat down the random errors and reveal any possible systematic effects. The control sequence uses the same detector pixels, on average, as those where the star resides, but is sampled out of phase with the variations in the star's raster motion during the MIPS photometry cycle. **c**, Histograms of intensity (lower abscissa scale) for the points in **a**, with bin width 0.1%, shown separately for the out-of-eclipse (black) and in-eclipse intervals (red).

We further illustrate the reality of the eclipse on Fig. 2. Now shifting the eclipse curve in phase, we find the best-fitting amplitude and χ^2 at each shift. This determines the best-fit central phase for the eclipse, and also further illustrates the statistical significance of the result. The thick line in Fig. 2a shows that the maximum amplitude (0.26%) is obtained at exactly phase 0.5 (which is also the minimum of χ^2). Further, we plot the eclipse "amplitude" versus central phase using 100 sets of synthetic data, consisting of gaussian noise with dispersion matching the real data, but without an eclipse. The amplitude (0.26%) of the eclipse in the real data stands well above the statistical fluctuations in the synthetic data.

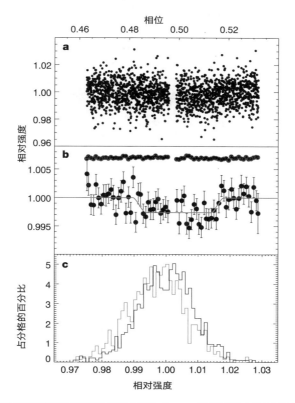

图 1. 观测展示了我们探测到的 HD 209458 系统中的次食。**a**，我们画出 1,696 个数据点的相对强度与该系统日心坐标系相位的关系图（横坐标在图的上方）。我们根据望远镜轨道位置的光传播时间对相位进行了修正。为将图像展示得更明了，我们没有画误差棒。相位 0.497 附近的数据间断是由于望远镜的非观测性活动造成的暂停产生的。系统的次食是存在的，但是仅为单独数据点噪声水平（约 1%）的 1/4 左右。**b**，将图 **a** 中的强度以 0.001 相位分格平均于每个小格中（横坐标在图的上方），同时也画出了 1σ 误差棒。误差棒是用统计的方法将单独点的误差合并计算得到的。红色线为最佳拟合的次食曲线（掩食深度为 0.26%），其中心相位被限制于 0.5。通过对传感器上 10×10 像素区域的强度求和，我们得到了一个对照序列，在图中是以蓝色显示的。我们使用该对照序列来减小随机误差的影响，同时揭示可能存在的系统误差影响。对照序列在传感器上使用的像素与恒星星像所处的像素基本相同，但在 MIPS 测光观测周期对它们采样时，恒星在传感器上的光栅位置是恰好错开的。**c**，用图 **a** 中的强度数据画出的直方图（横坐标位于图的下方），分格大小为 0.1%。次食区间内和次食区间外分别用红色和黑色标出。

我们利用图 2 来更深入地阐明次食的实际情况。我们移动次食曲线至不同的相位位置，并在每个移动的位置上找到拟合最好的幅度和 χ^2。该操作可以确定最佳拟合的次食中心相位，并可以进一步阐释结果的统计显著性。图 2a 中的粗线显示最大的幅度（0.26%）是准确地在 0.5 相位处获得的（该位置也是 χ^2 最小值获得处）。更进一步，我们用 100 组合成数据画出次食的"幅度"相对于中心相位的图像。这些数据包含了与真实数据相当的高斯噪声弥散，但并不含有次食事件。真实数据中次食的掩食深度（0.26%）显著高于合成数据的统计波动。

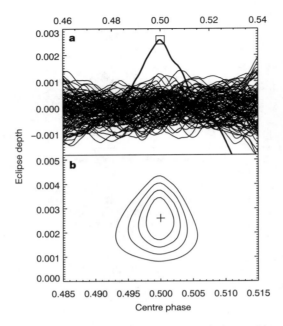

Fig. 2. Amplitude of the secondary eclipse versus assumed central phase, with confidence intervals for both. **a**, The darkest line shows the amplitude of the best-fit eclipse curve versus the assumed central phase (scale at top). The overplotted point marks the fit having smallest χ^2, which also has the greatest eclipse amplitude. The numerous thinner black lines show the effect of fitting to 100 synthetic data sets containing no eclipse, but having the same per-point errors as the real data. Their fluctuations in retrieved amplitude versus phase are indicative of the error in eclipse amplitude, and are consistent with $\sigma = 0.046\%$. Note that the eclipse amplitude found in the real data (0.26%) stands well above the error envelope at phase 0.5. **b**, Confidence intervals at the 1, 2, 3 and 4σ levels for the eclipse amplitude and central phase (note expansion of phase scale, at bottom). The plotted point marks the best fit (minimum χ^2) with eclipse depth of 0.26%, and central phase indistinguishable from 0.5. The centre of the eclipse occurs in our data at Julian day 2453346.5278.

Figure 2b shows confidence intervals on the amplitude and central phase, based on the χ^2 values. The phase shift of the eclipse is quite sensitive to eccentricity (e) and is given[25] as $\Delta t = 2Pe\cos(\omega)/\pi$, where P is the orbital period, and ω is the longitude of periastron. The Doppler data alone give $e = 0.027 \pm 0.015$ (Laughlin, G., personal communication), and allow a phase shift as large as ± 0.017 (87 min). We find the eclipse centred at phase 0.5, and we checked the precision using a bootstrap Monte Carlo procedure[26]. The 1σ phase error from this method is 0.0015 (~7 min), consistent with Fig. 2b. A dynamically significant eccentricity, $e \approx 0.03$ (refs 6, 7), constrained by our 3σ limit of $\Delta t < 21$ min, requires $|(\omega - \pi/2)| < 12$ degrees and is therefore only possible in the unlikely case that our viewing angle is closely parallel to the major axis of the orbit. A circular orbit rules out a promising explanation for the planet's anomalously large radius: tidal dissipation as an interior energy source to slow down planetary evolution and contraction[7]. Because the dynamical time for tidal decay to a circular orbit is short, this scenario posited the presence of a perturbing second planet in the system to continually force the eccentricity— a planet that is no longer necessary with a circular orbit for HD 209458b.

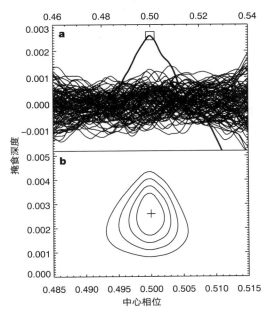

图 2. 次食深度与推定的中心相位关系图和二者各自的置信区间图。**a**，颜色最深的线展示了最佳拟合的次食曲线的幅度和推定的中心相位之间的关系（横坐标位于图的上方）。图中覆盖在粗线上方的点代表 χ^2 最小的拟合，该拟合结果的掩食深度也最大。旁边多条稍细的黑线展示了利用 100 组人造数据获得的结果。这些数据的单点误差和真实数据相同，但并不包含次食事件。人造数据拟合得到的掩食深度和相位之间的波动与 $\sigma = 0.046\%$ 相符，且可以大概标明从真实数据中得到的掩食深度的误差范围。可以看到，真实数据中得到的次食深度（0.26%）明显高于 0.5 相位处的误差范围。**b**，次食深度和中心相位分别在 1、2、3、4σ 处的置信区间（横坐标位于下方，请注意相位尺度的放大）。图中画出的点代表最佳拟合结果（最小的 χ^2），此时的次食深度为 0.26%，中心相位基本位于 0.5。在我们的数据中，次食中心发生在儒略日 2453346.5278。

图 2b 展示了幅度和中心相位基于 χ^2 的置信区间。次食的相移对于偏心率（e）较为敏感[25]，其表达式为 $\Delta t = 2Pe\cos(\omega)/\pi$，其中 P 为轨道周期，ω 为近星点经度。单独的多普勒数据给出的偏心率是 $e = 0.027 \pm 0.015$（劳克林，个人交流），该值所允许的最大相移为 ± 0.017（87 分钟）。我们发现掩食的中心在相位 0.5 处，然后利用自举蒙特卡罗方法来检测该结果的精度[26]。该方法所给出的 1σ 相位误差为 0.0015（约为 7 分钟），与图 2b 一致。利用前述结果可知 3σ 限制所对应的 $\Delta t < 21$ 分钟。在该约束条件下，若该系统有一个动力学显著的偏心率 $e \approx 0.03$[6,7]，则要求有 $|\omega - \pi/2| < 12°$。该条件成立的可能性不高，因为它只有在我们的观测方向和行星公转轨道的半长径方向较为平行的特殊情况下才可以满足。由于潮汐耗散作为内部能量源可以减慢行星演化和收缩，它是该行星拥有异常大半径的有效解释，但是该行星的圆轨道排除了这种可能性[7]。因为潮汐对轨道圆化的动力学时标较短，因此如果该行星有动力学显著的偏心率，则该偏心率需假定系统中还有第二个持续对 HD 209458b 摄动的行星来维持。但对于圆轨道的 HD 209458b 来说，第二颗行星便不再必要。

The infrared flux from the planet follows directly from our measured stellar flux (21.2 mJy) and the eclipse depth (0.26%), giving 55 ± 10 μJy. The error is dominated by uncertainty in the eclipse depth. Using the planet's known radius[5] and distance[13], we obtain a brightness temperature $T_{24} = 1{,}130 \pm 150$ K, confirming heating by stellar irradiation[2]. Nevertheless, T_{24} could differ significantly from the temperature of the equivalent blackbody (T_{eq}), that is, one whose bolometric flux is the same as the planet. Without measurements at shorter wavelengths, a model atmosphere must be used to estimate T_{eq} from the 24-μm flux. One such model is shown in Fig. 3, having $T_{eq} = 1{,}700$ K. This temperature is much higher than T_{24} (1,130 K) due to strong, continuous H_2O vapour absorption at 24 μm. The bulk of the planetary thermal emission derives ultimately from re-radiated stellar irradiation, and is emitted at 1–4 μm, between H_2O bands. However, our 24-μm flux error admits a range of models, including some with a significantly lower T_{eq} (for example, but not limited to, models with reflective clouds or less H_2O vapour).

Fig. 3. Flux from a model atmosphere shown in comparison to our measured infrared flux at 24 μm. A theoretical spectrum (solid line) shows that planetary emission (dominated by absorbed and re-radiated stellar radiation) should be very different from a blackbody. Hence, models are required to interpret the 24-μm flux measurement in terms of the planetary temperature. The model shown has $T_{eq} = 1{,}700$ K and was computed from a one-dimensional plane-parallel radiative transfer model, considering a solar system abundance of gases, no clouds, and the absorbed stellar radiation re-emitted on the day side only. Note the marked difference from a 1,700-K blackbody (dashed line), although the total flux integrated over the blackbody spectrum is equal to the total flux integrated over the model spectrum. (The peaks at short wavelength dominate the flux integral in the atmosphere model, note log scale in the ordinate.) The suppressed flux at 24 μm is due to water vapour opacity. This model lies at the hot end of the range of plausible models consistent with our measurement, but the error bars admit models with cooler T_{eq}.

Shortly after submission of this Letter, we became aware of a similar detection for the TrES-1 transiting planet system[27] using Spitzer's Infrared Array Camera[28]. Together, these Spitzer results represent the first measurement of radiation from extrasolar planets. Additional Spitzer observations should rapidly narrow the range of acceptable models, and reveal the atmospheric structure, composition, and other characteristics of close-in extrasolar giant planets.

(**434**, 740–743; 2005)

在测量出该行星主星的红外流量（21.2 mJy）和掩食深度（0.26%）后，来自行星的红外流量便可以直接得出，为 55±10 μJy。误差主要来源于掩食深度的不确定性。利用该行星已知的半径[5] 和距离[13]，我们可以得出其亮温度为 $T_{24} = 1,130 \pm 150$ K。这个结果证实了恒星辐射的加热作用[2]。尽管如此，T_{24} 也有可能与等效的黑体温度（T_{eq}），即用行星的热流量计算出的温度，有着显著的差别。在缺乏短波长区域测量的情况下，我们必须使用行星大气模型结合 24 微米处的流量来估计 T_{eq}。图 3 中展示了我们使用的一种模型，它得出的 $T_{eq} = 1,700$ K。该温度明显高出 T_{24}（1,130 K），主要原因是在 24 微米处有着水蒸气连续且较强的吸收。行星热辐射的主要部分最终的源头是对恒星辐射的再辐射，主要集中在 1～4 微米之间，介于水的波段之间。但是，我们所计算出的 24 微米处流量的误差使得很多种模型都有可能，其中就包括一些可以产生明显更低的 T_{eq} 的模型（比如有着反射性云层或者更少水蒸气的模型，但并不局限于此）。

图 3. 利用大气模型得到的流量与我们在 24 微米处测量得到流量的比较。该理论光谱（实线）表明行星辐射（由吸收和再辐射恒星辐射占主导）应与黑体非常不同。因此，合理的模型必须能够用行星温度来解释 24 微米处测量到的流量。图中所展示的是一个一维平面平行辐射转移模型的结果。在计算中，我们设定的条件为已知太阳系的气体丰度，无云，且只有行星的向昼侧会吸收恒星辐射并再辐射。此时得到的 $T_{eq} = 1,700$ K。注意一个 1,700 K 的黑体所发出的辐射（虚线）与模型的不同，尽管二者积分得到的总流量是相等的。（短波长附近的尖峰在大气模型的积分总流量中占据主导地位，请注意纵坐标为对数坐标）。24 微米处流量偏低是由于水蒸气的不透明度造成的。该模型在一系列与我们的测量相符合的可能模型中是偏热的，但是测量得到的误差棒是允许有其他 T_{eq} 较低的模型存在的。

在我们刚提交这篇文章后不久，我们了解到其他研究组使用了斯皮策望远镜[28] 的红外阵列相机对 TrES–1 凌星行星系统有过相似的观测[27]。与该工作一起，我们使用斯皮策望远镜得出的结果代表着首次对系外行星辐射的测量。更多使用斯皮策望远镜的观测应该会迅速地将可信模型的范围缩窄，同时也会揭示出密近太阳系外巨行星的大气结构、成分和其他的特性等信息。

（梁恩思 翻译；周济林 审稿）

Drake Deming[1], Sara Seager[3], L. Jeremy Richardson[2] & Joseph Harrington[4]

[1] Planetary Systems Laboratory and Goddard Center for Astrobiology, Code 693; [2] Exoplanet and Stellar Astrophysics Laboratory, Code 667, NASA's Goddard Space Flight Center, Greenbelt, Maryland 20771, USA

[3] Department of Terrestrial Magnetism, Carnegie Institution of Washington, 5241 Broad Branch Road NW, Washington DC 20015, USA

[4] Center for Radiophysics and Space Research, Cornell University, 326 Space Sciences Bldg, Ithaca, New York 14853-6801, USA

Received 3 February; accepted 28 February 2005; doi:10.1038/nature03507.
Published online 23 March 2005.

References:

1. Collier-Cameron, A. Extrasolar planets: what are hot Jupiters made of? *Astron. Geophys.* **43**, 421-425 (2002).

2. Seager, S. & Sasselov, D. D. Extrasolar giant planets under strong stellar irradiation. *Astrophys. J.* **502**, L157-L161 (1998).

3. Charbonneau, D., Brown, T. M., Latham, D. W. & Mayor, M. Detection of planetary transits across a sun-like star. *Astrophys. J.* **529**, L45-L48 (2000).

4. Henry, G. W., Marcy, G. W., Butler, R. P. & Vogt, S. S. A transiting "51 Peg-like" planet. *Astrophys. J.* **529**, L41-L44 (2000).

5. Brown, T. M., Charbonneau, D., Gilliland, R. L., Noyes, R. W. & Burrows, A. Hubble Space Telescope time-series photometry of the transiting planet of HD 209458. *Astrophys. J.* **552**, 699-709 (2001).

6. Bodenheimer, P., Lin, D. N. C. & Mardling, R. A. On the tidal inflation of short-period extrasolar planets. *Astrophys. J.* **548**, 466-472 (2001).

7. Laughlin, G. *et al.* A comparison of observationally determined radii with theoretical radius predictions for short-period transiting extrasolar planets. *Astrophys. J.* (in the press).

8. Burrows, A., Sudarsky, D. & Hubeny, I. in *The Search for Other Worlds: Proc. 14th Annu. Astrophys. Conf. in Maryland* (eds Holt, S. & Deming, D.) Vol. 713, 143-150 (American Institute of Physics, Melville, New York, 2003).

9. Werner, M. W. *et al.* The Spitzer Space Telescope mission. *Astrophys. J. Suppl.* **154**, 1-9 (2004).

10. Rieke, G. H. *et al.* The Multiband Imaging Photometer for Spitzer (MIPS). *Astrophys. J. Suppl.* **154**, 25-29 (2004).

11. Beichman, C. A. *et al.* Planets and IR excesses: preliminary results from a *Spitzer* MIPS survey of solar-type stars. *Astrophys. J.* (in the press).

12. Ribas, A. H., Solano, E., Masana, E. & Gimenez, A. Effective temperatures and radii of planet-hosting stars from IR photometry. *Astron. Astrophys.* **411**, L501-L504 (2003).

13. Perryman, M. A. C. (ed.) *The Hipparcos and Tycho Catalogues* (ESA SP-1200, European Space Agency, Noordwijk, 1997).

14. Kurucz, R. *Solar Abundance Model Atmospheres for 0, 1, 2, 4, and 8 km/s* CD-ROM 19 (Smithsonian Astrophysical Observatory, Cambridge, Massachusetts, 1994).

15. Horne, K. An optimal extraction algorithm for CCD spectrososcopy. *Publ. Astron. Soc. Pacif.* **98**, 609-617 (1986).

16. Krist, J. in *Astronomical Data Analysis Software and Systems IV* (eds Shaw, R. A., Payne, H. E. & Hayes, J. J. E.) Vol. 77, 349-352 (Astronomical Society of the Pacific, San Francisco, 1995).

17. Gordon, K. D. Reduction algorithms for the Multiband Imaging Photometer for SIRTF. *Publ. Astron. Soc. Pacif.* (in the press).

18. Rieke, G. H. *et al.* in *Proc. SPIE: Optical, Infrared, and Millimeter Space Telescopes* (ed. Mather, J. C.) Vol. 5487, 50-61 (SPIE, Bellingham, Washington, 2004).

19. Kelsall, T. *et al.* The COBE Diffuse Infrared Background Experiment (DIRBE) search for the cosmic infrared background. II. Model of the interplanetary dust cloud. *Astrophys. J.* **508**, 44-73 (1998).

20. Wittenmyer, R. A. *The Orbital Ephemeris of HD 209458b.* Master's thesis, San Diego State Univ. (2003).

21. Goukenleuque, C., Bezard, B., Joguet, B., Lellouch, E. & Freedman, R. A radiative equilibrium model of 51 Peg b. *Icarus* **143**, 308-323 (2000).

22. Seager, S., Whitney, B. A. & Sasselov, D. D. Photometric light curves and polarization of close-in extrasolar giant planets. *Astrophys. J.* **540**, 504-520 (2000).

23. Barman, T. S., Hauschildt, P. H. & Allard, F. Irradiated planets. *Astrophys. J.* **556**, 885-895 (2001).

24. Sudarsky, D., Burrows, A. & Hubeny, I. Theoretical spectra and atmospheres of extrasolar giant planets. *Astrophys. J.* **588**, 1121-1148 (2003).

25. Charbonneau, D. in *Scientific Frontiers in Research on Extrasolar Planets* (eds Deming, D. & Seager, S.) Vol. 294, 449-456 (Astronomical Society of the Pacific, San Francisco, 2003).

26. Press, W. H., Teukolsky, S. A., Vettering, W. T. & Flannery, B. P. *Numerical recipes in C* 2nd edn (Cambridge Univ. Press, Cambridge, 1992).

27. Alonso, R. *et al.* TrES-1, the transiting planet of a bright K0V star. *Astrophys. J.* **613**, L153-L156 (2004).

28. Charbonneau, D. *et al.* Detection of thermal emission from an extrasolar planet. *Astrophys. J.* (in the press).

Supplementary Information accompanies the paper on www.nature.com/nature.

Acknowledgements. We thank G. Laughlin for communicating the latest orbital eccentricity solutions from the Doppler data and for his evaluation of their status. We acknowledge informative conversations with D. Charbonneau, G. Marcy, B. Hansen, K. Menou and J. Cho. This work is based on observations made with the

Spitzer Space Telescope, which is operated by the Jet Propulsion Laboratory, California Institute of Technology, under contract to NASA. Support for this work was provided directly by NASA, and by its Origins of Solar Systems programme and Astrobiology Institute. We thank all the personnel of the Spitzer telescope and the MIPS instrument, who ultimately made these measurements possible. L.J.R. is a National Research Council Associate at NASA's Goddard Space Flight Center.

Competing interests statement. The authors declare that they have no competing financial interests.

Correspondence and requests for materials should be addressed to D.D. (Leo.D.Deming@nasa.gov).

Origin of the Cataclysmic Late Heavy Bombardment Period of the Terrestrial Planets

R. Gomes *et al.*

Editor's Note

The Moon seems to have experienced a large increase in strikes by comets and asteroids about 700 million years after the formation of the solar system. It is hard to understand why this is so; but here Alessandro Morbidelli and colleagues propose an explanation. They show that if the giant planets migrated slowly (Jupiter inward, Saturn, Uranus and Neptune outward), they could hit a "resonance" between the orbits of Jupiter and Saturn that would lead to very rapid migration. This gravitational churning of the solar system would cause objects from the disk of debris outside the orbit of Neptune to be pulled into the inner solar system, increasing the rate of impacts on planets and moons.

The petrology record on the Moon suggests that a cataclysmic spike in the cratering rate occurred ~700 million years after the planets formed[1]; this event is known as the Late Heavy Bombardment (LHB). Planetary formation theories cannot naturally account for an intense period of planetesimal bombardment so late in Solar System history[2]. Several models have been proposed to explain a late impact spike[3-6], but none of them has been set within a self-consistent framework of Solar System evolution. Here we propose that the LHB was triggered by the rapid migration of the giant planets, which occurred after a long quiescent period. During this burst of migration, the planetesimal disk outside the orbits of the planets was destabilized, causing a sudden massive delivery of planetesimals to the inner Solar System. The asteroid belt was also strongly perturbed, with these objects supplying a significant fraction of the LHB impactors in accordance with recent geochemical evidence[7,8]. Our model not only naturally explains the LHB, but also reproduces the observational constraints of the outer Solar System[9].

PREVIOUS work[9] explains the current orbital architecture of the planetary system by invoking an initially compact configuration in which Saturn's orbital period was less than twice that of Jupiter. After the dissipation of the gaseous circumsolar nebula, Jupiter's and Saturn's orbits diverged as a result of their interaction with a massive disk of planetesimals, and thus the ratio of their orbital periods, P_S/P_J, increased. When the two planets crossed their mutual 1:2 mean motion resonance (1:2 MMR, that is, $P_S/P_J = 2$) their orbits became eccentric. This abrupt transition temporarily destabilized the giant planets, leading to a short phase of close encounters among Saturn, Uranus and Neptune. As a result of these encounters, and of the interactions of the ice giants with the disk, Uranus

546

类地行星激变晚期重轰击期的起源

戈梅斯等

编者按

月球似乎在太阳系形成之后大约 7 亿年时，遭受到的彗星和小行星的撞击大大增加。这一现象的原因很难解释。但本文中亚历山德罗·莫尔比代利和他的同事就这一现象给出了一个解释。他们的研究显示，如果巨行星缓慢迁移（木星向内迁移，土星、天王星和海王星向外迁移），它们将使得木星和土星的轨道之间形成一种"共鸣"，从而导致非常迅速的迁移。这种太阳系重力的扰动会造成海王星轨道外碎屑盘的天体被吸引到内太阳系，从而增加了其对行星和月球造成影响的概率。

针对月球岩石学记录的研究表明，在行星形成后的大约 7 亿年，月球陨击率激增[1]，这一事件被称为晚期重轰击（LHB）。行星形成理论尚不能合理解释为何在太阳系演化历史如此晚的阶段，会突然出现这样强的星子轰击期[2]。为此，研究人员提出了若干理论解释这一晚期的撞击突增[3-6]，然而目前还尚无一种理论建立在太阳系演化的自洽框架之内。本文中，我们提出 LHB 是由于巨行星的快速迁移触发的，该时期出现于长时间的宁静期之后。在这次迁移爆发的过程中，位于行星轨道外侧的星子盘变得不稳定，从而导致星子突然向太阳系内侧运动。同时，小行星带也受到强烈的扰动，其中的天体构成了 LHB 撞击体的绝大部分，这与最近发现的地球化学证据相符[7-8]。我们的模型不仅自然解释了 LHB，而且重现了外太阳系的观测约束[9]。

已有的研究[9]通过引入一个最初致密的构型，在这一构型中土星的轨道周期小于木星轨道周期的两倍，从而可以解释当前行星系统的轨道体系。当气态环日星云耗散后，木星、土星与大质量星子盘发生相互作用，导致二者的轨道发生背离，所以二者的轨道周期之比 P_S/P_J 也随之增加。当木星和土星越过其 1∶2 平运动共振（MMR）时（即 $P_S/P_J = 2$），这两颗行星轨道变得越来越椭。这一突然转变暂时使得巨行星变得不稳定，从而导致土星、天王星以及海王星在短时间轨道发生近距离交会。由于上述交会以及带有盘的冰巨行星的相互作用，天王星和海王星到达目前的日心

and Neptune reached their current heliocentric distances and Jupiter and Saturn evolved to their current orbital eccentricities[9]. The main idea of this Letter is that the same planetary evolution could explain the LHB, provided that Jupiter and Saturn crossed the 1:2 MMR roughly 700 Myr after they formed. Thus, our goal is to determine if there is a generic mechanism that could delay the migration process.

In previous studies[9-12], planet migration started immediately because planetesimals were placed close enough to the planets to be violently unstable. Although this type of initial condition was reasonable for the goals of those studies, it is unlikely. Planetesimal-driven migration is probably not important for planet dynamics as long as the gaseous massive solar nebula exists. The initial conditions for the migration simulations should represent the system that existed at the time the nebula dissipated. Thus, the planetesimal disk should contain only those particles that had dynamical lifetimes longer than the lifetime of the solar nebula. In planetary systems like those we adopt from ref. 9, we find that they had to be beyond ~15.3 AU (Fig. 1), leading to the initial conditions illustrated in Fig. 2a.

Fig. 1. Disk location and LHB timing. **a**, The histogram reports the average dynamical lifetime of massless test particles placed in a planetary system (shown as triangles) with Jupiter, Saturn and the ice giants on nearly circular, co-planar orbits at 5.45, 8.18, 11.5 and 14.2 AU, respectively. Initially, we placed 10 particles with $e = i = 0$ (where e is eccentricity and i is inclination) and random mean anomaly at each semimajor axis. Stable Trojans of the planets have been removed from this computation. Each vertical bar in the plot represents the average lifetime for those 10 particles. We define "dynamical lifetime" as the time required for a particle to encounter a planet within a Hill radius. A comparison between the histogram and the putative lifetime of the gaseous nebula[20] argues that, when the latter dissipated, the inner edge of

距，而木星和土星轨道则经过演化形成目前的偏心率 [9]。本文的主要观点是，以上行星演化理论同样也可以用于解释 LHB，不过需要满足以下条件：木星和土星需要在形成后大约 7 亿年越过其 1:2 平运动共振。因此，我们的研究目的是确定是否存在可以推迟迁移进程的一般机制。

在以往的研究中 [9-12]，星子与行星的距离被认为足够近，从而使行星变得非常不稳定，进而导致行星瞬间开始迁移。尽管这种初始条件对那些研究而言也是合理的，但是实际上却不可能发生。只要大量的气态大质量太阳星云还存在，那么星子驱动的迁移对于行星动力学而言可能就不会很重要。用于仿真模拟迁移过程的初始条件应该表征星云耗散时刻的系统状态。因此，星子盘应该只含有动力学寿命长于太阳星云的那些粒子。在类似被采纳的行星系统中 [9]，我们发现这些星子的距离超过 ~ 15.3 AU（图 1），图 2a 对相应的初始条件进行了说明。

图 1. 星子盘的位置和 LHB 发生时间。**a**，直方图给出了无质量检验粒子的平均动力学寿命；这些粒子被置于与木星、土星和冷巨行星几乎共面的圆形轨道上，它们的轨道距离分别为 5.45 AU、8.18 AU、11.5 AU、14.2 AU，如图中三角所示。最初，我们放置了 10 颗粒子，其偏心率 e 和倾角 i 均为零，每个半长轴处的平近点角随机取值。在该计算中，我们没有考虑稳定的特洛伊型小行星。图中的每条垂直线代表着 10 颗粒子的平均寿命。我们将"动力学寿命"定义为粒子在希尔半径内交会行星所需要的时间。通过对比直方图和推定的气体星云的寿命可知 [20]，当星云耗散后，星子盘内边缘将超过最外层冰

the planetesimal disk had to be about 1–1.5 AU beyond the outermost ice giant. **b**, Time at which Jupiter and Saturn crossed the 1:2 MMR, as a function of the location of the planetesimal disk's inner edge, as determined from our first set of migration simulations. In all cases, the disk had a surface density equivalent to 1.9 M_E per 1 AU annulus. The outer edge of the disk was varied so that the total mass of the disk was 35 M_E. The disk was initially very dynamically cold, with $e = 0$ and $i < 0.5°$. A comparison between **a** and **b** shows that a disk that naturally should exist when the nebula dissipated would produce a 1:2 MMR crossing at a time comparable to that of the LHB event.

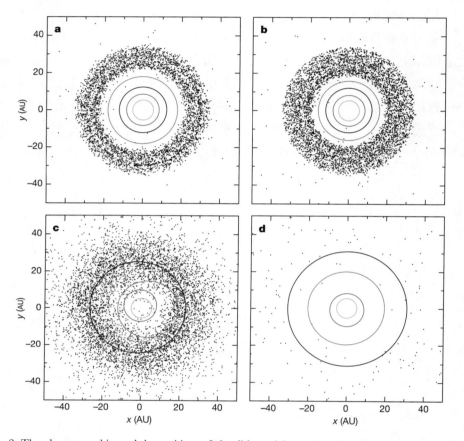

Fig. 2. The planetary orbits and the positions of the disk particles, projected on the initial mean orbital plane. The four panels correspond to four different snapshots taken from our reference simulation. In this run, the four giant planets were initially on nearly circular, co-planar orbits with semimajor axes of 5.45, 8.18, 11.5 and 14.2 AU. The dynamically cold planetesimal disk was 35 M_E, with an inner edge at 15.5 AU and an outer edge at 34 AU. Each panel represents the state of the planetary system at four different epochs: **a**, the beginning of planetary migration (100 Myr); **b**, just before the beginning of LHB (879 Myr); **c**, just after the LHB has started (882 Myr); and **d**, 200 Myr later, when only 3% of the initial mass of the disk is left and the planets have achieved their final orbits.

In this configuration, the initial speed of migration would be dependent on the rate at which disk particles evolve onto planet-crossing orbits. The time at which Jupiter and Saturn cross their 1:2 MMR depends on: (1) their initial distance from the location of the resonance, (2) the surface density of the disk near its inner edge, and (3) the relative location of the inner edge of the disk and the outer ice giant. On the basis of the above arguments, we initially

巨行星大约 1 ~ 1.5 AU。**b**，图中给出了木星和土星越过 1∶2 MMR 的时间与星子盘内边缘位置的函数关系，这一关系由我们第一组迁移的仿真模拟所确认。在所有的情况下，星子盘的密度等价于每 1 AU 环带 1.9 M_E。星子盘在最初动力学上是冷的，其偏心率 $e = 0$，倾角 $i < 0.5°$。比较图 **a** 和图 **b** 可知，当星云耗散后，自然存在的星子盘就会在与 LHB 事件相当的时间里越过 1∶2 MMR。

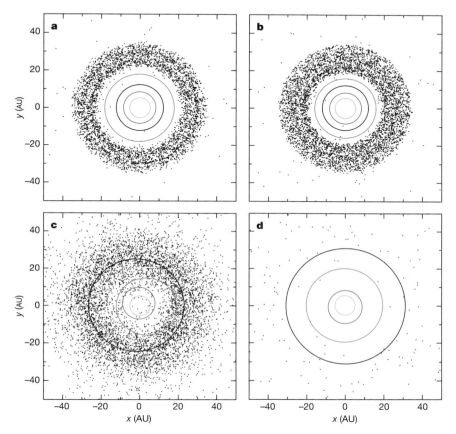

图 2. 在初始平均轨道平面上投影得到的行星轨道和星子盘粒子的位置。上面的四幅图片分别对应我们模拟过程中的四张快照。在我们的模拟中，四颗巨行星初始位置位于近圆形共面轨道上，其半长轴分别为 5.45 AU、8.18 AU、11.5 AU 和 14.2 AU。动力学上的冷星子盘的质量为 35 M_E，内边缘位于 15.5 AU，外边缘位于 34 AU。四幅图分别给出了行星系统在四个不同时期的状态：**a**，行星迁移的开始（1 亿年）；**b**，LHB 开始前不久（8.79 亿年）；**c**，LHB 开始后不久（8.82 亿年）；**d**，LHB 开始后的 2 亿年，这时星子盘只剩下 3% 的初始质量，各行星已经进入它们最终的轨道。

　　在这一构型中，行星迁移的初始速度将取决于星子盘粒子逸出至行星交会轨道的速率。木星和土星轨道越过 1∶2 MMR 的时间取决于：（1）它们与共振位置的初始距离；（2）靠近星子盘内边缘的表面密度；（3）星子盘内边缘与外侧冰巨行星的相对位置。基于以上参数，我们进行了八个仿真模拟，其中星子盘内边缘的位置设为唯

performed a series of eight simulations where the location of the inner edge of the disk was set as the unique free parameter (Fig. 1). As expected, we found a strong correlation between the location of the inner edge and the time of the 1:2 MMR crossing. For disks with inner edges near 15.3 AU (see above), we find crossing times between 192 Myr and 880 Myr (since the beginning of the simulation).

We also performed eight simulations where we varied the initial location of the ice giants by ~1 AU, Saturn's location by ~0.1 AU, the total mass of the disk by 5 Earth masses ($5\,M_E$), and its initial dynamical state by pushing the particles' eccentricities up to 0.1 and inclinations up to 3.5°. We found that we can delay the resonant crossing to 1.1 Gyr since the beginning of the simulation, although longer times are clearly possible for more extreme initial conditions. Therefore, we can conclude that the global instability caused by the 1:2 MMR crossing of Jupiter and Saturn could be responsible for the LHB, because the estimated date of the LHB falls in the range of the times that we found.

Figures 2 and 3 show the evolution of one of our runs from the first series of eight. Initially, the giant planets migrated slowly owing to leakage of particles from the disk (Fig. 3a). This phase lasted 880 Myr, at which point Jupiter and Saturn crossed the 1:2 MMR. After the resonance crossing event, the orbits of the ice giants became unstable and they were scattered into the disk by Saturn. They disrupted the disk and scattered objects all over the Solar System, including the inner regions. The solid curve in Fig. 3b shows the amount of material that struck the Moon as a function of time. A total of 9×10^{21} g struck the Moon after resonance crossing—roughly 50% of this material arrived in the first 3.7 Myr and 90% arrived before 29 Myr. The total mass is consistent with the estimate[4] of 6×10^{21} g, which was determined from the number and size distribution of lunar basins that formed around the time of the LHB epoch[1]. Such an influx spike happened in all our runs. The amount of cometary material delivered to the Earth is ~1.8×10^{23} g, which is about 6% of the current ocean mass. This is consistent with upper bounds on the cometary contribution to the Earth's water budget, based on D/H ratio measurement[13]. The average amount of material accreted by the Moon during this spike was $(8.4 \pm 0.3) \times 10^{21}$ g.

The above mass delivery estimate corresponds only to the cometary contribution to the LHB, as the projectiles originated from the external massive, presumably icy, disk. However, our scheme probably also produced an in flux of material from the asteroid belt. As Jupiter and Saturn moved from 1:2 MMR towards their current positions, secular resonances (which occur when the orbit of an asteroid processes at the same rate as a planet) swept across the entire belt[14]. These resonances can drive asteroids onto orbit with eccentricities and inclinations large enough to allow them to evolve into the inner Solar System and hit the Moon[4].

一的自由参量（图 1）。正如预期的那样，我们发现越过 1:2 MMR 的时间与星子盘内边缘的位置密切相关。当内边缘为 15.3 AU 时（见前述），相应的越过时间介于 1.92 到 8.80 亿年之间（从模拟启动开始计）。

同时，我们也进行了另外八个仿真模拟。在这些模拟中，我们设定冰巨行星的起始位置变化约 1 AU，土星的位置变化约 0.1 AU，星子盘的总质量变化 5 倍地球质量（5 M_E），并通过推动粒子的偏心率至 0.1 且推动倾角至 3.5° 来改变星子盘的起始动力学状态。通过这些模拟，我们发现可以将共振穿越的时间推迟到 11 亿年（从启动模拟开始计算）。当然，如果采用更为极端的初始条件，也可能得到更长的时间。因此，我们得出以下结论：越过木星和土星的 1:2 MMR 引起的全局不稳定性将会导致 LHB，因为推算出的 LHB 发生时间恰好落在我们模拟的时间范围内。

图 2 和图 3 展示了第一批八个模拟中的一次演化过程。最初，由于星子盘中粒子的渗漏，巨行星迁移得很缓慢，参见图 3a。这个阶段持续了 8.8 亿年，同时木星和土星在该时间越过了 1:2 MMR。共振穿越事件发生后，冰巨行星的轨道变得不稳定，并且通过土星散射入星子盘；这导致了星子盘的瓦解，并将其中的天体散射到太阳系各处，包括靠近太阳的区域。图 3b 中的实线给出了撞击月球的物质数量随时间的变化。共振穿越之后，总共有质量为 9×10^{21} g 的物质撞击了月球——其中，在前 370 万年有大约 50% 的物质达到月球，而在前 2,900 万年有 90% 的物质达到月球。通过分析 LHB 时期形成的月球盆地的数量和尺寸分布[1]，计算出的撞击物质总质量与预测结果一致，为 6×10^{21} g[4]。在我们所有的模拟中，均出现了这样的内向通量的峰值。该过程大约向地球释放了质量为 1.8×10^{23} g 的彗星物质，这大体相当于目前地球上海水总质量的 6%。该结果也与地球水量平衡中彗星贡献的上界相符，后者是基于 D/H 比值测量得到的[13]。在整个轰击峰值时期，月球增加的物质质量平均为 $(8.4 \pm 0.3) \times 10^{21}$ g。

以上输运质量的估计仅仅是对应在 LHB 时期的彗星物质贡献，即这些彗星抛射物质源自外部大质量的，推测可能是冰质的盘。然而，我们的体系中也存在源自小行星带的物质内向通量。随着木星和土星从 1:2 MMR 移动到目前的位置，当小行星带中的一颗小行星的轨道进动速率（这里指近星点进动速率）与一颗行星的进动速率相同时，就会发生扫过整个小行星带的长期共振[14]。这些长期共振驱使部分小行星进入偏心率和倾角较大的轨道，从而使得这些小行星足以进入太阳系内部区域并撞击月球[4]。

Fig. 3. Planetary migration and the associated mass flux towards the inner Solar System from a representative simulation. **a**, The evolution of the four giant planets. Each planet is represented by a pair of curves—the top and bottom curves are the aphelion and perihelion distances, Q and q, respectively. Jupiter and Saturn cross the 1:2 MMR at 880 Myr. The subsequent interaction between the planets and the disk led to the current planetary configuration as shown in ref. 9. **b**, The cumulative mass of comets (solid curve) and asteroids (dashed curve) accreted by the Moon. We have offset the comet curve so that the value is zero at the time of 1:2 MMR crossing. Thus, $\sim 5 \times 10^{21}$ g of comets was accreted before resonant crossing and 9×10^{21} g of cometary material would have struck the Moon during the LHB. Although the terrestrial planets were not included in our cometary simulations, we estimated the amount of material accreted by the Moon directly from the mass of the planetesimal disk by combining the particles' dynamical evolution with the analytic expressions in ref. 21. The impact velocity of these objects ranged from 10 to 36 km s^{-1} with an average of 21 km s^{-1}. Estimating the asteroidal flux first requires a determination of the mass of the asteroid belt before resonant crossing. This value was determined by first combining the percentage of asteroids remaining in the belt at the end of a simulation ($\sim 10\%$, very sensitive to planet migration rate and initial asteroid distribution) with estimates of the current mass of the belt to determine the initial asteroid belt mass ($\sim 5 \times 10^{-3}\ M_{\mathrm{E}}$). The flux was then again determined by combining the particles' dynamical evolution with the analytic expressions in ref. 21. The dashed curve shows a simulation where class 2 particles dominate. The average asteroidal impact velocity is 25 km s^{-1}.

We investigated the role of asteroid impactors in our LHB model by the following numerical integrations. The orbits of an asteroid belt, composed of 1,000 massless particles with semimajor axes between 2.0 and 3.5 AU, were integrated under the gravitational influence of the Sun, Venus, Earth, Mars, Jupiter and Saturn. Because formation models[15,16] predict that the asteroid belt was partially depleted and dynamically excited well before the LHB, we set the particles' eccentricities between 0 and 0.3 and inclinations between 0° and 30°, but kept the perihelion distances, q, > 1.8 AU and aphelion distances, Q, < 4 AU. Jupiter

图 3. 一次典型模拟中的行星迁移以及进入内太阳系相关的质量通量。**a**，图中给出了四颗巨行星的演化。图中每颗行星由两条曲线表示，上下两条曲线分别代表远日点（Q）和近日点（q）距离。木星和土星在 8.80 亿年越过 1:2 MMR。随后，行星和星子盘之间的相互作用形成了现在的行星系统构型[9]。**b**，图中给出了彗星和小行星撞击月球的累积质量，分别用实线和虚线表示。我们对彗星曲线进行了偏移，使得 1:2 MMR 穿越发生时刻的累积质量为零。因此，在共振穿越发生前大约质量为 5×10^{21} g 的彗星物质落在月球上，而在 LHB 期间总共有质量为 9×10^{21} g 的彗星物质撞击了月球。尽管我们在彗星模拟过程中并没有将类地行星也包含进来，但我们可以将粒子的动力学演化和参考文献 21 中的解析表达式结合起来，进而估算出星子盘物质撞击月球的质量。这些小型天体的撞击速度介于 10 至 36 km/s，平均速度为 21 km/s。为了估计小行星流量，需要首先确定共振穿越前的小行星带的质量。我们可以将模拟结束后的小行星在带中的剩余比例（约 10%，对行星迁移率和小行星初始分布十分敏感），与小行星带当前的估算质量综合起来，确定小行星带的初始质量（约 $5 \times 10^{-3} M_E$）。为了确定流量，我们可以将粒子动力学演化和参考文献 21 的解析表达式结合起来。图中虚线表明第二类粒子起主导作用的模拟结果。小行星的平均撞击速度为 25 km/s。

下面，我们借助数值积分的方法研究了 LHB 模型中小行星撞击体的作用。在太阳、金星、地球、火星、木星和土星的引力场的影响下，对以下小行星带进行积分：这是一条由 1,000 颗无质量粒子组成的小行星带，其中粒子的轨道半长轴介于 2.0 与 3.5 AU 之间。由于形成模型预测在 LHB 发生之前，这条小行星带就已经部分被清空并处于动力学上充分激发态[15-16]，因此我们将粒子的偏心率设在 0 到 0.3 之间，倾角

and Saturn were forced to migrate at rates that varied from run to run (adopted from ref. 9) by adding a suitably chosen drag-force term to their equations of motion.

We find that objects that reach Earth-crossing orbits follow one of two general paths. Some, referred to as class 1 particles, get trapped in the periapse secular resonance with Saturn (which affects eccentricities) and are driven directly onto Earth-crossing orbits. Other particles, referred to as class 2, stay in the asteroid belt, but are dynamically excited by resonant sweeping onto unstable orbits. These objects slowly leak out of the asteroid belt and can evolve into the inner Solar System. The two classes produce impact spikes with different temporal behaviours. Roughly 50% of class 1 particles arrive in the first 10 Myr, while 90% arrive within ~30 Myr. Conversely, the median arrival time for class 2 particles is ~50 Myr and 90% arrive within ~150 Myr. Class 2 particles dominated in our runs (Fig. 3). However, a preliminary investigation into this issue shows that this result is probably sensitive to the exact evolution of the giant planets and the dynamical state of the asteroid belt. Thus, the best we can conclude is that the impact spike due to asteroids is between these two extremes.

We find that $(3–8) \times 10^{21}$ g of asteroids hit the Moon during our simulations (Fig. 3). This amount is comparable to the amount of comets. So, our model predicts that the LHB impactors should have been a mixture of comets and asteroids. Unfortunately, we cannot say with any certainty the exact ratio of comets to asteroids in our model because, although the amount of cometary material is fairly well constrained (probably better than a factor of 2), the amount of asteroidal material is not well known (and could be outside the range reported above), because we do not have good estimates of the mass distribution in the asteroid belt before the LHB. It should also be noted that this ratio is probably a function of impactor size, because comets and asteroids probably have different size distributions. This ratio probably also varied with time. Within the first ~30 Myr comets dominated according to these simulations, but the last impactors were asteroidal. This is consistent with recent cosmochemical findings suggesting that some of the Moon's basins were formed by asteroids[7,8].

Our results support a cataclysmic model for the lunar LHB. Although many aspects of the LHB are not well known[1], our simulations reproduce two of the main characteristics attributed to this episode: (1) the 700 Myr delay between the LHB and terrestrial planet formation, and (2) the overall intensity of lunar impacts. Our model predicts a sharp increase in the impact rate at the beginning of the LHB. Unfortunately, the available lunar data are not yet capable of addressing this prediction.

Our model also has the advantage of supplying impactors that are a mixture of comets and asteroids. Our model predicts that the asteroid belt was depleted by a factor of ~10 during the LHB. This depletion does not contradict collisional evolution models[17,18]. On the contrary, the late secular resonance sweeping could explain why we do not see a large number of asteroid families that were produced during the LHB[18]. Our model predicts that the LHB lasted from between ~10 Myr and ~150 Myr. Correspondingly, the drop-off in

则介于 0 到 30°，近日点距离 q 满足 $q > 1.8$ AU，远日点距离 Q 满足 $Q < 4$ AU。通过在运动方程中加入合适的阻力项，木星和土星就会被迫以不断变化的速率迁移[9]。

我们发现，进入越地轨道的天体大致上遵循两条路径中的一条。一些天体被称为第一类粒子，它们会由于土星对偏心率的影响而被近星点长期共振俘获，而被直接拽入越地轨道。另一些粒子被称为第二类粒子，这类粒子位于小行星带中，但是会由共振清除作用被动力地激发到非稳定轨道上。这些小天体会逐渐脱离小行星带，然后进入内太阳系。以上两类粒子产生的撞击在时间分布上也不同。在第一类粒子中会有大约 50% 在最初的 1 千万年内发生撞击，大约 90% 会在约 3 千万年内发生撞击。对于第二类粒子，半数到达时间约为 5 千万年，90% 会在约 1.5 亿年内到达。如图 3 所示，在我们的计算机模拟中，第二类粒子起着主导作用。然而，我们的初步研究表明，以上问题的结果可能对巨行星的具体演化和小行星带的动力学状态十分敏感。因此，我们得出的最可信的结论是，小行星的撞击高峰期位于以上两个极值之间。

在模拟中，我们发现总质量为 $(3 \sim 8) \times 10^{21}$ g 的小行星撞击了月球，如图 3 所示。这一质量可以与彗星的质量相比较。因此，我们的模型预测 LHB 撞击体应该包含彗星和小行星。但是，我们并不能确定模型中彗星和小行星的确切比例。尽管可以较为准确地限定彗星物质的质量（可能优于因子 2），但是尚不清楚小行星物质的质量（可能在上述范围之外），这是因为我们尚不能很好地估计出 LHB 之前小行星带的质量分布。需要指出的是，彗星和小行星二者质量的比值可能也是撞击体尺寸的函数，因为彗星和小行星可能具有不同的尺寸分布。同时，这一比值也可能随时间变化。根据我们的模拟可知，在最初的约 3 千万年，彗星起主导作用；但是最后一批撞击体主要由小行星构成。这与最近的宇宙化学发现相符，其认为部分月球盆地是由于小行星撞击形成的[7,8]。

我们的结果支持月球 LHB 的灾变模型。尽管对于 LHB，有许多问题亟待解决，但是我们的模拟重现了这一事件的两个主要特征：（1）LHB 要比地球形成晚 7 亿年；（2）月球撞击的总强度。我们的模型也预测在 LHB 刚开始的时候，撞击率迅速增加。然而，目前的月球数据尚不能证实这一预测。

我们的模型另一个优点在于指出撞击体是彗星和小行星共同构成的。该模型预测，在 LHB 时期，整个小行星带经过耗损只剩下原先的约 1/10。这种耗损与碰撞演化模型并不矛盾[17,18]。相对地，晚期的长期共振清除机制可以解释为什么我们现在没有观察到大量产生于 LHB 时期的小行星族[18]。我们的模型预测，LHB 持续的时间介于 1 千万 ~ 1.5 亿年之间。相应的，这段时间内撞击率的衰减可以相当迅速

impact rates could be quite fast (with 50% of the impacts occurring in the first 3.7 Myr and 90% in 29 Myr) or moderately slow (with 50% of the impacts occurring in the first 50 Myr and 90% in 150 Myr). We are unable to pinpoint more exact values because the duration and the drop-off of the LHB depends on the relative contributions of class 1 asteroids, class 2 asteroids, and comets, which in turn are very sensitive to the pre-LHB orbital structure of the asteroid belt.

Most importantly, our scheme for the LHB is the result of a generic migration-delaying mechanism, followed by an instability, which is itself induced by a deterministic mechanism of orbital excitation of the planets[9]. This revised planetary migration scheme naturally accounts for the currently observed planetary orbits[9], the LHB, the present orbital distribution of the main-belt asteroids and the origin of Jupiter's Trojans[19].

(**435**, 466-469; 2005)

R. Gomes[1,2], H. F. Levison[2,3], K. Tsiganis[2] & A. Morbidelli[2]
[1] ON/MCT and GEA/OV/UFRJ, Ladeira do Pedro Antonio, 43 Centro 20.080-090, Rio de Janeiro, RJ, Brazil
[2] Observatoire de la Côte d' Azur, CNRS, BP 4229, 06304 Nice Cedex 4, France
[3] Department of Space Studies, Southwest Research Institute, 1050 Walnut Street, Suite 400, Boulder, Colorado, USA

Received 6 December 2004; accepted 18 April 2005.

References:

1. Hartmann, W. K., Ryder, G., Dones, L. & Grinspoon, D. in *Origin of the Earth and Moon* (eds Canup, R. & Righter, K.) 493-512 (Univ. Arizona Press, Tucson, 2000).

2. Morbidelli, A., Petit, J.-M., Gladman, B. & Chambers, J. A plausible cause of the Late Heavy Bombardment. *Meteorit. Planet. Sci.* **36**, 371-380 (2001).

3. Zappala, V., Cellino, A., Gladman, B. J., Manley, S. & Migliorini, F. Asteroid showers on Earth after family break-up events. *Icarus* **134**, 176-179 (1998).

4. Levison, H. F. *et al.* Could the lunar "Late Heavy Bombardment" have been triggered by the formation of Uranus and Neptune? *Icarus* **151**, 286-306 (2001).

5. Chambers, J. E. & Lissauer, J. J. A new dynamical model for the lunar Late Heavy Bombardment. *Lunar Planet. Sci. Conf.* **XXXIII**, abstr. 1093 (2002).

6. Levison, H. F., Thommes, E. W., Duncan, M. J., Dones, L. A. in *Debris Disks and the Formation of Planets: A Symposium in Memory of Fred Gillett (11-13 April 2002, Tucson, Arizona)* (eds Caroff, L., Moon, L. J., Backman, D. & Praton, E.) 152-167 (ASP Conf. Ser. 324, Astronomical Society of the Pacific, San Francisco, 2005).

7. Kring, D. A. & Cohen, B. A. Cataclysmic bombardment throughout the inner Solar System 3.9-4.0 Ga. *J. Geophys. Res. Planets* **107**(E2), 4-10 (2002).

8. Tagle, R. LL-ordinary chondrite impact on the Moon: Results from the 3.9 Ga impact melt at the landing site of Apollo 17. *Lunar Planet. Sci. Conf.* **XXXVI**, abstr. 2008 (2005).

9. Tsiganis, K., Gomes, R., Morbidelli, A. & Levison, H. F. Origin of the orbital architecture of the giant planets of the Solar System. *Nature* doi:10.1038/nature03539 (this issue).

10. Fernandez, J. A. & Ip, W.-H. Some dynamical aspects of the accretion of Uranus and Neptune—The exchange of orbital angular momentum with planetesimals. *Icarus* **58**, 109-120 (1984).

11. Hahn, J. M. & Malhotra, R. Orbital evolution of planets embedded in a planetesimal disk. *Astron. J.* **117**, 3041-3053 (1999).

12. Gomes, R. S., Morbidelli, A. & Levison, H. F. Planetary migration in a planetesimal disk: Why did Neptune stop at 30 AU? *Icarus* **170**, 492-507 (2004).

13. Morbidelli, A. *et al.* Source regions and timescales for the delivery of water to Earth. *Meteorit. Planet. Sci.* **35**, 1309-1320 (2000).

14. Gomes, R. S. Dynamical effects of planetary migration on the primordial asteroid belt. *Astron. J.* **114**, 396-401 (1997).

15. Wetherill, G. W. An alternative model for the formation of the asteroids. *Icarus* **100**, 307-325 (1992).

16. Petit, J., Morbidelli, A. & Chambers, J. The primordial excitation and clearing of the asteroid belt. *Icarus* **153**, 338-347 (2001).

17. Davis, D. R., Ryan, E. V. & Farinella, P. Asteroid collisional evolution: results from current scaling algorithms. *Planet. Space Sci.* **42**, 599-610 (1994).

18. Bottke, W. *et al.* The fossilized size distribution of the main asteroid belt. *Icarus* **175**(1), 111-140 (2005).

19. Morbidelli, A., Levison, H. F., Tsiganis, K. & Gomes, R. Chaotic capture of Jupiter's Trojan asteroids in the early Solar System. *Nature* doi:10.1038/nature03540 (this issue).

（50% 的撞击发生于开始的 370 万年，90% 的撞击发生于 2,900 万年内），或者适当减缓（50% 的撞击发生于开始的 5 千万年，90% 的撞击发生于 1.5 亿年内）。我们并不能更为精确的确定以上时间，因为 LHB 的持续和减弱依赖于第一类小行星、第二类小行星以及彗星的相对贡献，而这三者对 LHB 发生前的小行星带轨道结构颇为敏感。

最为重要的是，我们的 LHB 体系是由一般的迁移延迟机制造成的，随后出现的不稳定性本身又是由行星轨道的激发的决定性机制所诱发的 [9]。这一修正的行星迁移体系可以自然地将目前我们观测到的行星轨道 [9]、LHB、目前的主带小行星轨道分布以及木星–特洛伊族小行星的起源 [19] 纳入其中。

（金世超 翻译；季江徽 审稿）

20. Haisch, K. E., Lada, E. A. & Lada, C. J. Disk frequencies and lifetimes in young clusters. *Astrophys. J.* **553**, L153-L156 (2001).

21. Wetherill, G. W. Collisions in the asteroid belt. *J. Geophys. Res.* **72**, 2429-2444 (1967).

Acknowledgements. R.G. thanks Conselho Nacional de Desenvolvimento Científico e Tecnológico for support for his sabbatical year in the OCA observatory in Nice. K.T. was supported by an EC Marie Curie Individual Fellowship. A.M. and H.F.L. thank the CNRS and the NSF for funding collaboration between the OCA and the SWRI groups. H.F.L. was supported by NASA's Origins and PG&G programmes.

Author Information. Reprints and permissions information is available at npg.nature.com/reprintsandpermissions. The authors declare no competing financial interests. Correspondence and requests for materials should be addressed to A.M. (morby@obs-nice.fr).

Experimental Investigation of Geologically Produced Antineutrinos with KamLAND

T. Araki *et al.*

Editor's Note

The KamLAND anti-neutrino detector at the Kamioka mine in Japan was the first detector sensitive enough to detect neutrino oscillations—the spontaneous transformation of a neutrino from one type to another—by looking at anti-neutrinos from nuclear reactors. As Takeo Araki and colleagues note here, the detector was also sensitive enough to detect neutrinos produced in the Earth's interior from radioactive decay of uranium or thorium. Previous estimates of the energy released by such decays suggested that it accounted for fully half of the total energy dissipated inside the planet, making radioactivity a significant contributor to the heat of the deep earth. The results here broadly agree with the earlier figures, and put an improved upper limit on its value.

The detection of electron antineutrinos produced by natural radioactivity in the Earth could yield important geophysical information. The Kamioka liquid scintillator antineutrino detector (KamLAND) has the sensitivity to detect electron antineutrinos produced by the decay of ^{238}U and ^{232}Th within the Earth. Earth composition models suggest that the radiogenic power from these isotope decays is 16 TW, approximately half of the total measured heat dissipation rate from the Earth. Here we present results from a search for geoneutrinos with KamLAND. Assuming a Th/U mass concentration ratio of 3.9, the 90 per cent confidence interval for the total number of geoneutrinos detected is 4.5 to 54.2. This result is consistent with the central value of 19 predicted by geophysical models. Although our present data have limited statistical power, they nevertheless provide by direct means an upper limit (60 TW) for the radiogenic power of U and Th in the Earth, a quantity that is currently poorly constrained.

THE Kamioka liquid scintillator antineutrino detector (KamLAND) has demonstrated neutrino oscillation using electron antineutrinos ($\bar{\nu}_e$s) with energies of a few MeV from nuclear reactors[1,2]. Additionally, KamLAND is the first detector sensitive enough to measure $\bar{\nu}_e$s produced in the Earth from the ^{238}U and ^{232}Th decay chains. Using $\bar{\nu}_e$s to study processes inside the Earth was first suggested by Eder[3] and Marx[4], and has been reviewed a number of times[5-10]. As $\bar{\nu}_e$s produced from the ^{238}U and ^{232}Th decay chains have exceedingly small interaction cross-sections, they propagate undisturbed in the Earth's interior, and their measurement near the Earth's surface can be used to gain information on their sources. Although the detection of $\bar{\nu}_e$s from ^{40}K decay would also be of great interest in geophysics, with possible applications in the interpretation of geo-magnetism, their energies are too

KamLAND 对地质来源的
反中微子的实验研究

荒木岳夫等

编者按

KamLAND 反中微子探测器位于日本的神冈矿井下。它是第一个足够灵敏到通过监测来自反应堆的反中微子而探测到中微子振荡（即一种类型的中微子自发转变为另一种类型）的探测器。如荒木岳夫及其同事所指出的，该探测器也足够灵敏到可探测地球内部铀和钍放射性衰变产生的中微子。之前的估算表明，这些衰变产生的能量约占地球释放的总能量的一半，这使得放射性成为地球深部热能的一个主要来源。本文的结果与之前的数据大致吻合，并给出了更好的上限值。

探测地球中天然放射性产生的电子反中微子可以提供重要的地球物理信息。神冈液体闪烁体反中微子探测器（简称 KamLAND）可以探测到地球中放射元素 ^{238}U 和 ^{232}Th 衰变产生的电子反中微子（地球中微子）。地球组成模型表明，这些同位素衰变的放射性生热为 16 TW，大约占地球总散失热率测量值的一半。本文介绍了 KamLAND 探测地球中微子的结果。假设 Th/U 的质量丰度比为 3.9，探测到 90% 置信区间内地球中微子总数为 4.5 到 54.2 个。该结果与地球物理模型预测的中心值（19 个）一致。尽管现有数据统计量有限，这些数据仍然以直接的方式给出了此前知之甚少的地球中 U 和 Th 放射性生热的上限（60 TW）。

神冈液体闪烁体反中微子探测器（KamLAND）通过对来自核反应堆的几兆电子伏的电子反中微子（$\bar{\nu}_e$）的探测，证明了反应堆中微子振荡现象[1,2]。另外，KamLAND 也是第一个足够灵敏并探测到地球中 ^{238}U 和 ^{232}Th 衰变链产生的 $\bar{\nu}_e$ 的探测器。埃德[3] 和马克思[4] 第一次提出可利用 $\bar{\nu}_e$ 来测量地球内部性质，之后该观点被引述了数次[5-10]。^{238}U 和 ^{232}Th 衰变链产生的 $\bar{\nu}_e$ 具有极其小的相互作用截面，因此它们不受干扰地在地球内部传播，在地球表面附近对 $\bar{\nu}_e$ 进行测量可获得其产生来源的信息。尽管探测 ^{40}K 衰变产生的 $\bar{\nu}_e$ 对地球物理学也具有重要意义，可能用以解释地磁

low to be detected with KamLAND. The antineutrino flux above our detection threshold from other long-lived isotopes is expected to be negligible.

The Radiogenic Earth

The total power dissipated from the Earth (heat flow) has been measured with thermal techniques[11] to be 44.2 ± 1.0 TW. Despite this small quoted error, a more recent evaluation[12] of the same data (assuming much lower hydrothermal heat flow near mid-ocean ridges) has led to a lower figure of 31 ± 1 TW. On the basis of studies of chondritic meteorites[13] the calculated radiogenic power is thought to be 19 TW, 84% of which is produced by ^{238}U and ^{232}Th decay. Some models of mantle convection suggest that radiogenic power is a larger fraction of the total power[14,15].

^{238}U and ^{232}Th decay via a series of well-established α and β^- processes[16] terminating in the stable isotopes ^{206}Pb and ^{208}Pb, respectively. Each β^- decay produces a daughter nucleus, an electron and a $\bar{\nu}_e$. The $\bar{\nu}_e$ energy distribution is well established[17], and includes a correction for the electromagnetic interaction between the electron and the charge distribution of the daughter nucleus. Figure 1 shows the expected $\bar{\nu}_e$ distribution, $dn(E_\nu)/dE_\nu$, as a function of $\bar{\nu}_e$ energy, E_ν, for the ^{238}U and ^{232}Th decay chains.

Fig. 1. The expected ^{238}U, ^{232}Th and ^{40}K decay chain electron antineutrino energy distributions. KamLAND can only detect electron antineutrinos to the right of the vertical dotted black line; hence it is insensitive to ^{40}K electron antineutrinos.

Ignoring the negligible neutrino absorption, the expected $\bar{\nu}_e$ flux at a position $\mathbf{r}$ for each isotope is given by:

$$\frac{d\phi(E_\nu, \mathbf{r})}{dE_\nu} = A \frac{dn(E_\nu)}{dE_\nu} \int_{V_\oplus} d^3\mathbf{r}' \frac{a(\mathbf{r}')\rho(\mathbf{r}')P(E_\nu, |\mathbf{r}-\mathbf{r}'|)}{4\pi|\mathbf{r}-\mathbf{r}'|^2} \tag{1}$$

where A is the decay rate per unit mass, the integral is over the volume of the Earth, $a(\mathbf{r}')$ is the isotope mass per unit rock mass, $\rho(\mathbf{r}')$ is the rock density, and $P(E_\nu, |\mathbf{r}-\mathbf{r}'|)$ is the $\bar{\nu}_e$

现象，但是它们的能量太低，不能被 KamLAND 探测到。来自其他长寿命同位素且能量高于我们探测阈值的反中微子被认为可忽略不计。

地球的放射能

地球释放的总能量（热流）已通过热学方法[11] 测得，为 44.2±1.0 TW。尽管以上结果给出的误差很小，最近利用相同数据的推算[12]（假定洋中脊附近热液的热流低得多）给出一个更低的值 31±1 TW。基于对球粒陨石的研究[13]，计算出的放射性生热约为 19 TW，其中 84% 来自 ^{238}U 和 ^{232}Th 衰变。一些地幔对流模型给出的放射性生热占总能量的比例更高[14,15]。

^{238}U 和 ^{232}Th 经过一系列已知的 α 衰变和 β^- 衰变后[16]，最终分别变成稳定同位素 ^{206}Pb 和 ^{208}Pb。每次 β^- 衰变产生一个子核、一个电子和一个 $\bar\nu_e$。这个 $\bar\nu_e$ 的能谱已经比较精确[17]，包括对电子和子核电荷分布之间电磁相互作用的修正。图 1 是来自 ^{238}U 和 ^{232}Th 衰变链的预期 $\bar\nu_e$ 分布，即 $\mathrm{d}n(E_v)/\mathrm{d}E_v$，该结果是 $\bar\nu_e$ 能量（E_v）的函数。

图 1. 从 ^{238}U、^{232}Th 和 ^{40}K 衰变链产生的电子反中微子的预期能量分布。KamLAND 只能探测到黑竖点虚线右侧部分的电子反中微子，因此对 ^{40}K 电子反中微子不敏感。

忽略微不足道的中微子吸收，每种同位素在位置 **r** 处的 $\bar\nu_e$ 预期通量如下：

$$\frac{\mathrm{d}\phi(E_v, \mathbf{r})}{\mathrm{d}E_v} = A \frac{\mathrm{d}n(E_v)}{\mathrm{d}E_v} \int_{V_\oplus} \mathrm{d}^3\mathbf{r}' \frac{a(\mathbf{r}')\rho(\mathbf{r}')P(E_v, |\mathbf{r}-\mathbf{r}'|)}{4\pi|\mathbf{r}-\mathbf{r}'|^2} \tag{1}$$

其中 A 是单位质量的衰变率，积分针对整个地球的体积进行，$a(\mathbf{r}')$ 是每单位岩体质量的同位素质量，$\rho(\mathbf{r}')$ 是岩石密度，$P(E_v,|\mathbf{r}-\mathbf{r}'|)$ 是 $\bar\nu_e$ 穿过 $|\mathbf{r}-\mathbf{r}'|$ 距离后的"存活"

"survival" probability after travelling a distance $|\mathbf{r}-\mathbf{r}'|$. This probability derives from the now accepted phenomenon of neutrino oscillation, and can be written, for two neutrino flavours as[18]

$$P(E_v, L) \cong 1 - \sin^2 2\theta_{12} \sin^2 \left(\frac{1.27 \Delta m_{12}^2 [\text{eV}^2] L[\text{m}]}{E_v[\text{MeV}]} \right) \tag{2}$$

where $L = |\mathbf{r}-\mathbf{r}'|$. The neutrino oscillation parameters $\Delta m_{12}^2 = 7.9^{+0.6}_{-0.5} \times 10^{-5}$ eV^2 and $\sin^2 2\theta_{12} = 0.82 \pm 0.07$ are also determined with KamLAND[2] using reactor $\bar{\nu}_e$s with energies above those of geoneutrinos, combined with solar neutrino experiments[19]. Corrections from three flavour neutrino oscillation ($<5\%$) and "matter effects"[20] ($\sim1\%$) are ignored. For typical geoneutrino energies, the approximation $P(E_v, |L|) = 1 - 0.5\sin^2 2\theta_{12}$ only affects the accuracy of the integral in equation (1) at 1% owing to the distributed $\bar{\nu}_e$ production points. This approximation, used in this paper, neglects energy spectrum distortions.

Geoneutrino Detection

KamLAND is located in the Kamioka mine, 1,000 m below the summit of Mt Ikenoyama, Gifu prefecture, Japan (36° 25′ 36″ N, 137° 18′ 43″ E). It detects electron antineutrinos in ~1 kton of liquid scintillator via neutron inverse β-decay,

$$\bar{\nu}_e + p \rightarrow e^+ + n \tag{3}$$

which has a well-established cross-section[21] as a function of E_v. Scintillation light from the e^+, "prompt event", gives an estimate of the incident $\bar{\nu}_e$ energy, $E_v \approx E_{e^+} + 0.8$ MeV (neglecting the small neutron recoil), where E_{e^+} is the kinetic energy of the positron plus the electron–positron annihilation energy. With a mean time of ~200 µs, the neutron is captured by a proton, producing a deuteron and a 2.2 MeV γ-ray. The detection of scintillation light from this 2.2 MeV γ-ray is referred to as the "delayed event". The spatial and temporal coincidences between the prompt and delayed events provide a powerful tool for reducing backgrounds, which generally limit the sensitivity in low energy neutrino studies.

A reference model[22] is constructed using seismic data to divide the Earth into continental crust, oceanic crust, mantle, core and sediment. Some of these regions are further sub-divided, with each sub-region having different U and Th concentrations. This model assumes that U and Th are absent from the core. The expected geoneutrino flux at KamLAND, including a suppression factor of 0.59 due to neutrino oscillations, is 2.34×10^6 cm^{-2} s^{-1} and 1.98×10^6 cm^{-2} s^{-1} from the ^{238}U and ^{232}Th decay chains, respectively. Including the detection cross-section, the number of geoneutrinos expected at KamLAND from ^{238}U and ^{232}Th decay is 3.85×10^{-31} $\bar{\nu}_e$ per target proton per year, 79% of which is due to ^{238}U. Figure 2 shows that a large fraction of the expected geoneutrino flux originates in the area surrounding KamLAND. The effect of local geology was studied extensively in the context of the reference model[22] and was found to produce less than a 10% error on the total expected flux.

概率。该概率从已被证实的中微子振荡现象中得来。对两种中微子味道，该概率可写为[18]

$$P(E_v, L) \cong 1 - \sin^2 2\theta_{12}\sin^2\left(\frac{1.27\Delta m^2_{12}[\text{eV}^2]L[\text{m}]}{E_v[\text{MeV}]}\right) \qquad (2)$$

其中 $L = |\mathbf{r} - \mathbf{r}'|$。利用能量高于地球中微子的反应堆 $\bar{v}_e$ 的 KamLAND 实验[2]，并结合太阳中微子实验[19]，确定了中微子振荡参数的大小：$\Delta m^2_{12} = 7.9^{+0.6}_{-0.5} \times 10^{-5}$ eV^2，$\sin^2 2\theta_{12} = 0.82 \pm 0.07$。三味中微子振荡效应（<5%）和"物质效应"[20]（~ 1%）的修正可忽略。对典型的地球中微子能量，取 $P(E_v, |L|) = 1 - 0.5\sin^2 2\theta_{12}$ 的近似对公式（1）积分精度的影响只有 1%，主要来自分散的 $\bar{v}_e$ 产生地点。本文中使用这种近似，忽略了能谱的变形。

地球中微子探测

KamLAND 实验位于日本岐阜县池野山地下 1,000 米处的神冈矿井中（北纬 36°25′ 36″，东经 137°18′ 43″）。它通过中子反 β 衰变过程，在约 1 千吨的液体闪烁体中探测电子反中微子，

$$\bar{v}_e + p \rightarrow e^+ + n \qquad (3)$$

该过程的反应截面非常清楚[21]，是 E_v 的函数。来自 e^+ 的闪烁光被称为"快信号"，它给出入射 $\bar{v}_e$ 的能量的估计值，$E_v \approx E_{e^+} + 0.8$ MeV（忽略了小的中子反冲）。此处 E_{e^+} 是正电子动能加上电子–正电子的湮灭能。经过平均约 200 μs 的时间，中子被质子俘获，产生一个氘核和一个 2.2 MeV 的 γ 光子。探测到的 2.2 MeV γ 光子的闪烁光被称为"慢信号"。快慢信号在时间和位置上的符合提供了一个减少本底的强大工具。在低能中微子研究中，本底通常会制约实验灵敏度。

利用地震数据构建的一个参考模型[22] 将地球划分为陆壳、洋壳、地幔、地核和沉积层。部分上述区域可进一步细分，每个子区域有不同的 U 和 Th 丰度。这个模型假定地核里不含 U 和 Th。预期 KamLAND 实验站点来自 ^{238}U 和 ^{232}Th 衰变链的地球中微子通量分别为 2.34×10^6 cm^{-2} · s^{-1} 和 1.98×10^6 cm^{-2} · s^{-1}，其中考虑了来自中微子振荡的平均压低因子 0.59。考虑探测截面后，KamLAND 预期能捕获的来自 ^{238}U 和 ^{232}Th 衰变链的地球中微子事例率为 3.85×10^{-31} 个 $\bar{v}_e$ 每靶质子每年，其中 79% 来自 ^{238}U。从图 2 中可以看出，预期的地球中微子通量中，很大一部分在 KamLAND 附近区域产生。在参考模型中细致地研究了当地的地质效应[22]，发现导致的误差小于总预期通量的 10%。

Fig. 2. The expected total ^{238}U and ^{232}Th geoneutrino flux within a given distance from KamLAND[22]. Approximately 25% and 50% of the total flux originates within 50 km and 500 km of KamLAND, respectively. The line representing the crust includes both the continental and the almost negligible oceanic contribution.

The data presented here are based on a total detector live-time of 749.1 ± 0.5 d after basic cuts to ensure the reliability of the data. The number of target protons is estimated at $(3.46 \pm 0.17) \times 10^{31}$ on the basis of target proton density and a spherical fiducial scintillator volume with 5 m radius, resulting in a total exposure of $(7.09 \pm 0.35) \times 10^{31}$ target proton years. The overall efficiency for detecting geoneutrino candidates with energies between 1.7 and 3.4 MeV in the fiducial volume is estimated to be 0.687 ± 0.007. The energy range reaches below the inverse β-decay threshold owing to the detector energy resolution.

Backgrounds for geoneutrino candidates are dominated by $\bar{\nu}_e$s from nuclear reactors in the vicinity of the detector, and by α-particle induced neutron backgrounds due to radioactive contamination within the detector. Reactor $\bar{\nu}_e$s reach substantially higher energies, as shown in Fig. 3. Therefore, the oscillation parameters in ref. 2 were determined by analysing $\bar{\nu}_e$s with energies greater than 3.4 MeV, where there is no signal from the geoneutrinos. Using these parameters, the number of nuclear reactor $\bar{\nu}_e$ background events used by the "rate only" analysis discussed below is determined to be 80.4 ± 7.2.

The α-particle-induced neutron background is due to the ^{13}C$(\alpha,n)^{16}$O reaction where the α-particle is produced in ^{210}Po decay with a kinetic energy of 5.3 MeV. The ^{210}Po is produced by the decay of ^{210}Pb, which has a half-life of 22 yr. The ^{210}Pb resulted from the decay of ^{222}Rn contamination, and is distributed throughout the detector. The neutrons in the ^{13}C$(\alpha,n)^{16}$O reaction are produced with kinetic energy up to 7.3 MeV. Owing to scintillation light quenching for high ionization density, only about one-third of this energy is converted into "visible" energy as the neutrons thermalize. The thermal neutrons are captured by protons with a mean capture time of $\sim$200 μs, producing a delayed signal identical to that from neutron inverse β-decay. The number of ^{13}C nuclei in the fiducial volume is determined from the measured ^{13}C/^{12}C ratio in the KamLAND scintillator. On the basis of the ^{13}C$(\alpha,n)^{16}$O reaction cross-section[23], the α-particle energy loss in the scintillator[24], and the number of ^{210}Po decays, the total number of neutrons produced is

图 2. 在 KamLAND 不同距离范围内产生的 ^{238}U 和 ^{232}Th 地球中微子通量[22]。大约 25% 和 50% 的总通量来自 KamLAND 附近 50 km 和 500 km 范围内。图中地壳的贡献包括陆壳和几乎可忽略的洋壳的贡献。

本文中的数据经过了一些基本挑选，以确保数据的可靠性，总的探测器有效时间为 749.1±0.5 天。基于平均靶质子密度和半径为 5 m 的闪烁体球形有效体积，总的靶质子数估计为 $(3.46±0.17)×10^{31}$ 个，因此总的曝光量为 $(7.09±0.35)×10^{31}$ 靶质子·年。选取有效体积内能量在 1.7 MeV 到 3.4 MeV 之间的地球中微子候选者，总探测效率为 0.687±0.007。能量范围取到反 β 衰变的阈值以下是因为探测器存在能量分辨精度。

地球中微子候选者中的本底主要来自探测器附近核反应堆产生的电子反中微子，以及探测器中放射性杂质产生的 α 粒子引发的中子本底。如图 3 所示，反应堆中微子可达到的能量比地球中微子要高得多。因此参考文献 2 里的振荡参数通过分析能量大于 3.4 MeV 的 $\bar{\nu}_e$ 得到，此能量区间内无地球中微子信号。利用这些参数，得到反应堆中微子本底数为 80.4±7.2，下面将要介绍的"事例率"分析法中用到此值。

α 粒子引发的中子本底来自 ^{13}C$(\alpha,n)^{16}$O 反应，其中 α 粒子来自 ^{210}Po 衰变，动能为 5.3 MeV。^{210}Po 来自半衰期为 22 年的 ^{210}Pb 衰变。^{210}Pb 来自 ^{222}Rn 衰变，而 ^{222}Rn 污染分布在整个探测器内。^{13}C$(\alpha,n)^{16}$O 反应产生的中子最大动能为 7.3 MeV。由于闪烁光在高电离密度下的淬灭效应，当中子慢化时，只有约三分之一的能量转化为"可见"能量。热中子被质子所俘获，平均俘获时间约为 200 μs，产生一个与中子反 β 衰变相同的慢信号。^{13}C 原子核在探测器有效体积内的数量通过测量 KamLAND 闪烁体的 ^{13}C/^{12}C 比值得到。基于 ^{13}C$(\alpha,n)^{16}$O 的反应截面[23]、α 粒子在闪烁体里的能量损失[24]以及 ^{210}Po 衰变数，预期产生的总中子数为 93±22，误差主要由 ^{13}C$(\alpha,n)^{16}$O expected to be 93 ± 22. This error is dominated by estimated 20% and 14% uncertainties in the total $^{13}\text{C}(\alpha,n)^{16}\text{O}$ reaction cross-section and the number of ^{210}Po decays, respectively. The neutron energy distribution is calculated using the measured neutron angular distributions in the centre of mass frame[25,26]. Including the efficiency for passing the $\bar{\nu}_e$ candidate cuts, the number of (α,n) background events is estimated to be 42 ± 11.

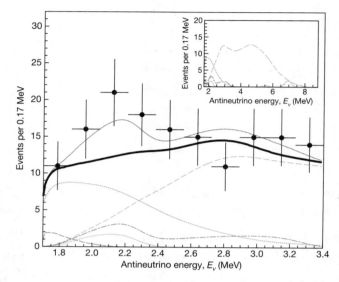

Fig. 3. $\bar{\nu}_e$ energy spectra in KamLAND. Main panel, experimental points together with the total expectation (thin dotted black line). Also shown are the total expected spectrum excluding the geoneutrino signal (thick solid black line), the expected signals from ^{238}U (dot-dashed red line) and ^{232}Th (dotted green line) geoneutrinos, and the backgrounds due to reactor $\bar{\nu}_e$ (dashed light blue line), $^{13}\text{C}(\alpha,n)^{16}\text{O}$ reactions (dotted brown line), and random coincidences (dashed purple line). Inset, expected spectra extended to higher energy. The geoneutrino spectra are calculated from our reference model, which assumes 16 TW radiogenic power from ^{238}U and ^{232}Th. The error bars represent ± 1 standard deviation intervals.

There is a small contribution to the background from random coincidences, $\bar{\nu}_e$s from the β^- decay of long lived nuclear reactor fission products, and radioactive isotopes produced by cosmic rays. Using an out-of-time coincidence cut from 10 ms to 20 s, the random coincidence background is estimated to be 2.38 ± 0.01 events. Using the expected $\bar{\nu}_e$ energy spectrum[27] for long lived nuclear reactor fission products, the corresponding background is estimated to be 1.9 ± 0.2 events. The most significant background due to radioactive isotopes produced by cosmic rays is from the β^- decay $^9\text{Li} \rightarrow 2\alpha + n + e^- + \bar{\nu}_e$, which has a neutron in the final state. On the basis of events correlated with cosmic rays, the estimated number of background events caused by radioactive ^9Li is 0.30 ± 0.05. Other backgrounds considered and found to be negligible include spontaneous fission, neutron emitters and correlated decays in the radioactive background decay chains, fast neutrons from cosmic ray interactions, (γ,n) reactions and solar ν_e induced break-up of ^2H. The total background is estimated to be 127 ± 13 events (1σ error).

The total number of observed $\bar{\nu}_e$ candidates is 152, with their energy distribution shown in

反应截面的 20% 不确定度和 ^{210}Po 衰变数的 14% 不确定度决定。通过在质心系下测量的中子角分布计算得到中子的能量分布 [25,26]，再考虑 $\bar{\nu}_e$ 事例挑选的效率，估算出 (α,n) 本底大约有 42 ± 11 个。

图 3. KamLAND 测得的电子反中微子能谱。主图为实验数据点和总的预期能谱（细黑点线）。同时显示了除地球中微子信号外所有预期能谱的总和（粗黑实线）、^{238}U 地球中微子预期信号（红点划线）、^{232}Th 地球中微子预期信号（绿点线）、反应堆中微子本底（浅蓝虚线）、^{13}C$(\alpha,n)^{16}$O 反应本底（棕点线）以及随机符合的本底（紫虚线）。小插图显示了延伸到更高能量下的预期能谱。地球中微子能谱从我们的参考模型计算而来，其中假定了 ^{238}U 和 ^{232}Th 共产生 16 TW 的放射性热能。误差棒代表 ±1 倍标准偏差。

其他较小的本底还包括随机符合本底、长寿命的反应堆裂变产物发生 β^- 衰变产生的 $\bar{\nu}_e$ 以及宇宙线产生的放射性同位素。根据信号时间窗以外的 10 ms 到 20 s 之间的符合情况来估算，约有 2.38 ± 0.01 个随机符合事例。根据长寿命的反应堆裂变产物的预期 $\bar{\nu}_e$ 能谱 [27]，相应的本底估计为 1.9 ± 0.2 个事例。宇宙线产生的最显著的放射性同位素本底来自末态有一个中子的 β^- 衰变 ^{9}Li$\rightarrow 2\alpha+n+e^-+\bar{\nu}_e$。基于与宇宙线关联的事例，由放射性的 ^{9}Li 产生的预期本底事例为 0.30 ± 0.05 个。其他考虑过但发现可忽略不计的本底还包括自发裂变、放射性本底衰变链中的中子发射和关联衰变、宇宙线产生的快中子、(γ,n) 反应以及太阳中微子引发的 ^{2}H 分解。总本底估计为 127 ± 13 个事例（1σ 误差）。

观测到的 $\bar{\nu}_e$ 候选者总数为 152 个，其能量分布显示在图 3 中。考虑到地球中微

Fig. 3. Including the geoneutrino detection systematic errors, parts of which are correlated with the background estimation errors, a "rate only" analysis gives 25^{+19}_{-18} geoneutrino candidates from the ^{238}U and ^{232}Th decay chains. Dividing by the detection efficiency, live-time, and number of target protons, the total geoneutrino detected rate obtained is $5.1^{+3.9}_{-3.6} \times 10^{-31}$ $\bar{\nu}_e$ per target proton per year.

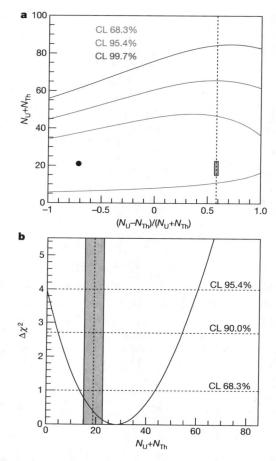

Fig. 4. Confidence intervals for the number of geoneutrinos detected. Panel **a** shows the 68.3% confidence level (CL; red), 95.4% CL (green) and 99.7% CL (blue) contours for detected ^{238}U and ^{232}Th geoneutrinos. The small shaded area represents the prediction from the geophysical model. The vertical dashed line represents the value of $(N_U - N_{Th})/(N_U + N_{Th})$ assuming the mass ratio, Th/U = 3.9, derived from chondritic meteorites, and accounting for the ^{238}U and ^{232}Th decay rates and the $\bar{\nu}_e$ detection efficiencies in KamLAND. The dot represents our best fit point, favouring 3 ^{238}U geoneutrinos and 18 ^{232}Th geoneutrinos. Panel **b** shows $\Delta\chi^2$ as a function of the total number of ^{238}U and ^{232}Th geoneutrino candidates, fixing the normalized difference to the chondritic meteorites constraint. The grey band gives the value of $N_U + N_{Th}$ predicted by the geophysical model.

We also perform an un-binned maximum likelihood analysis of the $\bar{\nu}_e$ energy spectrum between 1.7 and 3.4 MeV, using the known shape of the signal and background spectra. As the neutrino oscillation parameters do not significantly affect the expected shape of the

子探测的系统误差（其中一部分与本底估算误差相关联），采用事例率分析法，^{238}U 和 ^{232}Th 衰变链产生的地球中微子数为 25^{+19}_{-18}。该事例数除以探测器效率、取数时间以及靶质子数，探测到的地球中微子总事例率为每年每靶质子 $5.1^{+3.9}_{-3.6} \times 10^{-31}$ 个 $\bar{\nu}_e$。

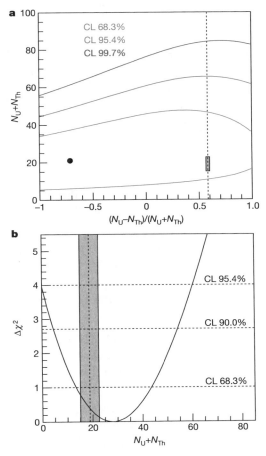

图 4. 探测到的地球中微子事例数的置信区间。图 **a** 是探测到的 ^{238}U 和 ^{232}Th 地球中微子数分别在 68.3% 置信度（红色）、95.4% 置信度（绿色）和 99.7% 置信度（蓝色）下的等值线。小的阴影区是地球物理模型的预期，竖虚线表示基于从球粒陨石推出的 Th/U 质量比 3.9，并考虑了 ^{238}U 和 ^{232}Th 衰变率以及 KamLAND 对 $\bar{\nu}_e$ 的探测效率等情况下的 $(N_U - N_{Th})$ 与 $(N_U + N_{Th})$ 的比值。黑点为最佳拟合点，倾向于 ^{238}U 地球中微子数为 3 个，^{232}Th 地球中微子数为 18 个。图 **b** 是 $\Delta\chi^2$ 随 ^{238}U 和 ^{232}Th 地球中微子总数的函数分布，其中归一化后的差别固定到球粒陨石的限制值。灰色区域带是地球物理模型预期的 $N_U + N_{Th}$ 值。

我们也利用已知的信号能谱和本底能谱的形状，对 1.7～3.4 MeV 区间的 $\bar{\nu}_e$ 能谱进行了一项不分能量区间的最大似然分析。中微子振荡参数对预期的地球中微子能谱形状影响很小，因此采用了无振荡的谱形。而反应堆中微子本底的谱形则包括

geoneutrino signal, the un-oscillated shape is assumed. However, the oscillation parameters are included in the reactor background shape. Figure 4a shows the confidence intervals for the number of observed ^{238}U and ^{232}Th geoneutrinos. Based on a study of chondritic meteorites[28], the Th/U mass ratio in the Earth is believed to be between 3.7 and 4.1, and is known better than either absolute concentration. Assuming a Th/U mass ratio of 3.9, we estimate the 90% confidence interval for the total number of ^{238}U and ^{232}Th geoneutrino candidates to be 4.5 to 54.2, as shown in Fig. 4b. The central value of 28.0 is consistent with the "rate only" analysis. At this point, the value of the fit parameters are $\Delta m_{12}^2 = 7.8 \times 10^{-5}$ eV^2, $\sin^2 2\theta_{12} = 0.82$, $p_\alpha = 1.0$, and $q_\alpha = 1.0$, where these last two parameters are defined in the Methods section. The 99% confidence upper limit obtained on the total detected ^{238}U and ^{232}Th geoneutrino rate is 1.45×10^{-30} $\bar{\nu}_e$ per target proton per year, corresponding to a flux at KamLAND of 1.62×10^7 cm^{-2} s^{-1}. On the basis of our reference model, this corresponds to an upper limit on the radiogenic power from ^{238}U and ^{232}Th decay of 60 TW.

As a cross-check, an independent analysis[29] has been performed using a partial data set, including detection efficiency, of 2.6×10^{31} target proton years. In this analysis, the ^{13}C$(\alpha,n)^{16}$O background was verified using the minute differences in the time structures of scintillation light from different particle species. Scintillation light in the prompt part of $\bar{\nu}_e$ events is caused by positrons, whereas scintillation light in the prompt part of ^{13}C$(\alpha,n)^{16}$O background events is caused by neutron thermalization. This alternative analysis produced a slightly larger geoneutrino signal, which is consistent with the results presented here.

Discussion and Future Prospects

In conclusion, we have performed the first experimental study of antineutrinos from the Earth's interior using KamLAND. The present measurement is consistent with current geophysical models, and constrains the $\bar{\nu}_e$ emission from U and Th in the planet to be less than 1.45×10^{-30} $\bar{\nu}_e$ per target proton per year at 99% confidence limits, corresponding to a flux of 1.62×10^7 cm^{-2} s^{-1}. There is currently a programme underway to reduce the ^{210}Pb content of the detector. This should help to reduce the substantial systematic error due to the ^{13}C$(\alpha,n)^{16}$O background. Further background reduction will require a new detector location, far away from nuclear reactors. The reported investigation of geoneutrinos should pave the way to future and more accurate measurements, which may provide a new window for the exploration of the Earth.

Methods

As shown in Fig. 5, KamLAND[1] consists of 1 kton of ultrapure liquid scintillator contained in a transparent nylon/EVOH (ethylene vinyl alcohol copolymer) composite film balloon suspended in non-scintillating oil. Charged particles deposit their kinetic energy in the scintillator; some of this energy is converted into scintillation light. The scintillation light is then detected by an array of 1,325 17-inch-diameter photomultiplier tubes (PMTs) and 554 20-inch-diameter PMTs mounted on the inner surface of an 18-m-diameter spherical stainless-steel containment vessel. A 3.2-

了振荡参数。图 4a 显示了观测到的 ^{238}U 和 ^{232}Th 地球中微子数的置信区间。基于对球粒陨石的研究 [28]，地球上 Th/U 的质量比被认为在 3.7 ~ 4.1 之间，相比于 Th 和 U 各自的绝对丰度，人们了解的 Th/U 质量比是更为准确的。假设 Th/U 的质量比为 3.9，我们估计 90% 置信区间内 ^{238}U 和 ^{232}Th 地球中微子总数为 4.5 到 54.2，如图 4b 所示。中心值 28.0 与前面事例率分析方法的结果一致。此处拟合参数的值分别为 $\Delta m_{12}^2 = 7.8 \times 10^{-5}$ eV^2、$\sin^2 2\theta_{12} = 0.82$、$p_\alpha = 1.0$、$q_\alpha = 1.0$，其中最后两个参数的定义在下面的方法章节中介绍。探测到的 ^{238}U 和 ^{232}Th 地球中微子总事例率的 99% 置信度上限为 1.45×10^{-30} 个 $\bar{\nu}_e$ 每靶质子每年，对应到达 KamLAND 的地球中微子通量为 1.62×10^7 cm$^{-2} \cdot$ s^{-1}。基于我们的参考模型，这相应于 ^{238}U 和 ^{232}Th 衰变的放射性功率上限为 60 TW。

作为验证，使用总量为 2.6×10^{31} 个靶质子·年的部分数据（包含探测器效率）进行了独立分析 [29]。在分析中，^{13}C$(\alpha,n)^{16}$O 本底通过不同粒子种类产生闪烁光的微小时间分布差异得到了验证。$\bar{\nu}_e$ 事例的快信号是由正电子产生的闪烁光，而 ^{13}C$(\alpha,n)^{16}$O 本底事例的快信号是中子慢化产生的闪烁光。此分析得到稍微大一点的地球中微子信号，与本文给出的结果一致。

讨论和前景

综上所述，我们利用 KamLAND 探测器，对来自地球内部的反中微子进行了首次实验研究。测量结果与现有的地球物理模型一致：在 99% 的置信限，限制了地球中 U 和 Th 发射的 $\bar{\nu}_e$ 数小于每靶质子每年 1.45×10^{-30} 个，对应于通量 1.62×10^7 cm$^{-2} \cdot$ s^{-1}。目前正在执行计划以减少探测器中 ^{210}Pb 的含量，这将帮助降低由 ^{13}C$(\alpha,n)^{16}$O 本底带来的较大的系统误差。进一步降低本底需要一个新的远离核反应堆的实验点。本文报告的对地球中微子的研究应该为未来更准确的测量铺平了道路，这可能为探索地球提供了一个新的窗口。

方　法

如图 5 所示，KamLAND[1] 由装在透明的尼龙/EVOH（乙烯–乙烯醇共聚物）复合膜气球里的 1 千吨超纯净的液体闪烁体组成，气球悬浮在不产生闪烁光的矿物油中。带电粒子在液体闪烁体里沉积能量，这些能量的一部分转化为闪烁光，被分布在四周的 1,325 个直径为 17 英寸的光电倍增管（PMT）和 554 个直径为 20 英寸的 PMT 探测到。PMT 安装在直径为 18 米的球形不锈钢容器的内表面。包围着球形容器的是装有 225 个直径为 20 英寸的 PMT 的 3.2

kton water-Cherenkov detector with 225 20-inch-diameter PMTs surrounds the containment sphere. This outer detector tags cosmic-ray muons and absorbs γ-rays and neutrons from the surrounding rock.

Fig. 5. Schematic diagram of the KamLAND detector.

The arrival times of photons at the PMTs allow us to determine the location of particle interactions inside the detector, and the amount of detected light after correcting for spatial variation of the detector response allows us to determine the particle's energy. The event location and energy determination is calibrated with γ-ray sources deployed vertically down the centre of the detector. To be classified as a $\bar{\nu}_e$ candidate, the time coincidence between the prompt and delayed events (ΔT) is required to satisfy $0.5\ \mu s < \Delta T < 500\ \mu s$. The position of the prompt ($\mathbf{r}_p$) and delayed ($\mathbf{r}_d$) events with respect to the centre of the detector are required to satisfy $|\mathbf{r}_p| < 5$ m; $|\mathbf{r}_d| < 5$ m and $|\mathbf{r}_p - \mathbf{r}_d| < 1.0$ m: The energy of the electron antineutrino is required to satisfy 1.7 MeV $< E_\nu < 3.4$ MeV and the energy of the delayed event (E_d) is required to satisfy 1.8 MeV $< E_d < 2.6$ MeV.

Given N_U and N_{Th} geoneutrinos detected from the ^{238}U and ^{232}Th decay chains, the expected energy distribution of the candidates is

$$\frac{\mathrm{d}\overline{N}(E_\nu)}{\mathrm{d}E_\nu} = N_U \frac{\mathrm{d}P_U(E_\nu)}{\mathrm{d}E_\nu} + N_{Th} \frac{\mathrm{d}P_{Th}(E_\nu)}{\mathrm{d}E_\nu} + \frac{\mathrm{d}N_r(E_\nu; \Delta m_{12}^2, \sin^2 2\theta_{12})}{\mathrm{d}E_\nu}$$

$$+ P_\alpha \frac{\mathrm{d}N_\alpha(E_\nu/q_\alpha)}{\mathrm{d}E_\nu} + \sum_k \frac{\mathrm{d}N_k(E_\nu)}{\mathrm{d}E_\nu}$$

(4)

where $\mathrm{d}P_U(E_\nu)/\mathrm{d}E_\nu$ and $\mathrm{d}P_{Th}(E_\nu)/\mathrm{d}E_\nu$ are the normalized expected geoneutrino spectra from ^{238}U and ^{232}Th decay chains. The third term on the right hand side of equation (4) is the energy spectrum of the expected $\bar{\nu}_e$ reactor background, which is a function of the neutrino oscillation parameters Δm_{12}^2

千吨水切伦科夫探测器，这个外部探测器用来标记宇宙线 μ 子并吸收来自周围岩石的 γ 射线和中子。

刻度装置

水切伦科夫
外部探测器

外部探测器的
光电倍增管

液体闪烁体
（1 千吨）

光电倍增管

不产生闪烁光的
矿物油

气球
（直径 13 米）

外部容器
（直径 18 米）

图 5. KamLAND 探测器的示意图。

根据光子到达 PMT 的时间分布可确定探测器内粒子发生相互作用的位置。修正探测器响应随位置的变化后，可通过探测到的总光子数确定粒子的能量。事例的位置和能量通过垂伸至探测器中心的 γ 源进行刻度。对 $\bar{\nu}_e$ 事例的挑选，要求满足以下条件：快慢信号之间的时间符合 (ΔT) 满足 $0.5\ \mu s < \Delta T < 500\ \mu s$；相对于探测器中心的快信号 $(\mathbf{r}_p)$ 和慢信号 $(\mathbf{r}_d)$ 的位置分别满足 $|\mathbf{r}_p| < 5\ m$，$|\mathbf{r}_d| < 5\ m$ 以及 $|\mathbf{r}_p - \mathbf{r}_d| < 1.0\ m$；电子反中微子的能量满足 $1.7\ MeV < E_\nu < 3.4\ MeV$；慢信号能量 E_d 满足 $1.8\ MeV < E_d < 2.6\ MeV$。

假定有 N_U 和 N_{Th} 个探测到的地球中微子分别来自 ^{238}U 和 ^{232}Th 衰变链，预期探测到的全部 $\bar{\nu}_e$ 候选者的能量分布为：

$$\frac{\mathrm{d}\overline{N}(E_\nu)}{\mathrm{d}E_\nu} = N_U \frac{\mathrm{d}P_U(E_\nu)}{\mathrm{d}E_\nu} + N_{Th} \frac{\mathrm{d}P_{Th}(E_\nu)}{\mathrm{d}E_\nu} + \frac{\mathrm{d}N_r(E_\nu; \Delta m_{12}^2, \sin^2 2\theta_{12})}{\mathrm{d}E_\nu}$$

$$+ P_\alpha \frac{\mathrm{d}N_\alpha(E_\nu/q_\alpha)}{\mathrm{d}E_\nu} + \sum_k \frac{\mathrm{d}N_k(E_\nu)}{\mathrm{d}E_\nu} \tag{4}$$

其中，$\mathrm{d}P_U(E_\nu)/\mathrm{d}E_\nu$ 和 $\mathrm{d}P_{Th}(E_\nu)/\mathrm{d}E_\nu$ 分别是 ^{238}U 和 ^{232}Th 衰变链产生的归一化后的预期地球中微子能谱，等式右边第三项是反应堆中微子本底的能谱，它是中微子振荡参数 Δm_{12}^2 和 $\sin^2 2\theta_{12}$ 的函数。$\mathrm{d}N_\alpha(E_\nu/q_\alpha)/\mathrm{d}E_\nu$ 是 $^{13}C(\alpha,n)^{16}O$ 本底经过能量和事例率的缩放因子 q_α 和 p_α 修正后的

and $\sin^2 2\theta_{12}$. $dN_\alpha(E_v/q_\alpha)/dE_v$ is the energy spectrum of the expected $^{13}C(\alpha,n)^{16}O$ background with energy and rate scaling factors q_α and p_α, respectively. The sum is over the other known backgrounds where $dN_k(E_v)/dE_v$ is the expected energy spectrum of the background. All expected spectra include energy smearing due to the detector energy resolution. Integrating equation (4) between 1.7 and 3.4 MeV gives the total number of expected candidates, $\overline{N}$.

The number of geoneutrinos from the ^{238}U and ^{232}Th decay chains is determined from an unbinned maximum likelihood fit. The log likelihood is defined by

$$\log L = -\frac{(N-\overline{N})^2}{2\left(\overline{N}+\sigma_{\overline{N}}^2\right)} + \sum_{i=1}^{N}\log\frac{1}{\overline{N}}\frac{d\overline{N}(E_i)}{dE_v} - \frac{(p_\alpha-1)^2}{2\sigma_p^2} - \frac{(q_\alpha-1)^2}{2\sigma_q^2}$$

$$-\frac{\chi^2(\Delta m_{12}^2, \sin^2 2\theta_{12})}{2}$$

(5)

where N is the total number of observed candidates and $\sigma_{\overline{N}}$ is the error on $\overline{N}$. E_i is the energy of the ith $\overline{v}_e$ candidate. $\sigma_p = 0.24$ and $\sigma_q = 0.1$ are the fractional errors on q_α and p_α, respectively. The term $\chi^2(\Delta m^2, \sin^2 2\theta)$ provides a constraint on the neutrino oscillation parameters from the KamLAND reactor measurements and the solar neutrino results[30]. $\log L$ is maximized at different values of N_U and N_{Th} by varying Δm_{12}^2, $\sin^2 2\theta_{12}$, p_α and q_α. The best fit point for N_U and N_{Th} corresponds to the maximum $\log L$. A $\Delta\chi^2$ is defined by

$$\Delta\chi^2 = 2(\log L_{max} - \log L)$$

(6)

where $\log L_{max}$ is the $\log L$ at the best fit point. The confidence intervals are calculated from this $\Delta\chi^2$.

(**436**, 499-503; 2005)

T. Araki[1], S. Enomoto[1], K. Furuno[1], Y. Gando[1], K. Ichimura[1], H. Ikeda[1], K. Inoue[1], Y. Kishimoto[1], M. Koga[1], Y. Koseki[1], T. Maeda[1], T. Mitsui[1], M. Motoki[1], K. Nakajima[1], H. Ogawa[1], M. Ogawa[1], K. Owada[1], J.-S. Ricol[1], I. Shimizu[1], J. Shirai[1], F. Suekane[1], A. Suzuki[1], K. Tada[1], S. Takeuchi[1], K. Tamae[1], Y. Tsuda[1], H. Watanabe[1], J. Busenitz[2], T. Classen[2], Z. Djurcic[2], G. Keefer[2], D. Leonard[2], A. Piepke[2], E. Yakushev[2], B. E. Berger[3], Y. D. Chan[3], M. P. Decowski[3], D. A. Dwyer[3], S. J. Freedman[3], B. K. Fujikawa[3], J. Goldman[3], F. Gray[3], K. M. Heeger[3], L. Hsu[3], K. T. Lesko[3], K.-B. Luk[3], H. Murayama[3], T. O'Donnell[3], A. W. P. Poon[3], H. M. Steiner[3], L. A. Winslow[3], C. Mauger[4], R. D. McKeown[4], P. Vogel[4], C. E. Lane[5], T. Miletic[5], G. Guillian[6], J. G. Learned[6], J. Maricic[6], S. Matsuno[6], S. Pakvasa[6], G. A. Horton-Smith[7], S. Dazeley[8], S. Hatakeyama[8], A. Rojas[8], R. Svoboda[8], B. D. Dieterle[9], J. Detwiler[10], G. Gratta[10], K. Ishii[10], N. Tolich[10], Y. Uchida[10], M. Batygov[11], W. Bugg[11], Y. Efremenko[11], Y. Kamyshkov[11], A. Kozlov[11], Y. Nakamura[11], H. J. Karwowski[12], D. M. Markoff[12], K. Nakamura[12], R. M. Rohm[12], W. Tornow[12], R. Wendell[12], M.-J. Chen[13], Y.-F. Wang[13] & F. Piquemal[14]

[1] Research Center for Neutrino Science, Tohoku University, Sendai 980-8578, Japan

[2] Department of Physics and Astronomy, University of Alabama, Tuscaloosa, Alabama 35487, USA

[3] Physics Department, University of California at Berkeley and Lawrence Berkeley National Laboratory, Berkeley, California 94720, USA

[4] W. K. Kellogg Radiation Laboratory, California Institute of Technology, Pasadena, California 91125, USA

[5] Physics Department, Drexel University, Philadelphia, Pennsylvania 19104, USA

[6] Department of Physics and Astronomy, University of Hawaii at Manoa, Honolulu, Hawaii 96822, USA

[7] Department of Physics, Kansas State University, Manhattan, Kansas 66506, USA

[8] Department of Physics and Astronomy, Louisiana State University, Baton Rouge, Louisiana 70803, USA

[9] Physics Department, University of New Mexico, Albuquerque, New Mexico 87131, USA

预期能谱；最后一项是对已知其他所有本底能谱 $dN_k(E_\nu)/dE_\nu$ 的求和。所有的能谱都包含了由探测器能量分辨引起的能量弥散。对公式 (4) 在 1.7～3.4 MeV 能量区间内进行积分给出总的预期 $\bar{\nu}_e$ 事例数 $\bar{N}$。

^{238}U 和 ^{232}Th 衰变链产生的地球中微子数目由不分能量区间的最大似然法拟合得到。对数似然函数的定义如下，

$$\log L = -\frac{(N-\bar{N})^2}{2\left(\bar{N}+\sigma_{\bar{N}}^2\right)} + \sum_{i=1}^{N}\log\frac{1}{\bar{N}}\frac{d\bar{N}(E_i)}{dE_\nu} - \frac{(p_\alpha-1)^2}{2\sigma_p^2} - \frac{(q_\alpha-1)^2}{2\sigma_q^2}$$

$$- \frac{\chi^2(\Delta m_{12}^2,\, \sin^2 2\theta_{12})}{2} \tag{5}$$

其中，N 是总的观测事例数，$\sigma_{\bar{N}}$ 是 $\bar{N}$ 的误差，E_i 是第 i 个 $\bar{\nu}_e$ 事例的能量，$\sigma_p = 0.24$ 和 $\sigma_q = 0.1$ 分别是 p_α 和 q_α 的相对误差。$\chi^2(\Delta m^2, \sin^2 2\theta)$ 项对 KamLAND 反应堆中微子测量和太阳中微子测量 [30] 得到的振荡参数提供了一个约束。通过改变 Δm_{12}^2、$\sin^2 2\theta_{12}$、p_α 和 q_α 这四个参数，将 $\log L$ 在不同 N_U 和 N_{Th} 值处最大化，最大的 $\log L$ 即是 N_U 和 N_{Th} 的最佳拟合点。$\Delta\chi^2$ 的定义如下

$$\Delta\chi^2 = 2(\log L_{max} - \log L) \tag{6}$$

其中 $\log L_{max}$ 是 $\log L$ 在最佳拟合点的值，而置信区间由 $\Delta\chi^2$ 计算得到。

（韩然 翻译；曹俊 审稿）

[10] Physics Department, Stanford University, Stanford, California 94305, USA

[11] Department of Physics and Astronomy, University of Tennessee, Knoxville, Tennessee 37996, USA

[12] Physics Department, Duke University, Durham, North Carolina 27008, USA, and Physics Department, North Carolina State, Raleigh, North Carolina 27695, USA, and Physics Department, University of North Carolina, Chapel Hill, North Carolina 27599, USA

[13] Institute of High Energy Physics, Beijing 100039, China

[14] CEN Bordeaux-Gradignan, IN2P3-CNRS and University Bordeaux I, F-33175 Gradignan Cedex, France

Received 25 May; accepted 4 July 2005.

References:

1. Eguchi, K. *et al.* First results from KamLAND: Evidence for reactor antineutrino disappearance. *Phys. Rev. Lett.* **90**, 021802 (2003).

2. Araki, T. *et al.* Measurement of neutrino oscillation with KamLAND: Evidence of spectral distortion. *Phys. Rev. Lett.* **94**, 081801 (2005).

3. Eder, G. Terrestrial neutrinos. *Nucl. Phys.* **78**, 657-662 (1966).

4. Marx, G. Geophysics by neutrinos. *Czech. J. Phys. B* **19**, 1471-1479 (1969).

5. Avilez, C., Marx, G. & Fuentes, B. Earth as a source of antineutrinos. *Phys. Rev. D* **23**, 1116-1117 (1981).

6. Krauss, L. M., Glashow, S. L. & Schramm, D. N. Antineutrino astronomy and geophysics. *Nature* **310**, 191-198 (1984).

7. Kobayashi, M. & Fukao, Y. The Earth as an antineutrino star. *Geophys. Res. Lett.* **18**, 633-636 (1991).

8. Raghavan, R. S. *et al.* Measuring the global radioactivity in the Earth by multidetector antineutrino spectroscopy. *Phys. Rev. Lett.* **80**, 635-638 (1998).

9. Rothschild, C. G., Chen, M. C. & Calaprice, F. P. Antineutrino geophysics with liquid scintillator detectors. *Geophys. Res. Lett.* **25**, 1083-1086 (1998).

10. Mantovani, F., Carmignani, L., Fiorentini, G. & Lissia, M. Antineutrinos from Earth: A reference model and its uncertainties. *Phys. Rev. D* **69**, 013001 (2004).

11. Pollack, H. N., Hurter, S. J. & Johnson, J. R. Heat flow from the Earth's interior: analysis of the global data set. *Rev. Geophys.* **31**, 267-280 (1993).

12. Hofmeister, A. M. & Criss, R. E. Earth's heat flux revised and linked to chemistry. *Tectonophysics* **395**, 159-177 (2005).

13. McDonough, W. F. & Sun, S.-s. The composition of the Earth. *Chem. Geol.* **120**, 223-253 (1995).

14. Jackson, M. J. & Pollack, H. N. On the sensitivity of parameterized convection to the rate of decay of internal heat sources. *J. Geophys. Res.* **89**, 10103-10108 (1984).

15. Richter, F. M. Regionalized models for the thermal evolution of the Earth. *Earth Planet. Sci. Lett.* **68**, 471-484 (1984).

16. Firestone, R. B. *Table of Isotopes* 8th edn (John Wiley, New York, 1996).

17. Behrens, H. & Jänecke, J. *Landolt-Börnstein - Group I, Elementary Particles, Nuclei and Atoms* Vol. 4 (Springer, Berlin, 1969).

18. McKeown, R. D. & Vogel, P. Neutrino masses and oscillations: triumphs and challenges. *Phys. Rep.* **394**, 315-356 (2004).

19. Ahmed, S. N. *et al.* Measurement of the total active ^{8}B solar neutrino flux at the Sudbury Neutrino Observatory with enhanced neutral current sensitivity. *Phys. Rev. Lett.* **92**, 181301 (2004).

20. Wolfenstein, L. Neutrino oscillations in matter. *Phys. Rev. D* **17**, 2369-2374 (1978).

21. Vogel, P. & Beacom, J. F. Angular distribution of neutron inverse beta decay, $\bar{\nu}_e + p \rightarrow e^+ + n$. *Phys. Rev. D* **60**, 053003 (1999).

22. Enomoto, S. *Neutrino Geophysics and Observation of Geo-neutrinos at KamLAND*. Thesis, Tohoku Univ. (2005); available at ⟨http://www.awa.tohoku.ac.jp/KamLAND/publications/Sanshiro_thesis.pdf⟩.

23. JENDL Japanese Evaluated Nuclear Data Library. ⟨http://wwwndc.tokai.jaeri.go.jp/jendl/jendl.html⟩ (2004).

24. Apostolakis, J. Geant—Detector description and simulation tool. ⟨http://wwwasd.web.cern.ch/wwwasd/geant/index.html⟩ (2003).

25. Walton, R. B., Clement, J. D. & Borlei, F. Interaction of neutrons with oxygen and a study of the $C^{13}(\alpha,n)O^{16}$ reaction. *Phys. Rev.* **107**, 1065-1075 (1957).

26. Kerr, G. W., Morris, J. M. & Risser, J. R. Energy levels of ^{17}O from $^{13}C(\alpha, \alpha_0)^{13}$C and $^{13}C(\alpha,n)^{16}$O. *Nucl. Phys. A* **110**, 637-656 (1968).

27. Kopeikin, V. I. *et al.* Inverse beta decay in a nonequilibrium antineutrino flux from a nuclear reactor. *Phys. Atom. Nuclei* **64**, 849-854 (2001).

28. Rocholl, A. & Jochum, K. P. Th, U and other trace elements in carbonaceous chondrites: Implications for the terrestrial and solar-system Th/U ratios. *Earth Planet. Sci. Lett.* **117**, 265-278 (1993).

29. Tolich, N. *Experimental Study of Terrestrial Electron Anti-neutrinos with KamLAND* Thesis, Stanford Univ. (2005); available at ⟨http://www.awa.tohoku.ac.jp/KamLAND/publications/Nikolai_thesis.pdf⟩.

30. KamLAND collaboration. Data release accompanying the 2nd KamLAND reactor result. ⟨http://www.awa.tohoku.ac.jp/KamLAND/datarelease/2ndresult.html⟩ (2005).

Acknowledgements. We thank E. Ohtani and N. Sleep for advice and guidance. The KamLAND experiment is supported by the COE program of the Japanese Ministry of Education, Culture, Sports, Science, and Technology, and by the United States Department of Energy. The reactor data were provided courtesy of the following associations in Japan: Hokkaido, Tohoku, Tokyo, Hokuriku, Chubu, Kansai, Chugoku, Shikoku and Kyushu Electric Power Companies, Japan Atomic Power Co. and Japan Nuclear Cycle Development Institute. Kamioka Mining and Smelting Company provided services for activity at the experimental site.

Author Information. Reprints and permissions information is available at npg.nature.com/reprintsandpermissions. The authors declare no competing financial interests. Correspondence and requests for materials should be addressed to S.E. (sanshiro@awa.tohoku.ac.jp) or N.T. (nrtolich@lbl.gov).

580

First Fossil Chimpanzee

S. McBrearty and N. G. Jablonski

Editor's Note

Fossil hominins are rare, but fossils of chimpanzees—our closest relatives—were entirely absent until this report of the remains of chimpanzee teeth from Kenya. The teeth are around half a million years old, and were buried alongside fossils attributable to our own genus, *Homo*. Most hominin fossils in Africa are found in the Rift Valley, whereas chimps are today confined to forested west and central Africa. But this discovery suggested that hominins and chimps once shared their environment. It still leaves open the question why chimpanzee fossils are so scarce, and why the fossil record of our other relation, the gorilla, is completely blank.

There are thousands of fossils of hominins, but no fossil chimpanzee has yet been reported. The chimpanzee (*Pan*) is the closest living relative to humans[1]. Chimpanzee populations today are confined to wooded West and central Africa, whereas most hominin fossil sites occur in the semi-arid East African Rift Valley. This situation has fuelled speculation regarding causes for the divergence of the human and chimpanzee lineages five to eight million years ago. Some investigators have invoked a shift from wooded to savannah vegetation in East Africa, driven by climate change, to explain the apparent separation between chimpanzee and human ancestral populations and the origin of the unique hominin locomotor adaptation, bipedalism[2-5]. The Rift Valley itself functions as an obstacle to chimpanzee occupation in some scenarios[6]. Here we report the first fossil chimpanzee. These fossils, from the Kapthurin Formation, Kenya, show that representatives of *Pan* were present in the East African Rift Valley during the Middle Pleistocene, where they were contemporary with an extinct species of *Homo*. Habitats suitable for both hominins and chimpanzees were clearly present there during this period, and the Rift Valley did not present an impenetrable barrier to chimpanzee occupation.

THE Kapthurin Formation forms the Middle Pleistocene portion of the Tugen Hills sequence west of Lake Baringo (Figs 1 and 2). It consists of a package of fluvial, lacustrine and volcanic sediments ~125 m thick, exposed over ~150 km^2 (refs 7–9) that contains numerous palaeontological and archaeological sites[9-11]. It is divided into five members informally designated K1–K5 (ref. 7), and the sequence is well calibrated by ^{40}Ar/^{39}Ar dating[12].

第一个黑猩猩化石

古人类化石是很罕见的，但是黑猩猩的化石——我们的近亲——在这篇来自肯尼亚的黑猩猩牙齿化石的报道之前是完全没有的。这些牙齿大约有 50 万年的历史，和我们人属的化石一起被埋葬。非洲的大部分古人类化石都是在东非大裂谷发现的，而今天的黑猩猩只能生活在非洲西部和中部的森林里。但本文发现表明，古人类和黑猩猩曾经共享它们的生存环境。为什么黑猩猩化石如此稀少？为什么我们的另一个亲戚大猩猩的化石记录是完全空白的？这些问题仍然悬而未决。

我们迄今已发现数以千计的古人类化石，但还没有黑猩猩化石被发现的报道。黑猩猩（黑猩猩属）是现存的与人类亲缘关系最近的动物[1]。今天的黑猩猩种群局限于树木繁茂的非洲西部和中部，而大多数古人类化石遗址都出现在半干旱的东非大裂谷。这种情形更加刺激了人们关于 500 万到 800 万年前人类和黑猩猩世系分叉脱离的有关原因的推测。一些研究者提出，在东非，气候变化引起的从森林到热带稀树草原植被的变化，导致黑猩猩与人类祖先种群之间的明显分离，以及古人类独特的运动方式适应——直立行走[2-5]。在某些情况下，东非大裂谷本身对黑猩猩的生存居住起到了障碍的作用[6]。在此我们报道第一个黑猩猩化石。来自肯尼亚卡普图林组的这些化石，显示黑猩猩属在中更新世期间就在东非大裂谷出现了，此时当地还存在着一种灭绝了的人属成员。很显然，这期间的生活环境适于黑猩猩与古人类生存，而且对于黑猩猩的生存居住，东非大裂谷并非不可逾越的障碍。

卡普图林组构成巴林戈湖西部图根丘陵层序的中更新世部分（图 1、图 2）。它由一套 ~125 米厚的河流、湖泊和火山沉积构成，出露约 150 平方千米（参考文献 7 ~ 9），其中有许多古生物和考古遗址[9-11]。它被非正式地划分为 K1 ~ K5（参考文献 7）5 层，且层序由 $^{40}Ar/^{39}Ar$ 测年标度校准[12]。

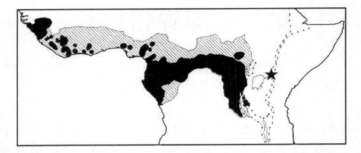

Fig. 1. Map showing current (solid black) and historical (stippled) ranges of *Pan* in equatorial Africa relative to major features of the eastern and western Rift Valleys. The Kapthurin Formation, Kenya, in the Eastern Rift Valley is marked by a star.

Fig. 2. Idealized stratigraphic column of the Kapthurin Formation, Kenya.

Hominin fossils attributed to *Homo erectus* or *Homo rhodesiensis* have been found in the fluvial sediments of K3 (refs 11, 13, 14). The new chimpanzee fossils were discovered at Locality (Loc.) 99 in K3′, the lacustrine facies of the same geological member. Loc. 99 consists of ~80 m² of exposures at an outcrop ~1 km northeast of site GnJh-19 where hominin mandible KNM-BK (Kenya National Museum-Baringo Kapthurin) 8518 was found[14]. Two chimpanzee fossils, KNM-TH (Kenya National Museum-Tugen Hills) 45519 and KNM-TH 45520, were found in surface context within an area of ~12 m² within Loc.

图 1. 与东非大裂谷西部与东部的主要特征相比，黑猩猩属在非洲赤道地区当前范围（实心黑色区）和历史范围（画点区），东非大裂谷肯尼亚卡普图林组用星形标出。

图 2. 肯尼亚卡普图林组的理想地层柱状图

属于直立人或罗得西亚人的化石已经在 K3 的河流沉积中发现（参考文献 11、13、14）。新的黑猩猩化石是在 99 号地点 K3 层中的湖相沉积（编为 K3′）中发现的。在 GnJh-19 遗址东北约 1 千米的断面上，99 号点有约 80 平方米的出露，在那里古人类下颌骨 KNM-BK（肯尼亚国家博物馆–巴林戈卡普图林）8518 被发现[14]。两个黑猩猩化石，KNM-TH（肯尼亚国家博物馆–图根丘陵）45519 和 KNM-TH 45520，

585

99; additional specimens (KNM-TH 45521 and KNM-TH 45522) were recovered from sieved superficial sediments within the same restricted area. The age of the chimpanzee fossils is constrained by $^{40}Ar/^{39}Ar$ dates of 545 ± 3 kyr (thousand years) on underlying K2 and 284 ± 12 kyr on overlying K4 (ref. 12). Because they are derived from a position low in this stratigraphic interval, they are probably closer to the maximum age of 545 kyr. *Homo* fossils KNM-BK 63-67 and KNM-BK 8518 from K3 are bracketed by $^{40}Ar/^{39}Ar$ dates of 543 ± 4 kyr and 509 ± 9 kyr[12] (Fig. 2).

K3′ sediments are exposed in an outcrop of ~ 1 km^2 in the eastern portion of the Kapthurin Formation. They consist of black and red zeolitized clays interbedded with sands and heavily altered volcanics. Sedimentary and geochemical features of the clays indicate that they were laid down in a shallow body of water that alternated between fresh and intensely saline-alkaline, probably as a response to changes in outflow geometry controlled by local volcanism[15]. Additional intermittent sources of fresh water are suggested by localized ephemeral stream channel features and the remains of an extensive fossil spring. Loc. 99 has produced fragmentary fossils representing suids, bovids, rodents, cercopithecoid primates and catfish. Eight additional faunal collecting areas in K3′ have also produced elephants, hippopotami, carnivores, crocodiles, turtles, gastropods and additional micromammals. Many K3′ taxa, notably hippopotami (*Hippopotamus*), crocodiles, catfish (*Clarias*), gastropods and turtles, reflect local aquatic conditions. The bulk of K3′ non-aquatic fauna, including a colobine monkey, the elephant, the bovids *Kobus*, *Tragelaphus* and specimens probably belonging to *Syncerus*, and the suids *Potamochoerus porcus* (bushpig) and the extinct *Kolpochoerus majus*[16], are consistent with a closed environment. The presence of the cane rat (*Thryonomys*) indicates localized patches of moist, marshy conditions.

Remains of *Homo* (KNM-BK 63-67 and KNM-BK 8518) were recovered at sites GnJh-01 and GnJh-19 by previous workers[11,13,14] from K3 fluvial sediments to the west that represent a system of braided streams, some of which seem to have debouched into the lake. Fluvial K3 deposits and lacustrine K3′ deposits are interstratified, indicating a shoreline that shifted in position in response to alterations in lake levels. The similarity in the array of fossils encountered in K3 and K3′ sediments suggests that Middle Pleistocene *Pan* and *Homo* lived, or at least died, in broadly similar environmental settings. Taken together, the evidence suggests a locally wooded habitat on the shore of an alternately fresh and saline-alkaline lake, fluctuating lake levels, ephemeral nearshore fluvial channels, a nearby freshwater spring, and a semi-arid climatic regime. These conditions are not unlike those found near the shore of Lake Baringo today, although dense human populations have eliminated much of the woodland that formerly supported chimpanzees and the faunal community of which they were a part.

The chimpanzee specimens comprise a minimum of three teeth, probably from the same individual. Two of these are right and left upper central permanent incisors (I^1; KNM-TH 45519 and KNM-TH 45521, respectively). They exhibit broad, spatulate and moderately worn crowns, with thin dental enamel (Fig. 3). The lingual tubercle is large and flanked at the base by deep mesial and distal foveae, characteristic of *Pan*. This feature imparts great

在 99 号点的地表约 12 平方米范围内发现。另外的标本（KNM-TH 45521 和 KNM-TH 45522）在相同的区域内，通过筛选表层堆积物获得。黑猩猩化石的年龄由 $^{40}Ar/^{39}Ar$ 测年限定在下部 K2 和上部 K4 层位之间，对应年代（54.5 万 ± 0.3 万年 ～ 28.4 万 ± 1.2 万年）（参考文献 12）。因为它们源于该地层间隔的低位，所以其年龄比较接近于最大年龄值 54.5 万年。人属化石 KNM-BK 63-67 和 KNM-BK 8518 由 $^{40}Ar/^{39}Ar$ 测年框定在 54.3 万 ± 4.3 万年和 50.9 万 ± 0.9 万年之间 [12]（图 2）。

在卡普图林组东部约 1 平方千米的露头里出露 K3′ 沉积。它们由黑色与红色沸石化黏土构成，并与砂及强变质火山岩互层。黏土的沉积学与地球化学特征显示它们是在淡水与强盐碱水之间交替变化的浅水体中沉积下来的。这种交替可能是作为被当地火山作用控制的流出物质几何学的一种响应 [15]。另外，局部的短暂溪流通道痕迹和泉水活动的相关遗迹提示有额外的间歇性淡水来源。99 号点已经出土的化石碎片分别代表猪科、牛科、啮齿动物、猕猴科灵长类和鲶鱼。在 K3′ 另外 8 个动物化石采集区也出土了象、河马、食肉动物、鳄鱼、海龟、腹足动物及另外的小型哺乳动物。K3′ 的许多动物类，特别是河马、鳄鱼、鲶鱼、腹足动物及海龟，反映了当地的水生环境。K3′ 的大部分非水生动物，包括非洲产疣猴、大象、牛羚、薮羚及可能属于非洲野牛属的标本 [16]，以及猪科的河猪（丛林猪）和灭绝了的阴野猪，是与封闭环境一致的。藤鼠的出现显示出局部有潮湿沼泽的小环境。

人属化石（KNM-BK 63-67 与 KNM-BK 8518）是前人 [11,13,14] 在 GnJh-01 与 GnJh-19 遗址，从 K3 河流沉积到代表辫流系统（其中某些辫流河似乎已经流到了湖里）的西部获得。河流相 K3 沉积与湖相 K3′ 沉积是互层的，这显示水滨线随着湖面变化而产生推移。K3 与 K3′ 沉积中，化石的排列类似，提示出在中更新世的黑猩猩属与人属，是生活在或者至少是死在大致相似的环境里。综上所述，证据提示出这样一个局部树木繁茂的湖岸生活环境：湖泊淡水与盐碱交替变化，湖面上下涨落，季节性近岸河道，靠近淡水泉，气候具有半干旱特征。这些环境条件与今天在靠近巴林戈湖的水岸发现的情况没有什么不同，尽管浓密的人口毁灭了以前黑猩猩赖以为生的很多林地以及它们所属的动物群落。

黑猩猩标本至少有 3 颗牙齿，可能都来自同一个个体的。其中两颗分别是左、右上颌中门齿（I^1，编号 KNM-TH 45519 和 KNM-TH 45521）。其齿冠宽阔，竹片状，磨损中等，釉质薄（图 3）。舌侧结节大，两侧基底连有近远中凹，这是黑猩猩属的

thickness to the labiolingual profiles of the teeth, and clearly distinguishes them from known hominins. The mesial and distal marginal ridges are well formed. The distal corners of the incisal edges are slightly chipped and the labial enamel surfaces exhibit pre-mortem wear as well as slight post-mortem surface weathering. The roots have closed apices and are straight, conical and relatively short. The incisal edges and lingual tubercles exhibit dentinal exposure resulting from wear. Measurements of the specimens, with comparisons to those of extant species of *Pan*, are provided in Table 1. The upper incisors are nearly identical to those of modern *Pan* in all aspects of morphology except their shorter root length. The sub-parallel mesial and distal margins of the incisors bestow a quadrate, rather than triangular, outline to the crowns, a feature that among living chimpanzees is considered to be more common among living *P. troglodytes* than *P. paniscus*[17]. The enamel and cementum coverings are in good condition and the perikymata on the labial surfaces of the crowns and the periradicular striae on the lingual surfaces of the roots can be easily seen. Several of the perikymata near the cervices of the teeth are faintly incised, indicating mild enamel hypoplasia having occurred at about the age of 5 years[18]. The well-matched mesial interproximal wear facets of the Kapthurin Formation *Pan* incisors (**KNM-TH 45519** and **KNM-TH 45521**), the comparable degree of wear on their incisal edges, and the continuity of the enamel hypoplasia on their crowns and the incremental markings on their roots suggest that the two teeth are antimeres.

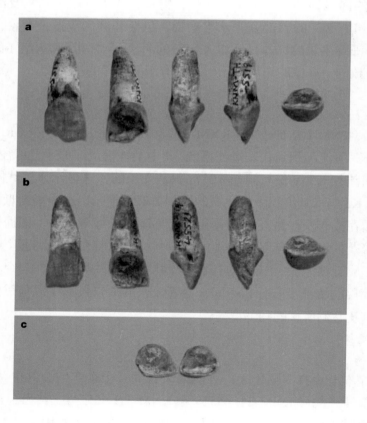

特征。较大的舌侧结节增加了齿冠的唇舌径，并使它们明显有别于已知的古人类。近远中边缘脊发育明显。门齿切缘的近中角有轻微缺口，齿冠唇侧表面有生前磨损和死后轻微风化痕迹。牙根直，尖端封闭，呈圆锥形，较短。门齿切缘和舌侧结节因为磨损而有齿质暴露。化石黑猩猩与其他现生黑猩猩属的测量数据对比列在了表 1 中。除了其牙根较短外，化石黑猩猩上中门齿的各方面形态特征与现生黑猩猩属几乎是一样的。门齿的近似平行的近远中边缘使牙冠排成的轮廓呈方形而不是三角形，这个特征在现生的黑猩猩属黑猩猩种中要比黑猩猩属倭黑猩猩种中更普遍 [17]。釉质和牙骨质状态良好，牙冠唇侧外面釉面横纹和齿根舌侧表面的根周带清晰可见。部分靠近齿颈线的釉面横纹有轻微蚀刻，显示在大约 5 岁时牙釉质出现轻微发育不全 [18]。黑猩猩属的门齿 (KNM-TH 45519 和 KNM-TH 45521) 相匹配的近中邻接面、程度相近的切缘磨耗、齿冠上对应的釉质发育不良、齿根上对应的生长线都提示这两颗牙齿源自同一个体的两侧。

Fig. 3. Central upper incisors of *Pan* from the Kapthurin Formation, Kenya. **a**, KNM-TH 45519. From left to right: labial, lingual, mesial, distal and incisal views. **b**, KNM-TH 45521. Images are in the same sequence as for the previous specimen. **c**, Enlargement of the incisal edge of KNM-TH 45519 (left) and KNM-TH 45521 (right), showing the extreme thinness of the enamel characteristic of modern chimpanzees. **d**, Labial and lingual views of KNM-TH 45519 and KNM-TH 45521.

The third tooth is a lightly worn crown of a left upper permanent molar (KNM-TH 45520) (Fig. 4). It can be problematic to distinguish first from second upper molars in *Pan*, but we identify KNM-TH 45520 as an M^1, judging from the relatively large size of its hypocone, as this cusp is known to decrease in size from M^1 to M^3 (ref. 19). The Kapthurin Formation M^1 is an extremely low molar crown that has lost most of the enamel on its mesial and lingual faces due to breakage after fossilization. The enamel surfaces are pockmarked as a result of chemical and physical weathering. The paracone and metacone are of approximately equal heights and are separated by a sharply incised buccal groove. The hypocone is lower than either of the buccal cusps, but is relatively large and well defined. A shallow trigon basin is delimited by a weak and obliquely oriented postprotocrista (crista obliqua). A deep but short distal fovea lies between the postprotocrista and the low distal marginal ridge. Despite marring of the enamel surface, perikymata are visible on the buccal and distal faces of the paracone, but there is no evidence of enamel hypoplasia. The relative thinness of the enamel can be discerned on the broken mesial and lingual faces of the tooth. The extremely low height of the M^1 crown and the pronounced thinness of the enamel distinguish the tooth from those of known fossil or modern hominins. Among living chimpanzees, the presence of a well-expressed hypocone is more common in *P. troglodytes* than in *P. paniscus*[20]. A fourth tooth (KNM-TH 45522), the crown and proximal roots of a tooth that may be plausibly identified as an aberrant right upper third molar (M^3), will be described elsewhere and is not further discussed here.

The state of wear on the incisors and the M^1 conforms to the known sequence of dental emergence in *Pan*[19,21], and it is likely that they come from the same individual. If they do represent the same animal, its age at death can be estimated at approximately 7–8 years based on standards derived from captive animals[22] and known dental maturation schedules for mandibular molars[23]. The presence of linear enamel hypoplasia on the incisors, but not on the molars, is common in modern apes and seems to be related to nutritional stress that is experienced by the animal after weaning[24].

图 3. 来自肯尼亚卡普图林组黑猩猩属的上中门齿。**a**，KNM-TH 45519。从左至右：唇侧，舌侧，近中，远中，切面（咬合面）。**b**，KNM-TH 45521。该牙齿的图片排列顺序与 KNM-TH 45519 一致。**c**，KNM-TH 45519（左）与 KNM-TH 45521（右）放大的切缘，显示出现代黑猩猩的牙釉质非常薄的特征。**d**，KNM-TH 45519 与 KNM-TH 45521 的唇侧和舌侧。

第三颗牙齿是左侧上颌臼齿（KNM-TH 45520）（图 4）轻度磨损的齿冠。要把黑猩猩属上颌第一臼齿和第二臼齿分开是成问题的，但是我们把 KNM-TH 45520 视为上颌第一臼齿，这主要是因为这颗牙齿的次尖较大，而次尖从上颌第一臼齿到上颌第三臼齿是不断减小的（参考 19）。卡普图林组上颌第一臼齿具有较低的齿冠，其近中和舌侧的大部分釉质因石化后遭受的破坏而丧失。釉质表面因为受到物理与化学风化而有麻子坑。前尖和后尖高度接近，被一条较深的颊侧沟分开。次尖比前尖和后尖都低，但尺寸仍然较大、轮廓清晰。发育较弱的斜脊在近中侧定义了一个较浅的三角座凹。斜脊和较低的远中边缘脊之间有一个深但短的远中凹。尽管釉质表面被损伤，但前尖颊侧和远中侧仍保留较明显的釉面横纹，无釉质发育不良。从破损的牙齿近中面和舌侧面可以看出其釉质较薄。较低的齿冠和较薄的釉质使得化石黑猩猩这颗上颌第一臼齿与已知化石及现代人类区分开。在现生黑猩猩中，发育较好的次尖在黑猩猩属黑猩猩种上比在黑猩猩属倭黑猩猩种上更普遍 [20]。第四颗牙齿（KNM-TH 45522），其牙冠和近齿冠的齿根部分似乎可以被认定为是一颗奇怪的上颌第三臼齿。这颗牙齿会在其他地方描述，在此不做更进一步的讨论。

门齿与上颌第一臼齿的磨耗级别符合黑猩猩属牙齿萌出顺序 [19,21]，且它们很可能来自同一个个体。如果它们确实是代表同一个个体，那么根据从圈养黑猩猩 [22] 身上得来的标准和已知的下颌骨臼齿的牙齿成熟时间表，可以估计这个化石黑猩猩的死亡年龄约为 7 ~ 8 岁 [23]。门齿上出现线状牙釉质发育不良，但臼齿上没有出现，这在现代猿类上很常见，而且似乎是与动物断奶后所经历的营养压力有关 [24]。

Fig. 4. Upper left first molar (KNM-TH 45520). From left to right: occlusal, labial, lingual, mesial and distal views. Note the thinness of the enamel on the broken mesial face of the paracone in the mesial view.

The morphology of the Kapthurin Formation teeth, especially the pronounced lingual tubercle on the incisors, the thickness of the bases of the incisors, the lowness of the molar crown, and the thinness of the enamel on all the teeth clearly supports their attribution to *Pan* rather than *Homo*. Specific diagnosis of isolated teeth within *Pan*, however, must be approached with caution, and for this reason we assign the Kapthurin Formation specimens to *Pan* sp. indet. Nonmetric characters that have been suggested as diagnostic criteria for *P. troglodytes*, such as a more quadrilateral outline shape to the upper central incisor crowns[17] and a better expressed hypocone on the maxillary molars[19,20], seem to suggest more similarity for the Kapthurin Formation fossils to *P. troglodytes* than to *P. paniscus*, but these features are variably expressed among the living species and subspecies of *Pan*[19,25]. Although mean tooth size is known to be significantly smaller in *P. paniscus* than in *P. troglodytes*[17,25,26], size ranges overlap (Table 1). Furthermore, apart from the present specimens, we lack a fossil record for the Pliocene and Pleistocene from which to assess past variability within the genus, and it is feasible that the Kapthurin Formation fossils represent members of an extinct lineage within the genus *Pan*.

Table 1. Dimensions of the Kapthurin Formation fossil chimpanzee teeth

Sample	Tooth	Mesiodistal dimension (mm)	Mesiodistal range (mm)	Buccolingual dimension (mm)	Buccolingual range (mm)
KNM-TH 45519	Right I¹	10.46	—	9.12	—
KNM-TH 45521	Left I¹	10.50	—	9.33	—
P. troglodytes (male)	I¹	12.6 (n = 14)	10.5–13.5	10.1 (n = 15)	9.0–11.3
P. troglodytes (female)	I¹	11.9 (n = 51)	10.0–13.4	9.6 (n = 50)	8.3–11.7
P. paniscus (male)	I¹	10.3 (n = 15)	8.9–11.9	7.9 (n = 15)	7.2–9.2
P. paniscus (female)	I¹	10.4 (n = 20)	9.0–11.5	7.6 (n = 21)	6.8–8.5
KNM-TH 45520	Left M¹	9.7 (estimate)	—	Damage prevents measurement	—
P. troglodytes (male)	M¹	10.3 (n = 19)	9.3–11.2	11.7 (n = 19)	10.7–13.2
P. troglodytes (female)	M¹	10.1 (n = 51)	9.0–11.9	10.9 (n = 50)	7.0–12.8

图 4. 左上第一臼齿（KNM-TH 45520）。从左至右：咬合面、颊侧、舌侧、近中侧、远中侧。注意在近中侧视图中前尖破裂的近中面上较薄的釉质。

卡普图林组牙齿的形态，尤其是门齿明显的舌侧结节，较厚的齿冠底部，低的臼齿齿冠，所有牙齿较薄的釉质，都明显地支持它们是属于黑猩猩属而不是人属成员。但是对黑猩猩属单颗牙齿的种一水平上的判断，必须要谨慎，因此我们将卡普图林组标本定为黑猩猩未定种。已经被提出来的非测量特征，比如上中门齿齿冠[17]的轮廓形状要更像四边形，上颌臼齿的次尖发育明显[19,20]，这似乎都提示卡普图林组化石更类似于黑猩猩属黑猩猩种，而与黑猩猩属倭黑猩猩种不同[19,25]。然而，这些特征在黑猩猩属的现生种和亚种上变异较大。虽然已经知道黑猩猩属倭黑猩猩种牙齿的平均尺寸要明显小于黑猩猩属黑猩猩种的[17,25,26]，但仍有重叠（表1）。此外，除了本文报道的标本外，我们还缺乏用来评估该属过去变异程度的上新世和更新世的化石材料。卡普图林组化石可能代表了黑猩猩属一个已灭绝的谱系成员。

表 1. 卡普图林组黑猩猩牙齿化石的尺寸

标　本	牙齿	近远中径（毫米）	近远中径范围（毫米）	颊舌径（毫米）	颊舌径范围（毫米）
KNM-TH 45519	右 I¹	10.46	–	9.12	–
KNM-TH 45521	左 I¹	10.50	–	9.33	–
黑猩猩属黑猩猩种（雄性）	I¹	12.6 (n = 14)	10.5 ~ 13.5	10.1 (n = 15)	9.0 ~ 11.3
黑猩猩属黑猩猩种（雌性）	I¹	11.9 (n = 51)	10.0 ~ 13.4	9.6 (n = 50)	8.3 ~ 11.7
黑猩猩属倭黑猩猩种（雄性）	I¹	10.3 (n = 15)	8.9 ~ 11.9	7.9 (n = 15)	7.2 ~ 9.2
黑猩猩属倭黑猩猩种（雌性）	I¹	10.4 (n = 20)	9.0 ~ 11.5	7.6 (n = 21)	6.8 ~ 8.5
KNM-TH 45520	左 M¹	9.7（估计）	–	因损坏而无法进行测量	–
黑猩猩属黑猩猩种（雄性）	M¹	10.3 (n = 19)	9.3 ~ 11.2	11.7 (n = 19)	10.7 ~ 13.2
黑猩猩属黑猩猩种（雌性）	M¹	10.1 (n = 51)	9.0 ~ 11.9	10.9 (n = 50)	7.0 ~ 12.8

Continued

Sample	Tooth	Mesiodistal dimension (mm)	Mesiodistal range (mm)	Buccolingual dimension (mm)	Buccolingual range (mm)
P. paniscus (male)	M¹	8.5 (n = 7)	7.9–9.4	9.5 (n = 6)	9.2–10.4
P. paniscus (female)	M¹	8.3 (n = 6)	7.6–8.8	9.7 (n = 6)	9.3–10.4

Comparative dimensions are given for modern *P. troglodytes* and *P. paniscus* from ref. 19.

The Kapthurin Formation fossils represent the first unequivocal evidence of *Pan* in the fossil record, and they demonstrate the presence of chimpanzees in the eastern Rift Valley of Kenya, ~600 km east of the limit of their current range (Fig. 1). The Rift Valley clearly did not pose a physiographical or ecological barrier to chimpanzee occupation. Chimpanzee habitat is now highly fragmented, in part by human activities, but in historic times chimpanzees ranged over a wide belt of equatorial Africa from southern Senegal to western Uganda and Tanzania (Fig. 1). Although much of this region is rainforest, chimpanzees currently also occupy dry forest, woodland and dry savannah, particularly near the eastern edge of their range[27-29]. The modern Baringo region ecosystem is a mosaic of semi-arid *Acacia* bushland and riverine woodland, with a significant substratum of perennial and annual grasses[30]. The Tugen Hills palaeosol carbon isotope record indicates that the woodland and grassland components of the vegetation have been present there from 16 Myr[30]. Representatives of both *Homo* and *Pan* are present in the same stratigraphic interval of the Kapthurin Formation at sites only ~1 km apart, and faunal data suggest that they occupied broadly similar environments in the Middle Pleistocene. This evidence shows that in the past chimpanzees occupied regions in which the only hominoid inhabitants were thought to have been members of the human lineage. Now that chimpanzees are known to form a component of the Middle Pleistocene fauna in the Rift Valley, it is quite possible that they remain to be recognized in other portions of the fossil record there, and that chimpanzees and hominins have been sympatric since the time of their divergence.

(**437**, 105-108; 2005)

Sally McBrearty[1] & Nina G. Jablonski[2]

[1] Department of Anthropology, University of Connecticut, Box U-2176, Storrs, Connecticut 06269, USA

[2] Department of Anthropology, California Academy of Sciences, 875 Howard Street, San Francisco, California 94103, USA

Received 31 January; accepted 4 July 2005.

References:

1. Ruvolo, M. E. Molecular phylogeny of the hominoids: inferences from multiple independent DNA sequence data sets. *Mol. Biol. Evol.* **14**, 248-265 (1997).

2. Darwin, C. *The Descent of Man and Selection in Relation to Sex* (John Murray, London, 1871).

3. Washburn, S. L. in *Changing Perspectives on Man* (ed. Rothblatt, B.) 193-201 (Univ. Chicago Press, Chicago, 1968).

4. Kortlandt, A. *New Perspectives on Ape and Human Evolution* (Univ. Amsterdam, Amsterdam, 1972).

5. Pilbeam, D. & Young, N. Hominoid evolution: synthesizing disparate data. *C. R. Palevol.* **3**, 305-321 (2004).

6. Coppens, Y. East side story: the origin of mankind. *Sci. Am.* **270**, 88-95 (1994).

7. Martyn, J. *The Geologic History of the Country Between Lake Baringo and the Kerio River, Baringo District, Kenya* (PhD dissertation, Univ. London, 1969).

8. Tallon, P. in *Geological Background to Fossil Man* (ed. Bishop, W. W.) 361-373 (Scottish Academic Press, Edinburgh, 1978).

标　本	牙齿	近远中径 (毫米)	近远中径范围 (毫米)	颊舌径 (毫米)	颊舌径范围 (毫米)
黑猩猩属倭黑猩猩种(雄性)	M¹	8.5 (n = 7)	7.9 ~ 9.4	9.5 (n = 6)	9.2 ~ 10.4
黑猩猩属倭黑猩猩种(雌性)	M¹	8.3 (n = 6)	7.6 ~ 8.8	9.7 (n = 6)	9.3 ~ 10.4

参考文献 19 给出了现生黑猩猩属黑猩猩种和黑猩猩属倭黑猩猩种的比较尺寸规格。

　　卡普图林组标本是第一个明确的黑猩猩属的化石证据，它们证明了在肯尼亚东非大裂谷东部，也就是在它们目前范围界限以东约 600 千米的地方，曾经生活着黑猩猩(图 1)。东非大裂谷在地形上、生态上对黑猩猩的生活栖息无疑都不是一个障碍。黑猩猩的栖息地由于人类活动而变得很零散，但在历史上，黑猩猩分布在非洲从塞内加尔南部到乌干达西部及坦桑尼亚这一广阔赤道地带(图 1)。虽然这个区域大部分为雨林，但黑猩猩现也生活在干燥森林、林地及干燥热带稀树草原，特别是靠近它们分布范围的东部边缘[27-29]。现代巴林戈区的生态系统，由半干旱金合欢矮灌丛地与有着多年生和一年生草的显著林下层的河边林地嵌合而成[30]。图根丘陵古土壤碳同位素记录显示，该地区植被的林地与草地成分已经存在了 1,600 万年[30]。典型的人属和黑猩猩属成员出现在卡普图林组同一地层范围，遗址仅相距大约 1 千米，动物群种类提示它们在中更新世所处环境相似。该证据显示在过去黑猩猩占据的区域中人科居民仅有人类世系成员。现在认为黑猩猩构成了东非大裂谷中更新世动物群的一个组成部分，很有可能在化石记录的其他部分里，它们可能会被发现；而且黑猩猩和古人类自从分离后，分布区一直是重叠的。

（田晓阳 翻译；邢松 审稿）

9. McBrearty, S., Bishop, L. C. & Kingston, J. Variability in traces of Middle Pleistocene hominid behaviour in the Kapthurin Formation, Baringo, Kenya. *J. Hum. Evol.* **30**, 563-580 (1996).

10. McBrearty, S. in *Late Cenozoic Environments and Hominid Evolution: a Tribute to Bill Bishop* (eds Andrews, P. & Banham, P.) 143-156 (Geological Society, London, 1999).

11. McBrearty, S. & Brooks, A. The revolution that wasn't: a new interpretation of the origin of modern human behaviour. *J. Hum. Evol.* **39**, 453-563 (2000).

12. Deino, A. & McBrearty, S. ⁴⁰Ar/³⁹Ar chronology for the Kapthurin Formation, Baringo, Kenya. *J. Hum. Evol.* **42**, 185-210 (2002).

13. Leakey, M., Tobias, P. V., Martyn, J. E. & Leakey, R. E. F. An Acheulian industry with prepared core technique and the discovery of a contemporary hominid at Lake Baringo, Kenya. *Proc. Prehist. Soc.* **35**, 48-76 (1969).

14. Wood, B. A. & Van Noten, F. L. Preliminary observations on the BK 8518 mandible from Baringo, Kenya. *Am. J. Phys. Anthropol.* **69**, 117-127 (1986).

15. Renaut, R. W., Tiercelin, J.-J. & Owen, B. in *Lake Basins Through Space and Time* (eds Gierlowski-Kordesch, E. H. & Kelts, K. R.) 561-568 (Am. Assoc. Petrol. Geol., Tulsa, Oklahoma, 2000).

16. Bishop, L. C., Hill, A. P. & Kingston, J. in *Late Cenozoic Environments and Hominid Evolution: a Tribute to Bill Bishop* (eds Andrews, P. & Banham, P.) 99-112 (Geological Society, London, 1999).

17. Johanson, D. C. Some metric aspects of the permanent and deciduous dentition of the pygmy chimpanzee (*Pan paniscus*). *Am. J. Phys. Anthropol.* **41**, 39-48 (1974).

18. Dean, M. C. & Reid, D. J. Perikymata spacing and distribution on hominid anterior teeth. *Am. J. Phys. Anthropol.* **116**, 209-215 (2001).

19. Swindler, D. R. *Primate Dentition: An Introduction to the Teeth of Non-Human Primates* (CUP, Cambridge, 2002).

20. Kinzey, W. G. in *The Pygmy Chimpanzee* (ed. Susman, R. L.) 65-88 (Plenum, New York, 1984).

21. Smith, B. H., Crummett, T. L. & Brandt, K. L. Ages of eruption of primate teeth: a compendium for aging individuals and comparing life histories. *Yearb. Phys. Anthropol.* **37**, 177-232 (1994).

22. Kuykendall, K. L., Mahoney, C. J. & Conroy, G. C. Probit and survival analysis of tooth emergence ages in a mixed-longitudinal sample of chimpanzees (*Pan troglodytes*). *Am. J. Phys. Anthropol.* **89**, 379-399 (1992).

23. Anemone, R. L., Watts, E. S. & Swindler, D. R. Dental development of known-age chimpanzees, *Pan troglodytes* (Primates, Pongidae). *Am. J. Phys. Anthropol.* **86**, 229-241 (1991).

24. Skinner, M. F. & Hopwood, D. Hypothesis for the causes and periodicity of repetitive linear enamel hypoplasia in large, wild African (*Pan troglodytes* and *Gorilla gorilla*) and Asian (*Pongo pygmaeus*) apes. *Am. J. Phys. Anthropol.* **123**, 216-235 (2004).

25. Uchida, A. *Craniodental Variation Among the Great Apes* (Harvard Univ. Peabody Mus., Cambridge, Massachusetts, 1996).

26. Johanson, D. C. *An Odontological Study of the Chimpanzee with Some Implications for Hominoid Evolution* (PhD dissertation, Univ. Chicago, 1974).

27. Kormos, R., Boesch, C., Bakarr, M. I. & Butynski, T. M. *West African Chimpanzees: Status Survey and Conservation Action Plan* (IUCN Publication Unit, Cambridge, 2003).

28. McGrew, W. C., Baldwin, P. J. & Tutin, C. E. G. Chimpanzees in a hot, dry and open habitat: Mt. Assirik, Senegal. *J. Hum. Evol.* **10**, 227-244 (1981).

29. McGrew, W. C., Marchant, L. F. & Nishida, T. *Great Ape Societies* (CUP, Cambridge, 1996).

30. Kingston, J. D., Marino, B. & Hill, A. P. Isotopic evidence for Neogene hominid palaeoenvironments in the Kenya Rift Valley. *Science* **264**, 955-959 (1994).

Acknowledgements. We wish to thank B. Kimeu, N. Kanyenze and M. Macharwas, who found the chimpanzee fossils reported here. Research in the Kapthurin Formation is carried out with the support of an NSF grant to S.M., and under a research permit from the Government of the Republic of Kenya and a permit to excavate from the Minister for Home Affairs and National Heritage of the Republic of Kenya. Both of these are issued to A. Hill and the Baringo Palaeontological Research Project, an expedition conducted jointly with the National Museums of Kenya. We also thank personnel of the Departments of Palaeontology, Ornithology and Mammalogy of the National Museums of Kenya, Nairobi; A. Zihlman; and Y. Hailie-Selassie, L. Jellema and M. Ryan for curation and access to specimens. We express gratitude to A. Hill for his comments on the manuscript. We also thank G. Chaplin for drafting Fig. 1, B. Warren for preparing Figs 3 and 4, and A. Bothell for help with submission of the figures. We are grateful to J. Kelley, J. Kingston, M. Leakey, R. Leakey, C. Tryon, A. Walker and S. Ward for discussions. We thank G. Suwa for his remarks.

Author Information. Reprints and permissions information is available at npg.nature.com/reprintsandpermissions. The authors declare no competing financial interests.

Correspondence and requests for materials should be addressed to S.M. (mcbrearty@uconn.edu).

Molecular Insights into Human Brain Evolution

R. S. Hill and C. A. Walsh

Editor's Note

The knowledge of the human genome is expected to have important consequences throughout biology—not least, to offer insights into how humans diverged from our ancestral species at the genetic level. This paper by two neuroscientists at Harvard Medical School uses information from the human genome sequence to make inferences about the evolution of the human brain. It argues that there has been significant genetic change relatively recently—that is, since the emergence of *Homo sapiens*—particularly in a gene called *FOXP2* associated with articulation and speech in humans. *FOXP2* is often now popularly called a "language gene", although that designation is far too simplistic.

Rapidly advancing knowledge of genome structure and sequence enables new means for the analysis of specific DNA changes associated with the differences between the human brain and that of other mammals. Recent studies implicate evolutionary changes in messenger RNA and protein expression levels, as well as DNA changes that alter amino acid sequences. We can anticipate having a systematic catalogue of DNA changes in the lineage leading to humans, but an ongoing challenge will be relating these changes to the anatomical and functional differences between our brain and that of our ancient and more recent ancestors.

SANTIAGO Ramon y Cajal, widely regarded as the founder of modern neuroscience, recognized as early as the turn of the twentieth century that the human brain was not just larger than that of our ancestors, but it differed in its circuitry as well. Over the course of the last century these differences have been extensively studied at a histological level, although specifying the exact changes that distinguish the human brain has been elusive.

"The opinion generally accepted at that time that the differences between the brain of [non-human] mammals (cat, dog, monkey, etc) and that of man are only quantitative, seemed to me unlikely and even a little offensive to the human dignity... My investigations showed that the functional superiority of the human brain is intimately bound up with the prodigious abundance and unusual wealth of forms of the so-called neurons with short axon." (Ref. 1, translated by J. DeFelipe).

Comparative Differences in Brain Structure

Understanding the genetic changes that distinguish our brain from that of our ancestors starts with defining the key structural and functional differences between the human brain and that of other primates. Our brain is roughly three times the size of the chimpanzee

从分子角度洞察人类大脑的演化

希尔，沃尔什

编者按

人类基因组的知识预计将在整个生物学领域产生重要影响，尤其是，它将为我们了解在基因层面上人类如何与我们的祖先物种分化提供见解。哈佛医学院的两位神经科学家利用人类基因组序列的信息，对人类大脑的演化做出了推断。该研究认为，自智人出现以来，人类最近发生了重大的基因变化，特别是在一种被称为 *FOXP2* 的基因中，这种基因与人类的发音和说话有关。*FOXP2* 现在通常被称为"语言基因"，尽管这个称谓过于简单了。

基因组结构和序列相关知识的迅速发展使得我们能够用新的手段分析与人类大脑和其他哺乳动物大脑的差异相关的特定 DNA 改变。最近的研究将演化改变归因于信使 RNA 和蛋白质表达水平，以及会改变氨基酸序列的 DNA 变化。我们可以预期将来在导致现代人产生的谱系中会有 DNA 变化的系统编目，而我们的大脑和我们远古的以及更近的祖先的大脑在解剖和功能上存在差异，我们正在面临的一项挑战就是如何将这些 DNA 的变化与这些差异联系起来。

圣地亚哥·拉蒙·卡哈尔，被认为是现代神经科学的创始人，早在十九和二十世纪之交就认识到人类的大脑不仅仅是比我们祖先的大，而且脑回路也不同。虽然在上个世纪这些差异已经在组织学层面上得到了广泛的研究，但是确定能够区别人脑的确切的改变仍然是难乎其难。

"在那个年代人们普遍接受的观点是，[非人类] 哺乳动物（猫、狗、猴子等）与人类大脑之间的不同仅仅是数量上的差异，在我看来这不太可能，甚至感觉是对人类尊严的冒犯……我的研究表明人类大脑的功能优越性，是与数量惊人、种类非同寻常的具有短轴突的神经元紧密相关的。"（参考文献 1，德费利佩译）

大脑结构的比较解剖差异

要理解将我们的大脑同祖先的大脑区分开来的遗传改变，需要首先确定人类的大脑与其他灵长类动物的大脑之间关键结构和功能上的不同。在七百万年至八百万

brain, our nearest living relative, from which we diverged 7–8 million years ago, and about twice the size of pre-human hominids living as recently as 2.5 million years ago[2]. The increased size particularly affects the cerebral cortex, the largest brain structure and seat of most higher cognitive functions. The cortex is a multi-layered sheet that is smooth in rodents, but folded in mammals with larger cortices (Fig. 1), allowing more cortex to squeeze into the limited volume of the head.

The enlarged cortex of great apes reflects a longer period of neuronal formation during pre-natal development, so that each dividing progenitor cell undergoes more cell cycles before stopping cell division[3]. Cortical progenitors undergo 11 rounds of cell division in mice[4], at least 28 in the macaque[3], and probably far more in human. In addition to making a larger cortex, the longer period of neurogenesis adds novel neurons to the cortex, so that the cortical circuit diagram differs between primates and other mammals (Fig. 1). Upper cortical layers, generated late in neurogenesis, are over-represented in the primate cerebral cortex, especially in humans[5]. Additionally, special cell types, such as spindle cells (specialized, deep-layer neurons[6]), are unique to primates. The upper-layer neurons that are so unusually common in great apes represent either locally projecting neurons—the "neurons with short axon" of Cajal—or neurons that connect the cortex to itself, but do not project out of the cortex (Fig. 1).

The cerebral cortex shows remarkable local specialization, reflected as functionally distinct cortical "areas" that are essentially a map of the behaviours and capabilities most essential to each species. For example, whereas rodents show relatively larger areas that respond to odours and sensation from the whiskers, they have small areas subserving their limited vision. In contrast, primates are highly visual, with more than a dozen distinct functional areas analysing various features of a visual scene. Recent work has compared functionally homologous visual regions between humans and macaques, suggesting that some areas are quite similar, whereas other visual areas have been either added or greatly modified during the course of evolution[7]. Primates also have particularly large areas of the frontal lobes anterior to the motor cortex (prefrontal cortex), whereas prefrontal cortex is tiny in non-primates. Prefrontal areas regulate many social behaviours and are preferentially enlarged in great apes. Although it has long been thought that prefrontal cortex is especially enlarged in humans, recent work suggests that other great apes may have equivalent proportions of prefrontal cortex[8].

The human cerebral cortex also shows functional asymmetries, with most of us being right handed and having language function preferentially localized in the left hemisphere. Chimpanzees do not show such strong asymmetry in handedness[9], although their brains show some asymmetries in frontal and temporal lobes (which correspond to language areas in humans)[10]. Recent evidence suggests that the left–right asymmetries of the human cerebral cortex are accompanied by asymmetric gene expression during early fetal development[11], although it is not known whether asymmetries of gene expression are seen in non-human primates. There is some evidence from fossil skulls for cortical asymmetry in human predecessors as well[12].

年前我们与关系最近的现生亲戚黑猩猩发生分化，我们大脑的大小是其 3 倍左右，而相比于近至 250 万年前的现代人之前的古人类，我们的大脑是其大脑的 2 倍[2]。大脑尺寸的增加尤其会影响大脑皮层，后者是大脑中最大的结构，也是大部分高级认知功能的所在地。大脑皮层在啮齿动物中是光滑的多层薄片，但在具有较大面积大脑皮层的哺乳动物中是折叠的(图 1)，这样可以将更多的皮层塞入有限的头部空间。

大猿类大脑皮层的增大反映了出生前发育过程中一个较长的神经元形成时期，因此每个将要分裂的祖细胞在细胞分裂停止之前都要经历更多的细胞周期[3]。大脑皮层祖细胞在小鼠中要经历 11 轮细胞分裂[4]，在猕猴中至少 28 轮[3]，而在人类中可能更多。除了形成一个更大的大脑皮层之外，更长的神经发生期还会在大脑皮层上增加新的神经元，因此灵长类动物和其他哺乳动物的大脑皮层回路图是不同的(图 1)。在神经发生晚期生成的上部皮层层次，在灵长类尤其是人类的大脑皮层中占有优势的比例[5]。除此之外，特殊的细胞类型，如梭形细胞(一类特化的深层神经元[6])，是灵长类独有的。在大猿中极其常见的上层神经元，要么是局部延伸的神经元，即卡哈尔的"短轴突神经元"，要么是将自己连接到皮层但并不延伸到皮层之外的神经元(图 1)。

大脑皮层有显著的区域特化，反映为功能截然不同的皮层"区域"，本质上就是对于每个物种最为根本的行为和能力的映射。例如，尽管啮齿类对气味和来自胡须的感觉做出反应的区域相对较大，但服务于其有限视力的区域却很小。相比之下，灵长类更加依赖视觉，有十几处不同的功能区域分析视觉场景中各种不同的特征。最近的研究比较了人和猕猴功能上同源的视觉区域，结果表明，尽管有些区域十分相似，但其他的视觉区域在演化过程中要么被添加要么被大幅度修改[7]。在运动皮层(前额叶皮层)前方灵长类也具有特别大的额叶区域，而在非灵长类中前额叶皮层很小。前额叶区调控着许多社会行为，在大猿当中该区域得到了优先增大。尽管长期以来人们一直认为，人的前额叶皮层尤其增大，但是最近的研究表明，其他的大猿可能具有相同比例的前额叶皮层[8]。

人类大脑皮层也表现出功能的不对称性，就像我们大部分人都是右利手，而语言功能被优先置于左半球。在使用右手或者左手的习惯上，黑猩猩在利手方面并没有表现出强烈的不对称性[9]，尽管它们的大脑在额叶和颞叶(与人类的语言区域相对应)上也表现出一些不对称性[10]。新的证据表明，人类大脑皮层的左右不对称性与胎儿早期发育过程中基因的不对称表达有关[11]，尽管在非人灵长类中还不知道是否也存在基因的不对称表达。也有来自化石头骨的证据表明在人类先祖中也存在皮层不对称性[12]。

Fig. 1. Differences in cerebral cortical size are associated with differences in the cerebral cortex circuit diagram. The top panel shows side views of the brain of a rodent (mouse), a chimpanzee and a human to show relative sizes. The middle panel shows a cross-section of a human and chimpanzee brain, with the cellular composition of the cortex illustrated in the bottom panel (adapted from ref. 5). The cerebral cortex derives from two developmental cell populations: the primordial plexiform layer (PPL) and the cortical plate (CP). The primordial plexiform layer seems to be homologous to simple cortical structures in Amphibia and Reptilia, and appears first temporally during mammalian brain development. The cortical plate develops as a second population that splits the primordial plexiform layer into two layers (layer I at the top and the subplate (SP) at the bottom; numbering follows the scheme of ref. 31). Cortical-plate-derived cortical layers are added developmentally from deeper first (VI, V) to more superficial (III, II) last. Cortical-plate-derived cortical layers are progressively elaborated in mammals with larger brains (for example, insectivores have a single layer II/III/IV that is progressively subdivided into II, III, IV, then IIa, IIb, and so on), so that humans have a larger proportion of these late-derived neurons, which project locally or elsewhere within the cortex. Images from the top and middle panels are from the Comparative Brain Atlas (http://www.brainmuseum.org).

Evolutionary Mechanisms

What sorts of genetic changes underlie diverse brain shape and size? Approaches to this question have come increasingly into focus, although the answers themselves await further

图 1. 大脑皮层大小的不同与大脑皮层回路图的不同相关。上面一排为啮齿动物（小鼠）、黑猩猩以及人类大脑的侧视图，显示相对大小。中间一排为人和黑猩猩大脑的截面，其皮层细胞组成在下面一排图中示意说明（修改自参考文献 5）。大脑皮层源自两种发育细胞群体：原丛状层（PPL）和皮质板（CP）。原丛状层似乎与两栖纲和爬行纲中简单的皮层结构同源，并且在哺乳动物大脑发育过程中首先出现。皮质板作为第二个细胞群体发育，将原丛状层分成两层（在顶部的 I 层和在底部的下板（SP）；编号遵循参考文献 31 的方案）。源自皮质板的皮层层次随着发育从较深层的最初（VI、V）到较浅层的最后（III、II）被逐渐添加。源自皮质板的皮层层次在具有较大大脑的哺乳动物中被逐步精心打造（例如，食虫类有一个单层的 II/III/IV，随着演化过程会被逐步细分成 II、III、IV，然后再分成 IIa、IIb 等），因此人类拥有很大比例的这些晚期衍生的神经元，它们在皮层中局部延伸或向别处延伸。上面和中间一排的图片引自大脑对比图集（http://www.brainmuseum.org）。

演 化 机 制

　　什么类型的基因改变决定了大脑形态和大小的不同呢？尽管答案本身仍然需要进一步的研究，但是解决问题的途径已经引起越来越多的关注。演化蜕变的三

work. Three major mechanisms of evolutionary changes include: (1) addition or subtraction of entire genes to or from the genome; (2) alterations in levels or patterns of gene expression; and (3) alterations in the coding sequence of genes. Recent evidence suggests roles for all of these mechanisms.

The recent completion of sequencing the chimpanzee genome emphasizes the highly similar composition of the human and chimpanzee genomes[13]. There is evidence for inactivation of genes, especially many olfactory receptor genes, by their conversion into pseudogenes[14]. However, there is currently little evidence to suggest that the addition of novel genes is a major mechanism in human brain evolution[13].

Recent studies suggest that human brain evolution is associated with changes in gene expression specifically within the brain as opposed to other tissues such as liver. A few studies suggest more-accelerated gene expression changes in the brain along the human lineage compared with the chimpanzee lineage[15]. Although the studies differ in design and principal conclusions, they share support for an increase in expression level in a subset of brain-expressed genes in the lineage leading to humans[16,17].

There is also accumulating evidence that some neural genes underwent important changes in their coding sequence over the course of recent brain evolution, although the proportion of neural genes that were targets of positive selection is still in debate. Genes strongly influenced by natural selection can be identified by comparing DNA changes that occur in different, closely related species, for example in different primate species. Synonymous DNA substitutions do not alter the amino acid sequence because they occur at degenerate sites in the codon (such as a CGT to CGG change, as both codons encode arginine). Because synonymous changes do not alter the biochemical properties of the encoded protein, they are usually evolutionarily neutral. In contrast, non-synonymous DNA changes alter the amino acid sequence. The vast majority of non-synonymous DNA changes represent disabling mutations that cause disease, hence decreasing the fitness of the organism, and so most non-synonymous DNA changes are subject to negative, or purifying, selection. In contrast, on rare occasions non-synonymous DNA changes might make the protein work slightly better, hence increasing the fitness of the organism and becoming subject to positive selection (that is, advantageous changes propagated to future generations). A ratio of non-synonymous (K_A) to synonymous (K_S) changes $\ll 1$ is typical of most proteins where change is detrimental[18]; rare proteins show $K_A/K_S > 1$, which can indicate positive selection.

In order to test whether genes expressed in the brain were frequent targets of positive selection in primates, one study[19] analysed 200 brain-expressed genes, comparing them to 200 widely expressed genes. They compared K_A/K_S ratios between rats and mice and between humans and macaque monkeys. They concluded that genes involved in brain development or function had a higher tendency to be under positive selection between macaques and humans than between mice and rats. In contrast, systematic surveys of K_A/K_S ratios across much larger numbers of genes between chimpanzees and humans failed to show that neural genes, as a group, have higher K_A/K_S ratios than genes expressed

个主要机制如下：(1) 从基因组中增加或者减除一个完整的基因；(2) 基因表达水平或者模式上的改变；(3) 基因编码序列的改变。新的证据表明以上所有这些机制都在起作用。

最近黑猩猩的基因组测序工作完成进一步表明人的基因组与黑猩猩基因组组成高度相似[13]。其中也存在基因失效转变成假基因的证据，尤其是许多嗅觉受体基因[14]。然而，目前还没有证据表明新基因的增加是人类大脑演化的主要机制[13]。

最近的研究表明人类大脑演化尤其与大脑内的基因表达变化有关，而与肝脏这样的其他的组织截然相反。一些研究发现与黑猩猩演化谱系相比，在人的演化谱系中大脑中的基因表达变化更加快速[15]。尽管这些研究在目的和主要结论上有所不同，但是他们都认为，在通往现代人的谱系中，大脑表达基因的一个子集的表达水平有所增加[16,17]。

越来越多的证据表明，一些神经基因在大脑最近的演化过程中编码序列发生了重大的变化，尽管作为正选择目标的神经基因所占的比例仍有争议。通过比较不同的或者紧密相关的物种中的 DNA 变化，就可以识别受自然选择强烈影响的基因，例如在不同灵长类物种之间。同义 DNA 替换并不会改变氨基酸序列，因为它们出现在密码子的简并位点（例如，CGT 变成 CGG，但两个密码子都编码精氨酸）。因为同义改变并不改变被编码蛋白质的生物化学性质，所以它们在演化上通常也是中性的。与之相反，非同义 DNA 变化会使氨基酸序列发生变化。绝大多数的非同义 DNA 变化都是失效突变，会引发疾病，从而降低生物的适应性，因此大部分非同义 DNA 变化往往会遭到负面选择或肃清。相比之下，在极少数情况下，非同义 DNA 变化可能会使蛋白质起到稍好的作用，从而提高生物的适应性，受到正选择（也就是说，这种有利的改变会传播给将来的世代）。对于大多数蛋白质来讲，非同义变化（K_A）与同义变化（K_S）的比值通常远小于 1，这些变化是有害的[18]；很少蛋白质显示 K_A/K_S 大于 1，这表明是正选择。

为了检验灵长类大脑中表达的基因是否是正选择的目标，一项研究[19]分析了 200 个大脑表达基因，并将它们同 200 个广泛表达的基因进行了比对。他们比较了大鼠和小鼠之间以及人和猕猴之间的 K_A/K_S 比率。他们得出结论，大脑发育或功能所涉及的基因，在猕猴和人之间比在小鼠和大鼠之间有更高的倾向受到正选择。相比之下，黑猩猩和人之间的更大数量基因的 K_A/K_S 比值的系统考察，并没有显示在这两个物种之间，作为一组的神经基因比大脑之外表达的基因有更高的 K_A/K_S 比值[20,21]。对 50 个 K_A/K_S 比值最高的基因进行分析后发现，它们中只有出奇的极少数

outside of the brain between these two species[20,21]. Analysis of the top 50 genes with the highest K_A/K_S ratios showed surprisingly few with known essential roles in the brain[20]. Analysis of the chimpanzee genome confirms that neural genes, as a group, have much lower average K_A/K_S ratios than genes expressed outside of the brain[13]. However, the more recent study suggested that a substantial fraction of the genes with the highest K_A/K_S ratios had roles in brain development or function[13]. These studies are most easily reconciled by suggesting that a small subset of neural genes may be targets for positive selection (see below), whereas neural genes as a whole are subject to intense negative selection due to the severe disadvantages conferred by mutations that disrupt brain function.

Correlation of Genetic Evolution with Human Brain Function

Whereas genome-wide analyses systematically highlight targets of positive genetic selection in the human lineage, there has been great interest in a subset of human genes that show positive evolutionary selection, and for which correlations between evolutionary patterns and gene function in humans are possible. For example, mutant alleles of *FOXP2* cause a severe disorder of articulation and speech in humans, yet subtle differences in *FOXP2* sequence between humans and non-humans show evidence of positive evolutionary selection by K_A/K_S ratio. Its involvement in speech production suggests that changes in *FOXP2* may have been important in the evolution of language[22,23]. Furthermore, analysis of *FOXP2*'s DNA sequence in diverse human populations suggests that the gene shows unusually low sequence diversity—that is, many human populations share a common ancestral sequence at the *FOXP2* locus. This evidence for a "selective sweep" (explained in detail in several recent reviews[2,24]) within humans suggests that evolutionary selection on this gene may have occurred very recently in human evolution; that is, after the appearance of *Homo sapiens*.

Two genes that cause microcephaly (small cerebral cortex) also show strong evidence for positive evolutionary selection. Microcephaly reduces the human brain to 50% or less of its normal mass; that is, to about the size of the brain of chimpanzees or our pre-human ancestors. Whereas marked mutations in abnormal spindle microcephaly (encoded by the *ASPM* locus) and microcephalin (encoded by the *MCPH1* locus) cause microcephaly, both genes show strong evidence that subtler sequence changes were subject to positive selection in the lineage leading to humans (manifested by a high K_A/K_S ratio)[25-29]. Although the precise functions of the two genes are unknown, both are highly expressed in dividing neural precursor cells in the cerebral cortex, and available evidence suggests roles in cell proliferation. Notably, just as neurons in the upper layers of the cerebral cortex (Fig. 1) are added last during development, and are most highly elaborated in humans and great apes, these upper-layer neurons are preferentially lost in many cases of microcephaly, supporting a requirement for microcephaly genes in the formation of the upper cortical layers.

AHI1, which is essential for axon pathfinding from the cortex to the spinal cord (and hence for normal coordination and gait), is another gene that causes a neurological disease

606

在大脑中有已知的重要功能[20]。对黑猩猩基因组的分析也确认了一点，神经基因，作为一组，相比在大脑外表达的基因有更低的 K_A/K_S 比值[13]。然而，更新的研究工作表明，有相当一部分具有最高 K_A/K_S 比值的基因在大脑发育和功能中发挥了作用[13]。这些研究最容易这样折中：神经基因的一个非常小的子集或许会是正选择的目标（见下文），而由于这些破坏大脑功能的基因突变所带来的严重的劣势，神经基因，作为一个整体，会遭受很强的负选择。

基因演化与人类大脑功能的相关性

由于基因组范围的分析系统地标明了人类谱系中基因正选择的目标，人类基因中显示正演化选择的一个子集引起了极大的关注，并且对于这些基因来讲，探讨人类中演化模式和基因功能的相关性是可能的。例如，在人类中 *FOXP2* 的突变等位基因会导致严重的语言和表达障碍，但是人类和非人类 *FOXP2* 基因序列的细微差异通过 K_A/K_S 比值显示该基因受到正演化选择。其参与语言产生的这个现象表明，*FOXP2* 中的变化在语言演化中起着很重要的作用[22,23]。况且，不同现代人群体的 *FOXP2* 的 DNA 序列表明该基因显示出非常低的序列多样性，也就是说，许多现代人群体在 *FOXP2* 位点上共有相同的祖先序列。这一人类内部"选择性清除"（在最近的几篇综述[2,24]中对此进行了详细解释）的证据表明，针对这一基因的演化选择在人类进化过程中可能出现得非常晚，也就是说，在智人出现之后。

导致小头畸形（大脑皮层小）的两个基因也显示出正演化选择强有力的证据。小头畸形会使人的大脑减小到正常体积的 50% 或更小，也就是说减小到大约相当于黑猩猩或现代人之前的祖先的脑的大小。尽管异常纺锤体小头畸形蛋白（由 *ASPM* 位点编码）和小头畸形素（由 *MCPH1* 位点编码）的显著突变会导致小头畸形，但是两个基因都显示出强有力的证据：较细微的序列变化在通往现代人的演化谱系中会受到正选择（表现为 K_A/K_S 比值很高）[25-29]。尽管两个基因的确切功能尚不清楚，但二者在要分裂的大脑皮层的神经先驱细胞中被高度表达，现有证据表明它们在细胞增殖中发挥了作用。值得注意的是，正如大脑皮层上层的神经元（图 1）是在发育的过程的最后被添加，并且在现代人和大猿中被最为精心打造一样，在很多小头畸形病例中，这些上层神经元会被专门丢弃，这证明了导致小头畸形的基因参与了皮层上部层次的形成。

AHI1 对于轴突从皮层到脊髓寻路是至关重要的基因（因此对正常的协调和步态也至关重要），该基因的突变也会导致神经系统疾病，但该基因在灵长类之间较细微

when mutated, but for which subtler changes between primate species suggest positive evolutionary selection in the lineage leading to humans[30]. Patients with *AHI1* mutations not only show mental retardation, but can also show symptoms characteristic of autism, such as antisocial behaviour. This raises the intriguing possibility that evolutionary differences in *AHI1* may relate not only to human patterns of gait, but potentially species-specific social behaviour.

The linkage of studies of gene function in humans with evolutionary analysis is just beginning, and is limited mainly by the rate at which the essential functional roles of genes in the human brain are elucidated. As a population, humans show many mutant alleles for every gene that has been extensively studied, so that the human population is likely to represent, to a first approximation, saturation mutagenesis, such that for each gene in the genome there is a human carrying a mutated allele for that gene. Many neurological diseases affect the very processes that define us evolutionarily as human: intelligence (mental retardation), social organization (autism and attention deficit disorder) and higher-order language (dyslexia). As the genes for these uniquely human disorders are characterized, they may give us new insight into our recent evolutionary history.

(**437**, 64-67; 2005)

Robert Sean Hill[1] & Christopher A. Walsh[1]

[1] Division of Neurogenetics and Howard Hughes Medical Institute, Beth Israel Deaconess Medical Center, and Department of Neurology, Harvard Medical School, Room 266, New Research Building, 77 Avenue Louis Pasteur, Boston, Massachusetts 02115, USA

References:

1. Ramon y Cajal, S. *Recuerdos de mi Vida* Vol. 2 *Historia de mi Labour Científica* 345-346 (Moya, Madrid, 1917).

2. Carroll, S. B. Genetics and the making of *Homo sapiens*. *Nature* **422**, 849-857 (2003).

3. Kornack, D. R. & Rakic, P. Changes in cell-cycle kinetics during the development and evolution of primate neocortex. *Proc. Natl Acad. Sci. USA* **95**, 1242-1246 (1998).

4. Takahashi, T., Nowakowski, R. S. & Caviness, V. S. Jr. The cell cycle of the pseudostratified ventricular epithelium of the embryonic murine cerebral wall. *J. Neurosci.* **15**, 6046-6057 (1995).

5. Marin-Padilla, M. Ontogenesis of the pyramidal cell of the mammalian neocortex and developmental cytoarchitectonics: a unifying theory. *J. Comp. Neurol.* **321**, 223-240 (1992).

6. Allman, J., Hakeem, A. & Watson, K. Two phylogenetic specializations in the human brain. *Neuroscientist* **8**, 335-346 (2002).

7. Orban, G. A., Van Essen, D. & Vanduffel, W. Comparative mapping of higher visual areas in monkeys and humans. *Trends Cogn. Sci.* **8**, 315-324 (2004).

8. Semendeferi, K., Lu, A., Schenker, N. & Damasio, H. Humans and great apes share a large frontal cortex. *Nature Neurosci.* **5**, 272-276 (2002).

9. Hopkins, W. D. & Cantalupo, C. Handedness in chimpanzees (*Pan troglodytes*) is associated with asymmetries of the primary motor cortex but not with homologous language areas. *Behav. Neurosci.* **118**, 1176-1183 (2004).

10. Cantalupo, C. & Hopkins, W. D. Asymmetric Broca's area in great apes. *Nature* **414**, 505 (2001).

11. Sun, T. *et al.* Early asymmetry of gene transcription in embryonic human left and right cerebral cortex. *Science* **308**, 1794-1798 (2005).

12. Broadfield, D. C. *et al.* Endocast of Sambungmacan 3 (Sm 3): a new *Homo erectus* from Indonesia. *Anat. Rec.* **262**, 369-379 (2001).

13. The Chimpanzee Sequencing and Analysis Consortium. Initial sequence of the chimpanzee genome and comparison with the human genome. *Nature* doi:10.1038/nature04072 (this issue).

14. Gilad, Y., Man, O. & Glusman, G. A comparison of the human and chimpanzee olfactory receptor gene repertoires. *Genome Res.* **15**, 224-230 (2005).

15. Enard, W. *et al.* Intra- and interspecific variation in primate gene expression patterns. *Science* **296**, 340-343 (2002).

16. Caceres, M. *et al.* Elevated gene expression levels distinguish human from non-human primate brains. *Proc. Natl Acad. Sci. USA* **100**, 13030-13035 (2003).

17. Uddin, M. *et al.* Sister grouping of chimpanzees and humans as revealed by genome-wide phylogenetic analysis of brain gene expression profiles. *Proc. Natl Acad. Sci. USA* **101**, 2957-2962 (2004).

的变化表明，在通向现代人的人类演化谱系中它是受到正选择的[30]。*AHI1* 基因突变的病人不仅表现为智力低下，而且还可能表现出自闭症的典型症状，比如反社会行为。这就产生了一种令人不解的可能性，即在 *AHI1* 基因上的演化差异可能不仅与人类的步态模式有关，而且还可能与物种特定的社会行为有关。

人类基因功能的研究与演化分析之间的结合只是刚刚开始，并且主要受限于阐明这些基因在人类大脑中的根本功能的研究速度。作为一个种群，人类被广泛研究的每一个基因都显示出许多突变等位基因，因此人类种群很可能大致上代表了饱和突变的发生，使得对于基因组中的每个基因，都有一个人携带着这个基因的突变等位基因。许多神经系统疾病会影响这个在演化意义上定义我们为人类的过程：智慧（智力低下），社会组织（自闭症和注意力缺陷症），高级语言（阅读障碍）。随着这些人类特有的疾病的基因的特征都得到详细的描绘，它们可能会让我们对人类最近的演化历史有一个全新的了解。

（吕静 翻译；张颖奇 审稿）

18. Goldman, N. & Yang, Z. A codon-based model of nucleotide substitution for protein-coding DNA sequences. *Mol. Biol. Evol.* **11**, 725-736 (1994).

19. Dorus, S. *et al.* Accelerated evolution of nervous system genes in the origin of *Homo sapiens*. *Cell* **119**, 1027-1040 (2004).

20. Nielsen, R. *et al.* A scan for positively selected genes in the genomes of humans and chimpanzees. *PLoS Biol.* **3**, e170 (2005).

21. Clark, A. G. *et al.* Inferring nonneutral evolution from human-chimp-mouse orthologous gene trios. *Science* **302**, 1960-1963 (2003).

22. Lai, C. S., Fisher, S. E., Hurst, J. A., Vargha-Khadem, F. & Monaco, A. P. A forkhead-domain gene is mutated in a severe speech and language disorder. *Nature* **413**, 519-523 (2001).

23. Enard, W. *et al.* Molecular evolution of *FOXP2*, a gene involved in speech and language. *Nature* **418**, 869-872 (2002).

24. Gilbert, S. L., Dobyns, W. B. & Lahn, B. T. Genetic links between brain development and brain evolution. *Nature Rev. Genet.* **6**, 581-590 (2005).

25. Bond, J. *et al.* *ASPM* is a major determinant of cerebral cortical size. *Nature Genet.* **32**, 316-320 (2002).

26. Evans, P. D., Anderson, J. R., Vallender, E. J., Choi, S. S. & Lahn, B. T. Reconstructing the evolutionary history of microcephalin, a gene controlling human brain size. *Hum. Mol. Genet.* **13**, 1139-1145 (2004).

27. Evans, P. D. *et al.* Adaptive evolution of *ASPM*, a major determinant of cerebral cortical size in humans. *Hum. Mol. Genet.* **13**, 489-494 (2004).

28. Kouprina, N. *et al.* Accelerated evolution of the *ASPM* gene controlling brain size begins prior to human brain expansion. *PLoS Biol.* **2**, E126 (2004).

29. Zhang, J. Evolution of the human *ASPM* gene, a major determinant of brain size. *Genetics* **165**, 2063-2070 (2003).

30. Ferland, R. J. *et al.* Abnormal cerebellar development and axonal decussation due to mutations in *AHI1* in Joubert syndrome. *Nature Genet.* **36**, 1008-1013 (2004).

31. Marin-Padilla, M. Dual origin of the mammalian neocortex and evolution of the cortical plate. *Anat. Embryol.* **152**, 109-126 (1978).

Acknowledgements. This work was supported by grants from the NINDS and Cure Autism Now. We thank M. Ruvolo and D. Reich for comments on an earlier version of this manuscript, and J. DeFilipe for the translation of the Cajal quotation. Owing to space limitations we were unable to cite directly some of the relevant work in this field. C.A.W. is an Investigator of the Howard Hughes Medical Institute.

Author Information. Reprints and permissions information is available at npg.nature.com/reprintsandpermissions. The authors declare no competing financial interests. Correspondence and requests for materials should be addressed to C.A.W. (cwalsh@bidmc.harvard.edu).

Anthropogenic Ocean Acidification over the Twenty-first Century and Its Impact on Calcifying Organisms

J. C. Orr *et al.*

Editor's Note

Acidification of the oceans is the other great environmental change besides raised temperatures that increased atmospheric carbon dioxide will cause. It could have profound effects on animals such as molluscs and coral, as a shift in the sea's carbon chemistry will make it harder to make calcium carbonate shells. This paper by James Orr and colleagues was one of those that raised the alarm, showing that the shells of planktonic molluscs begin to dissolve in water mimicking the ocean predicted for 2100 by a "business as usual" emission scenario. The effect is greater in cold water—placing corals in a climate-change pincer, as those reefs least at risk from bleaching in warmer water would be most at risk from acidification.

Today's surface ocean is saturated with respect to calcium carbonate, but increasing atmospheric carbon dioxide concentrations are reducing ocean pH and carbonate ion concentrations, and thus the level of calcium carbonate saturation. Experimental evidence suggests that if these trends continue, key marine organisms—such as corals and some plankton—will have difficulty maintaining their external calcium carbonate skeletons. Here we use 13 models of the ocean–carbon cycle to assess calcium carbonate saturation under the IS92a "business-as-usual" scenario for future emissions of anthropogenic carbon dioxide. In our projections, Southern Ocean surface waters will begin to become undersaturated with respect to aragonite, a metastable form of calcium carbonate, by the year 2050. By 2100, this undersaturation could extend throughout the entire Southern Ocean and into the subarctic Pacific Ocean. When live pteropods were exposed to our predicted level of undersaturation during a two-day shipboard experiment, their aragonite shells showed notable dissolution. Our findings indicate that conditions detrimental to high-latitude ecosystems could develop within decades, not centuries as suggested previously.

OCEAN uptake of CO_2 will help moderate future climate change, but the associated chemistry, namely hydrolysis of CO_2 in seawater, increases the hydrogen ion concentration [H^+]. Surface ocean pH is already 0.1 unit lower than preindustrial values. By the end of the century, it will become another 0.3–0.4 units lower[1,2] under the IS92a scenario, which translates to a 100–150% increase in [H^+]. Simultaneously, aqueous CO_2 concentrations [$CO_2(aq)$] will increase and carbonate ion concentrations [CO_3^{2-}] will decrease, making it more difficult for marine calcifying organisms to form biogenic calcium

21 世纪人类活动引起的海洋酸化效应及其对钙质生物的影响

奥尔等

编者按

大气中二氧化碳的持续增加，除了使得全球气温升高，也造成了另一个巨大的环境变化——海洋酸化。海洋酸化改变了海洋碳化学，使得贝类和珊瑚等动物产生碳酸钙壳体变得更加困难，因而产生深远的影响。詹姆斯·奥尔及其同事的这篇论文敲响了警钟，他们的研究表明，在模拟"照常排放"情景的 2100 年海洋的水体中，浮游软体动物的外壳会开始溶解。这样的效应在冷水中效果更大——就像是把珊瑚放在气候变化的困境里，因为那些冷水种珊瑚礁虽然躲开了在温暖的海水中白化的风险，却躲不了酸化的危机。

当今的海洋表层水中，碳酸钙处于饱和状态，然而随着大气二氧化碳浓度的升高，海水 pH 值会持续下降，碳酸根离子浓度也将不断降低，结果将导致海水中碳酸钙的饱和度下降。我们的实验证明，倘若这种趋势持续下去，海洋中的关键生物，如珊瑚和一些钙质浮游生物将很难保住他们的钙质外壳。我们利用 13 种海洋–碳循环模型，模拟在 IS92a "照常排放" 情景下，人为排放二氧化碳对于海洋碳酸钙的饱和度的影响。结果显示，到 2050 年，南大洋表层水将处于文石不饱和状态（文石是碳酸钙的一种亚稳定形式），而到了 2100 年，这种不饱和状态将扩展至整个南大洋并进入太平洋亚北极区海域。根据为期两天的船载实验，将翼足类暴露到模拟的不饱和度下，其文石外壳将遭受显著溶解。这说明，海洋酸化危害高纬度地区生态系统的情况也许几十年内就会出现，而不需要早先提出的几个世纪之久。

海洋对 CO_2 的吸收有助于减轻未来气候的变化，然而，与此相关的化学过程，即海水中 CO_2 的水解，却会使氢离子浓度（$[H^+]$）升高。目前表层海水的 pH 值已经比工业革命前降低了 0.1 个单位。根据 IS92a 排放情景，到 21 世纪末，pH 值可能还要降低 $0.3 \sim 0.4$ 个单位，也就是说 $[H^+]$ 将升高 $100\% \sim 150\%$。同时，海水溶解的 CO_2 浓度（$[CO_2(aq)]$）也将升高，而碳酸根离子浓度（$[CO_3^{2-}]$）则相应降低，由此导致海洋钙质生物难以沉淀生物源的碳酸钙（$CaCO_3$）。大量实验证明，在低纬度海

carbonate ($CaCO_3$). Substantial experimental evidence indicates that calcification rates will decrease in low-latitude corals[3-5], which form reefs out of aragonite, and in phytoplankton that form their tests (shells) out of calcite[6,7], the stable form of $CaCO_3$. Calcification rates will decline along with [CO_3^{2-}] owing to its reaction with increasing concentrations of anthropogenic CO_2 according to the following reaction:

$$CO_2 + CO_3^{2-} + H_2O \rightarrow 2HCO_3^-$$ (1)

These rates decline even when surface waters remain supersaturated with respect to $CaCO_3$, a condition that previous studies have predicted will persist for hundreds of years[4,8,9].

Recent predictions of future changes in surface ocean pH and carbonate chemistry have primarily focused on global average conditions[1,2,10] or on low latitude regions[4], where reef-building corals are abundant. Here we focus on future surface and subsurface changes in high latitude regions where planktonic shelled pteropods are prominent components of the upper-ocean biota in the Southern Ocean, Arctic Ocean and subarctic Pacific Ocean[11-15]. Recently, it has been suggested that the cold surface waters in such regions will begin to become undersaturated with respect to aragonite only when atmospheric CO_2 reaches 1,200 p.p.m.v., more than four times the preindustrial level ($4 \times CO_2$) of 280 p.p.m.v. (ref. 9). In contrast, our results suggest that some polar and subpolar surface waters will become undersaturated at $\sim 2 \times CO_2$, probably within the next 50 years.

Changes in Carbonate

We have computed modern-day ocean carbonate chemistry from observed alkalinity and dissolved inorganic carbon (DIC), relying on data collected during the CO_2 Survey of the World Ocean Circulation Experiment (WOCE) and the Joint Global Ocean Flux Study (JGOFS). These observations are centred around the year 1994, and have recently been provided as a global-scale, gridded data product GLODAP (ref. 16; see Supplementary Information). Modern-day surface [CO_3^{2-}] varies meridionally by more than a factor of two, from average concentrations in the Southern Ocean of 105 µmol kg^{-1} to average concentrations in tropical waters of 240 µmol kg^{-1} (Fig. 1). Low [CO_3^{2-}] in the Southern Ocean is due to (1) low surface temperatures and CO_2-system thermodynamics, and (2) large amounts of upwelled deep water, which contain high [$CO_2(aq)$] from organic matter remineralization. These two effects reinforce one another, yielding a high positive correlation of present-day [CO_3^{2-}] with temperature (for example, $R^2 = 0.92$ for annual mean surface maps). Changes in [CO_3^{2-}] and [$CO_2(aq)$] are also inextricably linked to changes in other carbonate chemistry variables (Supplementary Fig. S1).

区，利用文石来形成珊瑚礁的珊瑚[3-5]以及利用方解石（$CaCO_3$的稳固晶型）来形成外壳的浮游植物[6,7]的钙化速率都将降低。随着人类活动形成的CO_2浓度的不断升高，$[CO_3^{2-}]$因与CO_2发生反应而减少，导致钙化速率下降。CO_3^{2-}与CO_2的反应方程式如下：

$$CO_2 + CO_3^{2-} + H_2O \rightarrow 2HCO_3^-$$ (1)

钙化速率降低的趋势将会持续几百年[4,8,9]，即使表层水体中$CaCO_3$如早先预测的仍为过饱和。

近期对未来大洋表层 pH 值及碳酸盐化学变化的趋势预测研究主要集中于全球平均环境条件[1,2,10]或低纬度地区[4]，在这些地区造礁珊瑚非常丰富。本文则聚焦未来高纬度地区表层和次表层海水中将发生的变化，浮游带壳翼足类是这些区域（南大洋、北冰洋以及太平洋亚北极区）上层海洋主要的生物群组成[11-15]。近来有人提出，由于上述地区表层海水较冷，只有当大气CO_2浓度达到 1,200 ppmv 时，水环境才可能变为文石不饱和状态，而这一浓度是工业革命前CO_2浓度 280 ppmv 的 4 倍多（参考文献 9）。相反，我们的研究结果则表明，未来的 50 年内，当CO_2浓度约为现今的两倍时，极地、副极地的表层海水就会达到文石不饱和状态。

碳酸盐的变化

我们根据观测到的碱度及溶解无机碳（DIC）数据计算了现今海洋中的碳酸盐化学系统，其中所用数据来自世界大洋环流实验（WOCE）以及全球海洋通量联合研究（JGOFS）的CO_2研究结果。上述两项调查是在 1994 年前后进行的，并于近期形成了一个全球网格化产品 GLODAP（参考文献 16，见补充信息）。当代表层海水$[CO_3^{2-}]$在南北方向上变化，最大差异可达 2 倍以上，从南大洋平均浓度为 105 μmol·kg^{-1}到热带海域的 240 μmol·kg^{-1}（图 1）。南大洋表层水$[CO_3^{2-}]$较低的原因有：（1）表层温度以及CO_2体系的热力学活性较低；（2）南大洋有大量向上涌升的深层水，此深层水积累了大量有机质再矿化而来的高$[CO_2(aq)]$。两种效应相互促进，使得$[CO_3^{2-}]$与温度之间表现为非常好的正相关关系（比如，表层海洋年均分布图中 R^2 可以达到 0.92）。$[CO_3^{2-}]$和$[CO_2(aq)]$的变化也与其他碳酸盐化学参数的变化有着密不可分的关系（附图 S1）。

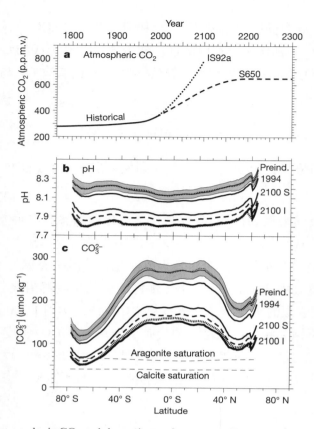

Fig. 1. Increasing atmospheric CO_2 and decreasing surface ocean pH and $[CO_3^{2-}]$. **a**, Atmospheric CO_2 used to force 13 OCMIP models over the industrial period ("Historical") and for two future scenarios: IS92a ("I" in **b** and **c**) and S650 ("S" in **b** and **c**). **b**, **c**, Increases in atmospheric CO_2 lead to reductions in surface ocean pH (**b**) and surface ocean $[CO_3^{2-}]$ (**c**). Results are given as global zonal averages for the 1994 data and the preindustrial ("Preind.") ocean. The latter were obtained by subtracting data-based anthropogenic DIC (ref. 17) (solid line in grey-shaded area), as well as by subtracting model-based anthropogenic DIC (OCMIP median, dotted line in grey-shaded area; OCMIP range, grey shading). Future results for the year 2100 come from the 1994 data plus the simulated DIC perturbations for the two scenarios; results are also shown for the year 2300 with S650 (thick dashed line). The small effect of future climate change simulated by the IPSL climate–carbon model is added as a perturbation to IS92a in the year 2100 (thick dotted line); two other climate–carbon models, PIUB-Bern and Commonwealth Scientific and Industrial Research Organisation (CSIRO), show similar results (Fig. 3a). The thin dashed lines indicating the $[CO_3^{2-}]$ for sea water in equilibrium with aragonite and calcite are nearly flat, revealing weak temperature sensitivity.

We also estimated preindustrial $[CO_3^{2-}]$ from the same data, after subtracting data-based estimates of anthropogenic DIC (ref. 17) from the modern DIC observations and assuming that preindustrial and modern alkalinity fields were identical (see Supplementary Information). Relative to preindustrial conditions, invasion of anthropogenic CO_2 has already reduced modern surface $[CO_3^{2-}]$ by more than 10%, that is, a reduction of 29 µmol kg^{-1} in the tropics and 18 µmol kg^{-1} in the Southern Ocean. Nearly identical results were found when, instead of the data-based anthropogenic CO_2 estimates, we used simulated anthropogenic CO_2, namely the median from 13 models that participated in the second

图 1. 大气 CO_2 含量的不断升高与大洋表层 pH 和 $[CO_3^{2-}]$ 的持续降低。图 a 为用来驱动 13 个 OCMIP 模型在工业革命时代（"历史"）以及两种未来情景——IS92a（图 b 和 c 中的"I"）和 S650（图 b 和 c 中的 "S"）排放情景下的大气 CO_2 浓度逐时变化。图 b 和 c 为随着大气 CO_2 浓度的上升，表层大洋 pH（图 b）和表层大洋 $[CO_3^{2-}]$（图 c）降低的南北分布图。图中给出了 1994 年及工业革命前全球海洋中的纬向平均值，后者是通过分别减去由数据获得的人为排放的 DIC（参考文献 17）（灰色阴影内的实线）和模拟的人为排放的 DIC 而得到的（灰色阴影内的点线表示 OCMIP 中值，阴影表示 OCMIP 的变化范围）。2100 年的结果是根据 1994 年的数据加上两种排放情景下 DIC 变化量的模拟值得到的；图中还给出了 S650 排放情景下 2300 年的情形（粗虚线）。IPSL 气候–碳元素模型得到的未来气候变化产生的微弱干扰也被加到了 IS92a 排放情景下 2100 年的值上（粗点线）；由另外两个模型 PIUB–伯尔尼和 CSIRO（澳大利亚联邦科学与工业研究组织）模型得到的结果与此相似（图 3a）。细虚线表示海水中文石与方解石平衡时的 $[CO_3^{2-}]$，该线近于水平，说明该参数对温度不敏感。

    我们还利用上述数据，假定工业革命以前海洋的碱度与现今的量级相同（见补充信息），根据现代海洋 DIC 的观测数据再减去用观测数据估算出的人为排放的 DIC（参考文献 17）之后，得到了工业革命以前的 $[CO_3^{2-}]$ 的估计值。相对于工业革命以前的水平，人为排放 CO_2 的剧增已使现今海表 $[CO_3^{2-}]$ 降低了 10% 以上，具体为热带地区降低了 29 $\mu mol \cdot kg^{-1}$，南大洋降低了 18 $\mu mol \cdot kg^{-1}$。当我们用模型估计的人为排放 CO_2（利用参与二期大洋碳循环模型国际对比项目（即 OCMIP-2）的 13 个模型模拟得到

phase of the Ocean Carbon-Cycle Model Intercomparison Project, or OCMIP-2 (Fig. 1c).

To quantify future changes in carbonate chemistry, we used simulated DIC from ocean models that were forced by two atmospheric CO_2 scenarios: the Intergovernmental Panel on Climate Change (IPCC) IS92a "continually increasing" scenario (788 p.p.m.v. in the year 2100) and the IPCC S650 "stabilization" scenario (563 p.p.m.v. in the year 2100) (Fig. 1). Simulated perturbations in DIC relative to 1994 (the GLODAP reference year) were added to the modern DIC data; again, alkalinity was assumed to be constant. To provide a measure of uncertainty, we report model results as the OCMIP median $\pm 2\sigma$. The median generally outperformed individual models in OCMIP model–data comparison (Supplementary Fig. S2). By the year 2100, as atmospheric CO_2 reaches 788 p.p.m.v. under the IS92a scenario, average tropical surface $[CO_3^{2-}]$ declines to 149 ± 14 µmol kg^{-1}. This is a 45% reduction relative to preindustrial levels, in agreement with previous predictions[4,8]. In the Southern Ocean (all waters south of $60°$ S), surface concentrations dip to 55 ± 5 µmol kg^{-1}, which is 18% below the threshold where aragonite becomes undersaturated (66 µmol kg^{-1}).

These changes extend well below the sea surface. Throughout the Southern Ocean, the entire water column becomes undersaturated with respect to aragonite. During the twenty-first century, under the IS92a scenario, the Southern Ocean's aragonite saturation horizon (the limit between undersaturation and supersaturation) shoals from its present average depth of 730 m (Supplementary Fig. S3) all the way to the surface (Fig. 2). Simultaneously, in a portion of the subarctic Pacific, the aragonite saturation horizon shoals from depths of about 120 m to the surface. In the North Atlantic, surface waters remain saturated with respect to aragonite, but the aragonite saturation horizon shoals dramatically; for example, north of $50°$ N it shoals from 2,600 m to 115 m. The greater erosion in the North Atlantic is due to deeper penetration and higher concentrations of anthropogenic CO_2, a tendency that is already evident in present-day data-based estimates[17,18] and in models[19,20] (Supplementary Figs S4 and S5). Less pronounced changes were found for the calcite saturation horizon. For example, in the year 2100 the average calcite saturation horizon in the Southern Ocean stays below 2,200 m. Nonetheless, in 2100 surface waters of the Weddell Sea become slightly undersaturated with respect to calcite.

In the more conservative S650 scenario, the atmosphere reaches $2 \times CO_2$ in the year 2100, 50 years later than with the IS92a scenario. In 2100, Southern Ocean surface waters generally remain slightly supersaturated with respect to aragonite. However, the models also simulate that the Southern Ocean's average aragonite saturation horizon will have shoaled from 730 m to 60 m, and that the entire water column in the Weddell Sea will have become undersaturated (Fig. 2). In the north, all surface waters remain saturated under the S650 scenario. North of $50°$ N, the annual average aragonite saturation horizon shoals from 140 m to 70 m in the Pacific, whereas it shoals by 2,000 m to 610 m in the North Atlantic. Therefore, under either scenario the OCMIP models simulated large changes in surface and

的中值）代替用实测数据估算的数值进行扣除时，得到了基本相同的结果（图 1c）。

为了量化海水碳酸盐体系未来的变化趋势，我们以两种大气 CO_2 排放情景——联合国政府间气候变化专门委员会（IPCC）的 IS92a"持续增加型"排放情景（到 2100 年为 788 ppmv）和 IPCC S650"稳定型"排放情景（到 2100 年为 563 ppmv）——为准，用模型得出了 DIC 在两种排放情景下各自的模拟结果（图 1）。同样仍假定碱度不随时间变化的条件下，我们将模拟出的 DIC 相对于 1994 年（GLODAP 的参考年份）的扰动值加到现代观测到的 DIC 数值上。为给出一个不确定度的衡量标准，我们将模拟结果用 OCMIP 中值 $\pm 2\sigma$ 来表示。该中值通常要优于 OCMIP 模拟–数据对照中所用的任一单个模型的分析结果（附图 S2）。根据 IS92a 排放情景，到 2100 年，大气 CO_2 浓度将达到 788 ppmv，热带海洋表层的 $[CO_3^{2-}]$ 的平均值将降低为 $149 \pm 14 \, \mu mol \cdot kg^{-1}$。该值比工业革命以前的浓度低 45%，这与之前的预测结果是一致的 [4,8]。在南大洋（60°S 以南的所有水体）中，表层浓度降至 $55 \pm 5 \, \mu mol \cdot kg^{-1}$，这一浓度比文石在海洋中能保持不溶解的极限 $[CO_3^{2-}]$（66 $\mu mol \cdot kg^{-1}$）还低 18%。

这些变化还将波及海洋表层以下的水体，到时整个南大洋的全水柱将都处于文石不饱和状态。根据 IS92a 排放情景，在 21 世纪，南大洋文石的饱和深度（指文石在水体中处于不饱和状态和过饱和状态之间交界的深度）将从现在的平均 730 m 深（附图 S3）一直升到海洋表层（意指全水柱文石将都处于不饱和状态）（图 2）。同时，亚北极太平洋的部分海域的文石饱和深度也将由 120 m 深处逐渐升至表层。而在北大西洋，表层水体仍处于文石过饱和状态，只是其文石饱和深度也明显变浅；比如，50°N 以北海域将由 2,600 m 深处升至 115 m 处。北大西洋海水的侵蚀作用愈加强烈，是因为人为排放 CO_2 的浓度越来越高，侵蚀的范围也越来越深，无论是根据实测数据得出的估算值 [17,18] 还是从模拟结果 [19,20] 来看，这种趋势都十分明显（附图 S4 和 S5）。而方解石饱和深度的变化则相对而言不那么明显。例如，到 2100 年南大洋方解石平均饱和深度仍将位于 2,200 m 以下。尽管如此，2100 年时威德尔海表层水体中的方解石也将呈轻微不饱和状态。

而在更为保守的 S650 排放情景下，到 2100 年大气中 CO_2 浓度将是现在的两倍，这比 IS92a 排放情景要晚 50 年的时间。到 2100 年时，南大洋表层水体中文石仍略处于过饱和状态。然而，模型结果同样显示，南大洋的平均文石饱和深度将由 730 m 处上升到 60 m 处，同时整个威德尔海的全水柱都变得文石不饱和（图 2）。在 S650 排放情景下，北半球的表层水体仍全部处于过饱和状态下。在 50°N 以北海域，文石的年均饱和深度在太平洋会从 140 m 处上升到 70 m 处，而在北大西洋则由 2,000 m 处上升到 610 m 处。因此，不管在何种排放情景下，OCMIP 模型的模拟结果都显示，表

subsurface $[CO_3^{2-}]$. Yet these models account for only the direct geochemical effect of increasing atmospheric CO_2 because they were all forced with prescribed modern-day climate conditions.

Fig. 2. The aragonite saturation state in the year 2100 as indicated by $\Delta[CO_3^{2-}]_A$. The $\Delta[CO_3^{2-}]_A$ is the *in situ* $[CO_3^{2-}]$ minus that for aragonite-equilibrated sea water at the same salinity, temperature and pressure. Shown are the OCMIP-2 median concentrations in the year 2100 under scenario IS92a: **a**, surface map; **b**, Atlantic; and **c**, Pacific zonal averages. Thick lines indicate the aragonite saturation horizon in 1765 (Preind.; white dashed line), 1994 (white solid line) and 2100 (black solid line for S650; black dashed line for IS92a). Positive $\Delta[CO_3^{2-}]_A$ indicates supersaturation; negative $\Delta[CO_3^{2-}]_A$ indicates undersaturation.

In addition to this direct geochemical effect, ocean $[CO_3^{2-}]$ is also altered by climate variability and climate change. To quantify the added effect of future climate change, we analysed results from three atmosphere–ocean climate models that each included an ocean carbon-cycle component (see Supplementary Information). These three models agree that twenty-first century climate change will cause a general increase in surface ocean $[CO_3^{2-}]$ (Fig. 3), mainly because most surface waters will be warmer. However, the models also agree that the magnitude of this increase in $[CO_3^{2-}]$ is small, typically counteracting less than 10% of the decrease due to the geochemical effect. High-latitude surface waters show the smallest increases in $[CO_3^{2-}]$, and even small reductions in some cases. Therefore, our analysis suggests that physical climate change alone will not substantially alter high-latitude surface $[CO_3^{2-}]$ during the twenty-first century.

层、次表层水体的 [CO_3^{2-}] 将发生明显变化。不过，这些模型仅考虑了大气 CO_2 升高后地球化学方面的直接变化，因为所有模型都是以现在的气候条件为基础的。

图 2. 以 $\Delta[CO_3^{2-}]_A$ 估算的 2100 年时文石的饱和状态。$\Delta[CO_3^{2-}]_A$ 指在盐度、温度和压力均相同的情况下原位 [CO_3^{2-}] 减去海水中文石饱和所需的 [CO_3^{2-}]。图中展示的是在 IS92a 排放情景下，2100 年时 OCMIP-2 估算浓度的中值：a 图为表层图；b 图为大西洋的纬向平均值；c 图为太平洋的纬向平均值。其中粗线分别表示 1765 年（工业革命前，白色虚线）、1994 年（白色实线）和 2100 年（黑色实线为 S650 排放情形，黑色虚线为 IS92a 排放情景下的情形）的文石饱和深度。$\Delta[CO_3^{2-}]_A$ 为正，表示过饱和；$\Delta[CO_3^{2-}]_A$ 为负，表示不饱和。

　　除地球化学方面的直接变化以外，海洋 [CO_3^{2-}] 还受气候变异性和气候变化的影响。为了量化未来气候变化对海洋 [CO_3^{2-}] 的影响，我们对三个海气气候模型的模拟结果作了分析，这三个模型中每一个都包含海洋碳循环的一个组分（见补充信息）。上述三个模型的结果一致显示，21 世纪气候变化将使大洋表层 [CO_3^{2-}] 普遍升高（图 3），这主要是由大部分表层水体的温度将升高所致。不过，模拟结果还显示，[CO_3^{2-}] 升高的幅度很小，一般仅仅可抵消地球化学变化引起的 [CO_3^{2-}] 降低值的 10%。高纬地区的表层水体中 [CO_3^{2-}] 升高最少，部分条件下甚至还会降低。因此，我们分析认为，在 21 世纪，仅仅物理层面上的气候变化不会使高纬地区表层海水的 [CO_3^{2-}] 发生很大变化。

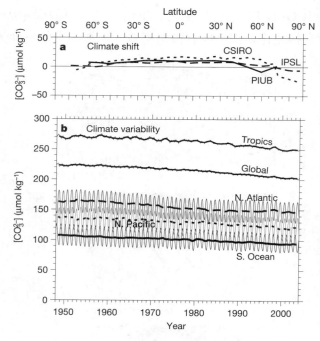

Fig. 3. Climate-induced changes in surface $[CO_3^{2-}]$. **a**, The twenty-first century shift in zonal mean surface ocean $[CO_3^{2-}]$ due to climate change alone, from three atmosphere–ocean climate models—CSIRO-Hobart (short dashed line), IPSL-Paris (long dashed line) and PIUB-Bern (solid line)—that each include an ocean carbon-cycle component (see Supplementary Information). **b**, The regional-scale seasonal and interannual variability is simulated by an ocean carbon-cycle model forced with reanalysed climate forcing.

Climate also varies seasonally and interannually, whereas our previous focus has been on annual changes. To illustrate how climate variability affects surface $[CO_3^{2-}]$, we used results from an ocean carbon-cycle model forced with the daily National Centers for Environmental Prediction (NCEP) reanalysis fields[21] over 1948–2003 (see Supplementary Information). These fields are observationally based and vary on seasonal and interannual timescales. Simulated interannual variability in surface ocean $[CO_3^{2-}]$ is negligible when compared with the magnitude of the anthropogenic decline (Fig. 3b). Seasonal variability is also negligible except in the high latitudes, where surface $[CO_3^{2-}]$ varies by about ± 15 μmol kg^{-1} when averaged over large regions. This is smaller than the twenty-first-century's transient change (for example, ~50 μmol kg^{-1} in the Southern Ocean). However, high-latitude surface waters do become substantially less saturated during winter, because of cooling (resulting in higher $[CO_2(aq)]$) and greater upwelling of DIC-enriched deep water, in agreement with previous observations in the North Pacific[22]. Thus, high-latitude undersaturation will be first reached during winter.

Our predicted changes may be compared to those found in earlier studies, which focused on surface waters in the tropics[8] and in the subarctic Pacific[22,23]. These studies assumed thermodynamic equilibrium between CO_2 in the atmosphere and the surface

图 3. 气候变化引起的表层 [CO₃²⁻] 改变。**a** 图为根据三个海气气候模型——CSIRO–霍巴特（短虚线），IPSL–巴黎（长虚线）和 PIUB–伯尔尼（实线）——得到的 21 世纪仅由气候变化引起的大洋表层 [CO₃²⁻] 纬向平均值的变化，这三个模型中每一个都包含一个碳循环组分（见补充信息）。**b** 图为气候变异性影响下的海洋碳循环模型对区域变化尺度与季节变化、年际变化尺度上的 [CO₃²⁻] 波动的模拟结果。

　　气候还存在季节变化以及年际变化，我们之前仅分析了一年内的变化。为了进一步阐释长期气候波动对表层水体中 [CO₃²⁻] 的影响，我们采用代入基于美国国家环境预报中心（NCEP）处理过的 1948～2003 年间每天天气场 [21]，运行海洋碳循环模型（见补充信息）。这些工作是根据观测数据得到的，其结果随季节和年际时间尺度上的变化而变化，与人为排放造成的 [CO₃²⁻] 降低的量级相比，模型得到的大洋表层 [CO₃²⁻] 的年际变化几乎可以忽略不计（图 3b）。除高纬度地区以外，季节变化也可忽略不计。如果考虑大范围内的平均值的话，高纬海域的表层 [CO₃²⁻] 的季节变化量可以达到 ±15 μmol·kg⁻¹。该值要小于 21 世纪的短期变化（例如，南大洋为 50 μmol·kg⁻¹ 左右）。不过，冬季时，由于水体温度降低（导致了 [CO₂(aq)] 升高）与更多富含 DIC 的深水的上涌，高纬度地区表层水体的文石饱和程度确实要低得多，这与之前在北太平洋观测到的结果 [22] 是一致的。因此，高纬度海域的海水文石不饱和状态将最先在冬季出现。

　　我们所预测出的变化可与早期主要集中于热带 [8] 和亚北极区太平洋海域 [22,23] 的表层水体的研究结果相对照。这些研究均假定，在原位碱度、温度和盐度下，大气 CO₂ 和表层水体中溶解的 CO₂ 之间处于热力学平衡状态。如果假设两者真的达到

waters at their *in situ* alkalinity, temperature and salinity. If, in the equilibrium approach, the p_{CO_2} is taken only to represent seawater p_{CO_2}, then the results agree with our non-equilibrium approach when the sets of carbonate chemistry constants are identical (Fig. 4). However, assuming equilibrium with the atmosphere leads to the prediction that future undersaturation will occur too soon (at lower atmospheric CO_2 levels), mainly because the anthropogenic transient in the ocean actually lags that in the atmosphere. For example, with the equilibrium approach, we predict that average surface waters in the Southern Ocean become undersaturated when atmospheric CO_2 is 550 p.p.m.v. (in the year 2050 under IS92a), whereas our non-equilibrium approach, which uses models and data, indicates that undersaturation will occur at 635 p.p.m.v. (in the year 2070). Despite these differences, both approaches indicate that the Southern Ocean surface waters will probably become undersaturated with respect to aragonite during this century. Conversely, both of these approaches disagree with a recent assessment[9] that used a variant of the standard thermodynamic equilibrium approach, where an incorrect input temperature was used inadvertently.

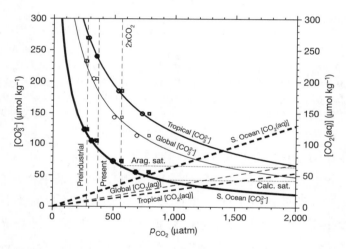

Fig. 4. Key surface carbonate chemistry variables as a function of p_{CO_2}. Shown are both [CO_3^{2-}] (solid lines) and [$CO_2(aq)$] (dashed lines) for average surface waters in the tropical ocean (thick lines), the Southern Ocean (thickest lines) and the global ocean (thin lines). Solid and dashed lines are calculated from the thermodynamic equilibrium approach. For comparison, open symbols are for [CO_3^{2-}] from our non-equilibrium, model-data approach versus seawater p_{CO_2} (open circles) and atmospheric p_{CO_2} (open squares); symbol thickness corresponds with line thickness, which indicates the regions for area-weighted averages. The nearly flat, thin dotted lines indicate the [CO_3^{2-}] for seawater in equilibrium with aragonite ("Arag. sat.") and calcite ("Calc. sat.").

Uncertainties

The three coupled climate–carbon models show little effect of climate change on surface [CO_3^{2-}] (compare Fig. 3a to Fig. 1) partly because air–sea CO_2 exchange mostly compensates for the changes in surface DIC caused by changes in marine productivity and circulation.

了热力学平衡，那么模型计算所用的二氧化碳分压(p_{CO_2}) 只能取海水中的 p_{CO_2} 的数值。在这种情况下，其他碳酸盐体系组分同时保持不变的条件下，平衡假设计算出的结果与我们用非平衡假设得到的结果才是一致的(图 4)。然而，采用海气热力学平衡假设(同时考虑大气 p_{CO_2} 的真实增加值)会导致海水预计的不饱和状态在未来会更早地出现(即大气 CO_2 浓度还较低时就会出现)，这主要是因为实际上海洋对人为排放 CO_2 的响应要滞后于大气。例如，在平衡假设下，我们预计当大气 CO_2 浓度为550 ppmv(根据 IS92a 排放情景应为 2050 年)时，南大洋的表层水体总体上将转变为不饱和状态。而根据我们采用的非平衡假设下的模型和数据来做的研究则显示，在大气 CO_2 浓度达到 635 ppmv(2070 年)时，海水的不饱和状态才会出现。尽管存在上述差异，两种方法的结果却都显示，本世纪南大洋的表层水体极有可能成为文石不饱和水体。反之，这两种方法都挑战了最近利用标准热动力平衡法得到的结论[9]，在该方法中，研究者因疏忽而输入了错误的温度值。

图 4. 主要的表层碳酸盐化学变量，以 p_{CO_2} 的函数表示。图中所示为 [CO_3^{2-}](实线) 和 [CO_2(aq)](虚线) 在热带海域(粗线)、南大洋(最粗线)和全球海洋(细线)表层水体中的平均值。实线和虚线是热动力平衡法计算而来的。为了展开比较，空心符号表示由我们的非平衡数据模拟法得到的 [CO_3^{2-}] 与海水的 p_{CO_2}(空心圆圈)和大气的 p_{CO_2}(空心方框)的比值;符号的粗细与线的粗细相对应，表示该区域面积所占的权重。图中近乎水平的细点线表示文石和方解石处于平衡状态时海水中的 [CO_3^{2-}]。

不 确 定 性

三个气候–碳耦合模型结果显示，气候变化对表层 [CO_3^{2-}] 的影响很小(比较图 3a 与图 1)，部分原因是大气与海洋之间的 CO_2 交换在很大程度上补偿了由海洋生产力和大洋循环的变化引起的表层 DIC 的变化。在缺乏类似补偿机制的次表层水体中，

In subsurface waters where such compensation is lacking, these models could under- or over-predict how much $[CO_3^{2-}]$ will change as a result of changes in overlying marine productivity. However, the models project a consistent trend, which only worsens the decline in subsurface $[CO_3^{2-}]$; that is, all coupled climate models predict increased evaporation in the tropics and increased precipitation in the high latitudes[24]. This leads to greater upper ocean stratification in the high latitudes, which in turn decreases nutrients (but not to zero) and increases light availability (owing to more shallow mixed layers). Thus, at $2 \times CO_2$ there is a 10% local increase in surface-to-deep export of particulate organic carbon (POC) in the Southern Ocean using the Institut Pierre Simon Laplace (IPSL)-Paris model[25]. Subsequent remineralization of this exported POC within the thermocline would increase DIC, which would only exacerbate the decrease in high-latitude subsurface $[CO_3^{2-}]$. For the twenty-first century, these uncertainties appear small next to the anthropogenic DIC invasion (see Supplementary Information).

The largest uncertainty by far, and the only means to limit the future decline in ocean $[CO_3^{2-}]$, is the atmospheric CO_2 trajectory. To better characterize uncertainty due to CO_2 emissions, we compared the six illustrative IPCC Special Reports on Emission Scenarios (SRES) in the reduced complexity, Physics Institute University of Bern (PIUB)-Bern model. Under the moderate SRES B2 scenario, average Southern Ocean surface waters in that model become undersaturated with respect to aragonite when atmospheric CO_2 reaches 600 p.p.m.v. in the year 2100 (Fig. 5). For the three higher-emission SRES scenarios (A1FI, A2 and A1B), these waters become undersaturated sooner (between the years 2058 and 2073); for the two lower-emission scenarios (A1T and B1), these waters remain slightly supersaturated in 2100. Thus, if atmospheric CO_2 rises above 600 p.p.m.v., most Southern Ocean surface waters will become undersaturated with respect to aragonite. Yet, even below this level, the Southern Ocean's aragonite saturation horizon will shoal substantially (Fig. 2). For a given atmospheric CO_2 scenario, predicted changes in surface ocean $[CO_3^{2-}]$ are much more certain than the related changes in climate. The latter depend not only on the model response to CO_2 forcing, but also on poorly constrained physical processes, such as those associated with clouds.

上述模型可能会低估或高估上层海洋生产力的变化所引起的 $[CO_3^{2-}]$ 的变化量。尽管如此，上述模型为我们指出了表层 $[CO_3^{2-}]$ 连续的变化趋势，而该降低趋势只会在次表层水体中更加严重。也就是说，所有耦合气候模型的预测结果都是：热带地区的蒸发量将不断增大，而在高纬地区降雨量则不断增多[24]。这将导致高纬度海区上层水体层化现象加重，进而使其营养盐含量降低（但不会降到零），同时对光的利用率增加（因为上混合层变浅）。因此，根据法国国家科研中心的皮埃尔·西蒙·拉普拉斯（IPSL）–巴黎模型[25]，当 CO_2 浓度达到现今的两倍时，南大洋中由表层向深处输出的颗粒态有机碳（POC）将升高 10%。这些输出的 POC 在温跃层中的再矿化将使 DIC 增加，进而加剧高纬度地区次表层 $[CO_3^{2-}]$ 的降低。不过，在 21 世纪，这种不确定性的影响与人为排放 DIC 的侵蚀相比还是较小（见补充信息）。

到目前为止，最大的不确定性就是大气中 CO_2 的变化趋势，了解该趋势也是限制未来海洋 $[CO_3^{2-}]$ 下降的唯一手段。为了更好地表征 CO_2 排放带来的不确定性，我们利用简化的伯尔尼大学物理研究所（PIUB）–伯尔尼模型，对 IPCC 的六份解释性排放情景特别报告（SRES）作了比较。在适中的 SRES B2 排放情景下，到 2100 年，大气 CO_2 浓度达到 600 ppmv 时，该模型得到的南大洋表层水体将处于文石不饱和状态（图 5）。对于三个排放量较高的 SRES 排放情景（A1FI、A2 和 A1B），水体达到不饱和的时间则早得多（在 2058 ~ 2073 年间）；而在其他两个排放量较低的排放情景（A1T 和 B1）下，上述水体到 2100 年还将处于轻微的过饱和状态。所以，倘若大气 CO_2 浓度升至 600 ppmv 以上，南大洋的大部分表层水体都将处于文石不饱和状态。然而，即便 CO_2 低于这一水平，南大洋中文石饱和深度也将明显变浅（图 2）。在某个给定大气 CO_2 排放情景下，所预测的大洋表层 $[CO_3^{2-}]$ 变化相对于气候变化可能带来的影响则要确定得多，后者并不仅仅取决于模型对 CO_2 强迫的响应，还受物理过程的影响，如云中发生的相关过程。

Fig. 5. Average surface $[CO_3^{2-}]$ in the Southern Ocean under various scenarios. Time series of average surface $[CO_3^{2-}]$ in the Southern Ocean for the PIUB-Bern reduced complexity model (see Fig. 3 and Supplementary Information) under the six illustrative IPCC SRES scenarios. The results for the SRES scenarios A1T and A2 are similar to those for the non-SRES scenarios S650 and IS92a, respectively.

Ocean CO₂ Uptake

With higher levels of anthropogenic CO_2 and lower surface $[CO_3^{2-}]$, the change in surface ocean DIC per unit change in atmospheric CO_2 (μmol kg^{-1} per p.p.m.v.) will be about 60% lower in the year 2100 (under IS92a) than it is today. Simultaneously, the $CO_3^{2-}/CO_2(aq)$ ratio will decrease from 4:1 to 1:1 in the Southern Ocean (Fig. 4). These decreases are due to the well-understood anthropogenic reduction in buffer capacity[26], already accounted for in ocean carbon-cycle models.

On the other hand, reduced export of $CaCO_3$ from the high latitudes would increase surface $[CO_3^{2-}]$, thereby increasing ocean CO_2 uptake and decreasing atmospheric CO_2. Owing to this effect, ocean CO_2 uptake could increase by 6–13 petagrams (Pg) C over the twenty-first century, based on one recent model study[27] that incorporated an empirical, CO_2-dependant relationship for calcification[7]. Rates of calcification could decline even further, to zero, if waters actually became undersaturated with respect to both aragonite and calcite. We estimate that the total shutdown of high-latitude aragonite production would lead to, at most, a 0.25 Pg C yr^{-1} increase in ocean CO_2 uptake, assuming that 1 Pg C yr^{-1} of $CaCO_3$ is exported globally[28], that up to half of that is aragonite[9,29,] and that perhaps half of all aragonite is exported from the high latitudes. The actual increase in ocean CO_2 uptake could be much lower because the aragonite fraction of the $CaCO_3$ may be only 0.1 based on low-latitude sediment traps[30], and the latitudinal distribution of aragonite export is uncertain. Thus, increased CO_2 uptake from reduced export of aragonite will provide little compensation for decreases in ocean CO_2 uptake due to reductions in buffer capacity. Of

图 5. 各种排放情景下，南大洋表层水体 $[CO_3^{2-}]$ 的平均值。利用 PIUB-伯尔尼简化模型（见图 3 及补充信息）得到的，在六种 IPCC SRES 排放情景下，南大洋表层平均 $[CO_3^{2-}]$ 的时间序列值。SRES A1T 和 A2 排放情景下的结果分别与非 SRES 的 S650 排放情景和 IS92a 排放情景相似。

海洋对 CO_2 的吸收

到 2100 年（根据 IS92a 排放情景），由于人为排放的 CO_2 含量较高而表层海水 $[CO_3^{2-}]$ 较低，大气 CO_2 浓度每改变一个单位（$\mu mol \cdot kg^{-1}$ 每 ppmv），大洋表层 DIC 发生的变化量将比现今的低 60%。与此同时，南大洋中 $CO_3^{2-}/CO_2(aq)$ 的比值由 4:1 降至 1:1（图 4）。这种下降是由人类排放引起的海水的缓冲能力降低所致[26]，海洋碳循环模型中已经考虑到了这一点。

另一方面，高纬度地区 $CaCO_3$ 输出量的减少会使表层海水中 $[CO_3^{2-}]$ 增加，从而促使海洋对 CO_2 的吸收能力增强，进而导致大气 CO_2 降低。根据最近的一项模型研究[27]，基于该效应，21 世纪海洋对 CO_2 的吸收能力可提高 6～13 Pg C（皮克碳），该模型包含经验的 CO_2 与钙化过程的相互关系[7]。倘若水体中文石和方解石均变为不饱和状态，钙化速率可能下降得更多，甚至变为 0。据我们估计，假设全球碳酸钙的输出通量为 1 Pg C·yr^{-1}[28]（其中一半的输出通量假设由文石贡献[9,29]，而其中文石一半又假设是由高纬度海域输出），那么高纬海域文石生产的消失，至多可使海洋对 CO_2 的吸收能力提高 0.25 Pg C·yr^{-1}。然而海洋对 CO_2 吸收能力的实际提高可能小得多，因为根据低纬海域沉积物捕获器的数据研究[30]，文石在输出 $CaCO_3$ 中所占的比例大约仅为 0.1，并且文石输出量的纬度分布也不确定。因此，由文石输出的减少所带来的海洋对 CO_2 吸收能力的增强，对因缓冲能力下降而导致的吸收能力的减弱所起到

greater concern are potential biological impacts due to future undersaturation.

Biological Impacts

The changes in seawater chemistry that we project to occur during this century could have severe consequences for calcifying organisms, particularly shelled pteropods: the major planktonic producers of aragonite. Pteropod population densities are high in polar and subpolar waters. Yet only five species typically occur in such cold water regions and, of these, only one or two species are common at the highest latitudes[31]. High-latitude pteropods have one or two generations per year[12,15,32], form integral components of food webs, and are typically found in the upper 300 m where they may reach densities of hundreds to thousands of individuals per m^3 (refs 11, 13–15). In the Ross Sea, for example, the prominent subpolar–polar pteropod *Limacina helicina* sometimes replaces krill as the dominant zooplankton, and is considered an overall indicator of ecosystem health[33]. In the strongly seasonal high latitudes, sedimentation pulses of pteropods frequently occur just after summer[15,34]. In the Ross Sea, pteropods account for the majority of the annual export flux of both carbonate and organic carbon[34,35]. South of the Antarctic Polar Front, pteropods also dominate the export flux of $CaCO_3$ (ref. 36).

Pteropods may be unable to maintain shells in waters that are undersaturated with respect to aragonite. Data from sediment traps indicate that empty pteropod shells exhibit pitting and partial dissolution as soon as they fall below the aragonite saturation horizon[22,36,37]. *In vitro* measurements confirm such rapid pteropod shell dissolution rates[38]. New experimental evidence suggests that even the shells of live pteropods dissolve rapidly once surface waters become undersaturated with respect to aragonite[9]. Here we show that when the live subarctic pteropod *Clio pyramidata* is subjected to a level of undersaturation similar to what we predict for Southern Ocean surface waters in the year 2100 under IS92a, a marked dissolution occurs at the growing edge of the shell aperture within 48 h (Fig. 6). Etch pits formed on the shell surface at the apertural margin (which is typically ~7-μm-thick) as the < 1-μm exterior (prismatic layer) peeled back (Fig. 6c), exposing the underlying aragonitic rods to dissolution. Fourteen individuals were tested. All of them showed similar dissolution along their growing edge, even though they all remained alive. If *C. pyramidata* cannot grow its protective shell, we would not expect it to survive in waters that become undersaturated with respect to aragonite.

的补偿作用很小。人们更需要关注的是未来的不饱和状态将引起的潜在的生物效应。

生物学影响

我们所预计的本世纪海水化学性质的变化将对钙质生物，特别是带壳的翼足类（文石的主要浮游生产者）有重大影响。在极地和副极地海域翼足类的种群密度相当高。不过在这些冷水区翼足类一般也只有 5 个种，其中仅有一到两个种在最高纬度的海域较常见 [31]。高纬地区的翼足类每年繁殖一到两代 [12,15,32]，形成了完整的食物网，而且它们一般生活在表层 300 m 处，在这里每立方米海水中可分布成千上万只翼足类（参考文献 11，13 ~ 15）。例如，在罗斯海中，主要的极地–副极地翼足类蠕虎螺（*Limacina helicina*）有时会取代磷虾在浮游动物中占据主导地位，这被认为是衡量生态系统健康状况的最全面的指标 [33]。在受季节变化影响很大的高纬地区，翼足类沉降输出的高峰一般出现在夏季刚刚结束 [15,34] 时。在罗斯海中，翼足类占碳酸盐和有机碳年输出通量的绝大部分 [34,35]。在南极锋面以南，翼足类也是 $CaCO_3$ 输出通量的主要来源（参考文献 36）。

在文石不饱和水体中，翼足类可能无法维持其壳体。来自沉积物捕获器的数据显示，一旦降落至文石饱和面以下，空的翼足类壳体上就会存在蚀损斑，而且壳体也将被部分溶解 [22,36,37]。体外实验也证实翼足类壳体的溶解速率非常快 [38]。新的实验证据表明，在文石不饱和的表层水体中，即使是活体，翼足类的壳体溶解速度也非常快 [9]。如图所示，当活着的亚北极区翼足类动物——尖菱蝶螺（*Clio pyramidata*）暴露于与 IS92a 排放情景下预测的 2100 年南大洋表层水体的不饱和度相当的环境中时，48 小时内其壳口生长边缘就会发生明显的溶解（图 6）。蚀坑形成于壳口边缘（通常厚度 7 μm 左右）的壳体表面，有小于 1 μm 的外壳（柱状层）向后剥蚀（图 6c），使下面的文石柱体暴露出来而受到溶解。在本实验中，我们共研究了 14 个个体。尽管所有个体都是活着的，但是沿其生长边缘仍都出现了类似的溶解现象。我们认为，倘若尖菱蝶螺不能让其保护壳继续生长，它将无法在文石不饱和的水体中生存。

Fig. 6. Shell dissolution in a live pteropod. **a–d**, Shell from a live pteropod, *Clio pyramidata*, collected from the subarctic Pacific and kept in water undersaturated with respect to aragonite for 48 h. The whole shell (**a**) has superimposed white rectangles that indicate three magnified areas: the shell surface (**b**), which reveals etch pits from dissolution and resulting exposure of aragonitic rods; the prismatic layer (**c**), which has begun to peel back, increasing the surface area over which dissolution occurs; and the aperture region (**d**), which reveals advanced shell dissolution when compared to a typical *C. pyramidata* shell not exposed to undersaturated conditions (**e**).

If the response of other high-latitude pteropod species to aragonite undersaturation is similar to that of *C. pyramidata*, we hypothesize that these pteropods will not be able to adapt quickly enough to live in the undersaturated conditions that will occur over much of the high-latitude surface ocean during the twenty-first century. Their distributional ranges would then be reduced both within the water column, disrupting vertical migration patterns, and latitudinally, imposing a shift towards lower-latitude surface waters that remain supersaturated with respect to aragonite. At present, we do not know if pteropod species endemic to polar regions could disappear altogether, or if they can make the transition to live in warmer, carbonate-rich waters at lower latitudes under a different ecosystem. If pteropods are excluded from polar and subpolar regions, their predators will be affected immediately. For instance, gymnosomes are zooplankton that feed exclusively on shelled pteropods[33,39]. Pteropods also contribute to the diet of diverse carnivorous zooplankton, myctophid and nototheniid fishes[40-42], North Pacific salmon[43,44], mackerel, herring, cod and baleen whales[45].

Surface dwelling calcitic plankton, such as foraminifera and coccolithophorids, may fare better in the short term. However, the beginnings of high-latitude calcite undersaturation will only lag that for aragonite by 50–100 years. The diverse benthic calcareous organisms in high-latitude regions may also be threatened, including cold-water corals which provide essential fish habitat[46]. Cold-water corals seem much less abundant in the North Pacific than in the North Atlantic[46], where the aragonite saturation horizon is much deeper (Fig. 2). Moreover, some important taxa in Arctic and Antarctic benthic communities secrete magnesian calcite, which can be more soluble than aragonite. These include gorgonians[46], coralline red algae and echinoderms (sea urchins)[47]. At $2 \times CO_2$, juvenile echinoderms stopped growing and produced more brittle and fragile exoskeletons in a subtropical six-

图 6. 一个活体翼足类壳体的溶解。图 a ~ d 为活体翼足类尖菱蝶螺的壳体，采自亚北极区太平洋海域，将其置于文石不饱和水中放置 48 小时。整个壳体（图 a）出现的白色矩形，对应着三处放大区域：壳体表面（图 b），出现深蚀坑并导致文石柱体暴露出来；柱状层（图 c），开始向后剥蚀，导致易被溶解的表面积增大；口缘区域（图 d），与未暴露到不饱和环境下的典型尖菱蝶螺（图 e）相比，最外缘的壳已被溶解。

倘若高纬翼足类的其他种对文石不饱和的响应也与尖菱蝶螺一致，我们就可以认为，这些翼足类将无法足够快地适应这种变化，以在不饱和环境中继续生存，而在 21 世纪大部分高纬海域的表层水体将呈现为不饱和状态。因此，到那时翼足类的分布范围将大大减小，不管是在垂向上（扰乱其垂向迁移的固有模式）还是纬向上（导致它们向仍处于文石饱和状态的低纬表层水域迁移）。目前我们并不清楚，极地海域的翼足类到底会全部消失，还是可以迁移至较温暖的水域生存，要知道低纬海域的富碳酸盐水体处于完全不同的生态系统之下。倘若极地和副极地海域的翼足类都不存在了，那么以它们为食的那些动物很快也将受到影响。例如，海天使就是一种专以带壳翼足类为食的浮游动物 [33,39]。翼足类还是其他许多食肉浮游动物，如蛇鼻鱼与南极鱼 [40-42]、北太平洋鲑鱼 [43,44]、鲭鱼、鲱鱼、鳕鱼以及须鲸等 [45] 的食物来源。

生活于表层的方解石质浮游生物，如有孔虫和颗石藻在短期内还不会受到影响。然而，高纬海域的方解石不饱和也仅会比文石不饱和滞后 50 ~ 100 年。除此之外，高纬地区的各种底栖钙质生物也将受到威胁，其中就包括冷水种珊瑚，而它又是许多鱼类基本生存居所的提供者 [46]。北太平洋海域的冷水种珊瑚远没有北大西洋丰富 [46]，因为北大西洋中文石的饱和深度要深得多（图 2）。不仅如此，南北两极底栖生物群中的一些重要种属分泌的是镁方解石，它比文石更易溶解。这些种属包括柳珊瑚 [46]、红珊瑚藻以及棘皮动物（海胆）[47] 等。根据在副热带地区进行的为期 6 个月的养殖实验发现，当大气 CO_2 浓度达到现今的两倍时，棘皮动物的幼体就会停

month manipulative experiment[48]. However, the responses of high-latitude calcifiers to reduced $[CO_3^{2-}]$ have generally not been studied. Yet experimental evidence from many lower-latitude, shallow-dwelling calcifiers reveals a reduced ability to calcify with a decreasing carbonate saturation state[9]. Given that at $2 \times CO_2$, calcification rates in some shallow-dwelling calcareous organisms may decline by up to 50% (ref. 9), some calcifiers could have difficulty surviving long enough even to experience undersaturation. Certainly, they have not experienced undersaturation for at least the last 400,000 years[49], and probably much longer[50].

Changes in high-latitude seawater chemistry that will occur by the end of the century could well alter the structure and biodiversity of polar ecosystems, with impacts on multiple trophic levels. Assessing these impacts is impeded by the scarcity of relevant data.

(**437**, 681-686; 2005)

James C. Orr[1], Victoria J. Fabry[2], Olivier Aumont[3], Laurent Bopp[1], Scott C. Doney[4], Richard A. Feely[5], Anand Gnanadesikan[6], Nicolas Gruber[7], Akio Ishida[8], Fortunat Joos[9], Robert M. Key[10], Keith Lindsay[11], Ernst Maier-Reimer[12], Richard Matear[13], Patrick Monfray[1]†, Anne Mouchet[14], Raymond G. Najjar[15], Gian-Kasper Plattner[7,9], Keith B. Rodgers[1,16]†, Christopher L. Sabine[5], Jorge L. Sarmiento[10], Reiner Schlitzer[17], Richard D. Slater[10], Ian J. Totterdell[18]†, Marie-France Weirig[17], Yasuhiro Yamanaka[8] & Andrew Yool[18]

[1] Laboratoire des Sciences du Climat et de l'Environnement, UMR CEA-CNRS, CEA Saclay, F-91191 Gif-sur-Yvette, France
[2] Department of Biological Sciences, California State University San Marcos, San Marcos, California 92096-0001, USA
[3] Laboratoire d'Océanographie et du Climat: Expérimentations et Approches Numériques (LOCEAN), Centre IRD de Bretagne, F-29280 Plouzané, France
[4] Woods Hole Oceanographic Institution, Woods Hole, Massachusetts 02543-1543, USA
[5] National Oceanic and Atmospheric Administration (NOAA)/Pacific Marine Environmental Laboratory, Seattle, Washington 98115-6349, USA
[6] NOAA/Geophysical Fluid Dynamics Laboratory, Princeton, New Jersey 08542, USA
[7] Institute of Geophysics and Planetary Physics, UCLA, Los Angeles, California 90095-4996, USA
[8] Frontier Research Center for Global Change, Yokohama 236-0001, Japan
[9] Climate and Environmental Physics, Physics Institute, University of Bern, CH-3012 Bern, Switzerland
[10] Atmospheric and Oceanic Sciences (AOS) Program, Princeton University, Princeton, New Jersey 08544-0710, USA
[11] National Center for Atmospheric Research, Boulder, Colorado 80307-3000, USA
[12] Max Planck Institut für Meteorologie, D-20146 Hamburg, Germany
[13] CSIRO Marine Research and Antarctic Climate and Ecosystems CRC, Hobart, Tasmania 7001, Australia
[14] Astrophysics and Geophysics Institute, University of Liege, B-4000 Liege, Belgium
[15] Department of Meteorology, Pennsylvania State University, University Park, Pennsylvania 16802-5013, USA
[16] LOCEAN, Université Pierre et Marie Curie, F-75252 Paris, France
[17] Alfred Wegener Institute for Polar and Marine Research, D-27515 Bremerhaven, Germany
[18] National Oceanography Centre Southampton, Southampton SO14 3ZH, UK
† Present addresses: Laboratoire d'Etudes en Géophysique et Océanographie Spatiales, UMR 5566 CNES-CNRS-IRD-UPS, F-31401 Toulouse, France (P.M.); AOS Program, Princeton University, Princeton, New Jersey 08544-0710, USA (K.B.R.); The Met Office, Hadley Centre, FitzRoy Road, Exeter EX1 3PB, UK (I.J.T.)

Received 15 June; accepted 29 July 2005.

634

止生长，同时其所形成的外骨骼更加脆弱和易碎[48]。不过高纬海域方解石钙质生物对 [CO_3^{2-}] 降低的响应目前还未得到广泛研究。尽管如此，来自低纬海域浅水钙质生物的大量实验证据已表明，随着碳酸盐饱和度的降低，方解石钙质生物的钙化能力会不断下降[9]。假设 CO_2 升高一倍，某些浅水钙质生物的钙化速率就可能降低 50%（参考文献 9），因此，在这种条件下某些种群可能都无法存活至水体方解石真正达到不饱和状态的那一天。当然，在过去 40 万年[49] 甚至更长的时间[50] 里，它们还从未经历过方解石不饱和环境。

本世纪末将要发生的高纬海域海水化学性质的变化可能会极大地改变极地生态系统的结构及其生物多样性，同时会对多个营养级都产生影响。由于缺乏相关数据，对上述影响的量化评估还无法实现。

（齐红艳 翻译；高树基 审稿）

References:

1. Haugan, P. M. & Drange, H. Effects of CO₂ on the ocean environment. *Energy Convers. Mgmt* **37**, 1019-1022 (1996).

2. Brewer, P. G. Ocean chemistry of the fossil fuel CO₂ signal: the haline signal of "business as usual". *Geophys. Res. Lett.* **24**, 1367-1369 (1997).

3. Gattuso, J.-P., Frankignoulle, M., Bourge, I., Romaine, S. & Buddemeier, R. W. Effect of calcium carbonate saturation of seawater on coral calcification. *Glob. Planet. Change* **18**, 37-46 (1998).

4. Kleypas, J. A. *et al.* Geochemical consequences of increased atmospheric carbon dioxide on coral reefs. *Science* **284**, 118-120 (1999).

5. Langdon, C. *et al.* Effect of elevated CO₂ on the community metabolism of an experimental coral reef. *Glob. Biogeochem. Cycles* **17**, 1011, doi:10.1029/2002GB001941 (2003).

6. Riebesell, U. *et al.* Reduced calcification of marine plankton in response to increased atmospheric CO₂. *Nature* **407**, 364-367 (2000).

7. Zondervan, I., Zeebe, R., Rost, B. & Riebesell, U. Decreasing marine biogenic calcification: A negative feedback on rising atmospheric p_{CO_2}. *Glob. Biogeochem. Cycles* **15**, 507-516 (2001).

8. Broecker, W. S. & Peng, T.-H. Fate of fossil fuel carbon dioxide and the global carbon budget. *Science* **206**, 409-418 (1979).

9. Feely, R. A. *et al.* The impact of anthropogenic CO₂ on the CaCO₃ system in the oceans. *Science* **305**, 362-366 (2004).

10. Caldeira, K. & Wickett, M. E. Anthropogenic carbon and ocean pH. *Nature* **425**, 365 (2003).

11. Urban-Rich, J., Dagg, M. & Peterson, J. Copepod grazing on phytoplankton in the Pacific sector of the Antarctic Polar Front. *Deep-Sea Res. II* **48**, 4223-4246 (2001).

12. Kobayashi, H. A. Growth cycle and related vertical distribution of the thecosomatous pteropod *Spiratella "Limacina" helicina* in the central Arctic Ocean. *Mar. Biol.* **26**, 295-301 (1974).

13. Pakhomov, E. A., Verheye, H. M., Atkinson, A., Laubscher, R. K. & Taunton-Clark, J. Structure and grazing impact of the mesozooplankton community during late summer 1994 near South Georgia, Antarctica. *Polar Biol.* **18**, 180-192 (1997).

14. Fabry, V. J. Aragonite production by pteropod molluscs in the subarctic Pacific. *Deep-Sea Res. I* **36**, 1735-1751 (1989).

15. Bathmann, U., Noji, T. T. & von Bodungen, B. Sedimentation of pteropods in the Norwegian Sea in autumn. *Deep-Sea Res.* **38**, 1341-1360 (1991).

16. Key, R. M. *et al.* A global ocean carbon climatology: Results from Global Data Analysis Project (GLODAP). *Glob. Biogeochem. Cycles* **18**, 4031, doi:10.1029/2004GB002247 (2004).

17. Sabine, C. L. *et al.* The ocean sink for anthropogenic CO₂. *Science* **305**, 367-370 (2004).

18. Gruber, N. Anthropogenic CO₂ in the Atlantic Ocean. *Glob. Biogeochem. Cycles* **12**, 165-191 (1998).

19. Sarmiento, J. L., Orr, J. C. & Siegenthaler, U. A perturbation simulation of CO₂ uptake in an ocean general circulation model. *J. Geophys. Res.* **97**, 3621-3645 (1992).

20. Orr, J. C. *et al.* Estimates of anthropogenic carbon uptake from four three-dimensional global ocean models. *Glob. Biogeochem. Cycles* **15**, 43-60 (2001).

21. Kalnay, E. *et al.* The NCEP/NCAR 40-year reanalysis project. *Bull. Am. Meteorol. Soc.* **77**, 437-471 (1996).

22. Feely, R. A. *et al.* Winter-summer variations of calcite and aragonite saturation in the northeast Pacific. *Mar. Chem.* **25**, 227-241 (1988).

23. Feely, R. A., Byrne, R. H., Betzer, P. R., Gendron, J. F. & Acker, J. G. Factors influencing the degree of saturation of the surface and intermediate waters of the North Pacific Ocean with respect to aragonite. *J. Geophys. Res.* **89**, 10631-10640 (1984).

24. Sarmiento, J. L. *et al.* Response of ocean ecosystems to climate warming. *Glob. Biogeochem. Cycles* **18**, 3003, doi:10.1029/2003GB002134 (2004).

25. Bopp, L. *et al.* Potential impact of climate change of marine export production. *Glob. Biogeochem. Cycles* **15**, 81-99 (2001).

26. Sarmiento, J. L., Le Quéré, C. & Pacala, S. Limiting future atmospheric carbon dioxide. *Glob. Biogeochem. Cycles* **9**, 121-137 (1995).

27. Heinze, C. Simulating oceanic CaCO₃ export production in the greenhouse. *Geophys. Res. Lett.* **31**, L16308, doi:10.1029/2004GL020613 (2004).

28. Iglesias-Rodriguez, M. D. *et al.* Representing key phytoplankton functional groups in ocean carbon cycle models: Coccolithophorids. *Glob. Biogeochem. Cycles* **16**, 1100, doi:10.1029/2001GB001454 (2002).

29. Berner, R. A. in *The Fate of Fossil Fuel CO₂ in the Oceans* (eds Andersen, N. R. & Malahoff, A.) 243-260 (Plenum, New York, 1977).

30. Fabry, V. J. Shell growth rates of pteropod and heteropod molluscs and aragonite production in the open ocean: Implications for the marine carbonate system. *J. Mar. Res.* **48**, 209-222 (1990).

31. Bé, A. W. H. & Gilmer, R. W. *Oceanic Micropaleontology* Vol. 1 (ed. Ramsey, A.) 733-808 (Academic, London, 1977).

32. Dadon, J. R. & de Cidre, L. L. The reproductive cycle of the Thecosomatous pteropod *Limacina retroversa* in the western South Atlantic. *Mar. Biol.* **114**, 439-442 (1992).

33. Seibel, B. A. & Dierssen, H. M. Cascading trophic impacts of reduced biomass in the Ross Sea, Antarctica: Just the tip of the iceberg? *Biol. Bull.* **205**, 93-97 (2003).

34. Accornero, A., Manno, C., Esposito, F. & Gambi, M. C. The vertical flux of particulate matter in the polynya of Terra Nova Bay. Part II. Biological components. *Antarct. Sci.* **15**, 175-188 (2003).

35. Collier, R., Dymond, J., Susumu Honjo, S. M., Francois, R. & Dunbar, R. The vertical flux of biogenic and lithogenic material in the Ross Sea: moored sediment trap observations 1996-1998. *Deep-Sea Res. II* **47**, 3491-3520 (2000).

36. Honjo, S., Francois, R., Manganini, S., Dymond, J. & Collier, R. Particle fluxes to the interior of the Southern Ocean in the western Pacific sector along 170° W. *Deep-Sea Res. II* **47**, 3521-3548 (2000).

37. Betzer, P. R., Byrne, R., Acker, J., Lewis, C. S. & Jolley, R. R. The oceanic carbonate system: a reassessment of biogenic controls. *Science* **226**, 1074-1077 (1984).

38. Byrne, R. H., Acker, J. G., Betzer, P. R., Feely, R. A. & Cates, M. H. Water column dissolution of aragonite in the Pacific Ocean. *Nature* **312**, 321-326 (1984).

636

39. Lalli, C. M. Structure and function of the buccal apparatus of *Clione limacina* (Phipps) with a review of feeding in gymnosomatous pteropods. *J. Exp. Mar. Biol. Ecol.* **4**, 101-118 (1970).

40. Foster, B. A. & Montgomery, J. C. Planktivory in benthic nototheniid fish in McMurdo Sound, Antarctica. *Environ. Biol. Fish.* **36**, 313-318 (1993).

41. Pakhomov, E., Perissinotto, A. & McQuaid, C. D. Prey composition and daily rations of myctophid fishes in the Southern Ocean. *Mar. Ecol. Prog. Ser.* **134**, 1-14 (1996).

42. La Mesa, M., Vacchi, M. & Sertorio, T. Z. Feeding plasticity of *Trematomus newnesi* (Pisces, Nototheniidae) in Terra Nova Bay, Ross Sea, in relation to environmental conditions. *Polar Biol.* **23**, 38-45 (2000).

43. Willette, T. M. *et al.* Ecological processes influencing mortality of juvenile pink salmon (*Oncorhynchus gorbuscha*) in Prince William Sound, Alaska. *Fish. Oceanogr.* **10**, 14-41 (2001).

44. Boldt, J. L. & Haldorson, L. J. Seasonal and geographical variation in juvenile pink salmon diets in the Northern Gulf of Alaska and Prince William Sound. *Trans. Am. Fisheries Soc.* **132**, 1035-1052 (2003).

45. Lalli, C. M. & Gilmer, R. *Pelagic Snails* (Stanford Univ. Press, Stanford, 1989).

46. Freiwald, A., Fosså, J. H., Grehan, A., Koslow, T. & Roberts, J. M. *Cold-water Coral Reefs: Out of Sight—No Longer Out of Mind* (No. 22 in Biodiversity Series, UNEP-WCMC, Cambridge, UK, 2004).

47. Dayton, P. K. in *Polar Oceanography, Part B: Chemistry, Biology and Geology* (ed. Smith, W. O.) 631-685 (Academic, San Diego, 1990).

48. Shirayama, Y. & Thornton, H. Effect of increased atmospheric CO_2 on shallow-water marine benthos. *J. Geophys. Res.* **110**, C09S09, doi:10.1029/2004JC002561 (2005).

49. Petit, J. R. *et al.* Climate and atmospheric history of the past 420,000 years from the Vostok ice core, Antarctica. *Nature* **399**, 429-436 (1999).

50. Pearson, P. N. & Palmer, M. R. Middle Eocene seawater pH and atmospheric carbon dioxide concentrations. *Science* **284**, 1824-1826 (1999).

Supplementary Information is linked to the online version of the paper at www.nature.com/nature.

Acknowledgements. We thank M. Gehlen for discussions, and J.-M. Epitalon, P. Brockmann and the Ferret developers for help with analysis. All but the climate simulations were made as part of the OCMIP project, which was launched in 1995 by the Global Analysis, Integration and Modelling (GAIM) Task Force of the International Geosphere–Biosphere Programme (IGBP) with funding from NASA (National Aeronautics and Space Administration). OCMIP-2 was supported by the European Union Global Ocean Storage of Anthropogenic Carbon (EU GOSAC) project and the United States JGOFS Synthesis and Modeling Project funded through NASA. The interannual simulation was supported by the EU Northern Ocean Carbon Exchange Study (NOCES) project, which is part of OCMIP-3.

Author Information. Reprints and permissions information is available at npg.nature.com/reprintsandpermissions. The authors declare no competing financial interests. Correspondence and requests for materials should be addressed to J.C.O. (orr@cea.fr).

Characterization of the 1918 Influenza Virus Polymerase Genes

J. K. Taubenberger *et al.*

Editor's Note

The 1918 "Spanish" influenza pandemic killed more people—about 50 million—than the First World War. There are fears that some recent flu strains could be similarly lethal. Here US virologist Jeffrey Taubenberger and colleagues analyse virus samples extracted from the lung tissue of one victim. They find that the lethal virus was not the result of an animal and human strain merging their DNA, but instead a bird strain that evolved to infect humans. The 1918 virus has some similarities to H5N1 avian flu, which can kill humans but cannot spread between them, and another avian strain, H7N7, which has also killed people, helping researchers identify what separates the relatively mild flu strains from the killers.

The influenza A viral heterotrimeric polymerase complex (PA, PB1, PB2) is known to be involved in many aspects of viral replication and to interact with host factors[1], thereby having a role in host specificity[2,3]. The polymerase protein sequences from the 1918 human influenza virus differ from avian consensus sequences at only a small number of amino acids, consistent with the hypothesis that they were derived from an avian source shortly before the pandemic. However, when compared to avian sequences, the nucleotide sequences of the 1918 polymerase genes have more synonymous differences than expected, suggesting evolutionary distance from known avian strains. Here we present sequence and phylogenetic analyses of the complete genome of the 1918 influenza virus[4-8], and propose that the 1918 virus was not a reassortant virus (like those of the 1957 and 1968 pandemics[9,10]), but more likely an entirely avian-like virus that adapted to humans. These data support prior phylogenetic studies suggesting that the 1918 virus was derived from an avian source[11]. A total of ten amino acid changes in the polymerase proteins consistently differentiate the 1918 and subsequent human influenza virus sequences from avian virus sequences. Notably, a number of the same changes have been found in recently circulating, highly pathogenic H5N1 viruses that have caused illness and death in humans and are feared to be the precursors of a new influenza pandemic. The sequence changes identified here may be important in the adaptation of influenza viruses to humans.

INFLUENZA A viruses cause annual outbreaks in humans and domestic animals. Periodically, new strains emerge in humans that cause global pandemics. The severe "Spanish" influenza pandemic of 1918–1919 infected hundreds of millions, and resulted in the death of approximately 50 million people[12]. We have previously used phylogenetic

1918 年流感病毒聚合酶基因的特点

陶本伯格等

编者按

1918 年的"西班牙"流感大流行造成的死亡人数超过第一次世界大战，约为 5,000 万。人们担心最近的一些流感病毒株可能具有同样的致命性。在这里，美国病毒学家杰弗里·陶本伯格及其同事分析了从一名受害者的肺组织中提取的病毒样本。他们发现这种致命的病毒不是动物和人类病毒株整合 DNA 的结果，而是由禽流感病毒株进化而来感染人类的。1918 年的流感病毒与 H5N1 禽流感病毒（它们可以感染并致人死亡但不能在人与人之间传播）以及另一种禽类病毒 H7N7（同样可以致人死亡）有一些相似之处，这有助于研究人员确定相对温和的流感病毒株与高致病性病毒株的区别。

已知甲型流感病毒异三聚体聚合酶复合体（PA、PB1、PB2）在病毒复制的多个方面发挥作用，并和宿主因子发生作用[1]，因此在宿主特异性中发挥作用[2,3]。1918 年人流感病毒的聚合酶蛋白序列只有少数氨基酸与禽流感病毒共有序列不同，从而支持了它们在大流行前不久由禽流感病毒产生的假说。但是，与禽流感序列相比较，1918 年病毒的聚合酶基因的核苷酸序列同义性差异大于预期，提示其与已知的禽流感毒株存在进化距离。这里我们给出了 1918 年流感病毒整个基因组序列并进行了系统发育分析[4-8]，提出 1918 年病毒不是一种基因重组病毒（如 1957 年和 1968 年大流行的病毒[9,10]），而更可能是能够感染人类的完全类似禽流感（病毒）的病毒。这些数据支持了先期系统发育研究结果，并表明 1918 年病毒来源于禽流感[11]。聚合酶蛋白中总共 10 个氨基酸的突变将 1918 年病毒以及随后的人类流感病毒序列同禽流感病毒序列区别开来。显而易见地，许多相同的突变在最近流行的高致病性 H5N1 病毒中被找到，该病毒已经造成了人类的疾病和死亡，并让人担心这是新的流感大流行的先兆。这里鉴定的序列突变可能对于流感病毒适应人类的过程非常重要。

甲型流感病毒每年都在人类和家畜中引起疫情暴发。新的毒株周期性地在人类中出现并引起全球大流行。1918～1919 年严重的"西班牙"流感大流行波及了数以亿计的人口，并导致了大约五千万人的死亡[12]。我们之前已经用系统发育分析来

analyses to help understand the origin of the pandemic virus[8,11]; functional studies to understand the pathogenicity of the 1918 virus are underway[6,13-17]. Recent data have shown that viral constructs bearing the 1918 haemagglutinin gene are pathogenic in a mouse model, but the genetic basis of this observation has not yet been mapped[6,13-17]. The overall goals of this project have been to understand the origin and unusual virulence of the 1918 influenza virus.

The influenza virus A polymerase functions as a heterotrimer formed by the PB2, PB1 and PA proteins (see ref. 1 for a review). An additional small open reading frame has recently been identified, coding for a peptide (PB1-F2) that is thought to play a role in virus-induced cell death[18]. It is not yet clear how the polymerase complex must change to adapt to a new host[3]. A single amino acid change in PB2, E627K, was shown (1) to be important for mammalian adaptation[2,3], (2) to distinguish highly pathogenic avian influenza (HPAI) H5N1 viruses in mice[19], and (3) to be present in the single fatal human infection during the HPAI H7N7 outbreak in the Netherlands in 2003 (ref. 20), and in some recent H5N1 isolates from humans in Vietnam and Thailand and wild birds in China[21-23].

The open reading frame sequences of segment 1 (PB2), segment 2 (PB1) and segment 3 (PA) of A/Brevig Mission/1/1918, and theoretical translations of the four identified reading frames, are shown in Supplementary Fig. 1a–c. The 1918 PB2 protein contained five changes from the avian consensus sequence (Table 1). Of these, A199S is in the area mapped as the PB1 binding site, and the L475M change is in a nuclear localization signal[24-26]. Three other changes at residues 567, 627 and 702 occur at sites that are not in known functional domains.

Table 1. Amino acid residues distinguishing human and avian influenza polymerases

Gene	Residue no.	Avian	1918	Human H1N1	Human H2N2	Human H3N2	Classical swine	Equine
PB2	199	A	S	S	S	S	S	A
PB2	475	L	M	M	M	M	M	L
PB2	567	D	N	N	N	N	D	D
PB2	627	E	K	K	K	K	K	E
PB2	702	K	R	R*	R	R	R	K
PB1	375	N/S/T†	S	S	S	S	S	S
PA	55	D	N	N	N	N	N	N
PA	100	V	A	A	A	A	V	A
PA	382	E	D	D	D	D	D	E
PA	552	T	S	S	S	S	S	T

* All human H1N1 PB2 sequences have an Arg residue at position 702, except that two out of three A/PR/8/34 sequences have a Lys residue.

† The majority of avian sequences have an Asn residue at position 375 of PB1, 18% have a Ser residue, 13% a Thr residue.

帮助了解这次大流行病毒的来源 [8,11]；了解 1918 年流感病毒致病性的功能研究正在进行中 [6,13-17]。最近的数据显示带有 1918 年血凝素基因的重组病毒在小鼠模型中具有致病性，但是这个现象的基因基础尚未明确 [6,13-17]。这个项目的总体目标就是了解1918 年流感病毒的起源和超常毒力。

甲型流感病毒聚合酶以 PB2、PB1 和 PA 蛋白异三聚体的形式发挥功能（见文献 1 综述）。最近发现了一个小的开放阅读框，它编码一种被认为在病毒诱导的细胞死亡中发挥作用的肽（PB1-F2）[18]。目前还不清楚聚合酶复合体必须如何改变以适应新的宿主 [3]。PB2 中的单个氨基酸突变——E627K 被发现：（1）对哺乳动物的适应性非常重要 [2,3]；（2）可用于鉴别小鼠中的高致病性禽流感病毒 H5N1[19]；（3）出现在 2003 年荷兰高致病性禽流感 H7N7 暴发期间的单例人致死感染（文献 20），以及最近从越南和泰国的人类及中国的野生鸟类中分离出的一些 H5N1 中 [21-23]。

A/布雷维格教区/1/1918，PB2、PB1 和 PA 的开放阅读框序列以及四个已识别的阅读框的理论蛋白翻译详见补充材料图 1a～1c。1918 年 PB2 蛋白含有五个相对于禽流感病毒共有序列的突变（表 1）。其中，A199S 位于 PB1 结合位点区域，L475M 突变位于核定位信号中 [24-26]。567、627 和 702 三个突变都位于目前已知的功能区域之外。

表 1. 区分人类和禽类流感聚合酶的氨基酸残基

基因	残基号	禽类	1918	人 H1N1	人 H2N2	人 H3N2	猪	马
PB2	199	A	S	S	S	S	S	A
PB2	475	L	M	M	M	M	M	L
PB2	567	D	N	N	N	N	D	D
PB2	627	E	K	K	K	K	K	E
PB2	702	K	R	R*	R	R	R	K
PB1	375	N/S/T†	S	S	S	S	S	S
PA	55	D	N	N	N	N	N	D
PA	100	V	A	A	A	A	V	A
PA	382	E	D	D	D	D	D	E
PA	552	T	S	S	S	S	S	T

* 除了三个 A/PR/8/34 序列中的两个含有赖氨酸残基，所有的人类 H1N1 PB2 序列在位点 702 含有精氨酸残基。
† 大部分禽类序列在 PB1 的位点 375 含有天冬酰胺残基，18% 含有丝氨酸残基，13% 含有苏氨酸残基。

The 1918 PB1 protein differed from the avian consensus by seven residues (one of which is shown in Table 1; see also Supplementary Fig. 2). Of these, K54R is in the overlapping binding domains for complementary (c)RNA and viral (v)RNA. Changes at residues 375, 383 and 473 all occur in between the four conserved polymerase motifs in the cRNA binding domain[27], and changes at residues 576, 645 and 654 occur in the vRNA binding domain[28].

Seven changes were noted in the 1918 PA protein compared with the avian consensus (four of which are shown in Table 1, the other three being C241Y, K312R and I322V). The C241Y change occurs in a nuclear localization signal, but the other six changes (at residues 55, 100, 312, 322, 382 and 552) occur at sites outside of known functional domains[24-26].

Representative phylogenetic analyses of the three polymerase genes are shown in Figs 1–3. The 1918 human pandemic viral polymerase genes were compared to representative avian influenza genes with regards to transition/transversion (T_i/T_v) ratio, synonymous/non-synonymous (S/N) ratio, and the numbers of differences at fourfold degenerate sites (defined in ref. 11). T_i/T_v ratios for most comparisons using the 1918 viral genes and representative sequences of either North American or Eurasian avian genes yielded values between 2 and 4. This range was similar to that observed for comparisons of various avian genes with one another, except for the PB1 gene. For PB1, comparisons of the 1918 viral gene with avian virus PB1 genes was always close to 2, whereas comparisons of various avian genes with one another were in the range of 6–10. There were fewer transversions in comparisons between avian PB1 genes than in comparisons between avian PB1 and 1918 human virus PB1, probably reflecting that transversions more often lead to non-synonymous changes.

S/N ratios for most comparisons using the 1918 viral genes and representative sequences of either North American or Eurasian avian genes usually yielded values in the range of 7–16 for both the PA and PB2 genes, as is the case for most avian versus avian PA and PB2 gene comparisons. Like the T_i/T_v ratios, the S/N ratios were somewhat higher with the PB1 gene (most of the comparisons yielded ratios in the range of 16–25), owing to a smaller number of non-synonymous changes in comparisons of avian PB1 genes with one another. These findings may reflect a more conservative evolution of PB1 in birds.

A subset of synonymous differences occurs at sites that are fourfold degenerate (that is, where a substitution with any base does not result in an amino acid replacement). As these sites are not subject to selective pressure at the protein level, base substitutions at many fourfold degenerate sites may accumulate rapidly. If influenza virus genes have been evolving in birds for long enough to reach evolutionary stasis, as is suggested by the high S/N ratios described above, one would predict that at many of the sites where fourfold degeneracy is possible, all four bases would be present in the avian clade unless the constraints of RNA secondary structure limit the accumulation of synonymous changes. In fact, when avian sequences from geographically distinct lineages (North American versus European) were compared, the per cent difference at fourfold degenerate sites yielded values in the 27–38% range. In contrast, calculating the per cent difference at fourfold degenerate

在蛋白序列上，1918 病毒株的 PB1 蛋白与禽流感株有七个氨基酸残基的差异（其中一个在表 1 中显示，也可见于补充材料图 2）。其中，K54R 位于互补（c）RNA 和病毒（v）RNA 的重叠结合域。375、383 和 473 处的突变都位于 cRNA 结合域的四个保守的聚合酶基序之间 [27]，而 576、645 和 654 处的突变位于 vRNA 结合域 [28]。

1918 病毒株 PA 蛋白与禽流感株在蛋白序列上的差别一共有七处（其中四个在表 1 中显示，其他三个是 C241Y、K312R 和 I322V）。C241Y 突变发生在核定位信号中，但是其他六个突变（55、100、312、322、382 和 552）均在已知的功能区域之外 [24-26]。

三个聚合酶基因的进化分析呈现在图 1 ~ 图 3 中。1918 年人类大流行病毒聚合酶基因与代表性的禽流感病毒基因进行了转换/颠换（T_i/T_v）比、同义/非同义（S/N）比和四倍简并位点（在文献 11 中定义）差别数目的对比。大部分 1918 年病毒基因和北美或者欧亚禽流感病毒基因的代表性序列进行对比获得的 T_i/T_v 数值都在 2 和 4 之间。该范围与不同禽类携带禽流感病毒基因之间对比所得到的结果类似，除了 PB1基因。对 PB1 基因来说，1918 年病毒基因与禽流感基因的对比始终接近 2，而不同禽类携带禽流感基因之间的对比都在 6 ~ 10 的范围内。禽流感 PB1 基因之间对比得到的颠换数少于禽流感和 1918 年人流感病毒 PB1 基因之间对比得出的颠换数，很可能反映了颠换更常导致非同义突变。

对 PA 和 PB2 基因来说，大部分用 1918 年病毒基因和北美或者欧亚任一禽类流感病毒基因的代表性序列进行对比获得的 S/N 比都在 7 ~ 16 的范围内，大部分禽流感病毒之间对比的结果范围也是一样。就像 T_i/T_v 比一样，PB1 基因的 S/N 比稍微高一些（大部分对比得出的数值在 16 ~ 25 范围内），因为相对于其他来说，禽流感病毒 PB1 基因的非同义突变数量少一些。这些发现可能反映了禽流感病毒 PB1 进化过程中的保守性更高。

一部分同义突变发生在四倍简并位点（即任何碱基的置换都不会造成氨基酸的替换）。由于这些位点不会在蛋白质水平面临选择压力，许多四倍简并位点的碱基置换可能会迅速地累积。如果流感病毒基因如上面所描述的高 S/N 比所揭示的那样，已经在鸟类中存在足够长的时间并达到进化停滞，我们能够预计在可能出现四倍简并的许多位点，所有四种碱基都可能出现在禽类分支上，除非 RNA 二级结构的限制约束了这种同义突变的积累。事实上，当对比地理上不同谱系（北美和欧亚）的禽类来源流感病毒序列时，四倍简并位点的百分比差别都在 27% ~ 38% 之间。相反的，对比 1918 年病毒的 PA、PB1、PB2 基因序列和禽流感病毒序列时，计算出四倍简

sites in comparisons of the 1918 viral PA, PB1 and PB2 gene sequences with avian sequences yielded consistently higher values (range 41–51%) for all three genes. As with the other 1918 genes[11], this suggests that the donor source of the 1918 virus was in evolutionary isolation from those avian influenza viruses currently represented in the databases.

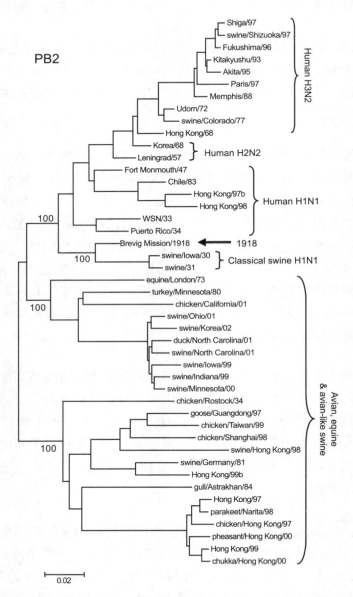

Fig. 1. Phylogenetic tree of the PB2 gene. Sequences were aligned and analysed for phylogenetic relationships using the NJ algorithm, with the proportion of sequence differences as the distance measure. Bootstrap values (100 replications) for key nodes are shown (for clarity, identical and nearly identical sequences have been removed from the trees). Major clades are identified with large brackets. The arrow identifies the position of the 1918 PB2 gene sequence. A distance bar is shown below the tree. Influenza strain abbreviations used in the analyses are listed in Supplementary Table 1.

并位点的百分比差别在三种基因中都处于高水平(41% ～ 51%)。和其他的 1918 年病毒基因一样 [11]，这提示 1918 年病毒的供体来源与目前数据库中显示的禽流感病毒在进化上是隔离的。

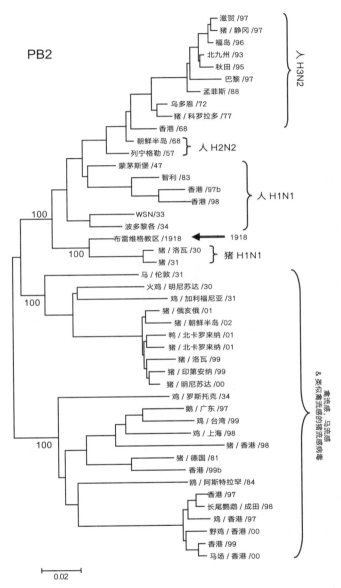

图 1. PB2 基因的系统发育树。用 NJ 算法排比和分析序列的分子进化关系，其距离的度量是序列差别的比例。图上标注了关键节点的自展值(100 个重复)(为了清晰起见，相同的和几乎相同的序列从树中移除)。主要分支用大括号标记出来。箭头指出了 1918 年病毒 PB2 基因序列的位置。距离的比例尺在树下面标出。分析中使用的流感病毒株系的缩写见补充信息表 1。

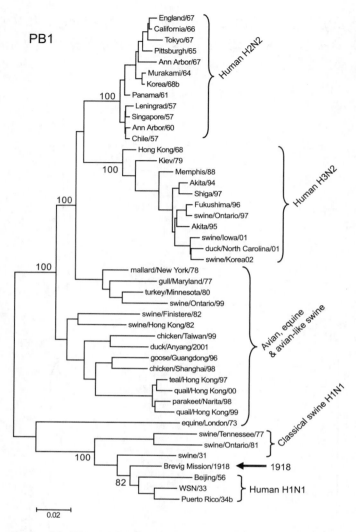

Fig. 2. Phylogenetic tree of the PB1 gene. Sequences were aligned and analysed as detailed in the legend to Fig. 1.

Emphasizing the avian-like nature of the 1918 influenza virus polymerase proteins, out of 19 total amino acid changes from the avian consensus, there are only 10 amino acid positions (out of 2,232 total codons) that consistently distinguish the 1918 and subsequent human polymerase proteins PB2, PB1 and PA from their avian influenza counterparts (these are defined as changes from avian sequences in the 1918 virus that are maintained without change in subsequent human viruses) (Table 1). It is likely that these changes have an important role in human adaptation. Seven of these ten changes were previously noted in an alignment between avian and human influenza polymerases[3]. What follows is a comparison between the 1918 virus changes and recent H5N1 isolates, in order to evaluate possible examples of parallel evolution in the adaptation of avian influenza viruses to humans.

图 2. PB1 基因的系统发育树。如图 1 图注中详细所述进行序列的排比和分析。

在和禽流感病毒共有序列不同的 19 个氨基酸中，只有 10 个氨基酸位置（总共 2,232 个密码子）始终如一地在 1918 年及之后的人类流感病毒聚合酶蛋白 PB2、PB1 和 PA 中与它们的禽流感病毒对应部分保持差别（这些被定义为 1918 年病毒中禽类 序列发生的突变，其在后续人类病毒中一直保持稳定）（表 1），这也突出了 1918 年 流感病毒聚合酶蛋白的类似禽流感病毒的性质。很有可能这些改变在适应人类的过 程中具有重要作用。在之前比对禽流感和人流感聚合酶时就发现了这 10 个突变中的 7 个 [3]。随后就是比较 1918 年病毒变化和最近的 H5N1 病毒分离株，目的是评估禽 流感病毒在适应人类的过程中发生平行进化的可能实例。

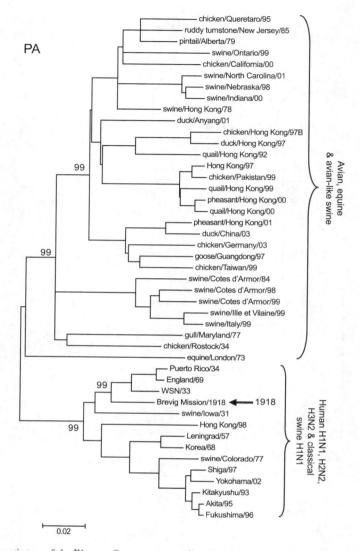

Fig. 3. Phylogenetic tree of the PA gene. Sequences were aligned and analysed as detailed in the legend to Fig. 1.

In the PB2 protein, five changes distinguish the human isolates from avian sequences (Table 1). Out of 253 available PB2 sequences from human H1N1, H2N2 and H3N2 isolates, these five changes are almost completely preserved, with the exception that two recent H3N2 isolates have the avian Lys residue at position 702. Only a small number of avian influenza isolates show any of these five changes, and it is intriguing that almost all of these isolates are from HPAI H5N1 or H7N7 viruses, or from the H9N2 lineage that infected a small number of humans in China in the late 1990s (ref. 29). Only 5 out of 282 available avian PB2 sequences have a Ser residue at position 199, four of these being 1997 H5N1 isolates from Hong Kong. The A199S change was also found in 5 out of 18 H5N1 strains isolated from humans (all five were from the 1997 Hong Kong outbreak). Of the avian viruses, 36 out of 336 have an Arg residue at position 702, 30 of which are H9N2 isolates from China

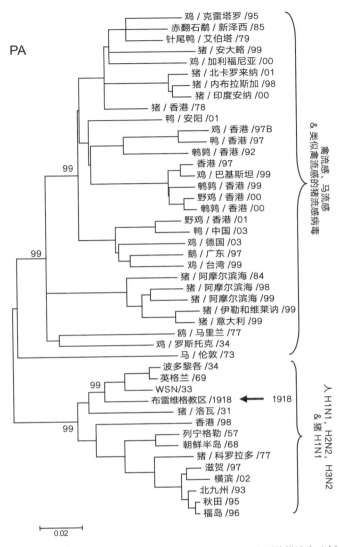

图 3. PA 基因的系统发育树。如图 1 图注中详细所述，进行序列的排比和分析。

在 PB2 蛋白中，人流感病毒分离株和禽病毒序列有 5 处差别（表 1）。在从人类 H1N1、H2N2 和 H3N2 病毒分离株获得的 253 个 PB2 序列中，这 5 处突变几乎完全保留，除了最近分离的两株 H3N2 在位点 702 具有禽流感的赖氨酸残基。只有少量的禽流感病毒分离株含有 5 种突变中的任意一种，而且有趣的是几乎所有含有这些突变的毒株都是从高致病性禽流感 H5N1 或者 H7N7 病毒中分离出来的，或者是从 20 世纪 90 年代晚期感染中国少部分人的 H9N2 病毒株中分离的（文献 29）。获得的 282 个禽流感 PB2 序列中只有 5 个在位点 199 是丝氨酸残基，其中 4 个来自香港的 1997 年 H5N1 病毒株。从人类中分离的 18 个 H5N1 株系中的 5 个发现了 A199S 突变（所有 5 个都来自 1997 年香港流感疫情）。336 个禽流感病毒中，只有 36 个在

around 1996–2000, and 5 are H5N1 isolates from Hong Kong in 1997 and 2001. Out of 18 available 1997 H5N1 strains isolated from humans, three have the K702R change.

Perhaps most interestingly, the 1918 virus and subsequent human isolates have a Lys residue at position 627. This residue has been implicated in host adaptation[2,3], and has previously been shown to be crucial for high pathogenicity in mice infected with the 1997 H5N1 virus[19]. Of the avian isolates, 19 out of 345 have a Lys residue at position 627, 18 of which are HPAI H5N1 or H7N7 avian influenza viruses. Sixteen of these were recently characterized H5N1 isolates from a die-off of wild waterfowl around Qinghai Lake in western China in 2005 (ref. 21). In human H5N1 isolates, 11 out of 37 have the E627K change: A/Hong Kong/483/1997 and A/Hong Kong/485/1997, four out of six isolates from Vietnam in 2004 (ref. 22), and two out of three isolates from Thailand in 2004 (ref. 23). The E627K mutation was seen in six out of seven H5N1 isolates from Thai tigers in 2004, and was also present in the H7N7 virus responsible for the single human fatality during the HPAI H7N7 outbreak in the Netherlands in 2003 (ref. 20). It was not noted in the contemporaneous chicken isolates.

At position 475, only one out of 355 avian isolates has a Met residue (an H5N1 HPAI virus from 2004). Similarly, only one out of 345 avian viruses has an Asn residue at position 567. None of the human H5N1 isolates has the L475M or the D567N changes. None of the available H5N1 or H7N7 sequences has more than one of the proposed human-adaptive PB2 changes determined for the 1918 virus.

The PA protein shows a similar pattern: four residues consistently differ between 1918 and subsequent human isolates and the avian consensus sequence (Table 1). Three other changes (C241Y, K312R and I322V) distinguish 1918, H1N1 and H2N2 human isolates, but most H3N2 isolates have the avian amino acid at these positions. Of 295 available sequences from human H1N1, H2N2 and H3N2 isolates, all have Asn at position 55 (except A/WSN/33), Ala at position 100 and Ser at position 552. Only 5 out of 295 human isolates have the avian Glu residue at position 382. Notably, these five isolates make up a minor clade of recent H3N2 isolates that have a number of unusual changes from typical human H3N2 viruses[30]. When avian influenza sequences are analysed, none (out of 209 sequences) has Asn at position 55 or Ser at position 552. Only 8 out of 209 avian PA protein sequences show the V100A change: six recent H6N2 isolates from chickens in California, and two HPAI 2002 H5N1 duck isolates from China. Of the 209 avian sequences, five have an Asp residue at position 382, including two HPAI H5N2 isolates from chickens in Mexico in 1994.

位点 702 是精氨酸残基，其中的 30 个是 1996 年 ~ 2000 年左右来自中国的 H9N2 分离株，5 个则是来自 1997 年和 2000 年香港的 H5N1 分离株。从人类中获得的 18 个 1997 年 H5N1 病毒株中，三个含有 K702R 突变。

可能最有趣的是，1918 年病毒和之后的人类分离株都在位点 627 含有一个赖氨酸残基。该残基与宿主的适应性相关 [2,3]，并且在之前的研究中已经被证实该位点对于 1997 年 H5N1 病毒感染小鼠时的高致病性非常关键 [19]。在 345 个禽流感分离株中，19 个在位点 627 含有赖氨酸残基，其中 18 个都是高致病性禽流感——H5N1 或者 H7N7 禽流感病毒。其中的 16 个是最近从 2005 年中国西部青海湖周围死去的野生水禽中分离出来的 H5N1 病毒株（文献 21）。在 37 个人类 H5N1 分离株中，11 个具有 E627K 突变：A/香港/483/1997 和 A/香港/485/1997，2004 年从越南分离出的 6 个病毒株中的 4 个（文献 22），以及 2004 年从泰国分离出的 3 个病毒株中的 2 个（文献 23）。该 E627K 突变在 2004 年从泰国老虎身上分离的 7 个 H5N1 毒株的 6 个中发现，并且存在于引起 2003 年荷兰高致病性禽流感 H7N7 大暴发时唯一人类死亡病例的 H7N7 病毒中（文献 20）。在同时期的鸡分离株中未发现该突变。

在位点 475，355 个禽类分离株中只有 1 个含有甲硫氨酸残基（2004 年分离的一个 H5N1 高致病性禽流感病毒）。类似的，345 个禽流感病毒株中只有 1 个在位点 567 含有天冬酰胺残基。人类 H5N1 分离株无 L475M 或者 D567N 突变。在获得的 H5N1 或者 H7N7 序列中，没有一个含有超过一种像 1918 年病毒那样的人类适应性 PB2 突变。

PA 蛋白表现出类似的模式：1918 年大流行及之后的人类分离株和禽类分离株相应序列之间有固定的 4 个残基的差别（表 1）。三个其他的改变（C241Y、K312R、I322V）将 1918 年、H1N1 和 H2N2 人类分离株区别开来，但是大部分 H3N2 分离株在这些位点都有禽流感的氨基酸。在 295 个从人类 H1N1、H2N2 和 H3N2 分离株中获得的序列中，全都在位点 55 含有天冬酰胺残基（除了 A/WSN/33），在位点 100 含有丙氨酸残基，位点 552 含有丝氨酸残基。295 个人类分离株中只有 5 个在位点 382 含有禽流感的谷氨酸残基。值得注意的是，这 5 个分离株形成了近期 H3N2 株的一个小的分支，与经典的人类 H3N2 毒株相比有一些不寻常的改变 [30]。当分析禽流感病毒序列时，没有一个序列（总共 209 个序列）在位点 55 含有天冬酰胺残基或者在位点 552 含有丝氨酸残基。209 个禽类 PA 蛋白序列中只有 8 个含有 V100A 突变：6 个来自近期加利福尼亚的鸡 H6N2 分离株，2 个来自中国 2002 年高致病性禽流感 H5N1 鸭分离株。在这 209 个禽类序列中，5 个在位点 382 含有天冬氨酸残基，包括 2 个从 1994 年墨西哥鸡中分离出的高致病性禽流感 H5N2 病毒。

The PB1 gene segment was replaced by reassortment in both the 1957 and 1968 pandemics[9]. We compared the PB1 protein from the 1918 human virus with those of the avian-derived PB1 segments from the 1957 and 1968 pandemics. Human H1N1, H2N2 and H3N2 viruses derived from the 1918, 1957 and 1968 pandemics, respectively, each possessed a uniquely derived avian-like PB1 gene segment, and so we sought to identify any parallel changes that might shed light on human adaptation. The three human pandemic PB1 proteins differ from the avian consensus by only 4–7 residues each (Supplementary Fig. 2). Only one of these changes is shared among the pandemic isolates: an N375S change. This change to a serine residue is also found in swine and equine influenza A isolates. With few exceptions, all human influenza PB1 proteins have Ser at this site. Of 230 human influenza sequences, only two H1N1 isolates (A/FM/47 and A/Beijing/1956) and the "minor clade" H3N2 isolates described above have the avian Asn residue[30]. In contrast, although this residue is maintained in almost all mammalian isolates, it is variable among avian PB1 proteins. Of 293 avian isolates, 66% have the consensus Asn residue at position 375, 18% have a Ser residue and 12% have a Thr residue.

The data presented here highlight the marked conservation of the PB1 protein in avian influenza viruses. PB1 functions as an RNA-dependent RNA polymerase, and so it is reasonable to hypothesize that its enzymatic function is optimal in this conserved form. In humans, the PB1 proteins experience linear change over time. Indeed, PB1 in humans acquires ~0.4 amino acid changes per year. As there is such strong antigenic selection on human viruses, it is possible that although the observed changes in PB1 are selectively beneficial with respect to antigenicity, they are mildly deleterious to enzyme function. Such complex fitness trade-offs are thought to be commonplace in RNA virus evolution. Supporting this hypothesis, a recent study examining combinations of avian and human influenza polymerases showed that the most efficient influenza transcriptional activity *in vitro* was seen with an avian-derived PB1, even if the PB2, PA and NP proteins were from a human virus[3]. Acquiring an avian PB1 by reassortment might provide a replicative advantage to the new virus, possibly explaining why both of the last two pandemics and the 1918 influenza virus all had very avian-like PB1 proteins.

Both the 1957 and 1968 pandemic influenza viruses were avian/human reassortants in which 2–3 avian gene segments were reassorted with the then-circulating, human-adapted virus[9,10]. Unlike the 1957 and 1968 pandemics, however, the 1918 virus was most likely not a human/avian reassortant virus, but rather an avian-like virus that adapted to humans *in toto*[8,11]. On the basis of amino acid replacement rates in human influenza virus polymerase genes, it is possible that these segments were circulating in human influenza viruses as early as 1900. However, proof that the 1918 virus did not retain gene segments from the previously circulating human influenza A strain would require discovery of a sample of the pre-1918 virus from archival material. The donor source, although avian-like at the protein level, may have come from a subset of avian influenza viruses not currently represented in the sequence databases and may have been in evolutionary isolation.

在 1957 年和 1968 年的大流行中，PB1 基因片段都发生了重组[9]。我们比较了 1918 年人类病毒的 PB1 蛋白与 1957 年和 1968 年大流行时禽类来源的 PB1 片段。分别来自 1918 年、1957 年和 1968 年大流行的人类 H1N1、H2N2 和 H3N2 病毒，每个都含有独特起源的类似禽流感的 PB1 基因片段，因此我们试图找到任何可能有助于人类适应性的平行突变。这三个人类大流行的 PB1 蛋白与禽类共有序列都仅有 4~7 个残基的差别（补充信息图 2）。只有一个突变在三个大流行分离株中都存在：N375S 突变。在猪和马的甲型流感分离株中也发现了这种到丝氨酸残基的突变。除了少数几个例外，所有的人类流感 PB1 蛋白在这个位点都是丝氨酸。在 230 个人类流感病毒序列中，只有两个 H1N1 分离株（A/FM/47 和 A/北京/1956）以及上面所述的 H3N2 分离株微小分支含有禽类天冬酰胺残基[30]。相反，尽管该残基在几乎所有的哺乳动物分离株中都存在，其在禽类 PB1 蛋白中是可变的。在 293 个禽类分离株中，66% 在位点 375 含有相同的天冬酰胺残基，18% 含有丝氨酸残基，12% 含有苏氨酸残基。

这里给出的数据凸显出了禽流感病毒 PB1 蛋白的显著保守性。PB1 作为一种 RNA 依赖的 RNA 聚合酶发挥功能，因此有理由假设在这种保守的形式下其酶功能是最佳的。在感染的人类中，PB1 蛋白随时间经历了线性的改变。实际上，PB1 在人群中每年获得大约 0.4 个氨基酸的改变。由于人类病毒存在很强的抗原性选择，尽管 PB1 的改变在抗原性方面具有选择优势，但它们在一定程度上降低了酶功能。这种复杂的适应性权衡被认为在 RNA 病毒的进化中非常普遍。最近一个研究支持了这个假设，它研究了禽流感和人流感聚合酶的组合，结果显示即使 PB2、PA 和 NP 蛋白都来源于人流感，含有禽类来源的 PB1 时，病毒的体外转录活性最有效率[3]。通过重组获得禽流感 PB1 蛋白可能给新病毒提供复制优势，这可能解释了为什么后两次大流行和 1918 年的流感病毒全都含有类似禽流感的 PB1 蛋白。

1957 年和 1968 年大流行的流感病毒都是禽类/人类的重组病毒，其中 2~3 个禽流感基因片段都与那时流行的适应人类的病毒发生了重组[9,10]。但是，不像 1957 年和 1968 年大流行，1918 年的病毒很可能不是禽类/人类的重组病毒，而是完全适应人类的类似禽流感的病毒[8,11]。根据人类流感病毒聚合酶基因氨基酸替换的速度，有可能这些片段早在 1900 年就在人类流感病毒中传播。但是，要证明 1918 年病毒是否保留先前传播的人类甲型流感病毒的基因片段，需要在档案材料中发现 1918 年之前的病毒样本。其来源尽管在蛋白质水平类似于禽流感，但可能是目前序列数据库中未显示的禽流感病毒亚类，并且已经出现了进化隔离。

The fact that amino acid changes identified in the 1918 analysis are also seen in HPAI strains of H5N1 and H7N7 avian viruses that have caused fatalities in humans is intriguing, and suggests that these changes may facilitate virus replication in human cells and increase pathogenicity. It is possible that the high pathogencity of the 1918 virus was related to its emergence as a human-adapted avian influenza virus. These changes may reflect a process of parallel evolution as avian influenza A viruses mutate in response to adaptational pressures, and suggest that the genetic basis of avian influenza virus adaptation to humans can be mapped.

Methods

RNA isolation, amplification and sequencing. RNA was isolated from frozen 1918 human lung tissue using Trizol (Invitrogen) according to the manufacturer's instructions. Each fragment was reverse transcribed, amplified, and sequenced at least twice. Reverse transcription polymerase chain reaction (RT–PCR), isolation of products and sequencing have been previously described[4]. Lists of primers and primer sequences are available upon request. Replicate RT–PCR reactions from independently produced RNA preparations gave identical sequence results. The 2,280-nucleotide complete coding sequence of PB2 was amplified in 33 overlapping fragments. The 2,274-nucleotide coding sequence of PB1 was amplified in 33 overlapping fragments. The 2,151-nucleotide coding sequence of PA was amplified in 32 overlapping fragments. The PCR products ranged in size from 77–138 bp.

Phylogenetic analyses. Phylogenetic analyses of the three polymerase genes were done using standard methods. We generated trees using the neighbour-joining (NJ) algorithm, with proportion of differences as the distance measure using MEGA version 2.1. Character evolution was analysed with the MacClade program after a parsimony analysis using PAUP version 4.0 beta, using ACTRAN as the optimization method. Trees were also generated using maximum-likelihood with midpoint rooting. All algorithms generated comparable trees, with major clades representing human, classical swine and avian-like viruses (NJ trees shown in Figs 1–3; complete data set available upon request). Polymerase segment sequences used in this analysis were obtained from GenBank and the Influenza Sequence Databank (ISD). (See Supplementary Table 1 for a list of sequences used.) For the PB2 gene, 83 sequences were used, all of which were full length. For the PB1 gene, 91 sequences were used, three of which were not full length. For the PA gene, 105 sequences were used, six of which were not full length.

(**437**, 889-893; 2005)

Jeffery K. Taubenberger[1], Ann H. Reid[1]†, Raina M. Lourens[1]†, Ruixue Wang[1], Guozhong Jin[1] & Thomas G. Fanning[1]

[1] Department of Molecular Pathology, Armed Forces Institute of Pathology, Rockville, Maryland 20850, USA

† Present addresses: Board on Life Sciences, The National Academies, 6th Floor, 500 Fifth Street N.W., Washington DC 20001, USA (A.H.R.); University of Iowa, Roy J. and Lucille A. Carver College of Medicine, 200 CMAB, Iowa City, Iowa 52242, USA (R.M.L.).

Received 30 June; accepted 19 September 2005.

　　1918 年病毒分析中得到的氨基酸改变也在导致人类死亡的 H5N1 和 H7N7 高致病性禽流感株中发现，这非常有意思；同时这也表明上述改变可能促进病毒在人细胞中复制并增加致病性。有可能 1918 年病毒的高致病性与其适应人类的禽流感病毒本质有关。这些改变可能反映了平行进化的过程，即甲型流感病毒（禽流感）应对适应压力做出的突变。它也表明我们可以绘制出禽流感病毒适应人类的遗传基础。

方　法

　　RNA 分离、扩增和测序　根据生产商的说明，用 Trizol 试剂（Invitrogen）从冰冻的 1918 年人肺组织中提取病毒 RNA。每个片段都进行至少两次逆转录、扩增和测序。逆转录聚合酶链式反应（RT-PCR）、产物的分离和测序之前已经描述过 [4]。引物和引物序列的列表可以向我们索取。从单独制备的 RNA 进行重复的 RT-PCR 反应得到了相同的序列产物。PB2 的 2,280 个核苷酸的完整编码序列在 33 个重叠的片段中扩增出来。PB1 的 2,274 个核苷酸的编码序列在 33 个重叠的片段中扩增出来。PA 的 2,151 个核苷酸的编码序列在 32 个重叠的片段中扩增出来。PCR 产物的大小在 77～138 bp 之间。

　　系统发育分析　三个聚合酶基因的系统发育分析用标准的方法进行。我们用邻接（NJ）算法绘制进化树，使用 MEGA 2.1 版将差异的比例作为距离度量。使用 ACTRAN 作为优化方法，在使用 PAUP 4.0 beta 版进行简易分析之后用 MacClade 程序分析特征进化。进化树也可用带有中点根的最大似然产生。所有的算法产生了可以比较的树，其主要的分支代表人类病毒、猪病毒和类似禽类的病毒（NJ 树在图 1～ 图 3 中显示；详细的数据可以向我们索取）。本分析中使用的聚合酶基因片段序列从 GenBank 和流感序列数据库获得。（使用的序列列表详见补充信息表 1）对于 PB2 基因，使用了 83 个序列，所有都是全长的。对于 PB1 基因，使用了 91 个序列，其中三个不是全长的。对于 PA 基因，使用了 105 个序列，其中六个不是全长的。

（毛晨晖 翻译；陈继征 审稿）

References:

1. Fodor, E. & Brownlee, G. G. in *Influenza* (ed. Potter, C. W.) 1-29 (Elsevier, Amsterdam, 2002).

2. Subbarao, E. K., London, W. & Murphy, B. R. A single amino acid in the PB2 gene of influenza A virus is a determinant of host range. *J. Virol.* **67**, 1761-1764 (1993).

3. Naffakh, N., Massin, P., Escriou, N., Crescenzo-Chaigne, B. & van der Werf, S. Genetic analysis of the compatibility between polymerase proteins from human and avian strains of influenza A viruses. *J. Gen. Virol.* **81**, 1283-1291 (2000).

4. Reid, A. H., Fanning, T. G., Hultin, J. V. & Taubenberger, J. K. Origin and evolution of the 1918 "Spanish" influenza virus hemagglutinin gene. *Proc. Natl Acad. Sci. USA* **96**, 1651-1656 (1999).

5. Reid, A. H., Fanning, T. G., Janczewski, T. A. & Taubenberger, J. K. Characterization of the 1918 "Spanish" influenza virus neuraminidase gene. *Proc. Natl Acad. Sci. USA* **97**, 6785-6790 (2000).

6. Basler, C. F. *et al.* Sequence of the 1918 pandemic influenza virus nonstructural gene (NS) segment and characterization of recombinant viruses bearing the 1918 NS genes. *Proc. Natl Acad. Sci. USA* **98**, 2746-2751 (2001).

7. Reid, A. H., Fanning, T. G., Janczewski, T. A., McCall, S. & Taubenberger, J. K. Characterization of the 1918 "Spanish" influenza virus matrix gene segment. *J. Virol.* **76**, 10717-10723 (2002).

8. Reid, A. H., Fanning, T. G., Janczewski, T. A., Lourens, R. & Taubenberger, J. K. Novel origin of the 1918 pandemic influenza virus nucleoprotein gene segment. *J. Virol.* **78**, 12462-12470 (2004).

9. Kawaoka, Y., Krauss, S. & Webster, R. G. Avian-to-human transmission of the PB1 gene of influenza A viruses in the 1957 and 1968 pandemics. *J. Virol.* **63**, 4603-4608 (1989).

10. Scholtissek, C., Rohde, W., Von Hoyningen, V. & Rott, R. On the origin of the human influenza virus subtypes H2N2 and H3N2. *Virology* **87**, 13-20 (1978).

11. Reid, A. H., Taubenberger, J. K. & Fanning, T. G. Evidence of an absence: the genetic origins of the 1918 pandemic influenza virus. *Nature Rev. Microbiol.* **2**, 909-914 (2004).

12. Johnson, N. P. & Mueller, J. Updating the accounts: global mortality of the 1918–1920 "Spanish" influenza pandemic. *Bull. Hist. Med.* **76**, 105-115 (2002).

13. Geiss, G. K. *et al.* Cellular transcriptional profiling in influenza A virus-infected lung epithelial cells: the role of the nonstructural NS1 protein in the evasion of the host innate defense and its potential contribution to pandemic influenza. *Proc. Natl Acad. Sci. USA* **99**, 10736-10741 (2002).

14. Tumpey, T. M. *et al.* Existing antivirals are effective against influenza viruses with genes from the 1918 pandemic virus. *Proc. Natl Acad. Sci. USA* **99**, 13849-13854 (2002).

15. Tumpey, T. M. *et al.* Pathogenicity and immunogenicity of influenza viruses with genes from the 1918 pandemic virus. *Proc. Natl Acad. Sci. USA* **101**, 3166-3171 (2004).

16. Kash, J. C. *et al.* The global host immune response: contribution of HA and NA genes from the 1918 Spanish influenza to viral pathogenesis. *J. Virol.* **78**, 9499-9511 (2004).

17. Kobasa, D. *et al.* Enhanced virulence of influenza A viruses with the haemagglutinin of the 1918 pandemic virus. *Nature* **431**, 703-707 (2004).

18. Chen, W. *et al.* A novel influenza A virus mitochondrial protein that induces cell death. *Nature Med.* **7**, 1306-1312 (2001).

19. Shinya, K. *et al.* PB2 amino acid at position 627 affects replicative efficiency, but not cell tropism, of Hong Kong H5N1 influenza A viruses in mice. *Virology* **320**, 258-266 (2004).

20. Fouchier, R. A. *et al.* Avian influenza A virus (H7N7) associated with human conjunctivitis and a fatal case of acute respiratory distress syndrome. *Proc. Natl Acad. Sci. USA* **101**, 1356-1361 (2004).

21. Chen, H. *et al.* Avian flu: H5N1 virus outbreak in migratory waterfowl. *Nature* **436**, 191-192 (2005).

22. Li, K. S. *et al.* Genesis of a highly pathogenic and potentially pandemic H5N1 influenza virus in eastern Asia. *Nature* **430**, 209-213 (2004).

23. Puthavathana, P. *et al.* Molecular characterization of the complete genome of human influenza H5N1 virus isolates from Thailand. *J. Gen. Virol.* **86**, 423-433 (2005).

24. Toyoda, T., Adyshev, D. M., Kobayashi, M., Iwata, A. & Ishihama, A. Molecular assembly of the influenza virus RNA polymerase: determination of the subunit-subunit contact sites. *J. Gen. Virol.* **77**, 2149-2157 (1996).

25. Masunaga, K., Mizumoto, K., Kato, H., Ishihama, A. & Toyoda, T. Molecular mapping of influenza virus RNA polymerase by site-specific antibodies. *Virology* **256**, 130-141 (1999).

26. Ohtsu, Y., Honda, Y., Sakata, Y., Kato, H. & Toyoda, T. Fine mapping of the subunit binding sites of influenza virus RNA polymerase. *Microbiol. Immunol.* **46**, 167-175 (2002).

27. Biswas, S. K. & Nayak, D. P. Mutational analysis of the conserved motifs of influenza A virus polymerase basic protein 1. *J. Virol.* **68**, 1819-1826 (1994).

28. Gonzalez, S. & Ortin, J. Distinct regions of influenza virus PB1 polymerase subunit recognize vRNA and cRNA templates. *EMBO J.* **18**, 3767-3775 (1999).

29. Guo, Y. J. *et al.* Characterization of the pathogenicity of members of the newly established H9N2 influenza virus lineages in Asia. *Virology* **267**, 279-288 (2000).

30. Holmes, E. C. *et al.* Whole-genome analysis of human influenza A virus reveals multiple persistent lineages and reassortment among recent H3N2 viruses. *PLoS Biol.* **3**, e300 (2005).

Supplementary Information is linked to the online version of the paper at www.nature.com/nature.

Acknowledgements. The research described in this report was done using stringent safety precautions to protect the laboratory workers, the environment and the public from this virus. The intention of this research is to provide the basis for understanding how influenza pandemic strains form and to help ascertain the risk of future influenza pandemics. This study was partially supported by a grant to J.K.T. from the National Institutes of Health, and by intramural funds from the Armed Forces Institute of Pathology. The opinions contained herein are the private views of the authors and are not to be construed as official or as reflecting the views of the US Department of the Army or the US Department of Defense.

Author Contributions. J.K.T. planned the project, and A.H.R., R.M.L., R.W. and G.J. generated the sequence data. J.K.T., A.H.R. and T.G.F. performed data analysis. J.K.T. wrote the manuscript.

Author Information. Coding sequences of the PB2, PB1 and PA genes have been deposited in GenBank under accession numbers DQ208309, DQ208310 and DQ208311, respectively. Reprints and permissions information is available at npg.nature.com/reprintsandpermissions. The authors declare no competing financial interests. Correspondence and requests for materials should be addressed to J.K.T. (taubenberger@afip.osd.mil).

Implications for Prediction and Hazard Assessment from the 2004 Parkfield Earthquake

W. H. Bakun *et al.*

Editor's Note

Whether earthquakes can be reliably predicted is still a contentious matter among geoscientists. This paper from a team mostly at the US Geological Survey argues that prediction is still very remote, if it is possible at all. It describes an earthquake that occurred on the Californian San Andreas fault in 2004, centred on the small community of Parkfield which has experienced rather regular quakes for the past 150 years. For this reason Parkfield is extremely well monitored for seismic activity, and the previous quasi-regular seismicity led to predictions of an earthquake before 1993 that was long "overdue" by 2004. Despite this intensive study, the timing of the 2004 quake was unanticipated, and it was accompanied by no obvious precursory activity.

Obtaining high-quality measurements close to a large earthquake is not easy: one has to be in the right place at the right time with the right instruments. Such a convergence happened, for the first time, when the 28 September 2004 Parkfield, California, earthquake occurred on the San Andreas fault in the middle of a dense network of instruments designed to record it. The resulting data reveal aspects of the earthquake process never before seen. Here we show what these data, when combined with data from earlier Parkfield earthquakes, tell us about earthquake physics and earthquake prediction. The 2004 Parkfield earthquake, with its lack of obvious precursors, demonstrates that reliable short-term earthquake prediction still is not achievable. To reduce the societal impact of earthquakes now, we should focus on developing the next generation of models that can provide better predictions of the strength and location of damaging ground shaking.

EARTHQUAKE prediction is the Holy Grail of seismology. Although the ability to predict the time and location of earthquakes remains elusive, predicting their effects, such as the strength and geographical distribution of shaking, is routine practice. The extent to which earthquake phenomena can accurately be predicted will ultimately depend on how well the underlying physical conditions and processes are understood. To understand earthquakes requires observing them up close and in detail—a difficult task because they are at present largely unpredictable, and so knowing where to put the instrumentation needed to make such observations is a challenge. The 40-km-long Parkfield section of the San Andreas fault was recognized two decades ago as a promising earthquake physics laboratory and an intensive experiment was established to record the next segment-rupturing earthquake there and provide the much-needed detailed

从 2004 年帕克菲尔德地震看地震预测和灾害评估的启示

巴昆等

编者按

地震能否被可靠地预测，仍然是地球科学家之间争论的事情。这篇论文来自一个研究团队，团队中多数研究人员在美国地质调查局工作。论文认为，假使确实有可能预测地震，但现在看来预测仍然非常遥不可及。这篇论文描述了 2004 年在加利福尼亚州圣安德烈亚斯断层上发生的地震，震中位于帕克菲尔德这个小社区。过去 150 年来，帕克菲尔德发生过具有一定规律的地震。因此，帕克菲尔德的地震活动得到了非常好的监测，根据先前准规律的地震活动性预测，1993 年前将发生一次地震，但到 2004 年地震才姗姗来迟。尽管研究人员进行了深入研究，但 2004 年地震发生的时间却在意料之外，而且此次地震没有伴随明显的前兆活动。

获得接近大地震的高质量测量并不容易：研究人员必须在正确的地点、正确的时间，使用正确的仪器。2004 年 9 月 28 日，当位于圣安德烈亚斯断层上的美国加利福尼亚州帕克菲尔德地震发生时，这种汇合发生了，这一地震正是发生在为监测帕克菲尔德地区地震而设计的密集地震台网的中心区域。得到的数据揭示了地震过程中一些前所未见的方面。在此，我们将展示这些数据，并与以前的帕克菲尔德地震数据结合，这为我们提供了有关地震物理和地震预测的信息。2004 年帕克菲尔德地震，由于缺乏明显的前兆，我们认为可靠的短期地震预测仍然无法实现。目前，为了降低地震的社会影响，我们应该集中精力开发下一代模型，以便更好地预测破坏性地面震动的强度和位置。

地震预测是地震学的"圣杯"。尽管预测地震的时间和位置仍然难以实现，但是预测地震造成的影响，例如震动的强度和地理位置分布，已是常规做法。地震现象能够精确预测的程度最终取决于对内在的物理条件及过程的理解程度。要了解地震，就需要对它们进行近距离细致的观测，这是一项艰巨的任务。因为目前地震在很大程度上是不可预测的，所以要知道在何处放置进行这种观测所需的仪器是一个挑战。圣安德烈亚斯断层的 40 km 长的帕克菲尔德段在 20 年前被公认是一个有希望的地震物理实验室，在此进行的密集实验用于记录下一个断层段破裂引起的地震，并提供迫切需要的详细观测结果。2004 年 9 月 28 日发生的预期矩震级 $M_W = 6.0$ 的地震（发震

observations. The occurrence of the anticipated moment magnitude $M_w = 6.0$ earthquake on 28 September 2004 (origin time 17:15:24 Coordinated Universal Time, UTC; epicentre location 35.815° N, 120.374° W; depth 7.9 km) fulfilled that promise.

The Parkfield section of the San Andreas fault is bounded on the northwest by a 150-km-long creeping section, where numerous small earthquakes occur, and on the southeast by hundreds of kilometres of locked fault where few earthquakes have been detected in the twentieth century (Fig. 1). The 1857 $M_w = 7.9$ Fort Tejon earthquake ruptured the locked fault southeast of Parkfield and is thought to have initiated near Parkfield[1]. On the Parkfield section, the motion of the Pacific plate relative to the North America plate is partly accommodated by repeating $M_w = 6.0$ earthquakes. The historical record of earthquakes at Parkfield includes at least six such events since 1857 (ref. 2; Supplementary Text 1, Supplementary Fig. 1 and Supplementary Table 1).

Fig. 1. Location of the 2004 Parkfield earthquake. The zone of surface rupture (yellow) is shown along the San Andreas fault (red lines). Locations of seismographs, strainmeters, creepmeters, magnetometers, and continuous GPS stations shown as squares. The strong-motion sensors (not shown here) are located on Fig. 4. Lower inset (same scale, in pale green) shows epicentres of 2004 aftershocks (black dots) plotted relative to fault traces[30]. Upper inset, map location.

The simple setting and apparent regularity of Parkfield earthquakes[3] offered the rationale

时刻 UTC 时间 17:15:24；震中位置 35.815°N，120.374°W；深度 7.9 km）实现了这一目标。

　　圣安德烈亚斯断层上，与帕克菲尔德段相邻的西北段是长为 150 km 的以小震密集活动为特征的蠕滑段，而东南则是长达数百千米的强闭锁段，20 世纪在这里几乎没有检测到地震（图 1）。在此强闭锁段上，上一次大地震是 1857 年发生的 $M_w = 7.9$ 蒂洪堡地震，该地震从帕克菲尔德附近开始破裂[1]。在帕克菲尔德断层段上，太平洋板块相对北美板块的运动，由多次 $M_w = 6.0$ 地震来部分调节。自 1857 年以来，帕克菲尔德地震的历史记录中至少包括 6 次这样的地震（参考文献 2，补充文本 1、补充图 1 和补充表 1）。

图 1. 2004 年帕克菲尔德地震的位置。地表破裂带（黄色）沿圣安德烈亚斯断层（红线）展布。地震仪、应变仪、蠕变仪、地磁仪和连续 GPS 站的位置以方块表示，强运动传感器的位置（未在此图标出）在图 4 中标出。图中下方插图（等比例尺，浅绿色）显示 2004 年余震震中（一系列黑点）相对于断层线的位置[30]，图中上方的插图显示了本图的位置。

　　帕克菲尔德地震具有简单的环境和明显的规律性[3]，这为科学的地震预测提供

for the only scientific earthquake prediction officially recognized by the United States government[4] and an opportunity to place instruments in the region before the anticipated earthquake. The primary goal of the Parkfield Earthquake Prediction Experiment[5] was to obtain a detailed understanding of the processes leading up to the anticipated earthquake; a secondary goal was to issue a public warning shortly before the earthquake. A variety of sensors were deployed in a dense network designed specifically to record the build-up of strain in the surrounding crust, monitor earthquakes and slip on the fault, and detect any precursors that might foreshadow a large earthquake. Complementary arrays of strong-ground-motion sensors were deployed to record shaking near the earthquake rupture zone[6].

A significant development of the Parkfield experiment has been the collaboration of federal, state and local officials to develop a protocol for issuing short-term earthquake alerts[7]; the protocol provided a template for communication between scientists and emergency responders and subsequently served as a prototype for volcanic hazard warning protocols[8]. Innovations in the collection, transmission and storage of Parkfield data included a pioneering effort to provide publicly available, near-real-time earth science data streams over the internet. The systems pioneered at Parkfield have become standard elements of seismic monitoring throughout the US and have set the foundation for the installation of the USGS Advanced National Seismic System (ANSS)[9]. The Parkfield dense instrumentation network, which includes a variety of geophysical sensors, motivated the placement of a scientific borehole, Earthscope's San Andreas Fault Observatory at Depth (SAFOD), at the northwestern end of the Parkfield segment[10,11] and served as a prototype for the geodetic networks that are part of Earthscope's Plate Boundary Observatory[11].

In 1985, the USGS issued a long-term prediction that an earthquake of approximately $M_w = 6$ would occur before 1993 on the San Andreas fault near Parkfield[4]. After the prediction window closed, *sans* earthquake, an independent evaluation of the Parkfield Earthquake Prediction Experiment was conducted by a Working Group of the National Earthquake Prediction Evaluation Council[12]. This working group recommended that monitoring be continued as a long-term effort to record the next earthquake at Parkfield. The failure of the long-term prediction of the time of the earthquake as well as certain aspects of the 2004 Parkfield earthquake (discussed below), have confounded nearly all simple earthquake models. However, the experiment's primary goal of observing a large earthquake near the rupture has been achieved. The instruments at Parkfield continue to operate and provide important data on postseismic deformation and other processes. Altogether, these recordings are providing a picture, at unprecedented resolution, of what occurred before, during and after the 2004 earthquake[13,14]. Although the analysis is far from complete, it is clear even now that the observations have important implications for nearly all areas of seismic hazard analysis and loss reduction.

了依据，该次地震预测成为唯一一次美国政府官方认可的预测[4]，从而有机会于预期地震发生前在该地区放置相关检测仪器。帕克菲尔德地震预测实验场[5]的首要目标是详细了解导致预期地震发生的过程，第二个目标是在地震前及时发布公共警报。各种传感器的安装形成了密集地震台网，专门用来记录周围地壳的应变积累，监测地震和断层滑动，探测可能预示大地震的任何前兆。在地震破裂带附近，部署强地面运动传感器作为补充阵列[6]，用来记录震动。

帕克菲尔德地震预测实验场有意义的工作进展之一是在美国联邦政府、州政府和地方政府的通力合作[7]下，建立了发布地震短期警报的预案。该预案提供了科学家和应急反应部门之间的实时通信联络模板，并以此作为火山灾害预警[8]的范例。在帕克菲尔德实验场，数据的收集、传输、存储等方面取得了开拓性进展，包括公共信息服务、准实时地球科学资料的网内数据流程等。实验场开发的数据系统已成为全美国地震监测的标准，并为美国地质调查局建立"国家级地震监测台网系统"（ANSS）奠定了基础[9]。帕克菲尔德密集仪器网络，包括各种地球物理传感器，催生了美国一系列科学项目的建立和实施，如在帕克菲尔德段的西北部安排了地震科学深钻，实施了地球透镜计划中的圣安德烈亚斯断层深部探测计划（SAFOD）[10,11]，实验场的应变观测台网作为板块边界观测计划的组成部分和地形变观测台网的向导[11]。

1985 年，美国地质调查局发布了一个长期地震预测，认为在 1993 年前帕克菲尔德附近的圣安德烈亚斯断层上将发生 $M_w = 6$ 左右的地震[4]。然而，当预测时间窗关闭后，地震并未发生。美国国家地震预测评审委员会组织专门工作组对帕克菲尔德地震预测实验场进行了独立评估[12]。该工作组提出尽管在预报期内未发生地震，但实验场的各种观测应继续下去，作为对帕克菲尔德未来地震的长期观测。地震长期预测在时间上的失败以及 2004 年帕克菲尔德地震的某些方面（将在后面章节讨论）使几乎所有的简单的地震模型失灵。然而，实验的首要目标，即在破裂带附近观测大地震已经实现。帕克菲尔德的观测仪器一直在持续运行，可以为震后形变及其他过程提供重要数据资料。总之，这些记录以前所未有的分辨率提供了 2004 年地震发生前、发生时和发生后的图像[13,14]。尽管分析远未结束，但目前很清楚的是观测几乎对地震灾害分析和减少损失等所有方面都有重要意义。

Precursors and Earthquake Prediction

The idea that detectable precursory processes precede earthquakes dates back to at least the seventeenth century[15]. However, with the exception of foreshocks, unambiguous and repeatable instrumental observations of such phenomena remain elusive. As noted, identical foreshocks preceded both the 1934 and 1966 Parkfield earthquakes by 17 min (ref. 16). However, such foreshocks did not precede the 1901 or 1922 events and so the Parkfield prediction experiment, which was designed to record potential foreshocks as well as other precursory signals, treated all precursors in a probabilistic manner[7]. At present, with the exception of an ambiguous low-level strain of $< 10^{-8}$ that occurred during the 24 h before the main shock, there is no evidence of any short-term precursory signal, either seismic or aseismic[13]. Even microseismicity, detectable at the $M = 0$ threshold in the epicentral region, was absent during the six days before the main shock[13]. Notable precursory signals are not evident in the magnetic field, telluric electric field, apparent resistivity, or creep observations[13]. This lack of short-term precursors emphasizes the difficulty of reliable short-term earthquake prediction (up to a few weeks before).

Subtle strain changes of a few nanostrain were recorded on several instruments in the 24 h before the earthquake. Such changes place important constraints on earthquake nucleation physics but are too small to provide a reliable basis for issuing public warnings that a damaging earthquake is imminent. The dense instrumentation arrays continue to uncover new processes, such as deep tremor under the locked section of the fault southeast of the Parkfield segment[17]. Future hopes for prediction will rest on whether such processes are precursory or simply commonplace.

Fault Structure and Segment Boundaries

The similar magnitude and rupture extent of the last six Parkfield earthquakes supports the concept of fault segmentation and the role of segment boundaries in influencing the rupture extent and magnitude of earthquakes. The nature of segment boundaries, however, is controversial. Fault geometry, rheological and frictional properties of materials, pore fluids and stress conditions have all been proposed to explain segment boundaries[18].

Lindh and Boore[19] suggested a fault-geometry-based explanation for the location of the boundaries of the Parkfield segment: a 5° bend in the fault trace to the northwest and a right-stepover to the southeast appeared to offer geometric obstacles that could limit earthquake rupture. The 2004 aftershocks relocated with a three-dimensional velocity model do not appear to show these features extending to depth (Fig. 2). Aftershocks and earlier seismicity[20] at depths below 6–7 km seem to be confined to a narrow band (see Supplementary Fig. 4). Because the fault seems straighter at depth, where large Parkfield earthquakes nucleate, than it does at the surface, it is possible that fault geometry is not the controlling factor in the location of the Parkfield segment boundaries[20]. However, the

前兆和地震预测

地震发生前具有可检测出的前兆过程，这一观点至少可追溯到 17 世纪 [15]。然而，除了前震以外，明确的、可重复观测到的前兆现象仍然难以捉摸。根据记录，1934 年和 1966 年两次帕克菲尔德地震发生前 17 分钟，有完全相同的前震活动出现（参考文献 16），而 1901 年和 1922 年两次地震前却没有出现这样的前震活动。因此，专门设计用来记录潜在的前震活动及其他前兆信号的帕克菲尔德地震预测实验场，所有前兆现象都被视为是以一定的概率出现 [7]。当今，除了在主震前 24 小时有十分模糊的低水平应变异常（$< 10^{-8}$）活动外，未发现地震学或其他学科的任何短期前兆信号 [13]。主震前 6 天，甚至阈值为 $M = 0$ 的微震，在震中区也未观测到 [13]。在地磁场、地电场、视电阻率和蠕变观测也都未见到值得注意的明显前兆信号 [13]。这种短期前兆的缺乏突显了可靠的短期地震预测的困难（地震发生前几周内）。

在地震发生前 24 小时内，多台仪器记录到了非常微弱的仅为几个纳米的应变变化。这些变化在地震成核物理过程中是重要的地震约束条件。但由于这些变化太小，无法为发布即将来临的破坏性地震的公众警报提供可靠的依据。密集的仪器台阵还继续揭示新的事件过程，如在帕克菲尔德东南断层闭锁段下的深部颤动 [17]。未来预测的成功与否将取决于这些事件是前兆还是正常的扰动。

断层结构和分段边界

最近 6 次的帕克菲尔德地震的震级和破裂长度都相似，这一点支撑了断层分段性的概念，以及分段边界在影响地震破裂长度和震级大小时起的作用。然而，断层分段边界性是有争议的。断层几何学、介质流变性与断层摩擦特性、孔隙流体与应力条件都被提出用以解释分段边界 [18]。

林德和布勒 [19] 建议基于断层几何学解释帕克菲尔德断层段边界的位置：断层西北端的 5° 弯曲和东南端的右移，似乎提供了限制地震破裂的几何障碍体。然而，用三维速度模型对 2004 年余震重定位的结果似乎没有显示这些表层弯曲特征延伸到深度（图 2）。余震和早期地震活动 [20] 在 6～7 km 深度处似乎局限在狭窄的条带内（见补充材料图 4）。由于断层在深处看起来比在地表更直，帕克菲尔德大型地震在深处成核，因此断层几何结构可能不是帕克菲尔德断层分段边界位置的控制因素 [20]。然而，复杂的地表几何结构可能是由孕震层深度的分段边界变形引起的。

complex surface trace geometry may result from deformation associated with the segment boundaries at seismogenic depth. That is, irregularities in the surface trace may reflect the presence of the boundaries at depth rather than being the primary cause of these boundaries.

Fig. 2. Spatial distribution of Parkfield aftershocks. Locations are listed in Supplementary Table S2. Aftershocks in 2004 are shown as red dots, those in 1966 as black diamonds. Aftershocks were relocated (Supplementary Text 3) using a three-dimensional velocity model[48] and the double difference relocation technique[44]. San Andreas fault traces (purple lines) and the 1966 (open star) and the 2004 (red star) main shock hypocentres are also shown. a, Map view. b, Along-fault section. c–g, Cross sections for the fault sections shown in a and b. The purple dots at zero depth indicate the traces shown in a. The aftershocks in f reveal multiple strands[49] activated by the main shock.

An alternative explanation for the boundaries of the Parkfield segment is based on fault zone rheology. This segment is adjoined on the northwest by a creeping section where, perhaps, stable sliding precludes large earthquakes and on the southeast by a locked section, which may fail only in infrequent great earthquakes[19,21]. The reasons for creep to the northwest and locking to the southeast are not clear. Properties of materials and fluid overpressure adjacent to the fault have been proposed to explain creeping and locked fault segments[20,22]. A better knowledge of the materials and conditions within the fault zone obtained from SAFOD[10] should help to discriminate between these possibilities. Ultimately, a combination of factors, including deep fault geometry, fault rheology, and stress level, may be necessary to explain why a fault creeps or is locked and what constitutes a segment boundary.

也就是说，断层在地表的不规则性可能反映出深度边界的存在，而不是产生这些边界的主要原因。

图 2. 帕克菲尔德余震的空间分布。位置在补充表 S2 中列出。2004 年的余震用红点表示，1966 年的余震用黑色菱形表示。利用三维速度模型[48]和双差重定位技术[44]重新定位余震（补充文本 3）。图中还显示了圣安德烈亚斯断层地表轨迹（紫色线），以及 1966 年（空心五角星）和 2004 年（红色五角星）的主要震源位置。图 a 为平面示意图。图 b 为沿断层的剖面。图 c~g 为图 a 和 b 中所示断层正交剖面，在 0 深度处的紫色点表示在图 a 中的地表断层。在图 f 中的余震表明主震破裂有多个分支[49]。

对帕克菲尔德分段边界的另一种解释是基于断层带的流变特性。帕克菲尔德分段在西北部与蠕滑段毗连，该蠕滑段稳定的滑动可能会阻止大地震的发生；而在东南部与闭锁段相连，该闭锁段可能比较少发生大地震[19,21]。西北部蠕滑和东南部闭锁的原因尚不清楚。介质特性和流体高压注入等被用于解释蠕滑段和闭锁段[20,22]。由 SAFOD 计划所获得的对断层带内介质性质和环境条件等的进一步认识[10]将有助于区别这些可能性。最终，包括深层断层几何学、断层流变性和应力水平等的多因素综合研究对于解释为什么断层是蠕滑或是闭锁，以及哪些因素构成了断层分段边界的条件等是很有必要的。

Seismic and Aseismic Slip

Over the long term, both seismic and aseismic slip along plate boundaries like the San Andreas fault accommodate the relative motion between the plates. To apply even the simplest mechanical model for the build-up of strain and its sudden release in earthquakes, one must account for slip on the fault that occurs aseismically. Aseismic slip has been recognized as a potentially important component of the slip budget on strike-slip faults in the San Francisco Bay area[23] and on megathrust faults along subduction plate boundaries in the Pacific Northwest region of the United States[24] and in Japan[25]. How seismic and aseismic slip are distributed over a fault and how much and where aseismic slip occurs during the times between large earthquakes are, however, not well resolved. Measurements of slip beginning shortly after the 1966 Parkfield earthquake[13,26] appear to provide some insight into these questions. The region of maximum slip in the 2004 event appears to partially fill a deficit in the distribution of slip that had accumulated beginning with the 1966 earthquake[13], but some slip-deficient regions apparently remain (Fig. 3).

Fig. 3. Distribution of slip on the San Andreas fault since 1966 estimated from geodetic data. **a, b, d, f**, Slip; **c, e, g**, accumulated slip. Slip in the 2004 earthquake (**d**) concentrated near an area with an apparent slip deficit (compare **c** and **d**). In **d** we overlay contours of slip, estimated using both geodetic and seismologic data, giving a higher-resolution image of the slip distribution with a peak slip of 77 cm (ref. 50). These slip models illustrate how slip in earthquakes (coseismic and postseismic) combines with aseismic slip between earthquakes to generate the cumulative offset across the fault. Slip values are listed in Supplementary Table S3.

地震滑动和无震滑动

从长期来看，沿着像圣安德烈亚斯断层这样的板块边界带，地震滑动和无震滑动都调节着板块之间的相对运动。因此，即使用最简单的力学模型来建立地震应变积累和瞬间释放，人们也必须考虑断层上发生的无震滑动。无论是在旧金山湾地区[23]走滑断层的滑动预估方面，还是沿着美国西北太平洋地区[24]和日本[25]俯冲板块边界的巨型逆冲断层的滑动预估方面，无震滑动都被认为是潜在的重要组成部分。然而，地震滑动和无震滑动在断层上是如何分布的，在大地震间隔期间有多少无震滑动，以及在何处发生无震滑动，都没有得到很好的解决。1966 年帕克菲尔德地震后不久很快开始的滑动测量[13,26]似乎可以对这些问题提供一些见解。2004 年地震的最大滑动地区似乎部分地填补了自 1966 年地震开始累积的滑移分布亏损[13]，但一些滑动亏损地区显然仍然存在（图 3）。

图 3. 由大地测量数据估计的自 1966 年以来圣安德烈亚斯断层的滑移量分布。图 a、b、d、f 表示滑移分布，图 c、e、g 表示累积滑移。2004 年地震（图 d）中的滑移集中分布在滑移明显亏损的地区附近（比较图 c 和图 d）。图 d 中的位移等值线是利用大地测量和地震学数据联合反演所得的高精度位错图像分布绘制而成，最大位错为 77 cm（参考文献 50）。这些位错模型说明了地震引起的位错（同震和震后）如何与震间的无震滑动共同作用构成了断层两侧的累积位错分布。滑移量值列在补充表 S3 中。

Postseismic surface slip of 35–45 cm was observed using alinement arrays following the 1966 Parkfield earthquake[27]. The 2004 Parkfield event, however, is the first at this location for which the geodetic data were recorded during and after the earthquake with sufficient temporal and spatial resolution to enable separation of the coseismic and postseismic signals. Postseismic slip equal to about 60% of the coseismic slip occurred in the first month after the 2004 event (Fig. 3f). Alinement array data from the 2004 earthquake suggest that near-surface slip will reach 20–50 cm over the next 2–5 yr (ref. 28), comparable to what was seen after the 1966 event[27]. Additionally, the Global Positioning System (GPS) data suggest that postseismic effects may persist for a decade, and that ultimately, the slip associated with this earthquake (coseismic plus postseismic) will balance the estimated slip deficit that existed on the fault at the time of the earthquake.

Prediction of Damaging Ground Motion

Most of the catastrophic damage in earthquakes occurs close to the earthquake source, but relatively few recordings of strong shaking close to an earthquake have been made. The ground motion near the 2004 earthquake[29] was recorded at eight sites within 1 km of the rupture and at 40 sites between 1 and 10 km from the rupture (Fig. 4), nearly doubling the global data set of strong-motion records within those distances. These records show the wavefield in unprecedented detail[14] and reveal large spatial variations in shaking amplitude.

The peak horizontal acceleration (PGA) for two of the records are greater than 1.0g (where g is the acceleration due to gravity) with one of these exceeding the instrument's recording capacity of 2.5g. Recordings of accelerations greater than 1g are rare, but they may not be anomalous at locations within a few kilometres of fault ruptures. Preliminary seismic slip models (see Fig. 3d for example) indicate slip was concentrated in two small regions, near the stations recording the strongest PGA. The local stress drop in these regions of concentrated slip appears to be more than an order of magnitude larger than the average stress drop of 0.2 MPa associated with the very smooth geodetic slip model (Fig. 3d). Temporal variations in rupture propagation, however, probably also influenced the radiation of the strongest shaking, as illustrated by the spatial variability in PGA (Fig. 4) and peak ground velocity close to the fault. Explaining the large variations in amplitude over distances of just a few kilometres continues to challenge our understanding of earthquake rupture dynamics and our ability to predict ground motions near the rupture (Fig. 4b and Supplementary Fig. S3).

1966 年帕克菲尔德地震后，研究人员利用线性台阵观测到 35～45 cm 的震后地表滑动 [27]。然而，2004 年帕克菲尔德地震是第一次在该地点对地震和震后进行大地测量观测记录，数据的时间和空间分辨率足以将同震和震后信号分离开来。2004 年震后一个月的滑移量约为同震滑移的 60%（图 3f）。2004 年地震的线性台阵数据表明，在未来 2～5 年内，近地表滑移量将达到 20～50 cm（参考文献 28），与 1966 年地震震后的情况相当 [27]。此外，全球定位系统（GPS）数据表明，震后效应可能会持续 10 年。最终，与这次地震相关的滑动（同震 + 震后）将平衡地震时断层上存在的预估滑移亏损。

破坏性的地面运动的预测

地震灾害大多发生在震源附近，但关于震源附近发生强烈震动的记录相对较少。2004 年地震附近的地面运动 [29]，在断裂带 1 km 内有 8 个台站记录到，在距离断裂带 1～10 km 范围内有 40 个台站记录到（图 4），几乎是全球关于这些距离内发生强地面运动记录数据集的两倍。这些记录比以往都详细地显示了波场 [14]，揭示了震动振幅在空间上的大幅度变化。

两个台站记录的峰值水平加速度（PGA）大于 1.0g（g 为重力加速度），其中一个超过仪器的记录范围 2.5g。加速度大于 1g 的记录很少，但它们在断层破裂数千米范围内可能并没有异常。初步的地震滑移模型（如图 3d 所示）表明，滑动集中在两个小区域内，靠近记录最强 PGA 的台站。与非常平滑的大地测量数据测得的位错模型所得的平均应力降 0.2 Mpa 相比，这些滑动集中区域的局部应力降大了至少一个量级（图 3d）。然而，如 PGA 的空间变化（图 4）和靠近断层的强地面运动峰值速度所示，破裂传播的时间变化也可能影响最强震动的辐射。对仅几千米距离内振幅的巨大变化的解释，继续挑战着我们对地震破裂动力学的理解以及预测破裂附近地面运动的能力（图 4b 和补充图 S3）。

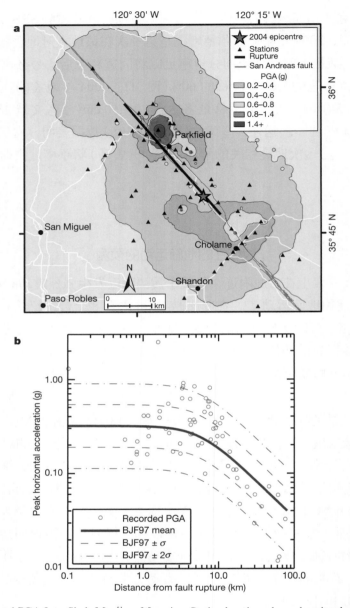

Fig. 4. Horizontal PGA from ShakeMap[51]. **a**, Map view. Station locations shown by triangles. The thin red line delineates the Alquist-Priolo fault traces[30] and the thick black line is the fault trace based on aftershock locations. **b**, Horizontal PGA as a function of distance from the fault rupture. The distances are based on the approximate projection of the fault to the ground surface. The mean (solid line) and $\pm 1\sigma$ (dashed lines) and $\pm 2\sigma$ (dash-dotted lines) for the Boore–Joyner–Fumal 1997 attenuation relation[52] are shown. The PGA which exceeded the 2.5g limit of the instrument is plotted at 2.5g.

Spatial variations in the intensity of shaking, such as peak ground acceleration and peak ground velocity, are often attributed to four factors: differences in soil conditions among sites, differences in the wave propagation to the sites, complexities of the rupture geometry, and heterogeneity of slip on the fault. Analysis of the strong-motion records from the 2004

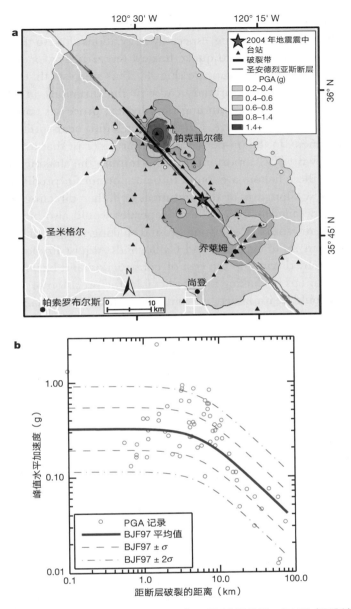

图 4. 震动图中的水平 PGA[51]。图 **a** 为地图，三角形表示观测台站位置，细红线表示阿尔奎斯特–普里奥洛断层 [30]，粗黑线表示基于余震位置勾勒出的断层。图 **b** 为水平 PGA，它是离断层破裂距离的函数。距离的计算基于断层在地表的近似投影。图中显示了布勒–乔伊纳–菲马尔 1997 衰减关系 [52]：平均值（实线）、±1σ（虚线）和 ±2σ（点划线）。在图中超过仪器 2.5g 限值的 PGA 用 2.5g 表示。

　　震动强度的空间变化，如强地面运动峰值加速度和强地面运动峰值速度，通常归因于四个因素：观测台站之间土壤条件的差异、波向各个台站传播的差异、破裂几何结构的复杂性和断层滑动的不均匀性。对 2004 年地震的强地面运动记录的分

673

earthquake should lead to a fuller understanding of how each of these factors contributes to the spatial variability in strong shaking, especially at locations close to the fault rupture. This has significant ramifications for earthquake hazard research. For example, the variability in PGA was greatest close to the rupture (Fig. 4). This suggests that complexities in the seismic source may have been the primary cause of the variations, in which case research with a greater emphasis on understanding the physical processes controlling complexity of the source would be most effective. On the other hand, near-surface soil conditions at the site and heterogeneity in the properties of the Earth's crust that influence seismic-wave propagation are known to be important for determining the shaking at locations farther from the rupture. If these factors are found to be important for predicting the distribution of shaking within a few kilometres of the rupture as well, then directing additional resources towards developing detailed maps of these properties would also be effective. The large uncertainties in current estimates of strong ground shaking require that societal guidelines, including the Uniform Building Code and California's Alquist-Priolo Fault Zoning Act[30], be conservative, thereby driving up the cost of construction and hazard mitigation. To the extent that such variations in shaking are predictable, the precision of seismic hazard maps and building codes could be improved, allowing necessarily limited hazard mitigation funds to be used more effectively.

Long-term Non-randomness of Earthquakes

The notion that large earthquakes tend to occur as similar-size "characteristic" events on fixed segments of a fault and that these segments are identifiable from geologic and geophysical data arose in the 1980s (refs 3, 19 and 31) and remains central to fault-based Probabilistic Seismic Hazard Analysis (PSHA). PSHA also includes other approaches such as smoothed seismicity models (see ref. 32), random events and multiple segment ruptures (see ref. 23). The sequence of earthquakes at Parkfield since 1857 has long been considered a prime example of the recurrence of a characteristic earthquake[3,5,23]. Two classes of characteristic earthquakes have been considered for these events. In the first, events have the same faulting mechanism and magnitude, and occur on the same fault segment[31]; this class of characteristic behaviour is most appropriate for long-term forecasting of earthquakes and is often inferred from paleoseismic investigations. In the second class, the events also have the same epicentre and rupture direction[3]. If events in the second class were further constrained to have the same rupture time history and distribution of slip, then this class of recurrent behaviour would imply low variability in the distribution of strong ground shaking among the recurrences of characteristic events.

The 1934, 1966 and 2004 Parkfield earthquakes are remarkably similar in size (see Fig. 5 for example) and location of rupture, albeit not in epicentre or rupture propagation direction. The aftershocks of the 1966 and 2004 earthquakes delineate many of the same fault structures (Fig. 2). Furthermore, most of the observations available for the Parkfield earthquakes in 1881, 1901 and 1922 are consistent with the hypothesis that these earlier earthquakes were similar in size and general location to the later events[3,5]. Owing to limited

析应能使人们更全面地了解这些因素如何分别对强震动的空间变化产生影响，尤其是在断层破裂附近的地方。这对地震灾害研究具有重要的影响。例如，在靠近破裂的地方，PGA 的变化最大（图 4）。这表明，震源的复杂性可能是造成这些变化的主要原因，在这种情况下，着重理解控制震源复杂性的物理过程的相关研究将是最有效的。另一方面，众所周知，台站近地表土壤条件和影响地震波传播的地壳介质的非均匀性，对于确定距离破裂较远位置的震动是非常重要的。如果这些因素被发现对于预测破裂带几千米范围内的震动分布也很重要，那么把更多的资源用于绘制具有这些介质属性的详细分布图，也将是有效的。目前，强震动的估计存在很大的不确定性，这需要保守的社会规范，包括统一建筑法规和加利福尼亚州的阿尔奎斯特–普里奥洛断层分区法[30]，从而提高了建设成本和减灾的成本。在这种程度下，震动变化是可预测的，地震灾害图的精度和建筑法规的精度可以得到改善，有限的减灾资金可以得到更有效的使用。

地震的长期非随机性

大地震往往在断层固定段落上以相似规模的"尺度特征"发生，关于这些断层分段的段落可以从地质和地球物理数据中识别的观点是从 20 世纪 80 年代形成的（参考文献 3、19 和 31），并一直在基于断层的地震危险性概率分析（PSHA）中居于核心地位。PSHA 还包括其他方法，如平滑地震活动模型（见参考文献 32）、随机地震事件和多段破裂（见参考文献 23）。自 1857 年以来，帕克菲尔德一连串的地震长期被认为是特征地震重复发生的主要例子[3,5,23]。其中，两类特征地震被考虑进来。在第一类中，地震具有相同的震源机制和震级，并且发生在同一断层段上[31]；这类特征地震行为最适合长期地震预测，通常从古地震调查中推断而来。在第二类中，地震也具有相同的震中和破裂方向[3]。如果第二类地震又具有相同的破裂时间历史和滑动分布，那么这类复发行为将意味着一组重复特征地震引起的强地面震动具有很小的分布变化。

1934 年、1966 年和 2004 年帕克菲尔德地震在大小（以图 5 为例）和破裂位置上极为相似，尽管在震中或破裂传播方向上不同。1966 年和 2004 年的余震勾勒出许多相同的断层结构（图 2）。此外，1881 年、1901 年和 1922 年帕克菲尔德地震的大多数观测结果都符合这样一个假设，即这些早期地震的大小及大体位置与后来的地震相似[3,5]。由于对这些早期地震的观测有限，对帕克菲尔德主震的严格定义必须限

observations of these earlier events, a rigorous definition of the Parkfield main shocks must be limited to their overall size and their location based on rupture along the Parkfield segment[33]. Michael and Jones' definition[33] was designed to encompass the Parkfield main shocks through 1966; the 2004 main shock also satisfies their definition. Thus, the Parkfield earthquakes are consistent with the first class of characteristic earthquake behaviour. However, the variability in the spatial distribution of slip for the last three events[34,35] and the different direction of rupture propagation in the 2004 event invalidates the application of the second class of characteristic behaviour to the Parkfield earthquakes.

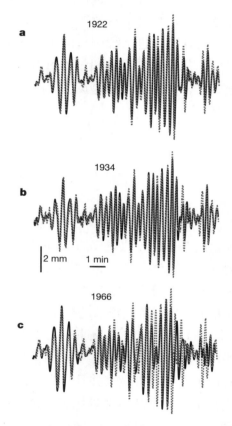

Fig. 5. Seismograms for Parkfield earthquakes at De Bilt, the Netherlands. North–south seismogram for the 2004 Parkfield earthquake (red dashed line) is plotted relative to the 1922, 1934, and 1966 Parkfield earthquakes in **a**, **b**, and **c** respectively. The 1922, 1934, and 1966 events were recorded by horizontal Galitzin seismographs. The 2004 signal, recorded by a three-component, broadband digital station located at the same site as the Galitzin seismograph, was digitally filtered to simulate a Galitzin seismograph. The similar amplitudes and waveforms imply the same seismic moment, focal mechanism, and teleseismic wave path.

We note that the six Parkfield earthquakes since 1857 have occurred with statistically significant (albeit imperfect) regularity in time—more regular than random but not sufficiently periodic to be predictable in any useful way beyond long-term statistical forecasts (Supplementary Text 2). This limited regularity underlies most of the long-term

制在沿着帕克菲尔德段破裂的总体尺寸和位置上 [33]。迈克尔和琼斯的定义 [33] 旨在涵盖 1966 年的帕克菲尔德主震，2004 年的主震也满足他们的定义。因此，帕克菲尔德地震符合第一类特征地震行为。然而，最近的三次地震 [34,35] 的滑动空间分布的变化，以及 2004 年地震破裂传播方向的不同，使得第二类特征行为不再适用于帕克菲尔德地震。

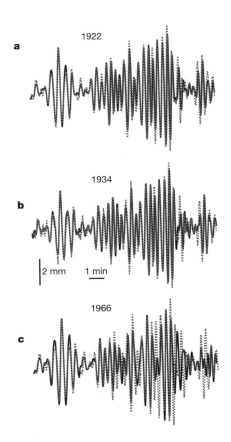

图 5. 帕克菲尔德地震在荷兰德比尔特测得的震波图。图 a、b、c 分别展示了 2004 年帕克菲尔德地震（红色虚线）相对于 1922 年、1934 年和 1966 年帕克菲尔德地震的北–南震波图。1922 年、1934 年和 1966 年地震都是由水平加利津地震仪记录的。2004 年的信号是由一个三分量的宽带数字观测站通过数字滤波模拟加利津地震仪记录的，该站与加利津地震仪位于同一站点。相似的振幅和波形意味着相同的地震矩、震源机制和远震地震波路径。

我们注意到，自 1857 年以来，6 次帕克菲尔德地震的发生时间在统计上具有显著（尽管不完美）的高于随机分布的规律性，但非完备的周期性，不可以用除长期统计预测外的任何有用方式进行预测（补充文本 2）。这种有限的规律性是多数长期地

prediction models proposed for the earthquakes[3,5]. The departures from perfectly regular occurrence of these earthquakes have been interpreted using physics-based variations upon the characteristic earthquake model. For example, the Parkfield Recurrence Model, used at the outset of the experiment in 1985, assumed a constant fault loading rate and failure threshold and allowed that main shocks could be triggered early by foreshocks, but did not allow for late events[5]. Consequently, it has been invalidated by the long time interval between the 1966 and 2004 main shocks. In a time-predictable model, the time between successive events is proportional to the slip of the prior event; in a slip-predictable model, the size of an earthquake is proportional to the time since the prior event[36]. Neither of these models is compatible with the sequence of Parkfield earthquake ruptures[34]. Various forms of fault interaction have been proposed to explain the variation in recurrence intervals of the earthquakes[37].

Statistical models of earthquake recurrence have also been applied to these events. The variability in the time between earthquakes implies a coefficient of variability (COV) of about 0.45 which is similar to the COV used in recent forecasts for the San Francisco Bay Area[23] but greater than that proposed in earlier models for the Parkfield sequence[38]. Earthquake activity over a wide range of smaller magnitudes ($M_w = 0$ to 5) also occurs at Parkfield. Clusters of microearthquakes that produce nearly identical waveforms repeatedly rupture small, fixed patches of the fault—some with remarkable regularity. Many of these clusters have characteristic recurrence times of months to years that scale with the magnitude of the repeating events. Changes in this recurrence time have been used to infer that slip rates over portions of the fault vary with time[39]. Similar to the Parkfield main shocks, models of these events suggest that they may balance their local slip budget with a mix of seismic and aseismic slip[40].

The earthquakes at Parkfield, both large and small, provide a fertile laboratory for testing and refining the characteristic earthquake concept by offering information on slip distribution, rupture dynamics and afterslip, and for testing models of earthquake recurrence and interaction, which are central to contemporary earthquake hazard assessment[23]. (The characteristic earthquake model can also be tested using global data sets. Kagan and Jackson[41] concluded that too few of Nishenko's[42] predicted gap-filling circum-Pacific earthquakes occurred in the first 5 yr.) Although the Parkfield earthquake history supports the use of characteristic events for earthquake forecasting, this topic remains controversial[42,43] and we must consider whether conclusions drawn from observations at Parkfield will transfer to other seismogenic regions. For instance, does the presence of aseismic slip to the north of and within the Parkfield segment yield unusual earthquake behaviour? Observations of the large amount of postseismic slip following the 2004 earthquake suggest that it may help to balance the slip budget. Faults that do not slip aseismically may exhibit more irregular behaviour because other large events are needed to balance the slip budget. There are other faults, however, with aseismic slip that produce small repeating events and may thus produce characteristic events similar to those observed at Parkfield. These include the Hayward and Calaveras faults in California and partially coupled subduction zones[44-46].

震预测模型的基础 [3,5]。与地震完备的规律的偏离，可以基于特征地震模型用物理基础的变化来解释。例如，1985 年的实验场开始时使用的帕克菲尔德重复地震模型，假设了恒定的断层加载速率和固定的失稳阈值，并认为主震可能由前震触发，然而后来的地震并非如此 [5]。因此，基于该重复地震模型给出的长期地震预测，被 1966 年和 2004 年两次主震间的长时间间隔所推翻。在时间可预测模型中，连续地震之间的时间与上一次地震的滑动量成比例；在震级可预测模型中，地震的大小与上一次地震以来的时间成比例 [36]。这两种模型都不适合帕克菲尔德地震序列 [34]。于是就提出了各种断层相互作用的理论，用于解释地震复发间隔的变化 [37]。

应用地震复发的多种统计模型来分析帕克菲尔德地震序列时发现，地震之间的时间变化表明可变化性系数（COV）为 0.45 左右，与最近用于预测旧金山湾区的 COV [23] 相当，但高于早期模型对帕克菲尔德序列所评估出的 COV 值 [38]。在帕克菲尔德也有较小震级（$M_w = 0 \sim 5$）的地震活动。微小地震群产生几乎相同的波形，并反复发生使小而固定的断层带破裂，其中一些具有显著的规律性。这些地震群中的许多地震具有几个月到几年的特征复发时间，特征复发时间与重复地震的震级成比例关系。复发时间的变化被用来推断断层段落的滑动速率随时间的变化 [39]。与帕克菲尔德主震相似，这些地震的模型表明，它们以地震滑动和无震蠕滑的形式来调节局部滑动预估 [40]。

帕克菲尔德地震，无论大小，都搭建了一个丰富的实验平台，通过提供有关滑动分布、破裂动力学和震后余滑的信息来检验和完善特征地震概念，并检验地震复发和相互作用的模型，这些模型在现代地震灾害评估中居于核心地位 [23]。（特征地震模型也可以使用全球数据集进行测试。卡根和杰克逊 [41] 得出的结论是，尼森科 [42] 预测的填充空区的环太平洋地震前 5 年发生得太少。）尽管帕克菲尔德地震历史支持使用特征地震进行地震预测，但这一问题仍存在争议 [42,43]，我们必须考虑从帕克菲尔德的观测中得出的结论是否可以用到其他孕震区。例如，在帕克菲尔德段的北部及其内部存在的无震滑动，会产生异常的地震行为吗？ 2004 年地震后，震后较大的滑动量观测结果表明，震后滑动可能有助于平衡滑动预估。不发生无震滑动的断层可能表现出更不规律的行为，因为需要其他大地震来平衡滑动预估。然而，还有其他一些进行无震滑动的断层，会产生小的重复地震，因此可能产生类似于在帕克菲尔德观测到的特征地震。这些断层包括加利福尼亚的海沃德断层和卡拉韦拉斯断层，以及部分耦合俯冲带 [44-46]。

Implications for Future Research

The magnitude and rupture extent of the 2004 Parkfield earthquake were correctly anticipated, but its time of occurrence clearly was not. This suggests that long-term earthquake forecasts require models that include higher degrees of variability (for example, see ref. 23). Although the 2004 Parkfield earthquake was ideally located within a dense monitoring network specifically designed to detect foreshocks and other possible short-term precursors, no significant signals were detected. This documented absence of clear precursory activity sets stringent bounds on the processes that preceded this earthquake. Attempts to detect short-term precursory strain changes near several other recent $M_w = 5.3$–7.3 earthquakes in California and Japan have also failed[47]. These experiences demonstrate that reliable short-term earthquake prediction (up to a few weeks in advance) will be very difficult at best. Although the search for precursors should not be abandoned, we should thoroughly explore other ways to mitigate losses in earthquakes.

Earthquake loss mitigation begins with hazard assessment. Improved hazard assessment will require incorporating the observed variability in both earthquake sources and the resulting ground motions into probabilistic seismic hazard analysis. The history of events at Parkfield and the detailed observations of the 2004 event have revealed variability in intervals between earthquakes, variations in slip distributions of large events, and spatial variations in strong ground motion. Incorporating realistic variability into hazard assessments will entail sophisticated three-dimensional numerical models that can accurately explore many seismic cycles and include the build-up of strain via plate motions, dynamic stress changes during rupture, and postseismic deformation. Such models must be able to explain the interaction of aseismic and seismic slip, the segmentation of faults, and the strong spatial variations in the intensity of strong shaking. Complementary data from *in situ* studies of the Earth's crust, such as SAFOD[10], laboratory experiments that recreate the conditions of faults in the Earth, and continued seismic monitoring will be needed to constrain the numerical models.

The value of the unique long-term record of crustal deformation being collected at Parkfield suggests that the monitoring there should continue. Parkfield-like experiments embedded within broader monitoring networks in other locations can provide similarly valuable data for faults in other tectonic contexts. Additional selected faults in California, which are already contained within sparse monitoring networks, should be densely instrumented. Large earthquakes are also anticipated on known fault segments in China, Japan, Turkey and elsewhere, and international cooperation should be sought to develop comprehensive monitoring in these regions. The Parkfield experiment showed that diligence is required to maintain these specialized networks until a large earthquake occurs, and the detailed observations made at Parkfield demonstrate how valuable such perseverance can be for advancing our understanding of earthquakes.

(**437**, 969-974; 2005)

对未来研究的启示

2004 年帕克菲尔德地震的震级和破裂程度得到了正确的预测，但对发震时间的预测显然不准。这意味着地震长期预测需要具有更高变化维度的模型（比如参考文献 23）。虽然 2004 年帕克菲尔德地震十分理想地发生在专门设计用于监测前震和其他可能的短期前兆的密集监测台网内，但监测台网并未观测到有意义的信号。明确的前兆活动的缺失对这次地震发生前的过程研究提出了非常严峻的挑战。在加利福尼亚州和日本的几次最近发生的 $M_w = 5.3 \sim 7.3$ 的地震附近，检测短期前兆应变变化的尝试也失败了 [47]。这些经验表明，可靠的短期地震预测（震前几周）无论如何都是非常困难的。尽管我们不应放弃对地震前兆的探索，但我们更应该深入探索减轻地震损失的其他多种途径。

减少地震损失从灾害评估开始。改进后的灾害评估需要将观测到的震源变化和由此产生的地面运动都纳入概率地震灾害分析中。帕克菲尔德地震的历史和 2004 年地震的详细观测已经揭示了地震时间间隔的可变动性、大地震滑动分布的变化以及强地面震动的空间变化。在灾害评估中考虑这些现实的可变动性需要复杂的三维数值模型，以准确地模拟多个地震周期并考虑板块运动中的应变累积、破裂过程中的动态应力变化和震后变形。这些模型必须能够解释无震滑动和地震滑动的相互作用、断层的分段性以及强震动的剧烈空间变化，从已有地壳研究的补充数据，如 SAFOD[10]，重建地球中断层活动的条件和实验环境，且以连续的地震监测来约束数值模型。

在帕克菲尔德收集到的地壳形变的唯一长期记录表明，该地区的监测应该继续下去。在其他地方配备更为广泛监测台网的类似帕克菲尔德的地震预测实验场，可以为当地的构造环境提供同样有价值的资料。加利福尼亚州地区，对已处于稀疏监测台网中的选定的断层，应该加密布置仪器观测。中国、日本、土耳其和其他地区，大地震也被预测在某些已知断层的段落上，这些地区应寻求国际合作开展综合监测。帕克菲尔德地震实验场表明，在发生大地震之前，这些专门的网络需要付出艰辛来继续坚持。在帕克菲尔德地区的详细观测表明，这种长期观测的坚持不懈对于增进我们对地震的理解是多么有价值。

（孙惠南 郭思彤 翻译；尹凤玲 审稿）

W. H. Bakun[1], B. Aagaard[1], B. Dost[2], W. L. Ellsworth[1], J. L. Hardebeck[1], R. A. Harris[1], C. Ji[3], M. J. S. Johnston[1], J. Langbein[1], J. J. Lienkaemper[1], A. J. Michael[1], J. R. Murray[1], R. M. Nadeau[4], P. A. Reasenberg[1], M. S. Reichle[5], E. A. Roeloffs[6], A. Shakal[5], R. W. Simpson[1] & F. Waldhauser[7]

[1] US Geological Survey, Menlo Park, California 94025, USA

[2] Royal Netherlands Meteorological Institute (KNMI), Seismology Division, PO Box 201, 3730AE De Bilt, The Netherlands

[3] Division of Geological and Planetary Sciences, Caltech, Pasadena, California 91125, USA

[4] University of California, Berkeley Seismological Laboratory, Berkeley, California 94720, USA

[5] California Geological Survey, Sacramento, California 95814, USA

[6] US Geological Survey, Vancouver, Washington 98683, USA

[7] Lamont-Doherty Earth Observatory, Columbia University, Palisades, New York 10964, USA

Received 28 January; accepted 10 July 2005.

References:

1. Sieh, K. E. Slip along the San Andreas Fault associated with the great 1857 earthquake. *Bull. Seismol. Soc. Am.* **68**, 1421-1447 (1978).

2. Toppozada, T. R., Branum, D. M., Reichle, M. S. & Hallstrom, C. L. San Andreas fault zone, California; M ≥ 5.5 earthquake history. *Bull. Seismol. Soc. Am.* **92**, 2555-2601 (2002).

3. Bakun, W. H. & McEvilly, T. V. Recurrence models and Parkfield, California, earthquakes. *J. Geophys. Res.* **89**, 3051-3058 (1984).

4. Shearer, C. F. Southern San Andreas fault geometry and fault zone deformation: implications for earthquake prediction (National Earthquake Prediction Council Meeting, March, 1985). *US Geol. Surv. Open-file Rep.* **85-507**, 173-174 (USGS, Reston, Virginia, 1985).

5. Bakun, W. H. & Lindh, A. G. The Parkfield, California, earthquake prediction experiment. *Science* **229**, 619-624 (1985).

6. Sherburne, R. W. Ground shaking and engineering studies near the San Andreas fault zone. *Calif. Geol.* **41**, 27-32 (1988).

7. Bakun, W. H. *et al.* Parkfield, California, earthquake prediction scenarios and response plans. *US Geol. Surv. Open-file Rep.* **87-192**, 1-45 (USGS, Reston, Virginia, 1987).

8. Hill, D. P. *et al.* Response plans for volcanic hazards in the Long Valley caldera and Mono Craters area, California. *US Geol. Surv. Open-file Rep.* **91-270**, 1-64 (USGS, Reston, Virginia, 1991).

9. USGS *Advanced National Seismic System* ⟨http://earthquake.usgs.gov/anss/⟩ (USGS Earthquake Hazards Program, 2000).

10. Hickman, S., Zoback, M. & Ellsworth, W. Introduction to the special section: preparing for the San Andreas Fault Observatory at depth. *Geophys. Res. Lett.* **31**, L12S01, doi:10.1029/2004GL020688 (2004).

11. Earthscope Project *Exploring the Structure and Evolution of the North American Continent* ⟨http://www.earthscope.org/⟩ (2003).

12. National Earthquake Prediction Evaluation Council Working Group. Earthquake research at Parkfield, California, 1993 and beyond—report of the NEPEC working group to evaluate the Parkfield earthquake prediction experiment. *US Geol. Surv. Circ.* **1116**, 1-14 (USGS, Reston, Virginia, 1994).

13. Langbein, J. *et al.* Preliminary report on the 28 September 2004, M6.0 Parkfield, California, earthquake. *Seismol. Res. Lett.* **76**, 10-26 (2005).

14. Shakal, A. *et al.* Preliminary analysis of strong-motion recordings from the 28 September 2004 Parkfield, California earthquake. *Seismol. Res. Lett.* **76**, 27-39 (2005).

15. Rikitake, T. *Earthquake Prediction* 7-26 (Elsevier, Amsterdam, Netherlands, 1976).

16. Bakun, W. H. & McEvilly, T. V. Earthquakes near Parkfield, California; comparing the 1934 and 1966 sequences. *Science* **205**, 1375-1377 (1979).

17. Nadeau, R. M. & Dolenc, D. Nonvolcanic tremors deep beneath the San Andreas fault. *Science* **307**, 389, doi:10.1126/science.1107142 (2004).

18. Harris, R. A. Numerical simulations of large earthquakes: Dynamic rupture propagation on heterogeneous faults. *Pure Appl. Geophys.* **161**, 2171-2181, doi:10.1007/s00024-004-2556-8(2004).

19. Lindh, A. G. & Boore, D. M. Control of rupture by fault geometry during the 1966 Parkfield earthquake. *Bull. Seismol. Soc. Am.* **71**, 95-116 (1981).

20. Eberhart-Phillips, D. & Michael, A. J. Three-dimensional velocity structure, seismicity, and fault structure in the Parkfield region, Central California. *J. Geophys. Res.* **98**, 15737-15758 (1993).

21. Liu, J., Klinger, Y., Sieh, K. & Rubin, C. Six similar sequential ruptures of the San Andreas Fault, Carrizo Plain, California. *Geology* **32**, 649-652 (2004).

22. Irwin, W. P. & Barnes, I. Effect of geologic structure and metamorphic fluids on seismic behaviour of the San Andreas fault system in central and northern California. *Geology* **3**, 713-716 (1975).

23. Working Group on California Earthquake Probabilities. Earthquake probabilities in the San Francisco Bay region: 2002-2031. *US Geol. Surv. Open-file Rep.* **03-214**, 1-340 (USGS, Reston, Virginia, 2003).

24. Dragert, H., Wang, K. L. & James, T. S. A silent slip event on the deeper Cascadia subduction interface. *Science* **292**, 1525-1528 (2001).

25. Kawasaki, I. *et al.* The 1992 Sanriku-Oki, Japan, ultra-slow earthquakes. *J. Phys. Earth* **43**, 105-116 (1995).

26. Harris, R. A. & Segall, P. Detection of a locked zone at depth on the Parkfield, California segment of the San Andreas fault. *J. Geophys. Res.* **92**, 7945-7962 (1987).

27. Lienkaemper, J. J. & Prescott, W. H. Historic surface slip along the San Andreas fault near Parkfield, California. *J. Geophys. Res.* **94**, 17647-17670 (1989).

28. Lienkaemper, J. J., Baker, B. & McFarland, F. S. Slip in the 2004 Parkfield, California earthquake measured on alinement arrays. *Eos* **85**(47), Abstr. S54B- 01 (2004).

29. CISN *Strong Motion Engineering Data Center* ⟨http://www.quake.ca.gov/cisn-edc/⟩ (2000).

682

30. California Geological Survey *Alquist-Priolo Earthquake Fault Zones* ⟨http://www.consrv.ca.gov/CGS/rghm/ap/⟩ (1998).

31. Schwartz, D. P. & Coppersmith, K. J. Fault behaviour and characteristic earthquakes; examples from the Wasatch and San Andreas fault zones. *J. Geophys. Res.* **89**, 5681-5698 (1984).

32. Frankel, A. D. *et al.* USGS national seismic hazard maps. *Earthq. Spect.* **16**, 1-19 (2000).

33. Michael, A. J. & Jones, L. M. Seismicity alert probabilities at Parkfield, California, revisited. *Bull. Seismol. Soc. Am.* **88**, 117-130 (1998).

34. Murray, J. R. & Segall, P. Testing time-predictable earthquake recurrence by direct measure of strain accumulation and release. *Nature* **419**, 287-291 (2002).

35. Segall, P. & Du, Y. How similar were the 1934 and 1966 Parkfield earthquakes? *J. Geophys. Res.* **98**, 4527-4538 (1993).

36. Shimazaki, K. & Nakata, T. Time-predictable recurrence model for large earthquakes. *Geophys. Res. Lett.* **7**, 279-282 (1980).

37. Ben-Zion, Y., Rice, J. R. & Dmowska, R. Interaction of the San Andreas fault creeping segment with adjacent great rupture zones, and earthquake recurrence at Parkfield. *J. Geophys. Res.* **98**, 2135-2144 (1993).

38. Savage, J. C. The Parkfield Prediction Fallacy. *Bull. Seismol. Soc. Am.* **83**, 1-6 (1993).

39. Nadeau, R. M. & McEvilly, T. V. Fault slip rates at depth from recurrence intervals of repeating earthquakes. *Science* **285**, 718-721 (1999).

40. Beeler, N. M., Lockner, D. A. & Hickman, S. H. A simple creep-slip and stick-slip model for repeating earthquakes and its application to micro-earthquakes at Parkfield. *Bull. Seismol. Soc. Am.* **91**, 1797-1804 (2001).

41. Kagan, Y. Y. & Jackson, D. D. New seismic gap hypothesis: Five years after. *J. Geophys. Res.* **100**, 3943-3959 (1995).

42. Nishenko, S. P. Circum-Pacific seismic potential—1989-1999. *Pure Appl. Geophys.* **135**, 169-259 (1991).

43. Main, I. *Is reliable earthquake prediction of individual earthquakes a realistic scientific goal?* ⟨http://www.nature.com/nature/debates/earthquake/equake_contents. html⟩ (Nature Debate 25 February to 8 April 1999).

44. Waldhauser, F. & Ellsworth, W. L. A double-difference earthquake location algorithm; method and application to the northern Hayward Fault, California. *Bull. Seismol. Soc. Am.* **90**, 1353-1368 (2000).

45. Schaff, D. P., Beroza, G. C. & Shaw, B. E. Post-seismic response of repeating earthquakes. *Geophys. Res. Lett.* **107**, B9, doi:10.1029/2001JB000633 (1998).

46. Uchida, N., Matsuzawa, T., Igarashi, T. & Hasegawa, A. Interplate quasi-static slip off Sanriku, NE Japan, estimated from repeating earthquakes. *Geophys. Res. Lett.* **30**, doi:10.1029/2003GL017452 (2003).

47. Johnston, M. J. S. & Linde, A. T. *Implications* of crustal strain during conventional, slow, and silent earthquakes. *Int. Handbk Earthq. Eng. Seismol.* **81A**, 589-605 (2002).

48. Michael, A. J. & Eberhart-Phillips, D. M. Relations among fault behaviour, subsurface geology, and three-dimensional velocity models. *Science* **253**, 651-654 (1991).

49. Waldhauser, F., Ellsworth, W. L., Schaff, D. P. & Cole, A. Streaks, multiplets, and holes: high-resolution spatio-temporal behaviour of Parkfield seismicity. *Geophys. Res. Lett.* **31**, L18608, doi:10.1029/2004GL020649 (2004).

50. Ji, C., Choi, K. K., King, N., Larson, K. M. & Hudnut, K. W. Co-seismic slip history and early afterslip of the Parkfield earthquake. *Eos* **85**(47), Abstr. S53D-04 (2004).

51. CISN ShakeMap. *Estimated Instrumental Intensity* ⟨http://www.quake.ca.gov/shake/index.html⟩ (1997).

52. Boore, D. M., Joyner, W. B. & Fumal, T. E. Equations for estimating horizontal response spectra and peak acceleration from Western North American earthquakes: A summary of recent work. *Seismol. Res Lett.* **68**, 128-153 (1997).

Supplementary Information is linked to the online version of the paper at www.nature.com/nature.

Acknowledgements. The Parkfield experiment has served as a model for the collaboration of federal and state agencies with researchers in academia and industry, and many, far too numerous to list here, have contributed to its successes. In particular, J. Davis, J. Filson, A. Lindh and T. McEvilly made the experiment happen. We thank T. Hanks, S. Hough, D. Jackson, Y. Kagan, A. Lindh, M. Rymer, W. Thatcher, D. Wald and M. L. Zoback for their comments and suggestions and L. Blair, J. Boatwright, M. Huang, and D. Wald for technical assistance.

Author Information. Reprints and permissions information is available at npg.nature.com/reprintsandpermissions. The authors declare no competing financial interests. Correspondence and requests for materials should be addressed to W.H.B. (bakun@usgs.gov).

A Haplotype Map of the Human Genome

The International HapMap Consortium[*]

Editor's Note

Three years after its official launch, the International HapMap Consortium revealed its completed haplotype map of the human genome. The map reveals the most common genetic differences found across the entire genome for 269 humans from four different populations. The research, led by geneticists David Altshuler and Peter Donnelly, groups single nucleotide polymorphisms (SNPs)—the single-letter differences in the DNA between individuals—into haplotypes, combinations of SNPs that have travelled together over evolutionary time. The goal is to understand the complex genetic changes underlying common diseases such as cardiovascular disease and cancer. Two years later the map was "upgraded" to a second-generation version of over 3 million SNPs.

Inherited genetic variation has a critical but as yet largely uncharacterized role in human disease. Here we report a public database of common variation in the human genome: more than one million single nucleotide polymorphisms (SNPs) for which accurate and complete genotypes have been obtained in 269 DNA samples from four populations, including ten 500-kilobase regions in which essentially all information about common DNA variation has been extracted. These data document the generality of recombination hotspots, a block-like structure of linkage disequilibrium and low haplotype diversity, leading to substantial correlations of SNPs with many of their neighbours. We show how the HapMap resource can guide the design and analysis of genetic association studies, shed light on structural variation and recombination, and identify loci that may have been subject to natural selection during human evolution.

DESPITE the ever-accelerating pace of biomedical research, the root causes of common human diseases remain largely unknown, preventative measures are generally inadequate, and available treatments are seldom curative. Family history is one of the strongest risk factors for nearly all diseases—including cardiovascular disease, cancer, diabetes, autoimmunity, psychiatric illnesses and many others—providing the tantalizing but elusive clue that inherited genetic variation has an important role in the pathogenesis of disease. Identifying the causal genes and variants would represent an important step in the path towards improved prevention, diagnosis and treatment of disease.

More than a thousand genes for rare, highly heritable "mendelian" disorders have been

---

* The full list of authors and affiliations has been removed. The original text is available in the *Nature* online archive.

人类基因组的单体型图谱

国际单体型图谱协作组[*]

编者按

计划正式启动三年后，国际 HapMap 协作组发布了完整的人类基因组单体型图谱。这份图谱揭示了来自四个不同种群的 269 个人类个体在整个基因组范围内的最常见的遗传差异。由遗传学家戴维·阿特舒勒和彼得·唐纳利领导的这项研究，将单核苷酸多态性 (SNP)——个体间 DNA 上单个字母的差异——集合成单体型，即随着时间共同演化的 SNP 组合。项目的目标是理解常见疾病如心血管疾病和癌症等背后的复杂的遗传变化。两年后这份图谱"升级"为包含超过 300 万个 SNP 的第二代版本。

遗传变异在人类疾病中有着重要作用，但这些作用大部分还未被阐明。在本文中我们报道了一个公开的人类基因组中常见变异的数据库，它包含超过 100 万个单核苷酸多态性 (SNP)。这些位点的准确而全面的基因型是通过来自四个种群的 269 份 DNA 样本获得的，我们也在 10 个 500 kb 的区域中提取了基本上所有的常见 DNA 变异的信息。这些数据证明了重组热点、连锁不平衡的区块结构和低单体型密度的普遍性，进而证实了 SNP 与很多邻近 SNP 的大量关联。我们展示了 HapMap 资源如何指导遗传学关联研究的设计和分析，为结构变异和重组提供线索，以及鉴定在人类演化过程中可能经历过自然选择的基因座。

尽管生物医学研究的步伐不断加速，但常见人类疾病的根本原因仍然大部分未知，预防措施普遍不足，现有的治疗手段鲜有疗效。对于几乎所有的疾病——包括心血管疾病、癌症、糖尿病、自身免疫病、精神疾病和很多其他的疾病，家族史是最强的风险因素之一，提供了诱人又难以捉摸的线索，即遗传变异在疾病的发病机理中有着重要的作用。在通往更好地预防、诊断和治疗疾病的道路上，鉴定导致疾病的基因和变异将代表着重要的一步。

对于罕见的、高度遗传的"孟德尔"疾病，已有超过 1,000 个基因被鉴定出来。

---

[*] 本书略去了作者和单位名单。原文可从《自然》在线数据库中获得。

identified, in which variation in a single gene is both necessary and sufficient to cause disease. Common disorders, in contrast, have proven much more challenging to study, as they are thought to be due to the combined effect of many different susceptibility DNA variants interacting with environmental factors.

Studies of common diseases have fallen into two broad categories: family-based linkage studies across the entire genome, and population-based association studies of individual candidate genes. Although there have been notable successes, progress has been slow due to the inherent limitations of the methods; linkage analysis has low power except when a single locus explains a substantial fraction of disease, and association studies of one or a few candidate genes examine only a small fraction of the "universe" of sequence variation in each patient.

A comprehensive search for genetic influences on disease would involve examining all genetic differences in a large number of affected individuals and controls. It may eventually become possible to accomplish this by complete genome resequencing. In the meantime, it is increasingly practical to systematically test common genetic variants for their role in disease; such variants explain much of the genetic diversity in our species, a consequence of the historically small size and shared ancestry of the human population.

Recent experience bears out the hypothesis that common variants have an important role in disease, with a partial list of validated examples including *HLA* (autoimmunity and infection)[1], *APOE4* (Alzheimer's disease, lipids)[2], Factor V[Leiden] (deep vein thrombosis)[3], *PPARG* (encoding PPARγ; type 2 diabetes)[4,5], *KCNJ11* (type 2 diabetes)[6], *PTPN22* (rheumatoid arthritis and type 1 diabetes)[7,8], insulin (type 1 diabetes)[9], *CTLA4* (autoimmune thyroid disease, type 1 diabetes)[10], *NOD2* (inflammatory bowel disease)[11,12], complement factor H (age-related macular degeneration)[13-15] and *RET* (Hirschsprung disease)[16,17], among many others.

Systematic studies of common genetic variants are facilitated by the fact that individuals who carry a particular SNP allele at one site often predictably carry specific alleles at other nearby variant sites. This correlation is known as linkage disequilibrium (LD); a particular combination of alleles along a chromosome is termed a haplotype.

LD exists because of the shared ancestry of contemporary chromosomes. When a new causal variant arises through mutation—whether a single nucleotide change, insertion/deletion, or structural alteration—it is initially tethered to a unique chromosome on which it occurred, marked by a distinct combination of genetic variants. Recombination and mutation subsequently act to erode this association, but do so slowly (each occurring at an average rate of about 10^{-8} per base pair (bp) per generation) as compared to the number of generations (typically 10^4 to 10^5) since the mutational event.

The correlations between causal mutations and the haplotypes on which they arose have long served as a tool for human genetic research: first finding association to a haplotype, and then subsequently identifying the causal mutation(s) that it carries. This was pioneered in studies of the *HLA* region, extended to identify causal genes for mendelian diseases

在这些疾病中，单个基因的变异对于导致疾病是必要且充分的。相比而言，常见疾病的研究已被证明更具挑战性，因为这些疾病被认为是源于很多不同的易感 DNA 变异与环境因素相互作用的组合效应。

常见疾病的研究分为两大类：基于家系的全基因组连锁研究和基于自然人群的对单个候选基因的关联研究。尽管这些研究已经有令人瞩目的成功，但是由于方法的内在限制，进展一直比较缓慢；连锁分析的效力通常很低，除非单个基因座能解释疾病的很大一部分，而一个或几个候选基因的关联研究则仅仅是检查了一个病人体内序列变异"宇宙"的很小一部分。

全面寻找遗传对疾病的影响将涉及在大量的病例和对照中研究所有的遗传差异。通过完整的基因组重测序，有可能最终实现这一点。同时，系统检测常见的遗传变异在疾病中的作用变得越来越可行；人类种群在历史上有着较小的规模和共同的祖先，因此这样的变异可以解释我们自身物种中很大一部分的遗传多样性。

最新的实践证明了常见变异在疾病中有着重要的作用这个假说，部分得到验证的例子包括 HLA（自身免疫病和感染）[1]、APOE4（阿尔茨海默病，脂质）[2]、V^Leiden 因子（深部静脉血栓形成）[3]、PPARG（编码 PPARγ；2 型糖尿病）[4,5]、KCNJ11（2 型糖尿病）[6]、PTPN22（类风湿性关节炎和 1 型糖尿病）[7,8]、胰岛素（1 型糖尿病）[9]、CTLA4（自身免疫性甲状腺病，1 型糖尿病）[10]、NOD2（炎性肠病）[11,12]、补体因子 H（老年性黄斑变性）[13-15] 和 RET（先天性巨结肠）[16,17]，此外还有很多。

某些个体如果在一个位点携带一个特定的 SNP 等位基因，则常常可预见地在邻近的其他变异位点也携带特定的等位基因，这个事实促进了对常见遗传变异的系统研究。这种关联被称为连锁不平衡（LD）；等位基因在一条染色体上特定的组合被称为单体型。

LD 存在是由于现在的染色体有着共同的祖先。当一种新的导致疾病的变异通过突变——不管是单核苷酸改变、插入/缺失或者结构变异——而产生时，它最初会局限于它所发生的染色体，以独特的遗传变异组合为特征。重组和突变随后削弱这种关联，但是相对于变异发生后的代数（通常 10^4 到 10^5），这种削弱是很缓慢的（分别以每代每碱基对（bp）大约 10^{-8} 的平均速率发生）。

导致疾病的变异与其所在的单体型的相关性早已被用作人类遗传研究的工具：首先发现与一个单体型的关联，然后鉴定该单体型含有的导致疾病的突变。这种方法最早应用在 HLA 区域的研究，后来拓展到孟德尔疾病（如囊性纤维化 [18] 和

(for example, cystic fibrosis[18] and diastrophic dysplasia[19]), and most recently for complex disorders such as age-related macular degeneration[13-15].

Early information documented the existence of LD in the human genome[20,21]; however, these studies were limited (for technical reasons) to a small number of regions with incomplete data, and general patterns were challenging to discern. With the sequencing of the human genome and development of high-throughput genomic methods, it became clear that the human genome generally displays more LD[22] than under simple population genetic models[23], and that LD is more varied across regions, and more segmentally structured[24-30], than had previously been supposed. These observations indicated that LD-based methods would generally have great value (because nearby SNPs were typically correlated with many of their neighbours), and also that LD relationships would need to be empirically determined across the genome by studying polymorphisms at high density in population samples.

The International HapMap Project was launched in October 2002 to create a public, genome-wide database of common human sequence variation, providing information needed as a guide to genetic studies of clinical phenotypes[31]. The project had become practical by the confluence of the following: (1) the availability of the human genome sequence; (2) databases of common SNPs (subsequently enriched by this project) from which genotyping assays could be designed; (3) insights into human LD; (4) development of inexpensive, accurate technologies for high-throughput SNP genotyping; (5) web-based tools for storing and sharing data; and (6) frameworks to address associated ethical and cultural issues[32]. The project follows the data release principles of an international community resource project (http://www.wellcome.ac.uk/doc_WTD003208.html), sharing information rapidly and without restriction on its use.

The HapMap data were generated with the primary aim of guiding the design and analysis of medical genetic studies. In addition, the advent of genome-wide variation resources such as the HapMap opens a new era in population genetics, offering an unprecedented opportunity to investigate the evolutionary forces that have shaped variation in natural populations.

The Phase I HapMap

Phase I of the HapMap Project set as a goal genotyping at least one common SNP every 5 kilobases (kb) across the genome in each of 269 DNA samples. For the sake of practicality, and motivated by the allele frequency distribution of variants in the human genome, a minor allele frequency (MAF) of 0.05 or greater was targeted for study. (For simplicity, in this paper we will use the term "common" to mean a SNP with MAF $\geq$ 0.05.) The project has a Phase II, which is attempting genotyping of an additional 4.6 million SNPs in each of the HapMap samples.

To compare the genome-wide resource to a more complete database of common variation—one in which all common SNPs and many rarer ones have been discovered and tested—a representative collection of ten regions, each 500 kb in length, was selected

畸形性骨发育不良[19])的致病基因的鉴定，最近则应用于复杂疾病，如老年性黄斑变性[13-15]。

早期的信息证实了人类基因组中 LD 的存在[20,21]；但是这些研究（由于技术原因）局限于数据不完整的少量区域，难以了解其一般的模式。随着人类基因组的测序和高通量基因组方法的发展，我们已经清楚，人类基因组一般比简单种群遗传模型[23]有着更多的 LD[22]，此外，与之前的预估相比，LD 在不同区域间的变化更大，也呈现更加分节段的结构[24-30]。这些现象说明，基于 LD 的方法总体来说将会有巨大的价值（因为邻近的 SNP 通常与很多附近的 SNP 关联），也说明需要通过实验研究种群样本中高密度的多态性来确定 LD 关系。

国际 HapMap 计划在 2002 年 10 月启动，目的是创建一个公开的、全基因组范围的人类常见序列变异数据库，为指导临床表型的遗传学研究提供所需要的信息[31]。这个计划由于以下内容的汇集而已经变得可行：(1) 人类基因组序列的获得；(2) 设计基因型分型所需的常见 SNP 数据库的完善（该数据库被此计划进一步丰富）；(3) 对人类 LD 的了解；(4) 廉价而准确的高通量 SNP 基因型分型技术的发展；(5) 基于网络的存储和分享数据的工具；以及 (6) 解决相关的伦理和文化问题的框架[32]。本计划遵循国际共享资源项目的数据释放原则（http://www.wellcome.ac.uk/doc_WTD003208.html），迅速分享信息，不限制使用。

HapMap 数据的主要目的是指导医学遗传学研究的设计和分析。另外，像 HapMap 这样的全基因组的变异资源将开启种群遗传学的新纪元，为研究在自然种群中塑造了变异的进化动力提供一个前所未有的机会。

第 I 阶段的 HapMap

HapMap 计划的第 I 阶段目标是，对于 269 个 DNA 样本的每一个，均能在全基因组范围内的每 5,000 个碱基中至少对一个常见 SNP 进行基因分型。为了实用，同时根据人类基因组中变异的等位基因频率分布，我们选择研究最小等位基因频率（MAF）大于或等于 0.05 的 SNP。（为了简便，本文中我们使用"常见的"表示 MAF ≥ 0.05 的 SNP）本计划的第 II 阶段将在各个 HapMap 样本中对另外 460 万个 SNP 进行基因分型。

为了比较全基因组范围的资源与更完整的常见变异数据库——该数据库中所有的常见 SNP 和很多相对罕见的 SNP 已经被发掘和检验，我们从 ENCODE(DNA 元

from the ENCODE (Encyclopedia of DNA Elements) Project[33]. Each 500-kb region was sequenced in 48 individuals, and all SNPs in these regions (discovered or in dbSNP) were genotyped in the complete set of 269 DNA samples.

The specific samples examined are: (1) 90 individuals (30 parent–offspring trios) from the Yoruba in Ibadan, Nigeria (abbreviation YRI); (2) 90 individuals (30 trios) in Utah, USA, from the Centre d'Etude du Polymorphisme Humain collection (abbreviation CEU); (3) 45 Han Chinese in Beijing, China (abbreviation CHB); (4) 44 Japanese in Tokyo, Japan (abbreviation JPT).

Because none of the samples was collected to be representative of a larger population such as "Yoruba", "Northern and Western European", "Han Chinese", or "Japanese" (let alone of all populations from "Africa", "Europe", or "Asia"), we recommend using a specific local identifier (for example, "Yoruba in Ibadan, Nigeria") to describe the samples initially. Because the CHB and JPT allele frequencies are generally very similar, some analyses below combine these data sets. When doing so, we refer to three "analysis panels" (YRI, CEU, CHB+JPT) to avoid confusing this analytical approach with the concept of a "population".

Important details about the design of the HapMap Project are presented in the Methods, including: (1) organization of the project; (2) selection of DNA samples for study; (3) increasing the number and annotation of SNPs in the public SNP map (dbSNP) from 2.6 million to 9.2 million (Fig. 1); (4) targeted sequencing of the ten ENCODE regions, including evaluations of false-positive and false-negative rates; (5) genotyping for the genome-wide map; (6) intense efforts that monitored and established the high quality of the data; and (7) data coordination and distribution through the project Data Coordination Center (DCC) (http://www.hapmap.org).

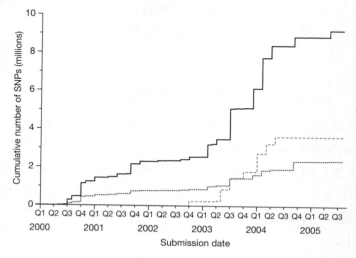

Fig. 1. Number of SNPs in dbSNP over time. The cumulative number of non-redundant SNPs (each mapped to a single location in the genome) is shown as a solid line, as well as the number of SNPs validated by genotyping (dotted line) and double-hit status (dashed line). Years are divided into quarters (Q1–Q4).

件百科全书)计划[33] 中选择了 10 个具有代表性的区域,每个区域的长度是 500 kb。先在 48 个个体中对这 10 个 500 kb 的区域进行测序,然后在全部 269 个 DNA 样本中对这些区域中所有的 SNP(新发现的或已收录在 dbSNP 数据库的)进行基因分型。

检测的样本包括:(1)尼日利亚伊巴丹市的 90 个(30 个亲本–子孙三联家系)约鲁巴人(简写为 YRI);(2)人类多态性研究中心收集的美国犹他州的 90 个(30 个三联家系)个体(简写为 CEU);(3)中国北京市的 45 个汉族中国人(简写为 CHB);(4)日本东京市的 44 个日本人(简写为 JPT)。

由于收集的这些样本并不是用来代表更大的种群如"约鲁巴人""北欧和西欧人""汉族中国人"或者"日本人"(更不代表"非洲""欧洲"或者"亚洲"的所有种群),一开始我们建议使用特定的局部地区标识(例如,"尼日利亚伊巴丹市的约鲁巴人")来描述样本。由于 CHB 和 JPT 等位基因频率大体上非常相似,下面的一些分析将其合并到一起。这样操作时,我们使用三个"分析小组"(YRI、CEU、CHB+JPT)的说法来避免将这种分析方法与"种群"的概念混淆。

关于 HapMap 计划设计的重要细节在方法部分中进行了描述,包括:(1)计划的组织;(2)用于研究的 DNA 样本的选择;(3)公共 SNP 图谱(dbSNP 数据库)中 SNP 的数量和注释的增长(从 260 万到 920 万)(图 1);(4)对 10 个 ENCODE 区域的靶向测序,包括假阳性率和假阴性率的评估;(5)全基因组图谱的基因分型;(6)为建立和监控数据的高质量所付出的巨大努力;(7)通过本计划的数据协调中心进行的数据协调和分配(http://www.hapmap.org)。

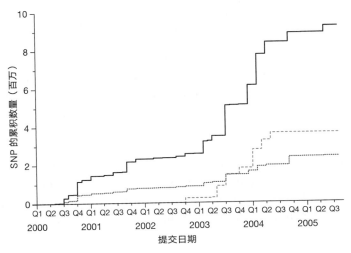

图 1. dbSNP 数据库中 SNP 数量随时间的变化。实线表示非冗余 SNP(各个 SNP 比对到基因组的单一位置)的累积数量,虚线表示被基因分型验证的 SNP 数量,短划线表示"双打击"状态。每年分为四个季度(Q1~Q4)。

Description of the data. The Phase I HapMap contains 1,007,329 SNPs that passed a set of quality control (QC) filters (see Methods) in each of the three analysis panels, and are polymorphic across the 269 samples. SNP genotyping was distributed across centres by chromosomal region, with several technologies employed (Table 1). Each centre followed the same standard rules for SNP selection, quality control and data release; all SNPs were genotyped in the full set of 269 samples. Some centres genotyped more SNPs than required by the rules.

Table 1. Genotyping centres

Centre	Chromosomes	Technology
RIKEN	5, 11, 14, 15, 16, 17, 19	Third Wave Invader
Wellcome Trust Sanger Institute	1, 6, 10, 13, 20	Illumina BeadArray
McGill University and Génome Québec Innovation Centre	2, 4p	Illumina BeadArray
Chinese HapMap Consortium*	3, 8p, 21	Sequenom MassExtend, Illumina BeadArray
Illumina	8q, 9, 18q, 22, X	Illumina BeadArray
Broad Institute of Harvard and MIT	4q, 7q, 18p, Y, mtDNA	Sequenom MassExtend, Illumina BeadArray
Baylor College of Medicine with ParAllele BioScience	12	ParAllele MIP
University of California, San Francisco, with Washington University in St Louis	7p	PerkinElmer AcycloPrime-FP
Perlegen Sciences	5 Mb (ENCODE) on 2, 4, 7, 8, 9, 12, 18 in CEU	High-density oligonucleotide array

* The Chinese HapMap Consortium consists of the Beijing Genomics Institute, the Chinese National Human Genome Center at Beijing, the University of Hong Kong, the Hong Kong University of Science and Technology, the Chinese University of Hong Kong, and the Chinese National Human Genome Center at Shanghai.

Extensive, blinded quality assessment (QA) exercises documented that these data are highly accurate (99.7%) and complete (99.3%, see also Supplementary Table 1). All genotyping centres produced high-quality data (accuracy more than 99% in the blind QA exercises, Supplementary Tables 2 and 3), and missing data were not biased against heterozygotes. The Supplementary Information contains the full details of these efforts.

Although SNP selection was generally agnostic to functional annotation, 11,500 non-synonymous cSNPs (SNPs in coding regions of genes where the different SNP alleles code for different amino acids in the protein) were successfully typed in Phase I. (An effort was made to prioritize cSNPs in Phase I in choosing SNPs for each 5-kb region; all known non-synonymous cSNPs were attempted as part of Phase II.)

数据的描述 HapMap 第 I 阶段包含 1,007,329 个在三个分析小组中均通过了一套质控(QC)过滤(详见方法),并且在 269 个样本中具有多态性的 SNP。SNP 基因分型任务按照染色体区域分配到各个中心,几种技术也部署到各个中心(表 1)。各个中心遵循相同的标准规则进行 SNP 挑选、质控和数据释放;所有的 SNP 都在整套 269 个样本中进行了基因分型。一些中心进行基因分型的 SNP 数量超出了规则所要求的。

表 1. 基因分型中心

中心	染色体	技术
日本理化研究所	5、11、14、15、16、17、19	Third Wave Invader
维康信托基金会桑格研究院	1、6、10、13、20	Illumina BeadArray
麦吉尔大学和基因组魁北克创新中心	2、4p	Illumina BeadArray
中国 HapMap 协作组 *	3、8p、21	Sequenom MassExtend, Illumina BeadArray
Illumina 公司	8q、9、18q、22、X	Illumina BeadArray
哈佛大学和麻省理工学院布罗德研究院	4q、7q、18p、Y、线粒体 DNA	Sequenom MassExtend, Illumina BeadArray
贝勒医学院和 ParAllele BioScience 公司	12	ParAllele MIP
加州大学旧金山分校和圣路易斯华盛顿大学	7p	PerkinElmer AcycloPrime-FP
Perlegen Sciences 公司	CEU 中 2、4、7、8、9、12、18 号染色体的 5 Mb 区域(ENCODE)	高密度寡核苷酸芯片

* 中国 HapMap 协作组包括北京基因组研究所、中国国家人类基因组北方研究中心、香港大学、香港科技大学、香港中文大学和中国国家人类基因组南方研究中心。

广泛的盲法质量评价(QA)发现这些数据是高度准确(99.7%)和完整的(99.3%,还可详见补充信息表 1)。所有的基因分型中心均产生高质量的数据(在盲法 QA 中准确度超过 99%,补充信息表 2 和 3),并且缺失的数据没有相对杂合子的偏倚。补充信息包含这些工作的所有细节。

尽管选择 SNP 时通常并不知晓功能注释,但是在第 I 阶段,有 11,500 个非同义 cSNP(即位于基因编码区,且不同的等位基因编码蛋白质的不同氨基酸的 SNP)被成功分型。(对于各个 5 kb 区域,选择 SNP 时优先选择第 I 阶段中的 cSNP;所有已知的非同义 cSNP 作为第 II 阶段的一部分。)

Table 2. ENCODE project regions and genotyping

Region name	Chromosome band	Genomic interval (NCBI) (base numbers)†	Gene density (%)‡	Conservation score (%)§	Pedigree-based recombination rate (cM Mb⁻¹)||	Population-based recombination rate (cM Mb⁻¹)¶	G+C content#	Available SNPs			Successfully genotyped SNPs††	Sequencing centre/genotyping centre(s)‡‡
								dbSNP☆	Sequence**	Total		
ENr112	2p16.3	51,633,239–52,133,238	0	3.8	0.8	0.9	0.35	1,570	1,762	3,332	2,275	Broad/McGill-GQIC
ENr131	2q37.1	234,778,639–235,278,638	4.6	1.3	2.2	2.5	0.43	1,736	1,259	2,995	1,910	Broad/McGill-GQIC
ENr113	4q26	118,705,475–119,205,474	0	3.9	0.6	0.9	0.35	1,444	2,053	3,497	2,201	Broad/Broad
ENm010	7p15.2	26,699,793–27,199,792	5.0	22.0	0.9	0.9	0.44	1,220	1,795	3,015	1,271	Baylor/UCSF-WU, Broad
ENm013*	7q21.13	89,395,718–89,895,717	5.5	4.4	0.4	0.5	0.38	1,394	1,917	3,311	1,807	Broad/Broad
ENm014*	7q31.33	126,135,436–126,632,577	2.9	11.2	0.4	0.9	0.39	1,320	1,664	2,984	1,966	Broad/Broad
ENr321	8q24.11	118,769,628–119,269,627	3.2	11.4	0.6	1.1	0.41	1,430	1,508	2,938	1,758	Baylor/Illumina
ENr232	9q34.11	127,061,347–127,561,346	5.9	8.3	2.7	2.6	0.52	1,444	1,523	2,967	1,324	Baylor/Illumina
ENr123	12q12	38,626,477–39,126,476	3.1	1.7	0.3	0.8	0.36	1,877	1,379	3,256	1,792	Baylor/Baylor
ENr213	18q12.1	23,717,221–24,217,220	0.9	7.4	1.2	0.9	0.37	1,330	1,459	2,789	1,640	Baylor/Illumina
Total	–	–	–	–	–	–	–	14,765	16,319	31,084	17,944	–

McGill-GQIC, McGill University and Génome Québec Innovation Centre.

*These regions were truncated to 500 kb for resequencing.

† Sequence build 34 coordinates.

‡ Gene density is defined as the percentage of bases covered either by Ensembl genes or human mRNA best BLAT alignments in the UCSC Genome Browser database.

§ Non-exonic conservation with mouse sequence was measured by taking 125 base non-overlapping sub-windows inside the 500,000 base windows. Sub-windows with less than 75% of their bases in a mouse alignment were discarded. Of the remaining sub-windows, those with at least 80% base identity were used to calculate the conservation

表 2. ENCODE 计划区域和基因分型

区域名称	染色体区带	基因组间距 (NCBI)† （碱基数量）	基因密度 (%)‡	保守性数值 (%)§	基于家系的重组率 (cM·Mb⁻¹)‖	基于种群的重组率 (cM·Mb⁻¹)¶	G+C 含量 #	已有的 SNP dbSNP☆	已有的 SNP 测序**	已有的 SNP 总计	成功基因分型的 SNP††	测序中心/基因分型中心‡‡
ENr112	2p16.3	51,633,239~52,133,238	0	3.8	0.8	0.9	0.35	1,570	1,762	3,332	2,275	布罗德/McGill-GQIC
ENr131	2q37.1	234,778,639~235,278,638	4.6	1.3	2.2	2.5	0.43	1,736	1,259	2,995	1,910	布罗德/McGill-GQIC
ENr113	4q26	118,705,475~119,205,474	0	3.9	0.6	0.9	0.35	1,444	2,053	3,497	2,201	布罗德/布罗德
ENm010	7p15.2	26,699,793~27,199,792	5	22.0	0.9	0.9	0.44	1,220	1,795	3,015	1,271	贝勒/UCSC-WU, 布罗德
ENm013*	7q21.13	89,395,718~89,895,717	5.5	4.4	0.4	0.5	0.38	1,394	1,917	3,311	1,807	布罗德/布罗德
ENm014*	7q31.33	126,135,436~126,632,577	2.9	11.2	0.4	0.9	0.39	1,320	1,664	2,984	1,966	布罗德/布罗德
ENr321	8q24.11	118,769,628~119,269,627	3.2	11.4	0.6	1.1	0.41	1,430	1,508	2,938	1,758	贝勒/Illumina
ENr232	9q34.11	127,061,347~127,561,346	5.9	8.3	2.7	2.6	0.52	1,444	1,523	2,967	1,324	贝勒/Illumina
ENr123	12q12	38,626,477~39,126,476	3.1	1.7	0.3	0.8	0.36	1,877	1,379	3,256	1,792	贝勒/贝勒
ENr213	18q12.1	23,717,221~24,217,220	0.9	7.4	1.2	0.9	0.37	1,330	1,459	2,789	1,640	贝勒/Illumina
合计	-	-	-	-	-	-	-	14,765	16,319	31,084	17,944	-

McGill-GQIC, 麦吉尔大学和基因组魁北克创新中心。

* 这些区域被削减到 500 kb 用于重测序。

† 34 版本序列坐标。

‡ 基因密度定义为被 Ensembl 基因或 UCSC 基因组浏览器数据库中人类 mRNA 最佳 BLAT 比对所覆盖的碱基的百分比。

§ 与小鼠序列的非外显子保守性是通过在 500,000 碱基窗口内取 125 碱基非重叠亚窗口来测定的。若一个亚窗口中小于 75% 的碱基比对到小鼠中，则该亚窗口被舍弃。剩下的亚窗口中，含有至少 80% 相同碱基的亚窗口用于计算保守性数值。小鼠比对中下列区域被舍弃：Ensembl 基因，所有的 GenBank mRNA Blastz 比对，FGenesh++ 基

score. The mouse alignments in regions corresponding to the following were discarded: Ensembl genes, all GenBank mRNA Blastz alignments, FGenesh++ gene predictions, Twinscan gene predictions, spliced EST alignments, and repeats.

‖ The pedigree-based sex-averaged recombination map is from deCODE Genetics[48].

¶ Recombination rate based on estimates from LDhat[46].

G+C content calculated from the sequence of the stated coordinates from sequence build 34.

☆ SNPs in dbSNP build 121 at the time the ENCODE resequencing began and SNPs added to dbSNP in builds 122–125 independent of the resequencing.

** New SNPs discovered through the resequencing reported here (not found by other means in builds 122–125).

†† SNPs successfully genotyped in all analysis panels (YRI, CEU, CHB+JPT).

‡‡ Perlegen genotyped a subset of SNPs in the CEU samples.

因预测，Twinscan 基因预测，剪接的 EST 比对以及重复。

‖ 基于家系的性别平均的重组图谱来自 deCODE Genetics[48]。

¶ 基于 LDhat[46] 估计的重组率。

G+C 含量根据来自序列版本 34 的相应序列计算。

☆ 在 ENCODE 重测序开始时 dbSNP 版本 121 中的 SNP，以及加入 dbSNP 的版本 122～125 中不依赖重测序结果的 SNP。

** 通过本文报道的重测序而新发现的 SNP（在版本 122～125 中通过其他方法未发现）。

†† 在所有分析小组（YRI、CEU、CHB+JPT）中被成功基因分型的 SNP。

‡‡ Perlegen 公司对 CEU 样本中一部分 SNP 进行了基因分型。

Across the ten ENCODE regions (Table 2), the density of SNPs was approximately tenfold higher as compared to the genome-wide map: 17,944 SNPs across the 5 megabases (Mb) (one per 279 bp).

More than 1.3 million SNP genotyping assays were attempted (Table 3) to generate the Phase I data on more than 1 million SNPs. The 0.3 million SNPs not part of the Phase I data set include 73,652 that passed QC filters but were monomorphic in all 269 samples. The remaining SNPs failed the QC filters in one or more analysis panels mostly because of inadequate completeness, non-mendelian inheritance, deviations from Hardy–Weinberg equilibrium, discrepant genotypes among duplicates, and data transmission discrepancies.

Table 3. HapMap Phase I genotyping success measures

SNP categories	Analysis panel		
	YRI	CEU	CHB+JPT
Assays submitted	1,273,716	1,302,849	1,273,703
Passed QC filters	1,123,296 (88%)	1,157,650 (89%)	1,134,726 (89%)
Did not pass QC filters*	150,420 (12%)	145,199 (11%)	138,977 (11%)
> 20% missing data	98,116 (65%)	107,626 (74%)	93,710 (67%)
> 1 duplicate inconsistent	7,575 (5%)	6,254 (4%)	10,725 (8%)
> 1 mendelian error	22,815 (15%)	13,600 (9%)	0 (0%)
< 0.001 Hardy–Weinberg P-value	12,052 (8%)	9,721 (7%)	16,176 (12%)
Other failures†	23,478 (16%)	17,692 (12%)	23,722 (17%)
Non-redundant (unique) SNPs	1,076,392	1,104,980	1,087,305
Monomorphic	156,290 (15%)	234,482 (21%)	268,325 (25%)
Polymorphic	920,102 (85%)	870,498 (79%)	818,980 (75%)
	All analysis panels		
Unique QC-passed SNPs	1,156,772		
Passed in one analysis panel	52,204 (5%)		
Passed in two analysis panels	97,231 (8%)		
Passed in three analysis panels	1,007,337 (87%)		
Monomorphic across three analysis panels	75,997		
Polymorphic in all three analysis panels	682,397		
MAF ≥ 0.05 in at least one of three analysis panels	877,351		

* Out of 95 samples in CEU, YRI; 94 samples in CHB+JPT.

† "Other failures" includes SNPs with discrepancies during the data transmission process. Some SNPs failed in more than one way, so these percentages add up to more than 100%.

SNPs on the Phase I map are evenly spaced, except on Y and mtDNA. The Phase I data

在 10 个 ENCODE 区域中（表 2），SNP 的密度大约是全基因组图谱的十倍：5 Mb 区域中有 17,944 个 SNP（每 279 bp 一个）。

我们对超过 130 万个 SNP 进行了基因分型（表 3），得到了第 I 阶段的超过 100 万个 SNP 的数据。30 万个不在第 I 阶段数据集的 SNP 包括 73,652 个通过了 QC 过滤但是在所有 269 个样本中都是单态性的 SNP。剩下的 SNP 则是在一个或更多分析小组中没有通过 QC 过滤的，这大多是因为完整性不足、非孟德尔遗传、偏离哈迪-温伯格平衡、重复间基因型不一致以及数据传送不一致。

表 3. 第 I 阶段 HapMap 成功的基因分型

SNP 类别	分析小组		
	YRI	CEU	CHB+JPT
提交的试验	1,273,716	1,302,849	1,273,703
通过 QC 过滤	1,123,296 (88%)	1,157,650 (89%)	1,134,726 (89%)
没有通过 QC 过滤 *	150,420 (12%)	145,199 (11%)	138,977 (11%)
缺失的数据 > 20%	98,116 (65%)	107,626 (74%)	93,710 (67%)
>1 个重复不一致	7,575 (5%)	6,254 (4%)	10,725 (8%)
>1 个孟德尔错误	22,815 (15%)	13,600 (9%)	0 (0%)
哈迪-温伯格平衡 P 值 < 0.001	12,052 (8%)	9,721 (7%)	16,176 (12%)
其他失败 †	23,478 (16%)	17,692 (12%)	23,722 (17%)
非冗余（唯一）SNP	1,076,392	1,104,980	1,087,305
单态性的	156,290 (15%)	234,482 (21%)	268,325 (25%)
多态性的	920,102 (85%)	870,498 (79%)	818,980 (75%)
	所有分析小组		
特定的通过 QC 的 SNP	1,156,772		
在一个分析小组中通过	52,204 (5%)		
在两个分析小组中通过	97,231 (8%)		
在三个分析小组中通过	1,007,337 (87%)		
在三个分析小组中的单态性	75,997		
在所有三个分析小组中的多态性	682,397		
在三个分析小组的至少一个中 MAF ≥ 0.05	877,351		

* 得自 95 个 CEU 和 YRI 样本；94 个 CHB+JPT 样本。
† "其他失败"包括在数据传输过程中不一致的 SNP。一些 SNP 存在不止一种失败，所以这些比例总计超过 100%。

除 Y 染色体和线粒体 DNA 上，第 I 阶段图谱中的 SNP 是均匀分布的　第 I 阶

include a successful, common SNP every 5 kb across most of the genome in each analysis panel (Supplementary Fig. 1): only 3.3% of inter-SNP distances are longer than 10 kb, spanning 11.9% of the genome (Fig. 2; see also Supplementary Fig. 2). One exception is the X chromosome (Supplementary Fig. 1), where a much higher proportion of attempted SNPs were rare or monomorphic, and thus the density of common SNPs is lower.

Fig. 2. Distribution of inter-SNP distances. The distributions are shown for each analysis panel for the HapMappable genome (defined in the Methods), for all common SNPs (with MAF ≥ 0.05).

Two intentional exceptions to the regular spacing of SNPs on the physical map were the mitochondrial chromosome (mtDNA), which does not undergo recombination, and the non-recombining portion of chromosome Y. On the basis of the 168 successful, polymorphic SNPs, each HapMap sample fell into one of 15 (of the 18 known) mtDNA haplogroups[34] (Table 4). A total of 84 SNPs that characterize the unique branches of the reference Y genealogical tree[35-37] were genotyped on the HapMap samples. These SNPs assigned each Y chromosome to 8 (of the 18 major) Y haplogroups previously described (Table 4).

Table 4. mtDNA and Y chromosome haplogroups

MtDNA haplogroup	DNA sample*			
	YRI (60)	CEU (60)	CHB (45)	JPT (44)
L1	0.22	–	–	–
L2	0.35	–	–	–
L3	0.43	–	–	–
A	–	–	0.13	0.04

段的数据在各个分析小组中大多数的基因组范围内每 5 kb 有一个成功分型的常见 SNP(补充信息图 1):只有 3.3% 的 SNP 间距超过 10 kb,占基因组的 11.9%(图 2;也可详见补充信息图 2)。X 染色体是一个例外(补充信息图 1),该染色体上罕见的或者单多态性的 SNP 的比例高得多,因而常见 SNP 的密度较低。

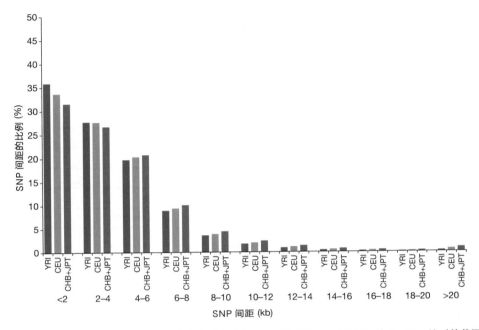

图 2. SNP 间距的分布。展示了各个分析小组中所有常见 SNP(MAF ≥ 0.05)在可被 HapMap 比对的基因组(在方法中有定义)中的分布。

物理图谱上 SNP 均匀间距的两个例外是不进行重组的线粒体染色体(mtDNA)和 Y 染色体的非重组部分。基于 168 个成功分型的多态性的 SNP,各个 HapMap 样本分别归属于 18 个已知 mtDNA 单倍体型中的 15 个[34](表 4)。总共 84 个表征参考 Y 染色体系统树独特分支的 SNP[35-37] 在 HapMap 样本中进行了基因分型。这些 SNP 将各个样本的 Y 染色体分配到 18 个主要的 Y 单体型中之前描述过的 8 个中(表 4)。

表 4. mtDNA 和 Y 染色体单体型

MtDNA 单体型	DNA 样本 *			
	YRI (60)	CEU (60)	CHB (45)	JPT (44)
L1	0.22	–	–	–
L2	0.35	–	–	–
L3	0.43	–	–	–
A	–	–	0.13	0.04

Continued

MtDNA haplogroup	DNA sample*			
	YRI (60)	CEU (60)	CHB (45)	JPT (44)
B	–	–	0.33	0.30
C	–	–	0.09	0.07
D	–	–	0.22	0.34
M/E	–	–	0.22	0.25
H	–	0.45	–	–
V	–	0.07	–	–
J	–	0.08	–	–
T	–	0.12	–	–
K	–	0.03	–	–
U	–	0.23	–	–
W	–	0.02	–	–
Y chromosome haplogroup	DNA sample*			
	YRI (30)	CEU (30)	CHB (22)	JPT (22)
E1	0.07	–	–	–
E3a	0.93	–	–	–
F, H, K	–	0.03	0.23	0.14
I	–	0.27	–	–
R1	–	0.70	–	–
C	–	–	0.09	0.09
D	–	–	–	0.45
NO	–	–	0.68	0.32

* Number of chromosomes sampled is given in parentheses.

Highly accurate phasing of long-range chromosomal haplotypes. Despite having collected data in diploid individuals, the inclusion of parent–offspring trios and the use of computational methods made it possible to determine long-range phased haplotypes of extremely high quality for each individual. These computational algorithms take advantage of the observation that because of LD, relatively few of the large number of possible haplotypes consistent with the genotype data actually occur in population samples.

The project compared a variety of algorithms for phasing haplotypes from unrelated individuals and trios[38], and applied the algorithm that proved most accurate (an updated version of PHASE[39]) separately to each analysis panel. (Phased haplotypes are available for download at the Project website.) We estimate that "switch" errors—where a segment of the maternal haplotype is incorrectly joined to the paternal—occur extraordinarily rarely in the trio samples (every 8 Mb in CEU; 3.6 Mb in YRI). The switch rate is higher in the CHB+JPT samples (one per 0.34 Mb) due to the lack of information from parent–

MtDNA 单体型	DNA 样本 *			
	YRI (60)	CEU (60)	CHB (45)	JPT (44)
B	–	–	0.33	0.30
C	–	–	0.09	0.07
D	–	–	0.22	0.34
M/E	–	–	0.22	0.25
H	–	0.45	–	–
V	–	0.07	–	–
J	–	0.08	–	–
T	–	0.12	–	–
K	–	0.03	–	–
U	–	0.23	–	–
W	–	0.02	–	–
Y 染色体单体型	DNA 样本 *			
	YRI (30)	CEU (30)	CHB (22)	JPT (22)
E1	0.07	–	–	–
E3a	0.93	–	–	–
F, H, K	–	0.03	0.23	0.14
I	–	0.27	–	–
R1	–	0.70	–	–
C	–	–	0.09	0.09
D	–	–	–	0.45
NO	–	–	0.68	0.32

* 染色体样本数在括号中给出。

远距离染色体单体型的精准确定　尽管收集的是二倍体个体的数据，亲本–子代三联家系的纳入和计算方法的使用使我们能够非常高质量地确定各个个体远距离的单体型。这些计算算法利用了这样一个现象：由于 LD 现象的存在，可能与基因型数据一致的大量单体型中，只有很少会实际存在于种群样本中。

本计划比较了各种来自不相关个体和三联家系[38]的单体型确定算法，并且分别对各个分析小组应用了被证明最准确的算法（PHASE 的一个最新版本[39]）。（确定的单体型数据可在本计划的网站上下载。）我们估计"转换"错误——母本单体型的一个片段错误地连到父本上——在三联家系样本中特别罕见（在 CEU 样本中每 8 Mb 一个；在 YRI 样本中每 3.6 Mb 一个）。由于缺少亲本–子代三联家系的信息，转换错

offspring trios, but even for the unrelated individuals, statistical reconstruction of haplotypes is remarkably accurate.

Estimating properties of SNP discovery and dbSNP. Extensive sequencing and genotyping in the ENCODE regions characterized the false-positive and false-negative rates for dbSNP, as well as polymerase chain reaction (PCR)-based resequencing (see Methods). These data reveal two important conclusions: first, that PCR-based sequencing of diploid samples may be biased against very rare variants (that is, those seen only as a single heterozygote), and second, that the vast majority of common variants are either represented in dbSNP, or show tight correlation to other SNPs that are in dbSNP (Fig. 3).

Fig. 3. Allele frequency and completeness of dbSNP for the ENCODE regions. **a–c**, The fraction of SNPs in dbSNP, or with a proxy in dbSNP, are shown as a function of minor allele frequency for each analysis panel (**a**, YRI; **b**, CEU; **c**, CHB+JPT). Singletons refer to heterozygotes observed in a single individual, and are broken out from other SNPs with MAF < 0.05. Because all ENCODE SNPs have been deposited in dbSNP, for this figure we define a SNP as "in dbSNP" if it would be in dbSNP build 125 independent of the HapMap ENCODE resequencing project. All remaining SNPs (not in dbSNP) were discovered only by ENCODE resequencing; they are categorized by their correlation (r^2) to those in dbSNP. Note that the number of SNPs in each frequency bin differs among analysis panels, because not all SNPs are polymorphic in all analysis panels.

误率在 CHB+JPT 样本中较高（每 0.34 Mb 一个），不过即使对于不相关的个体，单体型的统计学重建也是非常准确的。

SNP 发现和 dbSNP 数据库的特征估计　对 ENCODE 区域广泛的测序和基因分型，以及基于聚合酶链式反应（PCR）的重测序（详见方法），确定了 dbSNP 数据库的假阳性率和假阴性率。这些数据反映了两个重要的结论：第一，对二倍体样本进行基于 PCR 的测序，可能会在检测非常罕见的变异（即那些仅在单个杂合子中发现的变异）时产生偏倚；第二，大多数的常见变异要么收录在 dbSNP 中，要么与 dbSNP 中的其他 SNP 有紧密关联（图 3）。

图 3. ENCODE 区域的 dbSNP 等位基因频率和完整性。**a～c**，根据各个分析小组中最小等位基因频率表示 dbSNP 中或者在 dbSNP 中有代表物的 SNP 所占的比例（**a**，YRI；**b**，CEU；**c**，CHB+JPT）。单体指的是仅在单个个体中观察到的杂合子，是从 MAF < 0.05 的 SNP 中单独分出去的。因为所有的 ENCODE SNP 已经被收录到 dbSNP 中，所以对于这张图，如果一个 SNP 不是基于 HapMap ENCODE 重测序计划而被收录在 dbSNP 版本 125 中，我们就定义它为"在 dbSNP 中"。所有剩下的 SNP（不在 dbSNP 中）只通过 ENCODE 重测序而被发现，并根据与 dbSNP 中的 SNP 的关联（r^2）而进一步分类。注意，各个频率块中 SNP 的数量在不同分析小组中是不同的，因为不是所有 SNP 在所有分析小组中都是多态性的。

Allele frequency distributions within population samples. The underlying allele frequency distributions for these samples are best estimated from the ENCODE data, where deep sequencing reduces bias due to SNP ascertainment. Consistent with previous studies, most SNPs observed in the ENCODE regions are rare: 46% had MAF < 0.05, and 9% were seen in only a single individual (Fig. 4). Although most varying sites in the population are rare, most heterozygous sites within any individual are due to common SNPs. Specifically, in the ENCODE data, 90% of heterozygous sites in each individual were due to common variants (Fig. 4). With ever-deeper sequencing of DNA samples the number of rare variants will rise linearly, but the vast majority of heterozygous sites in each person will be explained by a limited set of common SNPs now contained (or captured through LD) in existing databases (Fig. 3).

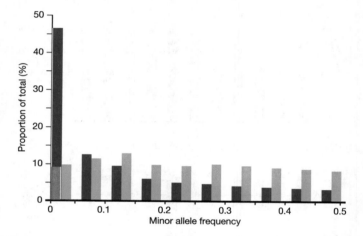

Fig. 4. Minor allele frequency distribution of SNPs in the ENCODE data, and their contribution to heterozygosity. This figure shows the polymorphic SNPs from the HapMap ENCODE regions according to minor allele frequency (blue), with the lowest minor allele frequency bin (< 0.05) separated into singletons (SNPs heterozygous in one individual only, shown in grey) and SNPs with more than one heterozygous individual. For this analysis, MAF is averaged across the analysis panels. The sum of the contribution of each MAF bin to the overall heterozygosity of the ENCODE regions is also shown (orange).

Consistent with previous descriptions, the CEU, CHB and JPT samples show fewer low frequency alleles when compared to the YRI samples (Fig. 5), a pattern thought to be due to bottlenecks in the history of the non-YRI populations.

In contrast to the ENCODE data, the distribution of allele frequencies for the genome-wide data is flat (Fig. 5), with much more similarity in the distributions observed in the three analysis panels. These patterns are well explained by the inherent and intentional bias in the rules used for SNP selection: we prioritized using validated SNPs in order to focus resources on common (rather than rare or false positive) candidate SNPs from the public databases. For a fuller discussion of ascertainment issues, including a shift in frequencies over time and an excess of high-frequency derived alleles due to inclusion of chimpanzee data in determination of double-hit status, see the Supplementary Information (Supplementary Fig. 3).

种群样本中的等位基因频率分布　对这些样本的潜在等位基因频率分布的最佳估计来自 ENCODE 数据，因为深度测序减少了确定 SNP 过程的偏倚。与之前的研究一致，ENCODE 区域内观察到的 SNP 大多数是罕见的：46% 的 MAF < 0.05，9% 仅在单个个体中存在（图 4）。尽管在种群中大多数变异位点是罕见的，但是在任何一个个体中，大多数杂合位点是常见 SNP。特别地，在 ENCODE 数据中，各个个体中 90% 的杂合位点是常见变异（图 4）。随着对 DNA 样本更加深度的测序，罕见变异的数量将会线性增长，但是每个个体中绝大多数的杂合位点仍可以用有限的一套已包含（或者通过 LD 而捕获）在已有数据库中的常见变异来解释（图 3）。

图 4. ENCODE 数据中 SNP 的最小等位基因频率分布和它们对杂合性的贡献。根据最小等位基因频率（蓝色）展示了来自 HapMap ENCODE 区域的多态性 SNP，最低的最小等位基因频率块（< 0.05）被分为单体（仅在一个个体中杂合的 SNP，用灰色表示）和在多于一个个体中杂合的 SNP。本分析中，MAF 是各分析小组的平均值。另外还展示了各个 MAF 块对 ENCODE 区域总体杂合性的贡献总和（橘色）。

与之前的描述一致，跟 YRI 样本相比，CEU、CHB 和 JPT 样本的低频等位基因更少（图 5），这种现象被认为是由于非 YRI 种群历史中的瓶颈效应。

与 ENCODE 数据相比，全基因组范围的等位基因频率分布是"平"的（图 5），在三个分析小组中的分布的相似性要高得多。这种模式可以用 SNP 筛选规则中固有的和人为的偏倚很好地进行解释：我们优先使用验证的 SNP，以便将资源集中于来自公共数据的常见的（而不是罕见或假阳性的）候选 SNP。对于确定 SNP 的问题的更加完整的讨论，包括频率随着时间的改变，以及在确定"双打击"状态时纳入黑猩猩数据而导致的高频率等位基因过量，详见补充信息（补充信息图 3）。

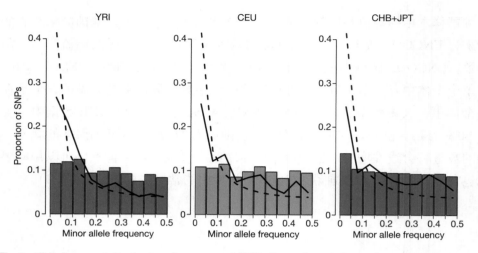

Fig. 5. Allele frequency distributions for autosomal SNPs. For each analysis panel we plotted (bars) the MAF distribution of all the Phase I SNPs with a frequency greater than zero. The solid line shows the MAF distribution for the ENCODE SNPs, and the dashed line shows the MAF distribution expected for the standard neutral population model with constant population size and random mating without ascertainment bias.

SNP allele frequencies across population samples. Of the 1.007 million SNPs successfully genotyped and polymorphic across the three analysis panels, only a subset were polymorphic in any given panel: 85% in YRI, 79% in CEU, and 75% in CHB+JPT. The joint distribution of frequencies across populations is presented in Fig. 6 (for the ENCODE data) and Supplementary Fig. 4 (for the genome-wide map). We note the similarity of allele frequencies in the CHB and JPT samples, which motivates analysing them jointly as a single analysis panel in the remainder of this report.

图 5. 常染色体 SNP 的等位基因频率分布。对于各个分析小组中所有第 I 阶段 HapMap 得到的频率大于零的 SNP，我们对其 MAF 分布作图（条形图）。实线表示 ENCODE SNP 的 MAF 分布，虚线表示基于恒定种群大小、随机交配以及无检测偏倚的标准中性种群模型得到的预期 MAF 分布。

种群样本间的 SNP 等位基因频率　三个分析小组共有 100.7 万成功基因分型并呈多态性的 SNP，其中只有一部分在三个分析小组中都是多态性的：YRI 中有 85%，CEU 中有 79%，CHB+JPT 中有 75%。种群间等位基因频率的联合分布见图 6（ENCODE 数据）和补充信息图 4（全基因组范围图谱）。我们注意到 CHB 和 JPT 样本等位基因频率相似，所以在这份报告的剩余部分将它们作为一个分析小组联合分析。

Fig. 6. Comparison of allele frequencies in the ENCODE data for all pairs of analysis panels and between the CHB and JPT sample sets. For each polymorphic SNP we identified the minor allele across all panels (**a–d**) and then calculated the frequency of this allele in each analysis panel/sample set. The colour in each bin represents the number of SNPs that display each given set of allele frequencies. The purple regions show that very few SNPs are common in one panel but rare in another. The red regions show that there are many SNPs that have similar low frequencies in each pair of analysis panels/sample sets.

A simple measure of population differentiation is Wright's F_{ST}, which measures the fraction of total genetic variation due to between-population differences[40]. Across the autosomes, F_{ST} estimated from the full set of Phase I data is 0.12, with CEU and CHB+JPT showing the lowest level of differentiation ($F_{ST} = 0.07$), and YRI and CHB+JPT the highest ($F_{ST} = 0.12$). These values are slightly higher than previous reports[41], but differences in the types of variants (SNPs versus microsatellites) and the samples studied make comparisons difficult.

As expected, we observed very few fixed differences (that is, cases in which alternate alleles are seen exclusively in different analysis panels). Across the 1 million SNPs genotyped, only 11 have fixed differences between CEU and YRI, 21 between CEU and CHB+JPT, and 5 between YRI and CHB+JPT, for the autosomes.

The extent of differentiation is similar across the autosomes, but higher on the X chromosome ($F_{ST} = 0.21$). Interestingly, 123 SNPs on the X chromosome were completely differentiated between YRI and CHB+JPT, but only two between CEU and YRI and one between CEU and CHB+JPT. This seems to be largely due to a single region near the centromere, possibly indicating a history of natural selection at this locus (see below; M. L. Freedman *et al.*, personal communication).

Haplotype sharing across populations. We next examined the extent to which haplotypes are shared across populations. We used a hidden Markov model in which each haplotype is modelled in turn as an imperfect mosaic of other haplotypes (see Supplementary Information)[42]. In essence, the method infers probabilistically which other haplotype in the sample is the closest relative (nearest neighbour) at each position along the chromosome.

图 6. ENCODE 数据中的等位基因频率在所有分析小组间以及 CHB 和 JPT 样本集间的比较。对于各个多态性 SNP，我们鉴定其在所有分析小组的最小等位基因 (a ~ d)，然后计算这个等位基因在各个分析小组/样本集的频率。各个块中的颜色代表显示特定等位基因频率集的 SNP 的数量。紫色区域表明非常少的 SNP 是在一个分析小组中常见而在另一个分析小组中罕见的。红色区域表明很多 SNP 在各对分析小组/样品集中有类似的低频率。

种群差异的一个简单的衡量方法是赖特的 F_{ST}，它测量总的遗传差异中由种群间差异导致的比例 [40]。对于常染色体，从全套第 I 阶段数据估计的 F_{ST} 是 0.12，其中 CEU 和 CHB+JPT 表现出最低水平的差异 (F_{ST} = 0.07)，而 YRI 和 CHB+JPT 则表现出最高的差异 (F_{ST} = 0.12)。这些数值略微高于之前的报道 [41]，但是变异类型的不同 (SNP 相对于微卫星) 和研究样本的差异使得比较变得困难。

正如预期的，我们观察到非常少的固定的差异 (即不同的等位基因特定地出现在不同的分析小组中的情况)。在进行了基因分型的 100 万 SNP 中，对于常染色体，只有 11 个 SNP 在 CEU 和 YRI 间有固定的差异，CEU 和 CHB+JPT 间有 21 个，YRI 和 CHB+JPT 间有 5 个。

种群差异的程度在常染色体间是类似的，但是在 X 染色体上更高 (F_{ST} = 0.21)。有趣的是，X 染色体上有 123 个 SNP 在 YRI 和 CHB+JPT 间完全不同，而 CEU 和 YRI 间仅有两个，CEU 和 CHB+JPT 间仅有一个。这或许在很大程度上是由于着丝粒附近的一个区域，可能暗示着该基因座被自然选择的历史 (见下文；弗里德曼等，个人交流)。

种群间共同的单体型 我们接下来检查了单体型在种群间一致的程度。我们使用的是隐马尔可夫模型，各个单体型依次被模型化为其他单体型的一个不完美镶嵌 (详见补充信息) [42]。本质上，这个方法概率地推断在染色体的各个位置上，样本中的哪一个其他单体型是最近的近亲 (近邻)。

Unsurprisingly, the nearest neighbour most often is from the same analysis panel, but about 10% of haplotypes were found most closely to match a haplotype in another panel (Supplementary Fig. 5). All individuals have at least some segments over which the nearest neighbour is in a different analysis panel. These results indicate that although analysis panels are characterized both by different haplotype frequencies and, to some extent, different combinations of alleles, both common and rare haplotypes are often shared across populations.

Properties of LD in the Human Genome

Traditionally, descriptions of LD have focused on measures calculated between pairs of SNPs, averaged as a function of physical distance. Examples of such analyses for the HapMap data are presented in Supplementary Fig. 6. After adjusting for known confounders such as sample size, allele frequency distribution, marker density, and length of sampled regions, these data are highly similar to previously published surveys[43].

Because LD varies markedly on scales of 1–100 kb, and is often discontinuous rather than declining smoothly with distance, averages obscure important aspects of LD structure. A fuller exploration of the fine-scale structure of LD offers both insight into the causes of LD and understanding of its application to disease research.

LD patterns are simple in the absence of recombination. The most natural path to understanding LD structure is first to consider the simplest case in which there is no recombination (or gene conversion), and then to add recombination to the model. (For simplicity we ignore genotyping error and recurrent mutation in this discussion, both of which seem to be rare in these data.)

In the absence of recombination, diversity arises solely through mutation. Because each SNP arose on a particular branch of the genealogical tree relating the chromosomes in the current populations, multiple haplotypes are observed. SNPs that arose on the same branch of the genealogy are perfectly correlated in the sample, whereas SNPs that occurred on different branches have imperfect correlations, or no correlation at all.

We illustrate these concepts using empirical genotype data from 36 adjacent SNPs in an ENCODE region (ENr131.2q37), selected because no obligate recombination events were detectable among them in CEU (Fig. 7). (We note that the lack of obligate recombination events in a small sample does not guarantee that no recombinants have occurred, but it provides a good approximation for illustration.)

毫不奇怪，最靠近的单体型大多来自同一分析小组，不过大约有10%的单体型与其他分析小组的单体型最匹配（补充信息图5）。所有个体都有一些片段，其最靠近的单体型存在于其他分析小组中。这些结果说明，尽管分析小组具有不同的单体型频率，在某种程度上还具有不同的等位基因组合，但是常见的以及罕见的单体型在不同种群间经常是一致的。

人类基因组中LD的特征

传统上，LD的描述集中于SNP对之间计算得到的测度，结果作为物理距离的函数取平均值。对HapMap数据的这种分析的例子在补充信息图6中有展示。对已知的混杂因素如样本量大小、等位基因频率分布、标志物密度和检测的区域长度进行校正后，这些数据跟之前发表的研究高度相似[43]。

因为LD在1~100 kb尺度上变化较大，而且经常是不连续的而非随距离平滑减少，因此取平均值会模糊LD结构的重要方面。对LD精细尺度结构更全面的探索，将不仅为LD的产生原因提供线索，也为它在疾病研究中的应用提供知识。

没有重组发生时LD模式是简单的　了解LD结构最自然的途径是首先考虑最简单的情况，即没有重组（或者基因转变）的情况，然后向模型中加入重组。（为了简便，在这部分分析中我们忽略了基因分型错误和频发突变，在这些数据中这两种情况看起来是罕见的。）

没有重组时，多样性只通过突变产生。因为各个SNP产生于系统树特定的分支，而该系统树与目前种群中的染色体相关，所以可观察到多个单体型。系统树相同分支上产生的SNP在样本中完美相关，而在不同分支上产生的SNP则不完美相关或者完全不相关。

我们利用实验观察到的基因型数据对这些概念进行了说明，这些数据来自一个ENCODE区域（ENr131.2q37）的36个相邻SNP，选择它们是因为在CEU中没有检测到它们有专性重组事件（图7）。（我们注意到，在小样本中没有专性重组事件并不能保证没有重组发生，但是它提供了一个很好的近似的例子。）

Fig. 7. Genealogical relationships among haplotypes and r^2 values in a region without obligate recombination events. The region of chromosome 2 (234,876,004–234,884,481 bp; NCBI build 34) within ENr131.2q37 contains 36 SNPs, with zero obligate recombination events in the CEU samples. The left part of the plot shows the seven different haplotypes observed over this region (alleles are indicated only at SNPs), with their respective counts in the data. Underneath each of these haplotypes is a binary representation of the same data, with coloured circles at SNP positions where a haplotype has the less common allele at that site. Groups of SNPs all captured by a single tag SNP (with $r^2 \geqslant 0.8$) using a pairwise tagging algorithm[53,54] have the same colour. Seven tag SNPs corresponding to the seven different colours capture all the SNPs in this region. On the right these SNPs are mapped to the genealogical tree relating the seven haplotypes for the data in this region.

In principle, 36 such SNPs could give rise to 2^{36} different haplotypes. Even with no recombination, gene conversion or recurrent mutation, up to 37 different haplotypes could be formed. Despite this great potential diversity, only seven haplotypes are observed (five seen more than once) among the 120 parental CEU chromosomes studied, reflecting shared ancestry since their most recent common ancestor among apparently unrelated individuals.

In such a setting, it is easy to interpret the two most common pairwise measures of LD: D' and r^2. (See the Supplementary Information for fuller definitions of these measures.) D' is defined to be 1 in the absence of obligate recombination, declining only due to recombination or recurrent mutation[27]. In contrast, r^2 is simply the squared correlation coefficient between the two SNPs. Thus, r^2 is 1 when two SNPs arose on the same branch of the genealogy and remain undisrupted by recombination, but has a value less than 1 when SNPs arose on different branches, or if an initially strong correlation has been disrupted by crossing over.

714

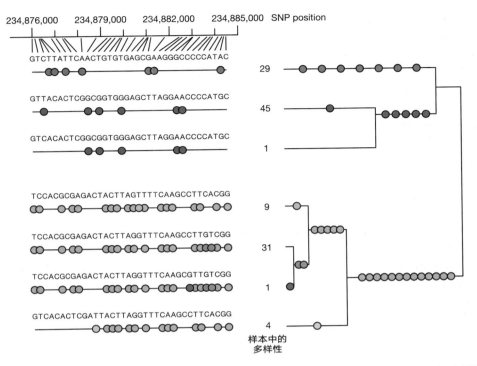

图 7. 没有专性重组事件的区域内单体型间的系谱关系和 r^2 值。2 号染色体 ENr131.2q37 区域
(234,876,004 ～ 234,884,481 bp；NCBI 版本 34) 包含 36 个 SNP，在 CEU 样本中没有专性重组事件。图
的左边部分表示在这个区域中观察到的七个不同的单体型（仅在 SNP 处标示等位基因），以及它们在数
据中各自的数量。在这些单体型各自的下面是相同数据的二进制表示，有颜色的圆圈表示单体型在该
位点含有相对不常见等位基因的 SNP 位置。相同的颜色表示的是利用成对标签算法 [53,54] 通过单个标签
SNP 捕获 ($r^2 \geqslant 0.8$) 的各组 SNP。对应于七种不同颜色的七个标签 SNP 捕获了该区域所有的 SNP。在
图的右边部分，这些 SNP 比对到系统树上，该系统树将该区域数据得到的七个单体型关联起来。

原则上，36 个这样的 SNP 能够产生 2^{36} 个不同的单体型。即使没有重组、基因
转变或者频发突变，也能够形成多达 37 个不同的单体型。尽管存在这种巨大的潜在
多样性，在研究的 120 个亲本 CEU 染色体中，只观察到七个单体型（其中五个观察
到超过一次），这反映了自它们最近的共同祖先之后明显不相关的个体也有着共同的
血统。

在这样的设定中，很容易解释这一对最常见的度量 LD 的方法：D' 和 r^2。（对于
这些度量方法更全面的定义见补充信息。）D' 在不存在专性重组时被定义为 1，只
由于重组或频发突变而减小 [27]。相反，r^2 就是简单的两个 SNP 间相关系数的平方。
因而，当两个 SNP 在系统树的同一分支上产生并且不受重组的破坏时，r^2 为 1；但
是当 SNP 在不同分支上产生，或者一个一开始很强的相关被互换所破坏时，r^2 值
小于 1。

In this region, $D' = 1$ for all marker pairs, as there is no evidence of historical recombination. In contrast, and despite great simplicity of haplotype structure, r^2 values display a complex pattern, varying from 0.0003 to 1.0, with no relationship to physical distance. This makes sense, however, because without recombination, correlations among SNPs depend on the historical order in which they arose, not the physical order of SNPs on the chromosome.

Most importantly, the seeming complexity of r^2 values can be deconvolved in a simple manner: only seven different SNP configurations exist in this region, with all but two chromosomes matching five common haplotypes, which can be distinguished from each other by typing a specific set of four SNPs. That is, only a small minority of sites need be examined to capture fully the information in this region.

Variation in local recombination rates is a major determinant of LD. Recombination in the ancestors of the current population has typically disrupted the simple picture presented above. In the human genome, as in yeast[44], mouse[45] and other genomes, recombination rates typically vary dramatically on a fine scale, with hotspots of recombination explaining much crossing over in each region[28]. The generality of this model has recently been demonstrated through computational methods that allow estimation of recombination rates (including hotspots and coldspots) from genotype data[46,47].

The availability of nearly complete information about common DNA variation in the ENCODE regions allowed a more precise estimation of recombination rates across large regions than in any previous study. We estimated recombination rates and identified recombination hotspots in the ENCODE data, using methods previously described[46] (see Supplementary Information for details). Hotspots are short regions (typically spanning about 2 kb) over which recombination rates rise dramatically over local background rates.

Whereas the average recombination rate over 500 kb across the human genome is about 0.5 cM[48], the estimated recombination rate across the 500-kb ENCODE regions varied nearly tenfold, from a minimum of 0.19 cM (ENm013.7q21.13) to a maximum of 1.25 cM (ENr232.9q34.11). Even this tenfold variation obscures much more dramatic variation over a finer scale: 88 hotspots of recombination were identified (Fig. 8; see also Supplementary Fig. 7)—that is, one per 57 kb—with hotspots detected in each of the ten regions (from 4 in 12q12 to 14 in 2q37.1). Across the 5 Mb, we estimate that about 80% of all recombination has taken place in about 15% of the sequence (Fig. 9, see also refs 46, 49).

在这个区域，由于没有证据表明历史上有过重组，对于所有的标志物对而言，$D' = 1$。相反，尽管单体型结构特别简单，r^2 值却呈现复杂的模式，在 0.0003 到 1.0 之间变化，与物理距离无关。这一点可以得到解释，因为在没有重组的情况下，SNP 间的相关依赖于它们出现的历史顺序，而不是它们在染色体上的物理顺序。

最重要的是，这种看起来复杂的 r^2 值能够以一种简单的方式去卷积：只有七种不同的 SNP 组合存在于这个区域，除了两条染色体外所有的染色体与五种常见的单体型相匹配，这些单体型能够通过输入特异的一组四个 SNP 而互相区分开来。也就是说，要完全捕获这个区域的信息，只需要检查少量的位点。

局部重组率的差异是 LD 的一个主要决定因素　现有种群的祖先中的重组通常已经破坏了上面呈现的简单图景。人类基因组与酵母[44]、小鼠[45] 和其他基因组一样，重组率一般在精细尺度上差异巨大，而重组热点解释了各个区域的很多互换[28]。这个模型的普遍性最近已经通过计算方法得到证实，这种计算方法能够从基因型数据估计重组率（包括热点和冷点）[46,47]。

ENCODE 区域中常见 DNA 变异的接近完整的信息使我们能够比任何之前的研究在大的区域中更加精确地估计重组率。利用之前描述的方法[46]，我们在 ENCODE 数据中估计了重组率，并且鉴定了重组热点（详见补充信息）。热点是短区域（一般长约 2 kb），其上的重组率比局部背景率高得多。

人类基因组中 500 kb 尺度上的平均重组率大约是 0.5 cM[48]。在 500 kb 的 ENCODE 区域中，重组率的变化幅度估计将近 10 倍，从最小的 0.19 cM（ENm013.7q21.13）到最大的 1.25 cM（ENr232.9q34.11）。然而这种 10 倍的差别仍然模糊了在更精细的尺度上更加巨大的差别：鉴定到 88 个重组热点（图 8；也可见补充信息图 7）——也就是每 57 kb 一个，并且存在于所有 10 个区域（从 12q12 区域的 4 个到 2q37.1 的 14 个）。在这个 5 Mb 的区域中，我们估计大约所有重组的 80% 发生在约 15% 的序列中（图 9，也可见参考文献 46、49）。

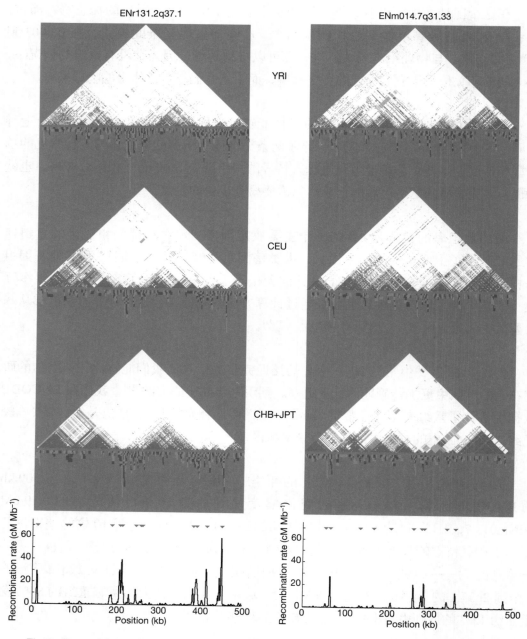

Fig. 8. Comparison of linkage disequilibrium and recombination for two ENCODE regions. For each region (ENr131.2q37.1 and ENm014.7q31.33), D' plots for the YRI, CEU and CHB+JPT analysis panels are shown: white, $D' < 1$ and LOD < 2; blue, $D' = 1$ and LOD < 2; pink, $D' < 1$ and LOD $\geq$ 2; red, $D' = 1$ and LOD $\geq$ 2. Below each of these plots is shown the intervals where distinct obligate recombination events must have occurred (blue and green indicate adjacent intervals). Stacked intervals represent regions where there are multiple recombination events in the sample history. The bottom plot shows estimated recombination rates, with hotspots shown as red triangles[46].

图 8. 两个 ENCODE 区域的 LD 和重组的比较。每个区域（ENr131.2q37.1 和 ENm014.7q31.33）的 YRI、CEU 和 CHB+JPT 分析小组的 D' 图：白色，$D' < 1$ 且 LOD < 2；蓝色，$D' = 1$ 且 LOD < 2；粉色，$D' < 1$ 且 LOD $\geqslant 2$；红色，$D' = 1$ 且 LOD $\geqslant 2$。各个图的下方展示了不同专性重组事件发生的区间（蓝色和绿色表示邻近的区间）。堆积的区间代表在样本历史中有多个重组事件发生的区域。底部的图展示估计的重组率，热点以红色三角形表示 [46]。

Fig. 9. The distribution of recombination events over the ENCODE regions. Proportion of sequence containing a given fraction of all recombination for the ten ENCODE regions (coloured lines) and combined (black line). For each line, SNP intervals are placed in decreasing order of estimated recombination rate[46], combined across analysis panels, and the cumulative recombination fraction is plotted against the cumulative proportion of sequence. If recombination rates were constant, each line would lie exactly along the diagonal, and so lines further to the right reveal the fraction of regions where recombination is more strongly locally concentrated.

A block-like structure of human LD. With most human recombination occurring in recombination hotspots, the breakdown of LD is often discontinuous. A "block-like" structure of LD is visually apparent in Fig. 8 and Supplementary Fig. 7: segments of consistently high D' that break down where high recombination rates, recombination hotspots and obligate recombination events[50] all cluster.

When haplotype blocks are more formally defined in the ENCODE data (using a method based on a composite of local D' values[30], or another based on the four gamete test[51]), most of the sequence falls into long segments of strong LD that contain many SNPs and yet display limited haplotype diversity (Table 5).

Table 5. Haplotype blocks in ENCODE regions, according to two methods

Parameter	YRI	CEU	CHB+JPT
Method based on a composite of local D' values[30]			
Average number of SNPs per block	30.3	70.1	54.4
Average length per block (kb)	7.3	16.3	13.2
Fraction of genome spanned by blocks (%)	67	87	81
Average number of haplotypes (MAF ≥ 0.05) per block	5.57	4.66	4.01
Fraction of chromosomes due to haplotypes with MAF ≥ 0.05 (%)	94	93	95
Method based on the four gamete test[51]			
Average number of SNPs per block	19.9	24.3	24.3

图 9. ENCODE 区域重组事件的分布。对于 10 个 ENCODE 区域（彩色线）和合并的全部区域（黑色线），含有特定比例重组的序列所占的比例。对于各条线，SNP 区间按估计的重组率逐渐减小的次序放置[46]，该重组率是各分析小组合计的，x 轴是累积的重组比例，y 轴是累积的序列比例。如果重组率是恒定的，各条线将会正好沿着对角线，所以偏向右边的线反映的是重组更加局部集中的区域所占的比例。

人类 LD 的区块样结构 大部分人类重组发生在重组热点处，LD 的分解常常是不连续的。LD 的"区块样"结构在图 8 和补充信息图 7 中看起来很明显：在高重组率、重组热点和专性重组事件[50]聚集的区域分成一段一段的高 D′ 的片段。

当单体型区块在 ENCODE 数据中更正规地定义时（利用基于局部 D′ 值组合的方法[30]，或者基于四配子检验的另一方法[51]），大部分的序列落入强 LD 的长片段，这些片段含有很多 SNP 但是表现出有限的单体型多样性（表 5）。

表 5. 根据两种方法得到的 ENCODE 区域的单体型块

参数	YRI	CEU	CHB+JPT
基于局部 D′ 值组合的方法[30]			
每个区块的 SNP 平均数量	30.3	70.1	54.4
每个区块平均长度（kb）	7.3	16.3	13.2
被区块横跨的基因组的比例（%）	67	87	81
每个区块的单体型（MAF ≥ 0.05）平均数量	5.57	4.66	4.01
MAF ≥ 0.05 的单体型占染色体的比例（%）	94	93	95
基于四配子检验的方法[51]			
每个区块的 SNP 平均数量	19.9	24.3	24.3

Continued

Parameter	YRI	CEU	CHB+JPT
Average length per block (kb)	4.8	5.9	5.9
Fraction of genome spanned by blocks (%)	86	84	84
Average number of haplotypes (MAF $\geq$ 0.05) per block	5.12	3.63	3.63
Fraction of chromosomes due to haplotypes with MAF $\geq$ 0.05 (%)	91	95	95

Specifically, addressing concerns that blocks might be an artefact of low marker density[52], in these nearly complete data most of the sequence falls into blocks of four or more SNPs (67% in YRI to 87% in CEU) and the average sizes of such blocks are similar to initial estimates[30]. Although the average block spans many SNPs (30–70), the average number of common haplotypes in each block ranged only from 4.0 (CHB+JPT) to 5.6 (YRI), with nearly all haplotypes in each block matching one of these few common haplotypes. These results confirm the generality of inferences drawn from disease-mapping studies[27] and genomic surveys with smaller sample sizes[29] and less complete data[30].

Long-range haplotypes and local patterns of recombination. Although haplotypes often break at recombination hotspots (and block boundaries), this tendency is not invariant. We identified all unique haplotypes with frequency more than 0.05 across the 269 individuals in the phased data, and compared them to the fine-scale recombination map. Figure 10 shows a region of chromosome 19 over which many such haplotypes break at identified recombination hotspots, but others continue. Thus, the tendency towards colocalization of recombination sites does not imply that all haplotypes break at each recombination site.

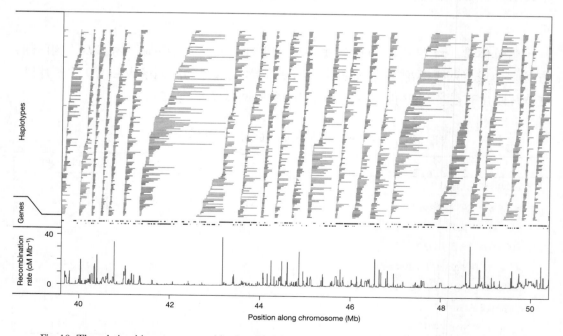

Fig. 10. The relationship among recombination rates, haplotype lengths and gene locations. Recombination

参数	YRI	CEU	CHB+JPT
每个区块的平均长度(kb)	4.8	5.9	5.9
被区块横跨的基因组的比例(%)	86	84	84
每个区块的单体型(MAF ≥ 0.05)平均数量	5.12	3.63	3.63
MAF ≥ 0.05 的单体型占染色体的比例(%)	91	95	95

特别地，在这些接近完整的数据中，大部分的序列落入含有四个或更多 SNP 的区块中(从 YRI 中的 67% 到 CEU 中的 87%)，而且这些区块的平均大小与之前的估计类似[30]，这解决了关于区块可能是低标签密度的假象的担忧[52]。尽管一般的区块横跨很多 SNP(30~70 个)，但是在各个区块中，常见单体型的平均数量只有 4.0 (CHB+JPT)到 5.6 个(YRI)，几乎所有的单体型都是不常见的单体型。这些结果证实了从样本量更小[29]、数据更不完整[30]的疾病遗传定位研究[27]以及基因组调查所得出的推断的普遍性。

远距离单体型和局部重组模式　尽管单体型经常在重组热点(和区块的边界)中断，这个趋势并不是一成不变的。我们鉴定了阶段性数据中所有在 269 个个体中频率均超过 0.05 的独特单体型，并将它们与精细尺度的重组图谱相比较。图 10 展示了 19 号染色体的一个区域，这个区域上很多这样的单体型在鉴定的重组热点位置中断，但是其他的则是连续的。因而，重组位点共定位的趋势并不意味着所有单体型在各个重组位点中断。

图 10. 重组率、单体型长度和基因位置之间的关系。重组率单位为 cM · Mb⁻¹(蓝色)。在 19 号染色体的

rates in cM Mb^{-1} (blue). Non-redundant haplotypes with frequency of at least 5% in the combined sample (bars) and genes (black segments) are shown in an example gene-dense region of chromosome 19 (19q13). Haplotypes are coloured by the number of detectable recombination events they span, with red indicating many events and blue few.

Some regions display remarkably extended haplotype structure based on a lack of recombination (Supplementary Fig. 8a, b). Most striking, if unsurprising, are centromeric regions, which lack recombination: haplotypes defined by more than 100 SNPs span several megabases across the centromeres. The X chromosome has multiple regions with very extensive haplotypes, whereas other chromosomes typically have a few such domains.

Most global measures of LD become more consistent when measured in genetic rather than physical distance. For example, when plotted against physical distance, the extent of pairwise LD varies by chromosome; when plotted against average recombination rate on each chromosome (estimated from pedigree-based genetic maps) these differences largely disappear (Supplementary Fig. 6). Similarly, the distribution of haplotype length across chromosomes is less variable when measured in genetic rather than physical distance. For example, the median length of haplotypes is 54.4 kb on chromosome 1 compared to 34.8 kb on chromosome 21. When measured in genetic distance, however, haplotype length is much more similar: 0.104 cM on chromosome 1 compared to 0.111 cM on chromosome 21 (Supplementary Fig. 9).

The exception is again the X chromosome, which has more extensive haplotype structure after accounting for recombination rate (median haplotype length = 0.135 cM). Multiple factors could explain different patterns on the X chromosome: lower SNP density, smaller sample size, restriction of recombination to females and lower effective population size.

A View of LD Focused on the Putative Causal SNP

Although genealogy and recombination provide insight into why nearby SNPs are often correlated, it is the redundancies among SNPs that are of central importance for the design and analysis of association studies. A truly comprehensive genetic association study must consider all putative causal alleles and test each for its potential role in disease. If a causal variant is not directly tested in the disease sample, its effect can nonetheless be indirectly tested if it is correlated with a SNP or haplotype that has been directly tested.

The typical SNP is highly correlated with many of its neighbours. The ENCODE data reveal that SNPs are typically perfectly correlated to several nearby SNPs, and partially correlated to many others.

We use the term proxy to mean a SNP that shows a strong correlation with one or more others. When two variants are perfectly correlated, testing one is exactly equivalent to testing the other; we refer to such collections of SNPs (with pairwise $r^2 = 1.0$ in the HapMap samples) as "perfect proxy sets".

一个高密度基因示例区域（19q13）内展示了在合并样本中频率至少为 5% 的非冗余单体型（棒状）和基因（黑色片段）。根据单体型区域内可检测的重组事件的数量，单体型标记为不同的颜色，红色代表更多的重组事件，而蓝色代表很少的重组事件。

由于缺少重组，一些区域表现出明显扩展的单体型结构（补充信息图 8a、8b）。最值得注意的是缺少重组的着丝粒区域：超过 100 个 SNP 组成的单体型横跨着丝粒前后数 Mb 的范围。X 染色体的多个区域含有范围非常大的单体型，而其他染色体则通常仅含有少量这样的区域。

当以遗传学距离而不是物理距离测量时，大多数对 LD 的全局性测量变得更加一致。例如，当针对物理距离作图时，成对 LD 的程度随染色体的不同而变化；当针对各条染色体上的平均重组率（估计自基于家系的遗传图谱）作图时，这些差异大部分消失了（补充信息图 6）。类似地，当以遗传学距离而不是物理距离测量时，单体型长度在染色体上的分布差异也更小。例如，单体型长度的中位数在 1 号染色体上是 54.4 kb，而在 21 号染色体上则是 34.8 kb。但是，当以遗传学距离测量时，单体型长度则接近得多：1 号染色体上是 0.104 cM，21 号染色体上是 0.111 cM（补充信息图 9）。

X 染色体同样是例外，扣除重组率的影响后，它含有范围更广的单体型结构（单体型长度中位数 = 0.135 cM）。有多个因素可以解释 X 染色体上呈现的不同模式：更低的 SNP 密度、更小的样本量、限于女性的重组以及更小的有效种群尺寸。

集中于潜在致病 SNP 的 LD 概览

尽管家系和重组为解释为什么邻近的 SNP 常常关联提供了线索，但是对于关联研究的设计和分析，SNP 中的冗余才是重中之重。一个真正全面的遗传关联研究必须考虑所有可能致病的等位基因，并且检验它们在疾病中潜在的作用。如果一个导致疾病的变异没有在疾病样本中被直接检验，但是它与一个已经被直接检验的 SNP 或单体型相关联，则它的作用就可以被间接检验。

一个典型的 SNP 与很多邻近 SNP 高度相关　ENCODE 数据反映了 SNP 通常与多个邻近的 SNP 完美相关，与很多其他的 SNP 部分相关。

我们使用术语"代理者"来表示与一个或者更多其他 SNP 高度相关的一个 SNP。当两个变异完美相关时，检验一个就完全等同于检验另一个；我们称这样的 SNP 集（在 HapMap 样本中成对的 $r^2 = 1.0$）为"完美的代理者集"。

Considering only common SNPs (the target of study for the HapMap Project) in CEU in the ENCODE data, one in five SNPs has 20 or more perfect proxies, and three in five have five or more. In contrast, one in five has no perfect proxies. As expected, perfect proxy sets are smaller in YRI, with twice as many SNPs (two in five) having no perfect proxy, and a quarter as many (5%) having 20 or more (Figs 11 and 12). These patterns are largely consistent across the range of frequencies studied by the project, with a trend towards fewer proxies at MAF < 0.10 (Fig. 11). Put another way, the average common SNP in ENCODE is perfectly redundant with three other SNPs in the YRI samples, and nine to ten other SNPs in the other sample sets (Fig. 13).

Fig. 11. The number of proxy SNPs ($r^2 \geq 0.8$) as a function of MAF in the ENCODE data.

只考虑 ENCODE 数据 CEU 中常见的 SNP(HapMap 计划的研究目标),则每五个 SNP 中有一个有 20 个或更多的完美代理者,有三个含有五个或更多的完美代理者,只有一个没有完美代理者。正如预期的,完美代理者集在 YRI 中更小,没有完美代理者的 SNP(每五个中有两个)是另两个小组的两倍,含有 20 个或更多代理者的 SNP(5%)是另两个小组的四分之一(图 11 和 12)。在计划所研究的频率范围内,这些模式大部分是一致的,并且表现出 MAF < 0.10 时代理者更少的趋势(图 11)。换句话说,ENCODE 中常见的 SNP,在 YRI 样本中平均跟三个其他 SNP 完全冗余,在其他样本集中平均跟 9 到 10 个 SNP 完全冗余(图 13)。

图 11. ENCODE 数据中不同 MAF 的 SNP 的代理者 SNP($r^2 \geq 0.8$)数量

Fig. 12. The number of proxies per SNP in the ENCODE data as a function of the threshold for correlation (r^2).

Fig. 13. Relationship in the Phase I HapMap between the threshold for declaring correlation between proxies and the proportion of all SNPs captured.

图 12. ENCODE 数据中不同相关性阈值 (r^2) 的每个 SNP 的代理者数量

图 13. 第 I 阶段 HapMap 中用于判定代理者间相关的阈值和所有捕获到的 SNP 的比例之间的关系

Of course, to be detected through LD in an association study, correlation need not be complete between the genotyped SNP and the causal variant. For example, under a multiplicative disease model and a single-locus χ^2 test, the sample size required to detect association to an allele scales as $1/r^2$. That is, if the causal SNP has an $r^2 = 0.5$ to one tested in the disease study, full power can be maintained if the sample size is doubled.

The number of SNPs showing such substantial but incomplete correlation is much larger. For example, using a looser threshold for declaring correlation ($r^2 \geq 0.5$), the average number of proxies found for a common SNP in CHB+JPT is 43, and the average in YRI is 16 (Fig. 12). These partial correlations can be exploited through haplotype analysis to increase power to detect putative causal alleles, as discussed below.

Evaluating performance of the Phase I map. To estimate the proportion of all common SNPs captured by the Phase I map, we evaluated redundancy among SNPs on the genome-wide map, and performed simulations based on the more complete ENCODE data. The two methods give highly similar answers, and indicate that Phase I should provide excellent power for CEU, CHB and JPT, and substantial power for YRI. Phase II, moreover, will provide nearly complete power for all three analysis panels.

Redundancies among SNPs in Phase I HapMap. Redundancy offers one measure that Phase I has sampled densely in comparison to the underlying scale of correlation. Specifically, 50% (YRI) to 75% (CHB+JPT, CEU) of all SNPs on the Phase I map are highly correlated ($r^2 \geq 0.8$) to one or more others on the map (Fig. 13; see also Supplementary Fig. 10). Over 90% of all SNPs on the map have highly statistically significant correlation to one or more neighbours. These partial correlations can be combined to form haplotypes that are even better proxies for a SNP of interest.

Modelling Phase I HapMap from complete ENCODE data. A second approach to evaluating the completeness of the Phase I data involves thinning the more complete ENCODE data to match Phase I for allele frequency and SNP density. Simulated Phase I HapMaps were used to evaluate coverage in relation to the full set of common SNPs (Table 6), and provided nearly identical estimates to those above: 45% (YRI) to 74% (CHB+JPT, CEU) of all common SNPs are predicted to have a proxy with $r^2 \geq 0.8$ to a SNP included in the Phase I HapMap (Supplementary Fig. 11).

Table 6. Coverage of simulated Phase I and Phase II HapMap to capture all common SNPs in the ten ENCODE regions

Analysis panel	Per cent maximum $r^2 \geq 0.8$	Mean maximum r^2
Phase I HapMap		
YRI	45	0.67
CEU	74	0.85
CHB+JPT	72	0.83

当然，为了能在关联研究中通过 LD 被检测到，基因分型的 SNP 和导致表型的变异间的相关性不需要是完全的。例如，在乘性疾病模型和单基因座 χ^2 检验下，检测一个等位基因的相关性所要求的样本大小是 $1/r^2$。也就是说，当在疾病研究中导致表型的 SNP 与被检验的 SNP 的 $r^2 = 0.5$ 时，如果样本大小翻倍就能够保持完全的效能。

表现出这种相当程度但不完全相关的 SNP 的数量大得多。例如，利用一个宽松的阈值来判定相关性（$r^2 \geqslant 0.5$），在 CHB+JPT 中一个常见 SNP 的代理者的平均数量是 43 个，在 YRI 中是 16 个（图 12）。正如下文讨论的，这些部分相关可以通过单体型分析而被挖掘，进而来增加检测可能导致表型的等位基因的能力。

第 I 阶段图谱质量的评估 为了估计第 I 阶段图谱捕获的所有常见 SNP 的比例，我们评估了全基因组范围图谱上 SNP 间的冗余，并且基于更完整的 ENCODE 数据进行了模拟。这两种方法给出了高度相似的答案，说明第 I 阶段图谱应该为 CEU、CHB 和 JPT 提供了非常好的效能，为 YRI 提供了相当程度的效能。并且，第 II 阶段将会为所有三个分析小组提供接近完全的效能。

第 I 阶段 HapMap 中 SNP 间的冗余 与潜在的相关性指标相比，冗余提供了一种测量手段，第 I 阶段图谱已经对其进行了密集取样。特别地，第 I 阶段图谱上所有 SNP 中的 50%（YRI）到 75%（CHB+JPT、CEU）与一个或更多其他 SNP 高度相关（$r^2 \geqslant 0.8$）（图 13；也可见补充信息图 10）。图谱上所有 SNP 中超过 90% 与一个或更多邻近 SNP 具有统计学意义上的高度相关。这些部分相关能被联合起来形成单体型，这些单体型对于感兴趣的 SNP 甚至是更好的代理者。

基于完整 ENCODE 数据的第 I 阶段 HapMap 建模 评估第 I 阶段数据完整性的第二个方法包括缩减更加完整的 ENCODE 数据来匹配第 I 阶段数据的等位基因频率和 SNP 密度。模拟的第 I 阶段 HapMap 被用于评估其相对全套常见 SNP 的覆盖度（表 6），它提供了跟上面几乎一致的估计值：所有常见 SNP 的 45%（YRI）到 74%（CHB+JPT、CEU）被预测在第 I 阶段的 HapMap 中有一个 $r^2 \geqslant 0.8$ 的代理者（补充信息图 11）。

表 6. 模拟的 HapMap 第 I 和第 II 阶段捕获 10 个 ENCODE 区域中所有常见 SNP 的覆盖度

分析小组	最大 r^2 值 $\geqslant 0.8$ 的比例	平均最大 r^2 值
第 I 阶段 HapMap		
YRI	45	0.67
CEU	74	0.85
CHB+JPT	72	0.83

Continued

Analysis panel	Per cent maximum $r^2 \geq 0.8$	Mean maximum r^2
Phase II HapMap		
YRI	81	0.90
CEU	94	0.97
CHB+JPT	94	0.97

Simulated Phase I HapMaps were generated from the phased ENCODE data (release 16c1) by randomly picking SNPs that appear in dbSNP build 121 (excluding "non-rs" SNPs in release 16a) for every 5-kb bin until a common SNP was picked (allowing up to three attempts per bin). The Phase II HapMap was simulated by picking SNPs at random to achieve an overall density of 1 SNP per 1 kb. These numbers are averages over 20 independent iterations for all ENCODE regions in all three analysis panels.

Statistical power in association studies may be more closely approximated by the average (maximal) correlation value between a SNP and its best proxy on the map, rather than by the proportion exceeding an arbitrary (and stringent) threshold. The average values for maximal r^2 to a nearby SNP range from 0.67 (YRI) to 0.85 (CEU and CHB+JPT).

Modelling Phase II HapMap from complete ENCODE data. A similar procedure was used to generate simulated Phase II HapMaps from ENCODE data (Table 6). Phase II is predicted to capture the majority of common variation in YRI: 81% of all common SNPs should have a near perfect proxy ($r^2 \geq 0.8$) to a SNP on the map, with the mean maximal r^2 value of 0.90. Unsurprisingly, the CEU, CHB and JPT samples, already well served by Phase I, are nearly perfectly captured: 94% of all common sites have a proxy on the map with $r^2 \geq 0.8$, with an average maximal r^2 value of 0.97.

These analyses indicate that the Phase I and Phase II HapMap resources should provide excellent coverage for common variation in these population samples.

Selection of Tag SNPs for Association Studies

A major impetus for developing the HapMap was to guide the design and prioritization of SNP genotyping assays for disease association studies. We refer to the set of SNPs genotyped in a disease study as tags. A given set of tags can be analysed for association with a phenotype using a variety of statistical methods which we term tests, based either on the genotypes of single SNPs or combinations of multiple SNPs.

The shared goal of all tag selection methods is to exploit redundancy among SNPs, maximizing efficiency in the laboratory while minimizing loss of information[24,27]. This literature is extensive and varied, despite its youth. Some methods require that a single SNP serve as a proxy for other, untyped variants, whereas other methods allow combinations of alleles (haplotypes) to serve as proxies; some make explicit use of LD blocks whereas others are agnostic to such descriptions. Although it is not practical to implement all such

分析小组	最大 r^2 值 ≥ 0.8 的比例	平均最大 r^2 值
第 II 阶段 HapMap		
YRI	81	0.90
CEU	94	0.97
CHB+JPT	94	0.97

模拟的第 I 阶段 HapMap 是从区分染色体的 ENCODE 数据（版本 16c1）产生的，方法是每 5 kb 随机选取出现在 dbSNP 版本 121（不包括版本 16a 中的"non-rs"SNP）中的 SNP，直到取到一个常见 SNP（每个 5 kb 区间允许三次尝试）。第 II 阶段 HapMap 的模拟是通过随机取 SNP 以达到总体每 1 kb 1 个 SNP 的密度。这些数值是三个分析小组中所有 ENCODE 区域 20 次独立迭代的平均值。

通过 SNP 和它在图谱上的最佳代理者的平均（最大）相关值，而不是通过超过一个主观设定的（并且严格的）阈值的比例，可以对关联研究中的统计效能进行更接近的估算。SNP 与附近 SNP 的最大 r^2 的平均值在 0.67（YRI）到 0.85（CEU 和 CHB+JPT）之间变化。

基于完整 ENCODE 数据的第 II 阶段 HapMap 建模　类似的步骤被用于从 ENCODE 数据产生模拟的第 II 阶段 HapMap（表 6）。第 II 阶段预计能捕获 YRI 中绝大多数的常见变异：所有常见 SNP 的 81% 应该在图谱上有一个接近完美的代理者（$r^2 ≥ 0.8$），平均最大 r^2 值是 0.90。与预期相符，CEU、CHB 和 JPT 样本已经在第 I 阶段满足要求，被近乎完美地捕获：所有常见位点的 94% 在图谱上有一个 $r^2 ≥ 0.8$ 的代理者，平均最大 r^2 值为 0.97。

这些分析说明第 I 和第 II 阶段 HapMap 的资源应该能够非常好地覆盖这些种群样本中的常见变异。

用于关联研究的标签 SNP 的选择

开展 HapMap 研究的一个主要的动力是指导疾病关联研究中 SNP 基因分型实验的设计和优先次序。我们称疾病研究中被基因分型的 SNP 集为标签。基于单个 SNP 或多个 SNP 的组合的基因型，利用我们称之为检验的各种统计学方法，可以分析一组给定的标签与某种表型的关联。

所有标签选择方法的共同目标是利用 SNP 间的冗余，最大化实验效率，同时最小化信息的丢失 [24,27]。尽管刚起步，但这样的文献广泛而多样。一些方法要求单个 SNP 作为其他未分型变异的代理者，而其他方法允许等位基因的组合（单体型）作为代理者；一些人明确使用 LD 区块，而其他人则没有这样的描述。尽管在本计划的

methods at the project website, the HapMap genotypes are freely available and investigators can apply their method of choice to the data. To assist users, both a single-marker tagging method and a more efficient multimarker method have been implemented at http://www.hapmap.org.

Tagging using a simple pairwise method. To illustrate general principles of tagging, we first applied a simple and widely used pairwise algorithm[53,54]: SNPs are selected for genotyping until all common SNPs are highly correlated ($r^2 \geq 0.8$) to one or more members of the tag set.

Starting from the substantially complete ENCODE data, the density of common SNPs can be reduced by 75–90% with essentially no loss of information (Fig. 14). That is, the genotyping burden can be reduced from one common SNP every 500 bp to one SNP every 2 kb (YRI) to 5 kb (CEU and CHB+JPT). Because LD often extends for long distances, studies of short gene segments tend to underestimate the redundancy across the genome[43].

Fig. 14. Tag SNP information capture. The proportion of common SNPs captured with $r^2 \geq 0.8$ as a function of the average tag SNP spacing is shown for the phased ENCODE data, plotted (left to right) for tag SNPs prioritized by Tagger (multimarker and pairwise) and for tag SNPs picked at random. Results were averaged over all the ENCODE regions.

Although tags selected based on LD offer the greatest improvements in efficiency and information capture, even randomly chosen subsets of SNPs offer considerable efficiencies (Fig. 14).

The data also reveal a rule of diminishing returns: a small set of highly informative tags captures a large fraction of all variation, with additional tags each capturing only one or a few proxies. For example, in CHB+JPT the most informative 1% of all SNPs (one per 50 kb) is able to proxy (at $r^2 \geq 0.8$) for 40% of all common SNPs, whereas a substantial proportion of SNPs have no proxies at all.

These observations are encouraging with respect to genome-wide association studies. A set of SNPs typed every 5–10 kb across the genome (within the range of current technology) can capture nearly all common variation in the genome in the CEU and CHB+JPT samples, with more SNPs required in the YRI samples.

734

网站上实现所有这些方法并不现实，但是 HapMap 的基因型数据是自由获取的，研究者可以用他们选择的方法分析这些数据。为了帮助使用者，单个标志物标签法和更有效的多标志物法都已经在 http://www.hapmap.org 网站上实现了。

使用简单成对方法进行的标记　为了说明标记的一般原则，我们首先应用了一个简单而广泛使用的成对算法[53,54]：选择 SNP 进行基因分型，直到所有常见 SNP 与一个或更多的标签集成员高度连锁（$r^2 \geqslant 0.8$）。

先以相当完整的 ENCODE 数据为例，常见 SNP 的密度能被减少 75%～90% 而基本不丢失信息（图 14）。也就是说，基因分型的负担能从每 500 bp 一个常见 SNP 减少到每 2 kb（YRI）或每 5 kb（CEU 和 CHB+JPT）一个 SNP。因为 LD 常常延伸很长距离，短基因片段的研究通常低估基因组中的冗余度[43]。

图 14. 标签 SNP 信息捕获。图中展示的是 ENCODE 数据中，被不同平均跨度的标签 SNP 捕获（$r^2 \geqslant 0.8$）的常见 SNP 的比例，从左到右依次为由 Tagger 软件（多标志物和成对标志物）定为优先级的标签 SNP 和随机选取的标签 SNP。结果是所有 ENCODE 区域的平均值。

基于 LD 选择的标签在效率和信息的捕获上提供了最大的改进，而即使是随机选择的 SNP 子集也提供了相当高的效率（图 14）。

这个数据还反映了一个回报不断减少的规律：一个小的高度富含信息的标签集可以捕获所有变异中的大部分，而增加的标签仅捕获一个或很少的代理者。例如，在 CHB+JPT 中，所有 SNP（每 50 kb 一个）中最富有信息的 1% 能够代理（$r^2 \geqslant 0.8$）所有常见 SNP 的 40%，而相当大比例的 SNP 完全没有代理者。

对于全基因组关联研究，这些现象是鼓舞人心的。对于 CEU 和 CHB+JPT 样本，在全基因组中每 5～10 kb 被分型的一组 SNP（现有技术的能力范围之内）就能够捕获基因组中几乎所有的常见变异，对于 YRI 样本则需要更多的 SNP。

Tagging from the genome-wide map. Whereas analysis of the complete ENCODE data set reveals the maximal efficiency likely to be possible with this tag selection strategy, analysis of the Phase I map illuminates the extent to which the current resource can be used for near-term studies. Specifically, using the same pairwise tagging approach above, 260,000 (CHB+JPT) to 474,000 (YRI) SNPs are required to capture all common SNPs in the Phase I data set (Table 7). That is, being incomplete and thus less redundant, the Phase I data are much less compressible by tag SNP selection than are the ENCODE data. Nevertheless, even at this level a half to a third of all SNPs can be selected as proxies for the remainder (and, by inference, the bulk of other common SNPs in the genome).

Table 7. Number of selected tag SNPs to capture all observed common SNPs in the Phase I HapMap

r^2 threshold*	YRI	CEU	CHB+JPT
$r^2 \geqslant 0.5$	324,865	178,501	159,029
$r^2 \geqslant 0.8$	474.409	293,835	259,779
$r^2 = 1.0$	604,886	447,579	434,476

Tag SNPs were picked to capture common SNPs in HapMap release 16c1 using the software program Haploview.
* Pairwise tagging at different r^2 thresholds.

Increasing the efficiency of tag SNPs. Although the pairwise method is simple, complete and straightforward, efficiency can be improved with a number of simple changes. First, relaxing the threshold on r^2 for tag SNP selection substantially reduces the number of tag SNPs selected, with only a modest decrease in the correlations among SNPs (Table 7). For example, reducing the r^2 threshold from 0.8 to 0.5 decreases the number of tag SNPs selected from the HapMap by 39% in CHB+JPT (260,000 to 159,000) and 32% in YRI (474,000 to 325,000). The average r^2 value between tags and other (unselected) SNPs falls much less dramatically than the number of tags selected, increasing efficiency. Whether such a loss of power is justified by the disproportionate reduction in work is a choice each investigator will need to make.

A second enhancement exploits multimarker haplotypes. Many investigators have discussed using multiple SNPs (in haplotypes and regression models) to serve as proxies for untyped sites[55-58], which may reduce the number of tags required and increase the power of analyses performed. Figure 14 illustrates the point with one such method[55], showing that a multimarker method allows greater coverage for a fixed set of markers (or, alternatively, fewer markers to achieve the same coverage). Although a full consideration of this issue is beyond the scope of this paper, the availability of these and other data should allow the comparison and application of such methods.

A third approach to increasing efficiency is to prioritize tags based on the number of other SNPs captured. Whereas 260,000 SNPs are required to provide $r^2 \geqslant 0.8$ for all SNPs in the Phase I HapMap (CHB+JPT), the best 10,000 such SNPs (4%) capture 22% of all common

从全基因组图谱进行的标签选取　尽管对完整 ENCODE 数据集的分析反映了利用这种标签选择策略可能具有的最大效率，对第 I 阶段图谱的分析则阐明了现有资源能够在多大程度上被用于近期的研究。特别地，利用相同的上述成对标签方法，为捕获第 I 阶段数据集中所有常见 SNP，需要 260,000(CHB+JPT)到 474,000(YRI)个 SNP(表 7)。也就是说，第 I 阶段数据不够完整因而冗余更少，与 ENCODE 数据相比，能够通过标签 SNP 选择而被压缩的程度要小很多。但是，即使在这种水平下，SNP 中的一半或三分之一可以被选作剩余 SNP(推断可知也是基因组中其他常见 SNP 的大部分)的代理者。

表 7. 为捕获第 I 阶段 HapMap 中观察到的所有常见 SNP 所选择的标签 SNP 的数量

r^2 阈值 *	YRI	CEU	CHB+JPT
$r^2 \geqslant 0.5$	324,865	178,501	159,029
$r^2 \geqslant 0.8$	474,409	293,835	259,779
$r^2 = 1.0$	604,886	447,579	434,476

标签 SNP 是利用软件 Haploview 选取的，以捕获 HapMap 版本 16c1 中常见的 SNP。
* 在不同 r^2 阈值下取成对的标签。

增加标签 SNP 的效率　尽管成对的方法简单、完整而直接，我们还是可以通过一些简单的改变提高效率。首先，放宽用于标签 SNP 选择的 r^2 的阈值，可以大大减少选择的标签 SNP 的数量，而在 SNP 间的相关性上仅稍有下降(表 7)。例如，r^2 阈值从 0.8 减少到 0.5，在 CHB+JPT 中减少了 39% 从 HapMap 选择的标签 SNP 的数量(从 260,000 到 159,000)，而在 YRI 中减少了 32%(从 474,000 到 325,000)。标签与其他(未选择)SNP 间平均 r^2 值下降的水平要比选择的标签数量的下降少得多，因而提高了效率。是否这样一种效能的损失会因为不成比例地减少工作量变得合理，是每个研究者需要作出的一个选择。

第二个提高的方法是利用多标志物单体型。很多研究者已经讨论了利用多个 SNP(在单体型和回归模型中)作为未分型位点的代理者[55-58]，这可能能够减少需要的标签的数量，并且增加分析的效能。图 14 利用一个这样的方法[55]说明了这一点，它表明，对于固定的一组标志物，多标志物方法能够达到更高的覆盖度(换言之，更少的标志物可以达到相同的覆盖度)。尽管全面考虑这个问题超出了本文的范畴，已有的这些以及其他数据足以对这样的方法进行比较和应用。

第三个增加效率的方法是基于捕获的其他 SNP 的数量对标签划分优先级。尽管要求 260,000 个 SNP 才能以 $r^2 \geqslant 0.8$ 捕获第 I 期 HapMap 里所有的 SNP (CHB+JPT)，其中最佳的 10,000 个 (4%) 就能以 $r^2 \geqslant 0.8$ 捕获所有常见变异位点的

variable sites with $r^2 \geqslant 0.8$ (Table 8). Such prioritization can be applied using different weights for SNPs based on genomic annotation (for example, non-synonymous coding SNPs, SNPs in conserved non-coding sequence, and candidate genes of biological interest).

Table 8. Proportion of common SNPs in Phase I captured by sets of tag SNPs

Tag SNP set size	Common SNPs captured (%)		
	YRI	CEU	CHB+JPT
10,000	12.3	20.4	21.9
20,000	19.1	30.9	33.2
50,000	32.7	50.4	53.6
100,000	47.2	68.5	72.2
250,000	70.1	94.1	98.5

As in Table 7, tag SNPs were picked to capture common SNPs in HapMap release 16c1 using Haploview, selecting SNPs in order of the fraction of sites captured. Common SNPs were captured by fixed-size sets of pairwise tags at $r^2 \geqslant 0.8$.

Tag transferability across populations. The most complete set of tags would be those based on all 269 samples; however, many studies may be performed in individuals more closely related to one particular HapMap population, and efficiency may be gained by selecting tags only from that population sample. (Selecting tags in a HapMap population sample that is known to be more distantly related than is another, for example, using CEU to pick tags for a study of Japanese, seems inefficient.)

An important question is how tags selected in one or more analysis panels will transfer to disease studies performed in these or other populations. Our data do not address this question directly, although the known similarity of allele and haplotype frequencies across populations within continents[41] is encouraging. More data are clearly needed, however.

Tag selection based on initial genotyping. Whereas the discussions above assume *de novo* selection of SNPs, many investigators will have already performed initial studies, and wish to design follow-on experiments. The HapMap data can be used to highlight SNPs that might potentially explain a positive association signal, or those that were poorly captured (and thus still need to be tested) after a negative scan. In cases where multiple SNPs are both associated with the trait and with each other, the HapMap data can be queried to identify whether samples from any other analysis panel show a breakdown of LD in that region, and thus the possibility of narrowing the span over which the causal variant may reside.

Applications to the Analysis of Association Data

Beyond guiding selection of tag SNPs, HapMap data can inform the subsequent analysis and interpretation in disease association studies.

22%(表 8)。这样的划分优先级法可以通过根据基因组注释对 SNP 使用不同的权重来应用(例如，非同义编码 SNP、在保守的非编码序列中的 SNP，以及有生物学意义的候选基因)。

表 8. 通过不同标签 SNP 集捕获的第 I 阶段中常见 SNP 的比例

标签 SNP 集大小	捕获的常见 SNP(%)		
	YRI	CEU	CHB+JPT
10,000	12.3	20.4	21.9
20,000	19.1	30.9	33.2
50,000	32.7	50.4	53.6
100,000	47.2	68.5	72.2
250,000	70.1	94.1	98.5

如表 7 一样，标签 SNP 是使用 Haploview 选取的，以捕获 HapMap 版本 16c1 中常见的 SNP，SNP 按捕获的位点的比例顺序选择。常见 SNP 被固定大小的一组成对标签以 $r^2 \geqslant 0.8$ 捕获。

标签在不同种群间的可转移性   最完整的一组标签是基于所有 269 个样本的标签；但是，很多研究可能是在与一个特定的 HapMap 种群亲缘关系更近的个体中进行的，因此效率仅在从那个种群样本中选择标签时可能会增加。(在亲缘关系更远的 HapMap 种群样本中选择标签看起来是低效的，例如使用 CEU 种群选取用于研究日本人的标签。)

一个重要的问题是：在一个或更多个分析小组中选择的标签如何转移到在这些或者其他种群中所开展的疾病研究。尽管已知的同一大陆上各个种群中等位基因和单体型频率的相似性[41]是令人鼓舞的，但是我们的数据并没有直接回答这个问题。很明显，要回答这个问题还需要更多的数据。

基于初步基因分型的标签选择   上述的讨论是假定从头选择 SNP 的，但是很多研究者已经进行了初步研究，希望在此基础上设计后续实验。HapMap 数据可以用来突出有望解释阳性关联信号的 SNP，或者经过阴性扫描不容易被捕获的(因而仍需要被检验)SNP。在多个 SNP 都跟性状关联并且 SNP 也彼此关联的情况下，可以查询 HapMap 数据来鉴定任一其他分析小组的样本是否在那个区域表现为 LD 的断裂，以及缩小导致性状的变异可能存在的区域范围的可能性。

在关联数据分析中的应用

在疾病关联研究中，HapMap 数据除了指导标签 SNP 的选择，还能够影响后续的分析和解释。

Analysis of an existing genotype data set. The HapMap can be used to inform association testing, regardless of how tags were selected. Specifically, as long as the SNPs genotyped in a disease study have also been typed in the HapMap samples, it is possible to identify which SNPs are well captured by the genotyped SNPs (either singly, or in haplotype combinations), and which are not[55].

This is of particular importance for genome-wide association studies performed using array-based, standardized genotyping reagents, which do not allow investigators to choose their own sets of tag SNPs. The Affymetrix 120K SNP array data included in Phase I of the HapMap provides a simple example: in CEU 48% of HapMap SNPs have substantial pairwise correlation ($r^2 \geqslant 0.5$) to one or more of the 120K SNPs on the array. An additional 13%, however, are not correlated to a single SNP, but are to a specific haplotype of two members of the 120K panel. By identifying such haplotype predictors in the HapMap, and testing them (in addition to the single SNPs) in a disease study, it is likely that power will be increased (I. Pe'er *et al.*, manuscript in preparation).

Evaluating statistical significance and interpreting results. An important challenge in genome-wide association testing is to develop statistical procedures that minimize false positives without greatly sacrificing true positives. The challenge is amplified by the correlated nature of polymorphism data, which makes simple frequentist approaches that assume independence (such as Bonferonni correction) highly conservative. To illustrate this point, we used the ENCODE data to estimate the "effective number of independent tests" (the statistical burden of testing all common ($MAF \geqslant 0.05$) variation) across large genomic regions. Specifically, we re-sampled from the phased ENCODE chromosomes to create mock case-control panels in which all common SNPs were observed, but there was not a causal allele. The resulting χ^2 distribution for association indicates that complete testing of common variation in each 500-kb region is equivalent to performing about 150 independent statistical tests (in CEU and CHB+JPT) and about 350 tests (in YRI). Although it will probably be desirable to perform such empirical estimates of significance within each disease study, these results illustrate how Bonferonni correction overestimates the statistical penalty of performing many correlated tests.

Study of less common alleles. We have focused primarily on the hypothesis that a single, common causal allele exists, and needs to be tested for association to disease. Of course, in many cases the causal allele(s) will be less common, and might be missed by such an approach.

It is possible to perform additional haplotype tests, beyond those that capture known polymorphisms, in the hope of capturing less common or unrepresented alleles[56]. Such haplotype analysis has a long history and proven value in mendelian genetics; the causal mutation is generally rare and unexamined during initial genotyping, but is frequently recognized by its presence on a long, unique haplotype of common alleles[18,19,59-62].

Admixture mapping. Although not designed specifically to enable admixture mapping[63],

对一个已有的基因型数据集的分析　HapMap 能够用于关联检验，而不受标签如何选择的影响。特别地，只要在疾病研究中被基因分型的 SNP 也在 HapMap 样本中被分型，就有可能鉴定哪些 SNP 被已进行基因分型的 SNP 较好地捕获（单一地或者在单体型组合中），哪些没有被捕获 [55]。

这对于使用基于芯片的、标准化的基因分型试剂所进行的全基因组关联研究特别重要，这些研究不允许研究者选择他们自己的标签 SNP 集。包含在第 I 阶段的 HapMap 的 Affymetrix 120K SNP 芯片数据提供了一个简单的例子：在 CEU 中，48% 的 HapMap SNP 与芯片上的 120K SNP 中的一个或者更多有着相当程度的成对相关性（$r^2 \geqslant 0.5$）。另外还有 13% 的 SNP 不与单个 SNP 相关，但是与 120K 组中两个成员组成的特定单体型相关。通过鉴定 HapMap 中这样的单体型预测者，并且在疾病研究中对它们（以及单个 SNP）进行检验，效能有可能会被提高（佩尔等，稿件准备中）。

统计学意义评估和结果解释　在全基因组关联检验中一个重要的挑战是开发最小化假阳性且不大幅牺牲真正阳性数据的统计学方法。多态性数据的关联特性将这个挑战进一步放大，使得假定独立的简单频率论方法（如邦费罗尼校正）高度保守。为了阐释这一点，我们使用 ENCODE 数据来估计在大的基因组区域内"独立检验的有效数量"（检验所有常见（MAF $\geqslant 0.05$）变异的统计学负担）。特别地，我们从区分染色体的 ENCODE 染色体中重新取样，进而产生模拟的样本–对照组，其中可观察到所有常见 SNP，但是没有引起疾病的等位基因。对于关联分析，得到的 χ^2 分布说明对各个 500 kb 区域内常见变异的完整检验等同于进行大约 150 次独立统计学检验（在 CEU 和 CHB+JPT 中）和大约 350 次检验（在 YRI 中）。尽管可能需要在各个疾病研究中都进行这样的对统计学意义的经验估计，这些结果阐释了邦费罗尼校正是如何高估了进行大量相关性检验的统计惩罚的。

不常见等位基因的研究　我们之前主要聚焦于这样的假说，即单个常见的引起疾病的等位基因是存在的，需要检验其与疾病的关联。当然，在很多情况下，导致疾病的等位基因是不常见的，可能被这样的方法所遗漏。

除了捕获已知的多态性的检验，还可以进行额外的单体型检验，以尝试捕获不常见或者无代表的等位基因 [56]。这种单体型分析有着很长的历史，已经证明在孟德尔遗传研究中具有价值；引起疾病的突变通常是罕见的，并且在一开始的基因分型中未被检测到，但是经常由于其存在于常见等位基因的长的唯一的单体型上而被识别 [18,19,59-62]。

混合作图　尽管没有特别设计来实现混合作图 [63]，但是 HapMap 已经为这种方

the HapMap has helped lay the groundwork for this approach. Admixture mapping requires a map of SNPs that are highly differentiated in frequency across population groups. By typing many SNPs in samples from multiple geographical regions, the data have helped to identify such SNPs for the design of genome-wide admixture mapping panels[64,65] and can be further used to identify candidate SNPs with large allele frequency differences for follow-up of positive admixture scan results[66].

Loss of heterozygosity in tumours. Loss of heterozygosity (LOH) in tumour tissue can be a powerful indicator of the location of tumour suppressor genes, and genome-wide, fine-scale LOH analysis has been empowered by genome-wide SNP arrays[67]. Germline DNA is not always available from the same subjects, however, and even if available, typing of germline DNA doubles project costs. In lower density scans for LOH (with markers far apart relative to the scale of LD), long runs of homozygosity in tumours are nearly always indicative of LOH. However, at higher densities runs of homozygosity can be due to haplotype homozygosity in the inherited germline DNA, rather than LOH.

The HapMap data can help minimize this difficulty; previous probabilities for homozygosity based on known frequencies of haplotypes in the HapMap data can be used to distinguish homozygosity due to haplotype sharing rather than LOH[68].

Identifying Structural Variants in HapMap Data

Structural variations—segments where DNA is deleted, duplicated, or rearranged—are common[69,70] and have an important role in diseases[71-73]. The HapMap can provide some insight into structural variation because, in many cases, structural variants reveal themselves through signatures in SNP genotype data. In particular, polymorphic deletions are important to discover, because loss of genetic material is of obvious functional relevance, and results in aberrant patterns of SNP genotypes. These include apparent non-mendelian inheritance of SNP alleles, null genotypes and deviations from Hardy–Weinberg equilibrium. However, such SNPs are routinely discarded as technical failures of genotyping.

Thus, we scanned the unfiltered Phase I HapMap data using an approach developed and validated to identify polymorphic deletions from clusters of SNPs with aberrant genotype patterns (calibrated across the multiple centres and genotyping platforms[74]). In total, 541 candidate deletion polymorphisms were identified, of which 150 were common enough to be observed as homozygotes.

The properties of these candidate deletions, including experimental validation of 90 candidates, are described in ref. 74. Validated polymorphisms include 10 that remove coding exons of genes, such that in many cases individuals are homozygous null for the encoded transcript. Analysis of confirmed deletions often shows strong LD with nearby SNPs, indicating that LD-based approaches can be useful for detecting disease associations due to structural (as well as SNP) variants.

法打下了基础。混合作图需要在不同种群中频率高度不同的一群 SNP 的图谱。通过对来自多个地理区域的样本的很多 SNP 进行分型,得到的数据已经帮助鉴定到可用于设计全基因组混合作图的 SNP[64,65],并且能被进一步用于鉴定后续阳性混合扫描结果所需的存在较大等位基因频率差异的候选 SNP[66]。

肿瘤中的杂合性缺失　肿瘤组织中的杂合性缺失(LOH)可以用作抑癌基因位置的强有力的指示物,全基因组 SNP 芯片使得全基因组范围的精细 LOH 分析成为可能[67]。然而,对于同一个个体,种系 DNA 并不总是能够获得的,而且即使获得了,对种系 DNA 的基因型分型也会使项目的花费加倍。在低密度扫描 LOH 时(相对于 LD 的尺度,标志物之间相距较远),肿瘤中纯合性的大量出现几乎总是提示 LOH 的存在。不过,在高密度扫描 LOH 时,纯合性的大量出现可能是由于遗传的种系 DNA 中单体型的纯合性,而不是 LOH。

HapMap 数据能够帮助将这种困难最小化;前期基于 HapMap 数据中单体型的已知频率得到的纯合性可能性可以用于区分单体型共享而非 LOH 导致的纯合性[68]。

HapMap 数据中结构变异的鉴定

结构变异——片段上发生 DNA 缺失、重复或重排——是常见的[69,70],并且在疾病中有着重要的作用[71-73]。HapMap 能够提供关于结构变异的信息,因为在很多情况下,结构变异可通过 SNP 基因型数据中的特征反映出来。发现多态性的缺失尤其重要,因为遗传材料的缺失是明显与功能相关的,并且会导致 SNP 基因型的异常模式。这包括 SNP 等位基因明显的非孟德尔遗传、频率为零的基因型和哈迪-温伯格平衡的偏离。然而,这样的 SNP 通常作为基因分型的技术问题而被弃掉。

因而,在扫描未过滤的第 I 阶段 HapMap 数据时,我们采用了一种为从带有异常基因型模式的 SNP 簇(在多个中心和基因分型平台进行了校准[74])中鉴定多态性缺失而开发和验证的方法。总共 541 个候选的缺失多态性被鉴定出来,其中 150 个较为常见,可观察到是纯合的。

这些候选缺失的组成,包括对 90 个候选者的实验验证,都在参考文献 74 中有所描述。得到验证的多态性中有 10 个使基因缺失外显子,在很多情况下,这种个体纯合缺少编码的转录本。对已证实的缺失的分析经常发现这种缺失与邻近 SNP 存在强 LD,表明基于 LD 的方法可以用于检测结构(以及 SNP)变异导致的疾病关联。

Polymorphic inversions may also be reflected in the HapMap data as long regions where multiple SNPs are perfectly correlated: because recombination between an inverted and non-inverted copy is lethal, the inverted and non-inverted copies of the region evolve independently. A striking example corresponds to the known inversion polymorphism on chromosome 17, present in 20% of the CEU chromosomes, that has been associated with fertility and total recombination rate in females among Icelanders[75]. Long LD may also arise, however, due to a low recombination rate or certain forms of natural selection, as discussed below.

Insights into Recombination and Natural Selection

In addition to its intended function as a resource for disease studies, the HapMap data provide clues about the biology of recombination and history of natural selection.

A genome-wide map of recombination rates at a fine scale. On the basis of the HapMap data, we created a fine-scale genetic map spanning the human genome (Supplementary Fig. 12), including 21,617 identified recombination hotspots (one per 122 kb).

Both the number and intensity of hotspots contribute to overall variation in recombination rate. For example, we selected 25 regions of 5 Mb as having the highest (> 2.75 cM Mb^{-1}) and lowest (< 0.5 cM Mb^{-1}) rates of recombination in the deCODE (pedigree-based) genetic map[48]. We detected recombination hotspots in all regions, even the lowest. But in the high cM Mb^{-1} regions hotspots are more closely spaced (one per 84 kb) and have a higher average intensity (0.124 cM) as compared to the low cM Mb^{-1} regions (one every 208 kb, and 0.051 cM, respectively).

Estimates of recombination rates and identified hotspots are robust to the specific markers and samples studied. Specifically, we compared these results to a similar analysis[76] of the data of ref. 77 (with about 1.6 million SNPs genotyped in 71 individuals). We find nearly complete correlation in rate estimates at a coarse scale (5 Mb) between these two surveys ($r^2 = 0.99$) and to the pedigree map ($r^2 = 0.95$). Very substantial correlation is found at finer scales: $r^2 = 0.8$ at 50 kb and $r^2 = 0.59$ at 5 kb. Moreover, of the 21,617 hotspots identified using the HapMap data, 78% (16,923) were also identified using the data of ref. 77.

The ability to detect events depends on marker density, with the larger number of SNPs studied by ref. 77 increasing power to detect hotspots, and presumably precision of rate estimates. There are, however, substantial genomic regions where the HapMap data have a higher SNP density. For example, more hotspots are detected on chromosomes 9 and 19 from the HapMap data. We expect that Phase II of HapMap will provide a genome-wide recombination map of substantially greater precision than either ref. 77, or Phase I, at fine scales.

744

多态性的倒位可能也在 HapMap 数据中有所反映，反映为多个 SNP 完美相关的长区域：因为倒位和非倒位拷贝间的重组是致死的，所以区域的倒位和非倒位拷贝各自独立进化。一个明显的例子是 17 号染色体上的一个已知的倒位多态性，它存在于 20% 的 CEU 染色体中，在冰岛女性中与生育力和总重组率相关[75]。不过，长 LD 也可能由于低重组率或者特定形式的自然选择而增加，详见下文的讨论。

对重组和自然选择的认识

除了原本预期的作为疾病研究的资源这一功能外，HapMap 数据还为研究重组的机理和自然选择的历史提供了线索。

重组率的全基因组精细图谱　基于 HapMap 数据，我们绘制了整个人类基因组的精细遗传学图谱（补充信息图 12），包括了鉴定到的 21,617 个重组热点（每 122 kb 一个）。

重组热点的数量和强度都对重组率的整体变化有所贡献。例如，我们选择了 deCODE（基于家系）遗传图谱[48]中含有最高重组率（> 2.75 cM · Mb^{-1}）和最低重组率（< 0.5 cM · Mb^{-1}）的 25 个 5 Mb 的区域。我们检测了所有区域中的重组热点，甚至是最低重组率的区域。不过，与低 cM · Mb^{-1} 区域相比，在高 cM · Mb^{-1} 区域中重组热点靠得更近（每 84 kb 一个），平均强度更高（0.124 cM）（低 cM · Mb^{-1} 区域分别是每 208 kb 一个和 0.051 cM）。

对重组率和鉴定到的重组热点的估计，对于特定标志物和研究样本而言是稳健的。特别地，我们将这些结果与参考文献 77 的数据（含有 71 个个体的大约 160 万个基因分型的 SNP）的一个类似的分析[76]进行了比较。我们发现，在粗略的尺度（5 Mb）上，这两项研究之间相比（$r^2 = 0.99$）以及与家系图谱相比（$r^2 = 0.95$），重组率的估计几乎完全相关。在更加精细的尺度上，我们也发现了相当程度的相关性：在 50 kb 上 $r^2 = 0.8$，在 5 kb 上 $r^2 = 0.59$。并且，利用 HapMap 数据鉴定到的 21,617 个重组热点中，有 78%（16,923 个）也在参考文献 77 的数据中鉴定到。

检测重组事件的能力取决于标志物的密度，参考文献 77 所研究的 SNP 数量更多，这增加了其检测重组热点的效能，并且很可能提高了重组率估计的准确性。不过，也有很大一部分基因组区域，其中 HapMap 数据有着更高的 SNP 密度。例如，在 9 号和 19 号染色体上，在 HapMap 数据中检测到了更多的重组热点。我们预期，第 II 阶段的 HapMap 将会提供一个在精细尺度上与参考文献 77 或者第 I 阶段 HapMap 相比准确度大大提高的全基因组范围的重组图谱。

Little is yet known about the molecular determinants of recombination hotspots. In an analysis of the data of ref. 77, another study (ref. 76) found significant evidence for an excess of the THE1A/B retrotransposon-like elements within recombination hotspots, and more strikingly for a sixfold increase of a particular motif (CCTCCCT) within copies of the element in hotspots, compared to copies of the element outside hotspots. In analysing the HapMap data, we confirmed these findings (Supplementary Fig. 13). Furthermore, THE1B elements with the motif are particularly enriched within 1.5 kb of the centre of the hotspots compared to flanking sequence ($P < 10^{-16}$).

Correlations of LD with genomic features. Variation in recombination rate is important, in large part, because of its impact on LD. We thus examined genome-wide LD for correlation to recombination rates, sequence composition and gene features.

We confirmed previous observations that LD is generally low near telomeres, elevated near centromeres, and correlated with chromosome length (Fig. 15; see also Supplementary Figs 8b and 14)[48,78-80]. These patterns are due to recombination rate variation as discussed above. We also confirmed previously described relationships between LD and G + C content[78,81,82], sequence polymorphism[83] and repeat composition[78,82].

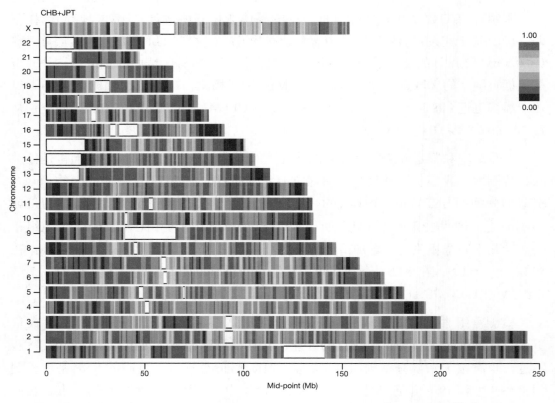

Fig. 15. Length of LD spans. We fitted a simple model for the decay of linkage disequilibrium[103] to windows of 1 million bases distributed throughout the genome. The results of model fitting are summarized for the CHB+JPT analysis panel, by plotting the fitted r^2 value for SNPs separated by 30 kb. The overall pattern

关于重组热点的分子机制目前还知之甚少。在分析参考文献 77 的数据时，另一项研究（参考文献 76）发现在重组热点中有明显的 THE1A/B 逆转录转座子样元件的富集，并且更明显地是，相对于重组热点外的元件，重组热点中的元件中一个特殊的模体（CCTCCCT）有六倍的增加。在分析 HapMap 数据的过程中，我们证实了这些发现（补充信息图 13）。并且，与旁侧序列相比，含有这个模体的 THE1B 元件在重组热点中心的 1.5 kb 范围内特别富集（$P < 10^{-16}$）。

LD 与基因组特征的相关性 重组率的变化的重要性很大程度上是由于它对 LD 的影响。因此我们研究了全基因组的 LD 与重组率、序列组成和基因特征的相关性。

我们证实了之前的发现，即 LD 普遍在端粒附近低，在着丝粒附近较高，并且与染色体的长度相关（图 15；也可见补充信息图 8b 和 14）[48,78-80]。正如上文的讨论，这种模式是由于重组率的变化。我们也证实了之前描述的 LD 与 G+C 含量[78,81,82]、序列多态性[83] 和重复序列组成[78,82] 的关系。

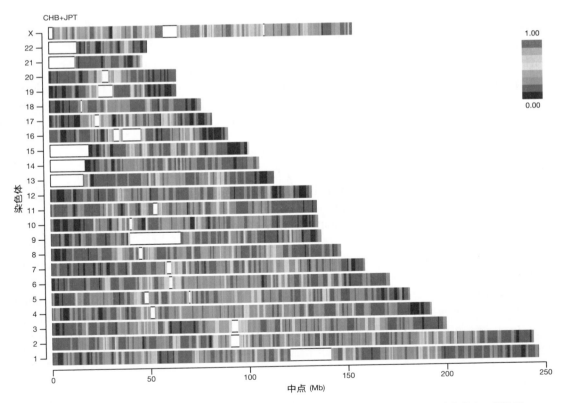

图 15. LD 横跨的长度。对于连锁不平衡的减弱[103]，我们以全基因组范围内的 100 万碱基为窗口拟合了一个简单的模型。通过画出相距 30 kb 的 SNP 的拟合 r^2 值，我们总结了 CHB+JPT 分析小组模型拟合

of variation was very similar in the other analysis panels[84] (see Supplementary Information).

We observe, for the first time, that LD tracks with both the density and functional classification of genes. We examined quartiles of the genome based on extent of LD, and looked for correlations to gene density. Surprisingly, we find that both the top and bottom quartiles of the genome have greater gene density as compared to the middle quartiles (6.7 as compared to 6.1 genes per Mb), as well as percentage of bases in codons (1.24% as compared to 1.08%). We have no explanation for this observation.

Although the majority of gene classes are equally divided between these two extreme quartiles of the genome, some classes of genes show a marked skew in their distribution[64,84,85]. Genes involved in immune responses and neurophysiological processes are more often located in regions of low LD, whereas genes involved in DNA and RNA metabolism, response to DNA damage and the cell cycle are preferentially located in regions of strong linkage disequilibrium. It is intriguing to speculate that the extent of LD (and sequence diversity) might track with gene function due to natural selection, with increased diversity being favoured in genes involved in interface with the environment such as the immune response[86], and disadvantageous for core cell biological processes such as DNA repair and packaging[87,88].

Natural selection. The preceding observation highlights the hypothesis that signatures of natural selection are present in the HapMap data. The availability of genome-wide variation data makes it possible to scan the genome for such signatures to discover genes that were subject to selection during human evolution[89]; the HapMap data also provide a genome-wide empirical distribution against which previous claims of selection can be evaluated (rather than relying solely on theoretical computer simulations).

Natural selection influences patterns of genetic variation in various ways, such as through the removal of deleterious mutations, the fixation of advantageous variants, and the maintenance of multiple alleles through balancing selection. Each form of selection may have occurred uniformly across the world (and thus be represented in all human populations) or have been geographically localized (and thus differ among populations).

Nearly all methods for recognizing natural selection rely on the collection of complete sequence data. The HapMap Project's focus on common variation—and the process of SNP selection that achieved a preponderance of high-frequency alleles (Fig. 5)—thus prevents their straightforward application. Adjusting for the effect of SNP choice is complex, moreover, because SNP choice varied over time as dbSNP evolved, and was implemented locally at each centre.

For these reasons, we focus here on two types of analysis. First, we examined the distributions of signatures of selection across the genome. Although the absolute value of these measures is difficult to interpret (owing to SNP ascertainment), the most extreme cases in a genome-wide distribution are important candidates to evaluate for selection. Second,

的结果。变异的总体模式在其他分析小组中是非常类似的[84](详见补充信息)。

我们第一次观察到 LD 与基因的密度和功能分类均同步。我们基于 LD 的含量研究了基因组的四分位数，寻找其与基因密度的相关性。令人惊奇的是，我们发现与中间四分位数相比，基因组的上四分位数和下四分位数均含有更高的基因密度（中间四分位数每 Mb 6.1 个基因，上、下四分位数每 Mb 6.7 个），位于编码区的碱基比例也是如此（前者为 1.08%，后者为 1.24%）。我们对这种现象还没有解释。

尽管大部分基因分类在基因组的两个极端四分位间是均等分布的，也有一些基因分类在分布上呈现明显的倾向性[64,84,85]。参与免疫反应和神经生理过程的基因更多位于低 LD 区域，而参与 DNA 和 RNA 代谢、DNA 损伤反应和细胞周期的基因更多位于强连锁不平衡的区域。一种有趣的猜测是，由于自然选择，LD 的含量（以及序列的多样性）可能与基因的功能同步，基因多样性的增加在环境界面如免疫反应相关的基因中是有利的[86]，而在核心细胞生物学过程如 DNA 修复和包装相关的基因中是不利的[87,88]。

自然选择　前面的发现突出了自然选择的特征存在于 HapMap 数据中这一假说。全基因组变异数据的获得，使得对这些特征进行全基因组扫描以发现在人类进化过程中被选择的基因成为可能[89]；HapMap 数据还提供了一个全基因组的经验分布，以此可以评估之前声称的自然选择（而不是仅仅依赖于理论上的计算机模拟）。

自然选择通过多种方式对遗传变异的模式产生影响，这些方式如去除有害突变，固定有利变异，以及通过平衡选择对多个等位基因进行保持。各种形式的选择可能在全世界一致地发生（因而在所有人类种群中都表现出来）或者局限于特定的地理位置（因而在不同种群中有差异）。

几乎所有识别自然选择的方法都依赖于收集完整的序列数据。HapMap 计划聚焦于常见变异——以及实现了高频等位基因的数量优势的 SNP 选择过程（图 5），因而使这些遗传变异不能直接应用。并且，调整 SNP 选择的影响是复杂的，因为随着 dbSNP 的演化，SNP 选择也随时间变化，并在各个中心中局部执行。

因为这些原因，我们这里聚焦于两种类型的分析。首先，我们研究了自然选择的特征在全基因组的分布。尽管这些测量的绝对值难以解释（原因在于 SNP 检测方法），但是对于自然选择，在基因组范围的分布中最极端的例子是重要的待评估的候

we compared across functional categories, because SNP choice was largely agnostic to such features, and thus systematic differences may be a sign of selection.

The outcomes of these analyses confirm a number of previous hypotheses about selection and identify new loci as candidates for selection.

Evidence for selective sweeps in particular genomic regions. First we consider population differentiation, generally accepted as a clue to past selection in one of the populations. The HapMap data reveal 926 SNPs with allele frequencies that differ across the analysis panels in a manner as extreme as the well-accepted example of selection at the Duffy (*FY*) locus (Supplementary Fig. 8c). Of these 926 SNPs, 32 are non-synonymous coding SNPs and many others occur in transcribed regions, making them strong candidates for functional polymorphisms that have experienced geographically restricted selection pressures (see Table 9 and Supplementary Information for details). In particular, the *ALMS1* gene on chromosome 2 has six amino acid polymorphisms that show very strong population differentiation.

Table 9. High-differentiation non-synonymous SNPs

Chromosome	Position (base number)	Gene*	SNP
1	54,772,383	*THEA*	rs1702003
1	156,000,000	*FY*	rs12075
1	244,000,000	Q8NGY8_human†	rs7555046
2	3,184,917	*COLEC11*	rs7567833
2	73,563,622	*ALMS1*	rs3813227
2	73,589,553	*ALMS1*	rs6546837
2	73,591,645	*ALMS1*	rs6724782
2	73,592,163	*ALMS1*	rs6546839
2	73,629,222	*ALMS1*	rs2056486
2	73,629,311	*ALMS1*	rs10193972
2	109,000,000	*EDAR*	rs3827760
3	182,000,000	*FXR1*	rs11499
3	185,000,000	*MCF2L2*	rs7639705
4	41,844,599	*SLC30A9*	rs1047626
4	46,567,077	ENSG00000172895.1	rs5825
4	101,000,000	*ADH1B*	rs1229984
8	10,517,787	*RP1L1*	rs6601495
8	146,000,000	*SLC39A4*	rs1871534
10	50,402,145	*ERCC6*	rs4253047
10	71,002,210	*NEUROG3*	rs4536103
11	46,701,579	*F2*	rs5896

选者。其次，我们比较了各个功能分类，因为 SNP 选择在很大程度上对于这些特征是不可知的，因而系统的差异可能是选择的一个标志。

这些分析的结果证实了大量的之前关于自然选择的假说，并且鉴定到了新的自然选择的候选基因座。

特定基因组区域内选择性清理的证据 首先，我们考虑了种群差异，它通常被认为是其中一个种群中以前的自然选择的线索。HapMap 数据发现了 926 个 SNP，其等位基因频率在各个分析小组中存在差异，且这种差异跟公认的在 Duffy(*FY*) 基因座的自然选择的例子一样极端(补充信息图 8c)。在这 926 个 SNP 中，有 32 个是非同义编码 SNP，并且很多其他的 SNP 位于转录区域中，使得它们成为经历过地理位置限制的选择压力的功能多态性的有力候选者(详见表 9 和补充信息)。特别地，2 号染色体上的 *ALMS1* 基因有六个表现出非常强的种群差异的氨基酸多态性。

表 9. 高度分化的非同义 SNP

染色体	位置（碱基数量）	基因 *	SNP
1	54,772,383	*THEA*	rs1702003
1	156,000,000	*FY*	rs12075
1	244,000,000	Q8NGY8_human†	rs7555046
2	3,184,917	*COLEC11*	rs7567833
2	73,563,622	*ALMS1*	rs3813227
2	73,589,553	*ALMS1*	rs6546837
2	73,591,645	*ALMS1*	rs6724782
2	73,592,163	*ALMS1*	rs6546839
2	73,629,222	*ALMS1*	rs2056486
2	73,629,311	*ALMS1*	rs10193972
2	109,000,000	*EDAR*	rs3827760
3	182,000,000	*FXR1*	rs11499
3	185,000,000	*MCF2L2*	rs7639705
4	41,844,599	*SLC30A9*	rs1047626
4	46,567,077	ENSG00000172895.1	rs5825
4	101,000,000	*ADH1B*	rs1229984
8	10,517,787	*RP1L1*	rs6601495
8	146,000,000	*SLC39A4*	rs1871534
10	50,402,145	*ERCC6*	rs4253047
10	71,002,210	*NEUROG3*	rs4536103
11	46,701,579	*F2*	rs5896

Continued

Chromosome	Position (base number)	Gene*	SNP
15	46,213,776	*SLC24A5*	rs1426654
15	61,724,262	*HERC1*	rs7162473
16	30,996,126	*ZNF646*	rs749670
16	46,815,699	*ABCC11*	rs17822931
17	26,322,430	*RNF135*	rs7225888
17	26,399,303	ENSG00000184253.2	rs6505228
18	66,022,323	*RTTN*	rs3911730
19	5,782,891	*FUT6*	rs364637
19	47,723,209	*CEACAM1*	rs8110904
22	18,164,095	*GNB1L*	rs2073770
X	65,608,007	*EDA2R*	rs1385699

* Where no standard gene abbreviation exists, the ENSEMBL gene ID has been given.
† It is unclear from current annotations whether this is a pseudogene.

Another signature of an allele having risen to fixation through selection is that all other diversity in the region is eliminated (known as a selective sweep). We identified extreme outliers in the joint distribution of heterozygosity (as assessed from shotgun sequencing SNP discovery projects) and either population differentiation or skewing of allele frequency towards rare alleles in each analysis panel (Supplementary Fig. 15). We identified 19 such genomic regions (13 on autosomes, 6 on the X chromosome) as candidates for future study (Supplementary Table 4); these include candidates for population-specific sweeps and sweeps in the ancestral population. Encouragingly, this analysis includes among its top-scoring results the *LCT* gene, which influences the ability to digest dairy products[90] and has been shown to be subject to past natural selection[91].

Long haplotypes as candidates for natural selection. Selective sweeps that fail to fix in the population, as well as balancing selection, lead to haplotypes that are relatively high in frequency and long in duration. In the *HLA* region (which is widely believed to have been influenced by balancing selection) multiple haplotypes of 500 SNPs that extend more than 1 cM in length are observed with a frequency in the HapMap samples of more than 1%. We identified other such occurrences of long haplotypes across the genome (Supplementary Fig. 8 and Supplementary Tables 5 and 6).

An approach to long haplotypes designed specifically to identify regions having undergone partial selective sweeps is the long range haplotype (LRH) test[91,92], which compares the length of each haplotype to that of others at the locus, matched across the genome based on frequency. Previously identified outliers to the genome-wide distribution for the LRH test (Fig. 16) that have been identified as candidates for selection include the *LCT* gene in the CEU sample (empirical *P*-value = 1.3×10^{-9}), which was an outlier for the

染色体	位置（碱基数量）	基因 *	SNP
15	46,213,776	*SLC24A5*	rs1426654
15	61,724,262	*HERC1*	rs7162473
16	30,996,126	*ZNF646*	rs749670
16	46,815,699	*ABCC11*	rs17822931
17	26,322,430	*RNF135*	rs7225888
17	26,399,303	ENSG00000184253.2	rs6505228
18	66,022,323	*RTTN*	rs3911730
19	5,782,891	*FUT6*	rs364637
19	47,723,209	*CEACAM1*	rs8110904
22	18,164,095	*GNB1L*	rs2073770
X	65,608,007	*EDA2R*	rs1385699

* 没有标准基因缩写的使用 ENSEMBL 基因 ID。
† 根据现有的注释不清楚它是否是一个假基因。

一个等位基因通过自然选择而被固定的另一个特征是区域内所有其他的多样性都被消除（这被称为选择性清除）。我们在杂合性（SNP 发现计划进行鸟枪法测序所检测的）与种群差异或各分析小组中等位基因频率向罕见等位基因的偏斜的联合分布中鉴定到了极端的离群值（补充信息图 15）。我们鉴定到了 19 个这样的基因组区域（13 个位于常染色体上，6 个位于 X 染色体上），将其作为下一步研究的候选者（补充信息表 4）；它们包括种群特异性的清理以及古老种群中的清理的候选者。鼓舞人心的是，这个分析在高分结果中包括了 *LCT* 基因，该基因影响消化奶制品的能力[90]，并且已经被发现经历过以前的自然选择[91]。

作为自然选择候选者的长单体型 没有在种群中固定下来的选择性清理，以及平衡选择，产生了频率相对较高且跨度相对较长的单体型。在 *HLA* 区域（普遍认为它被平衡选择所影响过）中，多个单体型含有 500 个 SNP，长度上超过 1 cM，在 HapMap 样本中频率超过 1%。我们还在全基因组中鉴定到了其他这样的长单体型情况（补充信息图 8 和补充信息表 5 和 6）。

长距离单体型（LRH）检验[91,92]是一种专门设计的用来鉴定经历过部分选择性清理的长单体型区域的方法，它是将各个单体型的长度与全基因中频率匹配的其他单体型的长度相比较。之前通过 LRH 检验鉴定到的相对于全基因组分布的（图 16），已经被认为是选择候选者的离群值，包括 CEU 样本中的 *LCT* 基因（经验 P 值 $= 1.3 \times 10^{-9}$）——上面提到的杂合性/等位基因频率检验的一个离群值，以及 YRI 样

heterozygosity/allele frequency test above, and the *HBB* gene (empirical *P*-value $= 1.39 \times 10^{-5}$) in the YRI sample. However, most of the strongest signals in the LRH test (Table 10) were not previously hypothesized as undergoing selection.

Fig. 16. The distribution of the long range haplotype (LRH[92]) test statistic for natural selection. In the YRI analysis panel, diversity around the *HBB* gene is highlighted by the red point. In the CEU analysis panel, diversity within the LCT gene region is similarly highlighted.

Table 10. Candidate loci in which selection occurred

Chromosome	Position (base number) at centre	Genes in region	Population	Haplotype frequency	Empirical *P*-value
2	137,224,699	*LCT*	CEU	0.65	1.25×10^{-9}
5	22,296,347	*CDH12, PMCHL1*	YRI	0.25	5.77×10^{-8}
7	79,904,387	*CD36*	YRI	0.24	2.72×10^{-6}
7	73,747,934	*PMS2L5, WBSCR16*	CEU	0.76	3.37×10^{-6}
12	109,892,896	*CUTL2*	CEU	0.36	7.95×10^{-9}
15	78,558,508	*ARNT2*	YRI	0.32	6.92×10^{-7}
16	75,661,011	Desert	YRI	0.46	5.01×10^{-7}
17	3,945,580	*ITGAE, GSG2*, HSA277841, *CAMKK1, P2RX1*	YRI	0.70	9.26×10^{-7}
18	24,502,756	Desert	CEU	0.57	2.23×10^{-7}
22	32,459,471	*LARGE*	YRI	0.36	7.82×10^{-9}
X	20,171,291	Desert	YRI	0.33	5.02×10^{-9}
X	64,323,320	*HEPH*	YRI	0.55	3.02×10^{-8}
X	42,763,073	*MAOB*	CEU	0.53	4.21×10^{-9}
X	34,399,948	Desert	CEU	0.57	8.85×10^{-8}

本中的 *HBB* 基因（经验 *P* 值 $= 1.39 \times 10^{-5}$）。不过，LRH 检验中大部分的最强信号（表 10）之前并不认为经历过自然选择。

图 16. 自然选择的长距离单体型（LRH[92]）检验统计量的分布。在 YRI 分析小组，*HBB* 基因周围的多样性通过红点突出显示。在 CEU 分析小组中，*LCT* 基因区域内的多样性以类似的方式突出显示。

表 10. 发生选择的候选基因座

染色体	中心位置（碱基数量）	区域内基因	种群	单体型频率	经验 *P* 值
2	137,224,699	*LCT*	CEU	0.65	1.25×10^{-9}
5	22,296,347	*CDH12*、*PMCHL1*	YRI	0.25	5.77×10^{-8}
7	79,904,387	*CD36*	YRI	0.24	2.72×10^{-6}
7	73,747,934	*PMS2L5*、*WBSCR16*	CEU	0.76	3.37×10^{-6}
12	109,892,896	*CUTL2*	CEU	0.36	7.95×10^{-9}
15	78,558,508	*ARNT2*	YRI	0.32	6.92×10^{-7}
16	75,661,011	Desert	YRI	0.46	5.01×10^{-7}
17	3,945,580	*ITGAE*、*GSG2*、HSA277841、*CAMKK1*、*P2RX1*	YRI	0.70	9.26×10^{-7}
18	24,502,756	Desert	CEU	0.57	2.23×10^{-7}
22	32,459,471	*LARGE*	YRI	0.36	7.82×10^{-9}
X	20,171,291	Desert	YRI	0.33	5.02×10^{-9}
X	64,323,320	*HEPH*	YRI	0.55	3.02×10^{-8}
X	42,763,073	*MAOB*	CEU	0.53	4.21×10^{-9}
X	34,399,948	Desert	CEU	0.57	8.85×10^{-8}

These four tests overlap only partially in the hypotheses they address—heterozygosity, for example, is sensitive to older sweeps, whereas the haplotype tests are most powerful for partial sweeps—but encouragingly some candidate regions are found by more than one test. In particular, six regions are identified both by long haplotypes and by low heterozygosity, and three regions (*LCT* on chromosome 2, and two regions on the X chromosome at 20 and 65 Mb) are identified by three different tests.

Confirming purifying selection at conserved non-coding elements. Finally, we used the HapMap data to test an important hypothesis from comparative genomics. Genomic sequencing has shown that about 5% of the human sequence is highly conserved across species, yet less than half of this sequence spans known functional elements such as exons[45]. It is widely assumed that conserved non-genic sequences lack diversity because of selective constraint (that is, purifying selection), but such regions may simply be coldspots for mutation, and thus be of little value as candidates for functional study.

Analysis of allele frequencies helps to resolve this uncertainty. Functional constraint, but not a low mutation rate, results in a downward skew in allele frequencies for conserved sequences as compared to neutral sequences[93,94]. We find that conserved non-genic sequences display a greater skew towards rare alleles than do intergenic regions, as predicted under purifying selection. This skew is less extreme than that observed for exons (Supplementary Fig. 16), reflecting either stronger purifying selection or the prioritization of coding SNPs for genotyping by the HapMap centres regardless of validation status. This novel evidence for ongoing constraint shows that conserved non-genic sequences are not mutational coldspots, and thus remain of high interest for functional study.

Conclusions

The International HapMap Project set out to create a resource that would accelerate the identification of genetic factors that influence medical traits. Analyses reported here confirm the generality of hotspots of recombination, long segments of strong LD, and limited haplotype diversity. Most important is the extensive redundancy among nearby SNPs, providing (1) the potential to extract extensive information about genomic variation without complete resequencing, and (2) efficiencies through selection of tag SNPs and optimized association analyses. Beyond the biomedical context, these data have made it possible to identify deletion variants in the genome, explore the nature of fine-scale recombination and identify regions that may have been subject to natural selection.

The HapMap Project (along with a previous genome-wide assessment of LD[77]) is a natural extension of the Human Genome Project. Where the reference sequence constructed by the Human Genome Project is informative about the vast majority of bases that are invariant across individuals, the HapMap focuses on DNA sequence differences among individuals. Our understanding of SNP variation and LD around common variants in the sampled populations is reasonably complete; the current picture is unlikely to change with additional

这四种检验提出的假设仅仅部分重合——例如，杂合性对更古老的清理敏感，而单体型检验对于部分清理最有效；但是令人鼓舞的是，一些候选区域在超过一种检验中发现。特别地，有六个区域同时被长单体型和低杂合性鉴定出来，有三个区域（2 号染色体上的 *LCT*，以及 X 染色体在 20 和 65 Mb 处的两个区域）被三种不同的检验同时鉴定出来。

在保守的非编码元件中验证纯化选择　最后，我们使用 HapMap 数据来检验一个来自比较基因组学的重要假说。基因组测序已经发现，大约 5% 的人类序列是在物种间高度保守的，但是其中横跨已知的功能元件如外显子 [45] 的只有不到一半。普遍认为，保守的非基因序列由于选择性限制（即纯化选择）而缺少多样性，但是，这样的区域也可能单纯是突变的冷点而几乎没有作为功能研究候选者的价值。

分析等位基因频率能帮助解决这种不确定性。功能限制，而非低突变率，会导致相比于中性序列，保守序列的等位基因频率向下偏斜 [93,94]。我们发现，保守的非基因序列比基因间区域表现出更大的向罕见等位基因的偏斜，这与在纯化选择压力下预测的一致。这种偏斜没有外显子中观察到的那么极端（补充信息图 16），不管验证状态如何，这反映了更强的纯化选择，或是 HapMap 中心对基因分型的编码 SNP 的优先选择。这个正在进行的限制的新证据表明，保守的非基因序列并不是突变冷点，因而在功能研究中仍然很有价值。

结　论

国际 HapMap 计划的建立是为了创造一种能够加快对影响医学特性的遗传因子的鉴定的资源。本文报道的分析结果验证了重组热点、强 LD 的长片段和有限的单体型多样性的普遍性。最重要的是邻近 SNP 间广泛的冗余性，这提供了 (1) 不需要全基因组重测序就可以提取大量基因组变异信息的可能，以及 (2) 通过标签 SNP 的选择和优化后的关联分析而提高的效率。除了生物医学方面，这些数据还使得鉴定基因组中的缺失突变，探索精细尺度上重组的本质以及鉴定可能经历过自然选择的区域成为可能。

HapMap 计划（以及之前的一项全基因组范围的对 LD 的评估 [77]）是人类基因组计划的自然的延伸。人类基因组计划搭建的参考序列表明绝大多数碱基在人与人之间是不变的，而 HapMap 聚焦于个体间存在差异的 DNA 序列。我们对于取样种群中的 SNP 变异和常见变异附近的 LD 的了解是相当完整的；即使再增加数据，目前

data. In other aspects—such as the fine details of local correlation among SNPs, rarer alleles, structural variants, and interpopulation differences—these resources are only a first step on the path towards a complete characterization of genetic variation of the human population. Planned extensions of the Phase I map include Phase II of HapMap, with genotyping of another 4.6 million SNPs attempted in the HapMap samples, and detailed genotyping of the HapMap ENCODE regions in additional members of each HapMap population sampled, as well as in samples from additional populations. These results should guide understanding of the robustness and transferability of LD inferences and tag SNPs selected from the current set of HapMap samples.

An important application of the HapMap data is to help make possible comprehensive, genome-wide association studies. There are now laboratory tools that make it practical to undertake such studies, and initial results are encouraging[13]. Given the low prior probability of causality for each SNP in the genome, however, rigorous standards of statistical significance will be needed to avoid a flood of false-positive results. Multiple replications in large samples provide the most straightforward path to identifying robust and broadly relevant associations. Given the potential for confusion if associations of uncertain validity are widely reported (and a persistent tendency towards genetic determinism in public discourse), we urge conservatism and restraint in the public dissemination and interpretation of such studies, especially if non-medical phenotypes are explored. It is time to create mechanisms by which all results of association studies, positive and negative, are reported and discussed without bias.

The success of the HapMap will be measured in terms of the genetic discoveries enabled, and improved knowledge of disease aetiology. Specifically, identifying which genes and pathways are causal in humans has the potential to provide a new and solid foundation for biomedical research. This is equally true whether the variants that lead to the discovery of those genes are themselves rare or common, or of large or small effect. The impact on diagnostics and targeted prevention, however, will depend on how predictive each given allele may be. Where genetic mechanisms underlie treatment responses, both more efficient trials and individualized preventive and treatment strategies may become practical[95].

Success identifying alleles conferring susceptibility or resistance to common diseases will also provide a deeper understanding of the architecture of disease: how many genes are involved in each case, whether and how alleles interact with one another[96] and with environmental exposures to shape clinical phenotypes. In this regard, it will be important to invest heavily in the discovery and characterization of relevant lifestyle factors, environmental exposures, detailed characterization of clinical phenotypes, and the ability to obtain such information in longitudinal studies of adequate size. Where environmental and behavioural factors vary across studies, replication will be hard to come by (as will clinical utility) unless we can learn to capture these variables with the same precision and completeness as genotypic variation. Technological innovation and international collaboration in these realms will probably be required (as they have been in the Human Genome Project and the HapMap) to advance the shared goal of understanding, and ultimately preventing, common human diseases.

的图景也基本不会改变。对于其他方面——比如 SNP 间局部相关性、更罕见的等位基因、结构变异和种群间差异等细节，这些资源仅仅是通往完整表征人类种群遗传变异的道路的第一步。第 I 阶段图谱的延伸计划包括 HapMap 的第 II 阶段，即在 HapMap 样本中对另外 460 万个 SNP 进行基因分型，以及在已取样的各 HapMap 种群的更多成员中和另外的种群的样本中，对 HapMap ENCODE 区域进行详细的基因分型。这些结果会对理解 LD 推断和从现有 HapMap 样本集中选择的标签 SNP 的稳健性和可转移性提供指导。

HapMap 数据的一个重要应用是帮助我们实现全面的全基因组关联研究。现有的实验工具已经使进行这样的研究切实可行，并且初步结果是令人鼓舞的[13]。但是，鉴于基因组中各个 SNP 导致疾病的先验概率偏低，统计显著性将需要严格的标准来避免大量的假阳性结果。大量样本中的多个重复提供了最直接的鉴定稳健且广泛相关的关联的方法。鉴于可能存在的对不确定有效的关联是否被广泛报道的困惑（以及公共讨论中朝向遗传决定论的持续倾向），我们呼吁在公开宣传和说明这样的研究时保持保守和克制，特别是研究非医学表型时。现在需要建立一种机制，以使所有关联研究的结果，无论阳性或阴性，都得到无偏倚的报道和讨论。

HapMap 的成功会通过它带来的遗传学发现和提高的病因知识来衡量。特别地，对人类中导致疾病的基因和通路的鉴定有望为生物医学研究提供新的坚实基础。不管使我们发现这些致病基因的遗传变异是罕见的还是常见的，效应是大还是小，这一点是始终成立的。不过，对诊断和靶向预防的影响将取决于各个给定的等位基因可以在多大程度上预测疾病发生。一旦清楚了治疗响应下的遗传机制，更加有效的试验和个性化预防与治疗策略都可能成为现实[95]。

成功鉴定影响常见疾病易感性或抵抗性的等位基因还将会帮助我们更加深入地理解疾病的机制：多少基因参与其中，等位基因间[96]以及等位基因与环境是否和如何相互作用进而影响临床表型。在这一点上，大力投入以发现和表征相关生活方式因子、环境暴露、详细的临床表型，以及在足够大的纵向研究中获取这种信息，将会十分重要。各个研究的环境和行为因子不同，除非我们能学会以与遗传学变异相同的准确度和完整性捕获这些变化，否则将难以进行重复（临床应用也是如此）。这些领域有可能需要技术的革新和国际合作（像人类基因组计划和 HapMap 那样），以推进理解和最终预防常见人类疾病这一共同的目标。

Methods

The project was undertaken by investigators from Japan, the United Kingdom, Canada, China, Nigeria and the United States, and from multiple disciplines: sample collection, sequencing and genotyping, bioinformatics, population genetics, statistics, and the ethical, legal, and social implications of genetic research. The Supplementary Information contains information about project participants and organization.

Choice of DNA samples. Any choice of DNA samples represents a compromise: a single population offers simplicity, but cannot be representative, whereas grid-sampling is representative of the current worldwide population, but is neither practical nor captures historical genetic diversity. The project chose to include DNA samples based on well-known patterns of allele frequencies across populations[41], reflecting historical genetic diversity[31,32].

For practical reasons, the project focused on SNPs present at a minor allele frequency (MAF) ≥ 0.05 in each analysis panel, and thus studied a sufficient number of individuals to provide good power for this frequency range[31]. Cell lines and DNA are available at the Coriell Institute for Medical Research (http://locus.umdnj.edu/nigms/products/hapmap.html).

Community engagement was employed to explain the project, and to learn how the project was viewed, in the communities where samples were collected[31,32]. Papers describing the community engagement processes are being prepared.

One JPT sample was replaced for technical reasons, but not in time for inclusion in this report. We surveyed cryptic relatedness among the study participants, and identified a small number of pairs with unexpectedly high allele sharing (Supplementary Information). As the total level of sharing is not great, and as a subset of analyses performed without these individuals were unchanged, we include these individuals in the data and analyses presented here.

Genome-wide SNP discovery. The project required a dense map of SNPs, ideally containing information about validation and frequency of each candidate SNP. When the project started, the public SNP database (dbSNP) contained 2.6 million candidate SNPs, few of which were annotated with the required information.

To generate more SNPs and obtain validation information, shotgun sequencing of DNA from whole-genome libraries and flow-sorted chromosomes was performed[31], augmented by analysis of sequence traces produced by Applied Biosystems[97,98], and information on 1.6 million SNPs genotyped by Perlegen Sciences[77], including 425,000 not in dbSNP when released (Supplementary Table 7). The HapMap Project contributed about 6 million new SNPs to dbSNP.

At the time of writing (October 2005) dbSNP (http://www.ncbi.nlm.nih.gov/projects/SNP/) contains 9.2 million candidate human SNPs, of which 3.6 million have been validated by both alleles having been seen two or more times during discovery ("double-hit" SNPs), and 2.4 million have genotype

方 法

本计划是由来自日本、英国、加拿大、中国、尼日利亚和美国的研究者实施的，这些研究者来自多个方向：样本收集，测序和基因分型，生物信息学，种群遗传学，统计学，以及遗传学研究的伦理、法律和社会影响。补充信息包括了参与本计划的人员和组织的信息。

DNA 样本的选择　任何一种 DNA 样本选择方法都代表着一种妥协：单一种群简单，但是不够有代表性，而网格采样代表了目前全球的种群，但是既不现实也不能捕获历史上的遗传多样性。本计划选择基于种群间等位基因频率的已知模式来纳入 DNA 样本[41]，进而反映历史上的遗传多样性[31,32]。

出于实际的原因，本计划聚焦于在各个分析小组中最小等位基因频率（MAF）≥ 0.05 的 SNP，因而研究了足量的个体来为这个频率段提供较好的效能[31]。细胞系和 DNA 可在科里尔医学研究所获取（http://locus.umdnj.edu/nigms/products/hapmap.html）。

本研究在样本采集的社区开展了参与活动，包括解释本计划，以及了解本计划是如何被看待的[31,32]。介绍社区参与过程的文章正在准备中。

只有一个 JPT 样本由于技术原因被替换掉，但是没有及时包含进本报道中。我们还调查了样本之间的隐性亲缘关系，鉴定到少量几对含有超预期的高等位基因共享性（详见补充信息）。由于总体的共享性水平并不高，以及不含这些个体的分析结果不变，我们在本文的数据和分析中还是包含了这些个体。

全基因组范围的 SNP 发现　本计划要求高密度的 SNP 图谱，最好包含各个候选 SNP 的验证和频率的信息。在本计划启动时，公共的 SNP 数据库（dbSNP）包含 260 万个候选 SNP，其中很少有所要求的注释信息。

为了产生更多的 SNP 并获得验证信息，我们对来自全基因组文库和流式筛选的染色体的 DNA 进行了鸟枪法测序[31]，并辅以 Applied Biosystems 公司的序列踪迹分析[97,98]，以及 Perlegen Sciences 公司基因分型的 160 万个 SNP 的信息[77]，这其中有 425,000 个在数据释放时并不在 dbSNP 中（补充信息表格 7）。HapMap 计划为 dbSNP 贡献了大约 600 万个新的 SNP。

在写作本文时（2005 年 10 月），dbSNP（http://www.ncbi.nlm.nih.gov/projects/SNP/）包含 920 万个候选人类 SNP，其中 360 万个 SNP 的两个等位基因都在发现过程中被观察到两次或更多

data (Fig. 1).

Comprehensive study of common variation across 5 Mb of DNA. To study patterns of genetic variation as comprehensively as possible, we selected ten 500-kb regions from the ENCODE Project[33]. These ten regions were chosen in aggregate to approximate the genome-wide average for G+C content, recombination rate, percentage of sequence conserved relative to mouse sequence, and gene density (Table 2).

In each such region additional sequencing and genotyping were performed to obtain a much more complete inventory of common variation. Specifically, bidirectional PCR-based sequencing was performed across each 500-kb region in 48 individuals (16 YRI, 16 CEU, 8 CHB, 8 JPT). Although the intent was for these same DNA samples to be included in Phase I, eight Yoruba and one Han Chinese sample used in sequencing were not among the 269 samples genotyped. (The nine samples are available from Coriell.)

All variants found by sequencing, and any others in dbSNP (build 121) not found by sequencing, were genotyped in all 269 HapMap samples. If the first attempt at genotyping was unsuccessful, a second platform was tried for each SNP.

False-positive and false-negative rates in PCR-based SNP discovery. The false-positive rate of SNP discovery by PCR-based resequencing was estimated at 7–11% (for the two sequencing centres), based on genotyping of each candidate SNP in the same samples used for discovery.

The false-negative rate of SNP discovery by PCR resequencing was estimated at 6%, using as the denominator a set of SNPs previously in dbSNP and confirmed by genotyping in the specific individuals sequenced. The false-negative rate was considerably higher, however, for singletons (SNPs seen only as a single heterozygote): 15% of singletons covered by high-quality sequence data were not detected by the trace analysis, and another 25% were missed due to a failure to obtain a high-quality sequence over the relevant base in the one heterozygous individual (D. J. Richter *et al.*, personal communication).

False-positive and false-negative rates in dbSNP. The false positive rate (candidate SNPs that cannot be confirmed as variable sites) estimated for dbSNP was 17%. This represents an upper bound, because dbSNP entries that are monomorphic in the 269 HapMap samples could be rare variants, or polymorphic in other samples. We note that as the catalogue of dbSNP gets deeper, the rate at which candidate SNPs are monomorphic in any given sample is observed to rise (Supplementary Table 8). This is expected because the number of rare SNPs and false positives scales with depth of sequencing, whereas the number of true common variants will plateau.

SNP genotyping for the genome-wide map. Genotyping assays were designed from dbSNP, with priority given to SNPs validated by previous genotyping data or both alleles having been seen more than once in discovery. Data from the Chimpanzee Genome Sequencing Project[99] were used in SNP validation if they confirmed the ancestral status of a human allele seen only once in discovery (Supplementary Information). Non-synonymous coding SNPs were also prioritized for genotyping.

762

次而得到验证（"双打击"的 SNP），240 万个含有基因型数据（图 1）。

对 5 Mb DNA 区域内常见变异的全面研究 为了尽可能全面地研究遗传变异的模式，我们从 ENCODE 计划中选择了 10 个 500 kb 区域[33]。这 10 个区域合起来可近似代表全基因组平均的 G+C 含量、重组率、相对于小鼠基因组保守序列的百分比，以及基因密度（表 2）。

在各个这样的区域中，我们进行了额外的测序和基因分型，以获得更加完整的常见变异清单。特别地，对 48 个个体（16 个 YRI、16 个 CEU、8 个 CHB、8 个 JPT）在各个 500 kb 区域上进行了基于双向 PCR 的测序。尽管目的是将这些用在测序中的 DNA 样本都包含进第 I 阶段 HapMap，但是其中有 8 个约鲁巴人和 1 个汉族中国人样本并没有包含在基因分型的 269 个样本当中。（这 9 个样本可从科里尔医学研究所获得。）

通过测序发现的所有变异，以及任何其他未被测序发现但在 dbSNP（版本 121）中的变异，都在所有 269 个 HapMap 样本中进行了基因分型。对于各个 SNP，如果第一次基因分型尝试不成功，则尝试第二个基因分型平台。

基于 PCR 的 SNP 发现中的假阳性率和假阴性率 通过基于 PCR 的重测序进行 SNP 发现，其假阳性率估计为 7%～11%（对于两个测序中心），这是基于在相同的样本中对各个候选 SNP 进行基因分型得出来的。

通过 PCR 重测序进行 SNP 发现，其假阴性率估计为 6%，这是使用之前在 dbSNP 中的并在被测序的特定个体中通过基因分型而被验证的 SNP 集作为分母得出来的。不过，对于单体 SNP（仅作为单个杂合子而被发现），假阴性率则高得多：被高质量的测序数据所覆盖的单体 SNP 中有 15% 没有被踪迹分析检测到，另外还有 25% 由于不能在唯一的杂合个体中获得相关碱基的高质量测序而被漏掉（里克特等，个人交流）。

dbSNP 中的假阳性率和假阴性率 对于 dbSNP，假阳性率（不能被证实在人群中存在变异的候选 SNP）估计为 17%。这代表着上限，因为在 269 个 HapMap 样本中呈单态性的 dbSNP 条目有可能是罕见变异，或者在其他样本中是多态性的。我们注意到，随着 dbSNP 目录的深入，候选 SNP 在任一给定样本中是单态性的比率是增加的（补充信息表 8）。这是符合预期的，因为罕见 SNP 和假阳性的数量与测序的深度成比例，而真正的常见变异的数量则将会保持稳定。

全基因组图谱的 SNP 基因分型 基因分型实验是根据 dbSNP 而设计的，首先针对由之前的基因分型数据验证过的 SNP，或者两个等位基因在发现过程中都被观察到超过一次的 SNP。对于在发现过程中仅被看到一次的人类等位基因，如果来自黑猩猩基因组测序计划[99] 的数据确认了该等位基因的祖先状态，这些数据就被用于 SNP 验证。非同义编码 SNP 也被

Two whole-genome, array-based genotyping reagents were used efficiently to increase SNP density: 40,000 SNPs from Illumina, and 120,000 SNPs from Affymetrix[100].

To monitor progress, the genome was partitioned into 5-kb bins, with genotyping continuing through iterative rounds until a set of predetermined "stopping rules" was satisfied in each analysis panel. (1) Minor allele frequency: in each analysis panel a common SNP (MAF ≥ 0.05) was obtained in each 5-kb bin. (2) Spacing: the distance between adjacent SNPs was 2–8 kb, with at least 9 SNPs across 50 kb. (3) "HapMappable" genome: with available technologies it is challenging to study centromeres, telomeres, gaps in genome sequence, and segmental duplications. The project identified such regions[101] (Supplementary Table 9), spanning 4.4% of the finished human genome sequence, in which only a single attempt to develop a genotyping assay was required. (4) Three strikes, you're out: if the above rules were not satisfied after three attempts to develop an assay in a given 5-kb region, or if all available SNPs in dbSNP had been tried, genotyping was considered complete for Phase I. Two attempts were considered sufficient if one attempt was of a SNP previously shown to have MAF ≥ 0.05 in the appropriate population sample in a previous genome-wide survey[77]. (5) Quality control: ongoing and standardized quality control (QC) filters and three rounds of quality assessment (QA) were used to ensure and document the high quality of the genotype data.

QC filters were systematically performed, with each SNP tested for completeness ($> 80\%$), consistency across five duplicate genotypes (≤ 1 discrepancy), mendelian inheritance in 60 trios (≤ 1 discrepancy in each of YRI and CEU), and Hardy–Weinberg equilibrium ($P > 0.001$[102]). SNPs in the Phase I data set passed all the QC filters in all the analysis panels and were polymorphic in the HapMap samples. Failing SNPs were released (with a special flag), as they can help to identify polymorphisms under primers, insertions/deletions, paralogous loci and natural selection.

Three QA exercises were carried out. First, a calibration exercise to "benchmark" each platform and laboratory protocol. Second, a mid-project evaluation of each genotyping centre. Third, a blind analysis of a random sample of the complete Phase I data set. A number of SNPs were genotyped more than once during the project, or by other investigators, providing additional information about data quality. See the Supplementary Information for full information about the QA exercises.

An exhaustive approach was taken to mtDNA. Alignment of more than 1,000 publicly available mtDNA sequences of African (n = 87), European (n = 928) and Asian (n = 238) geographical origin[34] was used to identify 210 common variants (MAF ≥ 0.05 in at least one continental region) that were attempted in the samples.

Data release. Data deposited at the Data Coordination Center and released at http://www.hapmap. org, a Japanese mirror site http://hapmap.jst.go.jp/ and dbSNP include ascertainment status of each SNP at the time of selection, primer sequences, protocols for genotyping, genotypes for each sample, allele frequencies, and, for SNPs that failed QC filters, a code indicating the mode(s) of failure.

Initially, because of concern that third parties might seek patents on HapMap data, users were required to agree to a web-based "click-wrap license", assenting that they would not prevent others from using the data (http://www.hapmap.org/cgi-perl/registration). In December 2004 this license

优先进行基因分型。两个全基因组的基于芯片的基因分型试剂被高效用于增加 SNP 密度：40,000 个 SNP 来自 Illumina，120,000 个 SNP 来自 Affymetrix[100]。

为了监控进度，基因组被分成 5 kb 的块，基因分型通过迭代循环持续进行，直到满足在各个分析小组中预先确定的一套"停止规则"。(1) 最小等位基因频率：在各个分析小组中每个 5 kb 块均获得一个常见 SNP(MAF ≥ 0.05)。(2) 间隔：相邻 SNP 间的距离是 2 ~ 8 kb，50 kb 区域内至少有 9 个 SNP。(3)"可被 HapMap 的"基因组：使用现有技术研究着丝粒、端粒、基因组序列缺口和片段重复还比较有挑战性。本计划鉴定了占已完成的人类基因组序列的 4.4% 的区域[101]（补充信息表 9），在这些区域内设计基因分型实验只需要尝试一次。(4) 三振出局：如果在一个给定的 5 kb 区域内设计一个基因分型实验时经过三次尝试而上述规则都不满足，或者如果 dbSNP 中所有 SNP 都已经被尝试了，则对于第 I 阶段 HapMap，基因分型被认为是完整的。如果其中一次尝试针对的是一个在之前的全基因组调查中在合适的种群样本中 MAF ≥ 0.05 的 SNP[77]，则两次尝试也被认为是足够的。(5) 质量控制：不间断的标准化质量控制(QC)过滤和三轮质量评估(QA)被用来确保和记录基因型数据的高质量。

我们系统实施了 QC 过滤，检验各个 SNP 的完整性(> 80%)、五个重复基因型间的一致性(≤ 1 个不一致)、60 个三联家系中的孟德尔遗传(在 YRI 和 CEU 中均 ≤ 1 个不一致)，以及哈迪–温伯格平衡($P > 0.001$[102])。第 I 阶段数据集中的 SNP 在所有分析小组中都通过了所有的 QC 过滤，并且在 HapMap 样本中是多态性的。失败的 SNP 也被释放（含有一个特殊的标记），因为它们能够帮助鉴定在引物、插入/缺失、同源基因座和自然选择下的多态性。

我们实施了三项 QA。第一是"基准"各个平台和实验室操作手册的一项校准。第二是在计划的中期对各个基因分型中心进行的评估。第三是对完整的第 I 阶段数据集的随机样本进行的盲分析。大量的 SNP 在计划中被基因分型超过一次，或者被其他的研究者进行过分型，这提供了额外的关于数据质量的信息。关于 QA 的完整信息见补充信息。

对于 mtDNA，我们采取了穷举的方法。超过 1,000 个可公开获得的来自非洲(n = 87)、欧洲(n = 928)和亚洲(n = 238)的 mtDNA 序列[34]被用来鉴定在样本中尝试过的 210 个常见变异（在至少一个大陆区域中 MAF ≥ 0.05）。

数据释放　储存在数据协调中心，并在 http://www.hapmap.org、一个日本镜像网站 http://hapmap.jst.go.jp/ 和 dbSNP 上释放的数据包括各个 SNP 在选择时的确定状态、引物序列、基因分型的操作手册、各个样本的基因型、等位基因频率，此外，对于未通过 QC 过滤的 SNP，数据还包含一个表示失败模式的编码。

最初，由于考虑到第三方可能会寻求 HapMap 数据的专利，所有的使用者都被要求同意一项基于网络的"点击同意许可"，表示其同意不会阻止其他人使用数据(http://www.hapmap.

was dropped, and all data were released without restriction into the public domain.

(**437**, 1299-1320; 2005)

Received 11 August; accepted 12 September 2005.

References:

1. Lechler, R. & Warrens, A. *HLA in Health and Disease* 2nd edn (Academic Press, San Diego, California, 2005).

2. Strittmatter, W. J. & Roses, A. D. Apolipoprotein E and Alzheimer's disease. *Annu. Rev. Neurosci.* **19**, 53-77 (1996).

3. Dahlbäck, B. Resistance to activated protein C caused by the factor V R^{506}Q mutation is a common risk factor for venous thrombosis. *Thromb. Haemost.* **78**, 483-488 (1997).

4. Altshuler, D. *et al.* The common PPARγ Pro12Ala polymorphism is associated with decreased risk of type 2 diabetes. *Nature Genet.* **26**, 76-80 (2000).

5. Deeb, S. S. *et al.* A Pro12Ala substitution in PPARγ 2 associated with decreased receptor activity, lower body mass index and improved insulin sensitivity. *Nature Genet.* **20**, 284-287 (1998).

6. Florez, J. C., Hirschhorn, J. & Altshuler, D. The inherited basis of diabetes mellitus: implications for the genetic analysis of complex traits. *Annu. Rev. Genomics Hum. Genet.* **4**, 257-291 (2003).

7. Begovich, A. B. *et al.* A missense single-nucleotide polymorphism in a gene encoding a protein tyrosine phosphatase (*PTPN22*) is associated with rheumatoid arthritis. *Am. J. Hum. Genet.* **75**, 330-337 (2004).

8. Bottini, N. *et al.* A functional variant of lymphoid tyrosine phosphatase is associated with type I diabetes. *Nature Genet.* **36**, 337-338 (2004).

9. Bell, G. I., Horita, S. & Karam, J. H. A polymorphic locus near the human insulin gene is associated with insulin-dependent diabetes mellitus. *Diabetes* **33**, 176-183 (1984).

10. Ueda, H. *et al.* Assocation of the T-cell regulatory gene *CTLA4* with susceptibility to autoimmune disease. *Nature* **423**, 506-511 (2003).

11. Ogura, Y. *et al.* A frameshift mutation in *NOD2* associated with susceptibility to Crohn's disease. *Nature* **411**, 603-606 (2001).

12. Hugot, J. P. *et al.* Association of NOD2 leucine-rich repeat variants with susceptibility to Crohn's disease. *Nature* **411**, 599-603 (2001).

13. Klein, R. J. *et al.* Complement factor H polymorphism in age-related macular degeneration. *Science* **308**, 385-389 (2005).

14. Haines, J. L. *et al.* Complement factor H variant increases the risk of age-related macular degeneration. *Science* **308**, 419-421 (2005).

15. Edwards, A. O. *et al.* Complement factor H polymorphism and age-related macular degeneration. *Science* **308**, 421-424 (2005).

16. Puffenberger, E. G. *et al.* A missense mutation of the endothelin-B receptor gene in multigenic Hirschsprung's disease. *Cell* **79**, 1257-1266 (1994).

17. Emison, E. S. *et al.* A common sex-dependent mutation in a *RET* enhancer underlies Hirschsprung disease risk. *Nature* **434**, 857-863 (2005).

18. Kerem, B. *et al.* Identification of the cystic fibrosis gene: genetic analysis. *Science* **245**, 1073-1080 (1989).

19. Hästbacka, J. *et al.* Linkage disequilibrium mapping in isolated founder populations: diastrophic dysplasia in Finland. *Nature Genet.* **2**, 204-211 (1992).

20. Pritchard, J. K. & Przeworski, M. Linkage disequilibrium in humans: models and data. *Am. J. Hum. Genet.* **69**, 1-14 (2001).

21. Jorde, L. B. Linkage disequilibrium and the search for complex disease genes. *Genome Res.* **10**, 1435-1444 (2000).

22. Reich, D. E. *et al.* Linkage disequilibrium in the human genome. *Nature* **411**, 199-204 (2001).

23. Kruglyak, L. Prospects for whole-genome linkage disequilibrium mapping of common disease genes. *Nature Genet.* **22**, 139-144 (1999).

24. Johnson, G. C. *et al.* Haplotype tagging for the identification of common disease genes. *Nature Genet.* **29**, 233-237 (2001).

25. Nickerson, D. A. *et al.* DNA sequence diversity in a 9.7-kb region of the human lipoprotein lipase gene. *Nature Genet.* **19**, 233-240 (1998).

26. Zhu, X. *et al.* Localization of a small genomic region associated with elevated ACE. *Am. J. Hum. Genet.* **67**, 1144-1153 (2000).

27. Daly, M. J., Rioux, J. D., Schaffner, S. F., Hudson, T. J. & Lander, E. S. High-resolution haplotype structure in the human genome. *Nature Genet.* **29**, 229-232 (2001).

28. Jeffreys, A. J., Kauppi, L. & Neumann, R. Intensely punctate meiotic recombination in the class II region of the major histocompatibility complex. *Nature Genet.* **29**, 217-222 (2001).

29. Patil, N. *et al.* Blocks of limited haplotype diversity revealed by high-resolution scanning of human chromosome 21. *Science* **294**, 1719-1723 (2001).

30. Gabriel, S. B. *et al.* The structure of haplotype blocks in the human genome. *Science* **296**, 2225-2229 (2002).

31. The International HapMap Consortium. The International HapMap Project. *Nature* **426**, 789-796 (2003).

32. The International HapMap Consortium. Integrating ethics and science in the International HapMap Project. *Nature Rev. Genet.* **5**, 467-475 (2004).

33. The ENCODE Project Consortium. The ENCODE (ENCyclopedia Of DNA Elements) Project. *Science* **306**, 636-640 (2004).

34. Herrnstadt, C. *et al.* Reduced-median-network analysis of complete mitochondrial DNA coding-region sequences for the major African, Asian, and European haplogroups. *Am. J. Hum. Genet.* **70**, 1152-1171 (2002).

35. Jobling, M. A. & Tyler-Smith, C. The human Y chromosome: an evolutionary marker comes of age. *Nature Rev. Genet.* **4**, 598-612 (2003).

36. The Y Chromosome Consortium. A nomenclature system for the tree of human Y-chromosomal binary haplogroups. *Genome Res.* **12**, 339-348 (2002).

37. Underhill, P. A. *et al.* The phylogeography of Y chromosome binary haplotypes and the origins of modern human populations. *Ann. Hum. Genet.* **65**, 43-62 (2001).

38. Marchini, J. *et al.* A comparison of phasing algorithms for trios and unrelated individuals. *Am. J. Hum. Genet.* (in the press).

org/cgi-perl/registration）。2004 年 12 月，这一许可被终止，所有数据面向公众无限制释放。

（李平 翻译；常江 审稿）

39. Stephens, M. & Donnelly, P. A comparison of Bayesian methods for haplotype reconstruction from population genotype data. *Am. J. Hum. Genet.* **73**, 1162-1169 (2003).

40. Wright, S. *Evolution and the Genetics of Populations Volume 2: the Theory of Gene Frequencies* 294-295 (Univ. of Chicago Press, Chicago, 1969).

41. Rosenberg, N. A. *et al.* Genetic structure of human populations. *Science* **298**, 2381-2385 (2002).

42. Li, N. & Stephens, M. Modeling linkage disequilibrium and identifying recombination hotspots using single-nucleotide polymorphism data. *Genetics* **165**, 2213-2233 (2003).

43. Pe'er, I. *et al.* Reconciling estimates of linkage disequilibrium in the human genome. *Genome Res.* (submitted).

44. Lichten, M. & Goldman, A. S. Meiotic recombination hotspots. *Annu. Rev. Genet.* **29**, 423-444 (1995).

45. Mouse Genome Sequencing Consortium. Initial sequencing and comparative analysis of the mouse genome. *Nature* **420**, 520-562 (2002).

46. McVean, G. A. *et al.* The fine-scale structure of recombination rate variation in the human genome. *Science* **304**, 581-584 (2004).

47. Crawford, D. C. *et al.* Evidence for substantial fine-scale variation in recombination rates across the human genome. *Nature Genet.* **36**, 700-706 (2004).

48. Kong, A. *et al.* A high-resolution recombination map of the human genome. *Nature Genet.* **31**, 241-247 (2002).

49. Winckler, W. *et al.* Comparison of fine-scale recombination rates in humans and chimpanzees. *Science* **308**, 107-111 (2005).

50. Myers, S. R. & Griffiths, R. C. Bounds on the minimum number of recombination events in a sample history. *Genetics* **163**, 375-394 (2003).

51. Hudson, R. R. & Kaplan, N. L. Statistical properties of the number of recombination events in the history of a sample of DNA sequences. *Genetics* **111**, 147-164 (1985).

52. Phillips, M. S. *et al.* Chromosome-wide distribution of haplotype blocks and the role of recombination hot spots. *Nature Genet.* **33**, 382-387 (2003).

53. Chapman, J. M., Cooper, J. D., Todd, J. A. & Clayton, D. G. Detecting disease associations due to linkage disequilibrium using haplotype tags: a class of tests and the determinants of statistical power. *Hum. Hered.* **56**, 18-31 (2003).

54. Carlson, C. S. *et al.* Selecting a maximally informative set of single-nucleotide polymorphisms for association analyses using linkage disequilibrium. *Am. J. Hum. Genet.* **74**, 106-120 (2004).

55. de Bakker, P. I. W. *et al.* Efficiency and power in genetic association studies. *Nature Genet.* Advance online publication, 23 October 2005 (doi:10.1038/ng1669).

56. Lin, S., Chakravarti, A. & Cutler, D. J. Exhaustive allelic transmission disequilibrium tests as a new approach to genome-wide association studies. *Nature Genet.* **36**, 1181-1188 (2004).

57. Weale, M. E. *et al.* Selection and evaluation of tagging SNPs in the neuronal-sodium-channel gene *SCN1A*: implications for linkage-disequilibrium gene mapping. *Am. J. Hum. Genet.* **73**, 551-565 (2003).

58. Stram, D. O. *et al.* Choosing haplotype-tagging SNPs based on unphased genotype data using a preliminary sample of unrelated subjects with an example from the Multiethnic Cohort Study. *Hum. Hered.* **55**, 27-36 (2003).

59. de la Chapelle, A. & Wright, F. A. Linkage disequilibrium mapping in isolated populations: the example of Finland revisited. *Proc. Natl Acad. Sci. USA* **95**, 12416-12423 (1998).

60. Mootha, V. K. *et al.* Identification of a gene causing human cytochrome c oxidase deficiency by integrative genomics. *Proc. Natl Acad. Sci. USA* **100**, 605-610 (2003).

61. Engert, J. C. *et al.* ARSACS, a spastic ataxia common in northeastern Québec, is caused by mutations in a new gene encoding an 11.5-kb ORF. *Nature Genet.* **24**, 120-125 (2000).

62. Richter, A. *et al.* Location score and haplotype analyses of the locus for autosomal recessive spastic ataxia of Charlevoix-Saguenay, in chromosome region 13q11. *Am. J. Hum. Genet.* **64**, 768-775 (1999).

63. Chakraborty, R. & Weiss, K. M. Admixture as a tool for finding linked genes and detecting that difference from allelic association between loci. *Proc. Natl Acad. Sci. USA* **85**, 9119-9123 (1988).

64. Smith, M. W. & O'Brien, S. J. Mapping by admixture linkage disequilibrium: advances, limitations and guidelines. *Nature Rev. Genet.* **6**, 623-632 (2005).

65. Smith, M. W. *et al.* A high-density admixture map for disease gene discovery in African Americans. *Am. J. Hum. Genet.* **74**, 1001-1013 (2004).

66. Zhu, X. *et al.* Admixture mapping for hypertension loci with genome-scan markers. *Nature Genet.* **37**, 177-181 (2005).

67. Zhao, X. *et al.* An integrated view of copy number and allelic alterations in the cancer genome using single nucleotide polymorphism arrays. *Cancer Res.* **64**, 3060-3071 (2004).

68. Huang, J. *et al.* Whole genome DNA copy number changes identified by high density oligonucleotide arrays. *Hum. Genomics* **1**, 287-299 (2004).

69. Iafrate, A. J. *et al.* Detection of large-scale variation in the human genome. *Nature Genet.* **36**, 949-951 (2004).

70. Sebat, J. *et al.* Large-scale copy number polymorphism in the human genome. *Science* **305**, 525-528 (2004).

71. Stankiewicz, P. & Lupski, J. R. Genome architecture, rearrangements and genomic disorders. *Trends Genet.* **18**, 74-82 (2002).

72. Gonzalez, E. *et al.* The influence of *CCL3L1* gene-containing segmental duplications on HIV-1/AIDS susceptibility. *Science* **307**, 1434-1440 (2005).

73. Singleton, A. B. *et al.* α-Synuclein locus triplication causes Parkinson's disease. *Science* **302**, 841 (2003).

74. McCarroll, S. *et al.* Common deletion variants in the human genome. *Nature Genet.* (in the press).

75. Stefansson, H. *et al.* A common inversion under selection in Europeans. *Nature Genet.* **37**, 129-137 (2005).

76. Myers, S., Bottolo, L., Freeman, C., McVean, G. & Donnelly, P. A fine-scale map of recombination rates and recombination hotspots in the human genome. *Science* **310**, 321-324 (2005).

77. Hinds, D. A. *et al.* Whole-genome patterns of common DNA variation in three human populations. *Science* **307**, 1072-1079 (2005).

78. Yu, A. *et al.* Comparison of human genetic and sequence-based physical maps. *Nature* **409**, 951-953 (2001).

79. Broman, K. W., Murray, J. C., Sheffield, V. C., White, R. L. & Weber, J. L. Comprehensive human genetic maps: individual and sex-specific variation in

recombination. *Am. J. Hum. Genet.* **63**, 861-869 (1998).

80. Weissenbach, J. *et al.* A second-generation linkage map of the human genome. *Nature* **359**, 794-801 (1992).

81. Fullerton, S. M., Bernardo Carvalho, A. & Clark, A. G. Local rates of recombination are positively correlated with GC content in the human genome. *Mol. Biol. Evol.* **18**, 1139-1142 (2001).

82. Dawson, E. *et al.* A first-generation linkage disequilibrium map of human chromosome 22. *Nature* **418**, 544-548 (2002).

83. Begun, D. J. & Aquadro, C. F. Levels of naturally occurring DNA polymorphism correlate with recombination rates in *D. melanogaster. Nature* **356**, 519-520 (1992).

84. Smith, A. V., Thomas, D. J., Munro, H. M. & Abecasis, G. R. Sequence features in regions of weak and strong linkage disequilibrium. *Genome Res.* **15**, 1519-1534 (2005).

85. The Gene Ontology Consortium. Gene ontology: tool for the unification of biology. *Nature Genet.* **25**, 25-29 (2000).

86. Trachtenberg, E. *et al.* Advantage of rare HLA supertype in HIV disease progression. *Nature Med.* **9**, 928-935 (2003).

87. Pehrson, J. R. & Fuji, R. N. Evolutionary conservation of histone macroH2A subtypes and domains. *Nucleic Acids Res.* **26**, 2837-2842 (1998).

88. Modrich, P. & Lahue, R. Mismatch repair in replication fidelity, genetic recombination, and cancer biology. *Annu. Rev. Biochem.* **65**, 101-133 (1996).

89. Nielsen, R. Human genomics: disclosure of variation. *Nature* **434**, 288-289 (2005).

90. Enattah, N. S. *et al.* Identification of a variant associated with adult-type hypolactasia. *Nature Genet.* **30**, 233-237 (2002).

91. Bersaglieri, T. *et al.* Genetic signatures of strong recent positive selection at the lactase gene. *Am. J. Hum. Genet.* **74**, 1111-1120 (2004).

92. Sabeti, P. C. *et al.* Detecting recent positive selection in the human genome from haplotype structure. *Nature* **419**, 832-837 (2002).

93. Dermitzakis, E. T. *et al.* Numerous potentially functional but non-genic conserved sequences on human chromosome 21. *Nature* **420**, 578-582 (2002).

94. Margulies, E. H., Blanchette, M., Haussler, D. & Green, E. D. Identification and characterization of multi-species conserved sequences. *Genome Res.* **13**, 2507-2518 (2003).

95. Need, A. C., Motulsky, A. G. & Goldstein, D. B. Priorities and standards in pharmacogenetic research. *Nature Genet.* **37**, 671-681 (2005).

96. Brem, R. B., Storey, J. D., Whittle, J. & Kruglyak, L. Genetic interactions between polymorphisms that affect gene expression in yeast. *Nature* **436**, 701-703 (2005).

97. Istrail, S. *et al.* Whole-genome shotgun assembly and comparison of human genome assemblies. *Proc. Natl Acad. Sci. USA* **101**, 1916-1921 (2004).

98. Venter, J. C. *et al.* The sequence of the human genome. *Science* **291**, 1304-1351 (2001).

99. The Chimpanzee Sequencing and Analysis Consortium. Initial sequence of the chimpanzee genome and comparison with the human genome. *Nature* **437**, 69-87 (2005).

100. Matsuzaki, H. *et al.* Genotyping over 100,000 SNPs on a pair of oligonucleotide arrays. *Nature Methods* **1**, 109-111 (2004).

101. Bailey, J. A. *et al.* Recent segmental duplications in the human genome. *Science* **297**, 1003-1007 (2002).

102. Wigginton, J. E., Cutler, D. J. & Abecasis, G. R. A note on exact tests of Hardy–Weinberg equilibrium. *Am. J. Hum. Genet.* **76**, 887-893 (2005).

103. Hill, W. G. & Weir, B. S. Maximum-likelihood estimation of gene location by linkage disequilibrium. *Am. J. Hum. Genet.* **54**, 705-714 (1994).

Supplementary Information is linked to the online version of the paper at www.nature.com/nature.

Acknowledgements. We thank many people who contributed to this project: J. Beck, C. Beiswanger, D. Coppock, A. Leach, J. Mintzer and L. Toji (Coriell Institute for Medical Research) for transforming the Yoruba, Japanese and Han Chinese samples, distributing the DNA and cell lines, storing the samples for use in future research, and producing the community newsletters and reports; J. Greenberg and R. Anderson (NIH National Institute of General Medical Sciences) for providing funding and support for cell line transformation and storage in the NIGMS Human Genetic Cell Repository at the Coriell Institute; T. Dibling, T. Ishikura, S. Kanazawa, S. Mizusawa and S. Saito (SNP Research Center, RIKEN) for help with genotyping; C. Hind and A. Moghadam for technical support in genotyping and all members of the subcloning and sequencing teams at the Wellcome Trust Sanger Institute; X. Ke (Wellcome Trust Centre for Human Genetics at the University of Oxford) for help with data analysis; Oxford E-Science Centre for provision of high-performance computing resources; H. Chen, W. Chen, L. Deng, Y. Dong, C. Fu, L. Gao, H. Geng, J. Geng, M. He, H. Li, H. Li, S. Li, X. Li, B. Liu, Z. Liu, F. Lu, F. Lu, G. Lu, C. Luo, X. Wang, Z. Wang, C. Ye and X. Yu (Beijing Genomics Institute) for help with genotyping and sample collection; X. Feng, Y. Li, J. Ren and X. Zhou (Beijing Normal University) for help with sample collection; J. Fan, W. Gu, W. Guan, S. Hu, H. Jiang, R. Lei, Y. Lin, Z. Niu, B. Wang, L. Yang, W. Yang, Y. Wang, Z. Wang, S. Xu, W. Yan, H. Yang, W. Yuan, C. Zhang, J. Zhang, K. Zhang and G. Zhao (Chinese National Human Genome Center at Shanghai) for help with genotyping; P. Fong, C. Lai, C. Lau, T. Leung, L. Luk and W. Tong (University of Hong Kong, Genome Research Centre) for help with genotyping; C. Pang (Chinese University of Hong Kong) for help with genotyping; K. Ding, B. Qiang, J. Zhang, X. Zhang and K. Zhou (Chinese National Human Genome Center at Beijing) for help with genotyping; Q. Fu, S. Ghose, X. Lu, D. Nelson, A. Perez, S. Poole, R. Vega and H. Yonath (Baylor College of Medicine); C. Bruckner, T. Brundage, S. Chow, O. Iartchouk, M. Jain, M. Moorhead and K. Tran (ParAllele Bioscience Inc.); N. Addleman, J. Atilano, T. Chan, C. Chu, C. Ha, T. Nguyen, M. Minton and A. Phong (UCSF) for help with genotyping, and D. Lind (UCSF) for help with quality control and experimental design; R. Donaldson and S. Duan (Washington University) for help with genotyping, and J. Rice and N. Saccone (Washington University) for help with experimental design; J. Wigginton (University of Michigan) for help with implementing and testing QA/QC software; A. Clark, B. Keats, R. Myers, D. Nickerson and A. Williamson for providing advice to NIH; J. Melone, M. Weiss and E. DeHaut-Combs (NHGRI) for help with project management; M. Gray for organizing phone calls and meetings; D. Leja for help with figures; the Yoruba people of Ibadan, Nigeria, the people of Tokyo, Japan, and the community at Beijing Normal University, who participated in public consultations and community engagements; the people in these communities who were generous in donating their blood samples; and the people in the Utah CEPH community who allowed the samples they donated earlier to be used for the Project. We also thank A. Clark, E. Lander, C. Langley and R. Lifton for comments on earlier drafts of the manuscript. This work was supported by the Japanese Ministry of Education, Culture,

Sports, Science, and Technology, the Wellcome Trust, Nuffield Trust, Wolfson Foundation, UK EPSRC, Genome Canada, Génome Québec, the Chinese Academy of Sciences, the Ministry of Science and Technology of the People's Republic of China, the National Natural Science Foundation of China, the Hong Kong Innovation and Technology Commission, the University Grants Committee of Hong Kong, the SNP Consortium, the US National Institutes of Health (FIC, NCI, NCRR, NEI, NHGRI, NIA, NIAAA, NIAID, NIAMS, NIBIB, NIDA, NIDCD, NIDCR, NIDDK, NIEHS, NIGMS, NIMH, NINDS, NLM, OD), the W.M. Keck Foundation, and the Delores Dore Eccles Foundation.

Author Contributions. David Altshuler, Lisa D. Brooks, Aravinda Chakravarti, Francis S. Collins, Mark J. Daly and Peter Donnelly are members of the writing group responsible for this manuscript.

Author Information. Reprints and permissions information is available at npg.nature.com/reprintsandpermissions. The authors declare competing financial interests: details accompany the paper at www.nature.com/nature. Correspondence and requests for materials should be addressed to D.A. (altshuler@molbio.mgh.harvard.edu) or P.D. (donnelly@stats.ox.ac.uk).

Rain, Winds and Haze during the Huygens Probe's Descent to Titan's Surface

M. G. Tomasko *et al.*

Editor's Note

The Cassini spacecraft carried the Huygens mission, whose goal was to land on the surface of Saturn's largest moon, Titan. During Huygens' parachute descent, an array of instruments studied the moon's atmosphere, winds and surface. The lander survived on the surface for about three hours. This paper is one of two presenting the key findings of the mission. It reports that the moon's surface contains features resembling those made by flowing liquid on Earth, presumably due to liquid hydrocarbons. The landing site looks like a dry river or lake bed, scattered with small rounded "rocks", which are probably hydrocarbon-coated water ice. The atmospheric haze that obscures the surface from telescopes is made of small particles, most probably of complex and as yet poorly characterized organic matter.

The irreversible conversion of methane into higher hydrocarbons in Titan's stratosphere implies a surface or subsurface methane reservoir. Recent measurements from the cameras aboard the Cassini orbiter fail to see a global reservoir, but the methane and smog in Titan's atmosphere impedes the search for hydrocarbons on the surface. Here we report spectra and high-resolution images obtained by the Huygens Probe Descent Imager/Spectral Radiometer instrument in Titan's atmosphere. Although these images do not show liquid hydrocarbon pools on the surface, they do reveal the traces of once flowing liquid. Surprisingly like Earth, the brighter highland regions show complex systems draining into flat, dark lowlands. Images taken after landing are of a dry riverbed. The infrared reflectance spectrum measured for the surface is unlike any other in the Solar System; there is a red slope in the optical range that is consistent with an organic material such as tholins, and absorption from water ice is seen. However, a blue slope in the near-infrared suggests another, unknown constituent. The number density of haze particles increases by a factor of just a few from an altitude of 150 km to the surface, with no clear space below the tropopause. The methane relative humidity near the surface is 50 per cent.

THE surface of Titan has long been studied with various instruments, including those on the Hubble Space Telescope (HST) and ground-based adaptive optics systems[1]. More recently, Cassini investigations using the charge-coupled device (CCD) camera[2], the

惠更斯空间探测器下落至土卫六
表面过程中的雨、风和雾霾

托马斯科等

编者按

卡西尼号土星探测器承担着惠更斯计划，惠更斯号探测器的目标是在土星最大的卫星土卫六的表面着陆。在惠更斯号打开降落伞的降落阶段，一系列探测仪器研究了土卫六的大气、风以及地表。着陆器在卫星表面工作了约3个小时。本文是报道本次探测任务主要发现的两篇文章之一，文章指出卫星的表面存在一些地貌特征，类似地球表面上液体流动留下的痕迹，推测可能和液态的烃有关。着陆点看起来像干涸的河床或者湖床，遍布圆球形的小"岩石"，这些很有可能是烃包被的水冰。由于大气中雾霾的存在，使得从望远镜只能观察到模糊的地表影像。雾霾是由细小粒子构成的，很可能成分复杂且存在迄今为止不为人知的有机物质。

在土卫六平流层探测到甲烷转变为高级烃的不可逆过程，这意味着土卫六的表面或地下存在甲烷储备。最近卡西尼轨道飞行器上搭载的照相机进行的观测并没能发现全球性的甲烷储备，但是土卫六大气中的甲烷和浓雾阻碍了在其表面寻找烃的工作。本文中，我们将报道惠更斯探测器在土卫六大气降落过程中，搭载的惠更斯降落成像仪/光谱辐射计测得的光谱和高分辨率图像。尽管这些图像并没有直接展现土卫六表面的液态烃湖，但是确实存在液态物质在土卫六表面流过留下的痕迹。土卫六上的地貌与地球表面有惊人的相似性，比较明亮的高地区域存在复杂交错的沟渠系统，它们汇入平坦而阴暗的低地。惠更斯号着陆后拍摄的照片显示的环境是一处干涸的河床。土卫六表面测得的红外反射光谱，不同于太阳系内任何其他已知的天体，在其光学波段的红端（较大波长）存在倾斜谱结构（红坡），这与一类有机物质（比如索林斯）的光谱特征相一致，水冰的吸收峰是可见的。尽管如此，近红外区域的蓝端倾斜结构（蓝坡）则预示另外一种未知的成分的存在。雾霾颗粒的数量密度从150 km的海拔到表面增大了数倍，并且在对流顶层以下没有明显的净空区域。甲烷在地表附近的相对湿度为50%。

借助包括哈勃空间望远镜（HST）搭载的仪器和地基自适应光学系统等在内的各种仪器，人们已经对土卫六的表面进行了长期的研究[1]。最近，卡西尼号飞船使用

Visible and Infrared Mapping Spectrometer (VIMS) instrument[3], and the Radio Detection and Ranging (RADAR) imaging system[4] have provided more detailed views of Titan's surface in the hope of revealing how the methane in Titan's atmosphere is replenished from the surface or interior of Titan. Of the Cassini imagers, the Imaging Science Subsystem (ISS) camera is potentially capable of the greatest spatial resolution, but Titan's obscuring haze limits its resolution on the surface to about 1 km, a value roughly similar to that available from VIMS and the radar imaging system. At this resolution, the bright and dark regions observed on the surface of Titan have proved difficult to interpret. Owing to its proximity to the surface, the Descent Imager/Spectral Radiometer (DISR) camera on the Huygens probe was capable of a linear resolution of some metres from a height of 10 km. In addition, the lower the probe descended, the less haze lay between the camera and the ground. The DISR was capable of linear resolution orders of magnitude better than has been available from orbit, although of a much smaller portion of Titan's surface. Also, a lamp was used at low altitude to measure the continuous reflectance spectrum of the surface without the complications introduced by observations through large amounts of methane and aerosol haze[5].

In addition to studying the surface of Titan, the DISR took measurements of solar radiation in the atmosphere. Spectrometers looking upward at continuum wavelengths (between the major methane absorptions) as well as downward measured the vertical distribution and wavelength dependence of the aerosol haze opacity. Measurements of the polarization of light at a scattering angle of $90°$ constrained the small dimension of the haze particles. Measurements of the brightness in the solar aureole around the Sun determined the projected area of the haze particles. Observations in the methane bands determined the methane mole fraction profile.

Data collection during the descent proceeded mostly, although not exactly, as planned. Turbulence during the first half of the descent tipped the probe more rapidly than expected, causing the Sun sensor to remain locked on the azimuth of the Sun for only a few successive rotations at a time. Below about 35 km, the signal from the direct solar beam was lost by the Sun sensor owing to the unexpectedly low temperature of this detector. These effects caused data from each of the DISR sub-instruments to be collected at mostly random, instead of specific, azimuths. Additionally, the probe rotated in the intended direction for only the first ten minutes before rotating in the opposite sense for the remainder of the descent. This resulted in ineffective baffling of the direct solar beam for the upward-looking visible spectrometer and the solar aureole camera. Consequently, some measurements made by the solar aureole camera are saturated, and the separation of the direct and diffuse solar beams in the visible spectral measurements must be postponed until a good model of the probe attitude versus time is available. Finally, the loss of one of the two radio communication channels in the probe receiver aboard the orbiter resulted in the loss of half the images as well as several other low-altitude spectrometer measurements.

Despite these misfortunes, the DISR instrument collected a unique and very useful data set. Images of the surface with unprecedented resolution were collected over the boundary

774

自身搭载的电荷耦合器件（CCD）照相机 [2]、可见光和红外测绘光谱仪（VIMS）[3] 以及雷达成像系统 [4]，对土卫六表面进行了更加仔细的观测，并期望能够揭示土卫六上的甲烷是如何从地表或地下重新回到大气中的。在卡西尼号所有的成像仪中，成像科学子系统（ISS）有能力可以获得最高的空间分辨率，但是在土卫六表面雾霾的影响下，其分辨率被限制在与 VIMS 以及雷达成像系统大致相当的水平，仅为 1 km 左右。在这一分辨率下，土卫六表面上被观测到的明亮和阴暗的区域被证明是难以解译的。由于惠更斯空间探测器接近土卫六表面，它搭载的降落成像仪 / 光谱辐射计（DISR）相机在 10 km 的高度可以获得米量级的线性分辨率。此外，探测器高度越低，则相机与地面之间的雾霾的厚度越小。这样，DISR 可以获得比在轨道上高数个量级的线性分辨率，但观测到的土卫六地表范围减小很多。同时，惠更斯号在较低的高度借助照明灯测量了表面的连续反射光谱，这样避免了透过大量的甲烷和气溶胶薄雾进行观测所引起的光谱复杂性 [5]。

除了研究土卫六表面，DISR 系统还测量了大气中的太阳辐射。采用连续波段（甲烷主吸收峰之间的波段），光谱仪分别朝上和朝下测量了薄雾在垂直方向上的分布及其不同波长的不透明度。在 90° 散射角处测量光的偏振可以约束雾霾颗粒是小颗粒的，而对太阳周围的日晕亮度的测量可以确定雾霾颗粒的投影面积。甲烷波段的观测可以确定甲烷的摩尔分数。

在惠更斯号降落过程中，尽管数据的采集工作基本按预定计划进行，但也出现了一些意外情况。在降落过程的前半段，湍流造成的探测器的倾斜比预期要快很多，这导致探测器每次保持太阳传感器锁定在太阳所在的方向角的姿态只能持续几次探测器旋转周期。降至约 35 km 以下，由于探测器的温度出乎意料的低，太阳传感器无法感应来自太阳光直射的信号。以上意外导致 DISR 子设备得到的数据并没能像预计的一样从特定的方位角方向获取，大部分都有随机的方位角。另一件意料之外的事情是，探测器仅仅在前 10 分钟内按照预定的方向旋转，然后在剩余的下降时间就一直以相反的方向转动。这导致与朝上观测的可见光谱分析仪和太阳光晕照相机有关的直射太阳光没有被有效地遮挡。因此，太阳光晕照相机进行的某些测量过度曝光，可见光谱测量中的直射太阳光束与弥散太阳光束暂时也难以有效分离，除非找到关于探测器姿态与时间关系的合理模型。最后，轨道器搭载的探测器接收天线损失掉了两个无线电通信频道中的一个，造成一半图像丢失，同时也造成光谱仪部分低空测量数据的丢失。

尽管遭遇了这些不幸，DISR 中的设备还是采集到了一个独一无二且非常有用的数据集。轨道器拍摄到了明亮区域和暗区域之间的边界地带史无前例的高分辨率图

between bright and dark terrain seen from the orbiter. Owing to redundant transmission over both communication channels during most of the descent, almost all of the spectral and solar aureole observations were received. A very large set of high-quality spectra were obtained with good altitude resolution and with good coverage in azimuth both away from and towards the Sun. The images, the spectra, the Sun sensor pulses, the recording of the gain in the Cassini radio receiver, and information from Very Long Baseline Interferometry (VLBI) observations from Earth together will permit reconstruction of the probe attitude relative to the Sun as a function of time during the descent, enabling a full analysis of the spectral data. The large number of solar aureole measurements included several acquired near the Sun and many polarization measurements opposite to the Sun. The surface science lamp worked exactly as planned, permitting surface reflection measurements even in strong methane absorption bands. Operations after landing included the collection of successive images as well as spectral reflectance measurements of the surface illuminated by the lamp from an assumed height of roughly 30 cm.

Taken together, the new observations shed substantial light on the role played by methane in forming the surface of Titan and how it is recycled into the atmosphere. The substantial relative humidity of methane at the surface and the obvious evidence of fluid flow on the surface provide evidence for precipitation of methane onto the surface and subsequent evaporation. Some indications of cryovolcanic flows are also seen. The vertical distribution and optical properties of Titan's haze have been characterized to aid the interpretation of remote measurements of the spectral reflection of the surface. The speed and direction of Titan's winds has also been measured for comparison with future dynamical models that include the radiative heating and cooling rates implied by the haze.

Physical Processes That Form the Surface

The imagers provided views of Titan's previously unseen surface, thus allowing a deeper understanding of the moon's geology. The three DISR cameras were designed to provide overlapping coverage for an unbroken 360°-wide swath stretching from nadir angles between 6° and 96°. Some 20 sets of such images were planned during the descent. Because of the opacity of the haze in the passband of our imager, surface features could be discerned in the images only below about 50 km, limiting the number of independent panoramic mosaics that can be made of the surface. The loss of half of the images meant that Titan's surface was not covered by systematic overlapping triplets, as expected. Three different views of Titan's surface are shown in Figs 1 to 3. A view of Titan's surface after the Huygens landing is shown in Fig. 4.

The highest view (Fig. 1), projected from an altitude of 34 km, displays an albedo variation very similar to the highest-resolution images provided by the ISS or VIMS cameras on the Cassini orbiter. It shows Titan's surface to consist of brighter regions separated by lanes or lineaments of darker material. No obvious impact features are visible, although craters less than roughly 10 km should not be abundant as a result of atmospheric shielding[6]. In the

像。在下降过程的大部分时间，两个通信频道都进行了冗余传输，这使得我们可以接收到大部分光谱以及太阳光晕的观测结果。惠更斯探测器获得了大量高质量的光谱，并且无论是朝向太阳还是背向太阳都具有极佳的高度分辨率和方位覆盖。通过获得的图像、光谱、太阳传感器脉冲、卡西尼无线电接收机的增益记录以及地球上甚长基线干涉测量（VLBI）信息，我们可以重建出下降阶段中探测器相对太阳的姿态随时间的变化函数，从而使我们能够全面地分析光谱数据。所获得的大量的太阳光晕测量包括在指向太阳方向附近进行的一些测量和大量的背向太阳方向的偏振测量。用于土卫六表面测量的科学照明灯完全按预期进行工作，使得即使是在强甲烷吸收波段中，也可以进行表面反射光谱的相关测量。探测器着陆后的操作包括采集连续图像以及测量地表的光谱反射率，其中反射率测量中照明灯在高度约为 30 cm 提供照明。

综上，惠更斯探测器进行的最新观测在相当程度上揭示了甲烷在土卫六地表形成过程中的作用，以及甲烷是如何通过循环进入大气的。地表附近甲烷有较高的相对湿度，而且地表明显存在液体流动的痕迹，这些证据表明甲烷经历了凝结降落以及再蒸发的循环过程。同时，也发现了冰火山作用相关的流动构造的迹象。土卫六上雾霾的垂直分布和光学属性也被确定，有助于解释地表谱反射率的遥测结果。另外，探测器对土卫六上的风速和风向也进行了测量，可以用于和将来的动力学模型的对比，模型将包含由雾霾得出的辐射加热速率与冷却速率。

形成土卫六表面的物理过程

惠更斯探测器上的成像仪提供了大量前所未有的关于土卫六地表的信息，使得更加深入地了解这颗卫星的地质情况成为可能。DISR 系统的三台照相机可以提供 360° 水平无缝覆盖全景图像，其天底角介于 6° 到 96° 之间。探测器原本预计在下降过程中拍摄大约 20 组这样的照片。由于雾霾对于成像仪的滤波通带的不透明性，只有在约 50 km 以下高度拍摄的照片中才能分辨出地表特征，从而也限制了不同的表面全景拼接图像的数量。同时，前面提到的图像丢失一半意味着土卫六的表面不能够按预期那样被三台照相机所拍摄的照片系统的交叠全部覆盖。图 1 到图 3 给出了土卫六表面的三幅图片。图 4 给出了惠更斯探测器着陆后拍摄的一幅地表图片。

视角最高的视图（图 1）是以 34 km 高度作为基点进行的投影，表明星体反照率的变化，这种变化与卡西尼轨道器上的 ISS 或 VIMS 照相机提供的最高分辨率图像非常相似。从图像中可知，土卫六表面由明亮区域以及分割这些区域的较暗的水道或线性构造构成。尽管由于大气的遮挡可以观察到的直径小于 10 km 的陨石坑应该

rightmost (eastern) part of the mosaic the images become sharper as the lower altitude of the camera causes the scale to decrease and the contrast to increase. More than a dozen brighter areas in that region seem to be elongated along a direction parallel with the main bright/dark boundary of that region. At the limit of resolution, narrow dark channels cut the bright terrain.

Fig. 1. View of Titan from 34 km above its surface. High-altitude (49 to 20 km) panoramic mosaic constructed from the DISR High and Medium Resolution Imagers (HRI and MRI) as projected from 34 km. The preliminary ground-track solution (indicated as small white points on gnomonic ground projection) represents the location of the probe when data were collected; north points up; scale indicated (although subsequent analysis indicates that north lies some 5–10° to the left of straight up in this and the two subsequent figures). Starting from the first surface image at 49 km, the probe moves in an east-northeastwardly direction at an initial speed of 20 m s⁻¹. Brighter regions separated by lanes or lineaments of darker material are seen. No obvious crater-like features are visible. The circle indicates the outline of the next-lowest pan, in Fig. 2. The method used for construction of panoramic mosaics incorporates knowledge of the probe's spatial location (longitude, latitude and altitude) and attitude (roll, pitch and yaw) at each image. With the exception of altitude, provided by the Huygens Atmospheric Structure Instrument[12] pressure sensor, none of these variables was directly measured. They are found through an iterative process in which a panorama is created, providing an improved ground-track and azimuth model, which results in an upgraded trajectory, which can improve the panorama, and so on. The current lack of pitch and roll knowledge constitutes the main source of error in the current composition and quality of the panoramas as well as the ground-track and wind speed determination reported below. Vigorous contrast-stretching in the images is required to reveal details washed out by the haze particle density at all altitudes in Titan's atmosphere. This contrast-stretching also displays the occasional ringing of the Discrete Cosine Transform data compressor, which appear as regular lines of bright and dark patterns, particularly in the MRI images.

The next view, Fig. 2, projected from an altitude of 8 km, reveals a large number of these channels (detailed in Fig. 5). The channel networks have two distinct patterns: short stubby

不会很多，图像中没有看到明显的陨石坑地貌[6]。在拼接图像的最右侧（东侧），图像变得锐度增加，这是由于照相机拍摄时的高度降低，从而使拍摄范围变小，对比度增加。图中十多块明亮区域看似沿主要的明暗边界方向被拉伸了。在现有的最高分辨率下，图中的较为阴暗的狭谷截切了明亮区域。

15 km

图 1. 土卫六上空 34 km 高度拍摄的图像。通过 DISR 高分辨率成像仪和中分辨率成像仪（即 HRI 和 MRI）构成的高空（49～20 km）全景拼接图，以 34 km 高度处作为基点投影。图中用小白点标出了探测器飞行轨迹在地面上的球心投影，这一初步的探测器飞行轨迹地表投影给出了探测器采集数据时的位置。图中正上方为北，比例尺标于图中（后续分析表明，图中实际的北方应该相对竖直向上方向向左偏移约 5°～10°，后面的两幅图也是如此）。探测器从 49 km 的高度开始拍摄第一幅照片，然后以 20 m/s 的初始速度向东北偏东方向飞行。由图可知，较亮的区域被较暗的水道或线性构造分开，但没有发现明显的类似环形山的地貌。图中的圆圈表示下一个全景镜头的轮廓，如图 2 所示。全景图像拼接的构建方法将探测器在拍摄每张照片时的空间定位（经度、纬度和高度）与姿态（滚动、俯仰和偏航）两方面的数据纳入考量。对于以上变量，除了高度可以通过惠更斯大气构造探测仪上的压强传感器直接测量[12]，其他变量都不能被直接测量。以上参数可以通过构建全景图像的迭代过程得到，该迭代过程可以改进探测器轨道的地表投影和方位模型，而模型又可以反过来校正探测器飞行轨道，进一步改善全景图像质量等。俯仰和滚动等姿态信息的缺乏，是目前全景图合成及其图像品质，以及后文轨迹的地面投影和风速确定中误差的主要来源。土卫六大气中的雾霾颗粒将使图像变得模糊不清，因此需要进行足够的对比度增强才能够显示更多的细节。对比度增强的操作也会偶尔表现出离散余弦变换数据压缩器的振荡效应，表现为规律性重复出现的明暗相间的条纹，这种效应对于中分辨率图像的影响特别严重。

下一幅拼接图如图 2 所示，以 8 km 的高度作为基点作投影，展现了大量的沟渠结构（具体细节如图 5 所示）。图中的沟渠网络具有两种明显不同的样式：一种是短

779

features and dendritic features with many branches. The region of the stubby network towards the west is significantly brighter than the dendritic region. The stubby channels are shorter, wider and relatively straight. They are associated with and often begin or end in dark circular areas, which suggest ponds or perhaps pits. The morphology of rectilinear networks with stubby heads is consistent with spring-fed channels or arroyos.

Fig. 2. View from 8 km. Medium-altitude (17 to 8 km) panoramic mosaic projected from 8 km. As in Fig. 1, the preliminary ground-track solution is indicated as points; north is up; scale indicated. At 11 km, the wind direction is at 0° (eastward), reaching −20° (southeastward) at an altitude of 8.5 km. The narrow dark lineaments, interpreted as channels, cut brighter terrain. The circle indicates the outline of the low-altitude pan in Fig. 3.

The dendritic network is consistent with rainfall drainage channels, implying a distributed rather than a localized source of a low-viscosity liquid. Stereo analysis of the dendritic region indicates an elevation of 50–200 m relative to the large darker plain to the south. It suggests that the brighter areas within the darker terrain are higher as well. The topographic differences are evident in Figs 6 and 7, which are three-dimensional renderings of the area just north of the landing site produced from the DISR images. They include the major bright–dark interface seen from above in Fig. 5. Figure 2 depicts many examples of these darker lanes of material between topographically higher, brighter areas. In fact the low contrast of the lowland plane argues that the entire dark region floods, and as the liquid drains the local topography drives flows as seen in the images. If the darker region is interpreted as a dried lakebed, it is too large to have been caused by the creeks and channels visible in the images. It may have been created by other larger river systems or some large-scale catastrophic event, which predates deposition by the rivers seen in these images.

而粗的断株状结构，另一种是具有很多分支的树枝状结构。前者相对更短、更宽和更直。图中指向西侧的断株样网络所在的区域明显比树枝状区域更加明亮。这些断株样沟渠通常起始或终止于深色的圆形区域，这一区域可能是池塘或深坑。以短粗结构为端点的直线网络地貌符合源于泉水的河道或河谷地貌特征。

图 2.8 km 高度的视图，是中空（17~8 km）所拍摄照片的全景拼接图。就像图 1 那样，探测器轨迹地面投影用点表示，图片正上方为北，比例尺标于图中。在 11 km 高度，探测到的风向位于 0°（朝正东方向）；在 8.5 km 高度，探测到的风向变为 −20°（朝东南方向）。图中细窄而暗的线性构造被解译为沟渠，截切了明亮区域。图中圆圈标记出了图 3 中的全景图像轮廓范围。

树枝状网络的地貌特征与降雨控制的水系河道相符，这意味着存在广泛分布的而非局域性的低黏度的液态物质。关于树枝状区域的立体信息分析显示，该区域相对南部的较暗的大型平原地区抬高了 50~200 m；这说明暗色区域内部的亮色区块同样会比周围的暗色区域更高。图 6 和图 7 是通过 DISR 图像生成的着陆点北部区域的三维效果图，它们包含了图 5 俯视图中主要的明暗分界，显然明暗区域的地貌特征存在很大区别。图 2 显示了多个存在于地形较高、较明亮的区域之间的较暗的带状分布的物质的实例。事实上，低地平原的较小的起伏说明整个暗色区域被液态物质湮没，而且地势会驱动液态物质的流动，表现出图像中所见的地貌。如果认为较暗的区域是干涸的湖床，显然面积太大，图像中所见到的小溪和河道不可能汇成这样大的湖泊。因此，暗色区域可能是由其他较大的河流系统汇成或者由某种大尺度的灾变造成，但这种灾变要早于图像中所见的河流沉积地貌。

The interpretation of the dark lanes within the brighter highlands as drainage features is so compelling as to dominate subsequent interpretation of other areas of images such as Figs 2 and 3. The prevailing bright–dark boundary of the region becomes a coastline, the bright areas separated from this boundary become islands. Bright streaks running parallel to the albedo boundary may be drift deposits or splays fractured off the bright highlands owing to faulting along the shoreline.

Fig. 3. View from 1.2 km. Low-altitude (7 to 0.5 km) panoramic mosaic projected from 1,200 m. As in Figs 1 and 2, the preliminary ground track is indicated as points; north is up; scale indicated. The probe's steady east-northeast drift halts altogether at an altitude of 7 km and reverses, moving west-northwest for some 1 km during the last 15 min of descent. Note the ridge near the centre, cut by a dozen darker lanes or channels. The projected landing site is marked with an "X" near the continuation of one of the channels, whose direction matches the orientation of the stream-like clearing in the near-foreground of the southward-looking surface image, Fig. 4.

When coupled with Fig. 4, which is an image of a typical offshore dark region, it is clear that the analogy has a limit. At present there is no liquid in the large dark lakebed imaged in Figs 1 to 5. The bright lobate feature, split by an apparently straight dark lane in the western part of the mosaic in Fig. 2, is a possible fissure-fed cryovolcanic flow. However, Fig. 4 also reveals rocks which—whether made of silicates or, more probably hydrocarbon-coated water-ice—appear to be rounded, size-selected and size-layered as though located in the bed of a stream within the large dark lakebed. Rounded stones approximately 15 cm in diameter and probably composed of water-ice, lie on top of a darker, finer-grained surface.

将明亮高地区域内的暗色条带看作用于排水的河道是非常可信的一种解释，以至于可以直接主导了图 2 和图 3 等其他图像的解译。这样的话，这一区域内主要的明暗边界可以被认为是海岸线，而被这些边界围限的明亮区域可以解释成岛屿。平行于反照率差异边界延伸的明亮条纹可能是冰川沉积物或者是沿海岸线发生断层活动由明亮高地断裂形成的斜面。

图 3. 1.2 km 高度处的视图。在 7 km ~ 0.5 km 范围内拍摄的图像，被用于制作以 1,200 m 为基点的投影全景图像。如图 1 和图 2，初步推测的探测器轨迹地面投影用点表示，图片正上方为北，比例尺标于图中。探测器首先朝东北偏东方向稳定飘移，到达 7 km 高度时完全停止，后反向运动，在下降阶段的最后 15 分钟探测器向西北偏西移动了大约 1 km。值得注意的是，图中心附近的山脊被若干暗色河道切割。探测器的着陆地点在图中的投影位置用"X"标记出，该位置靠近一条渠道的延长段；渠道与图 4 中显示的视角朝南的地表图像靠近前景的类似溪流的净空地带的延伸方向相一致。

图 4 是一片典型的离岸的暗色区域的图像，结合该图可知以上类比显然存在局限性。目前，图 1 至图 5 中的巨型暗色湖床区域并不存在液体。图 2 中西侧被一条直的暗色河道分隔的明亮叶状结构，可能是发源于裂缝的冰岩浆流。然而，图 4 展现的石块就好像是处在大型暗色湖床上的河床内，有较好的磨圆度、分选度和粒序层理，石块的成分可能是硅酸盐，或者更有可能是烃包被的水冰。这些直径大约为 15 cm、可能是由水冰构成的圆形石块位于由更细粒物质构成的更暗的表面之上。

Fig. 4. The view from Titan's surface. Merged MRI and SLI images acquired after the Huygens probe soft-landing. Horizon position implies a pitch of the DISR nose upward by $1.7 \pm 0.2°$ with no measurable roll. "Stones" 10–15 cm in size lie above darker, finer-grained substrate in a variable spatial distribution. Brightening of the upper left side of several rocks suggests solar illumination from that direction, implying a southerly view, which agrees with preliminary evidence from other data sets. A region with a relatively low number of rocks lies between clusters of rocks in the foreground and the background and matches the general orientation of channel-like features in the low-altitude pan of Fig. 3. The bright spot in the lower right corner is the illumination of the DISR surface science lamp.

It is interesting to compare the brightness and colour of the scene shown in Fig. 4 with that of a similar scene on the Earth. The brightness of the surface of the Earth illuminated by full sunlight is about half a million times greater than when illuminated by a full moon. The brightness of the surface of Titan is about a thousand times dimmer than full solar illumination on the Earth (or 500 times brighter than illumination by full moonlight). That is, the illumination level is about that experienced about 10 min after sunset on the Earth. The colour of the sky and the scene on Titan is rather orange due to the much greater attenuation of blue light by Titan's haze relative to red light. If the Sun is high in the sky, it is visible as a small, bright spot, ten times smaller than the solar disk seen from Earth, comparable in size and brightness to a car headlight seen from about 150 m away. The Sun casts sharp shadows, but of low contrast, because some 90% of the illumination comes from the sky. If the Sun is low in the sky, it is not visible.

The sizes of the more than 50 stones in the image in Fig. 4 vary between 3 mm in diameter, the resolution limit of the imager, and 15 cm. No rocks larger than 15 cm are seen. The resolution of the last images taken before landing from a height of 200–300 m would be sufficient to identify metre-sized objects, and none are seen in the 40×35 m field of view. Figure 8 shows the R value, a measure of the fraction of the surface covered by rocks of

图 4. 土卫六表面的图像。该图像是由惠更斯探测器软着陆后拍摄的 MRI 与 SLI 图像拼接而成。由地平线的位置可知 DISR 的仰角为 1.7°±0.2°，但没有可见的左右倾斜。粒径 10～15 cm 的"石块"不均匀地散布在更暗更细粒的基底上。几块岩石的左上部分被照亮，指示了太阳光的照射位于这一方向，即来自南方，这与其他数据得到的初步结论相符。图中前景石块群和远景石块群之间存在石块数量相对较少的区域，其延伸方向与图 3 低空拼接图中沟渠地貌的大体指向相匹配。图中右下角的亮斑是 DISR 地表科学照明灯的照明。

　　将图 4 中场景的亮度、颜色与地球上类似的场景进行比较会是非常有趣的。在地球表面上，太阳直射亮度是满月照射亮度的约 50 万倍。而土卫六表面的亮度是地球上太阳直射亮度的约 1,000 分之一，或者约为地球满月照射亮度的 500 倍。即，这一照明水平相当于地球上日落 10 分钟后的情形。土卫六天空和景观呈现橙色，这是由于土卫六上的雾霾对蓝光的衰减作用远大于对红光的作用。因此，如果太阳高悬于天空，看起来就像一个非常小的亮点，是地球上看到的日面的 10 分之一，其尺寸和亮度与在约 150 m 远的地方看一辆小汽车的前灯的情况相当。太阳在土卫六表面投射下清晰的阴影，但是对比度较低，因为大约 90% 的照明来源于天空。如果太阳在天空的位置较低，则无法看到太阳。

　　对图 4 中 50 多块石头的尺寸进行统计，发现它们的直径尺寸介于 3 mm（成像仪分辨率的极限）到 15 cm 之间，没有发现大于 15 cm 的石块。探测器着陆前的最后一组图像拍摄于 200～300 m 高度，其分辨率足以识别出米量级的物体，然而在 40 m × 35 m 的视场中并没有发现任何这一尺寸的物体。R 值通常被用于表现陨石坑及其周围的溅射物的尺寸–密度分布，在这里表征了土卫六地表被给定尺寸的岩石

a given size frequently used to describe the size distribution of impact craters or crater ejecta. A larger fraction of the surface is covered with rocks greater than 5 cm as opposed to smaller pebbles. The dominance of the cobbles 5–15 cm in size suggests that rocks larger than ~15 cm cannot be transported to the lakebed, while small pebbles (< 5 cm) are quickly removed from the surface. Figure 8 confirms the visual impression given by Fig. 4 that the surface coverage of rocks in the foreground of the image (< 80 cm horizontal distance from the probe) is higher than in the region beyond (about 80–160 cm). However, this trend is not seen for the pebbles less than 5 cm in size.

Elongated dark trails aligned with the general trend of the possible stream-bed visible in the centre of Fig. 4 extend from several of the distant boulders. The direction of the trails agrees with the general northwest–southeast alignment of the stream-like features shown in Fig. 3, because the last upward-looking spectra indicate that the probe settled with DISR facing southward. Images taken from the surface show no traces of the landing of the probe. The viewing direction is probably generally not downwind (the parachute is not visible).

Fig. 5. View of "shoreline" and channels. Panoramic mosaic projected from 6.5 km. showing expanded view of the highlands and bright-dark interface. As in previous figures, north is up; scale indicated. Branching and rectilinear channel networks of dark lanes are shown along an albedo boundary approximately 12 km long.

When coupled with the shapes, size selection and layering of the stones in Fig. 4, the elongated islands and their orientation parallel to the coastline in Fig. 1, the stubby and dendritic channel networks, as well as the ponds in Fig. 2 and Fig. 5, the major elements of the Titan surface albedo variations can be interpreted to be controlled by flow of low-viscosity fluids driven by topographic variation, whether caused by precipitation (the dendritic networks) or spring-fed flows (the stubby networks). We thus interpret the bright–dark albedo difference as follows: irrigation of the bright terrain results in darker material being removed and carried into the channels, which discharge it into the region offshore,

覆盖的比例，图 8 给出了 R 值。土卫六表面大部分被尺寸大于 5 cm 的岩石覆盖而不是更小的卵石，5～15 cm 的鹅卵石占主体，表明尺寸大于 ~15 cm 的石块不能够被运移到湖床，而尺寸较小的卵石（<5 cm）则会很快地被从地表运移走。图 8 中 R 值的分布进一步证实了图 4 给人的视觉印象，即图像前景区域（与探测器的水平距离小于 80 cm）的石块覆盖率高于更远的区域（大约在 80～160 cm）。然而，尺寸小于 5 cm 的石子并没有表现出这种趋势。

从远处几块巨砾延伸出拉长的暗色尾迹，其延伸方向与图 4 中心可辨的疑似河床地形的总体走势平行。同时，尾迹的方向与图 3 中河流状地貌西北–东南的大体走向也相符。因为最后一批朝上拍摄的光谱显示探测器着陆后 DISR 是面向南方的，DISR 在土卫六表面拍摄的图像没有显示探测器着陆的痕迹。视野方向可能不是大体上的下风向（视野内并没有看到降落伞）。

图 5. "海岸线" 和河道的图像。6.5 km 高度投影得到的全景拼接图。该图对高地区域和明暗分界进行了放大。与前面的图像一样，其正上方为北，比例尺标于图中。图上展现了沿大约 12 km 长的反照率边界分布的暗色河道的分支和直线网络。

综合图 4 中石块的形状、尺寸筛选以及层状分布，图 1 中和海岸线平行的拉长的岛屿，以及图 2 和图 5 中的断株状、树枝状河道网络及池塘，可以认为形成土卫六表面反照率变化的主要因素是地形起伏驱动的低黏度流体的流动，这些流体可能是源于降雨（对应树枝状河道网络）或源于泉（对应断株状河道网络）。因此，我们对明暗反照率的不同作以下解释：对明亮地带的冲刷将导致较暗物质被带离并被搬运进河道。河流在离岸区域将这些暗色物质卸载，因此这些区域变暗。如阵风等风成

thereby darkening it. Eolian processes such as wind gusts coupled with Titan's low gravity (compared to Earth) may aid this migration.

The dark channels visible in the lowest panorama (Fig. 3) seem to suggest south-easterly fluid flow across the lower plane, depositing or exposing the brighter materials (water ice?) along the upstream faces of the ridges.

Stereographic rendering of the dendritic channels just north of the probe landing site (Figs 6 and 7) shows that the slopes in bright terrain being dissected by the putative methane river channels are extremely rugged; slopes of the order of 30° are common. This suggests relatively rapid erosion by flows in the river beds, resulting in the deeply incised valleys. Erosion by steep landslides on slopes approaching the angle of repose is probably the primary mechanism by which the rugged topography is formed. Figure 7 shows two stereographic views of the shoreline and hillside north of the landing site.

Fig. 6. Topographic model of highland region ~5 km north of the Huygens landing site. The top panel shows an orthorectified HRI image from stereo pair (vertical view). The middle panel shows a perspective view of the topographic model with ~50° tilt angle. No vertical exaggeration was applied (it is 1:1). The bottom panel shows profiles (a–b and c–d from the top panel) that illustrate the extremely steep topography in the region dissected by the drainages. All dimensions are in metres. A DISR stereo pair (using HRI frame 450 and MRI frame 601) was photogrammetrically analysed using a digital stereo workstation. The overlapping area of stereo coverage is about 1 × 3 km; the convergence angle is ~25°. The coincidence of the drainage patterns with the valley floors gives confidence in the reality of the topographic model;

过程和土卫六（相比地球）较低的引力相结合可能有助于这一物质运移过程。

从图 3 全景图像中的暗色河道看，流体是流向东南方向，穿过低地平原，沿山脊面向上游的坡面沉积下或暴露出明亮的物质（水冰？）。

图 6 和图 7 给出了探测器着陆点北侧的树枝状河道的立体影像，显示被假定的甲烷河流分隔的明亮地带中的斜坡是非常崎岖的，其坡度一般在 30°的量级。这意味着河床遭受了流体相对快速的侵蚀，从而形成了深切河谷。河岸两侧的斜坡经过滑坡作用的侵蚀接近休止角，这种侵蚀过程可能是形成崎岖地形的主要机制。图 7 给出了着陆点北侧海岸线和山坡的立体影像。

图 6. 惠更斯号着陆点北侧约 5 km 处高地区域的地貌模型。其中，上图表示一对立体图（垂直视图）经过正射校正合成的 HRI 图像；中图表示以约 50°倾角观察地貌模型的透视图，其垂直方向比例尺没有放大（1:1）；下图给出了上图中从 a 到 b 以及从 c 到 d 点的地形剖面，展示了被河流系统所分割区域的极为陡峭的地形，三维坐标的单位都是米。我们借助数字立体影像工作站，对两幅 DISR 立体图像（HRI 第 450 帧和 MRI 第 601 帧）进行了摄影测绘分析。两幅立体图像的交叠面积大约为 1 km×3 km，会聚角约为 25°。河流系统的分布与谷底位置的相符使我们相信该地貌模型的真实性，其中高度的精确

the height accuracy is ~20 m. This preliminary model has been arbitrarily levelled so that the elevation differences are only relative.

Figure 7. Titan's surface. Perspective view of Titan's surface using a topographic model of the highland region ~5 km north of the Huygens probe landing site derived from the DISR images. The model in greyscale and false colour shows the elevation (pale white highest). The lowland plane or lakebed is to the left side of the display (in blue); the northern highlands (with the dendritic channels) is to the right.

Fig. 8. Distribution of rock on the surface. Rocks larger than 1.63 cm as an R-plot, frequently used to describe size distribution of impact craters or crater ejecta. If N is the number of rocks per centimetre increment of rock size, the fraction of the surface area A covered by rocks with diameters between d and $d + \Delta d$ is approximately $N \times \Delta d \times d^2 / A$. By keeping the size bin Δd proportional to the diameter d, the quantity $N \times d^3 / A$ (the R value) is also proportional to the surface fraction covered by rocks of diameter d (with a proportionality constant of ~3). The plot shows R values derived from rock counts from the SLI and MRI surface images. For the SLI, R values from counts up to a distance from the probe of 73 cm and up to 161 cm are presented in separate curves. The comparison between the two curves suggests that the count is complete in the displayed size range. The increase of the R value with size corresponds to a higher fraction of the surface covered with large rocks than with smaller ones.

度约为 20 m。值得注意的是，这一初步模型的基准面高度是随意选取的，所以高程的变化是相对的。

图 7. 土卫六表面的图像。由 DISR 图像得到的、惠更斯号探测器着陆点北侧约 5 km 处高地区域的地貌模型的透视图。其中，模型中的灰度和假彩色表示地形的高度（浅白色代表最高）。图中左侧的蓝色区域代表低地或者湖床，而右侧是布满树枝状沟渠的北方高地。

图 8. 地表岩石分布。图中给出了尺寸大于 1.63 cm 的石块的 R 值图，其中 R 通常被用于描述陨石坑及陨石坑周围溅射物的尺寸分布。如果用 N 表示石块尺寸每增加一厘米间隔范围内的石块数量，那么直径介于 d 和 $d+\Delta d$ 之间的石块在大小为 A 的表面积内的覆盖比例为 $N \times \Delta d \times d^2/A$。如果令尺寸间隔 Δd 正比于石块直径 d，则 R 值的大小 $N \times d^3/A$，也正比于直径为 d 的石块覆盖的面积比例，比例常数约为 3。图中 R 值是通过统计 SLI 和 MRI 表面图像中的石块得到的。对于 SLI，距离探测器 73 cm ~ 161 cm 的石块统计结果由单独的一条曲线表现。通过比较这两条曲线可知，计数统计在所示的尺寸范围内都是完整的。图中 R 值随石块尺寸增加而增加，符合大石块的表面覆盖率高于较小石块的现象。

The Wind Profile

Assembly of the panoramic mosaics leads to the construction of a descent trajectory as part of an iterative process of image reconstruction. The trajectory can be used to derive the probe ground track and extract the implied wind velocity as a function of altitude. Correlation of the roughly 200 usable images acquired by DISR during its descent resulted in longitude and latitude values versus time, displayed in Fig. 9. Fitted by polynomials, these ground tracks were differentiated with respect to time and scaled to derive the horizontal wind speed and direction as functions of altitude.

Fig. 9. Probe ground track. **a**, Sub-probe west longitude and latitude histories of the Huygens probe derived from panoramic image reconstructions. Arrows indicate the appropriate vertical axis. The image data points from which the latitude and longitude were derived are shown as triangles and dots respectively. The dotted and solid lines show polynomial fits to the data. Results adjusted to agree with the Descent Trajectory Working Group (DTWG-3) values at 2,200 s after T_0 (mission time). **b**, Probe longitude versus latitude (thicker line) and versus altitude (thinner line). The altitude axis needs to be expanded by a factor of almost six to recover one-to-one correspondence on a linear scale because the total longitudinal variation is less than 4 km. Using the Doppler Wind Experiment's (DWE) high-altitude references[33], the touchdown point (the predicted landing site) was extrapolated to west longitude 192.34°, latitude −10.34°. Using DTWG-3 high-altitude references, the touchdown point was extrapolated to 192.36°, latitude −10.36°.

The results indicate that the probe's steadily increasing eastward drift caused by Titan's

风 况 描 述

构建全景拼接图像的同时可以构造出质量较好的探测器降落过程的空间运动轨迹，这也是图像重建迭代过程的重要部分。通过轨迹可以推导出探测器轨迹在地面上的投影，并且可以提取出不同高度的风速信息。我们将 DISR 在下降阶段获取的大约 200 幅有用图像相互关联，以此计算出探测器的经度和纬度随时间的变化，如图 9 所示。我们对轨迹地面投影进行多项式拟合，然后对时间做微分并换算成实际空间距离，可以得出水平的风速和风向随高度变化的函数。

图 9. 探测器轨迹地面投影。**a**, 根据全景图像重建获得的惠更斯着陆探测器的西经和纬度随时间的变化。图中的箭头指向各自对应的纵轴，三角和圆点分别表示用于推出纬度和经度的图像数据点。图中的点线和实线是对以上数据的拟合曲线。结果已经经过校正以符合下降轨迹工作组（DTWG-3）在 T_0（任务时间）之后 2,200 s 的值。**b**, 探测器经度与纬度（粗线）以及经度与高度（细线）的关系。由于经向距离总变化小于 4 km，与高度对应的轴需要放大接近 6 倍才能实现比例尺上的一一对应。使用多普勒风实验仪（DWE）中的高空数据作为参照 [31]，推算出降落点（预计的着陆点）为西经 192.34°，纬度为 −10.34°。采用 DTWG-3 的高空数据作为参照，则推算出着陆点位于西经 192.36°，纬度 −10.36°。

以上结果表明，探测器从 50 km 高度下降至 30 km 高度过程中，由于土卫六风

prograde winds, as shown in Fig. 10, slowed from near 30 to 10 m s[-1] between altitudes of 50 and 30 km and slowed more rapidly (from 10 to 4 m s[-1]) between altitudes of 30 and 20 km. The winds drop to zero and reverse at around 7 km, near the expected top of the planetary boundary layer, producing a west-northwestwardly motion extending for about 1 km during the last 15 min of the descent (see Fig. 3). The generally prograde nature of the winds between 50 and 10 km agrees with models of Titan's zonal winds available before the arrival of Cassini or the Huygens probe[7], although the wind speed is somewhat less than the average predicted before entry.

Fig. 10. Observed winds. Horizontal wind speed and direction (counter-clockwise from east) as a function of altitude. The green lines are the DISR data and the blue lines are the high altitude DWE data[33] (showing reasonable consistency between the two). The lines on the left show the wind-speed profile, and on the right is the wind direction. The wind is computed from the combined longitude and latitude reconstructions displayed in Fig. 9. Titan's prograde winds slow from about 28 m s[-1] at 50 km to 10 m s[-1] near 30 km altitude, then decrease more rapidly from 30 km (10 m s[-1]) down to 7 km where they drop to zero. Below 7 km (which is near the expected top of the planetary boundary layer) the winds reverse and become retrograde, and the speed increases to about 1 m s[-1] around 2–3 km before dropping to almost zero (~0.3 m s[-1]) near the surface. The direction begins as due east, and then turns through south (beginning between 9–7 km) to the west-northwest between 7–5 km. The winds are extrapolated to be retrograde at the surface, but the two-sigma error bars (not shown) of 1 m s[-1] at the surface could include surface prograde winds. The error bars at 55 km altitude (4 m s[-1]) are consistent with continuity from the DWE measurements.

The planetary boundary layer is calculated to have a thickness of between 4 and 8 km, based on scaling the Earth's near-equatorial planetary-boundary-layer thickness of 1–2 km by the inverse square-rooted ratio of the planetary rotation rates. The minimum horizontal wind speed at 7 km can thus be an indication of entry into the boundary layer[8]. The reversal of wind direction at this altitude is also consistent with the Voyager-derived equatorial temperature profile[9], wherein the temperature gradient changes from dry adiabatic to a sub-adiabatic temperature gradient above 4 km altitude, indicating the top of the boundary layer.

The current ground-track and wind-speed analysis predicts winds of about 0.3 to 1 m s[-1] near the surface. This velocity can be produced by any number of sources including pressure and temperature gradients and tides[10].

的顺行影响平稳地向东飘移，如图 10 所示，但速度从大约 30 m/s 降至 10 m/s；在从 30 km 高度下降至 20 km 高度过程中，速度迅速地从 10 m/s 降至 4 m/s。当探测器降至大约 7 km 高度（靠近预测的行星边界层顶部）时，风速减为零，然后风向改为相反的方向，造成探测器在降落阶段的最后 15 分钟朝西北偏西的方向飘移了约 1 km，如图 3 所示。50 km 到 10 km 高度的风向和土卫六转动的方向相同，这与卡西尼或惠更斯探测器到达前就已提出的土卫六纬向风模型相一致 [7]，但风速比探测器进入前的预测平均值略小。

图 10. 观测到的风况。图中给出了水平风速和风向（自东沿逆时针方向）与高度的关系。其中，绿线代表 DISR 数据，而蓝线代表高空 DWE 数据 [33]，二者之间显示出合理的一致性。图中左侧曲线给出了风速剖面，而右侧曲线给出了风向，这两条曲线由图 9 中的经纬度信息重建得到。土卫六上的顺行风的风速由 50 km 高度处大约 28 km/s 下降到 30 km 高度附近约 10 m/s，最后在 7 km 高度迅速降为 0。在 7 km（靠近预期的行星边界层顶部）以下，风向则变为逆行方向，并且风速在 2～3 km 高度增加到 1 m/s 左右，在到达表面附近时则几乎为 0（～0.3 m/s）。风向首先向正东，然后转向南（起始于 9～7 km），并在 7～5 km 转为西北偏西。尽管地表附近风向的推断结果是反向风，但地表附近 1 m/s 风速的 2σ 误差范围（未在图中显示）包含了一部分顺向风的区间。55 km 高度处（对应风速 4 m/s）的误差范围与 DWE 测量得到的连续性相一致。

对土卫六和地球的旋转速率比值的平方根取倒数，并乘以地球赤道附近的行星边界层厚度（1～2 km），就可以计算出土卫六的行星边界层厚度为 4～8 km。7 km 高度处的最小水平风速，可以被认为是进入行星边界层的信号 [8]。而在 7 km 高度处的风向改变也与旅行者号飞船得出的赤道温度剖面相符 [9]。旅行者号的测量表明，在大于 4 km 的高度，温度梯度从干绝热变化到亚绝热，这意味着边界层的顶部。

目前，通过对探测器轨迹地面投影和风速分析，预测土卫六地表附近的风速大约为 0.3～1 m/s，这一速度可能是由气压、温度梯度和潮汐等因素引起 [10]。

Migration of Surface Material

The acquisition of visible spectra at known locations in the images allowed correlation of the reflectance spectra with different types of terrain. The Downward-Looking Visible Spectrometer (DLVS) was an imaging spectrometer measuring light between 480 and 960 nm as it projected the image of the slit onto the ground into up to 20 spatial resolution elements for nadir angles from 10° to 50°. Spectra were collected at nominally the same azimuths as the images, though often at slightly different altitudes (on different probe rotations). Interpolation between the times at which the spectral and image data were obtained located the spectra within the images. Determination of the surface reflectivity was hindered by scattering from the haze between the camera and the surface as well as by methane absorption. Correlation of the spectra with images was therefore best performed on measurements during which the altitude changed only slightly.

The centre of the image in Fig. 11 is displayed in true colour (that is, as the human eye would see it under Titan's atmosphere) using actual spectral data from one panorama. The area between the spectra is interpolated in azimuth. The coverage with spectra is similar to that shown in Fig. 12. The orange colour is due mainly to the illumination of the surface. Scattering and absorption (which dominate in the blue) cause the perceived true colour of the surface to change from yellow to orange with decreasing altitude. Note that the passband of the cameras peaked in the near infrared (at 750 nm), and therefore the brightness variations in the images would not necessarily be seen by the human eye.

Fig. 11. The surface of Titan displayed in true colour. As seen from an altitude of 8 km. See Fig. 12 for the location of the spectrometer's footprints. Some bright features appear to be overexposed because they are

地表物质的运移

通过采集图像中已知位置的可见光谱，可以将反射光谱与不同类型的地形建立联系。探测器采用俯视可见光谱分析仪（DLVS），是一种用于测量 480～960 nm 波段光线的成像光谱分析仪，它将分析仪狭缝的像投影到地面上，在 10°到 50°的天底角最多可以覆盖 20 个空间分辨单元。虽然标称可以测量与图像相同方位角的光谱，但光谱与对应图像的采集高度往往略有不同（探测器未发生明显的偏转）。通过对光谱和图像数据的采集时刻进行内插分析，可以在图像中确定光谱数据对应的覆盖区域。照相机和土卫六地表之间的雾霾的散射作用和甲烷吸收的影响阻碍了地表反射率的确定。因此，测量过程中探测器高度改变较轻微的情况下，光谱和图像之间会有较好的相关性。

借助全景照片的真实光谱数据，图 11 中心附近的图像可以以真实彩色呈现（即和人眼在土卫六大气下实际看到的颜色一样）。光谱之间的区域按方位进行内插。光谱覆盖范围类似于图 12 所示。橙色的色调主要是由于地面被照亮。随着高度的降低，散射和吸收（主要作用在蓝色波段）将使地面的真实颜色从黄色变为橙色。需要注意的是，照相机的滤波通带峰值处在近红外 750 nm，因此，人眼实际观察不一定看到图像中那样的亮度变化。

图 11. 真实颜色下的土卫六表面图像。从 8 km 高度看到的图像，图 12 标注了光谱仪覆盖区域的位置。图中亮度主要是根据近红外光谱得出的，部分地貌单元由于颜色过亮而产生过曝。真实彩色表达为红绿

too bright for their colour (the brightness in this image mainly derives from the near-infrared spectrum). True colour is expressed in red-green-blue (RGB) values that are derived by multiplying the spectra with the Commission Internationale de l'Eclairage colour-matching functions (with the 6,500-K correlated colour temperature, the D65 white point). The circle shown is the extent of the lowest panorama (Fig. 3).

Fig. 12. Reflectivity samples of Titan's surface. A panorama of Titan's surface overlaid with DLVS footprints coloured according to the 827 nm/751 nm intensity ratio, coded from red (high) to green (low). Spectral footprints (the small rectangles) selected for analysis in Fig. 13 are outlined in white. The panorama shows an area of 23 by 23 km. Areas A, B and C are referred to in Fig. 13.

In Fig. 12 the images are correlated with the ratio of the intensity in two methane windows (827 nm/751 nm) located in the infrared part of the spectrum where scattering is minimal and the systematic variability with nadir angle can be ignored. Reddening (high 827 nm/751 nm ratio) is concentrated at the area covered with drainage channels (north and northwest in the pan of Fig. 12) and to a lesser degree to the lake area adjacent to the coastline. The lake area in the southeast is not reddened. A preliminary analysis of spectra recorded in other panoramic cycles indicates that the land area in the northeast, which is not covered by drainage channels, is only moderately reddened compared to the river area. The reddening is not restricted to these two methane windows. Figure 13 shows that, in fact, it is present over the whole visual range, amounting to about 6% per 100 nm (note that atmospheric backscatter dominates over surface reflection at wavelengths below 600 nm).

蓝（RGB）颜色值，这些值是由光谱乘以国际照明委员会颜色匹配函数（具有 6,500 K 色温，D65 白点）得到的。图中圆圈给出了最低全景图像（如图 3）的范围。

图 12. 土卫六地表的反射率样例。图中将土卫六表面的全景图像与 DLVS 的覆盖区域叠加在一起，其中 DLVS 覆盖区域按照 827 nm/751 nm 两波段强度之比的大小着色，即比值越大则为红色，比值较小则为绿色。图 13 分析的光谱覆盖区用白色矩形框标记出。全景图像的面积为 23 km × 23 km。而区域 A、B、C 光谱具体情况可以参考图 13。

在图 12 中，图像与两个甲烷窗口信号（827 nm/751 nm）的强度之比关联起来，这两个窗口位于红外波段，在该波段散射效应最小，并且天底角的系统性变化可以忽略。红化（即高 827 nm/751 nm 比值）集中在排水河道分布的区域（图 12 中的北侧和西北侧）；在靠近海岸线的湖区也存在相对较弱的红化。位于东南侧的湖区没有红化。我们对其他全景拍摄周期记录的光谱数据进行了初步分析，发现东北方向的陆地区域（未分布排水河道）相对于河流区域只是被中等红化。红化现象并不是局限在两个甲烷观测窗口。如图 13 所示，实际上红化存在于整个可见光波段，相当于每100 nm 大约为 6% 的变化（值得注意的是对于小于 600 nm 的波段，大气背散射的影响显著地强于表面反射）。

Fig. 13. Spectral comparison of bright highlands and dark lowlands. Spectra of the dendritic river highlands and lakebed lowlands areas are compared. To restrict the influence of the atmosphere, only spectra recorded at the same nadir angle are selected. The solid and dashed curves are the average spectra associated with the two spectral pixels outlined in white near the areas marked "A" (dendritic highlands, solid) and "B" (dark lakebed, dashed), respectively in Fig. 12. The two pixels bordering "C" in Fig. 12 yield a spectrum intermediate to the "A" and "B" spectra. The spectra have been corrected for albedo by dividing by the total intensity to emphasize the difference in slope. Not shown here is that the reflectivity of the dendritic area ("A") is higher than that of the lakebed area ("B") at all wavelengths by roughly a factor of two. The asterisks denote the methane windows taken for the reddening ratio in Fig. 12.

The DLVS data clearly show that the highlands (high-albedo area) are redder than the lakebed (low-albedo area). Spectra of the lakebed just south of the coastline are less red than the highlands but clearly more red than the lakebed further away (that is, to the southeast). The data suggests that the brighter (redder) material of the hilly area may be of local origin, and is corrugated by rivers and drainage channels, and that the darker material (less red) is a substance that seems to be washed from the hills into the lakebed. It could be connected to the alteration of the highland terrain, either by precipitation, wind and/or cryoactivity. Additionally, it could indicate that the surface of the lowland area may be covered by different materials in regions that exhibit diverse morphology.

Surface Reflectivity and Methane Mole Fraction

Spectra taken near Titan's surface allow measurement of its reflectance and determination of the local methane mole fraction. These measurements provide clues as to the make-up of Titan's crust. The Downward-Looking and Upward-Looking Infrared Spectrometers (DLIS and ULIS) cover the region from 840 to 1,700 nm with a resolution of 15 to 20 nm. The ULIS looks up at a half-hemisphere through a diffuser while the DLIS projects its slit into a 3 by 9° field centred at a 20° nadir angle. Below 700 m altitude, a 20-W lamp was turned on to illuminate the surface at wavelengths where solar light had been completely absorbed by methane in Titan's atmosphere. At low altitudes we took repeated DLIS and ULIS spectra at short integration times (1 s). Nine DLIS and seven ULIS spectra were received between 734 and 21 m altitude. The DLIS continued to measure surface spectra free of atmospheric

图 13. 较亮高地和较暗低地的光谱对比。我们在图中将分布有树枝状河流的高地的光谱与湖床低地区域的光谱进行了对比。为了限制大气的影响，我们只挑选了以相同天底角采集的光谱。图中实线（虚线）分别表示图 12 中 A(B) 区域附近白框标示的两个光谱像素的平均光谱，A 区域是树枝状高地，用实线表示；B 区域是暗的湖床，用虚线表示。而图 12 中 C 区周围的两个像素的平均光谱介于 A 和 B 光谱之间。图中光谱已经通过除以总亮度进行了反照率校正，从而可以突出光谱斜率的不同。图中未显示的信息是，在整个波段范围，树枝状区域（A 区域）的反射率是湖床区域（B 区域）的 2 倍左右。图中星号表示两个甲烷吸收窗波段，这两个波段用于表征图 12 中的红化程度。

　　DLVS 数据清楚地表明，具有高反照率的高地比低反照率的湖床红化程度更高，紧邻海岸线南侧的湖床的光谱比高地的红化要弱，但比离岸更远些（即东南方向）的湖床红化明显更强。数据说明丘陵地带的更亮（更红）物质可能是在原位形成的，并在河流的作用下形成波状褶皱结构，而较暗（更不红）的物质则看起来像是被从山地冲洗进湖床的。这可能与高原地形的改造有关，可能是降雨、风和（或者）冰冻等机制造成的。此外，低地地区的一些地区展现出地貌的多样性，这些区域的表面可能覆盖着不同的物质。

表面反射率与甲烷摩尔分数

　　在接近土卫六表面得到的光谱使我们可以测量其反射率，并确定局部的甲烷摩尔分数。这些测量计算可以为确定土卫六地壳组成提供线索。探测器采用的俯视红外光谱分析仪（DLIS）和仰视红外光谱分析仪（ULIS）可以覆盖从 840 nm 到 1,700 nm 的波段，其分辨率为 15 ~ 20 nm。ULIS 可以通过漫射器向上观测整个半球，而 DLIS 则将其狭缝投影到以 20° 天底角为中心、大小为 3°×9° 的视场。在小于 700 m 高度，一盏功率为 20 W 的照明灯被开启用来照射土卫六表面，其发光波长恰是太阳光被土卫六大气中的甲烷完全吸收的波段。在低空，我们以较短的积分时间（1 s）不断重复测量 DLIS 和 ULIS 光谱。在 734 m 到 21 m 的下降高度之间，探测器总共

methane absorption after landing. About 20 such identical spectra were acquired from a distance of a few tens of centimetres of the surface.

DLIS spectra at all altitudes clearly showed an additional signal when the lamp was on. However, at the highest altitudes, the lamp reflection from the surface was negligible, so the additional signal was solely due to scattered light from the lamp into the instrument. This scattered light was estimated from the intensity level in the strong methane bands in the highest-altitude spectrum recorded with the lamp on, and removed from all DLIS spectra. After this correction, only spectra at 36 m and especially 21 m showed significant signal from the lamp. This signal dominated the upward intensity due to solar illumination in all regions of strong and moderate methane absorption, while the latter dominated in the methane windows.

This spectrum, which represents the product of the ground reflectivity and the two-way methane transmission, is shown in Fig. 14 and compared to synthetic spectra with methane mole fractions of 3%, 5% and 7%. The ground reflectivity assumed in these model calculations is shown in the inset. Four methane bands are seen in the lamp-only spectrum. The good correlation with the models, notably in the weak structures at 1,140, 1,370 and 1,470 nm, indicates a high signal-to-noise ratio of about 50. The best fit is achieved with a methane mole fraction of 5%, which is in firm agreement with the 4.9% *in situ* measurements made by the Gas Chromatograph Mass Spectrometer[11]. Most structures are well reproduced; notable exceptions are the detailed shape of the 1,000 nm band and the absorption shoulder near 1,320 nm.

Fig. 14. Derivation of methane mole fraction. Lamp-only downward-looking spectrum from altitude of 21 m (black data points). The red line with three-sigma error bars indicate absolute reflectivity in methane windows estimated from infrared measurements. This spectrum is compared to three models: 3% (blue), 5% (green), and 7% (red) methane mole fractions. These models make use of surface reflectivity at seven

采集了9张 DLIS 光谱和7张 ULIS 光谱。探测器着陆后，DLIS 在没有大气甲烷吸收影响的情况下继续测量土卫六表面的光谱；在距离表面大约数十厘米的位置获得了大约20张这样的光谱。

所有高度的 DLIS 光谱都清楚地显示，当照明灯打开后，出现了一个额外的信号。然而当探测器位于最高的高度时，地面对照明灯光的反射则可以忽略，因此光谱中的额外信号应该仅仅是来自照明灯光的散射。根据照明灯打开后记录的最高高度光谱中的强甲烷吸收带的强度，可以估算出照明灯散射光的强度值，并将其从所有的 DLIS 光谱中剔除掉。经过此校正之后，只有在36 m，尤其是21 m 高度处的光谱还存在明显的照明灯信号。该信号决定了向上的光强，这是由于太阳光的所有波段都有强–中等的甲烷吸收，而后者只是在甲烷窗口才起决定作用。

图14中给出的光谱是地面反射率与来回两次通过甲烷的穿透率的乘积所给出的结果，并与甲烷摩尔分数分别为3%、5%以及7%的合成光谱相比较。图14右上角的插图给出了计算模型中采用的反射率。在只有照明灯情况下的光谱中可以观察到四个甲烷吸收带。测量数据与模型符合得很好，在1,140 nm、1,370 nm 和1,470 nm 位置均出现了较弱的吸收结构，这表明了约为50的高信噪比。甲烷摩尔分数为5%时，可以实现最佳拟合，这与使用气相色谱–质谱联用仪进行原位测量得到的4.9%的甲烷摩尔分数严格一致[11]。光谱中大多数结构都可以被很好地重现，但1,000 nm处吸收带以及1,320 nm 附近的吸收肩的细节存在明显的差异。

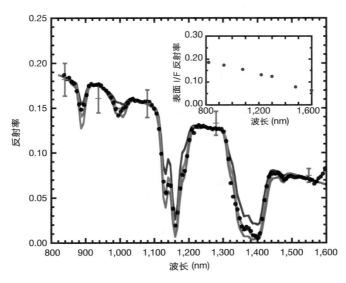

图14. 甲烷摩尔分数的推导。图中给出了开启照明灯后，在21 m 高度测量得到的俯视光谱（黑点表示数据点）。红线表示通过红外测量估计得到的甲烷窗口绝对反射率，同时给出了3σ 误差区间。作为对比，图中也给出了甲烷摩尔分数分别为3%、5% 和7% 的三种模型结果，分别用蓝线、绿线和红线表示。这些模型结果通过对7个波长处的表面反射率（如图中右上小图中蓝点所示；其中 I/F 表示谱强度与太阳

wavelengths (shown in inset by the blue points; I/F is the ratio of the intensity to the solar flux divided by π) and linearly interpolated between. From the lamp-on infrared spectra, a lamp-only spectrum at 21 m (representing the spectrum observed by DLIS in the absence of solar illumination) was obtained as follows. First, the reflectivity in regions of negligible methane absorption (at 840, 940, 1,070, 1,280 and 1,500–1,600 nm) was estimated by the ratio of mean upward intensity (measured by DLIS) to mean downward intensity (measured by ULIS). The mean upward intensity is the average measured over the seven low-altitude DLIS spectra showing no contribution from the lamp (734 to 53 m). The mean downward intensity was obtained by averaging the strongest intensity with the weakest intensity. This average gives reasonable approximation of the downward flux divided by π. The ratio of the mean upward intensity to the mean downward intensity gives reflectivity. Two corrections were required in this analysis: correction for the spatial response of the ULIS diffuser and correction for the solar illumination in the DLIS 21-m spectrum. The correction for diffuser response ranged from 15% (840 nm) to 25% (1,550 nm), assuming a haze optical depth of ~2 at 938 nm. The contribution of solar illumination in the DLIS spectrum at 21 m was eliminated by subtracting the average of the DLIS spectra at 85 and 109 m where the lamp contribution was negligible. The difference spectrum was then divided by the spectral response of the lamp and scaled by a constant to match the continuum reflectivities inferred previously, producing the lamp-only spectrum at 21 m.

We conclude that the methane abundance is $5 \pm 1\%$ in the atmosphere near the surface. The corresponding (two-way, and including the 20° lamp inclination) methane column abundance in the spectrum is 9.6 m-amagat (or a column 9.6 m high at the standard temperature and pressure of 273 K and 1 atmosphere). With a temperature of 93.8 K and pressure of 1467.6 mbar (ref. 12), the relative humidity of methane is about 50% using Brown and Ziegler's saturation law[13]. Therefore, methane near the surface is not near saturation, and ground fogs caused by methane in the neighbourhood of the landing site are unlikely.

The ratio of the observed spectrum to the methane transmission, restricted to spectral regions where the latter is higher than 90%, is shown in Fig. 15a ("plus" symbols). It is compared to one of the DLIS spectra after landing, divided by the lamp spectral response and rescaled by a constant reflectivity factor. Note that although this spectrum shows signs of methane absorption at 1,140–1,160 nm and 1,300–1,400 nm, no attempt of correction was made, in the absence so far of accurate information on the absorption path lengths. The agreement between the shapes of the two independent determinations of the ground reflectivity adds confidence to the result.

The four major characteristics of the surface spectrum are: (1) a relatively low albedo, peaking around 0.18 at 830 nm; (2) a red slope in the visible range; (3) a quasilinear decrease of the reflectivity by a factor of about two between 830 and 1,420 nm; and (4) a broad absorption, by ~30% of the local continuum, apparently centred near 1,540 nm (although its behaviour beyond 1,600 nm is poorly constrained) as seen in Fig. 15b. This spectrum is very unusual and has no known equivalent on any other object in the Solar System.

通量的比值除以 π) 进行线性插值得到。根据开启照明灯后的红外光谱可以推出 21 m 高度处只有照明灯信号的光谱 (代表了没有太阳光照环境下的 DLIS 观测光谱),具体步骤如下。首先,在某些甲烷吸收可以忽略的波段 (如 840 nm、940 nm、1,070 nm、1,280 nm 以及 1,500~1,600 nm),反射率可以通过向上的平均谱强度 (DLIS 测量得到) 与向下的平均谱强度 (ULIS 测量得到) 的比值估计出来。其中,向上的平均谱强度由不存在照明灯光影响的 7 个低高度 DLIS 光谱测量值 (734 m 到 53 m) 的平均后得到。通过对最大强度和最小强度取平均可以求出向下的平均谱强度;该平均值是向下光通量除以 π 的结果的合理近似。向上的平均谱强度与向下的平均谱强度的比值给出了反射率。在该分析中,需要考虑两种校准:ULIS 漫射器的空间响应的校准和 21 m 高度处 DLIS 光谱的太阳光照的校准。假设雾霾在 938 nm 处的光学深度约为 2,则散射器响应的校准范围介于 15% (对应 840 nm) 和 25% (对应 1,550 nm) 之间。由于在 85 m 和 109 m 高度处照明灯对 DLIS 光谱的贡献可以忽略,因此通过减去这两个高度的 DLIS 光谱平均值,从而消除 21 m 高度处 DLIS 光谱中太阳光照的贡献。然后用相减后得到的光谱除以照明灯的光谱响应,并乘以一个常数,从而与前面推论的连续谱反射率相符;这样就得到了只考虑照明灯情况的 21 m 高度处的反射率光谱。

因此我们得出以下结论:近地表大气中甲烷的丰度为 5%±1%。相应的 (双程的且包括了 20 度照明灯倾角的) 谱中甲烷柱丰度为 9.6 米阿马加 (即相当于 273 K 的标准温度和 1 个标准大气压下 9.6 米高度柱)。在实际温度为 93.8 K 和气压为 1467.6 mbar 的条件下[12],利用布朗和齐格勒的饱和定律[13],可以计算出甲烷的相对湿度大约为 50%。因此,地表附近的甲烷并未接近饱和,着陆点附近的雾不太可能是由甲烷形成的。

图 15a 给出了光谱区域内观测到的光谱数据与甲烷穿透率的比值 (用加号表示),限制在后者高于 90% 的区域内。图中也从着陆后的 DLIS 光谱中选择了一个与之进行比较,其中该光谱曲线是除以照明灯的光谱响应并利用常量反射率因子重新调整后的结果。值得注意的是,尽管该光谱在 1,140~1,160 nm 和 1,300~1,400 nm 波段出现了甲烷吸收的迹象,由于迄今还未获得关于吸收波程长度的精确信息,因此我们并没有尝试对光谱进行校正。由该图可知,通过两种独立方法确定的地面反射率符合得很好,从而进一步提高了结果的可信度。

表面光谱主要有以下四个特征:(1) 相对较低的反照率,在 830 nm 达到峰值约 0.18;(2) 在可见光波段存在红坡;(3) 反射率从 830 nm 到 1,420 nm 准线性地降低了约一半;(4) 如图 15b 所示,存在以 1,540 nm 附近为中心的较宽的吸收峰 (波段宽度约占局域连续谱的 30%),但是在大于 1,600 nm 的情况未得到很好的约束。该光谱特别不同寻常,在太阳系的其他天体上还未发现这样的情况。

Fig. 15. Reflectance of Titan's surface. **a**, Reflectivity measured from 21 m altitude ("plus" symbols) compared to the reflectivity after landing (solid curve). The methane absorption bands are indicated by the CH₄ symbol. **b**, Surface reflectivity as measured after landing (red line). It is compared with a simulation (blue line) of a mixture of large-grained (750 μm) low-temperature water ice, yellow tholins, and an unknown component with featureless blue slope between 850 and 1,500 nm. Spectra of two different organic tholins: a yellow tholin (dashed line) and a dark tholin (solid black line) from ref. 18 are also shown for comparison (reflectance scale reduced by a factor of 4). We are attempting to identify or synthesize the missing blue material in our laboratory.

Ground-based spectroscopic observations have provided strong evidence, although spectrally restricted to the methane windows, for the presence of water ice on Titan's surface[14], coexisting in variable proportions with a dark component, presumably of organic nature[15,16]. Water ice may explain the 1,540 nm band, as illustrated in Fig. 15b by a simulation of the reflectance spectrum of a mixture of low-temperature water ice[17], yellow tholins[18] and a spectrally neutral dark component. This identification is reasonable in the context of the light-coloured rocks present at the landing site (Fig. 4), but not conclusive, because some organics do show absorption at a similar wavelength. This is the case, notably, for bright yellow-orange tholins produced in laboratory experiments[19,20] (shown in Fig. 15b), which partly contribute to this band in the simulation and which may account for the red slope in the visible range of the surface spectrum. It is probably this material, existing as aerosol particles, that absorbs the blue wavelengths, which would explain the yellow-orange colour of Titan's atmosphere as seen from space or from the surface.

We note the remarkable absence of other absorption features in the surface spectrum along with the 1,540 nm band. This is at odds with predictions that some specific chemical bonds,

图 15. 土卫六地表的反射率。**a**, 在 21 m 高度测量得到的反射率 (加号表示) 与着陆后测量的反射率 (实线表示) 的对比。图中的 CH₄ 标出了甲烷吸收波段的位置。**b**, 探测器着陆后测量得到的表面反射率 (红线) 与模拟结果 (蓝线) 的对比。其中, 模拟曲线采用的是包含大颗粒 (750 μm) 的低温水冰、黄色的索林斯以及一种在 850 ~ 1,500 nm 之间存在无特征斜坡的未知成分的混合物。同时图中还给出了黄色索林斯 (虚线) 和暗色索林斯 (黑色实线) 两种有机物的谱线用于对比 (反射强度的纵坐标比例尺缩小为四分之一)[18]。目前, 我们正在实验室尝试识别或合成这种缺失的蓝色物质。

尽管基于地表的光谱观测结果限制在几个甲烷窗口内, 但该结果也提供了强有力的证据表明土卫六表面存在水冰[14]; 这些水冰与某种可能具有有机物特性的较暗的成分以变化的比例共存[15,16]。水冰也许可以解释 1,540 nm 处的吸收峰, 图 15b 中给出了低温水冰[17]、黄色索林斯[18] 以及一种光谱呈中性的暗色组分的混合物的反射率模拟结果。由于着陆点附近的岩石颜色较淡 (见图 4), 前文所作的鉴别具有合理性但不是结论性的, 因为一些有机物在相似的波段也具有吸收峰。实验室制备的亮橘黄色的索林斯尤其如此[19,20] (如图 15b 所示), 它对于模拟中出现的吸收峰具有一定的贡献, 同时可能用于解释表面光谱可见光范围内的红端斜坡。或许就是这种物质以气溶胶粒子的形式存在并吸收了蓝色光波段的光, 造成了从太空或从土卫六表面观察到的土卫六大气呈现橘黄色。

我们注意到表面光谱中并没有与 1,540 nm 吸收带共存的其他吸收结构, 这与以往研究得出的预测不符。根据先前的研究, 在表面光谱中, 将会出现某些化学键

in particular C–H or C≡N, and possibly the individual bands of atmospherically abundant species, such as ethane (C_2H_6), acetylene (C_2H_2), propane (C_3H_8), ethylene (C_2H_4), hydrogen cyanide (HCN) and their polymers, would show up as signatures in the surface spectrum.

The most intriguing feature in the surface spectrum is its quasilinear featureless "blue slope" between 830 and 1,420 nm. As briefly illustrated in Fig. 15b, a featureless blue slope is not matched by any combination of laboratory spectra of ices and complex organics, including various types of tholins. Depending on their composition and structural state (for example, abundance, extension and/or clustering of sp^2 carbon bonds), organic materials in the near-infrared exhibit either distinct absorption bands (for example, bright yellow-orange tholins, Fig. 15b), or a feature-poor red slope (for medium to low-albedo organics), or a very dark and flat spectrum[18,21].

Assessing the material responsible for the blue slope is a major challenge and also a prerequisite for a secure identification of the 1,540 nm band. If this band is indeed mostly due to water ice, an intimate mixing of this ice with a material displaying a strong "infrared-blue" absorption would explain the absence of the weaker H_2O bands at 1.04 and 1.25 µm in the surface spectrum, as demonstrated for several dark icy satellites, where these bands are hidden by the presence of an organic component (but neutral or reddish). Decreasing the water-ice grain size alone cannot suppress the 1.04- and 1.25-µm bands and at the same time maintain the apparent blue slope that is produced by large-grained water ice (considering only the continuum absorption between the infrared bands). To hide these weak water bands efficiently, the mixture would need to be ice and a material having a stronger and decreasing-with-wavelength infrared absorption.

Haze Particle Size

The haze particles in Titan's atmosphere have long been known to produce both high linear polarization and strong forward scattering. This has been taken to imply that the particles are aggregates of small "monomers" in open structures. The amount of linear polarization constrains the size of the small dimension (monomer radius) while the forward scattering or wavelength dependence of extinction optical depth determines the overall size of the particle or the number of monomers constituting the aggregate.

The DISR instrument measured the degree of linear polarization of scattered sunlight by measuring a vertical strip of sky in two bands centred at 492 and 934 nm. Some 50 measurements of this type were collected during the Titan descent. For the small monomer sizes expected, the direction of polarization would be perpendicular to the scattering plane and reach a maximum near 90° scattering angle at an azimuth opposite to the Sun, and would have a maximum electric field vector in the horizontal direction. We eliminated any polarization measurements made by the DISR that did not have this character, assuming that they were not made at the desired azimuth.

（尤其是 C–H 或 C≡N 键）的特征谱结构，也会出现大气中丰度较高的化合物的特征吸收带，例如乙烷（C_2H_6）、乙炔（C_2H_2）、丙烷（C_3H_8）、乙烯（C_2H_4）、氢氰酸（HCN）以及它们的聚合物。

表面光谱中最有趣的特征是位于 830 nm ~ 1,420 nm 之间的准线性无特征"蓝坡"结构。该斜坡结构还不能与水冰和复杂有机物（包括各种索林斯）的实验室光谱的任何组合相匹配。基于以上物质的不同组成和结构状态（比如，sp^2 碳化学键的丰度、延展和（或）成簇），得到的有机物质在近红外波段或者显示出明显的吸收峰（比如明亮的橘黄色索林斯，如图 15b 所示），或者显示出无特征的红坡（对于中低反照率的有机物），或者显示出非常暗的平坦谱线 [18,21]。

确定"蓝坡"光谱结构产生于何种物质是一项主要的挑战，这也是正确识别 1,540 nm 吸收带的前提。如果这一波段确实是主要由水冰造成的，这种冰与具有强"红外–蓝"吸收特征的物质的均匀混合将解释表面光谱 1.04 μm 和 1.25 μm 处更弱的 H_2O 吸收峰的缺失。这已经在数颗暗色的冰卫星上得到证实，这是因为这些吸收峰被有机物的谱结构（但是呈现出中性或红色的特征）所掩盖。仅仅减小水冰的晶粒尺寸并不能既抑制 1.04 μm 和 1.25 μm 处的吸收峰，又保持明显的蓝坡，因为蓝坡结构是由较大的水冰晶粒产生的（只考虑了红外波段吸收峰之间的连续吸收结构）。为了能够有效遮盖这些较弱的水的吸收峰，这种混合物质应该包含水冰和另一种具有更强的、但随波长增加而减弱的红外波段吸收特征的物质。

雾霾颗粒的尺寸

人们早就知道土卫六大气中的雾霾颗粒可以产生高度线偏振以及很强的前向散射。这意味着这些颗粒是较小的"单体"通过开放式结构构成的聚集体。线偏振的量约束了颗粒具有小维度的尺寸（单体的半径），而通过前向散射或消光光学深度与波长的关系可以确定颗粒的整体尺寸或构成聚集体的单体数目。

DISR 设备在以 492 nm 和 934 nm 为中心的两个波段，通过测量天空的一段垂直条带，得到太阳散射光的线偏振度。类似的测量在探测器降落过程中大约进行了 50 次。对于预期的较小单体尺寸，偏振方向将垂直于散射面并在背向太阳的方向达到最大偏振度（接近 90°），同时，在水平方向上具有最大电场矢量。我们假定不满足以上特征的偏振测量结果是由于 DISR 没有朝向预期的方位上，因此我们将这些结果进行了剔除。

Several polarization measurements showing the expected behaviour in Titan's atmosphere were obtained. A gradual rise to a maximum near a scattering angle of 90° was observed, followed by a decrease on the other side of this peak. The solar aureole camera made several of these measurements at different times through the descent that show a smooth decrease in polarization with increasing optical depth into the atmosphere (Fig. 16). Figure 16a shows a maximum degree of linear polarization of about 60% at altitudes above 120 km in the 934-nm channel. Below, we show that the optical depth at 934 nm is a few tenths at this location in the descent. Comparisons of this degree of polarization with model computations for different-sized fractal aggregate particles produced by binary cluster collision aggregation indicate that the radii of the monomers comprising the aggregate particles is near 0.05 µm, almost independent of the number of monomers in the particle.

Fig. 16. Haze properties. **a**, The maximum degree of linear polarization measured opposite to the Sun as a function of altitude in our 500-nm channel (triangles) and in the 935-nm channel (dots). **b**, Extinction optical depth versus altitude for three wavelengths, 531 (top), 829 (middle) and 1,500 nm (bottom). The dashed curves correspond to $N = 256$ monomers, and the solid curves correspond to $N = 512$ monomers of the aggregate particles that make up Titan's haze. Note that the 531 (top) curve was constrained above 40 km and extrapolated to the ground. More explicit constraints from the infrared spectrometer will be available after the probe azimuth with time is determined.

Haze Optical Depth and Vertical Distribution

Before the Huygens probe descent, several workers considered the possibility that the haze in Titan's atmosphere clears below an altitude of some 50 or 70 km (ref. 22) owing to condensation of hydrocarbon gases produced at high altitudes that diffuse to lower,

我们获得了数个与预期的土卫六大气特征相符的偏振测量的结果。我们观察到偏振在 90° 散射角附近逐渐增至最大值，然后在此峰值另一侧逐渐减小。日晕照相机在下降阶段的不同时间对偏振进行了数次测量，结果表明偏振随着大气光学深度的增加而平稳减小（图 16）。其中，由图 16a 可知，934 nm 观测通道的线偏振度在大于 120 km 的高度达到最大值，约为 60%。而图 16b 则表明在下降过程中这一地点934 nm 通道测量的光深大小仅为十分之几。我们把二元团簇碰撞聚集产生的不同尺寸的分形聚集颗粒带入模型进行计算，并与偏振度的测量结果进行比较，发现构成聚集体颗粒的单体的半径大约为 0.05 μm，且单体的半径几乎与颗粒中单体的数量无关。

图 16. 雾霾的特性。**a**, 在背向太阳方向，500 nm 和 935 nm 两个通道测量得到的最大线偏振度与高度的关系，分别用三角和圆点表示出。**b**, 图中给出了在三个不同的波长（即 531 nm、829 nm 以及 1,500 nm）处，消光光深与高度的关系，对应曲线分别位于图上部、中部、下部。图中虚线对应组成土卫六雾霾的聚集颗粒的单体数量 $N = 256$ 的情况，实线则对应单体数量 $N = 512$ 的情况。值得注意的是，531 nm（上部）的曲线仅仅在 40 km 以上被约束，40 km 高度到地面的曲线由外推获得。在确定探测器方位随时间变化的关系后，还能进一步从红外光谱分析仪获得更精确的约束。

雾霾的光深和垂直分布

在惠更斯探测器降落之前，若干研究者认为当低于某一高度（约 50 km 或70 km）时 [22]，土卫六大气中的雾霾可能会消失，这是因为生成于高层大气的碳氢化

colder, levels of the stratosphere. If such a clearing were to occur in Titan's atmosphere, the intensity seen by the downward-looking DISR spectrometer would be relatively constant below the altitude at which the clearing began.

The brightness looking downward averaged along the DLVS slit and averaged over azimuth increases by a factor of two from the surface to 30 km altitude at a wavelength of 830 nm as shown in Fig. 17a. The increase at 830 nm is due almost solely to scattering by haze between 30 km and the surface. These observations demonstrate that there is significant haze opacity at all altitudes throughout the descent, extending all the way down to the surface.

The brightness of the visible spectra looking upward depends on the azimuth relative to the Sun. Although the probe attitude is not yet well known, it is clear that the minimum intensities are found looking away from the Sun. The upward-looking spectra looking away from the Sun start with low intensities at the highest altitudes and increase in intensity as the altitude decreases from 140 to about 50 km (see Fig. 17b). Below 50 km the intensity decreases at short wavelengths as altitude decreases, while the intensity in continuum regions longer than 700 nm continues to increase, as shown in Fig. 17c.

合物气体向下扩散到平流层较冷较低的平面，从而发生凝聚。如果确实如此的话，则当惠更斯探测器降至某一高度后，由于雾霾开始消失，俯视 DISR 光谱分析仪观察到的强度将保持相对固定。

俯视观测到的沿 DLVS 狭缝亮度的以及对方位平均的 830 nm 波长处的平均亮度，从地表到 30 km 高度增加了一倍，如图 17a 所示。这种增加主要是由于 30 km 高度与地表之间的雾霾产生的散射效应。这些观测证实了在整个下降的不同高度，直至土卫六表面都存在显著的由雾霾引起的不透明度。

仰视观测到的可见光谱的亮度则与相对太阳的方位角相关。尽管探测器的姿态尚未完全确定，但探测到的最小强度显然位于背向太阳的方向。在探测器位于最高高度时，背离太阳方向的仰视光谱测量得到的光谱强度较低；随着高度从 140 km 逐渐降低到 50 km，光谱强度逐渐增加，如图 17b 所示。在 50 km 高度以下，短波长波段的强度随着高度降低而减小，但大于 700 nm 的连续波段的强度则继续增加，如图 17c 所示。

Fig. 17. Atmospheric spectra. **a**, The average intensity looking downward averaged over azimuth and over the length of the slit (10° to 50° nadir angle) as a function of wavelength for several altitudes as labelled. **b**, The intensity measured by the Upward-Looking Visible Spectrometer in the direction opposite the Sun as a function of wavelength for several altitudes as labelled. Note that the brightness begins at a low level at 140 km, and increases as altitude decreases. **c**, Same as **b** but for altitudes below 50 km. Note that the brightness away from the Sun decreases with decreasing altitude at short wavelengths, but increases in continuum regions longward of 700 nm.

The intensity looking upward away from the Sun, and the azimuthally averaged intensity looking downward at each continuum wavelength as functions of altitude, constrain the vertical distribution of aerosol opacity in the atmosphere as well as the aerosol single-scattering albedo. With the monomer radius fixed at 0.05 μm from the polarization measurements, the adjustable parameters include the number of monomers in each aggregate particle, N, as well as the local particle number density, n, in cm^{-3} as a function of altitude. An algorithm developed by (and available from) M.L. was used to determine the single-scattering phase function, the single-scattering albedo, and the extinction cross-section for each aggregate particle as functions of the wavelength, the real and imaginary refractive indices, the monomer radius, and the number of monomers per aggregate particle. This algorithm is based on the discrete dipole approximation and the T-matrix method (M. Lemmon, personal communication) to evaluate the single-scattering properties of the aggregate particles. These computations are most accurate at relatively small particle sizes and depend on extrapolation for N of 256 or larger.

For large particles the wavelength dependence of the extinction optical depth is smaller than for small particles. An N larger than about 100 is required to fit the observations. Hence, models with $N = 256$ or 512 monomers per particle are shown, even though for these values of N the single-scattering algorithm is not as accurate as desired. For these initial models, the real and imaginary refractive indices for the aerosols are taken from the measurements of laboratory tholins in ref. 23.

The radius, R_p, of the circle having the same projected area as an aggregate particle is given

814

图 17. 大气光谱。**a**, 图中给出了几个不同高度下俯视光谱平均强度与波长的关系（见图中标注），其中平均强度是基于方位角和狭缝长度方向（天底角 10° 到 50° 之间）的平均。**b**, 在背向太阳的方向，仰视可见光波段光谱仪测量得到的不同高度下的强度与波长的关系（见图中标注）。值得注意的是，140 km 高度对应的起始亮度较低，但亮度随着高度的下降而增加。**c** 与 **b** 图表示的关系相同，但曲线对应的 50 km以下的高度。值得注意的是，背向太阳方向的光亮度在短波长波段随着高度的减小而减小，但是在大于700 nm 的波段则随高度减小而增加。

　　背向太阳方向的仰视测量强度和在各个连续波段得到的对方位平均的俯视强度相对于高度的变化函数，可以用于确定大气中气溶胶不透明度的垂直分布以及气溶胶单散射反照率。根据偏振测量，单体半径固定值为 0.05 μm，那么可调参量包括每个聚集体中颗粒的单体数量 N 以及粒子数局部密度 n（单位为个/cm³）的高度变化函数。利用莱蒙提出的算法（可联系莱蒙获取），可以确定单散射相函数、单散射反照率、每个聚集颗粒的消光截面（波长的函数）、折射指数的实部和虚部、单体的半径以及每个聚集体中的单体数量。该算法基于离散偶极子近似和 T 矩阵方法（莱蒙，个人交流），可以评估聚集颗粒的单散射属性。以上计算对于相对较小的颗粒尺寸具有最高的精确度，而且依托于 $N \geqslant 256$ 的外推。

　　对于较大颗粒而言，较小颗粒的消光光深与波长的关系更加密切。为了拟合观测结果，N 的取值需要大于 100，因此我们在模型中设定每个颗粒中的单体数为 256或 512。尽管对于这样的 N 取值，单散射算法不如想要的那样精确。对于以上初始模型，气溶胶折射指数的实部和虚部取自实验室中索林斯的测量结果 [23]。

　　设某一圆面积与单一的聚集颗粒的投影面积相同，则该圆的半径 R_p 可以由公式

by $R_p = r \sqrt{(N^{0.925})}$, where r is the monomer radius and N is the number of monomers. Particles with 256 or 512 monomers have the same projected areas (which control their forward scattering properties) as circles with radii 0.65 and 0.9 µm, respectively.

Fig. 18. Haze models versus observations. **a**, Measured upward-looking intensity (points) away from the Sun versus altitude for 531 (blue) and 829 nm (red). Three models are shown compared to the observations at each wavelength. The solid curves are for 512 monomers in each aggregate particle. The model at 531 nm has 12 particles cm^{-3} above 80 km and 18 particles cm^{-3} below that altitude. The corresponding model at 829 nm has 20 particles cm^{-3} above 80 km and 60 cm^{-3} below. The models indicated by long-dashed lines have 256 monomers per particle and at 531 nm the number density is 20 particles cm^{-3} above 80 km and 40 cm^{-3} below. At 829 nm the number density is 30 cm^{-3} above 80 km and 100 cm^{-3} below. The number density of particles differs slightly with wavelength because the model of fractal aggregate particles does not yet reproduce the wavelength dependence of the cross-section to high accuracy. The models indicated by short-dashed lines have 256 monomers per particle, and have the same number of total particles as the models indicated by long-dashed lines, but all the particles are concentrated above 72 km with a clear space below. Such models with clear spaces are clearly not in agreement with the observations. **b**, Downward-looking measured intensities versus altitude (plotted as points) for 531 (blue points) and 829 nm (red points). The two models (plotted as curves) are the same models as those shown by long-dashed lines and solid curves in **a**.

$R_\mathrm{p} = r\sqrt{N^{0.925}}$ 计算得到，其中 r 表示单体的半径，N 表示单体的数量。不妨设两种颗粒分别由 256 个单体和 512 个单体组成，则与二者投影面积（决定着前向散射性质）相等的圆的半径分别为 0.65 μm 和 0.9 μm。

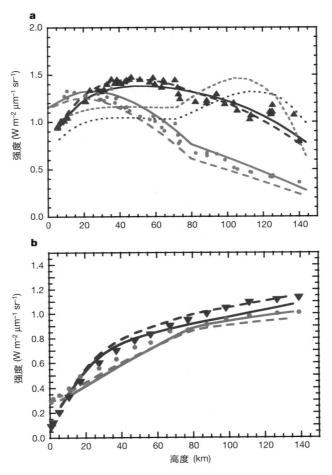

图 18. 雾霾模型与观测结果的对比。**a**, 图中给出了在背向太阳的方向仰视强度（用点表示）与高度的关系，蓝色与红色分别对应 531 nm 和 829 nm 观测通道。同时作为对比，对于每个通道还给出了三个模型的结果。其中，实线代表每个聚集颗粒包含 512 个单体的情况。对于 531 nm 通道，该模型在大于 80 km 高度的粒子数密度为 12 个/cm³，在低于 80 km 的高度则为 18 个/cm³。对于 829 nm 通道，该模型大于 80 km 高度的粒子数密度为 20 个/cm³，在低于 80 km 的高度则为 60 个/cm³。图中用长虚线标示的模型代表每个聚集颗粒包含 256 个单体，对于 531 nm 通道，大于 80 km 高度的粒子数密度为 20 个/cm³，在低于 80 km 的高度则为 40 个/cm³；对于 829 nm 通道，大于 80 km 高度的粒子数密度为 30 个/cm³，在低于 80 km 的高度则为 100 个/cm³。由以上数据可知，粒子数密度随波长变化而有些许变化，这是因为我们根据分形颗粒模型得出的截面积与波长的关系准确度并不高。图中短虚线表示每个颗粒由 256 个单体构成的模型结果，粒子（颗粒）总数与长虚线相同，但是所有的粒子都集中在 72 km 高度以上，低于 72 km 的空间则没有粒子。显然这样一种存在粒子净空层的模型与观测结果不符。**b**, 图中数据点标示了 531 nm 和 829 nm 两个通道测量得到的俯视测量的强度与高度的关系，分别用蓝色点和红色点表示。拟合曲线采用的两种模型与图 **a** 中长虚线和实线所代表的模型一致。

Comparison of the observed downward-streaming intensity looking away from the Sun at wavelengths of 531 and 829 nm with plane-parallel radiative transfer models constrains the vertical distribution of optical depth in Titan's atmosphere. The vertical distribution of particles can be adjusted to fit these curves arbitrarily well. In this preliminary work, only one constant number density above an altitude of 80 km and a second constant number density below 80 km were considered for models with $N = 256$ and $N = 512$, as shown in Fig. 18a. The number densities are larger in the lower half of the atmosphere than the upper half, but only by modest factors of two to three. The number densities are not exactly equal in the models at different wavelengths, but this is probably due to the extrapolation in the wavelength dependence of the cross-sections in the models for these relatively large N values at the shortest wavelengths (and largest size parameters). Average number densities in the entire atmosphere between 30 and 65 cm^{-3} are required if the number of monomers per particle is 256. Average number densities between 15 and 40 cm^{-3} are required if N is 512.

Models with a clear space below an altitude of 72 km are also shown in Fig. 18a. It is apparent that no such clear space exists in the region of the probe's entry. It will be interesting to examine the range of parameters in cloud physics models needed to reproduce the continuous variation of haze opacity throughout Titan's atmosphere.

Haze models must reproduce the upward-streaming intensity observed in the atmosphere as well as the downward-streaming intensity. Models with $N = 256$ and 512 at 531 and 829 nm are compared to the upward intensity averaged in azimuth and along the slit in Fig. 18b. While the fit is not exact, it is clear that the models that fit the downward intensity away from the Sun are also in reasonable agreement with the measured upward intensities. It is interesting to note the ground reflectivity implied by the measurements at 531 and 829 nm. These values include the true shape of the diffuser in the Upward-Looking Visible Spectrometer and produce ground reflectivities of 0.13 at 531 nm and 0.19 at 829 nm. The corrected value at 829 nm is in good agreement with the value measured by the Infrared Spectrometer (0.18) when a correction for the diffuser's non-ideal shape is made to the infrared spectrometer measurements.

Haze Structure and Methane Absorptions

Haze models must fit the observations at all wavelengths. How well do the models derived from the visible spectrometer fit the DISR observations in the infrared? The ULIS spectra in Fig. 19 clearly show absorption by the methane bands around 890, 1,000, 1,160 and 1,380 nm. The depths of these bands increase with decreasing altitude as a result of increasing methane column density. They are correctly reproduced by radiative transfer calculations based on an exponential sum formulation for the methane absorption and a stratospheric methane mole fraction of 1.6% (ref. 24). The agreement is worse at low altitudes in the troposphere, probably owing to inaccuracies in the methane absorption

将 531 nm 和 829 nm 两个波长观测到的背向太阳的下行辐射流强度，与平行平面的辐射传输模型进行比较，可以约束土卫六大气中光深的垂直分布。通过调整颗粒的垂直分布，可以对这些曲线进行很好的拟合。在前期工作中，对于 $N = 256$ 和 $N = 512$ 两种模型，我们只假设 80 km 以上的高度具有某一恒定粒子数密度 $N = 256$，而 80 km 以下高度具有另一恒定粒子数密度 $N = 512$，如图 18a 所示。下半层大气层中的粒子数密度比上半层大气层中的粒子数密度大，但只是上半层的 2 到 3 倍。但是在不同波长的模型中，粒子数密度并不是完全相同的，这可能是因为模型引入的截面与波长的关系在短波长和较大 N 取值条件（参数达到最大）下的外推造成的。如果每个颗粒的单体数量为 256，则整个大气层中的平均粒子数密度需要介于 30 个/cm³ 到 65 个/cm³ 之间。如果每颗粒的单体数量为 512，则整个大气层中的平均粒子数密度需要介于 15 个/cm³ 到 40 个/cm³ 之间。

同时，图 18a 还给出了假定 72 km 以下高度不存在雾霾的模型结果。显然，在探测器进入的区域并不存在这样的情况。检验用于重现土卫六大气中薄雾不透明度连续变化的云层物理模型参量的范围将是一项非常有意思的工作。

雾霾模型必须能够重现大气中的仰视方向辐射流强度和俯视方向辐射流强度。我们在 531 nm 和 829 nm 分别将 $N = 256$ 和 $N = 512$ 代入模型，并将模型结果与在不同方位上做平均并沿狭缝做平均后的向上辐射流强度进行比较，如图 18b 所示。尽管拟合还不够精确，但是可以清晰地看出用于拟合背向太阳的向下辐射流强度的模型也可以在一定程度上拟合向上辐射流强度。值得注意的是，在 531 nm 和 829 nm 测量可以得到包括仰视可见光谱仪中漫射器的真实形状等值，并以此获得在 531 nm 和 829 nm 测得的地面反射率（分别对应 0.13 和 0.19）。以上校正后的 829 nm 反射率与经过校正（考虑了红外光谱仪测量过程中漫射器的非理想形状）后的红外光谱仪的测量结果（0.18）相吻合。

雾霾的结构和甲烷的吸收

雾霾模型必须在所有波长都能拟合观测结果。那么根据可见光谱分析仪得到的模型在多大程度上可以拟合 DISR 在红外波段的观测结果呢？图 19 中的 ULIS 光谱清楚地显示，在 890 nm、1,000 nm、1,160 nm 以及 1,380 nm 附近存在甲烷的吸收峰。由于甲烷柱密度随着高度的降低而增加，所以这些吸收峰的深度也随着高度的降低而增加。根据甲烷吸收的指数求和公式以及平流层甲烷摩尔分数 1.6%，以上吸收带可以由辐射传输理论准确地计算出来 [24]。但是在对流层的较低高度，理论计算和实测结果的吻合度较差，这可能是由于采用的甲烷吸收系数不够准确。在甲烷窗

coefficients. In the methane windows the downward average intensity varies by 25% or less between 104 and 10 km, indicating relatively low aerosol absorption in the infrared range.

Fig. 19. Vanishing sunlight. ULIS spectra (points) recorded at various altitudes and showing the growth of the methane-band absorption with depth in the atmosphere. The spectra at altitudes greater than 3.5 km have been integrated over several probe rotations and correspond approximately (but not exactly) to azimuth-averaged intensities. The full analysis of these observations must await refinement of the attitude of the probe as a function of time, a task still in progress. Models, with a methane mole fraction of 1.6% in the stratosphere increasing to 5% at the surface, are shown for comparison (lines). At low altitudes (< 20 km), the mismatch between model and observations in the methane windows, specifically around 1,280 and 1,520–1,600 nm, is probably due to errors in the methane absorption coefficients at long path-lengths. The model slightly overestimates the intensity in the 104-km spectrum, because the latter does not correspond to an exact azimuth average. Radiative transfer calculations were based on a 16-term exponential-sum formulation of the methane absorption properties. In the near-infrared ($\lambda > 1,050$ nm), these absorption coefficients were calculated from a band model with a modified temperature dependence designed to better match the low-temperature observations. In the visible ($\lambda < 1,050$ nm), the absorption coefficients of Karkoschka[34] were used. In practice, for 30 pressure–temperature conditions representative of 30 levels in Titan's atmosphere[12], methane transmissions were calculated for 60 different paths, convolved to the resolution of the DISR spectrometers, and this ensemble of convolved transmissions was fitted each time with an exponential-sum model.

At altitudes less than 3.5 km, we used single short exposures for the infrared spectra rather than long time averages. The 940 nm intensity in the last three ULIS spectra is about four times larger that in the first three spectra, indicating that the Sun is located in their field of view (see Fig. 20). The contrast between the most intense spectrum (with the Sun in the field of view) and the weakest one (with the Sun out of the field of view) increases with wavelength, reaching 17 at 1,550 nm, a consequence of the decreasing haze optical depth. This contrast can be used to constrain the haze optical depth, assuming that the spectra correspond approximately to solar azimuths of 0 and 180°. A satisfactory model, using aggregate particles of 256 monomers, a 0.05-μm monomer radius, and a uniform concentration of 52 particles cm^{-3}, indicates an optical depth of about 2 at 940 nm, decreasing to 0.5 at 1,550 nm. Models with one-half and twice the particle density (and

口，向下平均强度在 104 km 到 10 km 高度之间变化了 25% 或者更小，这说明气溶胶在红外波段的吸收相对较弱。

图 19. 逐渐消失的阳光。不同高度处的 ULIS 光谱记录（图中标示为数据点），表明甲烷吸收峰的强度随着进入大气层深度的增加而增加。大于 3.5 km 高度的光谱是对若干个探测器旋转周期进行积分的结果，大体上（但不是完全地）对应了方位平均强度。关于这些观测结果的全面分析尚需精确确定探测器高度与时间的关系，这一工作目前正在进行中。图中的曲线给出了我们采用的模型结果（用实线表示）作为对比，其中采用的甲烷摩尔分数在平流层为 1.6%，然后在表面处增加到 5%。对于较低的高度（＜20 km），模型与观测结果在甲烷吸收窗口，特别是在 1,280 nm、1,520～1,600 nm 附近，存在较大差异；这可能是由于甲烷吸收系数存在误差经过长光程的放大导致的。模型稍稍高估了 104 km 高度处的光谱强度，因为该光谱并不精确地匹配方位平均。辐射传输计算主要基于甲烷吸收特性的 16 项多项式求和公式。在近红外区域（λ＞1,050 nm），通过吸收波段模型可以计算出吸收系数，其中，为更好地拟合低温观测结果，我们对温度的依赖关系进行了修正。在可见光波段（λ＜1,050 nm），则采用了卡尔科施卡计算的吸收系数[34]。实际操作中，对于代表土卫六大气 30 个高度的 30 个气压–温度条件[12]，为 60 条不同的路径计算甲烷的穿透率，并与 DISR 光谱分析仪的分辨率作卷积，作卷积后的穿透率每次用一个指数求和模型进行拟合。

在低于 3.5 km 的高度，我们采用单次短时曝光（而不是长时曝光取平均）测量红外光谱。最后的三张 ULIS 光谱中 940 nm 的强度大约是最先三张 ULIS 光谱中 940 nm 强度的 4 倍，这说明太阳位于后三张光谱的拍摄视场中，参见图 20。当太阳位于视野之内时光谱强度显然最高，当太阳位于视野之外时光谱强度则最低；最强与最弱光谱之间对比度随着波长增加而增加，并在 1,550 nm 处达到 17，这是由于雾霾的光深随波长减小。假设以上光谱对应的太阳方位角分别约为 0° 和 180°，则以上对比度可以用来确定雾霾的光深。假设聚集颗粒由 256 个单体组成，每个单体的半径为 0.05 μm，粒子的均匀密度为 52 个/cm³，这一可以被接受的模型可以计算得到：940 nm 处对应的光深大约为 2，在 1,550 nm 处降为 0.5。如果采用粒子数密度

hence optical depth) yield a contrast between spectra with the Sun in and out of the field about twice as large and half as large (respectively) as observed.

Fig. 20. Determination of total haze optical depth. ULIS spectra (black points) recorded at 734 m (diamonds) and 53 m (squares) above the surface with integration times of 1 s. The one with the highest intensity (734 m) has the Sun in its field of view; the lower one (53 m) does not. The contrast between the two in the methane windows increases with wavelength and is a sensitive function of the haze optical depth. The nominal model, shown for comparison (green line), has an optical depth of 2 at 940 nm decreasing to 0.5 at 1,550 nm. Calculations correspond to intensities averaged over the field of view and azimuths of 0 and 180 degrees with respect to the Sun. Other models show the effect of doubling (red) and halving (blue) the particle concentration. Solid lines show model intensity towards the Sun while the dashed lines show the intensity with the instrument facing away from the Sun.

The methane bands are prominent in the DLIS spectra at all altitudes (see Fig. 21a). The residual intensity in the cores of these bands is due to scattering by aerosol particles between the probe and the surface. Its variation provides a constraint of the vertical profile of the haze particles between approximately 150 and 40 km, as illustrated in Fig. 21a. The method is not sensitive at low altitudes because of absorption of the downward solar flux in the methane bands. A model with a constant particle concentration with altitude provides a good fit of the methane bands. Moderate variations of the particle concentration with height are also acceptable, but a model with a clear space in the lower stratosphere is inconsistent with the data.

The optical depths in the models that fit the visible and infrared spectral observations with $N = 256$ and 512 are shown as functions of altitude in Fig. 16b. The number density was assumed to be 52 cm^{-3}, independent of altitude for the infrared models with $N = 256$. The models computed for comparison with the visible spectrometer contained constant and different number densities above and below 80 km. The average number density above and below 80 km for the models with $N = 256$ (30 and 65) are in reasonable agreement with the single value used in the models derived from the infrared spectrometer. The same particle number densities give the required optical depths from 900 to 1,550 nm, indicating that the algorithm for generating cross-sections from particle sizes is working in a consistent manner. At shorter wave-lengths (531 nm), the size parameter is sufficiently large that the cross-

分别另取为以上粒子数密度（也是光学深度）的 1/2 和两倍的模型，则相应的太阳在视场内外两种光谱的对比度分别为观测值的两倍和一半。

图 20. 雾霾总光深的确定。图中给出了土卫六地表之上 734 m（标示为菱形）和 53 m（标示为方形）处的 ULIS 光谱，积分时间为 1 s。其中，734 m 高度的光谱强度最大，视场中包含了太阳，而强度较弱的 53 m 光谱视场中没有太阳。两个甲烷窗口的对比度随着波长的增加而增加，并且对雾霾光深的变化很敏感。图中给出了标准模型作对比（绿线），其雾霾光深在 940 nm 处为 2，然后逐渐降至 1,550 nm 处的 0.5。计算得到的强度是对视场和相对太阳的 0 和 180° 方位角进行平均后的结果。其他模型表明粒子浓度加倍（红）或减半（蓝）的效应。图中实线表示朝向太阳的光谱强度，而虚线表示仪器背向太阳的光谱强度。

　　如图 21a 所示，在所有高度的 DLIS 光谱中，甲烷对应的吸收峰都是非常明显的。图中吸收峰核心区内存在强度残差，这是探测器与地表之间的气溶胶粒子散射造成的。这一强度的变化可以用于确定约 150～40 km 高度之间的雾霾颗粒的垂直分布，如图 21a 所示。但该方法在较低高度并不灵敏，因为向下照射的太阳光通量在甲烷吸收峰内被吸收。如果假定粒子浓度不随高度变化，那么相应的模型可以较好地拟合甲烷吸收峰。粒子浓度随高度有适度的变化的模型也是可接受的；但平流层下部有净空层的模型与数据不符。

　　图 16b 给出了与可见光和红外观测结果吻合的模型中光深与高度的关系，其中 N 的取值分别为 256 和 512。在红外模型（$N = 256$）中假设粒子数密度为 52 个/cm³，并且与高度变化无关。用于与可见光谱分析仪对比的模型中，以 80 km 高度为界，上下分别采用了恒定但彼此不同的粒子数密度。$N = 256$ 的模型中 80 km 上下的平均粒子数密度（分别为 30 与 65），和基于红外光谱分析仪的模型采用的单值粒子数密度相符。相同的粒子数密度给出了 900～1,500 nm 范围的光深，这说明根据颗粒尺寸推出截面积的算法始终是适用的。在较短的波长（531 nm），粒子尺寸参量过大，

section algorithm is not as accurate, and the number density is decreased slightly to give models that fit the observations. The variation of optical depth with wavelength is modest, decreasing by only about a factor of 2.8 from 500 to 1,000 nm. If 512 monomers are used for the particles, the wavelength dependence is even less steep. The haze optical depth as a function of wavelength is presented in Fig. 21b.

Fig. 21. Haze vertical structure and total optical depth. **a**, DLIS spectra recorded at three altitudes: 104 km (top, dots), 82 km (middle, squares), and 57 km (bottom, diamonds). The intensities for the higher altitudes have been displaced in 0.3 increments for clarity. The points are measured data; the lines are the nominal model; the dashed lines are a modified model with the same optical depth as the nominal model, but with all the haze particles concentrated above 72 km (clearing below). The residual intensity in the core of the methane bands is a sensitive indicator of the presence of scattering particles beneath the probe. The model with the clearing produces too much emission in the core of the CH_4 bands at high altitude and not enough at low altitude. **b**, Total extinction optical depth of the haze alone versus wavelength. The triangles are for models with 256 monomers per particle. The points at the two shortest wavelengths are from models that fit the visible spectrometer measurements. The other four points are from models that fit the infrared spectrometer measurements. The dots are for models with 512 monomers per particle that fit the visible spectrometer measurements.

导致截面算法不够准确，粒子数密度需要略微减小才能使模型与观测结果相符。当波长从 500 nm 增加到 1,000 nm，光深减小为原光深的 2.8 分之一，这一变化并不很大。如果聚集颗粒为 512 个单体构成，则这种变化会更小。图 21b 给出了雾霾光深与波长的关系。

图 21. 雾霾的垂直结构和总光深。**a**, 图中分别给出了高度为 104 km（上部圆点）、82 km（中部方块）以及 57 km（下部菱形）的 DLIS 光谱测量数据。为更清楚地显示在一幅图中，较高高度的光谱分别相对较低高度的光谱向上移动 0.3 个单位。图中点表示测得的数据，实线表示标称模型，虚线表示与标称模型具有相同光深的修正模型，其所有的雾霾颗粒都集中在大约 72 km 高度以上（下面没有雾霾颗粒）。图中甲烷吸收峰核心区域存在的强度残差是探测器下面存在散射粒子的很敏感的指示物。对于较高的高度，修正模型在甲烷吸收峰核心附近的辐射强度过大，而对于较低的高度又过小。**b**, 图中给出了雾霾的总消光光深与波长的关系。其中三角表示每个聚集颗粒由 256 个单体构成的模型，最短的两个波长处的数据点源自可见光谱仪测量结果的拟合模型，而另外四个数据点则源自红外光谱仪测量结果的拟合模型。图中圆点代表了与可见光谱仪测量结果拟合的表示每个聚集颗粒由 512 个单体构成的模型。

A Thin Layer of Haze near 21 km Altitude

Many workers have suggested that hydrocarbons produced at very high altitudes could diffuse downward to cooler levels where they could condense on haze particles. Do our intensity profiles looking towards the horizon detect any thin haze layers at specific altitudes that might be due to this mechanism?

Figure 22 shows the normalized profile of intensity measured by the Side-Looking Imager (SLI) compared to a model. The left-hand side of the plot shows normalized intensity as a function of nadir angle for the observations at altitudes ranging from 20.4 to 22.3 km. The observations at 22.1 km and above and at 20.4 km and below show smooth functions of nadir angle. However, for the measurement at 20.8, and the two measurements at 20.9 km altitude, a dip of about 2% is seen near a nadir angle of 90°.

Fig. 22. Thin cloud layer observation at 21 km. In the left-hand side are the intensity profiles as a function of nadir angle divided by the average intensity profile measured by the SLI at the altitudes indicated. The right-hand side of the figure shows the model intensity profiles computed for a cloud layer of absorption optical depth 0.001 which is 1 km thick at an altitude of 21 km. The model is able to reproduce the 2% contrast feature seen in the observations at altitudes of 20.8 and 20.9 km. If the layer is mostly illuminated by diffuse light, the absorption optical depth is equal to total optical depth times the difference between the single-scattering albedos of the material in the layer and the albedo of the background haze. If the layer is primarily illuminated by direct sunlight, the absorption optical depth of the haze is proportional to the total optical depth of the haze times the difference between the phase functions of the material in the layer and the background haze at the scattering angles for any observation.

The curves in the right-hand side of Fig. 22 show the intensities of a model having a thin additional layer of haze at an altitude of 20.9 km. The haze layer of vertical absorption optical depth within a factor of two of 0.001 with a gaussian profile between 1 and 2 km thick can reproduce the depth of the feature. The location of the layer is at 21.0 ± 0.5 km, where the local temperature is 76 K and the pressure is 450 mbar (ref. 12).

This feature at 21 km occurs in the troposphere and may be an indication of methane condensation. It is the only indication of a thin layer seen in the set of SLI images taken from 150 km to the surface. Evidence of condensation of hydrocarbons in the lower stratosphere, where several hydrocarbons might be expected to condense[25], has not yet been

21 km 高度附近的雾霾薄层

许多研究者认为，非常高的大气中产生的碳氢化合物，可以向下扩散到较冷的层位，并在那里凝结成雾霾颗粒。那么我们朝向地平线方向的光谱强度剖面，是否会探测到某一高度存在由于以上机制形成的雾霾薄层呢？

图 22 给出了侧视成像仪 (SLI) 测量得到的归一化的强度分布曲线，以及与相应模型的比较。图中左侧表示归一化强度与天底角的关系曲线，对应的观测高度从 20.4 km 到 22.3 km。测量曲线在 22.1 km 及以上的区间和 20.4 km 以下的区间内都平滑连续，但是对于位于 20.8 km 高度的一条测量曲线和位于 20.9 km 高度的两条测量曲线，在天底角 90° 附近均存在一个大约 2% 的凹陷。

图 22. 21 km 高度处薄云层的观测结果。图中左侧给出了 SLI 在不同高度测量得到的强度与天底角的关系曲线，其中强度是实际强度除以平均强度后的结果。右侧则给出了对厚度为 1 km 的云层的模型计算结果，其中该云层的高度为 21 km，吸收光深为 0.001。该模型可以重现观测结果中 20.8 km 和 20.9 km 曲线 2% 的下陷结构。如果该云层主要由漫射光照亮，则吸收光深等于总光深乘以云层物质的单散射反照率与背景雾霾反照率之差。如果云层主要受直射阳光照亮，对于任何观测，雾霾的吸收光深正比于雾霾的总光深乘以云层物质与散射角方向处的背景雾霾之间的相位函数之差。

图 22 右侧给出了模型的强度曲线，其中该模型在 20.9 km 的高度附加了一层较薄的雾霾。如果这层薄雾霾的垂直吸收光深在 1 ~ 2 km 的厚度范围内为高斯分布，并且其值在 0.001 的两倍范围内变化，则该模型也可以产生类似左图的凹陷结构。该层薄雾霾的高度为 21.0 ± 0.5 km，局域温度为 76 K，压强为 450 mbar[12]。

21 km 处的雾霾薄层位于对流层内，可能意味着甲烷的凝结。SLI 在探测器从 150 km 高度到着陆过程中拍摄的图像里，这是唯一预示雾霾薄层存在的观测结果。但是目前尚未发现人们预期的碳氢化合物在平流层底层的凝结现象（人们预测有几

found, but the search is continuing.

Unravelling Titan's Mysteries

Some of the major questions about Titan concern the nature of the source of methane that replaces the irreversible loss at high altitudes by photochemistry that produces a host of complex organic compounds. Open pools of liquid hydrocarbons on the surface have been suggested, as well as cryovolcanism. Also, if methane photochemistry has been occurring over the lifetime of the Solar System the organic products of these processes should have accumulated to significant depths on the surface and should be seen in images and spectra of the surface.

Although no such liquid bodies were directly imaged by DISR, there is compelling evidence for fluid flow on the surface of Titan, including the dendritic and stubby drainage channel networks, the rounded and size-graded "rocks" at the surface landing site, and the morphology of the shoreline, offshore structures, and the appearance of the darker lakebed region. The stubby networks may imply sapping or spring-fed flows, as the existence of liquid pools on the surface and the frequency of precipitation that could cause the deep dendritic drainage channels are both still unconfirmed. In addition, there are at least a few structures that suggest cryovolcanic flows on the surface.

The ground track derived by the image correlations demonstrates a zonal wind field that is mostly prograde. The general altitude profile and shape agree with predicted average models of the zonal wind flow between 50 and 10 km altitude[7], although with a reduced intensity. Below 10 km, falling wind speeds and an abrupt change of wind direction indicate a planetary boundary layer some 7–8 km thick, scaling nicely from near-equatorial terrestrial boundary layers.

Spatially resolved spectral reflectance measurements of different regions on the surface suggest that the uplands are redder than the lowland lakebed regions. The regions near the mouths of the rivers are also redder than the lake regions. A host of questions about the sequence of flooding and formation of these structures is suggested by these observations.

The reflectivity of the surface at the landing site was measured from 480 nm to 1,600 nm without the interference of methane absorption bands or haze opacity. The peak reflectivity in the dark regions is about 0.18 at 830 nm and decreases towards longer and shorter wavelengths. The red slope in the visible is consistent with organic material, such as tholins, but the blue infrared slope is still unexplained. Between 1,500 and 1,600 nm the reflectivity is low (0.06) and flat, consistent with water ice. Nevertheless, the decrease in reflectivity from 900 to 1,500 nm does not show the expected weak absorption bands of water ice near 1,000 and 1,200 nm, and the identity of the surface component responsible for this blue slope remains unknown.

种碳氢化合物应该会在那里凝结[25]），相关搜寻正在进行中。

揭秘土卫六

关于土卫六的一些主要问题都涉及了甲烷的来源问题。在高层大气中，不可逆光化学反应通过消耗甲烷不断产生大量有机化合物，而源源不断进入大气、填补这一消耗的甲烷来自哪里呢？人们认为土卫六表面存在着液态烃构成的露天水池以及冰火山活动。同时，如果甲烷光化学反应在太阳系整个寿命周期中都不断进行，那么该过程中产生的有机产物就会在土卫六表面积累并达到明显的厚度，从而可以在图像和光谱中被观测到。

然而，DISR 图像并没有直接观测到这样的液体，不过还是有令人信服的证据支持土卫六表面存在液体的流动。这些证据包括树枝状和断株状沟渠网络，着陆点附近有分选性的圆"石"，海岸线地形结构，离岸的各种结构以及较暗的湖床区域的外观。其中，这些断株状网络可能意味着液体下切侵蚀的河道或者源自泉眼的液体流；而表面存在液体湖泊以及形成较深的树枝状排水沟道的频繁降雨，这两者尚未得到证实。此外，至少有几处结构表明地表存在冰火山作用相关的流动构造。

根据图像关联性推出的探测器轨迹地面投影说明了该处的风场是一个总体上与土卫六自转同向的纬向风场。该风场的大体高度剖面和速度曲线的形状与 50~10 km 高度之间的纬向风模型的预测相一致[7]，虽然风的强度相比于模型有所减小。在 10 km 高度以下，风速的降低和风向的骤然改变表明，行星边界层厚度大约为 7~8 km，与地球赤道附近的行星边界层有很好的对应关系。

土卫六表面的空间分辨光谱反射率测量表明，高地比湖床低地区域红化程度更高，河口附近的区域也比湖区更加红化。这些观测结果向我们提出了与洪水活动的顺序以及这些地形结构如何形成等相关的许多问题。

在不受甲烷吸收峰和雾霾不透明度干扰的情况下，探测器在着陆点附近测量了 480~1,600 nm 波段的表面反射率。暗色区域的反射率在 830 nm 处到达峰值，大约为 0.18，然后随着波长的增加和减小都降低。其中，可见光波段的红坡与有机物质（如索林斯）的结果相符，但是红外波段的蓝坡目前尚未得到解释。从 1,500 nm 到 1,600 nm 的范围内，反射率较低（0.06）且比较平坦，与水冰的特征相符。不过，从 900 nm 到 1,500 nm 反射率的下降过程中并未发现 1,000 nm 和 1,200 nm 附近预期存在的较弱的水冰吸收峰。是什么表面物质导致了这一蓝坡结构目前还不得而知。

The nature of the haze aerosols measured by DISR is different in significant ways from the view before the Huygens mission. Before the Huygens probe, cloud physics models with sedimentation and coagulation predicted a strong increase in haze density with decreasing altitude[9]. In addition, measurements of the high degree of linear polarization in light scattered from Titan near a phase angle of 90° by the Pioneer and Voyager spacecraft could only be matched by spherical particles having radii less than or equal to 0.1 μm. Such small particles produced a strong increase in optical depth with decreasing wavelength shortward of 1,000 nm. Fitting the strong methane band at 890 nm constrained the amount of haze at high altitudes. This haze became optically much thicker at the wavelength of the weaker methane band at 619 nm. To fit the observed strength of this band it was necessary to remove the haze permitted by the cloud physics calculations at altitudes below about 70 km by invoking condensation of organic gases produced at very high altitudes as they diffused down to colder levels[26]. The condensation of many organic gases produced by photochemistry at high altitudes on Titan was suggested by Sagan and Thompson in ref. 25, and seemed consistent with this view.

The next development in Titan haze models (pioneered by R.W., P.S., Cabane, M. and M.L.) included the use of fractal aggregate haze particles that had a small component (monomer) with a radius of about 0.06 μm to produce strong linear polarization[26-30]. These monomers stuck together in an aggregation of many tens (or more) monomers. The large size of the aggregation could produce the strong forward scattering required from the Titan haze aerosols while preserving the high degree of linear polarization. However, it was quite laborious to compute the single-scattering properties of such aggregate particles for more than about 100 monomers at visible wavelengths. Particles with an effective radius of about 0.35 μm were required to produce the degree of forward scattering observed by Voyager[31]. This required the number of monomers in an aggregate particle to be about 45, and permitted single-scattering computations of the cross-section and phase function of the particles over the visible range. Of course, even larger numbers of monomers per particle would have matched the observations at high phase angles on Voyager, but these were difficult to perform and have largely gone unexplored. If larger particles had been used, however, the optical depth of the aerosols at shorter wavelengths would not have been nearly so large, and the clear space below 70 km may well not have been necessary.

The new DISR observations give a measurement of the monomer radius of 0.05 μm, in good agreement with previous estimates. Significantly, however, they show that the haze optical depth varies from about 2 at 935 nm to only about 4.5 at 531 nm, and the number of monomers in a haze particle is therefore probably several hundred. A value of 256 for N gives a projected area equal to that of a sphere of radius 0.65 μm, about twice as large as previously assumed. With $N = 512$, the equivalent sphere with the same projected area has a radius of 0.9 μm, nearly three times the size previously used. In any case, it seems that the size of the aggregate particles is several times as large as in some of the older models. A better estimate of the particle size will be available after the analysis of the solar aureole measurements of the variation in brightness near the Sun. In addition, measurements by the DISR violet photometer will extend the optical measurements of the haze to

由 DISR 测量得到的土卫六上的雾霾气溶胶的特性与惠更斯任务之前的观点是非常不同的。在惠更斯探测器之前，考虑了凝固和沉积作用的云层物理模型预测随着高度的降低，雾霾的密度将有较大的增幅[9]。此外，先驱者号和旅行者号飞船在 90° 相位角测量了土卫六的散射光，发现存在高度线偏振，两个飞船的测量结果只有在球形颗粒的半径小于或等于 0.1 μm 的情况下才能吻合。这么小的颗粒随着波长（小于 1,000 nm 范围内）的减小，其光深大幅增加。通过拟合 890 nm 的甲烷强吸收峰，可以约束高空雾霾的总量。但在 619 nm 的甲烷弱吸收峰，这些雾霾的光学厚度则要大得多。为了拟合该吸收峰的观测强度，有必要援引产生于高层大气的有机气体扩散到下面较冷的大气层后将发生凝结的观点[26]，以此来移除云层物理模型中允许的 70 km 以下高度的雾霾。萨根和汤普森在参考文献 25 中提出了土卫六高层大气中的许多有机气体通过光化学发生凝结的观点，看似与上述观点相符。

通过引入雾霾颗粒分形聚集，进一步发展了土卫六雾霾模型（由韦斯特、史密斯、卡班和莱蒙率先提出），其采用的小成分（单体）的半径约为 0.06 μm，可以产生很强的线偏振[26-30]。聚集颗粒由数十个（或更多）单体彼此吸附而成。这么大的聚集颗粒不但可以产生土卫六雾霾气溶胶需要的非常强的前向散射，而且能够保持高度线偏振。然而，如果构成颗粒的单体超过 100 个，则计算这么大颗粒在可见光波段的单散射特性是非常艰难的。为了解释旅行者号观测到的前向散射度，聚集颗粒的有效半径需要大约为 0.35 μm[31]，则相应的单体数量大约为 45，这样就可以在可见光范围进行粒子的截面积和相函数的单散射计算。当然，每个颗粒有更大的单体数量也能匹配旅行者号在高相位角的观测结果，但是这是很难计算的，并且在很大程度上也未探索过。然而，如果采用较大的聚集颗粒，这些气溶胶在短波长波段的光深并不一定这么大，而且也没必要假设 70 km 以下存在净空层。

最近的 DISR 观测结果表明，构成雾霾颗粒的单体的半径为 0.05 μm，这与先前的估计相符。但是，明显地，雾霾的光深从 935 nm 处大约为 2 变到 531 nm 处的 4.5，而雾霾颗粒中的单体数量可能高达数百个。如果假设单体数量 $N = 256$，则其投影面积相当于一个半径为 0.65 μm 球体，相当于先前假定值的两倍。如果假设单体数量 $N = 512$，则相同投影面积的等价球体的半径为 0.9 μm，该尺寸几乎是先前值的三倍。无论哪种情况，聚集颗粒的尺寸看起来都是原先的模型中对应值的数倍。通过对太阳光晕进行太阳周围亮度的变化测量并进行分析，可以更好地估计出粒子的尺寸。此外，DISR 紫外光度计的测量可以将雾霾的光学测量范围扩展到更短的波

wavelengths as short as the band from 350 to 480 nm, also helping to constrain the size of the haze particles.

The number density of the haze particles does not increase with depth nearly as dramatically as predicted by the older cloud physics models. In fact, the number density increases by only a factor of a few over the altitude range from 150 km to the surface. This implies that vertical mixing is much less than had been assumed in the older models where the particles are distributed approximately as the gas is with altitude. In any case, no clear space at low altitudes, which was suggested earlier[32], was seen.

The methane mole fraction of 1.6% measured in the stratosphere by the Composite Infrared Spectrometer (CIRS) and the Gas Chromatograph Mass Spectrometer is consistent with the DISR spectral measurements. At very low altitudes (20 m) DISR measured $5 \pm 1\%$ for the methane mole fraction.

Finally, the entire set of DISR observations gives a new view of Titan, and reinforces the view that processes on Titan's surface are more similar to those on the surface of the Earth than anywhere else in the Solar System.

(**438**, 765-778; 2005)

M. G. Tomasko[1], B. Archinal[2], T. Becker[2], B. Bézard[3], M. Bushroe[1], M. Combes[3], D. Cook[2], A. Coustenis[3], C. de Bergh[3], L. E. Dafoe[1], L. Doose[1], S. Douté[4], A. Eibl[1], S. Engel[1], F. Gliem[5], B. Grieger[6], K. Holso[1], E. Howington-Kraus[2], E. Karkoschka[1], H. U. Keller[6], R. Kirk[2], R. Kramm[6], M. Küppers[6], P. Lanagan[1], E. Lellouch[3], M. Lemmon[7], J. Lunine[1,8], E. McFarlane[1], J. Moores[1], G. M. Prout[1], B. Rizk[1], M. Rosiek[2], P. Rueffer[5], S. E. Schröder[6], B. Schmitt[4], C. See[1], P. Smith[1], L. Soderblom[2], N. Thomas[9] & R. West[10]

[1] Lunar and Planetary Laboratory, University of Arizona, 1629 E. University Blvd, Tucson, Arizona 85721-0092, USA

[2] US Geological Survey, Astrogeology, 2225 N. Gemini Drive, Flagstaff, Arizona 86001, USA

[3] LESIA, Observatoire de Paris, 5 place Janssen, 92195 Meudon, France

[4] Laboratoire de Planétologie de Grenoble, CNRS-UJF, BP 53, 38041 Grenoble, France

[5] Technical University of Braunschweig, Hans-Sommer-Str. 66, D-38106 Braunschweig, Germany

[6] Max Planck Institute for Solar System Research, Max-Planck-Str. 2, D-37191 Katlenburg-Lindau, Germany

[7] Department of Physics, Texas A&M University, College Station, Texas 77843-3150, USA

[8] Istituto Nazionale di Astrofisica — Istituto di Fisica dello Spazio Interplanetario (INAF-IFSI ARTOV), Via del Cavaliere, 100, 00133 Roma, Italia

[9] Department of Physics, University of Bern, Sidlerstr. 5, CH-3012 Bern, Switzerland

[10] Jet Propulsion Laboratory, 4800 Oak Grove Drive, Pasadena, California 91109, USA

Received 26 May; accepted 8 August 2005. Published online 30 November 2005.

References:

1. Coustenis, A. *et al.* Maps of Titan's surface from 1 to 2.5 μm. *Icarus* **177**, 89-105 (2005).

2. Porco, C. C. *et al.* Imaging of Titan from the Cassini spacecraft. *Nature* **434**, 159-168 (2005).

3. Sotin, C. *et al.* Infrared images of Titan. *Nature* **435**, 786-789 (2005).

4. Elachi, C. *et al.* Cassini radar views the surface of Titan. *Science* **308**, 970-974 (2005).

5. Tomasko, M. G. *et al.* The Descent Imager/Spectral Radiometer (DISR) experiment on the Huygens entry probe of Titan. *Space Sci. Rev.* **104**, 469-551 (2002).

6. Ivanov, B. A., Basilevski, A. T. & Neukem, G. Atmospheric entry of large meteoroids: implication to Titan. *Planet. Space Sci.* **45**, 993-1007 (1997).

7. Flasar, F. M., Allison, M. D. & Lunine, J. I. Titan zonal wind model. *ESA Publ.* **SP-1177**, 287-298 (1997).

段(350~480 nm),这也有助于约束雾霾颗粒的尺寸大小。

雾霾颗粒的粒子数密度,并不像早期的云层物理模型预测的那样随着深度的增加而急剧增加。事实上,粒子数密度从 150 km 高度到表面仅仅增加了几倍。这意味着垂直混合程度要比早期模型的假设小得多,后者认为粒子随高度的分布大体和气体的分布是一样的。总之,和先前的研究一样[32],并没有在较低高度发现雾霾净空层。

合成红外光谱仪(CIRS)和气相色谱-质谱联用分析仪测得的甲烷摩尔分数为 1.6%,这与 DISR 光谱测量结果相一致。在非常低的高度(20 m),DISR 给出的甲烷摩尔分数为 5%±1%。

最后,DISR 的整个观测使我们对土卫六有了全新的认识,使我们进一步意识到土卫六表面上发生的各种过程比太阳系内其他任何天体都更类似于地球表面上发生的过程。

(金世超 翻译;陈含章 审稿)

8. Bond, N. A. Observations of planetary boundary-layer structure in the eastern equatorial Pacific. *J. Atmos. Sci.* **5**, 699-706 (1992).

9. Lindal, G. F., Wood, G. E., Hotz, H. B. & Sweetnam, D. N. The atmosphere of Titan: An analysis of the Voyager 1 radio occultation measurements. *Icarus* **53**, 348-363 (1983).

10. Tokano, T. & Neubauer, F. M. Tidal winds on Titan caused by Saturn. *Icarus* **158**, 499-515 (2002).

11. Niemann, H. B. *et al.* The abundances of constituents of Titan's atmosphere from the GCMS instrument on the Huygens probe. *Nature* doi:10.1038/nature04122 (this issue).

12. Fulchignoni, M. *et al. In situ* measurements of the physical characteristics of Titan's environment. *Nature* doi:10.1038/nature04314 (this issue).

13. Brown, G. N. Jr & Ziegler, W. T. in *Advances in Cryogenetic Engineering* (ed. Timmerhaus, K. D.) Vol. 25, 662-670 (Plenum, New York, 1980).

14. Griffith, C. A., Owen, T., Geballe, T. R., Rayner, J. & Rannou, P. Evidence for the exposure of water ice on Titan's surface. *Science* **300**, 628-630 (2003).

15. Coustenis, A., Lellouch, E., Maillard, J.-P. & McKay, C. P. Titan's surface: composition and variability from the near-infrared albedo. *Icarus* **118**, 87-104 (1995).

16. Lellouch, E., Schmitt, B., Coustenis, A. & Cuby, J.-G. Titan's 5-μm lightcurve. *Icarus* **168**, 204-209 (2004).

17. Grundy, W. & Schmitt, B. The temperature-dependent near-infrared absorption spectrum of hexagonal H_2O ice. *J. Geophys. Res. E* **103**, 25809-25822 (1998).

18. Bernard, J.-M. *et al.* Evidence for chemical variations at the micrometric scale of Titan's tholins: Implications for analysing Cassini-Huygens data. *Icarus* (submitted).

19. Coll, P. *et al.* Experimental laboratory simulation of Titan's atmosphere: aerosols and gas phase. *Planet. Space Sci.* **47**, 1331-1340 (1999).

20. Bernard, J.-M. *et al.* Experimental simulation of Titan's atmosphere: detection of ammonia and ethylene oxide. *Planet. Space Sci.* **51**, 1003-1011 (2003).

21. Moroz, L. V., Arnold, G., Korochantsev, A. V. & Wäsch, R. Natural solid bitumens as possible analogs for cometary and asteroid organics. 1. Reflectance spectroscopy of pure bitumens. *Icarus* **134**, 253-268 (1998).

22. Toon, O. B., McKay, C. P., Griffith, C. A. & Turco, R. P. A physical model of Titan's aerosols. *Icarus* **95**, 24-53 (1992).

23. Khare, B. N. *et al.* Optical constants of organic tholins produced in a simulated Titanian atmosphere—From soft X-ray to microwave frequencies. *Icarus* **60**, 127-137 (1984).

24. Flasar, F. M. *et al.* Titan's atmospheric temperatures, winds, and composition. *Science* **308**, 975-978 (2005).

25. Sagan, C. & Thompson, W. R. Production and condensation of organic gases in the atmosphere of Titan. *Icarus* **59**, 133-161 (1984).

26. Lemmon, M. T. *Properties of Titan's Haze and Surface*. PhD dissertation, (Univ. Arizona, 1994).

27. West, R. A. & Smith, P. H. Evidence for aggregate particles in the atmospheres of Titan and Jupiter. *Icarus* **90**, 330-333 (1991).

28. Cabane, M., Chassefière, E. & Israel, G. Formation and growth of photochemical aerosols in Titan's atmosphere. *Icarus* **96**, 176-189 (1992).

29. Cabane, M., Rannou, P., Chassefière, E. & Israel, G. Fractal aggregates in Titan's atmosphere. *Planet. Space Sci.* **41**, 257-267 (1993).

30. West, R. A. Optical properties of aggregate particles whose outer diameter is comparable to the wavelength. *Appl. Opt.* **30**, 5316-5324 (1991).

31. Rages, K. B. & Pollack, J. Vertical distribution of scattering hazes in Titan's upper atmosphere. *Icarus* **55**, 50-62 (1983).

32. McKay, C. P. *et al.* Physical properties of the organic aerosols and clouds on Titan. *Planet. Space Sci.* **49**, 79-99 (2001).

33. Bird, M. K. *et al.* The vertical profile of winds on Titan. *Nature* doi:10.1038/nature04060 (this issue).

34. Karkoschka, E. Methane, ammonia, and temperature measurements of the Jovian planets and Titan from CCD-spectrophotometry. *Icarus* **133**, 134-146 (1998).

Acknowledgements. We thank the people from the following organizations whose dedication and effort have made this project successful: AETA (Fontenay-aux-Roses, France), Alcatel Space (Cannes, France), Collimated Holes Inc., EADS Deutschland GmbH (formerly Deutsche Aerospace AG, Munich, Germany), ETEL Motion Technology (Mortiers, Switzerland), The European Space Agency's (ESA) European Space and Technology Centre (ESTEC), The European Space Operations Centre (ESOC), The Jet Propulsion Laboratory (JPL), Laboratoire de Planétologie de Grenoble (CNRS-UJF), Loral Fairchild (Tustin, California, USA), Martin Marietta Corporation (Denver, Colorado, USA), Max-Planck-Institut für Sonnensystemforschung (Katlenburg-Lindau, Germany), Observatoire de Paris (Meudon, France), Technische Universität Braunschweig (TUB), Thomson-CSF (Grenoble, France), University of Arizona's Kuiper Lunar and Planetary Laboratory (LPL), and the US Geological Survey (Flagstaff, Arizona, USA).

Author Information. Reprints and permissions information is available at npg.nature.com/reprintsandpermissions. The authors declare no competing financial interests. Correspondence and requests for materials should be addressed to C.S. (csee@lpl.arizona.edu).

Discovery of a Cool Planet of 5.5 Earth Masses through Gravitational Microlensing

J.-P Beaulieu *et al.*

Editor's Note

The search for extrasolar planets continues apace, with nearly 4,000 known in mid-2019. It is difficult from the surface of the Earth to find planets of about the mass of the Earth using the traditional Doppler technique of looking for the wobble in the parent star's position. Here Jean-Philippe Beaulieu and his colleagues report a planet of only 5.5 Earth masses, found using gravitational microlensing (the bending and focusing of light rays by gravity). The planet is about 2.6 astronomical units (the Earth–Sun distance) from its parent star—about where the asteroid belt is in our solar system. The planet orbits the star acting as a lens, which passed between our solar system and a more distant, lensed star.

In the favoured core-accretion model of formation of planetary systems, solid planetesimals accumulate to build up planetary cores, which then accrete nebular gas if they are sufficiently massive. Around M-dwarf stars (the most common stars in our Galaxy), this model favours the formation of Earth-mass ($M_\oplus$) to Neptune-mass planets with orbital radii of 1 to 10 astronomical units (AU), which is consistent with the small number of gas giant planets known to orbit M-dwarf host stars[1-4]. More than 170 extrasolar planets have been discovered with a wide range of masses and orbital periods, but planets of Neptune's mass or less have not hitherto been detected at separations of more than 0.15 AU from normal stars. Here we report the discovery of a $5.5^{+5.5}_{-2.7}M_\oplus$ planetary companion at a separation of $2.6^{+1.5}_{-0.6}$ AU from a $0.22^{+0.21}_{-0.11}M_\odot$ M-dwarf star, where $M_\odot$ refers to a solar mass. (We propose to name it OGLE-2005-BLG-390Lb, indicating a planetary mass companion to the lens star of the microlensing event.) The mass is lower than that of GJ876d (ref. 5), although the error bars overlap. Our detection suggests that such cool, sub-Neptune-mass planets may be more common than gas giant planets, as predicted by the core accretion theory.

G RAVITATIONAL microlensing events can reveal extrasolar planets orbiting the foreground lens stars if the light curves are measured frequently enough to characterize planetary light curve deviations with features lasting a few hours[6-9]. Microlensing is most sensitive to planets in Earth-to-Jupiter-like orbits with semi-major axes in the range 1–5 AU. The sensitivity of the microlensing method to low-mass planets is restricted by the finite angular size of the source stars[10,11], limiting detections to planets of a few $M_\oplus$ for giant

通过微引力透镜发现一颗 5.5 倍地球质量的冷行星

博利厄等

编者按

搜寻系外行星的工作进展迅速,截至 2019 年年中,已有将近 4,000 颗系外行星被发现。在地表利用传统的多普勒技术探测母恒星位置移动,进而发现与地球质量相当的行星是十分困难的。本文中,让–菲利普·博利厄与他的同事报道了通过微引力透镜(光线被引力弯曲和聚焦)找到的一颗仅有地球质量 5.5 倍的行星。这颗行星大致距离其母恒星 2.6 个天文单位(日地距离),大约对应于太阳系中小行星带所处的位置。围绕母星转动的行星与其母星,在经过我们的太阳系与更遥远的、被透镜的恒星之间时,表现为一个"透镜"。

核吸积模型是当前较为流行的行星系统形成模型,该模型认为微行星会聚集形成一个致密的行星核。如果它们的质量足够大,那么它们将逐渐吸积星云气体。M 型矮星是银河系中最常见的恒星,根据核吸积模型,在它们附近形成的行星质量通常介于地球质量($M_\oplus$)和海王星质量之间,相应的轨道半径为 1~10 个天文单位(AU)。这个预言与实际观测结果相符合,因为已知围绕 M 型矮星运动的气体巨行星的数目很少 [1-4]。目前,人们已经发现了超过 170 颗的系外行星,其质量和轨道周期的范围跨度很大,但是迄今尚未发现与正常恒星相距超过 0.15AU、质量与海王星相当或略小的行星。在本文中,我们发现了一颗质量为 $5.5^{+5.5}_{-2.7}M_\oplus$ 的类行星伴天体,其宿主恒星是质量为 $0.22^{+0.21}_{-0.11}M_\odot$ 的 M 型矮星($M_\odot$ 表示太阳的质量),二者相距 $2.6^{+1.5}_{-0.6}$ AU。我们建议将这颗星体命名为 OGLE-2005-BLG-390Lb,用以表示是微引力透镜事件中与恒星一起组成透镜系统的行星伴星。相比 GJ8764d,虽然两者的误差棒相互重叠,但是这颗行星的质量更小 [5]。我们的探测研究结果表明,同核吸积模型预测的一样,这些温度偏低的亚海王星质量的行星可能比气体巨行星更为普遍。

如果光变曲线的采样频率足够高,以致能够识别时标为几个小时的行星光变曲线偏移特征,微引力透镜事件可以揭示围绕前景透镜恒星转动的系外行星 [6-9]。微引力透镜对于探测那些轨道半长轴介于 1~5 AU 之间(对应从地球到木星之间的轨道范围)的行星最为灵敏。该方法在探测低质量行星方面的灵敏度主要受限于背景源恒星有限的角尺度 [10,11],因此,对于巨型源恒星,行星质量的探测下限大致为几个

source stars, but allowing the detection of planets as small as $0.1 M_\oplus$ for main-sequence source stars in the Galactic Bulge. The PLANET collaboration[12] maintains the high sampling rate required to detect low-mass planets while monitoring the most promising of the > 500 microlensing events discovered annually by the OGLE collaboration, as well as events discovered by MOA. A decade of pioneering microlensing searches has resulted in the recent detections of two Jupiter-mass extrasolar planets[13,14] with orbital separations of a few AU by the combined observations of the OGLE, MOA, MicroFUN and PLANET collaborations. The absence of perturbations to stellar microlensing events can be used to constrain the presence of planetary lens companions. With large samples of events, upper limits on the frequency of Jupiter-mass planets have been placed over an orbital range of 1–10 AU, down to $M_\oplus$ planets[15-17] for the most common stars of our galaxy.

On 11 July 2005, the OGLE Early Warning System[18] announced the microlensing event OGLE-2005-BLG-390 (right ascension $\alpha = 17$ h 54 min 19.2 s, declination $\delta = -30° \, 22'$ $38''$, J2000) with a relatively bright clump giant as a source star. Subsequently, PLANET, OGLE and MOA monitored it with their different telescopes. After peaking at a maximum magnification of $A_{max} = 3.0$ on 31 July 2005, a short-duration deviation from a single lens light curve was detected on 9 August 2005 by PLANET. As described below, this deviation was due to a low-mass planet orbiting the lens star.

From analysis of colour-magnitude diagrams, we derive the following reddening-corrected colours and magnitudes for the source star: $(V-I)_0 = 0.85$, $I_0 = 14.25$ and $(V-K)_0 = 1.9$. We used the surface brightness relation[20] linking the emerging flux per solid angle of a light-emitting body to its colour, calibrated by interferometric observations, to derive an angular radius of 5.25 ± 0.73 µas, which corresponds to a source radius of $9.6 \pm 1.3 R_\odot$ (where $R_\odot$ is the radius of the Sun) if the source star is at a distance of 8.5 kpc. The source star colours indicate that it is a 5,200 K giant, which corresponds to a G4 III spectral type.

Figure 1 shows our photometric data for microlensing event OGLE-2005-BLG-390 and the best planetary binary lens model. The best-fit model has $\chi^2 = 562.26$ for 650 data points, seven lens parameters, and 12 flux normalization parameters, for a total of 631 degrees of freedom. Model length parameters in Table 1 are expressed in units of the Einstein ring radius R_E (typically ~2 AU for a Galactic Bulge system), the size of the ring image that would be seen in the case of perfect lens–source alignment. In modelling the light curve, we adopted linear limb darkening laws[21] with $\Gamma_I = 0.538$ and $\Gamma_R = 0.626$, appropriate for this G4 III giant source star, to describe the centre-to-limb variation of the intensity profile in the I and R bands. Four different binary lens modelling codes were used to confirm that the model we present is the only acceptable model for the observed light curve. The best alternative model is one with a large-flux-ratio binary source with a single lens, which has gross features that are similar to a planetary microlensing event[22]. However, as shown in Fig. 1, this model fails to account for the PLANET-Perth, PLANET-Danish and OGLE

太阳质量。但对于星系核球中的主序源恒星，则允许探测到 0.1 个太阳质量大小的行星。PLANET 合作组织 [12] 每年对光学引力透镜实验（OGLE）合作组织以及天文物理微透镜观测（MOA）合作组织发现的超过 500 个最有可能的微引力透镜事件进行监控，其采样频率足够高，可以满足低质量行星探测的要求。结合过去十年 OGLE、MOA、MicroFUN 和 PLANET 合作组织对微引力透镜早期搜寻的观测结果，人们最近发现了两颗质量与木星相当、轨道半径相差几个 AU 的系外行星 [13,14]。无扰动的恒星微引力透镜事件可以用来限制透镜中行星伴星的存在。基于大样本的微引力透镜事件，人们不仅对轨道半径在 1 ~ 10 AU 范围内木星质量的行星出现频率给出了上限，还对于银河系中最常见的恒星周围低至 $M_\oplus$ 的行星出现频率给出了限制 [15-17]。

2005 年 7 月 11 日，OGLE 的预警系统 [18] 报告发现了微引力透镜事件 OGLE-2005-BLG-390（赤经 $\alpha = 17$ h 54 min 19.2 s，赤纬 $\delta = -30°22'38''$，J2000），其源恒星为一颗相对明亮的团簇巨星。随后，PLANET、OGLE 和 MOA 分别利用望远镜对其进行了监控观测。在 2005 年 7 月 31 日该引力透镜事件的放大率达到峰值 $A_{max} = 3.0$ 之后，2005 年 8 月 9 日 PLANET 探测到一个短时偏离单透镜光变曲线的现象。如下所述，这种偏离是由一颗围绕透镜恒星运动的低质量行星引起的。

通过分析颜色–星等图，我们可以推知这颗源恒星经过红化校正后的颜色和星等，结果如下：$(V-I)_0 = 0.85$，$I_0 = 14.25$，$(V-K)_0 = 1.9$。我们利用面亮度关系 [20] 将发光天体单位立体角内的辐射通量与颜色联系起来。经过干涉观测校正，我们推导出源恒星的角半径为 5.25 ± 0.73 μas。如果这颗源恒星的距离为 8.5 kpc，那么上述角半径值对应的物理半径为 $9.6 \pm 1.3 R_\odot$，其中 $R_\odot$ 表示太阳的半径。这颗源恒星的颜色表明，它是一颗温度为 5,200 K 的巨星，对应于 G4 III 光谱类型。

图 1 给出了微引力透镜事件 OGLE-2005-BLG-390 的测光数据以及最佳的行星双透镜模型。最优拟合模型的 $\chi^2 = 562.26$，该拟合具有 650 个数据点、7 个透镜参数、12 个通量归一化参数，总自由度为 631。表 1 给出的模型长度参数以爱因斯坦环半径 R_E（对于一个银河系核球系统而言，其典型值约为 2 AU）为单位，这个爱因斯坦环的半径对应当透镜、源恒星以及观测者精确排列在一条直线上时所能观测到的环形图像的尺寸。在建模光变曲线时，我们采用线性临边昏暗定律 [21] 来描述 I 和 R 波段从中心到边缘的发光强度轮廓，参数取值为 $\Gamma_I = 0.538$，$\Gamma_R = 0.626$，适用于 G4 III 巨型源恒星。四套不同的双透镜建模代码被用来验证我们这里所展示的模型，是针对观测到的光变曲线的唯一可接受模型。最好的替代模型包含单一的前景透镜恒星，背景源为具有大流量比的双星，该模型可以粗略地产生类似于行星微引力透镜事件的特征 [22]。然而，如图 1 所示，这一模型无法解释由 PLANET-Perth 天文台

measurements near the end of the planetary deviation, and it is formally excluded by $\Delta\chi^2 = 46.25$ with one less model parameter.

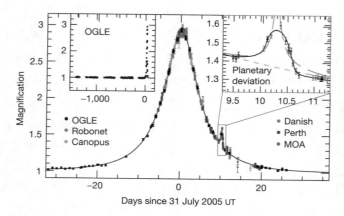

Fig. 1. The observed light curve of the OGLE-2005-BLG-390 microlensing event and best-fit model plotted as a function of time. Error bars are 1σ. The data set consists of 650 data points from PLANET Danish (ESO La Silla, red points), PLANET Perth (blue), PLANET Canopus (Hobart, cyan), RoboNet Faulkes North (Hawaii, green), OGLE (Las Campanas, black), MOA (Mt John Observatory, brown). This photometric monitoring was done in the I band (with the exception of the Faulkes R-band data and the MOA custom red passband) and real-time data reduction was performed with the different OGLE, PLANET and MOA data reduction pipelines. Danish and Perth data were finally reduced by the image subtraction technique[19] with the OGLE pipeline. The top left inset shows the OGLE light curve extending over the previous 4 years, whereas the top right one shows a zoom of the planetary deviation, covering a time interval of 1.5 days. The solid curve is the best binary lens model described in the text with $q = 7.6 \pm 0.7 \times 10^{-5}$, and a projected separation of $d = 1.610 \pm 0.008R_E$. The dashed grey curve is the best binary source model that is rejected by the data, and the dashed orange line is the best single lens model.

Table 1 Microlensing fit parameters

d	$1.610 \pm 0.008R_E$
q	$(7.6 \pm 0.7) \times 10^{-5}$
Closest approach	$0.359 \pm 0.005R_E$
Einstein ring radius crossing time	11.03 ± 0.11 days
Time of closest approach	31.231 ± 0.005 July 2005 UT
Source star radius crossing time	0.282 ± 0.010 days
θ	2.756 ± 0.003 rad

The parameters for the best binary lens model for the OGLE 2005-BLG-390 microlensing event light curve are shown with their 1σ uncertainties. Some of these parameters are scaled to the Einstein ring radius, which is given by $R_E = 2\sqrt{GMD_L(D_S - D_L)/(c^2 D_S)}$, where M is the mass of the lens, G is the newtonian constant of gravitation, c is the speed of light in vacuum, and D_L and D_S are the lens and source distances, respectively.

The planet is designated OGLE-2005-BLG-390Lb, where the "Lb" suffix indicates the secondary component of the lens system with a planetary mass ratio. The microlensing fit

望远镜、PLANET-Danish 天文台望远镜以及 OGLE 观测到的行星偏离末段附近的数据，该模型缺少一个模型参数，因 $\Delta\chi^2 = 46.25$ 从严格意义上被排除。

图 1. 观测到的 OGLE-2005-BLG-390 微引力透镜事件的光变曲线以及最佳拟合模型（横轴为时间）。误差棒为 1σ。图中共有 650 个数据点，分别来源于 PLANET-Danish 天文台望远镜（拉西亚欧南台（ESO），红色）、PLANET-Perth 天文台望远镜（蓝色）、PLANET-Canopus 天文台望远镜（霍巴特，青色）、RoboNet 北福克斯望远镜（夏威夷，绿色）、OGLE（拉斯坎帕纳斯，黑色）以及 MOA（约翰山天文台，棕色）。其中，除福克斯望远镜采用 R 波段数据，MOA 采用特制的红色通带外，其他测光监测均在 I 波段进行。我们采用 OGLE、PLANET 以及 MOA 不同的数据处理软件对数据进行实时处理。PLANET-Danish 和 PLANET-Perth 天文台望远镜的数据最终通过 OGLE 数据处理中的图像扣除技术 [19] 进行处理。左上方的插图给出了前四年里的 OGLE 测得的光变曲线，右上方插图给出了行星偏离部分的放大图，其时间跨度为 1.5 天。实线表示文中所述的最佳双透镜模型的理论预言，$q = 7.6 \pm 0.7 \times 10^{-5}$，投影间隔 $d = 1.610 \pm 0.008 R_E$。图中灰色虚线表示不被数据支持的最佳双源模型的理论预言。图中橙色虚线表示最佳单透镜模型的理论预言。

表 1. 微引力透镜的拟合参数

d	$1.610 \pm 0.008 R_E$
q	$(7.6 \pm 0.7) \times 10^{-5}$
最接近点	$0.359 \pm 0.005 R_E$
爱因斯坦环半径的穿越时间	11.03 ± 0.11 天
最接近点时间	31.231 ± 0.005 2005 年 7 月 UT
源恒星半径的穿越时间	0.282 ± 0.010 天
θ	2.756 ± 0.003 rad

上表给出了用于拟合 OGLE 2005-BLG-390 透镜事件光变曲线的最佳双透镜模型的参数值，同时给出了各参数 1σ 不确定度。表中部分参数以爱因斯坦半径 R_E 作为单位，$R_E = 2\sqrt{GMD_L(D_S - D_L)/(c^2 D_S)}$，其中 M 代表透镜的质量，G 表示牛顿万有引力常数，c 表示真空中的光速，D_S 和 D_L 分别表示透镜距离和源距离。

这颗行星被命名为 OGLE-2005-BLG-390Lb，其中后缀"Lb"表示透镜系统包含具有行星质量的次等组分。微引力透镜拟合仅直接确定行星与恒星的质量比

only directly determines the planet–star mass ratio, $q = 7.6 \pm 0.7 \times 10^{-5}$, and the projected planet–star separation, $d = 1.610 \pm 0.008 R_{\mathrm{E}}$. Although the planet and star masses are not directly determined for planetary microlensing events, we can derive their probability densities. We have performed a bayesian analysis[23] employing the Galactic models and mass functions described in refs 11 and 23. We averaged over the distances and velocities of the lens and source stars, subject to the constraints due to the angular diameter of the source and the measured parameters given in Table 1. This analysis gives a 95% probability that the planetary host star is a main-sequence star, a 4% probability that it is a white dwarf, and a probability of < 1% that it is a neutron star or black hole. The host star and planet parameter probability densities for a main sequence lens star are shown in Fig. 2 for the Galactic model used in ref. 23. The medians of the lens parameter probability distributions yield a companion mass of $5.5^{+5.5}_{-2.7} M_{\oplus}$ and an orbital separation of $2.6^{+1.5}_{-0.6}$ AU from the $0.22^{+0.21}_{-0.11} M_{\odot}$ lens star, which is located at a distance of $D_{\mathrm{L}} = 6.6 \pm 1.0$ kpc. These error bars indicate the central 68% confidence interval. These median parameters imply that the planet receives radiation from its host star that is only 0.1% of the radiation that the Earth receives from the Sun, so the probable surface temperature of the planet is ~50 K, similar to the temperatures of Neptune and Pluto.

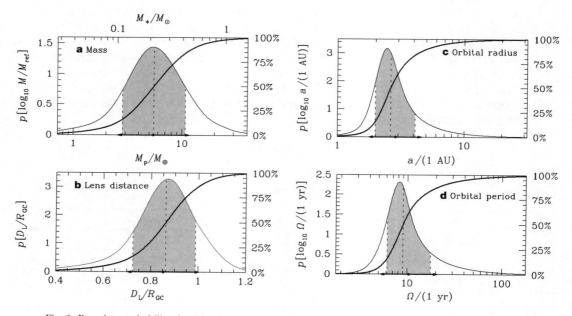

Fig. 2. Bayesian probability densities for the properties of the planet and its host star. **a**, The masses of the lens star and its planet (M_* and M_{p} respectively), **b**, their distance from the observer (D_{L}), **c**, the three-dimensional separation or semi-major axis a of an assumed circular planetary orbit; and **d**, the orbital period Ω of the planet. (In **a**, M_{ref} refers to $M_{\oplus}$ on the upper x axis and $M_{\odot}$ on the lower x axis.) The bold, curved line in each panel is the cumulative distribution, with the percentiles listed on the right. The dashed vertical lines indicate the medians, and the shading indicates the central 68.3% confidence intervals, while dots and arrows on the abscissa mark the expectation value and standard deviation. All estimates follow from a bayesian analysis assuming a standard model for the disk and bulge population of the Milky Way, the stellar mass function of ref. 23, and a gaussian prior distribution for $D_{\mathrm{S}} = 1.05 \pm 0.25 R_{\mathrm{GC}}$ (where $R_{\mathrm{GC}} = 7.62 \pm 0.32$ kpc for the Galactic Centre distance). The medians of these distributions yield a $5.5^{+5.5}_{-2.7} M_{\oplus}$

$q = 7.6 \pm 0.7 \times 10^{-5}$，以及行星与恒星的投影距离，$d = 1.610 \pm 0.008 R_{\mathrm{E}}$。尽管我们不能通过行星微引力透镜事件直接确定恒星和行星的质量，但是却可以推导出它们的概率密度。我们通过引入银河系模型和质量函数[11,23]，进行了贝叶斯分析[23]。基于源的角直径以及表 1 中测量参数的限制，我们对透镜和源恒星在距离和速度上进行了平均。该分析结果表明，该行星宿主恒星是一颗主序恒星的概率为 95%，是一颗白矮星的概率为 4%，是一颗中子星或黑洞的概率小于 1%。图 2 给出了银河系模型[23]下透镜系统中以主序星作为宿主恒星及其行星各参数的概率密度。透镜参数概率分布的中值表明伴星的质量为 $5.5^{+5.5}_{-2.7} M_{\oplus}$，围绕质量为 $0.22^{+0.21}_{-0.11} M_{\odot}$ 的透镜恒星运动，轨道半径为 $2.6^{+1.5}_{-0.6}$ AU，整个透镜系统与我们的距离为 $D_{\mathrm{L}} = 6.6 \pm 1.0$ kpc。图中误差棒给出了中心附近 68% 的置信区间。这些中值参数表明该行星从宿主恒星接收到的辐射，仅为地球从太阳接收到的辐射的 0.1%，因此这颗行星的表面温度很可能仅为 50 K 左右，类似于海王星和冥王星。

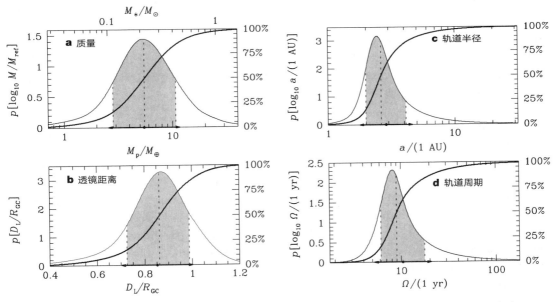

图 2. 行星及其宿主恒星属性的贝叶斯概率密度。a，透镜恒星及其行星的质量，分别用 M_* 和 M_{p} 表示；b，透镜恒星及其行星与观测者的距离 (D_{L})；c，假定圆形行星轨道的三维间隔或半长轴 a；d，行星的轨道周期 Ω。（在图 a 中，M_{ref} 表示在顶部 x 轴以 $M_{\odot}$ 为单位，在底部 x 轴以 $M_{\oplus}$ 为单位）在每幅图中，加粗曲线表示累计分布，右侧坐标轴给出了相应的百分比值。图中垂直虚线表示中值，阴影部分给出了中心附近 68.3% 的置信区间，横坐标轴上的点和箭头分别标记出期望值和标准差。以上所有估算均是在假定一个标准的银河系盘和核球模型，文献 23 中的恒星质量函数以及 $D_{\mathrm{S}} = 1.05 \pm 0.25 R_{\mathrm{GC}}$ 满足高斯先验分布（其中 R_{GC} 代表银河中心的距离，$R_{\mathrm{GC}} = 7.62 \pm 0.32$ kpc）的情况下利用贝叶斯分析得到的。这些分布的中值表明行星的质量为 $5.5^{+5.5}_{-2.7} M_{\oplus}$，在银河系核球区域的 M 型矮星的质量为 $0.22^{+0.21}_{-0.11} M_{\odot}$，二者相距 $2.6^{+1.5}_{-0.6}$ AU，而整个透镜系统与太阳的距离为 $D_{\mathrm{L}} = 6.6 \pm 1.0$ kpc。行星的中值周期为 9^{+9}_{-4} 年。对概率分布取对数平均（遵循开普勒第三定律），可知这颗行星的轨道周期为 10.4 年，与宿主恒星的距离为 2.9 AU，恒星和行星的质量分别为 $0.22 M_{\odot}$ 和 $5.5 M_{\oplus}$。每幅图中的纵坐标的方括号中列出了该概率密度的独

planetary companion at a separation of $2.6^{+1.5}_{-0.6}$ AU from a $0.22^{+0.21}_{-0.11}M_\odot$ Galactic Bulge M-dwarf at a distance of 6.6 ± 1.0 kpc from the Sun. The median planetary period is 9^{+9}_{-3} years. The logarithmic means of these probability distributions (which obey Kepler's third law) are a separation of 2.9 AU, a period of 10.4 years, and masses of $0.22M_\odot$ and $5.5M_\oplus$ for the star and planet, respectively. In each plot, the independent variable for the probability density is listed within square brackets. The distribution of the planet–star mass ratio was taken to be independent of the stellar mass, and a uniform prior distribution was assumed for the planet–star separation distribution.

The parameters of this event are near the limits of microlensing planet detectability for a giant source star. The separation of $d = 1.61$ is near the outer edge of the so-called lensing zone[7], which has the highest planet detection probability, and the planet's mass is about a factor of two above the detection limit set by the finite size of the source star. Planets with $q > 10^{-3}$ and $d \approx 1$ are much easier to detect, and so it may be that the parameters of OGLE-2005-BLG-390Lb represent a more common type of planet. This can be quantified by simulating planetary light curves with different values of q and θ (where θ is the angle of source motion with respect to the lens axis) but the remaining parameters are fixed to the values for the three known microlensing planets. We find that the probability of detecting a $q \approx 4-7 \times 10^{-3}$ planet, like the first two microlens planets[13,14], is ~50 times larger than the probability of detecting a $q = 7.6 \times 10^{-5}$ planet like OGLE-2005-BLG-390Lb. This suggests that, at the orbital separations probed by microlensing, sub-Neptune-mass planets are significantly more common than large gas giants around the most common stars in our Galaxy. Similarly, the first detection of a sub-Neptune-mass planet at the outer edge of the "lensing zone" provides a hint that these sub-Neptune-mass planets may tend to reside in orbits with semi-major axes $a > 2$ AU.

The core-accretion model of planet formation predicts that rocky/icy $5-15M_\oplus$ planets orbiting their host stars at $1-10$ AU are much more common than Jupiter-mass planets, and this prediction is consistent with the small fraction of M-dwarfs with planets detected by radial velocities[3,5] and with previous limits from microlensing[15]. Our discovery of such a low-mass planet by gravitational microlensing lends further support to this model, but more detections of similar and lower-mass planets over a wide range of orbits are clearly needed. Planets with separations of ~0.1 AU will be detected routinely by the radial velocity method or space observations of planetary transits in the coming years[24-27], but the best chance to increase our understanding of such planets over orbits of $1-10$ AU in the next $5-10$ years is by future interferometer programs[28] and more advanced microlensing surveys[11,29,30].

(**439**, 437-440; 2006)

立变量。这里认为行星–恒星质量比的分布与恒星的质量无关，并假定行星与宿主恒星之间的距离分布服从均匀的先验分布。

这次事件的各参数值接近巨型源恒星的微引力透镜探测极限。恒星、行星相距 $d = 1.61$ 已接近所谓的"透镜区域"的外边界 [7]，从而具有最高的行星探测概率；同时行星的质量是由源恒星的有限尺度所设定的探测极限的 2 倍。显然，那些 $q > 10^{-3}$ 且 $d \approx 1$ 的行星更加容易探测到，因此 OGLE-2005-BLG-390Lb 可能代表了一类更为普遍的行星。这可以在不同 q 和 θ 取值条件下通过对行星光变曲线进行模拟仿真而被量化（其中 θ 表示源恒星运动相对透镜主轴的角度），而剩余参量则对应已知的三个微透镜行星取固定值。我们发现，探测到一颗 $q \approx 4 \sim 7 \times 10^{-3}$ 的行星（类似首先发现的两颗透镜行星）的概率是探测到一颗 $q = 7.6 \times 10^{-5}$ 的行星（类似 OGLE-2005-BLG-390Lb）的概率的约 50 倍。这说明，在微引力透镜可探测的轨道间隔的范围内，对于我们星系中的众多恒星，其四周具有亚海王星质量的行星比大型气态巨行星明显更加普遍。类似地，在"透镜区域"外边缘首次探测到亚海王星质量的行星，暗示着这类行星的轨道半长轴倾向于 >2 AU。

行星形成的核吸积模型预测，在宿主恒星附近普遍存在的是质量为 $5 \sim 15 M_{\oplus}$、轨道半长轴在 $1 \sim 10$ AU 范围内的行星，而不是木星质量大小的行星。这与运用径向速度法很少探测到 M 型矮星附近的行星 [3,5] 的观测结果相吻合，同时也与过去的微引力透镜限制一致 [15]。我们通过微引力透镜方法发现的这样一颗低质量的行星，进一步支持了该模型，但是我们仍需探测更多类似的位于不同轨道上的低质量行星来验证这一模型。在未来几年中，通过径向速度法或空间观测掩食法探测轨道半长轴约为 0.1 AU 的行星 [24-27] 将成为一种常态。然而，未来 $5 \sim 10$ 年里，借助将来的干涉仪探测项目 [29] 以及更为先进的微引力透镜巡天 [11,28,30] 是进一步了解那些轨道介于 $1 \sim 10$ AU 的行星性质的最好的方法。

（金世超 刘项琨 翻译；李然 审稿）

J.-P. Beaulieu[1,4], D. P. Bennett[1,3,5], P. Fouqué[1,6], A. Williams[1,7], M. Dominik[1,8], U. G. Jørgensen[1,9], D. Kubas[1,10], A. Cassan[1,4], C. Coutures[1,11], J. Greenhill[1,12], K. Hill[1,12], J. Menzies[1,13], P. D. Sackett[1,14], M. Albrow[1,15], S. Brillant[1,10], J. A. R. Caldwell[1,16], J. J. Calitz[1,17], K. H. Cook[1,18], E. Corrales[1,4], M. Desort[1,4], S. Dieters[1,12], D. Dominis[1,19], J. Donatowicz[1,20], M. Hoffman[1,19], S. Kane[1,21], J.-B. Marquette[1,4], R. Martin[1,7], P. Meintjes[1,17], K. Pollard[1,15], K. Sahu[1,22], C. Vinter[1,9], J. Wambsganss[1,23], K. Woller[1,9], K. Horne[1,8], I. Steele[1,24], D. M. Bramich[1,8,24], M. Burgdorf[1,24], C. Snodgrass[1,25], M. Bode[1,24], A. Udalski[2,26], M. K. Szymański[2,26], M. Kubiak[2,26], T. Więckowski[2,26], G. Pietrzyński[2,26,27], I. Soszyński[2,26,27], O. Szewczyk[2,26], Ł. Wyrzykowski[2,26,28], B. Paczyński[2,29], F. Abe[3,30], I. A. Bond[3,31], T. R. Britton[3,15,32], A. C. Gilmore[3,15], J. B. Hearnshaw[3,15], Y. Itow[3,30], K. Kamiya[3,30], P. M. Kilmartin[3,15], A. V. Korpela[3,33], K. Masuda[3,30], Y. Matsubara[3,30], M. Motomura[3,30], Y. Muraki[3,30], S. Nakamura[3,30], C. Okada[3,30], K. Ohnishi[3,34], N. J. Rattenbury[3,28], T. Sako[3,30], S. Sato[3,35], M. Sasaki[3,30], T. Sekiguchi[3,30], D. J. Sullivan[3,33], P. J. Tristram[3,32], P. C. M. Yock[3,32] & T. Yoshioka[3,30]

[1] PLANET/RoboNet Collaboration (http://planet.iap.fr and http://www.astro.livjm.ac.uk/RoboNet/)

[2] OGLE Collaboration (http://ogle.astrouw.edu.pl)

[3] MOA Collaboration (http://www.physics.auckland.ac.nz/moa)

[4] Institut d'Astrophysique de Paris, CNRS, Université Pierre et Marie Curie UMR7095, 98bis Boulevard Arago, 75014 Paris, France

[5] University of Notre Dame, Department of Physics, Notre Dame, Indiana 46556-5670, USA

[6] Observatoire Midi-Pyrénées, Laboratoire d'Astrophysique, UMR 5572, Université Paul Sabatier—Toulouse 3, 14 avenue Edouard Belin, 31400 Toulouse, France

[7] Perth Observatory, Walnut Road, Bickley, Perth, WA 6076, Australia

[8] Scottish Universities Physics Alliance, University of St Andrews, School of Physics and Astronomy, North Haugh, St Andrews KY16 9SS, UK

[9] Niels Bohr Institutet, Astronomisk Observatorium, Juliane Maries Vej 30, 2100 København Ø, Denmark

[10] European Southern Observatory, Casilla 19001, Santiago 19, Chile

[11] CEA DAPNIA/SPP Saclay, 91191 Gif-sur-Yvette cedex, France

[12] University of Tasmania, School of Mathematics and Physics, Private Bag 37, Hobart, TAS 7001, Australia

[13] South African Astronomical Observatory, PO Box 9, Observatory 7935, South Africa

[14] Research School of Astronomy and Astrophysics, Australian National University, Mt Stromlo Observatory, Weston Creek, ACT 2611, Australia

[15] University of Canterbury, Department of Physics and Astronomy, Private Bag 4800, Christchurch 8020, New Zealand

[16] McDonald Observatory, 16120 St Hwy Spur 78 #2, Fort Davis, Texas 79734, USA

[17] Boyden Observatory, University of the Free State, Department of Physics, PO Box 339, Bloemfontein 9300, South Africa

[18] Lawrence Livermore National Laboratory, IGPP, PO Box 808, Livermore, California 94551, USA

[19] Universität Potsdam, Institut für Physik, Am Neuen Palais 10, 14469 Potsdam, Astrophysikalisches Institut Potsdam, An der Sternwarte 16, D-14482, Potsdam, Germany

[20] Technische Universität Wien, Wiedner Hauptstrasse 8/020 B.A. 1040 Wien, Austria

[21] Department of Astronomy, University of Florida, 211 Bryant Space Science Center, Gainesville, Florida 32611-2055, USA

[22] Space Telescope Science Institute, 3700 San Martin Drive, Baltimore, Maryland 21218, USA

[23] Astronomisches Rechen-Institut (ARI), Zentrum für Astronomie, Universität Heidelberg, Mönchhofstrasse 12-14, 69120 Heidelberg, Germany

[24] Astrophysics Research Institute, Liverpool John Moores University, Twelve Quays House, Egerton Wharf, Birkenhead CH41 1LD, UK

[25] Astronomy and Planetary Science Division, Department of Physics, Queen's University Belfast, Belfast, UK

[26] Obserwatorium Astronomiczne Uniwersytetu Warszawskiego, Aleje Ujazdowskie 4, 00-478 Warszawa, Poland

[27] Universidad de Concepcion, Departamento de Fisica, Casilla 160-C, Concepcion, Chile

[28] Jodrell Bank Observatory, The University of Manchester, Macclesfield, Cheshire SK11 9DL, UK

[29] Princeton University Observatory, Peyton Hall, Princeton, New Jersey 08544, USA

[30] Solar-Terrestrial Environment Laboratory, Nagoya University, Nagoya 464-860, Japan

[31] Institute for Information and Mathematical Sciences, Massey University, Private Bag 102-904, Auckland, New Zealand

[32] Department of Physics, University of Auckland, Private Bag 92019, Auckland, New Zealand

[33] School of Chemical and Physical Sciences, Victoria University, PO Box 600, Wellington, New Zealand

[34] Nagano National College of Technology, Nagano 381-8550, Japan

[35] Department of Astrophysics, Faculty of Science, Nagoya University, Nagoya 464-860, Japan

Received 28 September; accepted 14 November 2005.

References:

1. Safronov, V. *Evolution of the Protoplanetary Cloud and Formation of the Earth and Planets* (Nauka, Moscow, 1969).

2. Wetherill, G. W. Formation of the terrestrial planets. *Annu. Rev. Astron. Astrophys* **18**, 77-113 (1980).

3. Laughlin, G., Bodenheimer, P. & Adams, F. C. The core accretion model predicts few jovian-mass planets orbiting red dwarfs. *Astrophys. J.* **612**, L73-L76 (2004).

4. Ida, S. & Lin, D. N. C. Toward a deterministic model of planetary formation. II. The formation and retention of gas giant planets around stars with a range of metallicities. *Astrophys. J.* **616**, 567-572 (2004).

5. Rivera, E. *et al.* A ~7.5 Earth-mass planet orbiting the nearby star, GJ 876. *Astrophys. J.* (in the press).

6. Mao, S. & Paczynski, B. Gravitational microlensing by double stars and planetary systems. *Astrophys. J.* **374**, L37-L40 (1991).

7. Gould, A. & Loeb, A. Discovering planetary systems through gravitational Microlenses. *Astrophys. J.* **396**, 104-114 (1992).

8. Wambsganss, J. Discovering Galactic planets by gravitational microlensing: magnification patterns and light curves. *Mon. Not. R. Astron. Soc.* **284**, 172-188 (1997).

9. Griest, K. & Safizadeh, N. The use of high-magnification microlensing events in discovering extrasolar planets. *Astrophys. J.* **500**, 37-50 (1998).

10. Bennett, D. P. & Rhie, S. H. Detecting Earth-mass planets with gravitational microlensing. *Astrophys. J.* **472**, 660-664 (1996).

11. Bennett, D. P. & Rhie, S. H. Simulation of a space-based microlensing survey for terrestrial extrasolar planets. *Astrophys. J.* **574**, 985-1003 (2002).

12. Albrow, M. *et al.* The 1995 pilot campaign of PLANET: searching for microlensing anomalies through precise, rapid, round-the-clock monitoring. *Astrophys. J.* **509**, 687-702 (1998).

13. Bond, I. A. *et al.* OGLE 2003-BLG-235/MOA 2003-BLG-53: A planetary microlensing event. *Astrophys. J.* **606**, L155-L158 (2004).

14. Udalski, A. *et al.* A jovian-mass planet in microlensing event OGLE-2005-BLG- 071. *Astrophys. J.* **628**, L109-L112 (2005).

15. Gaudi, B. S. *et al.* Microlensing constraints on the frequency of Jupiter-mass companions: analysis of 5 years of PLANET photometry. *Astrophys. J.* **566**, 463-499 (2002).

16. Abe, F. *et al.* Search for low-mass exoplanets by gravitational microlensing at high magnification. *Science* **305**, 1264-1267 (2004).

17. Dong, S. *et al.* Planetary detection efficiency of the magnification 3000 microlensing event OGLE-2004-BLG-343. *Astrophys. J.* (submitted); preprint at ⟨http://arXiv.org/astro-ph/0507079⟩ (2005).

18. Udalski, A. The optical gravitational lensing experiment. Real time data analysis systems in the OGLE-III survey. *Acta Astron.* **53**, 291-305 (2003).

19. Alard, C. Image subtraction using a space-varying kernel. *Astron. Astrophys. Suppl.* **144**, 363-370 (2000).

20. Kervella, P. *et al.* Cepheid distances from infrared long-baseline interferometry. III. Calibration of the surface brightness-color relations. *Astron. Astrophys.* **428**, 587-593 (2004).

21. Claret, A., Diaz-Cordoves, J. & Gimenez, A. Linear and non-linear limb-darkening coefficients for the photometric bands R I J H K. *Astron. Astrophys. Suppl.* **114**, 247-252 (1995).

22. Gaudi, B. S. Distinguishing between binary-source and planetary microlensing perturbations. *Astrophys. J.* **506**, 533-539 (1998).

23. Dominik, M. Stochastical distributions of lens and source properties for observed galactic microlensing events. *Mon. Not. R. Astron. Soc.* (submitted); preprint at ⟨http://arXiv.org/astro-ph/0507540⟩ (2005).

24. Vogt, S. S. *et al.* Five new multicomponent planetary systems. *Astrophys. J.* **632**, 638-658 (2005).

25. Mayor, M. *et al.* The CORALIE survey for southern extrasolar planets. XII. Orbital solutions for 16 extrasolar planets discovered with CORALIE. *Astron. Astrophys.* **415**, 391-402 (2004).

26. Borucki, W. *et al.* in *Second Eddington Workshop: Stellar Structure and Habitable Planet Finding* (eds Favata, F., Aigrain, S. & Wilson, A.) 177-182 (ESA SP-538, ESA Publications Division, Noordwijk, 2004).

27. Moutou, C. *et al.* Comparative blind test of five planetary transit detection algorithms on realistic synthetic light curves. *Astron. Astrophys.* **437**, 355-368 (2005).

28. Sozzeti, A. *et al.* Narrow-angle astrometry with the space interferometry mission: the search for extrasolar planets. I. Detection and characterization of single planets. *Pub. Astron. Soc. Pacif.* **114**, 1173-1196 (2002).

29. Bennett, D. P. in *ASP Conf. Ser. on Extrasolar Planets: Today and Tomorrow* (eds Beaulieu, J.-P., Lecavelier des Etangs, A. & Terquem, C.) Vol. 321, 59-68 (ASP, 2004).

30. Beaulieu, J. P. *et al.* PLANET III: searching for Earth-mass planets via microlensing from Dome C? *ESA Publ. Ser.* **14**, 297-302 (2005).

Acknowledgements. PLANET is grateful to the observatories that support our science (the European Southern Observatory, Canopus, Perth; and the South African Astronomical Observatory, Boyden, Faulkes North) and to the ESO team in La Silla for their help in maintaining and operating the Danish telescope. Support for the PLANET project was provided by CNRS, NASA, the NSF, the LLNL/NNSA/DOE, PNP, PICS France-Australia, D. Warren, the DFG, IDA and the SNF. RoboNet is funded by the UK PPARC and the FTN was supported by the Dill Faulkes Educational Trust. Support for the OGLE project, conducted at Las Campanas Observatory (operated by the Carnegie Institution of Washington), was provided by the Polish Ministry of Science, the Foundation for Polish Science, the NSF and NASA. The MOA collaboration is supported by MEXT and JSPS of Japan, and the Marsden Fund of New Zealand.

Author Information. The photometric data set is available at planet.iap.fr and ogle.astrouw.edu.pl. Reprints and permissions information is available at npg.nature.com/reprintsandpermissions. The authors declare no competing financial interests. Correspondence and requests for materials should be addressed to J.P.B. (beaulieu@iap.fr) or D.P.B. (bennett@nd.edu).

Folding DNA to Create Nanoscale Shapes and Patterns

P. W. K. Rothemund

Editor's Note

Organizing molecules into structures with dimensions of several nanometres is a key objective in nanotechnology. DNA has emerged as a particularly versatile material for such molecular engineering, because it can be programmed to self-assemble in highly specific and selective ways, governed by the rules of complementary base-pairing. Artificial DNA strands had previously been used to make topologically complex molecules. But the strategy described here by Paul Rothemund at the California Institute of Technology goes much further, enabling the design of DNA that can be folded into just about any arbitrary two-dimensional pattern. Rothemund's DNA map of the world at a scale of $1:2 \times 10^{14}$ is emblematic of the power of contemporary nanotechnology.

"Bottom-up fabrication", which exploits the intrinsic properties of atoms and molecules to direct their self-organization, is widely used to make relatively simple nanostructures. A key goal for this approach is to create nanostructures of high complexity, matching that routinely achieved by "top-down" methods. The self-assembly of DNA molecules provides an attractive route towards this goal. Here I describe a simple method for folding long, single-stranded DNA molecules into arbitrary two-dimensional shapes. The design for a desired shape is made by raster-filling the shape with a 7-kilobase single-stranded scaffold and by choosing over 200 short oligonucleotide "staple strands" to hold the scaffold in place. Once synthesized and mixed, the staple and scaffold strands self-assemble in a single step. The resulting DNA structures are roughly 100 nm in diameter and approximate desired shapes such as squares, disks and five-pointed stars with a spatial resolution of 6 nm. Because each oligonucleotide can serve as a 6-nm pixel, the structures can be programmed to bear complex patterns such as words and images on their surfaces. Finally, individual DNA structures can be programmed to form larger assemblies, including extended periodic lattices and a hexamer of triangles (which constitutes a 30-megadalton molecular complex).

IN 1959, Richard Feynman put forward the challenge of writing the *Encyclopaedia Britannica* on the head of a pin[1], a task which he calculated would require the use of dots 8 nm in size. Scanning probe techniques have essentially answered this challenge: atomic force microscopy[2] (AFM) and scanning tunnelling microscopy[3,4] (STM) allow us to manipulate individual atoms. But these techniques create patterns serially (one line or

折叠 DNA 以形成纳米尺度
的形状和图案

罗特蒙德

编者按

将分子在几个纳米的尺度上组织起来是纳米技术的一个重要目标。DNA 已经成为分子工程中用途非常广泛的材料，因为它可以在遵循碱基互补配对的前提下，通过编程方法以高度特异性和选择性的方式自组装。之前人工合成 DNA 链已经被用来组装具有复杂拓扑结构的分子。但是本文中美国加州理工学院的保罗·罗特蒙德所描述的方法远远跨出一步，这种方法能够设计 DNA 使其折叠成几乎任意的二维图案。罗特蒙德设计的比例尺为 $1:2 \times 10^{14}$ 的 DNA 世界地图，标志着当代纳米技术的巨大力量。

"自下而上的组装方法"，即通过原子与分子的固有性质以指导其自组装过程，被广泛地用来制造相对简单的纳米结构。这一方法的核心目标之一在于创造出具有高度复杂性的纳米结构，其复杂性程度可与一般通过"自上而下"方法所得到的相媲美。DNA 分子的自组装为这一目标的实现提供了一个引人关注的途径。本文中我要描述一种简单的方法，它能够将长的单链 DNA 分子折叠成任意的二维形状。在设计所需形状时，先将一条 7,000 多个碱基的单链脚手架链像光栅一样填充起来，再选取 200 多条短链的低聚核苷酸"订书针链"将模板在合适的位置固定。合成并混合后，订书针链和脚手架链就会通过单步反应完成自组装。所得 DNA 结构直径大约为 100 nm，并且接近所需形状，如正方形、圆盘和五角星等，其空间分辨率为 6 nm。由于每个低聚核苷酸可以充当一个 6 nm 的像素，因此可以通过编程在该结构表面上设计诸如词汇和图像等复杂图案。最后，单个 DNA 结构可以通过编程形成更大的组装，包括扩展的周期性晶格和一个三角形六聚体(构成一个 30 兆道尔顿的分子复合物)等。

1959 年，理查德·费曼发起了在针头上写下《大英百科全书》的挑战 [1]，根据他的计算，实现这一任务需要使用大小为 8 nm 的像素点。扫描探针技术实际上已经能够应对这一挑战：原子力显微镜 [2] (AFM) 和扫描隧道显微镜 [3,4] (STM) 使我们能够对单个原子进行操纵。但是这些技术只能逐次创造图案(一次一条线或一个像素)，

one pixel at a time) and tend to require ultrahigh vacuum or cryogenic temperatures. As a result, methods based on self-assembly are considered as promising alternatives that offer inexpensive, parallel synthesis of nanostructures under mild conditions[5]. Indeed, the power of these methods has been demonstrated in systems based on components ranging from porphyrins[6] to whole viral particles[7]. However, the ability of such systems to yield structures of high complexity remains to be demonstrated. In particular, the difficulty of engineering diverse yet specific binding interactions means that most self-assembled structures contain just a few unique positions that may be addressed as "pixels".

Nucleic acids can help overcome this problem: the exquisite specificity of Watson–Crick base pairing allows a combinatorially large set of nucleotide sequences to be used when designing binding interactions. The field of "DNA nanotechnology"[8,9] has exploited this property to create a number of more complex nanostructures, including two-dimensional arrays with 8–16 unique positions and less than 20 nm spacing[10,11], as well as three-dimensional shapes such as a cube[12] and truncated octahedron[13]. However, because the synthesis of such nanostructures involves interactions between a large number of short oligonucleotides, the yield of complete structures is highly sensitive to stoichiometry (the relative ratios of strands). The synthesis of relatively complex structures was thus thought to require multiple reaction steps and purifications, with the ultimate complexity of DNA nanostructures limited by necessarily low yields. Recently, the controlled folding of a long single DNA strand into an octahedron was reported[14], an approach that may be thought of as "single-stranded DNA origami". The success of this work suggested that the folding of long strands could, in principle, proceed without many misfoldings and avoid the problems of stoichiometry and purification associated with methods that use many short DNA strands.

I now present a versatile and simple "one-pot" method for using numerous short single strands of DNA to direct the folding of a long, single strand of DNA into desired shapes that are roughly 100 nm in diameter and have a spatial resolution of about 6 nm. I demonstrate the generality of this method, which I term "scaffolded DNA origami", by assembling six different shapes, such as squares, triangles and five-pointed stars. I show that the method not only provides access to structures that approximate the outline of any desired shape, but also enables the creation of structures with arbitrarily shaped holes or surface patterns composed of more than 200 individual pixels. The patterns on the 100-nm-sized DNA shapes thus have a complexity that is tenfold higher than that of any previously self-assembled arbitrary pattern and comparable to that achieved using AFM and STM surface manipulation[4].

Design of Scaffolded DNA Origami

The design of a DNA origami is performed in five steps, the first two by hand and the last three aided by computer (details in Supplementary Note S1). The first step is to build a geometric model of a DNA structure that will approximate the desired shape. Figure 1a shows an example shape (outlined in red) that is 33 nm wide and 35 nm tall. The shape

而且往往需要超高真空或者超低温。因此，基于自组装过程的方法被认为是最有发展前景的选择，它成本低，且能在温和条件下并行合成纳米结构[5]。事实上，这种方法的力量已经在基于从卟啉[6]到整个病毒颗粒[7]等组分的各种系统中得到证实。但是，利用这种方法来制备高度复杂性结构的能力有待于进一步的验证。尤其是设计多种具有特异性的相互作用这点非常困难，这使得大多数自组装结构只包含很少可以被称为"像素"的独特部位。

核酸有助于克服这一难题：沃森－克里克碱基配对结构的高度特异性使得我们在设计相互作用时可以使用组合学意义上的大量核苷酸序列。"DNA 纳米技术"[8,9]领域便是要探索这一性质以创造出多种更为复杂的纳米结构，其中包括具有 8~16 个独特部位和间隔不到 20 nm 的二维阵列[10,11]，以及诸如立方体[12]和截角八面体[13]等三维形状。但是，由于上述纳米结构的合成涉及大量短链低聚核苷酸之间的相互作用，于是完整结构的产率很容易受到化学计量比（各链的相对比例）的影响。因此一般认为相对复杂结构的合成需要多步反应与纯化，DNA 纳米结构的最终复杂性必定受到低产率的限制。最近，有人报道将长的单链 DNA 可控折叠成八面体[14]，这种方法被认为是"单链 DNA 折纸术"。这一研究的成功意味着，在原则上，长链的折叠可以准确无误地进行，而且避免了使用大量短链 DNA 组装时涉及的化学计量与纯化的问题。

现在我将提出一种通用的而又简单的"一锅法"，利用大量短的单链 DNA 来指导一条长的单链 DNA 折叠成所需形状，其直径约为 100 nm 且具有约 6 nm 的空间分辨率。我将通过组装诸如正方形、三角形和五角星等六种不同的形状来阐明这种被我称之为"脚手架式 DNA 折纸术"方法的普遍性。我要指出的是，这种方法不仅提供了构建所需形状的轮廓的途径，而且还能够创造出由 200 多个独立像素点构成的具有任意形状的孔洞或表面图案的结构。因此 100 nm 大小的 DNA 表面上的图案，其复杂度是此前所得到的任何一种自组装图案的复杂度的十倍，并且可以与利用 AFM 和 STM 表面操纵技术所得到的图案[4]相媲美。

脚手架式 DNA 折纸术的设计

DNA 折纸术的设计是通过五步来进行的，前两步由手工实现，后三步则需计算机辅助（细节见附注 S1）。第一步是搭建一个与所需形状相似的 DNA 结构的几何模型。图 1a 展示了一个示例形状（其外廓为红色），宽 33 nm，高 35 nm。用偶数个平

is filled from top to bottom by an even number of parallel double helices, idealized as cylinders. The helices are cut to fit the shape in sequential pairs and are constrained to be an integer number of turns in length. To hold the helices together, a periodic array of crossovers (indicated in Fig. 1a as small blue crosses) is incorporated; these crossovers designate positions at which strands running along one helix switch to an adjacent helix and continue there. The resulting model approximates the shape within one turn (3.6 nm) in the x-direction and roughly two helical widths (4 nm) in the y-direction. As noticed before in DNA lattices[15], parallel helices in such structures are not close-packed, perhaps owing to electrostatic repulsion. Thus the exact y-resolution depends on the gap between helices. The gap, in turn, appears to depend on the spacing of crossovers. In Fig. 1a crossovers occur every 1.5 turns along alternating sides of a helix, but any odd number of half-turns may be used. In this study, data are consistent with an inter-helix gap of 1 nm for 1.5-turn spacing and 1.5 nm for 2.5-turn spacing, yielding a y-resolution of 6 or 7 nm, respectively.

Fig. 1. **Design of DNA origami. a**, A shape (red) approximated by parallel double helices joined by periodic crossovers (blue). **b**, A scaffold (black) runs through every helix and forms more crossovers (red). **c**, As first designed, most staples bind two helices and are 16-mers. **d**, Similar to **c** with strands drawn

行的双螺旋从顶部至底部将该形状填满（理想化地表示为圆柱形）。将螺旋进行剪切形成连续碱基对并且将其长度限制在整数个螺旋。为将螺旋维持在一起，要建立一种周期性的交叉阵列（在图 1a 中用小的蓝色交叉表示）；这些交叉指明了沿着某一螺旋延伸的链转向一个邻近螺旋并继续延伸的位点。所得模型模拟的形状在 x 方向上 1 个螺距内（3.6 nm），在 y 方向上则大致两个螺旋宽度（4 nm）。如同之前已在 DNA 晶格中注意到的那样 [15]，这种结构中的平行螺旋并不是密堆积的，这可能是由于静电斥力。因此 y 方向上精确的分辨率取决于螺旋之间的空隙。反过来，空隙则取决于交叉的间隔。在图 1a 中，交叉沿着螺旋的侧面交替出现，每 1.5 个螺距出现一次，但是半个螺距的奇数倍都是可以用的。在这项研究中，所有数据符合 1.5 个螺距有 1 nm 的交叉螺旋空隙，2.5 个螺距有 1.5 nm 空隙，因此 y 方向上的分辨率分别为 6 nm 或 7 nm。

图 1. **DNA 折纸术的设计。a**，用周期性交叉（蓝色）连接起来的平行双螺旋所模拟而成的形状（红色）。**b**，一根遍及每一螺旋并且形成更多交叉（红色）的脚手架（黑色）。**c**，如同最初所设计的，大多数订书针链连接两个螺旋，长度为 16 个碱基。**d**，类似于 **c**，其中的订书针链画成螺旋。红色三角形指的是脚

as helices. Red triangles point to scaffold crossovers, black triangles to periodic crossovers with minor grooves on the top face of the shape, blue triangles to periodic crossovers with minor grooves on bottom. Cross-sections of crossovers (1, 2, viewed from left) indicate backbone positions with coloured lines, and major/minor grooves by large/small angles between them. Arrows in **c** point to nicks sealed to create green strands in **d**. Yellow diamonds in **c** and **d** indicate a position at which staples may be cut and resealed to bridge the seam. **e**, A finished design after merges and rearrangements along the seam. Most staples are 32-mers spanning three helices. Insets show a dumbbell hairpin (**d**) and a 4-T loop (**e**), modifications used in Fig. 3.

Conceptually, the second step (illustrated in Fig. 1b) proceeds by folding a single long scaffold strand (900 nucleotides (nt) in Fig. 1b) back and forth in a raster fill pattern so that it comprises one of the two strands in every helix; progression of the scaffold from one helix to another creates an additional set of crossovers, the "scaffold crossovers" (indicated by small red crosses in Fig. 1b). The fundamental constraint on a folding path is that the scaffold can form a crossover only at those locations where the DNA twist places it at a tangent point between helices. Thus for the scaffold to raster progressively from one helix to another and onto a third, the distance between successive scaffold crossovers must be an odd number of half turns. Conversely, where the raster reverses direction vertically and returns to a previously visited helix, the distance between scaffold crossovers must be an even number of half-turns. Note that the folding path shown in Fig. 1b is compatible with a circular scaffold and leaves a "seam" (a contour which the path does not cross).

Once the geometric model and a folding path are designed, they are represented as lists of DNA lengths and offsets in units of half-turns. These lists, along with the DNA sequence of the actual scaffold to be used, are input to a computer program. Rather than assuming 10.5 base pairs (bp) per turn (which corresponds to standard B-DNA twist), the program uses an integer number of bases between periodic crossovers (for example, 16 bp for 1.5 turns). It then performs the third step, the design of a set of "staple strands" (the coloured DNA strands in Fig. 1c) that provide Watson–Crick complements for the scaffold and create the periodic crossovers. Staples reverse direction at these crossovers; thus crossovers are antiparallel, a stable configuration well characterized in DNA nanostructures[16]. Note that the crossovers in Fig. 1c are drawn somewhat misleadingly, in that single-stranded regions appear to span the inter-helix gap even though the design leaves no bases unpaired. In the assembled structures, helices are likely to bend gently to meet at crossovers so that only a single phosphate from each backbone occurs in the gap (as ref. 16 suggests for similar structures). Such small-angle bending is not expected to greatly affect the width of DNA origami (see also Supplementary Note S2).

The minimization and balancing of twist strain between crossovers is complicated by the non-integer number of base pairs per half-turn (5.25 in standard B-DNA) and the asymmetric nature of the helix (it has major and minor grooves). Therefore, to balance the strain[15] caused by representing 1.5 turns with 16 bp, periodic crossovers are arranged with a glide symmetry, namely that the minor groove faces alternating directions in alternating columns of periodic crossovers (see Fig. 1d, especially cross-sections 1 and 2). Scaffold crossovers are not balanced in this way. Thus in the fourth step, the twist of scaffold

手架交叉，黑色三角形对应的周期性交叉处小沟在底面，蓝色三角形对应的交叉处小沟在顶面。交叉的横截面（1，2，从左面看去）上以有色线段显示出骨架的位置，而大 / 小沟则用它们之间的大 / 小角度来表现。c 中的箭头表示缺口，它们闭合起来以产生 d 中的绿色订书针链。c 和 d 中的黄色菱形指出订书针链可以在此处被截短并重新闭合而将接缝连接起来。e，沿接缝经过合并重排后的设计。大多数订书针链长度为 32 个碱基，跨越 3 个螺旋。小图显示了一个哑铃形发卡结构（d）和一个 4-T 环（e），图 3 中用它们进行了修饰。

从概念上讲，第二步（如图 1b 所示）是通过将一条长的脚手架单链（图 1b 中所示为 900 个核苷酸（nt））在光栅中来回折叠以填充图形，从而使其构成每个双螺旋中的一条链；脚手架从一个螺旋到另一个螺旋的推进产生一组附加的交叉，即"脚手架交叉"（在图 1b 中用小的红色交叉表示）。对于折叠路径的基本限制是，只有在那些 DNA 扭转出现在两个螺旋间切点的位置时，脚手架才能形成交叉。因此当脚手架在光栅中从一个螺旋渐次移向下一个以及第三个时，连续的脚手架交叉点之间的距离必定是半螺距的奇数倍。反过来，当光栅在垂直方向上反转过来并返回之前曾到达的螺旋时，脚手架交叉点之间的距离必定是半螺距的偶数倍。注意图 1b 中所显示的折叠路径是与环形脚手架相一致的，并且留下了一条"接缝"（一条折叠路径未曾穿过的周线）。

一旦设计好几何模型和折叠路径，便可以将 DNA 的长度以及补偿以半螺旋为单位进行列表。将这些列表连同实际应用的脚手架的 DNA 序列，输入到计算机程序之中。程序并未假定每个螺距有 10.5 个碱基对（bp）（相当于标准 B-DNA 扭转），而是在周期性交叉点之间使用整数个碱基（例如每 1.5 个螺距有 16 bp）。接着便实施第三步，用沃森–克里克互补准则为脚手架设计一系列"订书针链"（图 1c 中彩色 DNA 链）产生周期性的交叉。订书针链在这些交叉处倒转方向；因此交叉是反平行的，这是一种很好地表征过的 DNA 纳米结构的稳定构型[16]。注意图 1c 中的交叉的画法是有些误导性的，因为单链区域似乎跨越了螺旋间空隙，然而设计中没有留下未配对碱基。在组装结构中，螺旋应该微微有些弯曲使其能在交叉处相遇，因而每一骨架中只有一个磷酸酯出现在空隙中（如同参考文献 16 所提出的类似结构那样）。预期这种小角度弯曲不会显著地影响 DNA 折叠结构的宽度（另见附注 S2）。

由于每半个螺距之中的非整数碱基对（标准 B-DNA 中是 5.25）以及螺旋的不对称性（其中有大沟和小沟），最小化和平衡交叉之间的扭曲张力是非常复杂的。因此，为了平衡采用 1.5 个螺距中 16 bp 产生的张力[15]，周期性交叉的排列具有滑移对称性，即小沟在交替的周期性交叉列中面朝交替的方向（见图 1d，尤其是横截面 1 和 2）。脚手架交叉不是以这种方式来平衡的。于是在第四步中，计算出脚手架交

crossovers is calculated and their position is changed (typically by a single bp) to minimize strain; staple sequences are recomputed accordingly. Along seams and some edges the minor groove angle (150°) places scaffold crossovers in tension with adjacent periodic crossovers (Fig. 1d, cross-section 2); such situations are left unchanged.

Wherever two staples meet there is a nick in the backbone. Nicks occur on the top and bottom faces of the helices, as depicted in Fig. 1d. In the final step, to give the staples larger binding domains with the scaffold (in order to achieve higher binding specificity and higher binding energy which results in higher melting temperatures), pairs of adjacent staples are merged across nicks to yield fewer, longer, staples (Fig. 1e). To strengthen a seam, an additional pattern of breaks and merges may be imposed to yield staples that cross the seam; a seam spanned by staples is termed "bridged". The pattern of merges is not unique; different choices yield different final patterns of nicks and staples. All merge patterns create the same shape but, as shown later, the merge pattern dictates the type of grid underlying any pixel pattern later applied to the shape.

Folding M13mp18 Genomic DNA into Shapes

To test the method, circular genomic DNA from the virus M13mp18 was chosen as the scaffold. Its naturally single-stranded 7,249-nt sequence was examined for secondary structure, and a hairpin with a 20-bp stem was found. Whether staples could bind at this hairpin was unknown, so a 73-nt region containing it was avoided. When a linear scaffold was required, M13mp18 was cut (in the 73-nt region) by digestion with *Bsr*BI restriction enzyme. While 7,176 nt remained available for folding, most designs did not fold all 7,176 nt; short (≤ 25 nt) "remainder strands" were added to complement unused sequence. In general, a 100-fold excess of 200–250 staple and remainder strands were mixed with scaffold and annealed from 95 °C to 20 °C in < 2 h. When samples were deposited on mica, only folded DNA structures stuck to the surface while excess staples remained in solution; AFM imaging thus proceeded under buffer without prior purification. Six different folds were explored; Fig. 2 gives their folding paths and their predicted and experimentally observed DNA structures. (Models and staple sequences are given in Supplementary Note S3, final designs appear in Supplementary Note S12. Experimental methods are given in Supplementary Note S4, results described here but not shown are in Supplementary Note S5.) Of the products imaged by AFM, a particular structure was considered qualitatively "well-formed" if it had no defect (hole or indentation in the expected outline) greater than 15 nm in diameter. For each fold the fraction of well-formed structures, as a percentage of all distinguishable structures in one or more AFM fields, was calculated as a rough estimate of yield. I note that while some structures classified as well-formed had 15-nm defects, most had no defects greater than 10 nm in diameter.

叉的扭曲并改变其位置(典型情况下是变动一个 bp)以使张力最小化;相应地,订书针链的序列被重新指定。沿着接缝和某些棱处,小沟角度(150°)使脚手架交叉与其毗邻的周期性交叉产生张力(图 1d,横截面 2);这种情况并未被改变。

无论两个订书针链在哪里相遇,骨架中都会有一个缺口。缺口出现在螺旋的顶部和底部的面上,如图 1d 所示。在最后一步中,为了使订书针链与脚手架链具有更大的连接范围(目的是获得更高的连接特异性和更高的结合能,从而具有更高的熔点),将邻近的各对订书针链跨过缺口合并,以产生出更少、更长的订书针链(图 1e)。为了使接缝更坚固,可以额外打断并连接一些订书针链使其穿过接缝;被订书针所横跨的接缝称为"桥联的"。接合的图案并不唯一;不同的选择导致最终图案中的缺口和订书针链不同。全部接合图案制造出相同的形状,但是如同后面将会指出的,接合图案决定了后面将会应用于此形状的任何像素图案的背景光栅类型。

将 M13mp18 基因组 DNA 折叠成型

为了检验该方法,选取来自病毒 M13mp18 的圆形基因组 DNA 作为脚手架。对其天然的 7,249 个核苷酸序列进行二级结构的检测,发现其中具有一个茎长 20 bp 的发夹状结构。由于不知道订书针链能否在这个发夹结构上弯曲,因此避开包含它的 73 个核苷酸区域。在需要线性的脚手架链时,用 *Bsr*BI 限制性内切酶通过降解作用将 M13mp18(在 73 个核苷酸区域中)切开。尽管可供折叠用的部分还有 7,176 个核苷酸,大多数设计却并不折叠全部 7,176 个核苷酸;而是用短的(≤25 个核苷酸)"余链"以互补未用到的序列。一般而言,将有 100 倍过量的 200~250 个的订书针和余链与脚手架混合,并在 2 小时内从 95 ℃退火到 20 ℃。将样品沉积在云母上之后,只有折叠的 DNA 结构才能固定在表面上,而多余的订书针则留在溶液中;因此可以不经过预先提纯而在缓冲液中进行 AFM 成像。我们尝试了 6 种不同的折叠;图 2 给出了它们的折叠路径和预测的以及实验测得的 DNA 结构。(附注 S3 中给出了模型和订书针的序列,最终设计出现在附注 S12 中。附注 S4 中给出了实验方法,这里只描述而并没有显示的结果则见于附注 S5。)在用 AFM 成像的结果中,如果没有直径超过 15 nm 的缺陷(洞或者是预期外廓中的锯齿形缺口),可以从质量上认为"良好地形成"一种特定的结构。对每一种折叠,用良好形成的部分的比例来估算产率,并用在一个或多个 AFM 场中占所有可区分结构的百分数表示。我注意到,尽管某些划归到良好形成类的结构具有 15 nm 的缺陷,但大多数结构没有直径超过 10 nm 的缺陷。

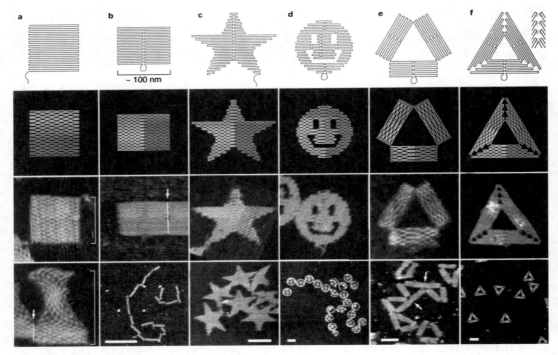

Fig. 2. **DNA origami shapes.** Top row, folding paths. **a**, square; **b**, rectangle; **c**, star; **d**, disk with three holes; **e**, triangle with rectangular domains; **f**, sharp triangle with trapezoidal domains and bridges between them (red lines in inset). Dangling curves and loops represent unfolded sequence. Second row from top, diagrams showing the bend of helices at crossovers (where helices touch) and away from crossovers (where helices bend apart). Colour indicates the base-pair index along the folding path; red is the 1st base, purple the 7,000th. Bottom two rows, AFM images. White lines and arrows indicate blunt-end stacking. White brackets in **a** mark the height of an unstretched square and that of a square stretched vertically (by a factor > 1.5) into an hourglass. White features in **f** are hairpins; the triangle is labelled as in Fig. 3k but lies face down. All images and panels without scale bars are the same size, 165 nm × 165 nm. Scale bars for lower AFM images: **b**, 1 μm; **c–f**, 100 nm.

First, a simple 26-helix square was designed (Fig. 2a). The square had no vertical reversals in raster direction, required a linear scaffold, and used 2.5-turn crossover spacing. Most staples were 26-mers that bound each of two adjacent helices as in Fig. 1c, but via 13 bases rather than 8. The design was made assuming a 1.5-nm inter-helix gap; an aspect ratio of 1.05 (93.9 nm × 89.5 nm) was expected. By AFM, 13% of structures were well-formed squares (out of $S = 45$ observed structures) with aspect ratios from 1.00 to 1.07 and bore the expected pattern of crossovers (Fig. 2a, upper AFM image). Of the remaining structures, ~25% were rectangular fragments, and ~25% had an hourglass shape that showed a continuous deformation of the crossover lattice (Fig. 2a, lower AFM image). Sequential imaging documented the stretching of a square into an hourglass, suggesting that hourglasses were originally squares that stretched upon deposition or interaction with the AFM tip. No subsequent designs exhibited stretching. Other designs had either a tighter 1.5-turn spacing with 32-mer staples spanning three helical domains (Fig. 2b–d, f) or smaller domains that appeared to slide rather than stretch (Fig. 2e).

858

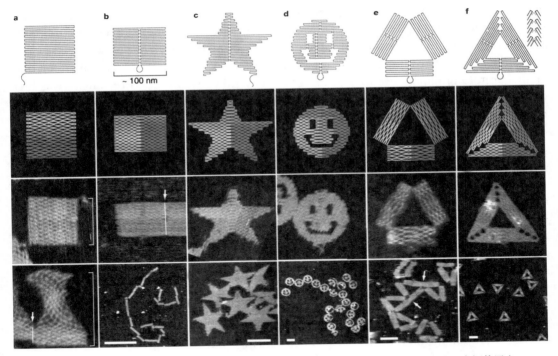

图 2. **DNA 折纸术造型**。顶行，折叠路径。**a**，正方形；**b**，矩形；**c**，五角星形；**d**，有三个洞的圆盘；**e**，由矩形区域构成的三角形；**f**，由梯形区域构成并且其间有桥联（小图中的红色线段）的锐角三角形。摇摆的曲线和环表示未折叠的序列。从顶部数第二行，图片显示螺旋在交叉处（螺旋发生接触）有弯曲而后远离交叉（螺旋分开）。颜色指示沿折叠路径的碱基对顺序；红色是第一个碱基，紫色是第 7,000 个；底部的两行是 AFM 图像。白线和箭头表示平端的堆积。**a** 中的白色括弧标示出一个未拉伸正方形的高度和一个在垂直方向上拉伸（＞1.5 倍）为沙漏形的正方形的高度。**f** 中的白色特征为发夹结构；三角形的标记如同图 3k 中那样，不过面朝下放置。所有没有比例尺的图像和画板都具有相同的尺寸，165 nm×165 nm。下方 AFM 图像的比例尺：**b**，1 μm；**c~f**，100 nm。

首先设计一个简单的 26 螺旋正方形（图 2a）。该正方形在光栅方向上没有垂直的反转，它需要一根线性脚手架，并且要用到 2.5 螺距交叉间隔。大多数订书针长度是 26 个碱基，如图 1c 所示那样将两个邻近螺旋连接起来，不过是借助于 13 个碱基而不是 8 个碱基。设计时假定螺旋间的空隙有 1.5 nm；预期会有 1.05 的纵横比（93.9 nm×89.5 nm）。根据 AFM 可知，13% 的结构是良好形成的正方形（在 $S=45$ 观测到的结构中），其纵横比为 1.00 到 1.07，并且具有预期的交叉图案（图 2a，上方的 AFM 图像）。在其余结构中，约 25% 具有矩形形态，还有约 25% 具有沙漏形状并且显示出交叉晶格的连续形变（图 2a，下方的 AFM 图像）。连续成像证实了从正方形到沙漏形的拉伸过程，表明沙漏最初本是正方形，由于沉积作用或者与 AFM 探针的相互作用而拉伸。后续设计都没有呈现出拉伸。其他设计或者是具有更为紧凑的 1.5 螺距间隔，长度为 32 个碱基的订书针跨越 3 个螺旋区域（图 2b~d，f）；或者是更小些的区域，它们更倾向于滑移而不是拉伸（图 2e）。

To test the formation of a bridged seam, a rectangle was designed (Fig. 2b) according to the scheme outlined in Fig. 1e using 1.5-turn crossover spacing, 32-mer staples and a circular scaffold. As seen in Fig. 2b, the central seam and associated pattern of crossovers was easily visualized (upper AFM image). Rectangles stacked along their vertical edges, often forming chains up to 5 μm long (lower AFM image). The yield of well-formed rectangles was high (90%, $S = 40$), and so rectangles were used to answer basic questions concerning inter-helix gaps, base-stacking, defects and stoichiometry. AFM drift often distorts aspect ratios so that inter-helix gaps cannot be inferred from the aspect ratio of a single rectangle. A range of aspect ratios implied a gap size from 0.9 to 1.2 nm; later designs assume 1 nm. Whatever the exact value, it is consistent: aspect ratios were invariant along stacked chains with dozens of rectangles. Such stacking was almost completely abolished by omitting staples along vertical edges. On the other hand, stacking across the seam of an unbridged rectangle (as in Fig. 1c) kept 65% of structures ($S = 40$) well-formed; the rest showed some degree of dislocation at the seam. Other defects, such as the intentional omission of single staples, could be visualized as 5–10-nm holes. However, sharp tips and high tapping amplitudes were required; repeated scanning created holes difficult to distinguish from holes due to missing strands. This effect also increased uncertainty when stoichiometry was varied. When staple excesses of approximately 100:1 and 9:1 were used, the frequencies of 5–10-nm holes (a few per rectangle) were indistinguishable. At 2:1, rectangles were similar; perhaps a greater fraction were malformed. At 1.5:1, rectangles formed but had holes up to ~10% of their area in size. At a 1:1 ratio, < 1% of structures were rectangular.

To demonstrate the creation of arbitrary shapes, a five-pointed star was designed with 1.5-turn spacing, 32-mer staples and a linear rather than circular scaffold (Fig. 2c). Designed assuming a 1.5-nm inter-helix gap (the work was carried out before the gap for 1.5-turn spacing was measured), the stars are somewhat squat (Fig. 2c, upper AFM image). Still, the stars show that the width of a shape may be approximated to within one DNA turn. Many of the structures observed were star fragments (Fig. 2c, lower AFM image), and only 11% ($S = 70$) were well-formed. The low yield of stars (and squares, see above) may be due to strand breakage occurring during *Bsr*BI digestion or subsequent steps to remove the enzyme; when untreated circular scaffold was folded into stars, 63% ($S = 43$) were well-formed. To show that DNA origami need not be topological disks, and that scaffolds can be routed arbitrarily through shapes, a three-hole disk was designed (Fig. 2d). Although the shape approximated is symmetric, the folding path is highly asymmetric and has five distinct seams. Unlike the rectangles, which rarely break or fold, three-hole disks exhibit several characteristic deformations (Fig. 2d, lower AFM image); still, 70% ($S = 90$) were well-formed.

DNA origami is not limited to the approximation of shapes by raster fill: some shapes can be created more exactly by combining distinct raster fill domains in non-parallel arrangements. Figure 2e shows a triangle built from three separate, 2.5-turn spacing rectangular domains; only single covalent bonds along the scaffold hold the domains together. But the desired equiangular triangles (upper AFM image) were rarely observed (< 1%, $S = 199$). As seen in

为了检验桥联接缝的形成，根据图 1e 中所描绘的概图设计一个矩形（图 2b），其中用到 1.5 螺距交叉间隔，长度 32 个碱基的订书针和一根圆形脚手架。如同在图 2b 中所看到的，中心接缝和相关的交叉图案很容易看到（上方的 AFM 图像）。矩形沿着它们的垂直边堆叠，经常会形成长达 5 μm 的链（下方的 AFM 图像）。良好形成的矩形的产率很高（90%，$S = 40$），因此可以用矩形来研究与螺旋间空隙、碱基堆叠、缺陷和化学计量比等有关的基本问题。AFM 漂移经常会扭曲纵横比，使得螺旋间空隙不能利用单个矩形的纵横比推断出来。从纵横比范围可以推测出空隙大小为 0.9 ~ 1.2 nm；后面的设计假定为 1 nm。不管具体数值是多少，它是前后一致的：纵横比对于沿着堆叠链方向的数十个矩形是不变的。如果去掉沿垂直棱的订书针的话，这种堆叠几乎被完全破坏。另一方面，穿过非桥联矩形的接缝的堆叠（如图 1c 所示）则保持着 65%（$S = 40$）的良好形成的结构；其余部分在接缝处表现出不同程度的位错。其他缺陷，例如有意去掉某条订书针，可以看到一个 5 ~ 10 nm 的洞。但是，需要尖锐的针尖和高的敲击幅度；重复的扫描产生出的洞很难与归因于缺失链的洞相区分。这种效应增加了在改变化学计量比时的不确定性。当所用的订书针的过量值近似为 100∶1 和 9∶1 时，5 ~ 10 nm 洞的出现频率（每个矩形有若干个）是不可区分的。在过量值为 2∶1 时，矩形是相似的；可能会有较大比例是畸形的。在 1.5∶1 时，能够形成矩形，但是洞占总面积多达 10% 左右。在 1∶1 的比例时，＜1% 的结构是矩形的。

为了证明这种方法能制备任意的形状，用 1.5 螺距间隔，长度为 32 个碱基的订书针和一根线性而不是圆形的脚手架设计了一个五角星（图 2c）。设计时假定螺旋间的空隙为 1.5 nm（这项工作是在测定 1.5 螺距间隔的空隙之前进行的），因此所得五角星似乎有些矮胖（图 2c，上方 AFM 图像）。五角星的情形再一次表明，形状的宽度可以近似地在一个 DNA 螺距之内。所观测到的很多结构是星形的碎片（图 2c，下方的 AFM 图像），只有 11%（$S = 70$）是良好形成的。星形的低产率（正方形的，见上）可以归结为在 BsrBI 降解或随后移除酶的过程中发生的链断裂；在用未经处理的圆形脚手架折叠成星形时，有 63%（$S = 43$）是良好形成的。为了说明 DNA 折纸术并不一定需要拓扑意义上的圆盘，其脚手架可以转变为任意形状，我设计了一个有 3 个洞的圆盘（图 2d）。尽管所模拟的形状是对称的，折叠路径却是高度不对称的，而且具有 5 个不同的接缝。与几乎不会破裂或弯折的矩形不同，三洞圆盘呈现出几种特征性的变形（图 2d，下方 AFM 图像）；仍然有 70%（$S = 90$）是良好形成的。

DNA 折纸术用来模拟形状的方法并不限于光栅填充：某些形状能够通过将不同的光栅填充区域合并为非平行排布而更为准确地制造出来。图 2e 显示了一个三角形，它是用 3 个独立的、2.5 螺距间隔的矩形区域搭建起来的；只有沿着脚手架上的单个共价键将各区域维持在一起。但是所需的正三角形（上方的 AFM 图像）却很少

the lower AFM image, stacking caused rectangular domains of separate triangles to bind; this effect and the flexibility of the single-bond joints at the vertices may account for the ease with which these triangles deform. To solve these problems, "sharp triangles", built from trapezoidal domains with 1.5-turn spacing, were designed (Fig. 2f). The slanted edges of the trapezoids meet at the triangle vertices and allow the addition of bridging staples along these interfaces. Sharp triangles remained separated and equiangular (Fig. 2f, lower AFM image); 88% were well-formed ($S = 78$). Even when bridging staples at the vertices were not used, a large number of sharp triangles were well-formed (55%, $S = 22$). These "weakened" sharp triangles provided the most stringent test of the estimated inter-helix gap, because too high or low an estimate would have caused gaps or overlaps between trapezoids. Gaps of 10 nm occasionally appeared but overlaps were never observed, suggesting that 1 nm may be a slight underestimate of the inter-helix gap.

Patterning and Combining DNA Origami

In addition to binding the DNA scaffold and holding it in shape, staple strands provide a means for decorating shapes with arbitrary patterns of binary pixels. Given a shape, the original set of staples is taken to represent binary "0"s; a new set of labelled staples, one for each original staple, is used to represent binary "1"s. Patterns are created by mixing appropriate subsets of these strands. In this way, any desired pattern can be made.

In principle, a variety of DNA modifications—for example, biotin or fluorophores—could serve as labels. Here, "dumbbell hairpins" (Fig. 1d inset, Supplementary Note S6), designed to avoid dimerization at high concentration, were added to the middle of 32-mer staples at the position of merges made during design. Depending on the merge pattern, the resulting pixel pattern was either rectilinear, with adjacent columns of hairpins on alternate faces of the shape, or staggered and nearly hexagonally packed, with all hairpins on the same face. In AFM images labelled staples give greater height contrast (3 nm above the mica) than unlabelled staples ($\sim$1.5 nm), which results in a pattern of light "1" and dark "0" pixels. Several patterns (Fig. 3), each with $\sim$200 pixels, illustrate the generality of this technique.

能被看到（< 1%，$S = 199$）。如同在下方 AFM 图像中所看到的那样，堆叠导致不同三角形中的矩形区域结合起来；这种效应加上顶点处单键结合的易变性，可以解释这些三角形为什么这么容易变形。为了解决这些问题，设计了"锐角三角形"（图 2f），它是用有 1.5 螺距间隔的梯形区域搭建起来的。梯形的斜边在三角形顶点处相遇，并且允许在界面处加入桥联的订书针。锐角三角形保持着等角并彼此独立（图 2f，下方 AFM 图像）；88%（$S = 78$）是良好形成的。即使在顶点处没有使用桥联订书针，仍然有大量锐角三角形是良好形成的（55%，$S = 22$）。这些"弱化的"锐角三角形为所估计的螺旋间空隙提供了最为严格的检验，因为过高或者过低的估计值都可能会导致梯形之间的空隙或重叠。偶尔会出现 10 nm 的空隙，但是未曾观测到重叠，这意味着 1 nm 对于螺旋间空隙来说可能是一个略微偏低的估值。

DNA 折纸术的绘图与合并

除去将 DNA 脚手架结合并保持其形状之外，订书针链还提供了一种以任意二元像素图案修饰该形状的方法。假定一个形状，最初的一组订书针用来表示二进制的"0"；另一组标记了的订书针，每条都对应于最初的每条订书针，用来表示二进制的"1"。通过混合这些订书针链的适当子集，即可创造出图案。利用这种方法，能得到任何预想的图案。

原则上讲，有很多种 DNA 修饰——例如生物素或荧光团——可以充当标记。本文中，将为避免高浓度时的二聚作用而设计了的"哑铃型发夹"（图 1d 小图，附注 S6），在设计订书针的接合时加入长度为 32 个碱基的订书针的中部。所得到的像素图案取决于接合图案：或者是直线形，其中发夹的相邻列位于该式样中交替的面上；或者是交错的近似于六方堆积，其中所有的发夹都位于相同的面上。在 AFM 图像中，标记的订书针表现出比未标记的订书针（约 1.5 nm）更大的高度对比（3 nm，在云母表面），结果是图案中的像素"1"明亮而"0"灰暗。各自具有大约 200 像素的几种图案（图 3）说明了这种技术的普适性。

Fig. 3. **Patterning and combining DNA origami. a**, Model for a pattern representing DNA, rendered using hairpins on a rectangle (Fig. 2b). **b**, AFM image. One pixelated DNA turn (~100 nm) is 30 × the size of an actual DNA turn (~3.6 nm) and the helix appears continuous when rectangles stack appropriately. Letters are 30 nm high, only 6 × larger than those written using STM in ref. 3; 50 billion copies rather than 1 were formed. **c, d**, Model and AFM image, respectively, for a hexagonal pattern that highlights the nearly hexagonal pixel lattice used in **a–i**. **e–i**, Map of the western hemisphere, scale $1:2 \times 10^{14}$, on a rectangle of different aspect ratio. Normally such rectangles aggregate (**h**) but 4-T loops or tails on edges (white lines in e) greatly decrease stacking (**i**). **j–m**, Two labellings of the sharp triangle show that each edge may be distinguished. In **j–u**, pixels fall on a rectilinear lattice. **n–u**, Combination of sharp triangles into hexagons (**n, p, q**) or lattices (**o, r–u**). Diagrams (**n, o**) show positions at which staples are extended (coloured protrusions) to match complementary single-stranded regions of the scaffold (coloured holes). Models (**p, r**) permit comparison with data (**q, s**). The largest lattice observed comprises only 30 triangles (**t**). **u** shows close association of triangles (and some breakage). **d** and **f** were stretched and sheared to correct for AFM drift. Scale bars: **h, i**, 1 μm; **q, s–u**, 100 nm.

Yields of patterned origami were similar to those of unpatterned origami; for the pattern in Fig. 3a, 91% ($S = 85$) of rectangles were well-formed. Because rectilinear patterns imaged poorly, only staggered patterns were examined quantitatively. Distances measured between pairs of "1" pixels in alternating columns (two pixel widths: 11.5 ± 0.9 nm, mean ± s.d., $n = 26$) and adjacent rows (one pixel height: 6.6 ± 0.5 nm, $n = 24$) are consistent with the theoretically expected pixel size of 5.4 nm × 6 nm. Most defects take the form of "missing pixels"; that is, pixels that should image as "1"s but image as "0"s instead. 94% of "1" pixels (of 1,080 observed) were visualized. Whether missing pixels represent real defects or artefacts

图 3. **DNA 折纸术的绘图与结合。a**，呈现 DNA 的图像的模型，利用矩形上的发夹来实现 (图 2b)。**b**，AFM 图像。单像素的一个 DNA 螺距 (约 100 nm) 的大小是一个实际 DNA 螺距 (约 3.6 nm) 的 30 倍，并且矩形以适当方式堆积时螺旋看来是连续的。字母高度为 30 nm，是参考文献 3 中用 STM 写成的那些字母的 6 倍；形成的副本是 500 亿而不是 1 份。**c，d**，分别为一个六边形图案的模型和 AFM 图像，它强调了 **a～i** 中所使用的近似六边形像素晶格。**e～i**，西半球的地图 (比例尺为 $1:2 \times 10^{14}$) 画在不同纵横比的矩形之上。正常情况下这些矩形会聚集 (**h**)，但是棱上的 4-T 环或尾部 (**e** 中的白色线段) 有效地避免了堆积 (**i**)。**j～m**，锐角三角形的两个标记表明各条边是可区分的。在 **j～u** 中，像素落在直线形晶格上。**n～u**，锐角三角形结合成六边形 (**n, p, q**) 或晶格 (**o, r～u**)。图像 (**n, o**) 显示出订书针进行扩展 (彩色的突起) 以便与脚手架的单链区域 (彩色的洞) 互补的部位。模型 (**p, r**) 与数据 (**q, s**) 是可比的。所观测到的最大晶格仅由 30 个三角形组成 (**t**)。**u** 显示出与三角形 (以及某些断裂) 的密切关联。**d** 和 **f** 被拉伸并切割，以修正 AFM 的漂移。比例尺：**h, i**，1 μm；**q, s～u**，100 nm。

有绘图的折纸术的产率与没有绘图的折纸术的产率相近；对于图 3a 中的图案而言，91% ($S = 85$) 的矩形是良好形成的。由于直线形图案成像不佳，因此只对交错型图案进行了定量检测。所测得的交替列 (两个像素宽度：11.5±0.9 nm，平均值 ± 标准差，$n = 26$) 与相邻行中 (一个像素的高度：6.6±0.5 nm，$n = 24$) 一对 "1" 像素之间的距离与理论预期的像素尺寸 5.4 nm × 6 nm 相吻合。大多数缺陷体现为 "丢失像素" 的形式；也就是说，这些像素应该描绘的是 "1" 但却描绘了 "0"。其中 94%

of imaging is unknown; sequential AFM images occasionally showed "1" pixels that later converted irreversibly to "0" pixels, suggesting tip-induced damage. Stoichiometric errors, synthetic errors, or unwanted secondary structure are not implicated for any particular strand, as the position of missing pixels appeared random (Fig. 3b, f and g).

Stacking of shapes along blunt-ended helices provides an uncontrolled mechanism for the creation of larger structures (Fig. 3b). Instead of removing staples on the edge of a rectangle to avoid stacking (as described previously), 4-T hairpin loops (four thymines in a row, Fig. 1e, inset) or 4-T tails can be added to edge staples (Fig. 3e, f); stacked chains of 3–5 rectangles still formed (Fig. 3g), but 30% of rectangles ($S = 319$) occurred as monomers (Fig. 3i). Without hairpins, all rectangles occurred in aggregates (Fig. 3h).

Controlled combination of shapes was achieved by designing "extended staples" that connected shapes along their edges. To create a binding interaction between two particular edges, extended staples were designed by merging and breaking normal staples along these edges (Supplementary Note S7). Starting with sharp triangles, this approach was used to create finite (hexagons; Fig. 3n, p, q) as well as periodic structures (triangular lattice; Fig. 3o, r–u). I note that the successful combination of shapes (unlike the successful formation of individual shapes) is in principle very sensitive to the concentrations of extended staples (which should ideally be equal to that of the scaffold). Poor stoichiometry may play a role in the poor yield of hexagons ($< 2\%$, $S = 70$) and lattices (not measured).

Discussion

The scaffolded self-assembly of DNA strands has been used to create linear structures[17,18] and proposed as a method for creating arbitrary patterns[18,19]. But the widespread use of scaffolded self-assembly, and in particular the use of long DNA scaffolds in combination with hundreds of short strands, has been inhibited by several misconceptions: it was assumed that (1) sequences must be optimized[20] to avoid secondary structure or undesired binding interactions, (2) strands must be highly purified, and (3) strand concentrations must be precisely equimolar. These three criteria are important for the formation of many DNA nanostructures and yet all three are ignored in the present method. For example, M13mp18 is essentially a natural sequence that has a predicted secondary structure which is more stable (lower in energy) than similar random sequences (Supplementary Note S8). Further, stocks of staples each contained a few per cent truncation products, stock concentrations were measured with at least 10% error, and staples were used successfully at stoichiometries that varied over an order of magnitude.

I suggest that several factors contribute to the success of scaffolded DNA origami (even though the method ignores the normal, careful practices of DNA nanotechnology).

的"1"像素(在 1,080 个观测到的像素之中)能被观察到。还不知道丢失像素所表现的究竟是真实的缺陷还是成像过程中的假象;连续的 AFM 成像偶尔会出现一开始为"1"像素随后不可逆地转变为"0"像素的情况,这意味着探针造成的损伤。对任一特定的链而言,化学计量误差、合成误差或者是不需要的二级结构都并未牵扯其中,因为丢失像素的部位似乎是随机的(图 3b,f 和 g)。

形状沿着平端螺旋的堆积为产生较大结构(图 3b)提供了一种无法控制的机制。不同于移除矩形边上的订书针以避免堆积(如同前面所描述的那样),4-T 发夹环(一行中有 4 个胸腺嘧啶,图 1e 小图)或 4-T 尾部可以加入边上的订书针中(图 3e 和 f);3~5 个矩形的堆叠链仍然会形成,但是 30% 的矩形($S = 319$)是作为单体而出现的(图 3i)。没有发夹的话,所有矩形都以聚集体形式出现(图 3h)。

通过设计"扩展型订书针"以沿形状的边将其连接,可以实现形状的可控结合。把沿着这些边的订书针链重新接合和打断,可以得到具有特定相互作用的两条边(附注 S7)。从锐角三角形开始,用这种方式可以创造有限的(六边形;图 3n,p 和 q)和周期性的结构(三角形晶格;图 3o,r~u)。我注意到,形状的成功结合(与单个形状的成功形成不同)在原则上极容易受到扩展型订书针浓度(在理想情况下,它应该等于脚手架的浓度)的影响。不准确的化学计量会导致六边形($< 2\%$,$S = 70$)和晶格(未检测)的低产率。

讨　论

DNA 链以脚手架方式进行的自组装已经被用来制造多种线形结构[17,18],而且被提出可作为一种能创造任意图案的方法[18,19]。但是脚手架式自组装的广泛应用,特别是长 DNA 脚手架在与数百个短订书针链相结合时的应用,却一直由于若干误解而不得发挥:人们假定(1)必须要对序列进行优化[20]以避免二级结构或不需要的结合作用,(2)DNA 链必须是高度纯化的,以及(3)DNA 链的浓度必须精确为等物质的量。这三个准则对于很多种 DNA 纳米结构的形成是重要的,但在我目前提出的这种方法中它们都是被忽略的。例如,M13mp18 实际上是一种天然序列,具有预期的二级结构,比类似的随机序列(附注 S8)更为稳定(能量更低)。此外,每个订书针的原料都含有少量百分比的截头产物,原料浓度的测定至少有 10% 的误差,而且当化学计量在一个数量级的水平上变动时仍可成功地使用订书针。

我认为,有几个因素对脚手架式 DNA 折纸术的成功很重要(尽管该方法忽略了 DNA 纳米技术常规的、谨慎的做法)。它们是:(1)链的进入,(2)过量订书针,

These are (1) strand invasion, (2) an excess of staples, (3) cooperative effects and (4) design that intentionally does not rely on binding between staples. Briefly (details are given in Supplementary Note S9), strand invasion may allow correct binding of excess full-length staples to displace unwanted secondary structure, incorrect staples, or grossly truncated staples. Further, each correct addition of a staple organizes the scaffold for subsequent binding of adjacent staples and precludes a large set of undesired secondary structures. Last, because staples are not designed to bind one another, their relative concentrations do not matter.

The method presented here is easy to implement, high yield and relatively inexpensive. Three months of effort went into the design program. In addition, each structure required about one week to design and one week to synthesize (commercially); the mixing and annealing of strands required a few hours. The greatest experimental difficulty was acquiring high-resolution AFM images, typically taking two days per structure. For rigid designs using circular scaffolds (rectangles with patterns, three-hole disks, and sharp triangles), yields of qualitatively well-formed structures were at least 70%. A better understanding of folding will depend on less-destructive imaging and quantification of small (< 15 nm) defects. A possible objection to the routine use of the method is the potential cost of staples; unlike the scaffold, staples cannot be cloned. However, unpurified strands are inexpensive so that the scaffold constitutes 80% of the cost, even when using a 100-fold excess of staples (Supplementary Note S10).

I believe that scaffolded DNA origami can be adapted to create more complex or larger structures. For example, the design of three-dimensional structures should be accessible using a straightforward adaptation of the raster fill method given here. If non-repetitive scaffolds of megabase length can be prepared, micrometre-size origami with 20,000 features may be possible. However, the requirement for unique sequence information means that the method cannot be scaled up arbitrarily; whenever structures above a critical size or level of complexity are desired, it will therefore be necessary to combine scaffolded DNA origami with hierarchical self-assembly[10,11], algorithmic self-assembly[22], or top-down fabrication techniques.

An obvious application of patterned DNA origami would be the creation of a "nanobreadboard", to which diverse components could be added. The attachment of proteins[23], for example, might allow novel biological experiments aimed at modelling complex protein assemblies and examining the effects of spatial organization, whereas molecular electronic or plasmonic circuits might be created by attaching nanowires, carbon nanotubes or gold nanoparticles[24]. These ideas suggest that scaffolded DNA origami could find use in fields as diverse as molecular biology and device physics.

(**440**, 297-302; 2006)

Paul W. K. Rothemund

Departments of Computer Science and Computation & Neural Systems, California Institute of Technology, Pasadena, California 91125, USA

(3) 协同效应和(4) 有意不依赖订书针间结合的设计。简单地说(附注 S9 中给出了细节)，链的进入使得过量的完整长度订书针正确结合，以取代那些不需要的二级结构、不正确的订书针或者是不准确的截头订书针。另外，每一个新的正确添加的订书针都会组织脚手架以使其适合与随后的相邻订书针的连接，从而排除了大量不需要的二级结构。最后，由于订书针并不是被设计成彼此连接的，因此它们的相对浓度并没有影响。

这里所介绍的方法容易施行，产率高而且成本相对较低。设计程序需要三个月的努力。此外，每一种结构大约需要一个星期来设计和一个星期来合成(商业化方式的)；订书针链的混合与退火需要几个小时。实验中最大的困难是获得高分辨率的 AFM 图像，通常情况下每个结构需要花两天时间。对于用圆形脚手架进行的稳定设计来说(有图案的矩形、三洞圆盘和锐角三角形)，从质量上看良好形成的结构的产率至少有 70%。对折叠过程更好的理解将取决于破坏更少的成像和对小(< 15 nm)缺陷的定量。反对把这一方法投入常规使用的理由可能是订书针的潜在消耗；与脚手架不同，订书针是不可复制的。但是，未经纯化的链成本很低，因此，即使是在使用 100 倍过量的订书针时，脚手架占成本消耗的 80%(附注 S10)。

我相信脚手架式 DNA 折纸术可以适用于创造更复杂或者更大的结构。例如，三维结构的设计应该可以通过直接改进本文中所给出的光栅填充方法而达到。如果能够制备出长达兆碱基的非重复性脚手架，那么具有 20,000 个特征的微米尺寸折纸结构就有可能实现。但是，对于独特的序列信息的需求意味着这种方法无法任意地按比例扩大；一旦需要超过某一临界尺寸或者是复杂性水平的结构，就必须要将脚手架式 DNA 折纸术与分级自组装 [10,11]、算法式自组装 [22] 或者自顶向下的技术相结合。

绘制图案的 DNA 折纸术的一个明显的应用，是"纳米模拟电路板"的制造，板上可以添加各种不同的组件。例如，蛋白质的附着 [23] 可能会使新型的生物学实验得以进行，这些实验将会有助于对复杂的蛋白质组装过程建立模型以及检测空间组织化过程的影响，而附着纳米导线、碳纳米管或者是金纳米颗粒 [24] 则有可能制造出分子电路或等离子电路。这些想法意味着脚手架式 DNA 折纸术可以在与分子生物学和器件物理学这种多样化的领域中找到应用。

(王耀杨 翻译；刘冬生 审稿)

Received 7 September 2005; accepted 12 January 2006.

References:

1. Feynman, R. P. There's plenty of room at the bottom. *Engineering and Science* 23 (5), 22-36 (Caltech, February, 1960).

2. Junno, T., Deppert, K., Montelius, L. & Samuelson, L. Controlled manipulation of nanoparticles with an atomic force microscope. *Appl. Phys. Lett.* **66**, 3627-3629 (1995).

3. Eigler, D. M. & Schweizer, E. K. Positioning single atoms with a scanning tunnelling microscope. *Nature* **344**, 524-526 (1990).

4. Heinrich, A. J., Lutz, C. P., Gupta, J. A. & Eigler, D. M. Molecular cascades. *Science* **298**, 1381-1387 (2002).

5. Whitesides, G. M., Mathias, J. P. & Seto, C. T. Molecular self-assembly and nanochemistry: a chemical strategy for the synthesis of nanostructures. *Science* **254**, 1312-1319 (1991).

6. Yokoyama, T., Yokoyama, S., Kamikado, T., Okuno, Y. & Mashiko, S. Self-assembly on a surface of supramolecular aggregates with controlled size and shape. *Nature* **413**, 619-621 (2001).

7. Mao, C. B. *et al.* Virus-based toolkit for the directed synthesis of magnetic and semiconducting nanowires. *Science* **303**, 213-217 (2004).

8. Seeman, N. C. Nucleic-acid junctions and lattices. *J. Theor. Biol.* **99**, 237-247 (1982).

9. Seeman, N. C. & Lukeman, P. S. Nucleic acid nanostructures: bottom-up control of geometry on the nanoscale. *Rep. Prog. Phys.* **68**, 237-270 (2005).

10. Chworos, A. *et al.* Building programmable jigsaw puzzles with RNA. *Science* **306**, 2068-2072 (2004).

11. Park, S. H. *et al.* Finite-size, fully-addressable DNA tile lattices formed by hierarchical assembly procedures. *Angew. Chem.* **118**, 749-753 (2006).

12. Chen, J. & Seeman, N. C. The synthesis from DNA of a molecule with the connectivity of a cube. *Nature* **350**, 631-633 (1991).

13. Zhang, Y. & Seeman, N. C. The construction of a DNA truncated octahedron. *J. Am. Chem. Soc.* **116**, 1661-1669 (1994).

14. Shih, W. M., Quispe, J. D. & Joyce, G. F. A 1.7-kilobase single-stranded DNA that folds into a nanoscale octahedron. *Nature* **427**, 618-621 (2004).

15. Rothemund, P. W. K. *et al.* Design and characterization of programmable DNA nanotubes. *J. Am. Chem. Soc.* **26**, 16344-16353 (2004).

16. Fu, T.-J. & Seeman, N. C. DNA double-crossover molecules. *Biochemistry* **32**, 3211-3220 (1993).

17. LaBean, T. H., Winfree, E. & Reif, J. H. in *DNA Based Computers V* (eds Winfree, E. & Gifford, D. K.) 123-140 (Vol. 54 of DIMACS, AMS Press, Providence, Rhode Island, 1999).

18. Yan, H., LaBean, T. H., Feng, L. & Reif, J. H. Directed nucleation assembly of DNA tile complexes for barcode-patterned lattices. *Proc. Natl Acad. Sci, USA* **100**, 8103-8108 (2003).

19. Reif, J. H. in *Proc. 29th Int. Colloquium on Automata, Languages, and Programming (ICALP)* (eds Widmayer, P., Ruiz, F. T., Bueno, R. M., Hennessy, M., Eidenbenz, S. & Conejo, R.) 1-21 (Vol. 2380 of Lecture Notes in Computer Science, Springer, New York, 2002).

20. Seeman, N. C. *De novo* design of sequences for nucleic acid structural engineering. *J. Biomol. Struct. Dyn.* **8**, 573-581 (1990).

21. Winfree, E. in *DNA Based Computers* (eds Lipton, R. J. & Baum, E. B.) 199-221 (Vol. 27 of DIMACS, AMS Press, Providence, Rhode Island, 1996).

22. Rothemund, P. W. K., Papadakis, N. & Winfree, E. Algorithmic self-assembly of DNA Sierpinski triangles. *PloS Biol.* **2**, e424 (2004).

23. Yan, H., Park, S. H., Finkelstein, G., Reif, J. H. & LaBean, T. H. DNA-templated self-assembly of protein arrays and highly conductive nanowires. *Science* **301**, 1882-1884 (2003).

24. Le, J. D. *et al.* DNA-templated self-assembly of metallic nanocomponent arrays on a surface. *Nano Lett.* **4**, 2343-2347 (2004).

Supplementary Information is linked to the online version of the paper at www.nature.com/nature.

Acknowledgements. I thank E. Winfree for discussions and providing a stimulating laboratory environment; B. Yurke for the term "nanobreadboard"; N. Papadakis, L. Adleman, J. Goto, R. Barish, R. Schulman, R. Hariadi, M. Cook and M. Diehl for discussions; B. Shaw for a gift of AFM tips; A. Schmidt for coordinating DNA synthesis; and K. Yong, J. Crouch and L. Hein for administrative support. This work was supported by National Science Foundation Career and Nano grants to E. Winfree as well as fellowships from the Beckman Foundation and Caltech Center for the Physics of Information.

Author Information. Reprints and permissions information is available at npg.nature.com/reprintsandpermissions. The author declares competing financial interests: details accompany the paper on www. nature.com/nature. Correspondence and requests for materials should be addressed to P.W.K.R. (pwkr@dna.caltech.edu).

Long γ-ray Bursts and Core-collapse Supernovae Have Different Environments

A. S. Fruchter *et al.*

Editor's Note

Long gamma-ray bursts (GRBs) are astrophysical phenomena generally believed to arise in the collapse and subsequent explosion of a very massive star. They had been associated with somewhat anomalous supernovae, but the nature of the link was unclear. Here Andrew Fruchter and colleagues report a careful analysis of galaxies hosting long GRBs and find that the bursts are far more concentrated in the brightest regions of galaxies than are the supernovae. These bright regions have the most massive stars. The authors conclude that bursts are best associated with such stars, and speculate that there is a preference for these stars to occur in environments relatively poor in elements heavier than helium.

When massive stars exhaust their fuel, they collapse and often produce the extraordinarily bright explosions known as core-collapse supernovae. On occasion, this stellar collapse also powers an even more brilliant relativistic explosion known as a long-duration γ-ray burst. One would then expect that these long γ-ray bursts and core-collapse supernovae should be found in similar galactic environments. Here we show that this expectation is wrong. We find that the γ-ray bursts are far more concentrated in the very brightest regions of their host galaxies than are the core-collapse supernovae. Furthermore, the host galaxies of the long γ-ray bursts are significantly fainter and more irregular than the hosts of the core-collapse supernovae. Together these results suggest that long-duration γ-ray bursts are associated with the most extremely massive stars and may be restricted to galaxies of limited chemical evolution. Our results directly imply that long γ-ray bursts are relatively rare in galaxies such as our own Milky Way.

IT is an irony of astrophysics that stellar birth is most spectacularly marked by the deaths of massive stars. Massive stars burn brighter and hotter than smaller stars, and exhaust their fuel far more rapidly. Therefore a region of star formation filled with low mass stars still early in their lives, and in some cases still forming, may also host massive stars already collapsing and producing supernovae. Indeed, with the exception of the now famous type Ia supernovae, which have been so successfully used for cosmological studies[1,2] and which are thought to be formed by the uncontrolled nuclear burning of stellar remnants comparable in mass to the Sun[3], all supernovae are thought to be produced by the collapse of massive stars. The collapse of the most massive stars (tens of solar masses) is thought to leave behind either black holes or neutron stars, depending largely on the state of chemical evolution of the material that formed the star, whereas the demise of stars between approximately 8 and 20 solar masses produces only neutron stars[4].

长伽马射线暴与核坍缩超新星
具有不同的环境

长时标伽马射线暴（简称长暴）一般被认为由大质量恒星的核坍缩及后续爆发所产生。它们与某些超新星成协出现，但成协的本质尚不清楚。本文中，安德鲁·弗鲁赫特与其合作者对长暴和超新星的宿主星系进行了细致的对比分析。他们发现相比于超新星，长暴发生位置更多地集中在星系中最亮的区域，而这些亮区域恰恰存在有超大质量的恒星。作者得出结论，长暴最有可能与星系中的超大质量恒星有着物理关联，并由此推测长暴仅发生在低金属丰度的宿主星系环境中。

当大质量恒星耗尽燃料，它们的内核会发生坍缩，接着星体常常会产生明亮的爆炸，该现象被称为核坍缩超新星。有时这种恒星坍缩会产生更亮的相对论性的爆炸，爆炸会产生持续时标超过两秒的伽马射线辐射，并且辐射能被空间高能卫星探测到。我们简称其为长时标伽马射线暴（即长暴）。一般会认为这些长暴和核坍缩超新星应该处于类似的星系环境中。但我们揭示这一预想是错误的。我们发现长暴比核坍缩超新星更加集中在宿主星系中最亮的区域。而且，长暴的宿主星系明显比核坍缩超新星的宿主星系更暗、更不规则。这些结论表明长暴和超大质量恒星成协，而且可能仅发生在金属丰度较低的星系中。我们的结果直接表明长暴很少会发生在类似银河系样的宿主星系中。

恒星诞生最显著的标志是大质量恒星的死亡，这可以说是天体物理学的一个讽刺。大质量恒星比小质量恒星燃烧时更亮更热，也更快地消耗完自己的燃料。因此在恒星诞生的区域，那里一方面遍布着处于生命期早期的小质量恒星，某些情况下仍有恒星生成；另一方面也可能包含已经坍缩并产生超新星的大质量恒星。诚然，除了最近著名的成功用作宇宙学研究[1,2]的 Ia 型超新星，其他类型超新星都被认为是由大质量恒星的核坍缩形成的。Ia 型超新星一般被认为是类似太阳质量大小的恒星遗迹在不可控制的核燃烧[3]下形成的。普遍认为，大多数大质量恒星（几十个太阳质量）坍缩后会留有黑洞或中子星，这主要取决于构成此恒星物质的化学演化状态。不过质量约为 8 到 20 倍太阳质量的恒星死亡后仅会产生中子星[4]。

Gamma-ray bursts (GRBs), like supernovae, are a heterogeneous population. GRBs can be divided into two classes: short, hard bursts, which last between milliseconds and about two seconds and have hard high-energy spectra, and long, soft bursts, which last between two and tens of seconds, and have softer high-energy spectra[5]. Only very recently have a few of the short bursts been well localized, and initial studies of their apparent hosts suggest that these bursts may be formed by the binary merger of stellar remnants[6,7]. In contrast, the afterglows of over 80 long GRBs (LGRBs) have been detected in the optical and/or radio parts of the spectrum. And as a result of these detections, it has become clear that LGRBs, like core-collapse supernovae, are related to the deaths of young, massive stars. It is these objects, born of the deaths of massive stars, that we study here.

LGRBs are generally found in extremely blue host galaxies[8-11] that exhibit strong emission lines[12,13], suggesting a significant abundance of young, very massive stars. Furthermore, whereas the light curves of the optical transients associated with LGRBs are often dominated by radiation from the relativistic outflow of the GRB, numerous LGRBs have shown late-time "bumps" in their light curves consistent with the presence of an underlying supernova[14-16]. In several cases spectroscopic evidence has provided confirmation of the light of a supernova superposed on the optical transient[17-20]. Indeed, given the large variations in the brightnesses of optical transients and supernovae, and the limited observations on some GRBs, it seems plausible that all LGRBs have an underlying supernova[21]. And although the energy released in a LGRB often appears to the observer to be orders of magnitude larger than that of a supernova, there is now good evidence suggesting that most LGRBs are highly collimated and often illuminate only a few per cent of the sky[22,23]. When one takes this into account, the energy released in LGRBs more closely resembles that of energetic supernovae. However, not all core-collapse supernovae may be candidates for the production of GRBs. The supernovae with good spectroscopic identifications so far associated with GRBs have been type Ic—that is, core-collapse supernovae that show no evidence of hydrogen or helium in their spectra. (Type Ib supernovae, which are often studied together with type Ic, have spectra that are also largely devoid of hydrogen lines but show strong helium features.) A star may therefore need to lose its outer envelope if a GRB is to be able to burn its way through the stellar atmosphere[24]. Studies that have compared the locations of type Ib/c supernovae with the more numerous type II supernovae (core-collapse supernovae showing hydrogen lines) in local galaxies so far show no differences in either the type of host or the placement of the explosion on the host[25,26]. This result led the authors of ref. 25 to argue that core-collapse supernovae all come from the same mass range of progenitor stars, but that type Ib/c supernovae may have had their envelopes stripped by interaction with a binary stellar companion. Whether type Ic supernovae come from single stars, or binary stars, or both, it is very likely that only a small fraction of these supernovae produce GRBs[27].

Given the common massive stellar origins of core-collapse supernovae and LGRBs, one might expect that their hosts and local environments are quite similar. It has long been argued that core-collapse supernovae should track the blue light in the Universe (the light from massive stars is blue), both in their distribution among galaxies and within their host galaxies themselves. One would expect similar behaviour from LGRBs, and indeed

伽马射线暴，类似于超新星，也分有子类。伽马暴可以分为两类：短硬暴，持续时间大约几毫秒到两秒，具有硬的高能能谱；长软暴，持续时间在两秒到几百秒之间，具有较软的高能能谱[5]。数个短暴的位置直到最近才得到确认。初步研究其宿主星系可知这些短暴可能由两颗恒星各自演化成最后状态的星体然后并合形成[6,7]。相比之下，在光学或射电波段探测到超过 80 个长暴余辉。这些探测结果显示长暴和核坍缩超新星一样与年轻大质量恒星的死亡有关。我们这里研究的正是这些从大质量恒星死亡中诞生的天体。

长暴一般在呈现强发射线[12,13]的极端蓝宿主星系中被发现[8-11]，这明显说明有大量的年轻的特大质量恒星存在。而且，尽管与长暴成协的光学暂现源通常由来自伽马暴相对论性外向流的辐射主导，还是有很多长暴在它们光变曲线的后期出现"隆起"，与潜在的超新星的出现一致[14-16]。在多个实例中，有光谱证据显示超新星的光线叠加在光学暂现源上[17-20]。确实，考虑到光学暂现源和超新星巨大的亮度变化范围以及对一些伽马暴的有限观测，似乎每颗长暴都具有成协的超新星[21]。尽管长暴释放的各向同性能量通常看来比超新星大几个量级，但是现在有很好的证据显示大多数长暴都高度准直且仅仅照亮几个百分比的天空[22,23]。考虑到这个因素，长暴释放的真实能量更接近能量更强的超新星。不过，不是所有核坍缩超新星都可能是产生伽马暴的候选体。目前与伽马暴成协光谱证认良好的超新星一般都是 Ic 型超新星——即光谱中没有氢线和氦线的核坍缩超新星（Ib 型超新星一般会与 Ic 型超新星一同被研究，其光谱大多也没有氢线，但表现出很强的氦线特征）。恒星需要失去外包层才能够使伽马暴冲破恒星外表面[24]。目前对邻近星系中 Ib/c 型超新星和数量更多的 II 型超新星（具有氢线的核坍缩超新星）位置的比较研究显示二者在宿主星系的类型或在宿主星系爆发的位置均没有差异[25,26]。这一结果使得文献 25 的作者得出结论，核坍缩超新星全部来自同一质量范围的前身星，但是 Ib/c 型超新星可能已经通过与双星中的伴星的相互作用被剥离了包层。不管 Ic 型超新星源自单星、双星抑或二者兼而有之，这些超新星中只有很少一部分会产生伽马暴[27]。

核坍缩超新星和长暴都起源于大质量恒星，我们预计它们的宿主星系与其当地环境都很相似。一直以来都有观点主张核坍缩超新星在星系里的分布和在宿主星系本身里的分布应该都可以示踪宇宙中的蓝光（来自大质量恒星的光是蓝色的）。对长暴也有类似的估计。事实上已经有研究报道了这一相关的粗略证据[28]。这里我们利

rough evidence for such a correlation has been reported[28]. Here we use the high resolution available from Hubble Space Telescope (HST) images, and an analytical technique developed by us that is independent of galaxy morphology, to study the correlation between these objects and the light of their hosts. We also compare the sizes, morphologies and brightnesses of the LGRB hosts with those of the supernovae. Our results reveal surprising and substantial differences between the birthplaces of these cosmic explosions. We find that whereas core-collapse supernovae trace the blue light of their hosts, GRBs are far more concentrated on the brightest regions of their hosts. Furthermore, while the hosts of core-collapse supernovae are approximately equally divided between spiral and irregular galaxies, the overwhelming majority of GRBs are on irregulars, even when we restrict the GRB sample to the same redshift range as the supernova sample. We argue that these results may be best understood if GRBs are formed from the collapse of extremely massive, low-metallicity stars.

Fig. 1. A mosaic of GRB host galaxies imaged by HST. Each individual image corresponds to a square region on the sky 3.75″ on a side. These images were taken with the Space Telescope Imaging Spectrograph (STIS), the Wide-Field and Planetary Camera 2 (WFPC2) and the Advanced Camera for Surveys (ACS) on HST. In cases where the location of the GRB on the host is known to better than 0.15″ the position of the GRB is shown by a green mark. If the positional error is smaller than the point spread function of the image (0.07″ for STIS and ACS, 0.13″ for WFPC2) the position is marked by a cross-hair;

用哈勃太空望远镜(HST)的高分辨率图像，以及我们提出的独立于星系形态的分析技术来研究这些天体和它们宿主星系光线之间的相关。我们也比较了长暴宿主星系和超新星宿主星系的大小、形态和亮度。结果显示这些宇宙爆炸诞生地存在令人惊讶的重大差异。我们发现尽管核坍缩超新星示踪宿主星系的蓝光，但伽马暴会更加集中于宿主星系的最亮区域。而且，核坍缩超新星的宿主星系中旋涡和不规则星系大致各占一半；甚至将伽马暴样本的选取限定在与超新星样本一样的红移区间时亦是如此。如果伽马暴形成于金属丰度低的超大质量恒星的坍缩，那么也许就能够理解这些结果。

图 1. HST 获得的伽马暴宿主星系拼接组合图。每幅单独的图像对应天球上单边 3.7″ 的正方形天区。这些图像来自 HST 上的太空望远镜成像摄谱仪(STIS)、大视场行星相机 2(WFPC2)和高新巡天相机(ACS)。位置精度优于 0.15″ 的伽马暴用绿色标记出来。位置误差小于图像的点扩散函数(STIS 和 ACS 为 0.07″，WFPC2 的为 0.13″)的伽马暴用十字标记；其他位置误差用圆圈表示。STIS 图像都是白光下拍摄的(没有滤光片)，WFPC2 和 ACS 的图像大部分是在 F606W 滤光片下拍摄的(有几种情况此滤光

otherwise the positional error is indicated by a circle. The STIS images were all taken in white light (no filter), and in most cases the WFPC2 and ACS images are in the F606W filter (though in a few cases where images in this filter were not available we have used images in F555W or F775W). The STIS and F606W images can be thought of as broad "V" or visual images, and are, for galaxies exhibiting typical colours of GRB hosts, the single most sensitive settings for these cameras. F555W is close to the ground-based Johnson V band, and F775W corresponds to the ground-based Johnson I band. Owing to the redshifts of the hosts, these images generally correspond to blue or ultraviolet images of the hosts in their rest frame, and thus detect light largely produced by the massive stars in the hosts.

The Sample

Over 40 LGRBs have been observed with the HST at various times after outburst. The HST is unique in its capability easily to resolve the distant hosts of these objects. Shown in Fig. 1 is a mosaic of HST images of the hosts of 42 bursts. These are all LGRBs with public data that had an afterglow detected with better than 3σ significance and a position sufficiently well localized to determine a host galaxy. A list of all the GRBs used in this work can be found in Supplementary Tables 1–3.

The supernovae discussed here were all discovered as part of the Hubble Higher z Supernova Search[29,30], which was done in cooperation with the HST GOODS survey[31]. The GOODS survey observed two ~150 arcmin^2 patches of sky five times each, in epochs separated by 45 days. Supernovae were identified by image subtraction. Here we discuss only the core-collapse supernovae identified in this survey. A list of the supernovae used is presented in Supplementary Table 4, and images of the supernova hosts can be seen in Fig. 2.

Positions of GRBs and Supernovae on Their Hosts

If LGRBs do in fact trace massive star formation, then in the absence of strong extinction we should find a close correlation between their position on their host galaxies and the blue light of those galaxies. However, many of the GRB hosts and quite a few of the supernova hosts are irregular galaxies made up of more than one bright component. As a result, the common astronomical procedure of identifying the centroid of the galaxy's light, and then determining the distance of the object in question from the centroid, is not particularly appropriate for these galaxies—the centroid of light may in fact lie on a rather faint region of the host (examine GRBs 000926 and 020903 in Fig. 1 for excellent illustrations of this effect). We have therefore developed a method that is independent of galaxy morphology. We sort all of the pixels of the host galaxy image from faintest to brightest, and ask what fraction of the total light of the host is contained in pixels fainter than or equal to the pixel containing the explosion. If the explosions track the distribution of light, then the fraction determined by this method should be uniformly distributed between zero and one. (A detailed exposition of this method can be found in Supplementary Information).

片下的图像无法获取，我们用 F555W 或 F775W 中的图像代替）。STIS 和 F606W 的图像可以被认为是宽"V"或者目视图像，而且对于呈现基本色彩的伽马暴宿主，这些相机的设置都是最为敏感的。F555W 接近于地基 Johnson V 波段，F775W 对应于地基 Johnson I 波段。由于宿主星系的红移，这些图像总体上都对应各自静止系的宿主星系的蓝或紫外图像，因此探测到的大部分光线都源自宿主星系里的大质量恒星。

样　　本

HST 在爆后不同时间内观测了超过 40 颗长暴。HST 分辨这些天体遥远的宿主星系的能力是独一无二的。图 1 展示的是 HST 测得的 42 颗伽马暴宿主星系的拼接组合图。这些皆是存在公开数据的长暴中测得的余辉，显著性优于 3σ，且具有足以定位到的宿主星系。这一工作中所有伽马暴都在补充表格 1～3 中列出。

本文讨论的超新星是哈勃高红移超新星搜寻项目中 [29,30] 发现的一部分超新星，该研究是与 HST GOODS 巡天合作完成的。GOODS 巡天观测了两块约 150 arcmin^2 的天区，每块天区观测 5 次，每次间隔 45 天。通过图像相减发现超新星。这里使用的超新星列在补充表格 4 中，超新星宿主星系的图像见图 2。

伽马暴和超新星在宿主星系的位置

如果长暴真的与大质量恒星密切相关，那么在没有强消光的情况下我们应该能够发现长暴在宿主星系的位置和星系蓝光具有很好的相关。不过，许多伽马暴宿主星系和一些超新星宿主星系是不规则星系，由多于 1 个亮成分组成。因此，尽管天文学普遍的处理步骤是先确定星系光的形心，然后确定要研究的天体离形心的距离，但对于这些星系不是特别适用——光的形心可能位于宿主星系的一个相当暗弱的区域（图 1 中伽马暴 000926 和 020903 很好地描述了这一效应）。我们因此创立了一种独立于星系形态的方法。我们把宿主星系的所有像素从暗到亮排序，然后分别找出像素中包含宿主全部光的部分与包含爆发的部分，再求得前者与后者相比同等亮或更为暗弱的像素的比例。如果爆炸示踪了光的分布，那么这种方法确定的比率应该从 0 到 1 均匀分布（此方法的具体说明见补充资料）。

Fig. 2. A mosaic of core-collapse supernova host galaxies imaged with HST as part of the GOODS programme. Each image in the mosaic has a width of 7.5″ on the sky, and thus twice the field of view of each image in the GRB mosaic. The position of each supernova on its host galaxy is marked. In all cases, these positions are known to sub-pixel accuracy. Supernovae in the GOODS sample were identified by ref. 30 as either type Ia or core-collapse supernovae on the basis of their colours, luminosities and light curves, as data allowed (a supernova exploding near the beginning or end of one of the multi-epoch observing runs would have much less data, and sometimes poor colour information). Thus bright type Ib and Ic supernovae, which have colours and luminosities similar to type Ia supernovae, would probably have been classified as type Ia (unless a grism spectrum was taken—however, only a small fraction of objects were observed spectroscopically). On the other hand, fainter type Ib and Ic supernovae ($M_B \gtrsim -18$) could in principle be identified from photometric data; however, in practice the data were rarely sufficient for a clear separation from other core-collapse supernovae. On the basis of surveys of nearby galaxies, one might expect approximately 20% of the core-collapse supernovae to be type Ib or Ic[49,50].

As can be seen in Fig. 3, the core-collapse supernovae do track the light of their hosts as well as could be expected given their small number statistics. A Kolmogorov–Smirnov (KS) test finds that the distribution of the supernovae is indistinguishable from the distribution of the underlying light. The situation is clearly different for LGRBs. As can be seen in Fig. 3, the GRBs do not simply trace the blue light of the hosts; rather, they are far more concentrated on the peaks of light in the hosts than the light itself. A KS test rejects the hypothesis that GRBs are distributed as the light of their hosts with a probability greater than 99.98%. Furthermore, this result is robust: it shows no dependence on GRB host size or magnitude. And in spite of the relatively small number of supernova hosts for which a comparison can be made, the two populations are found by the KS test to be drawn from different distributions with ~99% certainty. In the next section, we show that the surprising differences in the locations of these objects on the underlying light of their hosts may be due not only to the nature of their progenitor stars but also that of their hosts.

图 2. 作为 GOODS 项目一部分，HST 获得的核坍缩超新星宿主星系拼接组合图。拼接图中的每幅图像对应天球上单边 7.5″ 的天区，因此是伽马暴拼接图中每幅图像视场的两倍。宿主星系里超新星的位置都标记了出来。所有这些位置精度都是在亚像素级别的。GOODS 的超新星样本都在文献 30 中根据颜色、光度和光变曲线数据确定为 Ia 型或核坍缩超新星（如果超新星爆发时接近多次观测中某一次观测的开始或结束，则它的数据会比较少，有时颜色信息也很差）。因此具有类似 Ia 型超新星颜色和光度的亮 Ib 或 Ic 型超新星可能被分类作 Ia 型超新星（除非拍摄获得棱栅光谱——不过，只有对一小部分天体是可以通过光谱观测的）。另一方面，较暗弱的 Ib 或 Ic 型超新星（$M_B \geqslant -18$）原则上可以依据测光数据分类；不过，实际操作中，缺少充分的数据将其与另外的核坍缩超新星区分。在对附近星系的巡天基础上，估计大约有 20% 的核坍缩超新星是 Ib 或 Ic 型超新星[49,50]。

　　如图 3 所示，在小数目统计下，核坍缩超新星确实如预想的一样很好地示踪了宿主星系光线。柯尔莫戈洛夫 - 斯米尔诺夫（KS）检验发现，超新星的分布和基底光的分布难以区分。而对于长暴，情况则明显不同。如图 3 所示，伽马暴不仅示踪了宿主星系的蓝光，而且它们比光本身更加集中在宿主星系的光的峰值处。KS 检验有大于 99.8% 的概率否定伽马暴与宿主星系光具有相同分布的假设。而且这一结论是很可靠的：它与伽马暴宿主星系的大小或星等无关。尽管超新星宿主星系的数目较少，不足以做出比较，KS 检测发现这两个星族在约 99% 确定度下分布不同。在本文的下一节中，我们将展示这些天体在宿主星系基底光线位置的惊人差异可能不仅源自它们前身星的性质，同时也与其宿主星系的性质有关。

Fig. 3. The locations of the explosions in comparison to the host light. For each object, an arrow indicates the fraction of total host light in pixels fainter than or equal to the light in the pixel at the location of the transient. The cumulative fraction of GRBs or supernovae found at a given fraction of the total light is shown as a histogram. The blue arrows and histogram correspond to the GRBs, and the red arrows and histogram correspond to the supernovae. Were the GRBs and supernovae to track the light identically, their histograms would follow the diagonal line. Whereas the supernova positions do follow the light within the statistical error, the GRBs are far more concentrated on the brightest regions of their hosts. Thus although the probability of a supernova exploding in a particular pixel is roughly proportional to the surface brightness of the galaxy at that pixel, the probability of a GRB at a given location is effectively proportional to a higher power of the local surface brightness.

A Comparison of the Host Populations

An examination of the mosaics of the GRB and supernova hosts (Figs 1 and 2) immediately shows a remarkable contrast—only one GRB host in this set of 42 galaxies is a grand-design spiral, whereas nearly half of the supernova hosts are grand-design spirals. One might wonder if this effect is due to a difference in redshift distribution— the core-collapse supernovae discovered by the GOODS collaboration all lie at redshift $z < 1.2$, whereas LGRBs can be found at much larger redshifts where grand-design spirals are rare to non-existent. Yet if we restrict the GRB population to $z < 1.2$ (and thus produce a population with a nearly identical mean and standard deviation in redshift space compared to the GOODS core-collapse supernovae), the situation remains essentially unchanged: only one out of the eighteen GRB hosts is a grand-design spiral. (For a detailed comparison of GRB hosts to field galaxies, rather than the supernova selected galaxies shown here, see ref. 32.)

Were the difference in spiral fraction the only indication of a difference in the host populations, we could not rule out random chance—given the small number statistics, both populations are barely consistent with each other and a spiral fraction of ~25%. However,

图 3. 爆炸位置和宿主星系光线位置的比较。对于每个天体，箭头代表总宿主光线较暂现位置处光线暗弱或相等的像素的比重。在总光线的给定比例下找到的伽马暴或超新星的累积比重用直方图表示。蓝色箭头和直方图代表伽马暴，红色箭头和直方图代表超新星。如果伽马暴或超新星能同样跟踪光线，那么它们的直方图将沿着对角线分布。超新星位置在统计误差范围的确示踪了光线，而伽马暴的位置则更加集中于宿主星系的极亮区域。因此，尽管超新星在某个像素爆发的概率约正比于在该像素的星系表面亮度，但是在某个位置出现伽马暴的概率实际上正比于能量更高的近域表面亮度。

宿主星族的比较

检查伽马暴和超新星宿主星系的拼接图像（图 1 和图 2）立刻会发现二者的显著差异——在本组 42 个星系中只有一个伽马暴宿主星系是宏大的旋涡结构，而接近一半的超新星宿主星系是宏大旋涡结构。这不禁让人想知道这一效应是否是由于红移分布的不同导致的——GOODS 巡天发现的核坍缩超新星红移全部低于 1.2；长暴可以在更大红移处被发现，但那里却很少甚至没有宏大旋涡星系存在。不过如果我们将伽马暴族限制在 $z < 1.2$（从而产生平均值和标准偏差在红移空间与 GOODS 核坍缩超新星相当的星族），情况基本没有变化：18 个伽马暴宿主星系中只有一个是宏大旋涡星系。（如果相较于此处根据超新星而选择星系进行比较，读者想要获取伽马暴宿主星系和场星系的详细对比，请见文献 32。）

假如旋涡比率的差异是宿主星族的唯一指标，那么我们就不能排除随机因素的影响——因为在小数目统计资料下，星族之间几乎不可能出现彼此一致，旋涡比率约为

the host populations differ strongly in ways other than morphology.

In Fig. 4 we compare the 80% light radius (r_{80}) and absolute magnitude distributions of the GRB and supernova hosts. Included in the comparison are all LGRBs with known redshifts $z < 1.2$ at the time of submission and the 16 core-collapse supernovae of GOODS with spectroscopic or photometric redshifts (see the Supplementary Tables for a complete list of the GRBs, supernovae and associated parameters used in this study). The small minority of GRB hosts in this redshift range without HST imaging are compared only in absolute magnitude and not in size. The absolute magnitudes have been derived from the observed photometry using a cosmology of $\Omega_m = 0.27$, $\Lambda = 0.73$ and $H_0 = 71$ km s^{-1}Mpc^{-1}, and the magnitudes have been corrected for foreground Galactic extinction[33]. For a technical discussion of the determination of the magnitude and size of individual objects, see Supplementary Information.

Fig. 4. A comparison of the absolute magnitude and size distributions of the GRB and supernova hosts. In the main panel, the core-collapse supernova hosts are represented as red squares, and the LGRB hosts as blue circles. The absolute magnitudes of the hosts are shown on the x axis, and the lengths of the semi-major axes of the hosts on the y axis. The plot is then projected onto the two side panels where a histogram is displayed for each host population in each of the dimensions—absolute magnitude and semi-major axis. Shown as blue arrows are the absolute magnitudes of GRB hosts with $z < 1.2$ that have been detected from the ground but have not yet been observed by HST. These hosts are only included in the absolute magnitude histogram. The hosts of GRBs are both smaller and fainter than those of supernovae.

As can be readily seen, the two host populations differ substantially both in their intrinsic magnitudes and sizes. The GRB hosts are fainter and smaller than the supernova hosts. Indeed, KS tests reject the hypothesis that these two populations are drawn from the same population with certainties greater than 98.6% and 99.7% for the magnitude and size distributions, respectively.

25%的情况。不过，不同的宿主星系族除了形态之外，在其他方面也有很大的差异。

图 4 中我们对伽马暴和超新星宿主星系的 80% 光半径 (r_{80}) 和绝对星等分布进行了比较。包含的比较对象皆为截至投稿时间已知的红移 $z < 1.2$ 的长暴和 16 个具有光谱或测光红移 GOODS 的核坍缩超新星（伽马暴、超新星以及本研究相关参数的完整列表参见补充表格）。在此红移范围的小部分没有 HST 成像的伽马暴宿主星系仅比较绝对星等，不比较大小。绝对星等是在宇宙学参数 $\Omega_{M} = 0.27$，$\Lambda = 0.73$ 和 $H_0 = 71\ km \cdot s^{-1} \cdot Mpc^{-1}$ 的条件下，经过银河系前景消光修正后的测光观测数据获得的 [33]。获得单个天体星等和大小的技术讨论见补充资料。

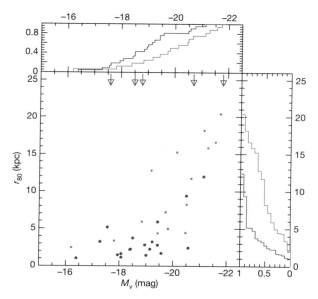

图 4. 伽马暴和超新星宿主星系绝对星等和大小分布的比较。在主图中，核坍缩超新星宿主星系用红色方块表示，长暴宿主星系用蓝色圆圈表示。x 轴表示宿主星系的绝对星等，y 轴表示半长轴的长度。图像投影到面板的两侧得到在每个纬度上——绝对星等和半长轴——各个宿主星系的直方图。蓝色箭头表示的是在地面探测到，但是没有在 HST 观测到的 $z < 1.2$ 伽马暴宿主星系的绝对星等。这些宿主星系只包含在绝对星等直方图中。伽马暴的宿主星系比超新星的更小更暗弱。

如上所示，两个宿主星系星族在本征星等和大小上都存在巨大差异。伽马暴宿主星系比超新星宿主星系更暗弱且更小。事实上，KS 检验分别在星等和大小分布上以高于 98.6% 和 99.7% 的确定度否定了这两类星系是同一种星系的假设。

Discussion

Although the evidence is now overwhelming that both core-collapse supernovae and LGRBs are formed by the collapse of massive stars, our observations show that the distribution of these objects on their hosts, and the nature of the hosts themselves, are substantially different. How then can this be? We propose here that these surprising findings are the result of the dependence of the probability of GRB formation on the state of the chemical evolution of massive stars in a galaxy.

Even before the association of LGRBs with massive stars had been established, a number of theorists had suggested that these objects could be formed by the collapse of massive stars, which would leave behind rapidly spinning black holes. An accretion disk about the black hole would power the GRB jet. These models, sometimes referred to as "hypernovae" or "collapsar" models, implicitly require very massive stars, as only stars greater than about 18 solar masses form black holes. But in fact it was widely suspected that even more massive stars would be required—if only to provide the required large energies, and to limit the numbers of supernovae progressing to GRBs.

We conclude that LGRBs do indeed form from the most massive stars and that this is the reason that they are even more concentrated on the blue light of their hosts than the light itself. The most massive stars (O stars) are frequently found in large associations. These associations can be extremely bright, and can indeed provide the peak of the light of a galaxy—particularly if that galaxy is a faint, blue irregular, as are the GRB hosts in general. Indeed, a connection of LGRBs with O stars (and perhaps Wolf–Rayet stars) is a natural one— given the strong emission lines (including Ne [III]) seen in many of these hosts[12,13] and the evidence for possible strong winds off the progenitors of the GRBs seen in absorption in some LGRB spectra[34,35].

However, O stars are found in galaxies of all sizes. Indeed, studies of the Magellanic clouds suggest that the initial distribution of masses of stars at formation in these dwarf galaxies is essentially identical to that in our much larger spiral, the Milky Way[36]. Therefore, a difference in the initial mass function of stars is unlikely to be responsible for the differences between the hosts. We propose that the fundamental differences between the LGRB and supernova host populations are not their size or luminosity, but rather their metallicity, or chemical evolution. Some evidence of this already exists. The hosts of seven LGRBs (GRBs 980425 (P.M.V., personal communication), 990712[13], 020903[37], 030323[38], 030329[17], 031203[39] and 050730[40]) have measurements of, or limits on, their metallicity, and in all cases the metallicity is less than one-third solar. The small size and low luminosity of the GRB hosts is then a result of the well known correlation between galaxy mass and metallicity (see ref. 41 and references therein).

But why do LGRBs occur in low-metallicity galaxies? This may be a direct result of the evolution of the most massive stars. It has recently been proposed that metal-rich stars

讨　论

尽管现在有决定性的证据表明核坍缩超新星与长暴是由大质量恒星坍缩而成，但是我们的观测显示这两者在宿主星系里的分布与宿主星系本身的性质上明显不同。这又是为什么呢？我们推测这些令人惊讶的发现是由于伽马暴的形成取决于星系中大质量恒星化学演化状态。

在确定长暴和大质量恒星的成协之前，很多理论已经提出这些天体可能是由大质量恒星坍缩形成，并留下一个快速自转的黑洞。黑洞周围的吸积盘将为伽马暴喷流提供能量。这些模型，即被人们称为"极超新星"或"坍缩星"的模型，内含了形成黑洞需要质量非常大的恒星的要求，例如只有大于 18 个太阳质量的恒星才能形成黑洞。但是实际上人们很大程度上猜测需要更大质量的恒星——如果仅仅是为了提供需要的巨大能量，并限制超新星演化到伽马暴的数目。

我们的结论是，长暴确实由最大质量恒星形成，这就是为什么它们在宿主星系的蓝光区比自身光区更集中。最大质量恒星（O 型星）经常在大的星协里被发现。这些星协极其亮，事实上能够提供星系的光线峰值——特别是如果那个星系是一个微弱的蓝色不规则星系，就像一般的伽马暴宿主星系一样。事实上，长暴和 O 型星（也可能沃尔夫－拉叶星）的关联是很自然的——因为在这些宿主星系里，很多都发现了强发射线（包括 Ne[III]）[12,13]，同时有证据显示在某些长暴光谱吸收中发现可能源自伽马暴前身星的强风 [34,35]。

不过，所有大小的星系中都有 O 型星。事实上，对麦哲伦云的研究显示在这些矮星系中恒星形成时的初始质量分布本质上与我们所生活的更大的旋涡星系——银河系——是一样的 [36]。因此，恒星初始质量分布的差异不太可能导致两类宿主星系的差异。我们认为长暴和超新星宿主星系星族的根本差异不在于其大小或者光度，而是金属丰度或者说化学演化。目前已经有一些这方面的证据。具有测量或极限金属丰度的 7 个长暴的宿主星系（伽马暴 980425（弗雷埃斯维克，个人交流），990712[13]，020903[37]，030323[38]，030329[17]，031203[39] 和 050730[40]），它们的金属丰度全都小于太阳水平的 1/3。伽马暴宿主星系的小尺度和低光度则由著名的星系质量和金属丰度相关导致的（见参考文献 41 及其中的文献）。

但是为什么长暴存在于低金属丰度星系？这可能是最大质量恒星演化直接导致的。最近有研究提出具有几十个太阳质量的富金属恒星的表面风很强（光压作用在富

with masses of tens of solar masses have such large winds off their surfaces (due to the photon pressure on their metal-rich atmospheres) that they lose most of their mass before they collapse and produce supernovae[4]. As a result they leave behind neutron stars, not the black holes necessary for LGRB formation. Ironically, stars of 15–30 solar masses may still form black holes, as they do not possess radiation pressure sufficient to drive off their outer envelopes. Direct evidence for this scenario comes from recent work showing that the Galactic soft γ-ray repeater, SGR 1820–06, is in a cluster of extremely young stars of which the most massive have only started to collapse[42]—yet the progenitor of SGR 1820–06 collapsed to a neutron star, not a black hole. Recent observations of winds from very massive (Wolf–Rayet) stars provide further support for this scenario: outflows from the low-metallicity stars in the Large Magellanic Cloud are substantially smaller than those seen from more metal-rich Galactic stars[43]. The possible importance of metallicity in LGRB formation has therefore not escaped the notice of theorists[44,45].

A preference for low metallicity may also explain one of the most puzzling results of GRB host studies. None of the LGRB hosts is a red, sub-millimetre bright galaxy. These highly dust-enshrouded galaxies at redshifts of ~1–3 are believed to be the sites of a large fraction of the star formation in the distant Universe[46]. And although some LGRB hosts do show sub-millimetre emission, none have the red colours characteristic of the majority of this population. However, it is likely that these red dusty galaxies have substantial metallicities at all redshifts. The low metallicity of hosts may also help explain the fact that a substantial fraction of high-redshift LGRB hosts display strong Lyman-α emission[47].

All well-classified supernovae associated with LGRBs are of type Ic, presumably because the presence of a hydrogen envelope about the collapsing core can block the emergence of a GRB jet[24]. Thus only those supernovae whose progenitors have lost some, but not too much, mass appear to be candidates for the formation of a GRB. Given the large numbers of type Ic supernovae in comparison to the estimated numbers of LGRBs, however, it is likely that only a small fraction of type Ic supernovae produce LGRBs. Indeed, even the number of unusually energetic type Ib/Ic supernovae appears to dwarf the LGRB population[48]. Another process, perhaps the spin-up of the progenitor in a binary[27], may decide which type Ic supernovae produce LGRBs. Interestingly, it was the similar distribution of supernovae on their hosts, and particularly the fact that type Ib/Ic were no more correlated than type II with the UV bright regions of their hosts, that led ref. 25 to the conclusion that type Ib/Ic supernovae form from binaries. LGRBs clearly track light differently from the general type Ic population. However, the samples used by refs 25 and 26 were from supernovae largely discovered on nearby massive galaxies—dwarf irregular hosts are underrepresented in these samples. It will be particularly interesting to see whether large unbiased supernova surveys at present underway produce similar locations for their supernovae.

We do not know, however, what separates the small fraction of low-metallicity type Ic supernovae that turn into LGRBs from the rest of the population. Potentially, the answer is the amount of angular momentum available in the core to form the jet. In this case, the

金属大气上导致），在它们坍缩形成超新星之前已经丢失了大部分质量[4]。因此它们留下的是中子星而不是形成长暴所需要的黑洞。具有讽刺意味的是，15～30 倍太阳质量的恒星仍然能形成黑洞，因为它们没有足够的辐射压以驱动它们的外包层。这个图景的直接证据来自最近的研究，研究显示银河系的软伽马射线复现源 SGR1820-06 处于由极年轻恒星组成的星团中，其中最大质量的一批恒星刚刚开始坍缩[42]——不过 SGR1820-06 的前身星已然坍缩成中子星，而不是黑洞。最近对来自超大质量恒星（沃尔夫－拉叶星）星风的观测也进一步支持了这个图景：大麦哲伦云里的低金属度星的外向流比银河系中更为富金属的恒星的外向流明显要小[43]。在长暴形成过程中可能起重要作用的金属丰度因此也没能逃出理论学家的注意[44,45]。

低金属丰度也可能用来解释关于伽马暴宿主星系研究中最困难的一个谜题。长暴宿主星系中没有一个是红的、亚毫米波的亮星系。这些红移约为 1～3 处的被尘埃掩盖的星系被认为是遥远宇宙大部分恒星形成之地[46]。尽管一些长暴宿主星系有亚毫米辐射，但是没有一个具有大部分这类星族的红色特征。不过，很可能这些红色的富尘埃星系在所有红移处都具有充足的金属丰度。宿主星系低金属丰度或许也能帮助解释一部分高红移长暴宿主星系呈现的强莱曼 α 辐射[47]。

所有与长暴成协的，类型确定的超新星都是 Ic 型，这大概是由于坍缩核外的氢包层阻止了伽马暴喷流出现[24]。因此只有那些前身星已经丢失一些质量，但又不是很多的超新星才可能是伽马暴的候选。不过，考虑到 Ic 型超新星数量相比长暴的估计数目大得多，可能只有一小部分 Ic 型超新星会形成长暴。事实上，甚至非正常的富能量 Ib/Ic 型超新星的数目看起来都使长暴族相形见绌[48]。另一个过程，可能是双星前身星的加速[27]，可能决定了哪一种 Ic 型超新星产生长暴。有意思的是，正是超新星在其宿主星系的相似分布，尤其是 Ib/Ic 型超新星和 II 型超新星与其各自宿主星系的 UV 亮区域之间的相关都不紧密，导致文献 25 得出 Ib/Ic 型超新星来自双星的结论。长暴的清晰示踪的光线和一般 Ic 型超新星不同。不过，文献 25 和 26 使用的样本大部分来自附近大质量宿主星系——矮且不规则的星系中发现的超新星，因而是取样不足的。目前正在进行的大型、无偏超新星巡天发现的超新星是否也具有类似的位置将具有非凡的意义。

不过，我们不知道是什么机制把贫金属 Ic 型超新星从星族分离出来变成长暴。答案有可能是核中角动量是否足够大到形成喷流。在此情形下，贫金属的倾向可能表明双星中单星的演化相比双星相互作用在长暴的形成过程中占主导作用。通过研

preference for low metallicity may indicate that single star evolution dominates over binary interaction in forming LGRBs. Deep, high-spectral-resolution studies of LGRB afterglows may provide insight here, by allowing studies of the winds off the progenitor and any binary companion.

Only a small fraction of LGRBs are found in spiral galaxies, even for LGRBs with redshifts $z < 1$ where spirals are much more common. However, the local metallicity in spirals is known to be anti-correlated with distance from the centre of the galaxy. Thus one might expect LGRBs in spirals to violate the trend that we have seen for the general LGRB population, and avoid the bright central regions of their hosts. The present number of LGRBs known in spirals is still too small to test this prediction. But a sample size a few times larger should begin to allow such a test. Additionally, a survey of the metallicity of the hosts of the GOODS supernovae should find a higher average metallicity than that seen in GRB hosts. Finally, if low metallicity is indeed the primary variable in determining whether LGRBs are produced, then as we observe higher redshifts, where metallicities are lower than in most local galaxies, LGRBs should be more uniformly distributed among star-forming galaxies. Indeed, some evidence of this may already be present in the data[32]. LGRBs, however, are potentially visible to redshifts as high as $z \approx 10$. At significant redshifts, where the metallicities of even relatively large galaxies are expected to be low, we may find that LGRBs do become nearly unbiased tracers of star formation.

(**441**, 463–468; 2006)

A. S. Fruchter[1], A. J. Levan[1,2,3], L. Strolger[1,4], P. M. Vreeswijk[5], S. E. Thorsett[6], D. Bersier[1,7], I. Burud[1,8], J. M. Castro Cerón[1,9], A. J. Castro-Tirado[10], C. Conselice[11,12], T. Dahlen[13], H. C. Ferguson[1], J. P. U. Fynbo[9], P. M. Garnavich[14], R. A. Gibbons[1,15], J. Gorosabel[1,10], T. R. Gull[16], J. Hjorth[9], S. T. Holland[17], C. Kouveliotou[18], Z. Levay[1], M. Livio[1], M. R. Metzger[19], P. E. Nugent[20], L. Petro[1], E. Pian[21], J. E. Rhoads[1], A. G. Riess[1], K. C. Sahu[1], A. Smette[5], N. R. Tanvir[3], R. A. M. J. Wijers[22] & S. E. Woosley[6]

[1] Space Telescope Science Institute, 3700 San Martin Drive, Baltimore, Maryland 21218, USA
[2] Department of Physics and Astronomy, University of Leicester, University Road, Leicester, LE1 7RH, UK
[3] Centre for Astrophysics Research, University of Hertfordshire, College Lane, Hatfield, AL10 9AB, UK
[4] Physics & Astronomy, TCCW 246, Western Kentucky University, 1 Big Red Way, Bowling Green, Kentucky 42101, USA
[5] European Southern Observatory, Alonso de Córdova 3107, Casilla 19001, Santiago, Chile
[6] Department of Astronomy & Astrophysics, University of California, 1156 High Street, Santa Cruz, California 95064, USA
[7] Astrophysics Research Institute, Liverpool John Moores University, Twelve Quays House, Egerton Wharf, Birkenhead, CH41 1LD, UK
[8] Norwegian Meteorological Institute, PO Box 43, Blindern, N-0313 Oslo, Norway
[9] Dark Cosmology Centre, Niels Bohr Institute, University of Copenhagen, DK-2100 Copenhagen, Denmark
[10] Instituto de Astrofísica de Andalucía (CSIC), Camino Bajo de Huétor, 50, 18008 Granada, Spain
[11] California Institute of Technology, Mail Code 105-24, Pasadena, California 91125, USA
[12] School of Physics and Astronomy, University of Nottingham, University Park, Nottingham, NG7 2RD, UK
[13] Department of Physics, Stockholm University, SE-106 91 Stockholm, Sweden
[14] Physics Department, University of Notre Dame, 225 Nieuwland Hall, Notre Dame, Indiana 46556, USA
[15] Vanderbilt University, Department of Physics and Astronomy, 6301 Stevenson Center, Nashville, Tennessee 37235, USA
[16] Code 667, Extraterrestial Planets and Stellar Astrophysics, Exploration of the Universe Division, [17] Code 660.1, Goddard Space Flight Center, Greenbelt, Maryland 20771, USA
[18] NASA/Marshall Space Flight Center, VP-62, National Space Science & Technology Center, 320 Sparkman Drive, Huntsville, Alabama 35805, USA

究前身星风和双子星伴星，长暴余辉的深、高光谱分辨率研究可能会为此问题提供一些思路。

　　即便在红移 $z < 1$ 里十分常见的旋涡星系，也只有小部分长暴被发现存在于其中。不过，旋涡星系的局部金属丰度与离星系中心的距离反相关。因此可以预测旋涡星系中的长暴与我们在一般长暴族观测到的趋势不同，它们将回避其宿主星系中心亮区域。目前已知的旋涡星系中的长暴数量还太少，不足以验证这个预测。等样本数量再增大几倍时就可以进行验证。另外，对 GOODS 超新星宿主星系金属丰度巡天发现的平均金属丰度应该超过伽马暴宿主星系的观测值。最后，如果贫金属丰度确实是决定是否形成长暴的主要参数，那么在更高红移处的金属丰度比大部分邻近星系低，应该看到更多的长暴不均匀地分布于正在形成恒星的星系中。确实，这个趋势可能已经在数据中有所展示 [32]。不过，长暴可能在红移 $z \approx 10$ 处都能看到。在显著的红移处，相对较大的星系的金属丰度预期会降低，因而我们可能会发现长暴成为恒星形成的无偏差示踪者。

（肖莉 翻译；徐栋 审稿）

[19] Renaissance Technologies Corporation, 600 Route 25A, East Setauket, New York 11733, USA

[20] Lawrence Berkeley National Laboratory, MS 50F-1650, 1 Cyclotron Road, Berkeley, California 94720, USA

[21] INAF, Osservatorio Astronomico di Trieste, Via G.B. Tiepolo 11, I-34131 Trieste, Italy

[22] Astronomical Institute "Anton Pannekoek", University of Amsterdam, Kruislaan 403, NL-1098 SJ Amsterdam, The Netherlands

Received 22 August 2005; accepted 5 April 2006. Published online 10 May 2006.

References:

1. Riess, A. G. *et al.* Observational evidence from supernovae for an accelerating universe and a cosmological constant. *Astron. J.* **116**, 1009-1038 (1998).

2. Perlmutter, S. *et al.* Measurements of Ω and Λ from 42 high-redshift supernovae. *Astrophys. J.* **517**, 565-586 (1999).

3. Branch, D., Livio, M., Yungelson, L. R., Boffi, F. R. & Baron, E. In search of the progenitors of type IA supernovae. *Publ. Astron. Soc. Pacif.* **107**, 1019-1028 (1995).

4. Heger, A., Fryer, C. L., Woosley, S. E., Langer, N. & Hartmann, D. H. How massive single stars end their life. *Astrophys. J.* **591**, 288-300 (2003).

5. Kouveliotou, C. *et al.* Identification of two classes of gamma-ray bursts. *Astrophys. J.* **413**, 101-104 (1993).

6. Gehrels, N. *et al.* A short γ-ray burst apparently associated with an elliptical galaxy at redshift z = 0.225. *Nature* **437**, 851-854 (2005).

7. Prochaska, J. X. *et al.* The galaxy hosts and large-scale environments of short-hard γ-ray bursts. *Astrophys. J. Lett.* (in the press): preprint at ⟨http://arxiv.org/astro-ph/0510022⟩ (2005).

8. Fruchter, A. S. *et al.* HST and Palomar imaging of GRB 990123: Implications for the nature of gamma-ray bursts and their hosts. *Astrophys. J.* **519**, 13-16 (1999).

9. Sokolov, V. V. *et al.* Host galaxies of gamma-ray bursts: Spectral energy distributions and internal extinction. *Astron. Astrophys.* **372**, 438-455 (2001).

10. Le Floc'h, E. *et al.* Are the hosts of gamma-ray bursts sub-luminous and blue galaxies? *Astron. Astrophys.* **400**, 499-510 (2003).

11. Christensen, L., Hjorth, J. & Gorosabel, J. UV star-formation rates of GRB host galaxies. *Astron. Astrophys.* **425**, 913-926 (2004).

12. Bloom, J. S., Djorgovski, S. G., Kulkarni, S. R. & Frail, D. A. The host galaxy of GRB 970508. *Astrophys. J.* **507**, L25-L28 (1998).

13. Vreeswijk, P. M. *et al.* VLT spectroscopy of GRB 990510 and GRB 990712: Probing the faint and bright ends of the gamma-ray burst host galaxy population. *Astrophys. J.* **546**, 672-680 (2001).

14. Bloom, J. S. *et al.* The unusual afterglow of the γ-ray burst of 26 March 1998 as evidence for a supernova connection. *Nature* **401**, 453-456 (1999).

15. Galama, T. J. *et al.* Evidence for a supernova in reanalyzed optical and near-infrared images of GRB 970228. *Astrophys. J.* **536**, 185-194 (2000).

16. Levan, A. *et al.* GRB 020410: A gamma-ray burst afterglow discovered by its supernova light. *Astrophys. J.* **624**, 880-888 (2005).

17. Hjorth, J. *et al.* A very energetic supernova associated with the γ-ray burst of 29 March 2003. *Nature* **423**, 847-850 (2003).

18. Stanek, K. Z. *et al.* Spectroscopic discovery of the supernova 2003dh associated with GRB 030329. *Astrophys. J.* 591, L17-L20 (2003).

19. Della Valle, M. *et al.* Evidence for supernova signatures in the spectrum of the late-time bump of the optical afterglow of GRB 021211. *Astron. Astrophys.* **406**, L33-L37 (2003).

20. Malesani, D. *et al.* SN 2003lw and GRB 031203: A bright supernova for a faint gamma-ray burst. *Astrophys. J.* **609**, L5-L8 (2004).

21. Zeh, A., Klose, S. & Hartmann, D. H. A systematic analysis of supernova light in gamma-ray burst afterglows. *Astrophys. J.* **609**, 952-961 (2004).

22. Panaitescu, A. & Kumar, P. Fundamental physical parameters of collimated gamma-ray burst afterglows. *Astrophys. J.* **560**, L49-L53 (2001).

23. Frail, D. A. *et al.* Beaming in gamma-ray bursts: Evidence for a standard energy reservoir. *Astrophys. J.* **562**, L55-L58 (2001).

24. MacFadyen, A. I., Woosley, S. E. & Heger, A. Supernovae, jets, and collapsars. *Astrophys. J.* **550**, 410-425 (2001).

25. van Dyk, S. D., Hamuy, M. & Filippenko, A. V. Supernovae and massive star formation regions. *Astron. J.* **111**, 2017-2027 (1996).

26. van den Bergh, S., Li, W. & Filippenko, A. V. Classifications of the host galaxies of supernovae, Set III. *Publ. Astron. Soc. Pacif.* **117**, 773-782 (2005).

27. Podsiadlowski, P., Mazzali, P. A., Nomoto, K., Lazzati, D. & Cappellaro, E. The rates of hypernovae and gamma-ray bursts: Implications for their progenitors. *Astrophys. J.* **607**, L17-L20 (2004).

28. Bloom, J. S., Kulkarni, S. R. & Djorgovski, S. G. The observed offset distribution of gamma-ray bursts from their host galaxies: A robust clue to the nature of the progenitors. *Astron. J.* **123**, 1111-1148 (2002).

29. Riess, A. G. *et al.* Identification of Type Ia supernovae at redshift 1.3 and beyond with the Advanced Camera for Surveys on the Hubble Space Telescope. *Astrophys. J.* **600**, L163-L166 (2004).

30. Strolger, L. G. *et al.* The Hubble Higher z Supernova Search: Supernovae to z~1.6 and constraints on Type Ia progenitor models. *Astrophys. J.* **613**, 200-223 (2004).

31. Giavalisco, M. *et al.* The Great Observatories Origins Deep Survey: Initial results from optical and near-infrared imaging. *Astrophys. J.* **600**, L93-L98 (2004).

32. Conselice, C. J. *et al.* Gamma-ray burst selected high redshift galaxies: Comparison to field galaxy populations to z~ 3. *Astrophys. J.* **633**, 29-40 (2005).

33. Schlegel, D. J., Finkbeiner, D. P. & Davis, M. Maps of dust infrared emission for use in estimation of reddening and cosmic microwave background radiation foregrounds. *Astrophys. J.* **500**, 525-553 (1998).

34. Mirabal, N. *et al.* GRB 021004: A possible shell nebula around a Wolf-Rayet star gamma-ray burst progenitor. *Astrophys. J.* **595**, 935-949 (2003).

35. Klose, S. *et al.* Probing a gamma-ray burst progenitor at a redshift of z = 2: A comprehensive observing campaign of the afterglow of GRB 030226. *Astron. J.* **128**, 1942-1954 (2004).

36. Weidner, C. & Kroupa, P. in *The Initial Mass Function 50 Years Later* (eds Corbelli, E., Plla, F. & Zinnecker, H.) 125-186 (Springer, Dordrecht, 2005).

37. Bersier, D. *et al.* Evidence for a supernova associated with the x-ray flash 020903. *Astrophys. J.* (submitted).

38. Vreeswijk, P. M. *et al.* The host of GRB 030323 at *z* = 3.372: A very high column density DLA system with a low metallicity. *Astron. Astrophys.* **419**, 927-940 (2004).

39. Prochaska, J. X. *et al.* The host galaxy of GRB 031203: Implications of its low metallicity, low redshift, and starburst nature. *Astrophys. J.* **611**, 200-207 (2004).

40. Chen, H.-W., Prochaska, J. X., Bloom, J. S. & Thompson, I. B. Echelle spectroscopy of a GRB afterglow at *z* = 3.969: A new probe of the interstellar and intergalactic media in the young Universe. *Astrophys. J.* **634**, L25-L28 (2005).

41. Kobulnicky, H. A. & Kewley, L. J. Metallicities of galaxies in the GOODS-North Field. *Astrophys. J.* **617**, 240-261 (2004).

42. Figer, D. F., Najarro, F., Geballe, T. R., Blum, R. D. & Kudritzki, R. P. Massive stars in the SGR 1806-20 cluster. *Astrophys. J.* **622**, L49-L52 (2005).

43. Crowther, P. A. & Hadfield, L. J. Reduced Wolf-Rayet line luminosities at low metallicity. *Astron. Astrophys.* **449**, 711-722 (2006).

44. Woosley, S. & Heger, A. The progenitor stars of gamma-ray Bursts. *Astrophys. J.* **637**, 914-921 (2005).

45. Yoon, S.-C. & Langer, N. Evolution of rapidly rotating metal-poor massive stars towards gamma-ray bursts. *Astron. Astrophys.* **443**, 643-648 (2005).

46. Chapman, S. C., Blain, A. W., Smail, I. & Ivison, R. J. A redshift survey of the submillimeter galaxy population. *Astrophys. J.* **622**, 772-796 (2005).

47. Fynbo, J. P. U. *et al.* On the Lyα emission from gamma-ray burst host galaxies: Evidence for low metallicities. *Astron. Astrophys.* **406**, L63-L66 (2003).

48. Soderberg, A. M., Nakar, E., Kulkarni, S. R. & Berger, E. Late-time radio observations of 68 Type Ibc supernovae: Strong constraints on off-axis gamma-ray bursts. *Astrophys. J.* **638**, 930-937 (2006).

49. van den Bergh, S. & Tammann, G. A. Galactic and extragalactic supernova rates. *Annu. Rev. Astron. Astrophys.* **29**, 363-407 (1991).

50. Mannucci, F. *et al.* The supernova rate per unit mass. *Astron. Astrophys.* **433**, 807-814 (2005).

Supplementary Information is linked to the online version of the paper at www.nature.com/nature.

Acknowledgements. Support for this research was provided by NASA through a grant from the Space Telescope Science Institute, which is operated by the Association of Universities for Research in Astronomy, Inc. Observations analysed in this work were taken by the NASA/ESA Hubble Space Telescope under programmes: 7785, 7863, 7966, 8189, 8588, 9074 and 9405 (Principal Investigator, A.S.F.); 7964, 8688, 9180 and 10135 (PI, S. R. Kulkarni); 8640 (PI, S.T.H.). We thank N. Panagia, N. Walborn and A. Soderberg for conversations; A. Filippenko and collaborators for early-time images of GRB 980326; and J. Bloom and collaborators for making public their early observations of GRB 020322.

Author Information. Reprints and permissions information is available at npg.nature.com/reprintsandpermissions. The authors declare no competing financial interests. Correspondence and requests for materials should be addressed to A.S.F. (fruchter@stsci.edu).

The Association of GRB 060218 with a Supernova and the Evolution of the Shock Wave

S. Campana *et al.*

Editor's Note

Although the association between gamma-ray bursts and a rare class of supernovae (exploding stars) is well established, how the jet that characterizes a burst emerges from the exploding star had been unclear. Here Sergio Campana and colleagues report observations of a fairly nearby burst, which they spotted very early and were thus able to study carefully its connection with the associated supernova. They conclude that the properties are best explained by the "break-out" of a shock wave formed when a fast-moving shell of detritus collided with a stellar wind surrounding the supernova's progenitor star. This means that they observed the supernova in the very act of exploding.

Although the link between long γ-ray bursts (GRBs) and supernovae has been established[1-4], hitherto there have been no observations of the beginning of a supernova explosion and its intimate link to a GRB. In particular, we do not know how the jet that defines a γ-ray burst emerges from the star's surface, nor how a GRB progenitor explodes. Here we report observations of the relatively nearby GRB 060218 (ref. 5) and its connection to supernova SN 2006aj (ref. 6). In addition to the classical nonthermal emission, GRB 060218 shows a thermal component in its X-ray spectrum, which cools and shifts into the optical/ultraviolet band as time passes. We interpret these features as arising from the break-out of a shock wave driven by a mildly relativistic shell into the dense wind surrounding the progenitor[7]. We have caught a supernova in the act of exploding, directly observing the shock break-out, which indicates that the GRB progenitor was a Wolf–Rayet star.

GRB 060218 was detected with the Burst Alert Telescope (BAT) instrument[8] onboard the Swift[9] space mission on 18.149 February 2006 Universal Time[5]. The burst profile is unusually long with a T_{90} (the time interval containing 90% of the flux) of $2{,}100 \pm 100$ s (Fig. 1). The flux slowly rose to the peak at 431 ± 60 s (90% containment; times are measured from the BAT trigger time). Swift slewed autonomously to the newly discovered burst. The X-ray Telescope (XRT)[10] found a bright source, which rose smoothly to a peak of ~ 100 counts s^{-1} (0.3–10 keV) at 985 ± 15 s. The X-ray flux then decayed exponentially with an e-folding time of $2{,}100 \pm 50$ s, followed around 10 ks later by a shallower power-law decay similar to that seen in typical GRB afterglows[11,12] (Fig. 2). The UltraViolet/Optical Telescope (UVOT)[13] found emission steadily brightening by a factor of 5–10 after the first detection, peaking in a broad plateau first in the ultraviolet (31.3 ± 1.8 ks at 188 nm) and later in the optical (39.6 ± 2.5 ks at 439 nm) parts of the spectrum. The light curves reached a minimum at about 200 ks, after which the ultraviolet light curves remained constant while

GRB 060218 与一个超新星成协
以及激波的演化

尽管γ射线暴与一类稀有的超新星（即爆炸的恒星）之间的成协已经确立，作为γ射线暴特征的喷流如何从爆炸恒星出现却一直不为人所知。本文作者塞尔希奥·坎帕纳与他的同事报道了他们对一个非常近的γ射线暴的观测。他们很早便开始观察，因而可以细致地研究这一个γ射线暴与成协的超新星之间的联系。他们得出结论，对于所观测到的一系列特征最好的解释是快速运动的爆炸残余物壳层与超新星前身星周围的星风碰撞时形成的激波的"突破"。这意味着他们观测到的超新星正处于爆炸进行之中。

尽管长γ射线暴（GRB）和超新星之间的关联已经被确定[1-4]，迄今尚未观测到超新星爆发的开始时期及其与GRB之间的紧密联系。尤其是，我们不知道刻画γ射线暴的喷流是如何从恒星的表面突现出来的，也不知道GRB的前身星是怎样爆发的。这里我们报道就相对较近的GRB 060218（参考文献5）及其与超新星SN 2006aj（参考文献6）之间的联系的观测。除了典型的非热辐射，GRB 060218 的X射线能谱还显示存在热成分，热成分随着时间推移逐渐变冷并转移到光学/紫外波段。我们将这些特征解释为由轻度相对论性壳层驱动的激波进入前身星周围的致密星风引发的激波暴[7]。我们正好捕捉到一颗超新星处于爆发之中，并直接观测到激波暴。此激波暴表明该GRB的前身星是一颗沃尔夫-拉叶星。

GRB 060218 是于世界时 2006 年 2 月 18.149 日利用载于雨燕[9]天文台上的γ暴预警望远镜（BAT）[8]观测到的[5]。这个γ暴的轮廓不寻常的长，T_{90}（包含 90% 流量的时间区间）为 2,100±100 s（图 1）。流量缓慢上升，在 431±60 s 时达到峰值（包含 90%；时间以 BAT 触发时间为起始）。雨燕自动转动到这个最新发现的γ暴。X射线望远镜（XRT）[10]发现了一颗亮源在平滑上升，并在 985±15 s 时到达峰值，约 100 次计数·s^{-1}（0.3～10 keV）。然后 X 射线流量指数衰减，e 折时间为 2,100±50 s，接下来约 10 ks 后是类似典型 GRB 余辉中看到的那种较缓的幂率衰减[11,12]（图 2）。紫外/光学望远镜（UVOT）[13]发现在第一次探测后辐射稳定变亮为原来的 5～10 倍，在一个宽的平台中达到峰值，首次是出现于频谱的紫外波段（31.3±1.8 ks，位于 188 nm），随后出现于光学波段（39.6±2.5 ks，位于 439 nm）。光变曲线在约 200 ks 时达到最低值，之后紫外波段光变曲线一直稳定，光学波段再次变亮，约在

a rebrightening was seen in the optical bands, peaking again at about 700–800 ks (Fig. 2).

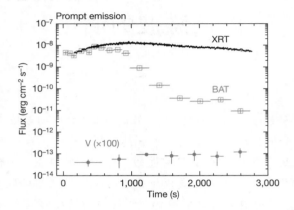

Fig. 1. Early Swift light curve of GRB 060218. GRB 060218 was discovered by the BAT when it came into the BAT field of view during a pre-planned slew. There is no emission at the GRB location up to −3,509 s. Swift slewed again to the burst position and the XRT and UVOT began observing GRB 060218 159 s later. For each BAT point we converted the observed count rate to flux (15–150 keV band) using the observed spectra. The combined BAT and XRT spectra were fitted with a cut-off power law plus a blackbody, absorbed by interstellar matter in our Galaxy and in the host galaxy at redshift $z = 0.033$. The host galaxy column density is $N_H^z = 5.0 \times 10^{21}$ cm^{-2} and that of our Galaxy is $(0.9–1.1) \times 10^{21}$ cm^{-2}. Errors are at 1σ significance. At a redshift $z = 0.033$ (corresponding to a distance of 145 Mpc with $H_0 = 70$ km s^{-1} Mpc^{-1}) the isotropic equivalent energy, extrapolated to the 1–10,000-keV rest-frame energy band, is $E_{iso} = (6.2 \pm 0.3) \times 10^{49}$ erg. The peak energy in the GRB spectrum is at $E_p = 4.9^{+0.4}_{-0.3}$ keV. These values are consistent with the Amati correlation, suggesting that GRB 060218 is not an off-axis event[26]. This conclusion is also supported by the lack of achromatic rise behaviour of the light curve in the three Swift observation bands. The BAT fluence is dominated by soft X-ray photons and this burst can be classified as an X-ray flash[27]. A V-band light curve is shown with red filled circles. For clarity the V flux has been multiplied by a factor of 100. Magnitudes have been converted to fluxes using standard UVOT zero points and multiplying the specific flux by the filter Full Width at Half Maximum (FWHM). Gaps in the light curve are due to the automated periodic change of filters during the first observation of the GRB.

Soon after the Swift discovery, low-resolution spectra of the optical afterglow and host galaxy revealed strong emission lines at a redshift of $z = 0.033$ (ref. 14). Spectroscopic indications of the presence of a rising supernova (designated SN 2006aj) were found three days after the burst[6,15] with broad emission features consistent with a type Ic supernova (owing to a lack of hydrogen and helium lines).

The Swift instruments provided valuable spectral information. The high-energy spectra soften with time and can be fitted with (cut-off) power laws. This power-law component can be ascribed to the usual GRB jet and afterglow. The most striking feature, however, is the presence of a soft component in the X-ray spectrum that is present in the XRT data up to ~10,000 s. The blackbody component shows a marginally decreasing temperature ($kT \approx 0.17$ keV, where k is the Boltzmann constant), and a clear increase in luminosity with time, corresponding to an increase in the apparent emission radius from $R_{BB}^X = (5.2 \pm 0.5) \times 10^{11}$ cm to $R_{BB}^X = (1.2 \pm 0.1) \times 10^{12}$ cm (Fig.3). During the rapid decay ($t \approx 7,000$ s), a blackbody component is still present in the data with a marginally cooler temperature ($kT = 0.10 \pm 0.05$ keV) and a comparable emission radius:

$700 \sim 800$ ks 再次达到峰值 (图 2)。

图 1. GRB 060218 的早期雨燕光变曲线。GRB 060218 是在 BAT 按预设回转时进入 BAT 的视野从而被发现的。直到 γ 暴前 3,509 s，在 GRB 的位置还没有辐射。雨燕重新回转到 γ 暴位置，XRT 和 UVOT 在 γ 暴后 159 s 开始观测 GRB 060218。对 BAT 的每个点，我们通过观测的能谱把观测计数率转化为流量 ($15 \sim 150$ keV 波段)。我们使用一个截断幂率谱加一个黑体谱来拟合 BAT 和 XRT 组合能谱，其中考虑了银河系和红移 $z = 0.033$ 的宿主星系中星际介质的吸收。宿主星系的柱密度为 $N_H = 5.0 \times 10^{21}$ cm^{-2}，而银河系的柱密度为 $(0.9 \sim 1.1) \times 10^{21}$ cm^{-2}。误差为 1σ。在红移 $z = 0.033$ 处 (对应距离 145 Mpc，$H_0 = 70$ km $\cdot$ s^{-1} $\cdot$ Mpc^{-1})，外推到静止参照系 $1 \sim 10,000$ keV 能量区间的各向同性等效能量为 $E_{iso} = (6.2 \pm 0.3) \times 10^{49}$ erg。GRB 能谱的峰值能量为 $E_p = 4.9^{+0.4}_{-0.3}$ keV。这些值和阿马蒂关系一致，表明 GRB 060218 不是一个偏轴的事件 [26]。光变曲线在雨燕的三个观测波段没有出现无色的上升行为也支持了这一观点。BAT 的能流主要由软 X 射线光子主导，所以这一 γ 暴被分类为 X 射线闪变 [27]。V 波段的光变曲线用红色实心圆表示。为了更清晰地呈现，这里将 V 波段的流量乘以因子 100。星等转化成流量的过程中利用了标准 UVOT 零点，并将此流量乘以滤波器的半高全宽 (FWHM)。光变曲线中的间断是由于第一次观测该 GRB 时滤波器的自动周期性改变所造成的。

在雨燕的发现之后不久，光学余辉和宿主星系的低分辨率光谱显示在红移 $z = 0.033$ 处有很强的发射线 (参考文献 14)。GRB 三天后 [6,15] 分光观测显示出现了一颗增亮中的超新星 (命名为 SN 2006aj)，宽线辐射特征表明其为 Ic 型超新星 (由于缺乏氢线和氦线)。

雨燕搭载的设备提供了丰富的光谱信息。高能光谱随着时间软化，并可以用 (截断的) 幂率谱进行拟合。这个幂率谱成分通常来自 GRB 的喷流和余辉。不过最显著的特征是，在 XRT 数据中 X 射线谱存在直到约 10,000 s 的软成分。黑体成分呈现温度微弱的降低 ($kT \approx 0.17$ keV，此处 k 为玻尔兹曼常数)，而光度随时间显著地增大，这对应于视辐射半径从 $R^X_{BB} = (5.2 \pm 0.5) \times 10^{11}$ cm 增大到 $R^X_{BB} = (1.2 \pm 0.1) \times 10^{12}$ cm (图 3)。在快速衰减的过程中 ($t \approx 7,000$ s) 中，黑体成分在数据中依然存在，具有一个稍微冷一点的温度 ($kT = 0.10 \pm 0.05$ keV) 和一个大小相当的辐射半径 $R^X_{BB} =$

Fig. 2. Long-term Swift light curve of GRB 060218. **a**, The XRT light curve (0.3–10 keV) is shown with open black circles. Count-rate-to-flux conversion factors were derived from time-dependent spectral analysis. We also plotted (filled grey circles) the contribution to the 0.3–10-keV flux by the blackbody component. Its percentage contribution is increasing with time, becoming dominant at the end of the exponential decay. The X-ray light curve has a long, slow power-law rise followed by an exponential (or steep power-law) decay. At about 10,000 s the light curve breaks to a shallower power-law decay (dashed red line) with an index of -1.2 ± 0.1, characteristic of typical GRB afterglows. This classical afterglow can be naturally accounted for by a shock driven into the wind by a shell with kinetic energy $E_{shell} \approx 10^{49}$ erg. The t^{-1} flux decline is valid at the stage where the shell is being decelerated by the wind with the deceleration phase beginning at $t_{dec} \lesssim 10^4$ s for $\dot{M} \gtrsim 10^{-4}(v_{wind}/10^8)M_\odot\,\mathrm{yr}^{-1}$ (where v_{wind} is in units of cm s^{-1}), consistent with the mass-loss rate inferred from the thermal X-ray component. Error bars are 1σ. **b**, The UVOT light curve. Filled circles of different colours represent different UVOT filters: red, V (centred at 544 nm); green, B (439 nm); dark blue, U (345 nm); light blue, UVW1 (251 nm); magenta, UVM1 (217 nm); and yellow, UVW2 (188 nm). Specific fluxes have been multiplied by their FWHM widths (75, 98, 88, 70, 51 and 76 nm, respectively). Data have been rebinned to increase the signal-to-noise ratio. The ultraviolet band light curve peaks at about 30 ks owing to the shock break-out from the outer stellar surface and the surrounding dense stellar wind, while the optical band peaks at about 800 ks owing to radioactive heating in the supernova ejecta.

$R_{BB}^{X} = (6.5^{+14}_{-4.4}) \times 10^{11}$ cm. In the optical/ultraviolet band at 9 hours (32 ks) the blackbody peak is still above the UVOT energy range. At 120 ks the peak of the blackbody emission is within the UVOT passband, and the inferred temperature and radius are $kT = 37^{+1.9}_{-0.9}$ eV and $R_{BB}^{UV} = 3.29^{+0.94}_{-0.93} \times 10^{14}$ cm, implying an expansion speed of $(2.7 \pm 0.8) \times 10^9$ cm s^{-1}. This estimate is consistent with what we would expect for a supernova and it is also consistent with the line broadening observed in the optical spectra.

The thermal components are the key to interpreting this anomalous GRB. The high temperature (two million degrees) of the thermal X-ray component suggests that the radiation is emitted by a shock-heated plasma. The characteristic radius of the emitting region, $R_{shell} \approx (E/aT^4)^{1/3} \approx 5 \times 10^{12}$ cm (E is the GRB isotropic energy and a is the radiation density constant), corresponds to the radius of a blue supergiant progenitor. However, the

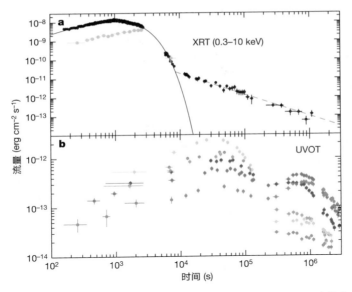

图 2. GRB 060218 的长期雨燕光变曲线。**a**，黑色空心圆代表 XRT(0.3 ~ 10 keV) 的光变曲线。计数率-流量转化因子来自依赖于时间的谱分析。我们也绘制了黑体成分对 0.3 ~ 10 keV 流量的贡献（灰色实心圆）。黑体成分的百分比随着时间而增大，在指数衰减的末期成为主导。X 射线光变曲线具有长而缓慢的幂率上升，然后指数（或以陡的幂率形式）衰减。在约 10,000 s 光变曲线偏折为较浅的幂率衰减（红色虚线），指数为 -1.2 ± 0.1，具有典型的 GRB 余辉的特征。这个典型余辉可以很自然地用被壳层驱动进入星风的激波来描述，壳层动能为 $E_{shell} \approx 10^{49}$ erg。壳层被星风减速，减速相开始于 $t_{dec} \lesssim 10^4$ s，此时 $\dot{M} \gtrsim 10^{-4}(v_{wind}/10^8)M_\odot \cdot yr^{-1}$（这里 v_{wind} 以 cm·s^{-1} 为单位），流量下降符合 t^{-1}。这与从热 X 射线成分推导出的质量损失率一致。误差棒为 1σ。**b**，UVOT 光变曲线。不同颜色的实心圈代表不同的 UVOT 滤光片：红色，V（中心位于 544 nm）；绿色，B（439 nm）；深蓝色，U（345 nm）；浅蓝色，UVW1（251 nm）；品红，UVW1（217 nm）；黄色，UVW2（188 nm）。具体的流量已经乘以了各自的半高全宽（分别为 75 nm，98 nm，88 nm，70 nm，51 nm 和 76 nm）。数据被重新分组以增加信噪比。紫外波段的光变曲线的峰值大约在 30 ks 处，这是由于激波需要从恒星外表面和周围致密星风物质突破出来。然而光学波段的峰值大约在 800 ks 处，源自超新星喷出物中的放射性加热。

$(6.5^{+14}_{-4.4}) \times 10^{11}$ cm。在光学/紫外波段黑体的峰在 9 小时（32 ks）时仍然高于 UVOT 的能量范围。在 120 ks 时黑体的峰落入 UVOT 能量范围内，估计的温度和半径分别为 $kT = 3.7^{+1.9}_{-0.9}$ eV 和 $R^X_{BB} = (3.29^{+0.94}_{-0.93}) \times 10^{14}$ cm，这表明膨胀速度为 $(2.7 \pm 0.8) \times 10^9$ cm·s^{-1}。这一估计与我们对超新星的预期一致，也与光谱中观测到的谱线展宽一致。

　　热成分是解释这一反常 GRB 的关键。X 射线热成分的较高温度（两百万度）表明辐射是由激波加热的等离子体发出。辐射区的特征半径为 $R_{shell} \approx (E/aT^4)^{1/3} \approx 5 \times 10^{12}$ cm（E 是 GRB 各向同性的能量，a 是辐射密度常数），对应于前身星为蓝巨星的半径。不过，超新星光谱缺少氢线表明它是一个更致密的源。大的辐射半径

lack of hydrogen lines in the supernova spectrum suggests a much more compact source. The large emission radius may be explained in this case by the existence of a massive stellar wind surrounding the progenitor, as is common for Wolf–Rayet stars. The thermal radiation is observed once the shock driven into the wind reaches a radius, $\sim R_{\text{shell}}$, where the wind becomes optically thin.

The characteristic variability time is $R_{\text{shell}}/c \approx 200$ s, consistent with the smoothness of the X-ray pulse and the rapid thermal X-ray flux decrease at the end of the pulse. We interpret this as providing, for the first time, a direct measurement of the shock break-out[16,17] of the stellar envelope and the stellar wind (first investigated by Colgate[18]). The fact that R_{shell} is larger than R_{BB}^{X} suggests that the shock expands in a non-spherical manner, reaching different points on the R_{shell} sphere at different times. This may be due to a non-spherical explosion (such as the presence of a jet), or a non-spherical wind[19,20]. In addition, the shock break-out interpretation provides us with a delay between the supernova explosion and the GRB start of $\lesssim 4$ ks (ref. 21; see Fig. 1).

As the shock propagates into the wind, it compresses the wind plasma into a thin shell. The mass of this shell may be inferred from the requirement that its optical depth be close to unity, $M_{\text{shell}} \approx 4\pi R_{\text{shell}}^2/\kappa \approx 5 \times 10^{-7} M_\odot$ ($\kappa \approx 0.34$ cm^2 g^{-1} is the opacity). This implies that the wind mass-loss rate is $\dot{M} \approx M_{\text{shell}} v_{\text{wind}}/R_{\text{shell}} \approx 3 \times 10^{-4} M_\odot$ yr^{-1}, for a wind velocity $v_{\text{wind}} = 10^8$ cm s^{-1}, typical for Wolf–Rayet stars. Because the thermal energy density behind a radiation-dominated shock is $aT^4 \approx 3\rho v_s^2$ (ρ is the wind density at R_{shell} and v_s the shock velocity) we have $\rho \approx 10^{-12}$ g cm^{-3}, which implies that the shock must be (mildly) relativistic, $v_s \simeq c$. This is similar to GRB 980425/SN 1998bw, where the ejection of a mildly relativistic shell with energy of $\simeq 5 \times 10^{49}$ erg is believed to have powered radio[22-24] and X-ray emission[7].

The optical–ultraviolet emission observed at an early time of $t \lesssim 10^4$ s may be accounted for as the low-energy tail of the thermal X-ray emission produced by the (radiation) shock driven into the wind. At a later time, the optical–ultraviolet emission is well above that expected from the (collisionless) shock driven into the wind. This emission is most probably due to the expanding envelope of the star, which was heated by the shock passage to a much higher temperature. Initially, this envelope is hidden by the wind. As the star and wind expand, the photosphere propagates inward, revealing shocked stellar plasma. As the star expands, the radiation temperature decreases and the apparent radius increases (Fig. 3). The radius inferred at the peak of the ultraviolet emission, $R_{\text{BB}}^{\text{UV}} \approx 3 \times 10^{14}$ cm, implies that emission is arising from the outer $\sim 4\pi (R_{\text{BB}}^{\text{UV}})^2/\kappa \approx 10^{-3} M_\odot$ shell at the edge of the shocked star. As the photosphere rapidly cools, this component of the emission fades. The ultraviolet light continues to plummet as cooler temperatures allow elements to recombine and line blanketing to set in, while radioactive decay causes the optical light to begin rising to the primary maximum normally seen in supernova light curves (Fig. 2).

可以用存在于前身星周围的大质量星风来解释，这对于沃尔夫–拉叶星来说很常见。一旦被驱动进入星风的激波到达半径 $\sim R_{shell}$，在此星风变得光薄，热辐射便会被观测到。

特征的变化时标为 $R_{shell}/c \approx 200$ s，这与平滑的 X 射线脉冲以及在脉冲末端热 X 射线流量的快速减少一致。我们对此的解释是，这是首次直接观测到激波从恒星包层和星风中突破出来的激波暴 [16,17]（科尔盖特 [18] 曾首次进行过研究）。R_{shell} 比 R_{BB}^{X} 大的事实表明激波以非球形的方式膨胀，在不同的时间到达 R_{shell} 球上的不同点。这可能是由非球形的爆炸（例如存在喷流）或者非球形的星风 [19,20] 引起。另外，激波暴的解释为我们提供了超新星爆炸和 GRB 开始之间延迟时间的限制，为 $\lesssim 4$ ks。

激波传播到星风后压缩星风等离子体成为一个薄壳层。这个壳层的质量可以从光深满足接近于 1 这一条件推出，$M_{shell} \approx 4\pi R_{shell}^2/\kappa \approx 5 \times 10^{-7} M_{\odot}$（$\kappa \approx 0.34$ cm$^2 \cdot$ g^{-1} 是不透明度）。这表明对星风速度为 $v_{wind} = 10^8$ cm $\cdot$ s^{-1} 的典型沃尔夫–拉叶星而言，星风质量损失为 $\dot{M} \approx M_{shell} v_{wind}/R_{shell} \approx 3 \times 10^{-4} M_{\odot}$ yr^{-1}。因为在辐射主导的激波之后的热能量密度为 $aT^4 \approx 3\rho v_s^2$（ρ 为 R_{shell} 处的星风密度，v_s 为激波速度），我们得到 $\rho \approx 10^{-12}$ g $\cdot$ cm^{-3}，这意味着激波必须是（轻度）相对论性的，$v_s \simeq c$。这与 GRB 980425/SN 1998bw 类似，我们相信其中是一个能量为 $\simeq 5 \times 10^{45}$ erg 的轻度相对论性壳层驱动了射电 [22-24] 和 X 射线辐射 [7]。

早期 $t \lesssim 10^4$ s 时观测到的光学–紫外辐射可能是来自（辐射）激波进入星风产生的热 X 射线辐射的低能尾巴。之后，光学–紫外的辐射明显亮于对星风中的（无碰撞）激波的预期。这个辐射最有可能来自膨胀的恒星包层，恒星星包由于激波经过而加热到一个大大增高的温度。起初，这个包层隐埋在星风里。当恒星和星风膨胀，光球层向内传播，逐渐显示出激波加速后的恒星等离子体物质。当恒星膨胀时，辐射温度降低，视半径增大（图 3）。紫外辐射达到峰值时推算出的半径 $R_{BB}^{UV} \approx 3 \times 10^{14}$ cm，这表明辐射来自经激波扫过的恒星外层约 $4\pi(R_{BB}^{UV})^2/\kappa \approx 10^{-3} M_{\odot}$ 的壳层。当光球快速冷却时，辐射的这一成分衰退。温度降低导致元素发生重合，并开始出现谱线覆盖，因而紫外光继续急速下降。然而放射性衰变而导致可见光开始上升，并达到通常在超新星光变曲线中常见到的主极大值（图 2）。

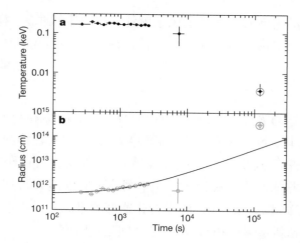

Fig. 3. Evolution of the soft thermal component temperature and radius. **a**, Evolution of the temperature of the soft thermal component. The joint BAT and XRT spectrum has been fitted with a blackbody component plus a (cut-off) power-law in the first ~3,000 s (see also the legend of Fig. 1). The last point (circled in green) comes from a fit to the six UVOT filters, assuming a blackbody model with Galactic reddening, $E(B-V) = 0.14$, and host galaxy reddening. This reddening has been determined by fitting the Rayleigh–Jeans tail of the blackbody emission at 32 ks (9 hours). The data require an intrinsic $E(B-V) = 0.20 \pm 0.03$ (assuming a Small Magellanic Cloud reddening law[28]). Error bars are 1σ. **b**, Evolution of the radius of the soft thermal component. The last point (circled in green) comes from the fitting of UVOT data. The continuous line represents a linear fit to the data.

Because the wind shell is clearly larger than the progenitor radius, we infer that the star radius is definitely smaller than 5×10^{12} cm. Assuming a linear expansion at the beginning (owing to light travel-time effects) we can estimate a star radius of $R_{star} \approx (4 \pm 1) \times 10^{11}$ cm. This is smaller than the radius of the progenitors of type II supernovae, like blue supergiants (4×10^{12} cm for SN 1987A, ref. 25) or red supergiants (3×10^{13} cm). Our results unambiguously indicate that the progenitor of GRB 060218/SN 2006aj was a compact massive star, most probably a Wolf–Rayet star.

(**442**, 1008-1010; 2006)

S. Campana[1], V. Mangano[2], A. J. Blustin[3], P. Brown[4], D. N. Burrows[4], G. Chincarini[1,5], J. R. Cummings[6,7], G. Cusumano[2], M. Della Valle[8,9], D. Malesani[10], P. Mészáros[4,11], J. A. Nousek[4], M. Page[3], T. Sakamoto[6,7], E. Waxman[12], B. Zhang[13], Z. G. Dai[13,14], N. Gehrels[6], S. Immler[6], F. E. Marshall[6], K. O. Mason[15], A. Moretti[1], P. T. O'Brien[16], J. P. Osborne[16], K. L. Page[16], P. Romano[1], P. W. A. Roming[4], G. Tagliaferri[1], L. R. Cominsky[17], P. Giommi[18], O. Godet[16], J. A. Kennea[4], H. Krimm[6,19], L. Angelini[6], S. D. Barthelmy[6], P. T. Boyd[6], D. M. Palmer[20], A. A. Wells[16] & N. E. White[6]

[1] INAF—Osservatorio Astronomico di Brera, via E. Bianchi 46, I-23807 Merate (LC), Italy
[2] INAF—Istituto di Astrofisica Spaziale e Fisica Cosmica di Palermo, via U. La Malfa 153, I-90146 Palermo, Italy
[3] UCL Mullard Space Science Laboratory, Holmbury St. Mary, Dorking, Surrey RH5 6NT, UK
[4] Department of Astronomy and Astrophysics, Pennsylvania State University, University Park, Pennsylvania 16802, USA
[5] Università degli studi di Milano Bicocca, piazza delle Scienze 3, I-20126 Milano, Italy
[6] NASA—Goddard Space Flight Center, Greenbelt, Maryland 20771, USA
[7] National Research Council, 2101 Constitution Avenue NW, Washington DC 20418, USA
[8] INAF—Osservatorio Astrofisico di Arcetri, largo E. Fermi 5, I-50125 Firenze, Italy
[9] Kavli Institute for Theoretical Physics, UC Santa Barbara, California 93106, USA

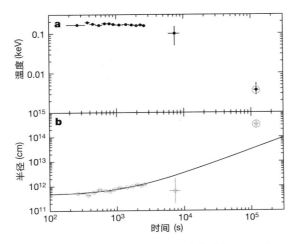

图 3. 软的热成分的温度和半径的演化。**a**，软的热成分温度的演化。BAT 和 XRT 的联合能谱在前约 3,000 s 用一个黑体成分加一个（截断的）幂率来拟合（见图 1 图注）。最后的点（绿色圆圈内）来自考虑了黑体模型在银河系红化 $E(B-V) = 0.14$ 和宿主星系红化后对 UVOT 的 6 个滤光片的拟合。红化值的确定来自对在 32 ks（9 小时）黑体辐射的瑞利–金斯尾的拟合。数据要求本征红化 $E(B-V) = 0.20 \pm 0.03$（假设为小麦哲伦云的红外定律[28]）。误差棒为 1σ。**b**，软的热成分的半径的演化。最后的点（绿色圆圈内）来自对 UVOT 数据的拟合。连续线代表对数据的线性拟合。

因为星风壳层明显比前身星半径大，我们推断恒星半径必然小于 5×10^{12} cm。假设起初星体是线性膨胀的，（由光行时间效应）我们估计恒星半径为 $R_{star} \approx (4 \pm 1) \times 10^{11}$ cm。这比 II 型超新星的前身星半径，比如蓝巨星（对 SN 1987A 而言是 4×10^{12} cm，参考文献 25）或红巨星（3×10^{13} cm）要小。我们的结果毫无疑问地证明了 GRB 060218/SN 2006aj 的前身星为致密的大质量恒星，而且最可能是沃尔夫–拉叶星。

（肖莉 翻译；黎卓 审稿）

[10] International School for Advanced Studies (SISSA-ISAS), via Beirut 2-4, I-34014 Trieste, Italy

[11] Department of Physics, Pennsylvania State University, University Park, Pennsylvania 16802, USA

[12] Physics Faculty, Weizmann Institute, Rehovot 76100, Israel

[13] Department of Physics, University of Nevada, Box 454002, Las Vegas, Nevada 89154-4002, USA

[14] Department of Astronomy, Nanjing University, Nanjing, 210093, China

[15] PPARC, Polaris House, North Star Avenue, Swindon SN2 1SZ, UK

[16] Department of Physics and Astronomy, University of Leicester, University Road, Leicester LE1 7RH, UK

[17] Department of Physics and Astronomy, Sonoma State University, Rohnert Park, California 94928-3609, USA

[18] ASI Science Data Center, via G. Galilei, I-00044 Frascati (Roma), Italy

[19] Universities Space Research Association, 10211 Wincopin Circle Suite 500, Columbia, Maryland 21044-3431, USA

[20] Los Alamos National Laboratory, PO Box 1663, Los Alamos, New Mexico 87545, USA

Received 13 March; accepted 10 May 2005.

References:

1. Woosley, S. E. Gamma-ray bursts from stellar mass accretion disks around black holes. *Astrophys. J.* **405**, 273-277 (1993).

2. Paczyński, B. Are gamma-ray bursts in star-forming regions? *Astrophys. J.* **494**, L45-L48 (1993).

3. MacFadyen, A. I. & Woosley, S. E. Collapsars: gamma-ray bursts and explosions in "failed supernovae". *Astrophys. J.* **524**, 262-289 (1999).

4. Galama, T. J. *et al.* An unusual supernova in the error box of the γ-ray burst of 25 April 1998. *Nature* **395**, 670-672 (1998).

5. Cusumano, G. *et al.* GRB060218: Swift-BAT detection of a possible burst. *GCN Circ.* 4775 (2006).

6. Masetti, N. *et al.* GRB060218: VLT spectroscopy. *GCN Circ.* 4803 (2006).

7. Waxman, E. Does the detection of X-ray emission from SN1998bw support its association with GRB980425? *Astrophys. J.* **605**, L97-L100 (2004).

8. Barthelmy, S. D. *et al.* The Burst Alert Telescope (BAT) on the SWIFT Midex Mission. *Space Sci. Rev.* **120**, 143-164 (2005).

9. Gehrels, N. *et al.* The Swift gamma ray burst mission. *Astrophys. J.* **611**, 1005-1020 (2004).

10. Burrows, D. N. *et al.* The Swift X-Ray Telescope. *Space Sci. Rev.* **120**, 165-195 (2005).

11. Tagliaferri, G. *et al.* An unexpectedly rapid decline in the X-ray afterglow emission of long γ-ray bursts. *Nature* **436**, 985-988 (2005).

12. O'Brien, P. T. *et al.* The early X-ray emission from GRBs. *Astrophys. J.* (submitted); preprint at ⟨http://arXiv.org/astro-ph/0601125l⟩ (2006).

13. Roming, P. W. A. *et al.* The Swift Ultra-Violet/Optical Telescope. *Space Sci. Rev.* **120**, 95-142 (2005).

14. Mirabal, N. & Halpern, J. P. GRB060218: MDM Redshift. *GCN Circ.* 4792 (2006).

15. Pian, E. *et al.* An optical supernova associated with the X-ray flash XRF 060218. *Nature* doi:10.1038/nature05082 (this issue).

16. Ensman, L. & Burrows, A. Shock breakout in SN1987A. *Astrophys. J.* **393**, 742-755 (1992).

17. Tan, J. C., Matzner, C. D. & McKee, C. F. Trans-relativistic blast waves in supernovae as gamma-ray burst progenitors. *Astrophys. J.* **551**, 946-972 (2001).

18. Colgate, S. A. Prompt gamma rays and X-rays from supernovae. *Can. J. Phys.* **46**, 476 (1968).

19. Mazzali, P. A. *et al.* An asymmetric, energetic type Ic supernova viewed off-axis and a link to gamma-ray bursts. *Science* **308**, 1284-1287 (2005).

20. Leonard, D. C. *et al.* A non-spherical core in the explosion of supernova SN2004dj. *Nature* **440**, 505-507 (2006).

21. Norris, J. P. & Bonnell, J. T. How can the SN-GRB time delay be measured? *AIP Conf. Proc.* **727**, 412-415 (2004).

22. Kulkarni, S. R. *et al.* Radio emission from the unusual supernova 1998bw and its association with the gamma-ray burst of 25 April 1998. *Nature* **395**, 663-669 (1998).

23. Waxman, E. & Loeb, A. A subrelativistic shock model for the radio emission of SN1998bw. *Astrophys. J.* **515**, 721-725 (1999).

24. Li, Z.-Y. & Chevalier, R. A. Radio supernova SN1998bw and its relation to GRB980425. *Astrophys. J.* **526**, 716-726 (1999).

25. Arnett, W. D. *et al.* Supernova 1987A. *Annu. Rev. Astron. Astrophys.* **27**, 629-700 (1989).

26. Amati, L. *et al.* GRB060218: $E_{p,i}$-E_{iso} correlation. *GCN Circ.* 4846 (2006).

27. Heise, J., *et al.* in *Proceedings of "Gamma-Ray Bursts in the Afterglow Era"* (eds Costa, E., Frontera, F. & Hjorth, J.) 16-21 (Springer, Berlin/Heidelberg, 2001).

28. Pei, Y. C. Interstellar dust from the Milky Way to the Magellanic Clouds. *Astrophys. J.* **395**, 130-139 (1992).

Acknowledgements. We acknowledge support from ASI, NASA and PPARC.

Author Information. Reprints and permissions information is available at www.nature.com/reprints. The authors declare no competing financial interests.

Correspondence and requests for materials should be addressed to S.C. (sergio.campana@brera.inaf.it).

904

Analysis of One Million Base Pairs of Neanderthal DNA

R. E. Green *et al.*

Editor's Note

Neanderthals were the closest relatives of modern humans. They lived in Europe and Western Asia about 400,000–24,000 years ago. As modern humans were present in Europe at least 41,000 years ago, there is much speculation about whether Neanderthals and modern humans interbred. The only way to decide this is from genome analysis. In this paper Svante Pääbo and colleagues describe the sequencing of a million base pairs of Neanderthal nuclear DNA from a bone from Croatia. The full genome sequence took a further four years to complete, and the analysis of this and other Neanderthal genomes suggests that around 4% of the DNA of modern Europeans is of Neanderthal origin.

Neanderthals are the extinct hominid group most closely related to contemporary humans, so their genome offers a unique opportunity to identify genetic changes specific to anatomically fully modern humans. We have identified a 38,000-year-old Neanderthal fossil that is exceptionally free of contamination from modern human DNA. Direct high-throughput sequencing of a DNA extract from this fossil has thus far yielded over one million base pairs of hominoid nuclear DNA sequences. Comparison with the human and chimpanzee genomes reveals that modern human and Neanderthal DNA sequences diverged on average about 500,000 years ago. Existing technology and fossil resources are now sufficient to initiate a Neanderthal genome-sequencing effort.

NEANDERTHALS were first recognized as a distinct group of hominids from fossil remains discovered 150 years ago at Feldhofer in Neander Valley, outside Düsseldorf, Germany. Subsequent Neanderthal finds in Europe and western Asia showed that fossils with Neanderthal traits appear in the fossil record of Europe and western Asia about 400,000 years ago and vanish about 30,000 years ago. Over this period they evolved morphological traits that made them progressively more distinct from the ancestors of modern humans that were evolving in Africa[1,2]. For example, the crania of late Neanderthals have protruding mid-faces, brain cases that bulge outward at the sides, and features of the base of the skull, jaw and inner ears that set them apart from modern humans[3].

The nature of the interaction between Neanderthals and modern humans, who expanded out of Africa around 40,000–50,000 years ago and eventually replaced Neanderthals

对尼安德特人 DNA 的一百万
碱基对的分析

格林等

编者按

尼安德特人是现代人类最近的亲戚。它们大约在 400,000 到 24,000 年前生活在欧洲和西亚。由于现代人类至少在 41,000 年前出现在欧洲，人们对尼安德特人和现代人类是否杂交有很多猜测。确定这一点的唯一方法是从基因组进行分析。在本文中，斯凡特·帕波及其同事描述了来自克罗地亚骨骼的尼安德特人核 DNA 的一百万个碱性对的测序。完整的基因组序列又用了四年时间才完成。对这个基因组序列和其他尼安德特人基因组的分析表明，现代欧洲人中约有 4% 的 DNA 来自尼安德特人。

尼安德特人是与当代人类亲缘关系最近的已经灭绝的人类类群，所以他们的基因组能为我们提供一个独特的机遇来了解解剖学意义上完全的现代人所特有的遗传变化。我们已经甄别选定了一件罕见不受现代人 DNA 污染的有着 38,000 年历史的尼安德特人化石。对该化石提取出的 DNA 进行的直接高通量测序，目前已经得到了 100 多万碱基对的类人猿核 DNA 序列。该序列与人和黑猩猩的基因组对比表明，现代人和尼安德特人的 DNA 序列平均大约在 500,000 年前发生分歧。现有的技术和化石资源足以支撑着手开展尼安德特人基因组测序工作。

基于 150 年前发现于德国杜塞尔多夫外的尼安德谷费尔德霍费尔山洞的化石遗存，尼安德特人最初被认为是一个独特的人类类群。后来欧洲和西亚的尼安德特人的发现显示具有尼安德特人特征的化石在欧洲和西亚的化石记录中出现于约 400,000 年前，消失于约 30,000 年前。在这期间，他们进化出了与当时正在非洲进化的现代人祖先渐行渐远的形态特征 [1,2]。例如，晚期尼安德特人的头骨有着突出的中面部，两侧向外突出的脑颅以及将他们与现代人区别开来的颅底、颌骨和内耳特征 [3]。

现代人大约于 40,000 到 50,000 年前走出非洲，并最终取代了尼安德特人和其他生活在旧大陆的古老型人类。这些现代人与尼安德特人间相互交流的本质至今仍是

as well as other archaic hominids across the Old World is still a matter of some debate. Although there is no evidence of contemporaneous cohabitation at any single site, there is evidence of geographical and temporal overlap in their ranges before the disappearance of Neanderthals. Additionally, late in their history, some Neanderthal groups adopted cultural traits such as body decorations, potentially through cultural interactions with incoming modern humans[4].

In 1997, a segment of the hypervariable control region of the maternally inherited mitochondrial DNA (mtDNA) of the Neanderthal type specimen found at Feldhofer was sequenced. Phylogenetic analysis showed that it falls outside the variation of contemporary humans and shares a common ancestor with mtDNAs of present-day humans approximately half a million years ago[5,6]. Subsequently, mtDNA sequences have been retrieved from eleven additional Neanderthal specimens: Feldhofer 2 in Germany[7], Mezmaiskaya in Russia[8], Vindija 75, 77 and 80 in Croatia[9,10], Engis 2 in Belgium, La Chapelle-aux-Saints and Rochers de Villeneuve in France[10], Scladina in Belgium[11], Monte Lessini in Italy[12], and El Sidron 441 in Spain[13]. Although some of these sequences are extremely short, they are all more closely related to one another than to modern human mtDNAs[9,11].

This fact, in conjunction with the absence of any related mtDNA sequences in currently living humans or in a small number of early modern human fossils[5,10] strongly suggests that Neanderthals contributed no mtDNA to present-day humans. On the basis of various population models, it has been estimated that a maximal overall genetic contribution of Neanderthals to the contemporary human gene pool is between 25% and 0.1% (refs 10, 14). Because the latter conclusions are based on mtDNA, a single maternally inherited locus, they are limited in their ability to detect a Neanderthal contribution to the current human gene pool both by the vagaries of genetic drift and by the possibility of a sex bias in reproduction. However, both morphological evidence[4,15] and the variation in the modern human gene pool[16] support the conclusion that if any genetic contribution of Neanderthals to modern human occurred, it was of limited magnitude.

Neanderthals are the hominid group most closely related to currently living humans, so a Neanderthal nuclear genome sequence would be an invaluable resource for annotating the human genome. Roughly 35 million nucleotide differences exist between the genomes of humans and chimpanzees, our closest living relatives[17]. Soon, genome sequences from other primates such as the orang-utan and the macaque will allow such differences to be assigned to the human and chimpanzee lineages. However, temporal resolution of the genetic changes along the human lineage, where remarkable morphological, behavioural and cognitive changes occurred, are limited without a more closely related genome sequence for comparison. In particular, comparison to the Neanderthal would enable the identification of genetic changes that occurred during the last few hundred thousand years, when fully anatomically and behaviourally modern humans appeared.

一个存在争议的问题。尽管没有证据显示他们在任何一个地点同时生存过，但是有证据表明在尼安德特人消失之前，他们彼此存在地理和时代分布的交叠。此外，在他们的历史的晚期，有些尼安德特人群体接纳了身体装饰等文化特征，可能是他们通过与迁徙而来的现代人之间进行文化交流而实现的[4]。

1997 年，对发现于费尔德霍费尔的尼安德特人模式标本的母系遗传的线粒体 DNA（mtDNA）的高变控制区的一个片段进行了测序。系统发育分析的结果表明，该序列落于当代人的变异范围之外，并且于大概 500,000 年前与当代人的 mtDNA 共有一个祖先[5,6]。接着，从另外 11 个尼安德特人标本得到了 mtDNA 序列，包括德国的费尔德霍费尔 2[7]，俄罗斯的梅兹迈斯卡亚[8]，克罗地亚的温迪迦 75、77 和 80[9,10]，比利时的英格斯 2，法国的拉沙佩勒–欧赛恩茨和维伦纽夫岩[10]，比利时的斯卡拉迪纳[11]，意大利的蒙蒂莱西尼[12]，以及西班牙的埃尔西德隆 441[13]。尽管其中有些序列非常短，但是比起与现代人 mtDNA 的关系，它们彼此的亲缘关系要近得多[9,11]。

这一事实与现存的人类或少量早期现代人化石[5,10]中缺少任何相关的 mtDNA 序列一起强烈表明尼安德特人对当代人的 mtDNA 没有贡献。基于各种人类群体模型，已估算出尼安德特人对当代人基因库的最大整体遗传贡献在 25% 到 0.1% 之间（参考文献 10 和 14）。因为后面的推论是根据 mtDNA 推导出来的，而 mtDNA 只是一个单一的母系遗传位点，所以遗传漂移的不确定性及繁殖过程中性别差异的可能性导致它们在检测尼安德特人对当前人类基因库的贡献度方面的能力是有限的。然而，形态学证据[4,15]和现代人类基因库的变异[16]都支持如下结论，即如果尼安德特人对现代人有过任何的遗传贡献的话，那么这种贡献程度也是有限的。

尼安德特人是与现存的人类亲缘关系最密切的人类类群，所以尼安德特人的核基因组序列对于注释人类基因组来说将是无价的资源。我们现存的至亲黑猩猩与人类的基因组之间大概存在 35,000,000 个核苷酸的差异[17]。不久的将来，其他灵长类（如猩猩和猕猴）的基因组序列也会支持这种差异添加到人类和黑猩猩的演化谱系中。但是，由于所发生的形态、行为和认知变化非常显著，如果没有与人类亲缘关系更加接近的基因组序列能够用来做比较，发生在人类演化谱系中遗传变化的年代分辨率会受到局限。特别是，通过与尼安德特人进行比较，就可以对过去几十万年里出现的解剖学和行为学上完全的现代人发生的遗传变化进行鉴别。

Identification of a Neanderthal Fossil for DNA Sequencing

Although it is possible to recover mtDNA[18] and occasionally even nuclear DNA sequences[19-22] from well-preserved remains of organisms that are less than a few hundred thousand years old, determination of ancient hominid sequences is fraught with special difficulties and pitfalls[18]. In addition to degradation and chemical damage to the DNA that can cause any ancient DNA to be irretrievable or misread, contamination of specimens, laboratory reagents and instruments with traces of DNA from modern humans must be avoided. In fact, when sensitive polymerase chain reaction (PCR) is used, human mtDNA sequences can be retrieved from almost every ancient specimen[23,24]. This problem is especially severe when Neanderthal remains are studied because Neanderthal and human are so closely related that one expects to find few or no differences between Neanderthals and modern humans within many regions[25], making it impossible to rely on the sequence information itself to distinguish endogenous from contaminating DNA sequences. A necessary first step for sequencing nuclear DNA from Neanderthals is therefore to identify a Neanderthal specimen that is free or almost free of modern human DNA.

We tested more than 70 Neanderthal bone and tooth samples from different sites in Europe and western Asia for bio-molecular preservation by removing samples of a few milligrams for amino acid analysis. The vast majority of these samples had low overall contents of amino acids and/or high levels of amino acid racemization, a stereoisomeric structural change that affects amino acids in fossils, indicating that they are unlikely to contain retrievable endogenous DNA[26]. However, some of the samples are better preserved in that they contain high levels of amino acids (more than 20,000 p.p.m.), low levels of racemization of amino acids such as aspartate that racemize rapidly, as well as amino acid compositions that suggest that the majority of the preserved protein stems from collagen.

From 100–200 mg of bone from six of these specimens we extracted DNA and analysed the relative abundance of Neanderthal-like mtDNA sequences and modern human-like mtDNA sequences by performing PCR with primer pairs that amplify both human and Neanderthal mtDNA with equal efficiency. The amplification products span segments of the hypervariable region of the mtDNA in which all Neanderthals sequenced to date differ from all contemporary humans. From subsequent cloning into a plasmid vector and sequencing of more than a hundred clones from each product, we determined the ratio of Neanderthal-like to modern human-like mtDNA in each extract. We used two different primer pairs that amplify fragments of 63 base pairs and 119 base pair to gauge the contamination levels for different lengths of DNA molecules.

Figure 1 shows that the level of contamination differs drastically among the samples. Whereas only around 1% of the mtDNA present in three samples from France, Russia and Uzbekistan was Neanderthal-like, one sample from Croatia and one from Spain contained around 5% and 75% Neanderthal-like mtDNA, respectively. One bone (Vi-80) from Vindija Cave, Croatia, stood out in that ~99% of the 63-base-pair mtDNA segments and

用于 DNA 测序的尼安德特人化石的甄选

尽管从保存良好且年龄小于几十万年的生物遗骸中得到 mtDNA[18]，极少数情况下甚至得到核 DNA 序列[19-22]也是可能的，但是古老人类序列的确定充满特殊的困难和陷阱[18]。除了导致古 DNA 不可获取或误读的 DNA 降解和化学损伤外，标本的污染、带有现代人 DNA 残留的实验室试剂和仪器也是必须要避免的。事实上，当使用敏感的聚合酶链式反应（PCR）时，几乎可以从每件古老的标本中得到人类 mtDNA 序列[23,24]。当研究尼安德特人时，这一问题尤为严重，因为尼安德特人与现代人的亲缘关系如此之近，所以研究者会预期在许多区域上现代人和尼安德特人之间都很少有或根本没有差异[25]，这使得仅仅依靠序列本身不可能将内源 DNA 与污染源 DNA 序列区别开。因此如果要对尼安德特人的核 DNA 进行测序，第一步必须要做的就是甄选一件没有或几乎没有受到现代人 DNA 污染的尼安德特人标本。

通过去除几毫克样品进行氨基酸分析，我们检测了欧洲和西亚的不同地点采集的 70 多个尼安德特人骨骼和牙齿样品以确认其生物分子保存状况。绝大部分样品的总氨基酸含量很低并且（或者）氨基酸外消旋化（一种对化石中的氨基酸产生影响的立体异构变化）水平很高，表明这些样本不可能含有可获取的内源 DNA[26]。然而，有些样本的保存情况较好，因为它们的氨基酸含量水平很高（大于 20,000 ppm）；而通常快速外消旋化的天冬氨酸等氨基酸的外消旋化水平很低；另外这些样本的氨基酸构成意味着大部分保存下来的蛋白质来源于胶原蛋白。

从其中六件标本的 100 mg 到 200 mg 骨骼样品中我们提取到了 DNA。通过执行等效引物对 PCR 扩增现代人和尼安德特人的 mtDNA，我们分析了似尼安德特人的 mtDNA 序列及似现代人的 mtDNA 序列的相对丰度。扩增产物涵盖了 mtDNA 高变区的片段。迄今为止，在这一区域中所有经过测序的尼安德特人与所有现代人都不一样。随后通过将 PCR 产物克隆到质粒载体中并对每个产物的一百多个克隆进行测序，我们确定了每个提取物中似尼安德特人 mtDNA 与似现代人 mtDNA 的比率。我们使用了两个不同引物对分别扩增 63 个碱基对（bp）和 119 个碱基对的片段，用以计量不同长度的 DNA 分子的污染水平。

图 1 显示样品间的污染水平显著不同。尽管来自法国、俄罗斯和乌兹别克斯坦的三个样品中只有 1% 左右的 mtDNA 是似尼安德特人的，而一个来自克罗地亚的样品和一个来自西班牙的样品分别含有 5% 和 75% 左右的似尼安德特人 mtDNA。来自克罗地亚温迪迦洞穴的一件骨骼标本（Vi-80）的数据异常突出，约 99% 的 63 bp

~94% of the 119-base pair segments are of Neanderthal origin. Assuming that the ratio of Neanderthal to contaminating modern human DNA is the same for mtDNA as it is for nuclear DNA, the Vi-80 bone therefore yields DNA fragments that are predominantly of Neanderthal origin and provided that the contamination rate was not increased during the downstream sequencing process, the extent of contamination in the final analyses is below ~6%.

Fig. 1. Ratio of Neanderthal to modern human mtDNA in six hominid fossils. For each fossil, primer pairs that amplify a long (119 base pairs; upper lighter bars) and short (63 base pairs; lower darker bars) product were used to amplify segments of the mtDNA hypervariable region. The products were sequenced and determined to be either of Neanderthal (yellow) or modern human (blue) type.

The Vi-80 bone was discovered by M. Malez and co-workers in layer G3 of Vindija Cave in 1980. It has been dated by carbon-14 accelerator mass spectrometry to $38,310 \pm 2,130$ years before present and its entire mtDNA hypervariable region I has been sequenced[10]. Out of 14 Neanderthal remains from layer G3 that we have analysed, this bone is one of six samples that show good bio-molecular preservation, while the other eight bones show intermediate to bad states of preservation that do not suggest the presence of amplifiable DNA. Preservation conditions in Vindija Cave thus vary drastically from bone to bone, a situation that may be due to different extents of water percolation in different parts of the cave.

Direct Large-scale DNA Sequencing from the Vindija Neanderthal

Because the Vi-80 Neanderthal bone extract is largely free of contaminating modern human mtDNA, we chose this extract to perform large-scale parallel 454 sequencing[27]. In this technology, single-stranded libraries, flanked by common adapters, are created from the DNA sample and individual library molecules are amplified through bead-based emulsion PCR, resulting in beads carrying millions of clonal copies of the DNA fragments from the samples. These are subsequently sequenced by pyrosequencing on the GS20 454 sequencing system.

For several reasons, the 454 sequencing platform is extremely well suited for analyses of bulk

的 mtDNA 片段和约 94% 的 119 bp 的 mtDNA 片段源自尼安德特人。假设尼安德特人的核 DNA 与现代人污染源的核 DNA 的比率与 mtDNA 的情况一样，那么从该 Vi-80 骨骼标本得到的 DNA 片段应该主要来自尼安德特人。那么，如果在下游测序过程中没有增加污染率的话，那么最终分析时的污染率应该低于大约 6%。

图 1. 六件人类化石标本中尼安德特人与现代人 mtDNA 的比例。对于每件化石标本，都使用了两个引物对来扩增 mtDNA 的高变区片段，其中一对扩增的产物较长（119 bp；上面的浅颜色横杠），另一对扩增的产物较短（63 bp；下面的深颜色横杠）。对产物进行了测序并确定其属于尼安德特人（黄色）类型还是现代人（蓝色）类型。

梅勒兹及其同事于 1980 年在温迪迦洞穴的 G3 层中发现了 Vi-80 骨骼标本。通过碳−14 加速器质谱法测定其年代为距今 38,310±2,130 年，其 mtDNA 高变区 I 已经完全测序[10]。我们已经对 G3 层发现的 14 个尼安德特人样本进行了分析，该骨骼标本是生物分子保存状况良好的六个样品之一，而其余八件骨骼标本则显示出中度至较差的保存状况，表明其不存在可扩增的 DNA。因此温迪迦洞穴中各骨骼标本彼此的保存状况非常不同，可能是由洞穴中不同部位的水渗透情况不同造成的。

温迪迦尼安德特人的直接大范围 DNA 测序

由于 Vi-80 尼安德特骨骼标本提取物基本排除了现代人 mtDNA 污染的可能，所以我们选择这一提取物来进行大范围平行 454 测序[27]。这一技术中，由 DNA 样本创建出两侧连有通用衔接子的单链 DNA 库，各个库中的分子通过磁珠乳液 PCR 进行扩增，于是就可以从样本中得到携带有数以百万计的 DNA 片段的克隆拷贝的磁珠。然后在 GS20 454 测序系统上通过焦磷酸测序法对这些 DNA 片段进行测序。

由于以下几个原因，454 测序平台非常适合于分析古代残骸中提取到的大量

DNA extracted from ancient remains[28]. First, it circumvents bacterial cloning, in which the vast majority of initial template molecules are lost during transformation and establishment of clones. Second, because each molecule is amplified in isolation from other molecules it also precludes template competition, which frequently occurs when large numbers of different DNA fragments are amplified together. Third, its current read length of 100–200 nucleotides covers the average length of the DNA preserved in most fossils[29]. Fourth, it generates hundreds of thousands of reads per run, which is crucial because the majority of the DNA recovered from fossils is generally not derived from the fossil species, but rather from organisms that have colonized the organism after its death[20,30]. Fifth, because each sequenced product stems from just one original single-stranded template molecule of known orientation, the DNA strand from which the sequence is derived is known[28]. This provides an advantage over traditional PCR from double-stranded templates, in which the template strand is not known, because the frequency of different nucleotide misincorporations can be deduced. For example, using 454 sequencing, the rate at which cytosine is converted to uracil and read as thymine can be distinguished from the rate at which guanine is converted to xanthine and read as adenine, whereas this is impossible using traditional PCR or bacterial cloning. This is important since nucleotide conversions and misincorporations in ancient DNA are caused by damage that affects different bases differently[28,31] and this pattern of false substitutions can be used to estimate the relative probability that a particular substitution (that is, the observation of a nucleotide difference between DNA sequences) represents the authentic DNA sequence of the organism versus an artefact from DNA degradation.

We recovered a total of 254,933 unique sequences from the Vi-80 bone (see Supplementary Methods). These were aligned to the human (build 36.1)[32], chimpanzee (build 1)[17] and mouse (build 34.1)[33] complete genome sequences, to environmental sample sequences in the GenBank *env* database (version 3, September 2005), and to the complete set of redundant nucleotide sequences in GenBank *nt* (version 3, September 2005, excluding EST, STS, GSS, environmental and HTGS sequences)[34] using the program BLASTN (NCBI version 2.2.12)[35]. The most similar database sequence for each query was identified and classified by its taxonomic order (Fig. 2) (see Supplementary Methods). No significant nucleotide sequence similarity in the databases was found for 79% of the fossil extract sequence reads. This is typical of large-scale sequencing both from other ancient bones[20,22,28] and from environmental samples[36,37], although some permafrost-preserved specimens can yield high amounts of endogenous DNA[22]. Sequences with similarity to a database sequence were classified by the taxonomic order of their most significant alignment. Actinomycetales, a bacterial order with many soil-living species, was the most populous order and accounted for 6.8% of the sequences. The second most populous order, to which 15,701 unique sequences or 6.2% of the sequence reads were most similar, was that of primates. All other individual orders were substantially less frequent. Notably, the average percentage identity for the primate sequence alignments was 98.8%, whereas it was 92–98% for the other frequently occurring orders. Thus, the primate reads, unlike many of the prokaryotic reads, are aligned to a very closely related species.

DNA[28]。首先，它绕过了细菌克隆，因为在转化和建立克隆的过程中会丢失绝大多数的初始模板分子。其次，由于每个分子都是同其他分子隔离开进行扩增的，所以可以预先排除模板竞争（模板竞争经常发生在同时扩增大量不同的 DNA 片段时）。第三，454 测序目前的读取长度是 100 到 200 个核苷酸，这一长度可以涵盖大部分化石中保存的 DNA 的平均长度[29]。第四，454 测序技术每次运行可以产生数十万个读取，这一特点是很重要的，因为大部分从化石中复原的 DNA 都不是来自化石物种本身，而是来自那些在化石物种死后聚居其上的生物[20,30]。第五，由于每个测序产物仅由一个已知方向的初始单链模板分子扩增而来，所以产生该序列的 DNA 链是已知的[28]。传统 PCR 中，我们不知道模板链是哪条，所以 454 测序技术比传统的从双链模板得到 PCR 产物的技术更具优越性，因为同时可以推导出不同核苷酸错配率。举例而言，使用 454 测序技术，可以将胞嘧啶被转变为尿嘧啶而被读为胸腺嘧啶的比率与鸟嘌呤被转变为黄嘌呤而被读成腺嘌呤的比率区别开来，而这在使用传统 PCR 或者细菌克隆时是不可能办到的。由于古 DNA 中的损伤会不同程度地影响不同碱基而发生核苷酸转变和错配，而且这种虚假的碱基替换模式可以用来估计代表生物真实 DNA 序列的特定碱基替换（即观察到的 DNA 序列间的核苷酸差异）与 DNA 降解所导致人为替代的相对概率，所以该测序技术的这一特点非常重要[28,31]。

　　我们总共从 Vi-80 骨骼标本中复原了 254,933 条不同序列（见补充方法）。使用 BLASTN 程序（NCBI 2.2.12 版本）[35] 将这些序列与人（版本 36.1）[32]、黑猩猩（版本 1）[17] 和小鼠（版本 34.1）[33] 的全基因组序列进行了对齐，与 GenBank *env* 数据库（2005 年 9 月第 3 版）中的环境样本序列进行了对齐，以及与 GenBank *nt*（2005 年 9 月第 3 版，不包括 EST、STS、GSS、环境和 HTGS 序列）[34] 中全套冗余核苷酸序列进行了对齐。根据"目"一级分类学单元将每次查询到的最相似的数据库序列进行确认并分类（图 2）（见补充方法）。其中 79% 的化石提取物的序列读取没有在数据库中找到有意义的核苷酸序列相似性。虽然一些永久冻土中保存的标本可以产生大量的内源 DNA[22]，但是对于其他古代骨骼[20,22,28] 和环境样品[36,37] 的大范围测序来说，这是很典型的现象。与数据库序列具有相似性的序列根据其最有意义的对齐的"目"一级分类学单元进行分类。放线菌目是一个含有许多生活在土壤中的种类的细菌目，是序列数目最多的细菌目，占序列的 6.8%。第二大目是灵长目，有 15,701 条不同序列或者说 6.2% 的序列读取与其最相似。所有其他的各目的频率都低得多。值得注意的是，灵长目序列对齐的平均百分率一致性达到了 98.8%，而其余经常出现的目是 92% 到 98%。因此，与许多原核生物的读取不同，灵长目的序列读取被对齐到了亲缘关系很近的物种上。

Fig. 2. Taxonomic distribution of DNA sequences from the Vi-80 extract. The taxonomic order of the database sequence giving the best alignment for each unique sequence read was determined. The most populous taxonomic orders are shown.

Neanderthal mtDNA Sequences

Among the 15,701 sequences of primate origin, we first identified all mtDNA in order to investigate whether their evolutionary relationship to the current human mtDNA pool is similar to what is known from previous analyses of Neanderthal mtDNA. A total of 41 unique DNA sequences from the Vi-80 fossil had their closest hits to different parts of the human mtDNA, and comprised, in total, 2,705 base pairs of unique mtDNA sequence. None of the putative Neanderthal mtDNA sequences map to the two hypervariable regions that have been previously sequenced in Neanderthals. We aligned these mtDNA sequences to the complete mtDNA sequences of 311 modern humans from different populations[38] as well as to the complete mtDNA sequences of three chimpanzees and two bonobos (Supplementary Information). A schematic neighbour-joining tree estimated from this alignment is shown in Fig. 3. In agreement with previous results, the Neanderthal mtDNA falls outside the variation among modern humans. However, the length of the branch leading to the Neanderthal mtDNA is 2.5 times as long as the branch leading to modern human mtDNAs. This is likely to be due to errors in our Neanderthal sequences derived from substitution artefacts from damaged, ancient DNA and from sequencing errors[28].

916

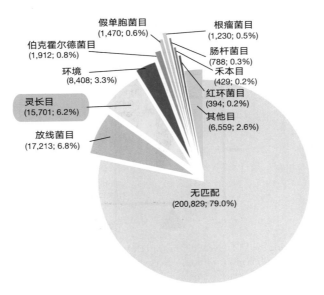

图 2. Vi-80 提取物的 DNA 序列的分类学分布情况。确定了与每条不同序列读取最佳对齐的数据库序列所属的分类学目。图中展示了序列数量最多的几个分类学目。

尼安德特人的 mtDNA 序列

在源于灵长目的 15,701 条序列中，我们首先鉴定了所有 mtDNA，以研究它们同现代人 mtDNA 库的演化关系是否与之前对尼安德特人 mtDNA 的分析结果相似。从 Vi-80 化石共得到 41 条与人类 mtDNA 的不同部位最为匹配的不同序列，总共包含 2,705 bp 的独特 mtDNA 序列。这些推定的尼安德特人 mtDNA 序列不能够映射到之前已测序的尼安德特人两个高变区。我们将这些 mtDNA 序列与来自不同人类群体的 311 个现代人的 mtDNA 全序列[38] 及三只黑猩猩和两只倭黑猩猩的 mtDNA 全序列进行了对齐（见补充信息）。由该对齐估算出的邻接树的示意图如图 3 所示。得到的结果与以前的研究一致，尼安德特人 mtDNA 也落在现代人的变异范围之外。然而，尼安德特人 mtDNA 分支的长度是现代人 mtDNA 分支长度的 2.5 倍。导致这种情况的原因可能是尼安德特人序列中存在的由受损古 DNA 导致的人为碱基替换错误以及测序错误[28]。

Fig. 3. Schematic tree relating the Vi-80 Neanderthal mtDNA sequences to 311 human mtDNA sequences. The Neanderthal branch length is given with uncorrected sequences (red triangle) and after correction of sequences via independent PCRs (black triangle). Chimpanzee and bonobo sequences (not shown) were used to root the neighbour-joining tree. Several substitution models (Kimura 2-parameter, Tajima-Nei, and Tamura 3-parameter with uniform or gamma-distributed ($\gamma = 0.5$–1.1) rates) yielded bootstrap support values for the human branch from 72–83%.

To analyse the extent to which errors occur in the Neanderthal mtDNA reads, we designed 29 primer pairs (Supplementary Methods) flanking all 39 positions at which the Vi-80 Neanderthal mtDNA sequences differed by substitutions from the consensus bases seen among the 311 human mtDNA sequences. These primer pairs, which are designed to yield amplification products that vary in length between 50 and 98 base pairs (including primers), were used in a multiplex two-step PCR[39] from the same Neanderthal extract that had been used for large-scale 454 sequencing. Twenty five of the PCR products, containing 34 of the positions where the Neanderthal differs from humans, were successfully amplified and cloned, and then six or more clones of each product were sequenced. The consensus sequence seen among these clones revealed the same nucleotides seen by the 454 sequencing at 20 of the 34 positions and no additional differences. Of the 14 positions found to represent errors in the sequence reads, seven were C to T transitions, four were G to A, two were G to T and one was T to C. This pattern of change is typical for ancient DNA, where deamination of cytosine residues[31] and, to a lesser extent, modifications of guanosine residues[28] have been found to account for the majority of nucleotide misincorporations during PCR.

These results also show that the likelihood of observing errors in the sequencing reads is drastically different depending on whether one considers nucleotide positions where a base in the Neanderthal mtDNA sequence differs from both the human and chimpanzee sequences, or positions where the Neanderthal differ from the humans but is identical to the chimpanzee mtDNA sequences. Among the mtDNA sequences analysed, there are 14 positions where the Neanderthal carries a base identical to the chimpanzee, and 13 of those were confirmed by PCR. In contrast, among the remaining 20 positions, where the Neanderthal sequences differed from both humans and chimpanzees, only seven were

图 3. Vi-80 尼安德特人 mtDNA 序列和 311 个人类的 mtDNA 序列的关系树示意图。尼安德特人分支的长度根据未修正序列（红色三角形）及通过独立 PCR 修正过的序列（黑色三角形）分别给出。黑猩猩和倭黑猩猩的序列（图中未示出）用来作为邻接树的根部。几种替换模型（替代速率为均匀分布或伽马分布（γ = 0.5 ～ 1.1）的 Kimura 双参数模型、Tajima-Nei 模型以及 Tamura 三参数模型）对人类分支的自举支持值达到了 72% 到 83%。

　　为了分析在尼安德特人 mtDNA 序列读取中发生错误的程度，我们设计了 29 个引物对（见补充方法），从两侧囊括了 39 个 Vi-80 尼安德特人 mtDNA 序列由于替换而与 311 个人类 mtDNA 序列中所见的合意碱基不同的位置。这些被设计为获取 50 bp 到 98 bp（包括引物）长度不等的扩增产物的引物对被用于大范围 454 测序的尼安德特人相同提取物的多重两步 PCR[39]。最终成功扩增及克隆了 25 个包含尼安德特人不同于人类的 34 个位置的 PCR 产物。随后对每个产物挑选了六个或者更多克隆进行了测序。这些克隆的合意序列与 454 测序法测得的序列相比，这 34 个位置中的 20 个位置的核苷酸是相同的，而且不存在此外的差异。在这 14 个被发现是错误的序列读取中，其中七个是 C → T 转换，四个 G → A 转换，两个 G → T 转换及一个 T → C 转换。这种变化模式是古 DNA 的典型变化类型。这当中，胞嘧啶残基的脱氨基作用 [31] 以及程度较弱的鸟嘌呤核苷残基的修改 [28] 导致了 PCR 过程中发生的大多数核苷酸错参。

　　这些结果也表明在测序序列读取当中观察到错误发生的可能性的显著差异取决于一个人是否考虑尼安德特人 mtDNA 中某些核苷酸位置上一个碱基与人和黑猩猩序列都不同，或者在这些位置上尼安德特人与现代人不同但与黑猩猩 mtDNA 序列完全相同。在所分析的 mtDNA 序列中，在 14 个位置上，尼安德特人所带的碱基与黑猩猩相同，其中 13 个通过 PCR 得到了确认。相比之下，余下的 20 个位置上，尼安德特人与人类和黑猩猩都不相同，其中只有 7 处得到了确认。当只使用经过 PCR confirmed. When only PCR-confirmed sequence data are used to estimate the mtDNA tree (Fig. 3), the Neanderthal branch has a length comparable to that of contemporary humans. This suggests that no large source of errors other than what is detected by the PCR analysis affects the sequences.

Using these PCR-confirmed substitutions and a divergence time between humans and chimpanzees of 4.7–8.4 million years[40-42], we estimate the divergence time for the mtDNA fragments determined here to be 461,000–825,000 years. This is in general agreement with previous estimates of Neanderthal–human mtDNA divergence of 317,000–741,000 years[6] based on mtDNA hypervariable region sequences and is compatible with our presumption that the mtDNA sequences determined from the Vi-80 extract are of Neanderthal origin.

Nuclear DNA Sequences

We next analysed the sequence reads whose closest matches are to the human or chimpanzee nuclear genomes and that are at least 30 base pairs long. Figure 4 shows where they map to the human karyotype (see Supplementary Methods). Overall, 0.04% of the autosomal genome sequence is covered by the Neanderthal reads—on average 3.61 bases per 10,000 bases. Both X and Y chromosomes are represented, with a lower coverage of 2.18 and 1.62 bases per 10,000, respectively, showing that the Vi-80 bone is derived from a male individual.

Fig. 4. Location on the human karyotype of Neanderthal DNA sequences. All sequences longer than 30 nucleotides whose best alignments were to the human genome are shown. The blue lines above each chromosome mark the position of all alignments that are unique in terms of bit-score within the human

确认过的序列数据来估算 mtDNA 树（图 3）时，尼安德特人分支的长度基本与现代人的分支长度相当。这表明除了 PCR 分析检测出的错误外，没有其他大的错误来源影响到序列的测定。

我们使用这些 PCR 确认过的碱基替换并采纳人类和黑猩猩间的分歧时间为距今 470 万年到 840 万年 [40-42]，由此估算出这里所确定的 mtDNA 片段的分歧时间是距今 461,000 年到 825,000 年。这与以前基于 mtDNA 高变区序列的尼安德特人–现代人 mtDNA 分歧时间为距今 317,000 年到 741,000 年 [6] 基本一致，也与我们的假定是相符的，即假定 Vi-80 提取物确定的 mtDNA 序列是源于尼安德特人的。

核 DNA 序列

接着我们分析了与现代人或黑猩猩核基因组最匹配的序列读取，这些序列至少 30 bp 长。图 4 展示了将它们映射到人类染色体核型上的情况（见补充方法）。总的来说，这些尼安德特人的序列读取涵盖了 0.04% 的常染色体基因组序列——平均每 10,000 碱基中有 3.61 个。其中也展示了 X 染色体和 Y 染色体的情况，涵盖范围比常染色体的稍低，分别是每 10,000 碱基有 2.18 个和 1.62 个，表明 Vi-80 骨骼标本是一个男性个体的。

图 4. 尼安德特人 DNA 序列在人类染色体核型上的位置。所有长度大于 30 个核苷酸的序列在现代人基因组中的最佳对齐位置都在此示出。每条染色体上部的蓝线表示在现代人基因组中具有唯一位分值的最

921

genome. Orange lines are alignments that have more than one alignment of equal bit-score. To the left of each chromosome, the average number of Neanderthal bases per 10,000 is given. Lines (Neanderthal, blue; human, red) within each chromosome show the hit density, on a log-base 2 scale, within sliding windows of 3 megabases along each chromosome. The centre black lines indicate the average hit-density for the chromosomes. The purple lines above and below indicate hit densities of 2X and 1/2X the chromosome average, respectively. On chromosome 5, an example of a region of increased sequence density is highlighted. Sequence gaps in the human reference sequence are indicated by dark grey regions. Chromosomal banding pattern is indicated by light grey regions.

The data presented in Fig. 4 show that when the hit density for sequences that have a single best hit in the human genome is plotted along the chromosomes, several suggestive local deviations from the average hit density are seen, which may represent copy-number differences in the Neanderthal relative to the human reference genome. For comparison, we generated 454 sequence data from a DNA sample from a modern human. Interestingly, some of the deviations seen in the Neanderthal are present also in the modern human, whereas others are not. The latter group of sequences may indicate copy-number differences that are unique to the Neanderthal relative to the modern human genome sequence. Thus, when more Neanderthal sequence is generated in the future, it may be possible to determine copy number differences between the Neanderthal, the chimpanzee and the human genomes.

Patterns of Nucleotide Change on Lineages

We generated three-way alignments between all Neanderthal sequences that map uniquely within the human genome and the corresponding human and chimpanzee genome sequences (see Supplementary Methods). An important artefact of local sequence alignments, such as those produced here, is that they necessarily begin and end with regions of exact sequence identity. The size of these regions is a function of the scoring parameters for the alignment. In this case, five bases at both ends of the alignments, amounting to ~14% of all data, needed to be removed (Supplementary Fig. 1) to eliminate biases in estimates of sequence divergence.

Each autosomal nucleotide position in the alignment that did not contain a deletion in the Neanderthal, the human or the chimpanzee sequences and was associated with a chimpanzee genome position with quality score ≥ 30 was classified according to which species share the same bases (Fig. 5). A total of 736,941 positions contained the same base in all three groups. The next largest category comprises 10,167 positions in which the human and Neanderthal base are identical, but the chimpanzee base is different. These positions are likely to have changed either on the hominid lineage before the divergence between human and Neanderthal sequences or on the chimpanzee lineage. At 3,447 positions, the Neanderthal base differs from both the human and chimpanzee bases, which are identical to each other. As suggested by the analysis of the mtDNA sequences, this category contains positions that have changed on the Neanderthal lineage, as well as a large proportion of errors that derive both from base damage that have accumulated in the ancient DNA and

佳对齐位置。橙色线表示具有相等位分值的超过一个的对齐位置。每条染色体的左侧给出了每 10,000 个碱基中尼安德特人碱基的平均数目。每条染色体内部的曲线（蓝色代表尼安德特人，红色代表现代人）表示沿每条染色体在三百万碱基滑动窗口内以 2 为底取对数的匹配密度。中间的黑线表示该染色体的平均匹配密度。上面和下面的紫色线分别表示相当于染色体平均数 2X 和 1/2X 的匹配密度。5 号染色体上，标出了一个序列密度增加的区域的例子。现代人参考序列中的序列间断用深灰色区域标出。染色体带型用浅灰色区域表示。

图 4 列出的数据表明当在现代人基因组中只有一个最佳匹配的序列的匹配密度沿着染色体被描绘的时候，能够看到几个平均匹配密度的提示性局部偏差，可能代表了尼安德特人相对于现代人参考基因组的拷贝数差异。为了进行比较，我们由一个现代人的 DNA 样本生成了 454 序列数据。有趣的是，某些在尼安德特人序列中看到的偏差同样也存在于现代人中，而其他却不存在。后一组序列可能暗示相对于现代人基因组序列而言，尼安德特人所特有的拷贝数差异。因此，如果将来可以生成更多的尼安德特人序列，那么就有可能确定尼安德特人、黑猩猩和现代人基因组间的拷贝数差异。

各谱系中的核苷酸变化模式

我们对所有在现代人基因组内有唯一映射的尼安德特人序列与相应的现代人和黑猩猩基因组序列进行了三重对齐（见补充方法）。就像这里的对齐一样，局部的序列对齐一个重要的人为因素就是它们必须以序列完全相同的区域开始和结束。这些区域的大小是对齐的评分参数的一个函数。这里，对齐两端各有五个碱基（补充图 1），占所有数据的约 14%，需要予以剔除，以消除估算序列分化时的偏差。

尼安德特人、现代人或者黑猩猩序列中不包含缺失，且在黑猩猩基因组中位置质量得分 ≥30 那些对齐中，每个常染色体核苷酸位置都根据共有相同碱基的物种进行分类（图 5）。所有三组中含有相同碱基的总共有 736,941 个位置。第二大类中，现代人和尼安德特人具有相同碱基但与黑猩猩不同的位置有 10,167 个。这些位置可能在现代人和尼安德特人序列发生分歧之前或者是黑猩猩谱系中就发生了变化。尼安德特人在 3,447 个位置的碱基与人类和黑猩猩都不同，但后两者完全相同。正如 mtDNA 序列分析所表明的那样，这一类别包含了尼安德特人谱系中发生改变的位置，也包含了由古 DNA 中累积的碱基损伤以及测序错误导致的大部分错误。现代

from sequencing errors. At 434 positions, the human base differs from both the Neanderthal and chimpanzee bases, which are identical to each other. These positions are likely to have changed on the human lineage after the divergence from Neanderthal. Finally, a total of 51 positions contain different bases in all three groups.

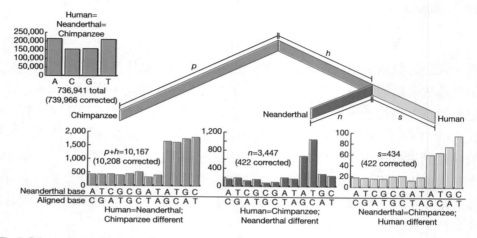

Fig. 5. Schematic tree illustrating the number of nucleotide changes inferred to have occurred on hominoid lineages. In blue is the distribution of all aligned positions that did not change on any lineage. In brown are the changes that occurred either on the chimpanzee lineage (p) or on the hominid lineage (h) before the human and Neanderthal lineages diverged. In red are the changes that are unique to the Neanderthal lineage (n), including all changes due to base-damage and base-calling errors. In yellow are changes unique to the human lineage. The distributions of types of changes in each category are also given. The numbers of changes in each category, corrected for base-calling errors in the Neanderthal sequence (see Supplementary Methods), are shown within parentheses.

Because the 454 sequencing technology allows the base in a base pair from which a sequence is derived to be determined, the relative frequencies of each of the 12 possible categories of base changes can be estimated for each evolutionary lineage. As seen in Fig. 5, the patterns of the chimpanzee-specific and human-specific changes are similar to each other in that the eight transversional changes are of approximately equal frequency and about fourfold less frequent than each of the four transitional changes, yielding a transition to transversion ratio of 2.04, typical of closely related mammalian genomes[43]. For the Neanderthal-specific changes the pattern is very different in that mismatches are dominated by C to T and G to A differences. Thus, the pattern of change seen among the Neanderthal-specific alignment mismatches is typical of the nucleotide substitution pattern observed in PCR of ancient DNA.

Consistent with this, modern human sequences determined by 454 sequencing show no excess amount of C to T or G to A differences (Supplementary Fig. 2), indicating that lesions in the ancient DNA rather than sequencing errors account for the majority of the errors in the Neanderthal sequences. Assuming that the evolutionary rate of DNA change was the same on the Neanderthal and human lineages, the majority of observed differences specific to the Neanderthal lineage are artefacts. All Neanderthal-specific changes were therefore

924

人在 434 个位置处的碱基与尼安德特人和黑猩猩都不同，而后两者是完全相同的。这些位置可能是人类与尼安德特人发生分歧之后才在人类谱系中发生了变化的。最后，有 51 个位置所有三组中的碱基均不同。

图 5. 人猿超科谱系上已发生的核苷酸变化数目的推测示意树。蓝色表示在任何谱系上都没有变化的对齐位置的分布情况。褐色表示在现代人和尼安德特人谱系分歧之前，黑猩猩谱系 (p) 或者人类谱系 (h) 上发生过的变化。红色表示尼安德特人谱系 (n) 独有的变化，包括碱基损伤和碱基识别错误等引起的所有变化。黄色是现代人谱系独有的变化。图中也给出了每个类别的变化类型的分布情况。圆括号中给出的是对尼安德特人序列碱基识别错误进行修正（见补充方法）后的每个类别的变化数目。

由于 454 测序技术能够确定序列来源的碱基对中的碱基，所以可以估算出每一演化谱系 12 个可能的碱基变化种类的每一种的相对发生频率。正如从图 5 中看到的，黑猩猩特有以及现代人特有的变化模式彼此很相似，因为八种颠换发生的频率基本相等，大概是四种转换中的每一种的发生频率的 1/4，产生了一个转换对颠换比率为 2.04 的结果，这对亲缘关系近的哺乳动物基因组而言是很具有代表性的[43]。尼安德特人特有的变化主要是 C 到 T 和 G 到 A 错配的差异，所以与上述模式很不一样。因此，尼安德特人特有的对齐中的错配的变化模式，是在古 DNA 的 PCR 中典型的核苷酸替换。

与此一致，454 测序技术确定的现代人序列显示出没有过量的 C 到 T 或 G 到 A 的差异（补充图 2），这表明造成尼安德特人序列中出现的错误，大部分是由于古 DNA 中的损伤而非测序错误。假定 DNA 变化的演化速率在尼安德特人和现代人谱系中是相等的，那么大部分观察到的尼安德特谱系特有的差异就都是人为噪音了。因此在接下来的分析中我们忽略了所有尼安德特人特有的变化，尼安德特人序列只

disregarded in the subsequent analyses and the Neanderthal sequences were used solely to assign changes to the human or chimpanzee lineage where the human and chimpanzee genome sequences differ and the Neanderthal sequence carries either the human or the chimpanzee base.

Genomic Divergence between Neanderthals and Humans

Assuming that the rates of DNA sequence change along the chimpanzee lineage and the human lineage were similar, it can be estimated that 8.2% of the DNA sequence changes that have occurred on the human lineage since the divergence from the chimpanzee lineage occurred after the divergence of the Neanderthal lineage. However, although the Neanderthal-specific changes that are heavily influenced by errors are not used for this analysis, some errors in the single-pass sequencing reads from the Neanderthal extract will create positions where the Neanderthal is identical either to human or chimpanzee sequences, and thus affect the estimates of sequence change on the human and chimpanzee lineages. When the effects of such errors in the Neanderthal sequences are quantified and removed (see Supplementary Methods), ~7.9% of the sequence changes along the human lineage are estimated to have occurred after divergence from the Neanderthal. If the human–chimpanzee divergence time is set to 6,500,000 years (refs 40, 41, 44), this implies an average human–Neanderthal DNA sequence divergence time of ~516,000 years. A 95% confidence interval generated by bootstrap re-sampling of the alignment data gives a range of 465,000 to 569,000 years. Obviously, these divergence estimates are dependent on the human–chimpanzee divergence time, which is a much larger source of uncertainty.

We analysed the DNA sequences generated from a contemporary human using the same sequencing protocol as was used for the Neanderthal. Although ancient DNA is degraded and damaged, this comparison controls for many of the aspects of the analysis including sequencing and alignment methodology. In this case, ~7.1% of the divergence along the human lineage is assigned to the time subsequent to the divergence of the two human sequences. The average divergence time between alleles within humans is thus ~459,000 years with a 95% confidence interval between 419,000 and 498,000 years. As expected, this estimate of the average human diversity is less than the divergence seen between the human and the Neanderthal sequences, but constitutes a large fraction of it because much of the human sequence diversity is expected to predate the human–Neanderthal split[25]. Neanderthal genetic differences to humans must therefore be interpreted within the context of human diversity.

Ancestral Population Size

Humans differ from apes in that their effective population size is of the order of 10,000 while those of chimpanzees, gorillas and orangutans are two to four times larger[45-47]. Furthermore, the population size of the ancestor of humans and chimpanzees was found to

用来在现代人和黑猩猩基因组序列不同的位置并且在该位置尼安德特人序列或者携带现代人或者携带黑猩猩碱基的情况下，将变化分配到现代人或者黑猩猩谱系中去。

尼安德特人和现代人基因组之间的分歧

假定黑猩猩谱系和人类谱系中 DNA 序列变化速率是相似的，那么可以估算出从人类与黑猩猩谱系发生分歧后所发生的 DNA 序列变化中，有 8.2% 是在与尼安德特人谱系发生分歧之后发生的。但是，尽管本分析中并未使用那些受错误严重影响的尼安德特人特有的变化，但是有些来自尼安德特人提取物的单通道测序读取错误能告知尼安德特人与现代人或者黑猩猩序列相同的位置，因此会影响到对现代人和黑猩猩谱系中发生的序列变化的估算。当把尼安德特人序列中这种错误的影响量化并且去除后（见补充方法），可以估算出，现代人谱系中的 7.9% 的序列变化是发生在与尼安德特人发生分歧之后。如果人类–黑猩猩分歧时间被设定在 6,500,000 年（参考文献 40、41、44），那么就意味着现代人–尼安德特人 DNA 序列的平均分歧时间约为距今 516,000 年。通过对对齐数据进行自举重新抽样产生的 95% 置信区间给出的范围是距今 465,000 年至 569,000 年。很明显，这些分歧估值取决于人类–黑猩猩的分歧时间，这是一个更大的不确定性来源。

我们使用与尼安德特人同样的测序方案分析了一例现代人产生的 DNA 序列。尽管古 DNA 会被降解和损坏，但是这一比较在包括测序和对齐方法论在内的很多方面对分析进行了控制。这里，现代人谱系中 7.1% 的分歧被分配到两条人类序列发生分歧之后的时间里。于是，现代人中等位基因之间的平均分歧时间大约是距今 459,000 年，95% 置信区间的范围在距今 419,000 年到 498,000 年间。正如预期的那样，这一平均人类多样性的估值比现代人和尼安德特人序列间的分歧要晚，但是因为现代人序列许多多样性理应早于现代人–尼安德特人分歧时间，所以年代范围占据了其中很大一部分 [25]。因此必须在现代人多样性这一背景下解读尼安德特人与现代人间的遗传差异。

祖先种群大小

人不同于猿，人的有效种群大小是 10,000，而黑猩猩、大猩猩和猩猩的有效种群大小是人类的两到四倍 [45-47]。此外，研究发现人类和黑猩猩的祖先的种群大小与

be similar to those of apes, rather than to humans[42,48]. The Neanderthal sequence data now allow us to ask if the effective size of the population ancestral to humans and Neanderthals was large, as is the case for apes and the human–chimpanzee ancestor, or small, as for present-day humans.

We applied a method[42] that co-estimates the ancestral effective population size and the split time between Neanderthal and human populations (Fig. 6a; see Supplementary Methods). As seen in Fig. 6b, we recover a line describing combinations of population sizes and split times compatible with the data and lack power to be more precise (see Supplementary Methods and Results). Using this line we can estimate the ancestral population size, given estimates about the population split time from independent sources. If we use a split time of 400,000 years inferred from the fossil record (J. J. Hublin, personal communication), then our point estimate of the ancestral population size is ~ 3,000. Given uncertainty in both the sequence divergence time and the population split time, our estimate of the ancestral population size varies from 0 to 12,000.

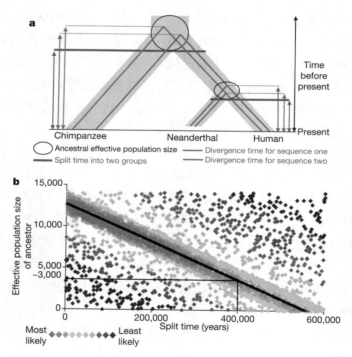

Fig. 6. Estimate of the effective population size of the ancestor of humans and Neanderthals. **a**, Schematic illustration of the model used to estimate ancestral effective population size. By split time, we mean the time, in the past, after which there was no more interbreeding between two groups. By divergence, we mean the time, in the past, at which two genetic regions separated and began to accumulate substitutions independently. Effective population size is the number of individuals needed under ideal conditions to produce the amount of observed genetic diversity within a population. **b**, The likelihood estimates of population split times and ancestral population sizes. The likelihoods are grouped by colour. The red–yellow points are statistically equivalent based on the likelihood ratio test approximation. The black line is the line of best fit to red–yellow points (see Supplementary Methods). This graph is scaled assuming a human–chimpanzee average sequence divergence time of 6,500,000 years.

猿类很相似，而非与人类相似[42,48]。现在，尼安德特人的序列数据允许我们提出如下问题，现代人和尼安德特人的祖先的有效种群大小是像猿类和人类-黑猩猩的祖先的种群一样大呢，还是像如今的现代人一样小？

　　我们运用了一种可以同时估算祖先有效种群大小和尼安德特人与现代人种群之间的分化时间的方法[42]（图 6a；见补充方法）。如图 6b 所示，我们复原了一条同时描述种群大小和分化时间组合且与数据相吻合的拟合线，但是统计学功效欠缺无法更加精确（见补充方法和结果）。使用这条拟合线，给定独立来源的种群的分化时间估值，我们可以估算出祖先种群的大小。如果我们使用根据化石记录推断的距今 400,000 年（胡布林，个人交流）作为分化时间的话，那么我们对祖先种群大小的点估计大约是 3,000。鉴于序列分歧时间和种群分化时间二者的不确定性，我们对祖先种群大小的估计从 0 到 12,000 不等。

图 6. 现代人和尼安德特人的祖先的有效种群大小的估计。a，用来估算祖先有效种群大小的模型的示意图。我们所说的分化时间是指过去的某一时间，在该时间之后两个群体之间不再有杂交。我们所说的分歧是指过去某一时间，在该时间两个遗传区域发生分离并且开始独立积累替换。有效种群大小是指理想条件下能在一个种群内产生特定数量的可见遗传多样性所需的个体数目。b，种群分化时间和祖先种群大小的可能性估计。用不同颜色对可能性进行了分组。红黄点根据似然比检验逼近在统计意义上是等同的。黑线是红黄点的最佳拟合线（见补充方法）。该图比例设定的是在假定人类-黑猩猩的平均序列分歧时间为距今 6,500,000 年的前提下。

These results suggest that the population ancestral to present-day humans and Neanderthals was similar to present-day humans in having a small effective size and thus that the effective population size on the hominid lineage had already decreased before the split between humans and Neanderthals. Therefore, the small effective population size seen in present-day human samples may not be unique to modern humans, but was present also in the common ancestor of Neanderthals and modern humans. We speculate that a small effective size, perhaps associated with numerous expansions from small groups, was typical not only of modern humans but of many groups of the genus *Homo*. In fact, the origin of *Homo erectus* may have been associated with genetic or cultural adaptations that resulted in drastic population expansions as indicated by their appearance outside Africa around two million years ago.

Neanderthal Sequences and Human Polymorphisms

Another question that can be addressed with these data is how often the Neanderthal has the ancestral allele (that is, the same allele seen in the chimpanzee) versus the derived (or novel) allele at sites where humans carry a single nucleotide polymorphism (SNP). The latter case identifies SNPs that were present in the common ancestor of Neanderthals and present-day humans. Using the SNPs that overlap with our data from two large genome-wide data sets (HapMap[49], 786 SNPs and Perlegen[50], 318 SNPs), we find that the Neanderthal sample has the derived allele in ~30% of all SNPs. This number is presumably an overestimate since the SNPs analysed were ascertained to be of high frequency in present-day humans and hence are more likely to be old. Nevertheless, this high level of derived alleles in the Neanderthal is incompatible with the simple population split model estimated in the previous section, given split times inferred from the fossil record. This may suggest gene flow between modern humans and Neanderthals. Given that the Neanderthal X chromosome shows a higher level of divergence than the autosomes (R.E.G., unpublished observation), gene flow may have occurred predominantly from modern human males into Neanderthals. More extensive sequencing of the Neanderthal genome is necessary to address this possibility.

Rationale and Prospects for a Neanderthal Genome Sequence

We demonstrate here that DNA sequences can be generated from the Neanderthal nuclear genome by massive parallel sequencing on the 454 sequencing platform. It is thus feasible to determine large amounts of sequences from this extinct hominid. As a corollary, it is possible to envision the determination of a Neanderthal genome sequence. For several reasons, we believe that this would represent a valuable genomic resource.

First, a Neanderthal genome sequence would allow all nucleotide sequence differences as well as many copy-number differences between the human and chimpanzee genomes to be temporally resolved with respect to whether they occurred before the separation of

这些结果表明如今的现代人和尼安德特人的祖先种群与如今的现代人相似，有效种群大小都比较小，所以人类谱系的有效种群大小在现代人和尼安德特人发生分化之前已经有所减少。因此，我们看到的如今的现代人样本中有效种群小的现象，可能并不是现代人特有的，而是早在尼安德特人和现代人的共同祖先时就具有的。我们推测，小规模有效种群可能与小群体的扩张有关，不仅在现代人中很典型，在人属的许多其他类群中也很典型。事实上，直立人的起源可能与遗传和文化适应有关，这导致了明显的种群扩张，正如大约两百万年前他们就出现在非洲之外所表明的那样。

尼安德特人序列和人类的遗传多态性

基于这些数据可以探讨的另一个问题是尼安德特人在现代人携带的单核苷酸多态性（SNP）的位点处出现祖先型等位基因（即在黑猩猩中也见到的同样的等位基因）与衍生的（或新型）等位基因的频率。后一种情况可以识别出存在于尼安德特人和现代人的共同祖先中的 SNP。我们使用两大全基因组数据库中与我们的数据相重叠的那些 SNP（HapMap[49] 有 786 个 SNP 及 Perlegen[50] 有 318 个 SNP），发现尼安德特人样品具有的衍生等位基因约占到了所有 SNP 的 30%。这一数字很可能是过高估算，因为已经查明所有纳入分析的 SNP 在如今的现代人中都有很高的出现频率，故而其年代更有可能比较久远。然而，根据由化石记录推断的分化时间，尼安德特人中这种高水平衍生等位基因与前一部分估算的简单种群分化模型是相矛盾的。这可能表明现代人和尼安德特人之间存在基因流。考虑到尼安德特人的 X 染色体显示出比常染色体更高水平的分歧（理查德·格林，未发表观察结果），因此基因流可能主要是从现代人男性流向尼安德特人的。要确认这一可能性，须要对尼安德特人基因组进行更广泛的测序。

尼安德特人基因组序列的缘由和前景

我们在此证明可以通过在 454 测序平台上进行大规模平行测序从尼安德特人核基因组生成 DNA 序列。因此从这种灭绝的人类确定大量序列是可行的。作为必然的结果，确定尼安德特人基因组序列是可能的。由于如下原因，我们相信这将是一种非常有价值的基因组资源。

首先，尼安德特人基因组序列使得人类与黑猩猩基因组之间所有的核苷酸序列差异以及许多拷贝数差异在时间上得到解决，即差异究竟是发生在现代人与尼安德

humans from Neanderthals, or whether they occurred after or at the time of separation. The latter class of changes is of interest, because some of them will be associated with the emergence of modern humans. A Neanderthal genome sequence would therefore allow the research community to determine whether DNA sequence differences between humans and chimpanzees that are found to be functionally important represent recent changes on the human lineage. No data other than a Neanderthal genome sequence can provide this information.

Second, the fact that Neanderthals carry the derived allele for a substantial fraction of human SNPs suggests a method of identifying genomic regions that have experienced a selective sweep subsequent to the separation of human and Neanderthal populations. Such selective sweeps in the human genome will make the variation in these regions younger than the separation of humans and Neanderthals. As we show above, in regions not affected by sweeps a substantial proportion of polymorphic sites in humans will carry derived alleles in the Neanderthal genome sequence, whereas no sites will do so in regions affected by sweeps. This represents an approach to identifying selective sweeps in humans that is not possible from other data.

Third, once large amounts of Neanderthal genome sequence is generated, it will become possible to estimate the misincorporation probabilities for each class of nucleotide differences between the Neanderthal and chimpanzee genomes with high accuracy by analysing regions covered by many reads such as mtDNA, repeated genome regions of high sequence identity, as well as single-copy regions covered by multiple reads. Once this is done, the confidence that any particular nucleotide position where the Neanderthal differs from human as well as chimpanzee is correct can be reliably estimated. In combination with future knowledge about the function of genes and biological systems, comprehensive information from the Neanderthal genome will then allow aspects of Neanderthal biology to be deciphered that are unavailable by any other means.

Are fossil and technical resources today sufficient to imagine the determination of a Neanderthal genome sequence? The results presented here are derived from approximately one fifteenth of an extract prepared from ~100 mg of bone. To achieve one-fold coverage of the Neanderthal genome (3 gigabases) without any further improvement in technology, about twenty grams of bone and 6,000 runs on the current version of the 454 sequencing platform would be necessary. Although this is at present a daunting task, technical improvements in the procedures described here that would make the retrieval of DNA sequences of the order of ten times more efficient can easily be envisioned (our unpublished results). In view of that prospect, we have recently initiated a project that aims at achieving an initial draft version of the Neanderthal genome within two years.

(**444**, 330-336; 2006)

特人分离之前，还是发生在分离之后或分离之时。后一类变化更加应该被关注，因为其中有些与现代人的出现有关。因此尼安德特人的基因组序列将令学术界能够确定人和黑猩猩间功能上重要的 DNA 序列差异是否代表了人类谱系最近发生的变化。除了尼安德特人的基因组序列外，没有其他数据能够提供这一信息。

其次，尼安德特人携带着大量人类 SNP 的衍生等位基因这一事实指明了一种识别基因组中在现代人与尼安德特人种群分离之后经历了选择性清除的区域的方法。人类基因组中的这些选择性清除会使这些区域内的变异比现代人和尼安德特人的分离年轻。正如我们上面所陈述的，在未受选择性清除影响的区域中，对于人类的大部分多态位点来说，尼安德特人基因组序列中会携带存在的衍生等位基因，然而在受选择性清除影响的区域中，没有位点会出现这种情况。这代表一种识别人类中的选择性清除的方法，其他数据是不可能做到这点的。

再者，一旦生成了大量尼安德特人基因组序列，通过分析像 mtDNA 那样由多读取覆盖的区域、序列高度等同的重复基因组区域以及多读取覆盖的单拷贝区域，以高精度估算尼安德特人和黑猩猩基因组间每类核苷酸差异的错配概率将成为可能。一旦完成了这一步，就能够可靠地估计出尼安德特人不同于现代人及黑猩猩的任何特定核苷酸位置的正确性的可信度。加上将来对基因功能和生物系统的进一步了解，尼安德特人基因组提供的全面信息就可以对尼安德特人生物学的方方面面进行解读，这是其他方式无法做到的。

现在的化石和技术资源足够让我们奢想确定尼安德特人基因组序列吗？这里介绍的结果源自由约 100 mg 骨骼样品产生的提取物的大概 1/15。在无须任何技术改进的基础上，为了得到尼安德特人整个基因组 (3 千兆碱基) 的信息，在现有版本的 454 测序平台上，将需要约 20 g 骨骼，进行 6,000 次运行。尽管目前这是一项令人畏惧的任务，但是对这里描述的步骤进行技术改良之后，很轻易就能够更有效地获取十倍的 DNA 序列 (我们尚未发表的结果)。鉴于这一前景，我们最近启动了一个旨在两年内完成尼安德特人基因组草图的项目。

（刘皓芳 翻译；张颖奇 审稿）

Richard E. Green[1], **Johannes Krause**[1], **Susan E. Ptak**[1], **Adrian W. Briggs**[1], **Michael T. Ronan**[2], **Jan F. Simons**[2], **Lei Du**[2], **Michael Egholm**[2], **Jonathan M. Rothberg**[2], **Maja Paunovic**[3‡] & **Svante Pääbo**[1]

[1] Max-Planck Institute for Evolutionary Anthropology, Deutscher Platz 6, D-04103 Leipzig, Germany

[2] 454 Life Sciences, 20 Commercial Street, Branford, Connecticut 06405, USA

[3] Institute of Quaternary Paleontology and Geology, Croatian Academy of Sciences and Arts, A. Kovacica 5/II, HR-10 000 Zagreb, Croatia

‡ Deceased

Received 14 July; accepted 11 October 2006.

References:

1. Bischoff, J. L. *et al.* The Sima de los Huesos hominids date to beyond U/Th equilibrium (> 350 kyr) and perhaps to 400–500 kyr: New radiometric dates. *J. Archaeol. Sci.* **30**, 275-280 (2003).

2. Hublin, J-J. (ed.) *Climatic Changes, Paleogeography, and the Evolution of the Neandertals* (Plenum Press, New York, 1998).

3. Franciscus, R. G. (ed.) *Neanderthals* (Oxford Univ. Press, Oxford, 2002).

4. Hublin, J. J., Spoor, F., Braun, M., Zonneveld, F. & Condemi, S. A late Neanderthal associated with Upper Palaeolithic artefacts. *Nature* **381**, 224-226 (1996).

5. Krings, M. *et al.* Neandertal DNA sequences and the origin of modern humans. *Cell* **90**, 19-30 (1997).

6. Krings, M., Geisert, H., Schmitz, R. W., Krainitzki, H. & Pääbo, S. DNA sequence of the mitochondrial hypervariable region II from the Neandertal type specimen. *Proc. Natl Acad. Sci. USA* **96**, 5581-5585 (1999).

7. Schmitz, R. W. *et al.* The Neandertal type site revisited: Interdisciplinary investigations of skeletal remains from the Neander Valley, Germany. *Proc. Natl Acad. Sci. USA* **99**, 13342-13347 (2002).

8. Ovchinnikov, I. V. *et al.* Molecular analysis of Neanderthal DNA from the northern Caucasus. *Nature* **404**, 490-493 (2000).

9. Krings, M. *et al.* A view of Neandertal genetic diversity. *Nature Genet.* **26**, 144-146 (2000).

10. Serre, D. *et al.* No evidence of Neandertal mtDNA contribution to early modern humans. *PLoS Biol.* **2**, 313-317 (2004).

11. Orlando, L. *et al.* Revisiting Neandertal diversity with a 100,000 year old mtDNA sequence. *Curr. Biol.* **16**, R400-R402 (2006).

12. Caramelli, D. *et al.* A highly divergent mtDNA sequence in a Neandertal individual from Italy. *Curr. Biol.* **16**, R630-R632 (2006).

13. Lalueza-Fox, C. *et al.* Neandertal evolutionary genetics: mitochondrial DNA data from the Iberian peninsula. *Mol. Biol. Evol.* **22**, 1077-1081 (2005).

14. Currat, M. & Excoffier, L. Modern humans did not admix with Neanderthals during their range expansion into Europe. *PLoS Biol.* **2**, e421 (2004).

15. Stringer, C. Modern human origins: progress and prospects. *Phil. Trans. R. Soc. Lond. B* **357**, 563-579 (2002).

16. Takahata, N., Lee, S. H. & Satta, Y. Testing multiregionality of modern human origins. *Mol. Biol. Evol.* **18**, 172-183 (2001).

17. Chimpanzee Sequencing and Analysis Consortium. Initial sequence of the chimpanzee genome and comparison with the human genome. *Nature* **437**, 69-87 (2005).

18. Pääbo, S. *et al.* Genetic analyses from ancient DNA. *Annu. Rev. Genet.* **38**, 645-679 (2004).

19. Greenwood, A. D., Capelli, C., Possnert, G. & Pääbo, S. Nuclear DNA sequences from late Pleistocene megafauna. *Mol. Biol. Evol.* **16**, 1466-1473 (1999).

20. Noonan, J. P. *et al.* Genomic sequencing of Pleistocene cave bears. *Science* **309**, 597-599 (2005).

21. Rompler, H. *et al.* Nuclear gene indicates coat-color polymorphism in mammoths. *Science* **313**, 62 (2006).

22. Poinar, H. N. *et al.* Metagenomics to paleogenomics: large-scale sequencing of mammoth DNA. *Science* **311**, 392-394 (2006).

23. Hofreiter, M., Serre, D., Poinar, H. N., Kuch, M. & Pääbo, S. Ancient DNA. *Nature Rev. Genet.* **2**, 353-359 (2001).

24. Malmstrom, H., Stora, J., Dalen, L., Holmlund, G. & Gotherstrom, A. Extensive human DNA contamination in extracts from ancient dog bones and teeth. *Mol. Biol. Evol.* **22**, 2040-2047 (2005).

25. Pääbo, S. Human evolution. *Trends Cell Biol.* **9**, M13-M16 (1999).

26. Poinar, H. N., Höss, M., Bada, J. L. & Pääbo, S. Amino acid racemization and the preservation of ancient DNA. *Science* **272**, 864-866 (1996).

27. Margulies, M. *et al.* Genome sequencing in microfabricated high-density picolitre reactors. *Nature* **437**, 376-380 (2005).

28. Stiller, M. *et al.* Patterns of nucleotide misincorporations during enzymatic amplification and direct large-scale sequencing of ancient DNA. *Proc. Natl Acad. Sci. USA* **103**, 13578-13584 (2006).

29. Pääbo, S. Ancient DNA: extraction, characterization, molecular cloning, and enzymatic amplification. *Proc. Natl Acad. Sci. USA* **86**, 1939-1943 (1989).

30. Höss, M., Dilling, A., Currant, A. & Pääbo, S. Molecular phylogeny of the extinct ground sloth *Mylodon darwinii. Proc. Natl Acad. Sci. USA* **93**, 181-185 (1996).

31. Hofreiter, M., Jaenicke, V., Serre, D., Haeseler Av, A. & Pääbo, S. DNA sequences from multiple amplifications reveal artifacts induced by cytosine deamination in ancient DNA. *Nucleic Acids Res.* **29**, 4793-4799 (2001).

32. International Human Genome Sequencing Consortium. Initial sequencing and analysis of the human genome. *Nature* **409**, 860-921 (2001).

33. Mouse Genome Sequencing Consortium. Initial sequencing and comparative analysis of the mouse genome. *Nature* **420**, 520-562 (2002).

34. Benson, D. A., Karsch-Mizrachi, I., Lipman, D. J., Ostell, J. & Wheeler, D. L. GenBank. *Nucleic Acids Res.* **34**, D16-D20 (2006).

35. Altschul, S. F. *et al.* Gapped BLAST and PSI-BLAST: a new generation of protein database search programs. *Nucleic Acids Res.* **25**, 3389-3402 (1997).

36. Beja, O. *et al.* Construction and analysis of bacterial artificial chromosome libraries from a marine microbial assemblage. *Environ. Microbiol.* **2**, 516-529 (2000).

934

37. Venter, J. C. *et al.* Environmental genome shotgun sequencing of the Sargasso Sea. *Science* **304**, 66-74 (2004).

38. Ingman, M. & Gyllensten, U. mtDB: Human Mitochondrial Genome Database, a resource for population genetics and medical sciences. *Nucleic Acids Res.* **34**, D749-D751 (2006).

39. Krause, J. *et al.* Multiplex amplification of the mammoth mitochondrial genome and the evolution of Elephantidae. *Nature* **439**, 724-727 (2006).

40. Kumar, S., Filipski, A., Swarna, V., Walker, A. & Blair Hedges, S. Placing confidence limits on the molecular age of the human-chimpanzee divergence. *Proc. Natl Acad. Sci. USA* **102**, 18842-18847 (2005).

41. Patterson, N., Richter, D. J., Gnerre, S., Lander, E. S. & Reich, D. Genetic evidence for complex speciation of humans and chimpanzees. *Nature* **441**, 1103-1108 (2006).

42. Wall, J. D. Estimating ancestral population sizes and divergence times. *Genetics* **163**, 395-404 (2003).

43. Yang, Z. & Yoder, A. D. Estimation of the transition/transversion rate bias and species sampling. *J. Mol. Evol.* **48**, 274-283 (1999).

44. Innan, H. & Watanabe, H. The effect of gene flow on the coalescent time in the human-chimpanzee ancestral population. *Mol. Biol. Evol.* **23**, 1040-1047 (2006).

45. Kaessmann, H., Wiebe, V., Weiss, G. & Pääbo, S. Great ape DNA sequences reveal a reduced diversity and an expansion in humans. *Nature Genet.* **27**, 155-156 (2001).

46. Yu, N., Jensen-Seaman, M. I., Chemnick, L., Ryder, O. & Li, W-H. Nucleotide diversity in gorillas. *Genetics* **166**, 1375-1383 (2004).

47. Fischer, A., Pollack, J., Thalmann, O., Nickel, B. & Pääbo, S. Demographic history and genetic differentiation in apes. *Curr. Biol.* **16**, 1133-1138 (2006).

48. Rannala, B. & Yang, Z. Bayes estimation of species divergence times and ancestral population sizes using DNA sequences from multiple loci. *Genetics* **164**, 1645-1656 (2003).

49. The International HapMap Consortium. A haplotype map of the human genome. *Nature* **437**, 1299-1320 (2005).

50. Hinds, D. A. *et al.* Whole genome patterns of common DNA variation in three human populations. *Science* **307**, 1072-1079 (2005).

Supplementary Information is linked to the online version of the paper at www.nature.com/nature.

Acknowledgements. We are indebted to G. Coop, W. Enard, I. Hellmann, A. Fischer, P. Johnson, S. Kudaravalli, M. Lachmann, T. Maricic, J. Pritchard, J. Noonan, D. Reich, E. Rubin, M. Slatkin, L. Vigilant and T. Weaver for discussions. We thank A. P. Derevianko, C. Lalueza-Fox, A. Rosas and B. Vandermeersch for fossil samples. We also thank the Croatian Academy of Sciences and Arts for support and the Innovation Fund of Max Planck Society for financial support. 454 Life Sciences thanks NHGRI for continued support for the development of this platform, as well as all of its employees who developed the sequencing system. R.E.G. is supported by an NSF postdoctoral fellowship in Biological Informatics.

Author Contributions. M.P. provided Neanderthal samples and palaeontological information; J.M.R. and S.P. conceived of and initiated the 454 Neanderthal sequencing approach; M.T.R. developed the library preparation method, and generated and processed the sequencing data; J.F.S. planned and coordinated library preparation and sequencing activities; L.D. processed and transferred data between 454 Life Sciences and the MPI; M.E. supervised, planned and coordinated research between MPI and 454 Life Sciences; J.K. and A.W.B. extracted ancient DNA and performed analyses in the "Identification of a Neanderthal fossil for DNA sequencing" section; J.K. and R.E.G. performed analyses in the "Neanderthal mtDNA sequences" section; R.E.G. performed the analyses in the sections "Direct large-scale DNA sequencing" to "Genomic divergence between Neanderthals and humans"; S.E.P. performed analyses in the sections "Ancestral population size" and "Neanderthal sequences and human polymorphisms"; S.P. conceived of the ideas presented in the section "Rationale and prospects for a Neanderthal genome sequence", and initiated, planned and coordinated the study; R.E.G., S.E.P., J.K. and S.P. wrote the paper.

Author Information. Neanderthal fossil extract sequences were deposited at EBI with accession numbers CAAN01000001-CAAN01369630. Reprints and permissions information is available at www.nature.com/reprints. The authors declare competing financial interests: details accompany the paper on www.nature.com/nature. Correspondence and requests for materials should be addressed to R.E.G. (green@eva.mpg.de).

Identification and Analysis of Functional Elements in 1% of the Human Genome by the ENCODE Pilot Project

The ENCODE Project Consortium[*]

Editor's Note

With the human genome sequence completed, the logical next step was to work out how cells interpret the genetic instructions. This paper reveals the first findings of the Encyclopedia of DNA Elements (ENCODE) project, an initiative aiming to identify the functional elements of the human genome. The pilot program, which scrutinizes just 1% of the genome, offers insights into the nature and evolution of DNA sequences. Around half the functional elements appear able to change sequence more freely than expected, challenging the idea that biologically relevant DNA resists change. The study also finds that most DNA is transcribed into RNA, undermining the common picture of our genome as a rather small number of discrete genes amidst a mass of inactive "junk DNA".

We report the generation and analysis of functional data from multiple, diverse experiments performed on a targeted 1% of the human genome as part of the pilot phase of the ENCODE Project. These data have been further integrated and augmented by a number of evolutionary and computational analyses. Together, our results advance the collective knowledge about human genome function in several major areas. First, our studies provide convincing evidence that the genome is pervasively transcribed, such that the majority of its bases can be found in primary transcripts, including non-protein-coding transcripts, and those that extensively overlap one another. Second, systematic examination of transcriptional regulation has yielded new understanding about transcription start sites, including their relationship to specific regulatory sequences and features of chromatin accessibility and histone modification. Third, a more sophisticated view of chromatin structure has emerged, including its inter-relationship with DNA replication and transcriptional regulation. Finally, integration of these new sources of information, in particular with respect to mammalian evolution based on inter- and intra-species sequence comparisons, has yielded new mechanistic and evolutionary insights concerning the functional landscape of the human genome. Together, these studies are defining a path for pursuit of a more comprehensive characterization of human genome function.

THE human genome is an elegant but cryptic store of information. The roughly three billion bases encode, either directly or indirectly, the instructions for synthesizing

---

[*] The full list of authors and affiliations has been removed. The original text is available in the *Nature* online archive.

通过 ENCODE 先导计划鉴定与分析人类基因组 1% 区域内的功能元件

ENCODE 计划协作组[*]

编者按

人类基因组测序完成后的下一步必然是阐释细胞如何执行这个遗传指南。DNA 元件百科全书（ENCODE）计划是一个旨在鉴定人类基因组功能元件的倡议，本文介绍了该计划的早期发现。先导项目仅仔细研究了 1% 的基因组，使人们对 DNA 序列的本质和进化有了初步了解。大约半数的功能元件看起来比预期能够更自由地改变序列，这对生物学相关的 DNA 抵抗改变的观点提出了挑战。大多数的 DNA 被转录成 RNA，这个发现颠覆了我们把基因组看作是相当少量且分散的基因位于大量不活跃的"垃圾 DNA"之间的通俗认识。

作为 ENCODE 计划先导阶段的一部分，针对人类基因组 1% 的目标区域进行了多种不同的实验，得到了功能数据，我们对这些功能数据的产生和分析进行了报道。这些数据已经通过大量的进化和计算分析被进一步整合和扩充。总的来说，我们的结果在几个主要方面增加了对人类基因组功能的认识。首先，我们的研究提供了令人信服的证据，证明了基因组是广泛转录的，以至于它的大部分碱基都可以在原始转录本中找到，这包括非蛋白质编码的转录本和广泛的互相重合的转录本。第二，转录调控的系统研究对转录起始位点产生了新的认识，这包括其与特定调控序列的关系、染色可接近性和组蛋白修饰的特征。第三，一个关于染色质结构的更加复杂精致的图景已经浮现，这包括它与 DNA 复制和转录调控的相互关系。最后，这些新的信息的整合，特别是基于物种间和物种内序列比较对哺乳动物进化的研究，已经对人类基因组的功能图景产生了机制和进化方面新的认识。总而言之，这些研究为进一步阐明人类基因组功能指明了道路。

人类基因组以简洁而隐晦的方式储存信息。大约 30 亿个碱基通过直接或间接的方式编码合成分子的指令，指导合成几乎所有构成人类细胞、组织和器官的分子。

---

* 作者和其他附加信息已经移除，原文可以从《自然》在线数据库中获得。

nearly all the molecules that form each human cell, tissue and organ. Sequencing the human genome[1-3] provided highly accurate DNA sequences for each of the 24 chromosomes. However, at present, we have an incomplete understanding of the protein-coding portions of the genome, and markedly less understanding of both non-protein-coding transcripts and genomic elements that temporally and spatially regulate gene expression. To understand the human genome, and by extension the biological processes it orchestrates and the ways in which its defects can give rise to disease, we need a more transparent view of the information it encodes.

The molecular mechanisms by which genomic information directs the synthesis of different biomolecules has been the focus of much of molecular biology research over the last three decades. Previous studies have typically concentrated on individual genes, with the resulting general principles then providing insights into transcription, chromatin remodelling, messenger RNA splicing, DNA replication and numerous other genomic processes. Although many such principles seem valid as additional genes are investigated, they generally have not provided genome-wide insights about biological function.

The first genome-wide analyses that shed light on human genome function made use of observing the actions of evolution. The ever-growing set of vertebrate genome sequences[4-8] is providing increasing power to reveal the genomic regions that have been most and least acted on by the forces of evolution. However, although these studies convincingly indicate the presence of numerous genomic regions under strong evolutionary constraint, they have less power in identifying the precise bases that are constrained and provide little, if any, insight into why those bases are biologically important. Furthermore, although we have good models for how protein-coding regions evolve, our present understanding about the evolution of other functional genomic regions is poorly developed. Experimental studies that augment what we learn from evolutionary analyses are key for solidifying our insights regarding genome function.

The Encyclopedia of DNA Elements (ENCODE) Project[9] aims to provide a more biologically informative representation of the human genome by using high-throughput methods to identify and catalogue the functional elements encoded. In its pilot phase, 35 groups provided more than 200 experimental and computational data sets that examined in unprecedented detail a targeted 29,998 kilobases (kb) of the human genome. These roughly 30 Mb—equivalent to ~1% of the human genome—are sufficiently large and diverse to allow for rigorous pilot testing of multiple experimental and computational methods. These 30 Mb are divided among 44 genomic regions; approximately 15 Mb reside in 14 regions for which there is already substantial biological knowledge, whereas the other 15 Mb reside in 30 regions chosen by a stratified random-sampling method (see http://www.genome.gov/10506161). The highlights of our findings to date include:

- The human genome is pervasively transcribed, such that the majority of its bases are associated with at least one primary transcript and many transcripts link distal regions to established protein-coding loci.

938

对人类基因组的测序 [1-3] 为 24 条染色体提供了高精度的 DNA 序列。但是目前，我们还不能完整理解基因组的蛋白质编码部分，而对于非蛋白质编码的转录本和在时空水平上调控基因表达的基因组元件，更是知之甚少。为了了解人类基因组，以及它调控的生物学过程和它的缺陷导致疾病的机制，我们需要对它所编码的信息有一个更清楚的认知。

在过去的 30 多年里，基因组信息指导合成不同生物分子的分子机制一直是很多分子生物学研究的焦点。之前的研究通常聚焦于单个基因，获得一般规律，进而促进对转录、染色质重塑、信使 RNA 剪接、DNA 复制和众多其他基因组学过程的认识。尽管许多这样的规律也适用于其他研究的基因，但是它们通常还未提供在全基因组范围内认识生物学功能的信息。

第一个在基因组层面阐明人类基因组功能的研究是关于进化的行为。随着越来越多的脊椎动物基因组被测序 [4-8]，人们越来越能够发现被进化的力量影响最多和最少的基因组区域。不过，尽管这些研究有力地表明，存在大量的基因组在进化上高度保守，但是这些研究在鉴定精确的保守碱基上还不够有力，对于为什么那些碱基在生物学上是重要的也几乎不能提供有用的信息。并且，尽管我们对于蛋白质编码区域如何进化有很好的模型，但是我们目前对其他有功能的基因组区域的了解还很欠缺。为了巩固我们对基因组功能的理解，通过实验研究扩充我们进化分析所得是关键。

DNA 元件百科全书（ENCODE）计划 [9] 旨在利用高通量方法对人类基因组所编码的功能元件进行鉴定和分类，进而提供人类基因组更加具有生物学信息的表征。在该计划的先导阶段，35 个课题组贡献了超过 200 个实验和计算数据集，以前所未有的详细度研究了人类基因组特定的 29,998 千碱基（kb）区域。这大约 30 Mb——相当于人类基因组的 ~ 1%——已经足够大和足够多样，可以严格地用来先期测试多种实验和计算方法。这 30 Mb 分布在 44 个基因组区域；大约 15 Mb 位于 14 个已经有大量的生物学知识的区域，而另外 15 Mb 则位于 30 个通过分层随机抽样方法选择的区域（见 http://www.genome.gov/10506161）。目前我们研究发现的亮点包括：

- 人类基因组是广泛转录的，以至于它的大部分碱基至少和一个原始转录本相关联，并且许多转录本将远端区域与已知的蛋白质编码基因座相关联。

- Many novel non-protein-coding transcripts have been identified, with many of these overlapping protein-coding loci and others located in regions of the genome previously thought to be transcriptionally silent.

- Numerous previously unrecognized transcription start sites have been identified, many of which show chromatin structure and sequence-specific protein-binding properties similar to well-understood promoters.

- Regulatory sequences that surround transcription start sites are symmetrically distributed, with no bias towards upstream regions.

- Chromatin accessibility and histone modification patterns are highly predictive of both the presence and activity of transcription start sites.

- Distal DNaseI hypersensitive sites have characteristic histone modification patterns that reliably distinguish them from promoters; some of these distal sites show marks consistent with insulator function.

- DNA replication timing is correlated with chromatin structure.

- A total of 5% of the bases in the genome can be confidently identified as being under evolutionary constraint in mammals; for approximately 60% of these constrained bases, there is evidence of function on the basis of the results of the experimental assays performed to date.

- Although there is general overlap between genomic regions identified as functional by experimental assays and those under evolutionary constraint, not all bases within these experimentally defined regions show evidence of constraint.

- Different functional elements vary greatly in their sequence variability across the human population and in their likelihood of residing within a structurally variable region of the genome.

- Surprisingly, many functional elements are seemingly unconstrained across mammalian evolution. This suggests the possibility of a large pool of neutral elements that are biochemically active but provide no specific benefit to the organism. This pool may serve as a "warehouse" for natural selection, potentially acting as the source of lineage-specific elements and functionally conserved but non-orthologous elements between species.

Below, we first provide an overview of the experimental techniques used for our studies, after which we describe the insights gained from analysing and integrating the generated data sets. We conclude with a perspective of what we have learned to date about this 1% of the human genome and what we believe the prospects are for a broader and deeper

- 许多新的非蛋白质编码转录本被鉴定，其中很多与蛋白质编码基因座重合，其他的则位于以前被认为是不转录的基因组区域。

- 大量的以前未被识别的转录起始位点被鉴定，其中很多具有与已知的启动子类似的染色质结构和序列特异的蛋白质结合特性。

- 转录起始位点附近的调控序列是对称分布的，并没有偏向上游区域。

- 染色质可接近性和组蛋白修饰特征不仅可以准确预测转录起始位点的存在，而且可以预测转录起始位点的活性。

- 远端的 DNA 酶 I 超敏感位点含有与启动子截然不同的组蛋白修饰特征；其中一些远端位点含有的标志物与绝缘子功能一致。

- DNA 复制时相与染色质的结构相关。

- 基因组总计 5% 的碱基可以明确地鉴定为在哺乳动物中进化保守；基于目前已有的实验结果，大约 60% 的保守碱基，有证据表明是有功能的。

- 尽管实验鉴定到的功能性基因组区域与进化保守的区域有广泛的重叠，但是这些实验确定的区域内，并非所有的碱基都有进化保守的证据。

- 不同的功能元件在人群中序列变异性方面以及位于基因组结构可变区的可能性方面差别很大。

- 出人意料的是，很多功能元件看起来在哺乳动物进化中并不保守。这暗示可能存在一个巨大的中性元件库，这些中性元件在生化上活跃，但是对机体并没有特别的益处。这个中性元件库可以作为一个用于自然选择的"仓库"，作为谱系特异元件以及种间功能保守但非同源元件的潜在来源。

接下来，我们首先概述我们研究中所用到的实验技术，然后描述由分析和整合这些实验产生的数据集所得到的见解。最后我们总结了目前 1% 的人类基因组中已有的发现，并对更广更深地研究人类基因组中的功能元件进行了展望。为了帮助读

investigation of the functional elements in the human genome. To aid the reader, Box 1 provides a glossary for many of the abbreviations used throughout this paper.

Box 1. Frequently used abbreviations in this paper

AR Ancient repeat: a repeat that was inserted into the early mammalian lineage and has since become dormant; the majority of ancient repeats are thought to be neutrally evolving

CAGE tag A short sequence from the 5′ end of a transcript

CDS Coding sequence: a region of a cDNA or genome that encodes proteins

ChIP-chip Chromatin immunoprecipitation followed by detection of the products using a genomic tiling array

CNV Copy number variants: regions of the genome that have large duplications in some individuals in the human population

CS Constrained sequence: a genomic region associated with evidence of negative selection (that is, rejection of mutations relative to neutral regions)

DHS DNaseI hypersensitive site: a region of the genome showing a sharply different sensitivity to DNaseI compared with its immediate locale

EST Expressed sequence tag: a short sequence of a cDNA indicative of expression at this point

FAIRE Formaldehyde-assisted isolation of regulatory elements: a method to assay open chromatin using formaldehyde crosslinking followed by detection of the products using a genomic tiling array

FDR False discovery rate: a statistical method for setting thresholds on statistical tests to correct for multiple testing

GENCODE Integrated annotation of existing cDNA and protein resources to define transcripts with both manual review and experimental testing procedures

GSC Genome structure correction: a method to adapt statistical tests to make fewer assumptions about the distribution of features on the genome sequence. This provides a conservative correction to standard tests

HMM Hidden Markov model: a machine-learning technique that can establish optimal parameters for a given model to explain the observed data

Indel An insertion or deletion; two sequences often show a length difference within alignments, but it is not always clear whether this reflects a previous insertion or a deletion

者阅读，框 1 提供了一个词汇表，里面有本论文所用的很多缩写词。

框 1. 本文常用的缩写词

AR 古老的重复：一种在早期就插入到哺乳动物谱系但自此休眠的重复；大部分古老的重复被认为正在进行中性进化

CAGE tag 转录本 5′ 端的短序列

CDS 编码序列：cDNA 区域或编码蛋白质的基因组区域

ChIP-chip 染色质免疫沉淀后利用基因组叠瓦式阵列检测产物

CNV 拷贝数变异：在人群中一些个体中发生大片段重复的基因组区域

CS 保守序列：有证据表明跟负选择相关的基因组区域（也就是，跟中性区域相比更排斥突变）

DHS DNA 酶 I 超敏感位点：跟附近区域相比，对 DNA 酶 I 非常敏感的基因组区域

EST 表达序列标签：表示在该点表达的 cDNA 短序列

FAIRE 基于甲醛的调控元件分离：一种检测开放染色质的方法，甲醛交联后利用基因组叠瓦式阵列检测产物

FDR 错误发现率：一种为统计学检验设定阈值以校正多重检验的统计学方法

GENCODE 通过人工审查和实验检测的方法，整合注释已知的 cDNA 和蛋白质资源，以定义转录本

GSC 基因组结构校正：一种适合统计学检验的方法，使其对基因组序列上的分布特征做出更少假设。这为标准检验提供了一种保守的校正

HMM 隐马尔可夫模型：一种机器学习技术，能为一个给定的模型建立最优的变量以解释观察到的数据

Indel 插入或缺失；在比对两个序列时经常出现长度不一的情况，但是有时并不清楚这反映的是一个插入还是缺失

PET A short sequence that contains both the 5′ and 3′ ends of a transcript

RACE Rapid amplification of cDNA ends: a technique for amplifying cDNA sequences between a known internal position in a transcript and its 5′ end

RFBR Regulatory factor binding region: a genomic region found by a ChIP-chip assay to be bound by a protein factor

RFBR-Seqsp Regulatory factor binding regions that are from sequence-specific binding factors

RT–PCR Reverse transcriptase polymerase chain reaction: a technique for amplifying a specific region of a transcript

RxFrag Fragment of a RACE reaction: a genomic region found to be present in a RACE product by an unbiased tiling-array assay

SNP Single nucleotide polymorphism: a single base pair change between two individuals in the human population

STAGE Sequence tag analysis of genomic enrichment: a method similar to ChIP-chip for detecting protein factor binding regions but using extensive short sequence determination rather than genomic tiling arrays

SVM Support vector machine: a machine-learning technique that can establish an optimal classifier on the basis of labelled training data

TR50 A measure of replication timing corresponding to the time in the cell cycle when 50% of the cells have replicated their DNA at a specific genomic position

TSS Transcription start site

TxFrag Fragment of a transcript: a genomic region found to be present in a transcript by an unbiased tiling-array assay

Un.TxFrag A TxFrag that is not associated with any other functional annotation

UTR Untranslated region: part of a cDNA either at the 5′ or 3′ end that does not encode a protein sequence

Experimental Techniques

Table 1 (expanded in Supplementary Information section 1.1) lists the major experimental techniques used for the studies reported here, relevant acronyms, and references reporting the generated data sets. These data sets reflect over 400 million experimental data points (603 million data points if one includes comparative sequencing bases). In describing the major

PET 同时包含一个转录本 5′和 3′端的短序列

RACE cDNA 末端快速扩增：一种扩增技术，扩增一个转录本中间的已知位置和它的 5′端之间的 cDNA 序列

RFBR 调控因子结合区域：ChIP-chip 实验发现的与蛋白质因子结合的基因组区域

RFBR-Seqsp 被序列特异的结合因子所结合的调控因子结合区域

RT–PCR 反转录酶聚合酶链式反应：扩增转录本特定区域的技术

RxFrag RACE 反应的片段：通过无偏性叠瓦式阵列实验在 RACE 产物中发现的基因组区域

SNP 单核苷酸多态性：人群中两个个体间单个碱基对的改变

STAGE 基因组丰度的序列标签分析：类似于 ChIP-chip 用于检测蛋白质因子结合区域的方法，不过是利用大量短序列确定，而不是基因组叠瓦式阵列实验

SVM 支持向量机：一种机器学习技术，能基于标记的训练数据建立最优的分类器

TR50 一种衡量复制时相的方法，对应于细胞周期中 50% 的细胞在特定的基因组位置复制 DNA 所用的时间

TSS 转录起始位点

TxFrag 转录本片段：通过无偏性叠瓦式阵列实验在转录本中发现基因组片段

Un.TxFrag 与任何功能注释均不关联的 TxFrag

UTR 非翻译区：位于 5′或 3′端的不编码蛋白质序列的部分 cDNA

实 验 技 术

表 1（在补充信息 1.1 中有扩充）列出了本文报道的研究所用的主要实验技术、相关的首字母缩略词以及报道这些实验技术所涉及的参考文献。这些数据集反映了超过 4 亿个实验数据点（如果包含比较测序的碱基则是 6.03 亿个数据点）。在描述主

results and initial conclusions, we seek to distinguish "biochemical function" from "biological role". Biochemical function reflects the direct behaviour of a molecule(s), whereas biological role is used to describe the consequence(s) of this function for the organism. Genome-analysis techniques nearly always focus on biochemical function but not necessarily on biological role. This is because the former is more amenable to large-scale data-generation methods, whereas the latter is more difficult to assay on a large scale.

Table 1. Summary of types of experimental techniques used in ENCODE

Feature class	Experimental technique(s)	Abbreviations	References	Number of experimental data points
Transcription	Tiling array, integrated annotation	TxFrag, RxFrag, GENCODE	117 118 19 119	63,348,656
5′ ends of transcripts*	Tag sequencing	PET, CAGE	121 13	864,964
Histone modifications	Tiling array	Histone nomenclature†, RFBR	46	4,401,291
Chromatin‡ structure	QT-PCR, tiling array	DHS, FAIRE	42 43 44 122	15,318,324
Sequence-specific factors	Tiling array, tag sequencing, promoter assays	STAGE, ChIP-Chip, ChIP-PET, RFBR	41, 52 11, 120 123 81 34, 51 124 49 33 40	324,846,018
Replication	Tiling array	TR50	59 75	14,735,740
Computational analysis	Computational methods	CCI, RFBR cluster	80 125 10 16 126 127	NA
Comparative sequence analysis*	Genomic sequencing, multi-sequence alignments, computational analysis	CS	87 86 26	NA
Polymorphisms*	Resequencing, copy number variation	CNV	103 128	NA

* Not all data generated by the ENCODE Project.

† Histone code nomenclature follows the Brno nomenclature as described in ref. 129.

‡ Also contains histone modification.

要的结果和初始的结论上，我们试着区分"生化功能"和"生物学功能"。生化功能反映的是一个或多个分子的直接行为，而生物学功能则用来描述这个功能对机体的影响。全基因分析技术几乎都是聚焦于生化功能，并不一定关心生物学功能。这是因为前者更容易被大规模数据产生方法所检验，而后者在大通量下却更难分析。

表 1. ENCODE 中使用的实验技术类型总结

特征分类	实验技术	缩写	参考文献	实验数据点的数量
转录	叠瓦式阵列、整合注释	TxFrag、RxFrag、GENCODE	117 118 19 119	63,348,656
转录本 5′端 *	标签测序	PET、CAGE	121 13	864,964
组蛋白修饰	叠瓦式阵列	组蛋白系统命名法†、RFBR	46	4,401,291
染色质结构‡	QT-PCR、叠瓦式阵列	DHS、FAIRE	42 43 44 122	15,318,324
序列特异因子	叠瓦式阵列、标签测序、启动子实验	STAGE、ChIP-chip、ChIP-PET、RFBR	41、52 11、120 123 81 34、51 124 49 33 40	324,846,018
复制	叠瓦式阵列	TR50	59 75	14,735,740
计算分析	计算方法	CCI、RFBR 簇	80 125 10 16 126 127	NA
序列比较分析 *	基因组测序、多重序列比对、计算分析	CS	87 86 26	NA
多态性 *	重测序、拷贝数目变异	CNV	103 128	NA

* 并非所有的数据都由 ENCODE 计划产生。

† 组蛋白密码系统命名法遵循参考文献 129 中描述的布尔诺系统命名法。

‡ 也包括组蛋白修饰。

The ENCODE pilot project aimed to establish redundancy with respect to the findings represented by different data sets. In some instances, this involved the intentional use of different assays that were based on a similar technique, whereas in other situations, different techniques assayed the same biochemical function. Such redundancy has allowed methods to be compared and consensus data sets to be generated, much of which is discussed in companion papers, such as the ChIP-chip platform comparison[10,11]. All ENCODE data have been released after verification but before this publication, as befits a "community resource" project (see http://www.wellcome.ac.uk/doc_wtd003208.html). Verification is defined as when the experiment is reproducibly confirmed (see Supplementary Information section 1.2). The main portal for ENCODE data is provided by the UCSC Genome Browser (http://genome.ucsc.edu/ENCODE/); this is augmented by multiple other websites (see Supplementary Information section 1.1).

A common feature of genomic analyses is the need to assess the significance of the co-occurrence of features or of other statistical tests. One confounding factor is the heterogeneity of the genome, which can produce uninteresting correlations of variables distributed across the genome. We have developed and used a statistical framework that mitigates many of these hidden correlations by adjusting the appropriate null distribution of the test statistics. We term this correction procedure genome structure correction (GSC) (see Supplementary Information section 1.3).

In the next five sections, we detail the various biological insights of the pilot phase of the ENCODE Project.

Transcription

Overview. RNA transcripts are involved in many cellular functions, either directly as biologically active molecules or indirectly by encoding other active molecules. In the conventional view of genome organization, sets of RNA transcripts (for example, messenger RNAs) are encoded by distinct loci, with each usually dedicated to a single biological role (for example, encoding a specific protein). However, this picture has substantially grown in complexity in recent years[12]. Other forms of RNA molecules (such as small nucleolar RNAs and micro (mi)RNAs) are known to exist, and often these are encoded by regions that intercalate with protein-coding genes. These observations are consistent with the well-known discrepancy between the levels of observable mRNAs and large structural RNAs compared with the total RNA in a cell, suggesting that there are numerous RNA species yet to be classified[13-15]. In addition, studies of specific loci have indicated the presence of RNA transcripts that have a role in chromatin maintenance and other regulatory control. We sought to assay and analyse transcription comprehensively across the 44 ENCODE regions in an effort to understand the repertoire of encoded RNA molecules.

Transcript maps. We used three methods to identify transcripts emanating from the ENCODE regions: hybridization of RNA (either total or polyA-selected) to unbiased tiling

ENCODE 先导计划旨在建立不同数据集发现结果的冗余。在一些情形下，这包括专门使用基于相似技术的不同实验结果，而在其他情形下，则是不同的技术测定同一生化功能。这种冗余使得不同方法可以进行比较，产生一致的数据集，这部分在关于比较的文章中有很多讨论，比如 ChIP-chip 平台的比较 [10,11]。作为一个"共享资源"计划，所有经过验证的 ENCODE 数据在本文发表前就已经发布了（详见 http://www.wellcome.ac.uk/doc_wtd003208.html）。验证的定义是实验被重复确认（详见补充信息 1.2）。UCSC 基因组浏览器提供获取 ENCODE 数据的主要入口（http://genome.ucsc.edu/ENCODE/）；除此之外还有多个其他的网站（详见补充信息 1.1）。

基因组分析的一个常见的特征是需要评估特征共发生的显著性，或者其他统计学检验的显著性。一个混淆因素是基因组的异质性，这会使得分布于基因组上的变量产生无意义的相关。我们已经开发和使用了一种统计学框架，它通过检验统计调整合适的零分布，以减少很多这样的隐含相关。我们将这种校正方法称为基因组结构校正（GSC）（详见补充信息 1.3）。

在接下来的五部分中，我们详细介绍 ENCODE 先导计划的各种生物学发现。

转　　录

概况　RNA 转录本通过直接作为生物学活性分子，或者间接编码其他活性分子，参与很多细胞功能。关于基因组结构，传统上认为，不同的 RNA 转录本（如信使 RNA）由不同的基因座编码，每一种 RNA 转录本通常具有单独一种生物学功能（如编码一个特定的蛋白质）。但是，近年来这种描述逐渐变得复杂起来 [12]，我们已经发现其他形式的 RNA 分子（如小核仁 RNA 和微 RNA（miRNA））的存在，它们大多间插在编码蛋白质的基因区域。众所周知，目前观察到的 mRNA 和大的结构性 RNA 水平与细胞总 RNA 水平不符，这与上述发现是一致的，说明还有大量的 RNA 类型未被归类 [13-15]。另外，特定基因座的研究已经表明，RNA 转录本的存在在染色质维持和其他调节控制中有重要作用。为了理解作为一种分子库的编码 RNA，我们全面地检测和分析了 44 个 ENCODE 区域的转录。

转录本图谱　我们使用了三种方法来鉴定 ENCODE 区域产生的转录本：RNA 杂交（总的或多聚 A 筛选的）到无偏性叠瓦式阵列（详见补充信息 2.1），在 5′端或

arrays (see Supplementary Information section 2.1), tag sequencing of cap-selected RNA at the 5′ or joint 5′/3′ ends (see Supplementary Information sections 2.2 and S2.3), and integrated annotation of available complementary DNA and EST sequences involving computational, manual, and experimental approaches[16] (see Supplementary Information section 2.4). We abbreviate the regions identified by unbiased tiling arrays as TxFrags, the cap-selected RNAs as CAGE or PET tags (see Box 1), and the integrated annotation as GENCODE transcripts. When a TxFrag does not overlap a GENCODE annotation, we call it an Un.TxFrag. Validation of these various studies is described in papers reporting these data sets[17] (see Supplementary Information sections 2.1.4 and 2.1.5).

These methods recapitulate previous findings, but provide enhanced resolution owing to the larger number of tissues sampled and the integration of results across the three approaches (see Table 2). To begin with, our studies show that 14.7% of the bases represented in the unbiased tiling arrays are transcribed in at least one tissue sample. Consistent with previous work[14,15], many (63%) TxFrags reside outside of GENCODE annotations, both in intronic (40.9%) and intergenic (22.6%) regions. GENCODE annotations are richer than the more-conservative RefSeq or Ensembl annotations, with 2,608 transcripts clustered into 487 loci, leading to an average of 5.4 transcripts per locus. Finally, extensive testing of predicted protein-coding sequences outside of GENCODE annotations was positive in only 2% of cases[16], suggesting that GENCODE annotations cover nearly all protein-coding sequences. The GENCODE annotations are categorized both by likely function (mainly, the presence of an open reading frame) and by classification evidence (for example, transcripts based solely on ESTs are distinguished from other scenarios); this classification is not strongly correlated with expression levels (see Supplementary Information sections 2.4.2 and 2.4.3).

Table 2. Bases detected in processed transcripts either as a GENCODE exon, a TxFrag, or as either a GENCODE exon or a TxFrag

	GENCODE exon	TxFrag	Either GENCODE exon or TxFrag
Total detectable transcripts (bases)	1,776,157 (5.9%)	1,369,611 (4.6%)	2,519,280 (8.4%)
Transcripts detected in tiled regions of arrays (bases)	1,447,192 (9.8%)	1,369,611 (9.3%)	2,163,303 (14.7%)

Percentages are of total bases in ENCODE in the first row and bases tiled in arrays in the second row.

Analyses of more biological samples have allowed a richer description of the transcription specificity (see Fig. 1 and Supplementary Information section 2.5). We found that 40% of TxFrags are present in only one sample, whereas only 2% are present in all samples. Although exon-containing TxFrags are more likely (74%) to be expressed in more than one sample, 45% of unannotated TxFrags are also expressed in multiple samples. GENCODE annotations of separate loci often (42%) overlap with respect to their genomic coordinates, in particular on opposite strands (33% of loci). Further analysis of GENCODE-annotated sequences with respect to the positions of open reading frames revealed that some component exons do not have the expected synonymous versus non-synonymous substitution patterns of protein-coding sequence (see Supplement Information section 2.6)

同时在 5′/3′ 端采用标签测序经帽子筛选的 RNA（详见补充信息 2.2 和 S2.3），以及通过计算、手工和实验方法整合注释已知互补的 DNA 和 EST 序列[16]（详见补充信息 2.4）。我们把经无偏性叠瓦式阵列鉴定到的区域简称为 TxFrag，将经帽子筛选的 RNA 称为 CAGE 或 PET 标签（详见框 1），将整合的注释称为 GENCODE 转录本。对于不与 GENCODE 注释重合的 TxFrag，我们称之为 Un.TxFrag。这些不同研究的验证在报道这些数据集的文章中有描述[17]（详见补充信息 2.1.4 和 2.1.5）。

这些方法虽然再现了之前的发现，但这次不仅有更多组织取样，还整合了三种不同的方法，从而提供了更高的分辨率（见表 2）。首先，我们的研究发现，无偏性叠瓦式阵列上的碱基有 14.7% 在至少一种组织样本中转录。与之前的研究一致[14,15]，很多（63%）TxFrag 位于 GENCODE 注释之外，内含子区有（40.9%），基因间区有（22.6%）。与相对保守的 RefSeq 或 Ensembl 注释相比，GENCODE 注释更丰富，2,608 个转录本聚集成 487 个基因座，平均每个基因座 5.4 个转录本。最后，对位于 GENCODE 注释之外的预测蛋白编码序列进行了广泛的检测，发现只有 2% 是阳性的[16]，这说明 GENCODE 注释涵盖了几乎所有的蛋白质编码序列。既可通过可能的功能（主要是开放阅读框的存在）也可通过类别证据（例如，仅基于 EST 的转录本跟其他类型是不同的）对 GENCODE 注释进行分类；这种分类跟表达水平并没有很强的相关性（详见补充信息 2.4.2 和 2.4.3）。

表 2. 在处理过的转录本中检测到的是 GENCODE 外显子、TxFrag 或两者其一的碱基

	GENCODE 外显子	TxFrag	GENCODE 外显子或 TxFrag
总的检测到的转录本（碱基）	1,776,157 (5.9%)	1,369,611 (4.6%)	2,519,280 (8.4%)
在阵列的叠瓦区域检测到的转录本（碱基）	1,447,192 (9.8%)	1,369,611 (9.3%)	2,163,303 (14.7%)

比例是第一行中 ENCODE 中总的碱基和第二行阵列中叠瓦的碱基。

对更多生物学样本的分析更加丰富了对转录本特异性的描述（详见图 1 和补充信息 2.5）。我们发现 40% 的 TxFrag 仅在一种样本中存在，只有 2% 的 TxFrag 在所有样本中都存在。尽管含有外显子的 TxFrag 更倾向于（74%）在超过一种样本中表达，45% 未被注释的 TxFrag 也在多种样本中表达。不同基因座 42% 的 GENCODE 注释大多与它们的基因组位置重合，特别是与另一条链（33% 的基因座）。根据开放阅读框的位置进一步分析 GENCODE 注释的序列，发现一些组成的外显子没有预期的蛋白质编码序列中同义和非同义替换情况（详见补充信息 2.6），一些外显子含

and some have deletions incompatible with protein structure[18]. Such exons are on average less expressed (25% versus 87% by RT–PCR; see Supplementary Information section 2.7) than exons involved in more than one transcript (see Supplementary Information section 2.4.3), but when expressed have a tissue distribution comparable to well-established genes.

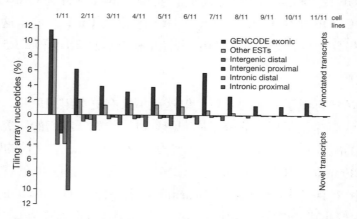

Fig. 1. Annotated and unannotated TxFrags detected in different cell lines. The proportion of different types of transcripts detected in the indicated number of cell lines (from 1/11 at the far left to 11/11 at the far right) is shown. The data for annotated and unannotated TxFrags are indicated separately, and also split into different categories based on GENCODE classification: exonic, intergenic (proximal being within 5 kb of a gene and distal being otherwise), intronic (proximal being within 5 kb of an intron and distal being otherwise), and matching other ESTs not used in the GENCODE annotation (principally because they were unspliced). The y axis indicates the per cent of tiling array nucleotides present in that class for that number of samples (combination of cell lines and tissues).

Critical questions are raised by the presence of a large amount of unannotated transcription with respect to how the corresponding sequences are organized in the genome—do these reflect longer transcripts that include known loci, do they link known loci, or are they completely separate from known loci? We further investigated these issues using both computational and new experimental techniques.

Unannotated transcription. Consistent with previous findings, the Un.TxFrags did not show evidence of encoding proteins (see Supplementary Information section 2.8). One might expect Un.TxFrags to be linked within transcripts that exhibit coordinated expression and have similar conservation profiles across species. To test this, we clustered Un.TxFrags using two methods. The first method[19] used expression levels in 11 cell lines or conditions, dinucleotide composition, location relative to annotated genes, and evolutionary conservation profiles to cluster TxFrags (both unannotated and annotated). By this method, 14% of Un.TxFrags could be assigned to annotated loci, and 21% could be clustered into 200 novel loci (with an average of ~7 TxFrags per locus). We experimentally examined these novel loci to study the connectivity of transcripts amongst Un.TxFrags and between Un.TxFrags and known exons. Overall, about 40% of the connections (18 out of 46) were validated by RT–PCR. The second clustering method involved analysing a time course (0, 2, 8 and 32 h) of expression changes in human HL60 cells following retinoic-acid

有与蛋白质结构不相容的缺失[18]。这种外显子(详见补充信息 2.7)比参与一种以上转录本的外显子(详见补充信息 2.4.3)平均表达水平更低(根据 RT–PCR 是 25% 比 87%),不过,当它们表达时,其组织分布与已确定的基因相比差别不大。

图 1. 不同细胞系中检测到的注释和未注释的 TxFrag。在指明数量的细胞系中检测到的不同类型的转录本的比例(从最左边的 1/11 到最右边的 11/11)。注释和未注释的 TxFrag 的数据分开展示,并且还基于 GENCODE 分类分成了不同的类别:外显子、基因间(距基因 5 kb 以内是近端,大于 5 kb 则是远端)、内含子(距内含子 5 kb 以内是近端,大于 5 kb 则是远端)和未在 GENCODE 注释中使用的匹配其他 EST(主要是因为它们没有剪接)。y 轴表示特定数量的样本(包括了细胞系和组织)特定分类下检测到的叠瓦式阵列核苷酸的百分比。

大量未注释转录本的存在带来了一个重要问题:它们相应的序列在基因组中是如何组织的——它们是否反映了包含已知基因座的更长转录本,它们是否与已知基因座有联系,或者它们是否完全独立于已知基因座之外?我们利用计算和新实验技术进一步探究了这些问题。

未被注释的转录 与之前的发现一致,没有证据表明 Un.TxFrag 编码蛋白质(详见补充信息 2.8)。我们期待 Un.TxFrag 在协调表达且在物种间有相似保守性的转录本中可能有关联。为检验这种猜测,我们利用两种方法将 Un.TxFrag 聚类。第一种方法[19]利用 11 种细胞系或条件下表达水平、二核苷酸构成、相对注释基因的位置和进化保守谱来聚类 TxFrag(未注释的和已注释的)。通过这种方法,14% 的 Un.TxFrag 能被分配到注释的基因座,21% 能被聚类成 200 个新的基因座(平均一个基因座大约 7 个 TxFrag)。我们利用实验检查了这些新的基因座,以研究 Un.TxFrag 内部以及 Un.TxFrag 跟已知的外显子间的转录本的关联性。总体上,大约 40% 的关联(46 个中有 18 个)被 RT–PCR 验证。第二种聚类方法是分析视黄酸刺激人 HL60 细胞后一段时间内(0、2、8 和 32 小时)的表达变化。这是一个描述注释基因座表达

stimulation. There is a coordinated program of expression changes from annotated loci, which can be shown by plotting Pearson correlation values of the expression levels of exons inside annotated loci versus unrelated exons (see Supplementary Information section 2.8.2). Similarly, there is coordinated expression of nearby Un.TxFrags, albeit lower, though still significantly different from randomized sets. Both clustering methods indicate that there is coordinated behaviour of many Un.TxFrags, consistent with them residing in connected transcripts.

Transcript connectivity. We used a combination of RACE and tiling arrays[20] to investigate the diversity of transcripts emanating from protein-coding loci. Analogous to TxFrags, we refer to transcripts detected using RACE followed by hybridization to tiling arrays as RxFrags. We performed RACE to examine 399 protein-coding loci (those loci found entirely in ENCODE regions) using RNA derived from 12 tissues, and were able to unambiguously detect 4,573 RxFrags for 359 loci (see Supplementary Information section 2.9). Almost half of these RxFrags (2,324) do not overlap a GENCODE exon, and most (90%) loci have at least one novel RxFrag, which often extends a considerable distance beyond the 5′ end of the locus. Figure 2 shows the distribution of distances between these new RACE-detected ends and the previously annotated TSS of each locus. The average distance of the extensions is between 50 kb and 100 kb, with many extensions (> 20%) being more than 200 kb. Consistent with the known presence of overlapping genes in the human genome, our findings reveal evidence for an overlapping gene at 224 loci, with transcripts from 180 of these loci (~50% of the RACE-positive loci) appearing to have incorporated at least one exon from an upstream gene.

Fig. 2. Length of genomic extensions to GENCODE-annotated genes on the basis of RACE experiments followed by array hybridizations (RxFrags). The indicated bars reflect the frequency of extension lengths among different length classes. The solid line shows the cumulative frequency of extensions of that length or greater. Most of the extensions are greater than 50 kb from the annotated gene (see text for details).

变化的协调性项目，通过跟无关外显子相比较描绘注释基因座外显子表达水平的皮尔逊相关值（详见补充信息 2.8.2）。同样，靠近的 Un.TxFrag 协调表达，虽然水平更低一些，但仍然与随机组显著不同。这两种聚类方法说明很多 Un.TxFrag 存在协调关系，这与它们位于相关联转录本上一致。

转录本的关联性　我们联合使用 RACE 和叠瓦式阵列[20]来研究蛋白质编码基因座产生的转录本的多样性。类似于 TxFrag，我们称 RACE 后杂交到叠瓦式阵列所检测到的转录本为 RxFrag。利用 12 种组织的 RNA，我们通过 RACE 检测了 399 个蛋白质编码基因座（这些基因座全部位于 ENCODE 区域），能够确定地在 359 个基因座检测到 4,573 个 RxFrag（详见补充信息 2.9）。这些 RxFrag 近乎半数（2,324 个）不与 GENCODE 外显子重合，并且大部分基因座（90%）至少有一个全新的 RxFrag，这些全新的 RxFrag 大多从基因座的 5′ 端延伸相当长的距离。图 2 展示了各个基因座中这些 RACE 检测到的全新的末端与已注释的 TSS 之间的距离的分布。延伸的平均距离在 50 kb 到 100 kb 之间，很多（> 20%）超过了 200 kb。与已知人类基因组中存在重合基因一致，我们发现 224 个基因座存在重合基因的证据，其中 180 个基因座（~50% 的 RACE 阳性基因座）的转录本看起来包含了上游基因的至少一个外显子。

图 2. 基于 RACE 实验结合微阵列杂交（RxFrag）得到 GENCODE 注释基因的延伸长度。各个条表示在不同长度类别下延伸长度的频率。实线表示特定长度及其以上的延伸的累积频率。大部分延伸距离注释基因超过 50 kb（详见正文）。

To characterize further the 5′ RxFrag extensions, we performed RT–PCR followed by cloning and sequencing for 550 of the 5′ RxFrags (including the 261 longest extensions identified for each locus). The approach of mapping RACE products using microarrays is a combination method previously described and validated in several studies[14,17,20]. Hybridization of the RT–PCR products to tiling arrays confirmed connectivity in almost 60% of the cases. Sequenced clones confirmed transcript extensions. Longer extensions were harder to clone and sequence, but 5 out of 18 RT–PCR-positive extensions over 100 kb were verified by sequencing (see Supplementary Information section 2.9.7 and ref. 17). The detection of numerous RxFrag extensions coupled with evidence of considerable intronic transcription indicates that protein-coding loci are more transcriptionally complex than previously thought. Instead of the traditional view that many genes have one or more alternative transcripts that code for alternative proteins, our data suggest that a given gene may both encode multiple protein products and produce other transcripts that include sequences from both strands and from neighbouring loci (often without encoding a different protein). Figure 3 illustrates such a case, in which a new fusion transcript is expressed in the small intestine, and consists of at least three coding exons from the *ATP5O* gene and at least two coding exons from the *DONSON* gene, with no evidence of sequences from two intervening protein-coding genes (*ITSN1* and *CRYZL1*).

Fig. 3. Overview of RACE experiments showing a gene fusion. Transcripts emanating from the region between the *DONSON* and *ATP5O* genes. A 330-kb interval of human chromosome 21 (within ENm005) is shown, which contains four annotated genes: *DONSON*, *CRYZL1*, *ITSN1* and *ATP5O*. The 5′ RACE products generated from small intestine RNA and detected by tiling-array analyses (RxFrags) are shown along the top. Along the bottom is shown the placement of a cloned and sequenced RT–PCR product that has two exons from the *DONSON* gene followed by three exons from the *ATP5O* gene; these sequences are separated by a 300 kb intron in the genome. A PET tag shows the termini of a transcript consistent with this RT–PCR product.

Pseudogenes. Pseudogenes, reviewed in refs 21 and 22, are generally considered non-functional copies of genes, are sometimes transcribed and often complicate analysis of transcription owing to close sequence similarity to functional genes. We used various computational methods to identify 201 pseudogenes (124 processed and 77 non-processed) in the ENCODE regions (see Supplementary Information section 2.10 and ref. 23). Tiling-array analysis of 189 of these revealed that 56% overlapped at least one TxFrag. However, possible cross-hybridization between the pseudogenes and their corresponding parent genes may have confounded such analyses. To assess better the extent of pseudogene transcription, 160 pseudogenes (111 processed and 49 non-processed) were examined for expression using RACE/tiling-array analysis (see Supplementary Information section 2.9.2). Transcripts were detected for 14 pseudogenes (8 processed and 6 non-processed) in at least

956

为了进一步研究 5′ RxFrag 延伸的特征，我们对 550 个 5′ RxFrag(包括各个基因座延伸最长的 261 个)进行了 RT-PCR，然后进行克隆和测序。通过微阵列检测 RACE 产物的方法是一种之前报道的并且被很多研究验证过的联合方法[14,17,20]。将 RT-PCR 产物杂交到叠瓦式阵列验证了几乎 60% 的连通情况。被测序的克隆验证了转录本的延伸。越长的延伸越难克隆测序，但是 18 个超过 100 kb 的 RT-PCR 阳性延伸中，有 5 个经测序验证(详见补充信息 2.9.7 和参考文献 17)。大量的 RxFrag 延伸被检测到，并且有证据表明有相当数量的内含子转录本存在，都说明蛋白质编码基因座的转录要比之前想象的更加复杂。传统的观点认为很多基因含有一个或多个选择性转录本，编码选择性蛋白质，而我们的数据则暗示一个特定的基因可能既编码多个蛋白质产物，又产生包含两条链以及附近基因座序列的其他转录本(大多不编码其他蛋白质)。图 3 展示了这样一个例子来加以说明，在这个例子中，一个新的融合转录本在小肠中表达，它含有 ATP5O 基因的至少三个编码外显子和 DONSON 基因的至少两个编码外显子，但是并没有证据显示它含有位于这两个干扰蛋白编码基因(ITSN1 和 CRYZL1)的序列。

图 3. 概述 RACE 实验，展示基因融合现象。转录本产生于 DONSON 和 ARP5O 基因间区域。图中展示了人类 21 号染色体的一段 330 kb 的区域(在 ENm005 中)，它包含四个注释基因：DONSON、CRYZL1、ITSN1 和 ATP5O。顶端展示的是叠瓦式阵列检测到的来自小肠 RNA 的 5′ RACE 产物(RxFrag)。底端展示的是克隆测序的 RT-PCR 产物的位置，该 PCR 产物含有 DONSON 基因的两个外显子和 ATP5O 基因的三个外显子；这些序列在基因组上被一个 300 kb 的内含子分开。PET 标签展示的与这个 RT-PCR 产物一致的一个转录本的末端。

假基因 假基因通常被认为是没有功能的基因拷贝，有时候会被转录，因为与正常基因序列的高度相似性常使转录分析变得复杂，在参考文献 21 和 22 中有对其的综述。利用多种计算方法，我们在 ENCODE 区域鉴定到 201 个假基因(124 个加工，77 个未加工)(见补充信息 2.10 和参考文献 23)。对其中的 189 个进行叠瓦式阵列分析，发现 56% 与至少一个 TxFrag 重合。不过，假基因可能和它们对应的亲本基因交叉杂交，进而可能使得上述分析产生混乱。为了更好地检测假基因转录的范围，利用 RACE/叠瓦式阵列检测 160 个假基因(111 个加工，49 个未加工)的表达(详见补充信息 2.9.2)。14 个假基因(8 个加工，6 个未加工)在 12 个 RNA 样本中的

one of the 12 tested RNA sources, the majority (9) being in testis (see ref. 23). Additionally, there was evidence for the transcription of 25 pseudogenes on the basis of their proximity (within 100 bp of a pseudogene end) to CAGE tags (8), PETs (2), or cDNAs/ESTs (21). Overall, we estimate that at least 19% of the pseudogenes in the ENCODE regions are transcribed, which is consistent with previous estimates[24,25].

Non-protein-coding RNA. Non-protein-coding RNAs (ncRNAs) include structural RNAs (for example, transfer RNAs, ribosomal RNAs, and small nuclear RNAs) and more recently discovered regulatory RNAs (for example, miRNAs). There are only 8 well-characterized ncRNA genes within the ENCODE regions (*U70, ACA36, ACA56, mir-192, mir-194-2, mir-196, mir-483* and *H19*), whereas representatives of other classes, (for example, box C/D snoRNAs, tRNAs, and functional snRNAs) seem to be completely absent in the ENCODE regions. Tiling-array data provided evidence for transcription in at least one of the assayed RNA samples for all of these ncRNAs, with the exception of mir-483 (expression of mir-483 might be specific to fetal liver, which was not tested). There is also evidence for the transcription of 6 out of 8 pseudogenes of ncRNAs (mainly snoRNA-derived). Similar to the analysis of protein-pseudogenes, the hybridization results could also originate from the known snoRNA gene elsewhere in the genome.

Many known ncRNAs are characterized by a well-defined RNA secondary structure. We applied two *de novo* ncRNA prediction algorithms—EvoFold and RNAz—to predict structured ncRNAs (as well as functional structures in mRNAs) using the multi-species sequence alignments (see below, Supplementary Information section 2.11 and ref. 26). Using a sensitivity threshold capable of detecting all known miRNAs and snoRNAs, we identified 4,986 and 3,707 candidate ncRNA loci with EvoFold and RNAz, respectively. Only 268 loci (5% and 7%, respectively) were found with both programs, representing a 1.6-fold enrichment over that expected by chance; the lack of more extensive overlap is due to the two programs having optimal sensitivity at different levels of GC content and conservation. We experimentally examined 50 of these targets using RACE/tiling-array analysis for brain and testis tissues (see Supplementary Information sections 2.11 and 2.9.3); the predictions were validated at a 56%, 65%, and 63% rate for Evofold, RNAz and dual predictions, respectively.

Primary transcripts. The detection of numerous unannotated transcripts coupled with increasing knowledge of the general complexity of transcription prompted us to examine the extent of primary (that is, unspliced) transcripts across the ENCODE regions. Three data sources provide insight about these primary transcripts: the GENCODE annotation, PETs, and RxFrag extensions. Figure 4 summarizes the fraction of bases in the ENCODE regions that overlap transcripts identified by these technologies. Remarkably, 93% of bases are represented in a primary transcript identified by at least two independent observations (but potentially using the same technology); this figure is reduced to 74% in the case of primary transcripts detected by at least two different technologies. These increased spans are not mainly due to cell line rearrangements because they were present in multiple tissue experiments that confirmed the spans (see Supplementary Information section 2.12).

至少 1 个样本中检测到转录本，大部分（9 个）在睾丸中被检测到（见参考文献 23）。另外，有证据表明 25 个假基因在转录，这是基于它们靠近（假基因末端距离 100 bp 以内）CAGE 标签（8 个）、PET（2 个）或 cDNA/EST（21 个）。总体来说，我们估计 ENCODE 区域内至少 19% 的假基因被转录，这与之前的估计是一致的[24,25]。

非蛋白质编码 RNA　非蛋白质编码 RNA(ncRNA) 包括结构 RNA(如转运 RNA、核糖体 RNA 和核内小 RNA) 和最近发现的调控 RNA(如 miRNA)。在 ENCODE 区域内只有 8 种熟知的 ncRNA 基因（*U70*、*ACA36*、*ACA56*、*mir-192*、*mir-194-2*、*mir-196*、*mir-483* 和 *H19*），其他类型（如 C/D 核仁小 RNA、tRNA 和功能性 snRNA）在 ENCODE 区域似乎完全不存在。叠瓦式阵列数据为所有这些 ncRNA 在至少一种被分析 RNA 样本中的转录提供了证据，这其中 mir-483 除外（mir-483 可能在胎肝中特异表达，而胎肝没有被检测）。也有证据表明 8 个 ncRNAs 假基因（主要是 snoRNA 产生的）中有 6 个转录。类似于蛋白质假基因的分析，杂交结果也可能是来源于基因组中其他地方的已知 snoRNA 基因。

很多已知的 ncRNA 具有明确的 RNA 二级结构。我们通过两种从头预测 ncRNA 的算法——EvoFold 和 RNAz，利用多物种序列比对来预测结构 ncRNA(详见下文、补充信息 2.11 和参考文献 26)。使用能检测所有已知的 miRNA 和 snoRNA 的敏感性阈值，我们通过 EvoFold 和 RNAz 分别鉴定到 4,986 和 3,707 个候选 ncRNA 基因座。只有 268 个基因座（分别是 5% 和 7%）在两个程序中都被发现，相对偶然概率有 1.6 倍富集；没有更高的重合是因为两个程序的最佳敏感性所要求的 GC 含量和保守性水平不同。我们使用 RACE/叠瓦式阵列实验在大脑和睾丸组织中检查了其中的 50 个（详见补充信息 2.11 和 2.9.3）；Evofold、RNAz 和两种方法联合预测的被验证率分别为 56%、65% 和 63%。

初级转录本　由于大量未被注释的转录本被检测到，加上我们对转录的基本复杂性认识的深入，使我们不得不检查初级（也就是未被剪接的）转录本在 ENCODE 区域内的分布范围。三个数据源为认识这些初级转录本提供了线索：GENCODE 注释、PET 和 RxFrag 延伸。图 4 总结了 ENCODE 区域内碱基与这些技术鉴定到的转录本重合的比例。值得注意的是，93% 的碱基位于被至少两种独立观察（但是有可能使用同一种技术）鉴定到的初级转录本中；如果是被至少两种不同的技术鉴定到的初级转录本，则这个数字下降到 74%。这些增加的跨度并不主要是由于细胞系的重排，因为在多种组织的实验中都验证了这种跨度的存在（详见补充信息 2.12）。这些

These estimates assume that the presence of PETs or RxFrags defining the terminal ends of a transcript imply that the entire intervening DNA is transcribed and then processed. Other mechanisms, thought to be unlikely in the human genome, such as *trans*-splicing or polymerase jumping would also produce these long termini and potentially should be reconsidered in more detail.

Fig. 4. Coverage of primary transcripts across ENCODE regions. Three different technologies (integrated annotation from GENCODE, RACE-array experiments (RxFrags) and PET tags) were used to assess the presence of a nucleotide in a primary transcript. Use of these technologies provided the opportunity to have multiple observations of each finding. The proportion of genomic bases detected in the ENCODE regions associated with each of the following scenarios is depicted: detected by all three technologies, by two of the three technologies, by one technology but with multiple observations, and by one technology with only one observation. Also indicated are genomic bases without any detectable coverage of primary transcripts.

Previous studies have suggested a similar broad amount of transcription across the human[14,15] and mouse[27] genomes. Our studies confirm these results, and have investigated the genesis of these transcripts in greater detail, confirming the presence of substantial intragenic and intergenic transcription. At the same time, many of the resulting transcripts are neither traditional protein-coding transcripts nor easily explained as structural non-coding RNAs. Other studies have noted complex transcription around specific loci or chimaeric-gene structures (for example refs 28–30), but these have often been considered exceptions; our data show that complex intercalated transcription is common at many loci. The results presented in the next section show extensive amounts of regulatory factors around novel TSSs, which is consistent with this extensive transcription. The biological relevance of these unannotated transcripts remains unanswered by these studies. Evolutionary information (detailed below) is mixed in this regard; for example, it indicates that unannotated transcripts show weaker evolutionary conservation than many other annotated features. As with other ENCODE-detected elements, it is difficult to identify clear biological roles for the majority of these transcripts; such experiments are challenging to perform on a large scale and, furthermore, it seems likely that many of the corresponding biochemical events may be evolutionarily neutral (see below).

估计假定如果存在定义转录本两个末端的 PET 或 RxFrag，就意味着整个中间 DNA 首先被转录，然后再被加工。被认为不可能存在于人类基因组的其他机制，例如反式剪接或者聚合酶跳跃，也会产生这种长末端，可能应该被更仔细地重新思考。

图 4. 原始转录本在 ENCODE 区域的覆盖度。三种不同的技术（来自 GENCODE、RACE 阵列实验（RxFrag）和 PET 标签的整合注释）被用来评估初级转录本中碱基的存在。这些技术的应用使人们有机会对每一个发现进行多次观察。图中展示了在 ENCODE 区域中被检测的基因组碱基与下列情形相关的各自所占的比例：被三种技术都检测到，被三种技术中的两种检测到，被一种技术但是多次观察到，以及被一种技术一次观察到。图中还展示了没有检测到初级转录本覆盖的基因组碱基所占的比例。

之前的研究已经表明人类[14,15]和小鼠[27]基因组都存在类似的大量转录。我们的研究验证了这些结果，并且还更详细地研究了这些转录本的产生，验证了大量基因内和基因间转录的存在。同时，得到的很多转录本既不是传统的蛋白质编码转录本，也不能简单地解释为结构性非编码 RNA。其他的研究已经注意到在特定基因座或者嵌合基因结构存在复杂的转录（如参考文献 28～30），但是这些常常被认为是特例，我们的数据说明复杂的有插入的转录在很多基因座是常见的。下一部分呈现的结果展示了在新的 TSS 周围有大量的调控因子，与这种广泛转录一致。这些研究还不能回答这些未注释转录本的生物学意义。进化的信息（下文有详细介绍）在这方面是混杂的，例如，它暗示未注释的转录本比很多其他注释特征表现为更弱的进化保守性。和其他 ENCODE 检测到的元件一样，这些转录本中的大多数难以鉴定明确的生物学功能。大规模地进行这种实验很有挑战性，再者，有可能很多对应的生化事件在进化上是中性的（见下文）。

Regulation of Transcription

Overview. A significant challenge in biology is to identify the transcriptional regulatory elements that control the expression of each transcript and to understand how the function of these elements is coordinated to execute complex cellular processes. A simple, commonplace view of transcriptional regulation involves five types of *cis*-acting regulatory sequences—promoters, enhancers, silencers, insulators and locus control regions[31]. Overall, transcriptional regulation involves the interplay of multiple components, whereby the availability of specific transcription factors and the accessibility of specific genomic regions determine whether a transcript is generated[31]. However, the current view of transcriptional regulation is known to be overly simplified, with many details remaining to be established. For example, the consensus sequences of transcription factor binding sites (typically 6 to 10 bases) have relatively little information content and are present numerous times in the genome, with the great majority of these not participating in transcriptional regulation. Does chromatin structure then determine whether such a sequence has a regulatory role? Are there complex inter-factor interactions that integrate the signals from multiple sites? How are signals from different distal regulatory elements coupled without affecting all neighbouring genes? Meanwhile, our understanding of the repertoire of transcriptional events is becoming more complex, with an increasing appreciation of alternative TSSs[32,33] and the presence of non-coding[27,34] and anti-sense transcripts[35,36].

To better understand transcriptional regulation, we sought to begin cataloguing the regulatory elements residing within the 44 ENCODE regions. For this pilot project, we mainly focused on the binding of regulatory proteins and chromatin structure involved in transcriptional regulation. We analysed over 150 data sets, mainly from ChIP-chip[37-39], ChIP-PET and STAGE[40,41] studies (see Supplementary Information section 3.1 and 3.2). These methods use chromatin immunoprecipitation with specific antibodies to enrich for DNA in physical contact with the targeted epitope. This enriched DNA can then be analysed using either microarrays (ChIP-chip) or high-throughput sequencing (ChIP-PET and STAGE). The assays included 18 sequence-specific transcription factors and components of the general transcription machinery (for example, RNA polymerase II (Pol II), TAF1 and TFIIB/GTF2B). In addition, we tested more than 600 potential promoter fragments for transcriptional activity by transient-transfection reporter assays that used 16 human cell lines[33]. We also examined chromatin structure by studying the ENCODE regions for DNaseI sensitivity (by quantitative PCR[42] and tiling arrays[43,44], see Supplementary Information section 3.3), histone composition[45], histone modifications (using ChIP-chip assays)[37,46], and histone displacement (using FAIRE, see Supplementary Information section 3.4). Below, we detail these analyses, starting with the efforts to define and classify the 5′ ends of transcripts with respect to their associated regulatory signals. Following that are summaries of generated data about sequence-specific transcription factor binding and clusters of regulatory elements. Finally, we describe how this information can be integrated to make predictions about transcriptional regulation.

962

转录的调控

概况　生物学中一个重大的挑战是鉴定控制各个转录本表达的转录调控元件，以及理解这些元件的功能是如何协调以完成复杂的细胞过程。对转录调控一个简单朴素的认识包括五种类型的顺式调控元件——启动子、增强子、沉默子、绝缘子和基因座控制区[31]。总体上，转录调控包括多种组分的相互作用，特定转录因子的可用性和特定基因组区域的开放性决定一个转录本的产生与否[31]。不过，目前对转录调控的认识被认为过于简单，很多细节还未完善。例如，转录因子结合位点的共有序列（通常 6 到 10 个碱基）含有相对很少的信息量，在基因组中大量存在，其中大部分并不参与转录调控。接下来，是否染色质结构决定这样一个序列是否具有调控作用？是否有复杂的因子间相互作用整合来自多个位点的信号？来自不同的远端调控元件的信号如何联系起来并且还不影响所有邻近的基因？同时，随着对可变 TSS[32,33] 认识的更加深入以及非编码[27,34] 和反义[35,36] 转录本的存在，我们对转录事件库的理解正变得更加复杂。

为更好地理解转录调控，我们开始为位于 44 个 ENCODE 区域内的调控元件编制目录。对于这个先导计划，我们主要关注调控蛋白的结合和参与转录调控的染色质结构。我们分析了超过 150 个数据集，这些数据集主要来自 ChIP-chip[37-39]，ChIP-PET 和 STAGE[40,41] 研究（详见补充信息 3.1 和 3.2）。这些方法使用染色质免疫沉淀结合特定的抗体从而物理靠近目标表位富集 DNA。这些富集的 DNA 可以利用芯片（ChIP-chip）或高通量测序（ChIP-PET 和 STAGE）分析。这样的实验包括 18 个序列特异的转录因子和基本转录机制的组分（如 RNA 聚合酶 II（Pol II）、TAF1 和 TFIIB/GTF2B）。另外，我们利用 16 个人细胞系，通过瞬时转染报告实验检测了超过 600 个潜在的启动子片段的转录活性[33]。我们还通过研究 ENCODE 区域的 DNaseI 敏感性（通过定量 PCR[42] 和叠瓦式阵列[43,44]，详见补充信息 3.3）、组蛋白构成[45]、组蛋白修饰（利用 ChIP-chip 实验）[37,46] 和组蛋白置换（使用 FAIRE，详见补充信息 3.4）检测了染色质的结构。下面，我们详细介绍这些信息，首先根据相关的调控信号来定义和分类转录本的 5′ 端；然后总结产生的关于序列特异转录因子结合和调控元件簇的数据；最后我们描述这些信息如何被整合起来，从而对转录调控做出预测。

Transcription start site catalogue. We analysed two data sets to catalogue TSSs in the ENCODE regions: the 5′ ends of GENCODE-annotated transcripts and the combined results of two 5′-end-capture technologies—CAGE and PET-tagging. The initial results suggested the potential presence of 16,051 unique TSSs. However, in many cases, multiple TSSs resided within a single small segment (up to ~200 bases); this was due to some promoters containing TSSs with many very close precise initiation sites[47]. To normalize for this effect, we grouped TSSs that were 60 or fewer bases apart into a single cluster, and in each case considered the most frequent CAGE or PET tag (or the 5′-most TSS in the case of TSSs identified only from GENCODE data) as representative of that cluster for downstream analyses.

The above effort yielded 7,157 TSS clusters in the ENCODE regions. We classified these TSSs into three categories: known (present at the end of GENCODE-defined transcripts), novel (supported by other evidence) and unsupported. The novel TSSs were further subdivided on the basis of the nature of the supporting evidence (see Table 3 and Supplementary Information section 3.5), with all four of the resulting subtypes showing significant overlap with experimental evidence using the GSC statistic. Although there is a larger relative proportion of singleton tags in the novel category, when analysis is restricted to only singleton tags, the novel TSSs continue to have highly significant overlap with supporting evidence (see Supplementary Information section 3.5.1).

Table 3. Different categories of TSSs defined on the basis of support from different transcript-survey methods

Category	Transcript survey method	Number of TSS clusters (non-redundant)*	P value†	Singleton clusters‡ (%)
Known	GENCODE 5′ ends	1,730	2×10^{-70}	25 (74 overall)
Novel	GENCODE sense exons	1,437	6×10^{-39}	64
	GENCODE antisense exons	521	3×10^{-8}	65
	Unbiased transcription survey	639	7×10^{-63}	71
	CpG island	164	4×10^{-90}	60
Unsupported	None	2,666	–	83.4

* Number of TSS clusters with this support, excluding TSSs from higher categories.

† Probability of overlap between the transcript support and the PET/CAGE tags, as calculated by the Genome Structure Correction statistic (see Supplementary Information section 1.3).

‡ Per cent of clusters with only one tag. For the "known" category this was calculated as the per cent of GENCODE 5′ ends with tag support (25%) or overall (74%).

Correlating genomic features with chromatin structure and transcription factor binding. By measuring relative sensitivity to DNaseI digestion (see Supplementary Information section 3.3), we identified DNaseI hypersensitive sites throughout the ENCODE regions. DHSs and TSSs both reflect genomic regions thought to be enriched for regulatory information and many DHSs reside at or near TSSs. We partitioned DHSs into those within 2.5 kb of a TSS (958; 46.5%) and the remaining ones, which were classified

转录起始位点的分类　我们分析了两个数据集，进而对 ENCODE 区域的 TSS 进行分类：GENCODE 注释的转录本的 5′ 端和两个 5′ 端捕获技术——CAGE 和 PET 标签的综合结果。起初的结果表明有 16,051 个唯一的 TSS 的潜在存在。但是，在很多情况下，多个 TSS 位于同一个小的片段内（最多 ~ 200 碱基），这是因为一些含有 TSS 的启动子含有很多非常靠近的精确的起始位点[47]。为了使这种影响正常化，我们将相距 60 或者更少碱基的 TSS 归为一个簇，并且在这种情况下把频率最高的 CAGE 或 PET 标签（或者对于仅在 GENCODE 数据鉴定到 TSS 则是最 5′ 的 TSS）作为这个簇的代表用于下游分析。

上述分析在 ENCODE 区域产生了 7,157 个 TSS 簇。我们将这些 TSS 分为三类：已知的（在 GENCODE 确定的转录本的末端存在），全新的（被其他证据支持的）和不被支持的。基于支持的证据的性质，全新的 TSS 被进一步分类（详见表 3 和补充信息 3.5），利用 GSC 统计发现，产生的 4 个亚类都与实验证据高度重合。当仅分析单一标签时，尽管单一标签的相对比例在新类里更大，但是全新的 TSS 仍然与支持证据高度重合（详见补充信息 3.5.1）。

表 3. 基于支持不同转录本鉴定方法而定义的不同类的 TSS

类别	转录本鉴定方法	TSS 簇的数量（非冗余的）*	P 值†	单一簇‡(%)
已知的	GENCODE 5′ 端	1,730	2×10^{-70}	25(总共 74)
全新的	GENCODE 正义链外显子	1,437	6×10^{-39}	64
	GENCODE 反义链外显子	521	3×10^{-8}	65
	无偏性的转录鉴定	639	7×10^{-63}	71
	CpG 岛	164	4×10^{-90}	60
不被支持的	无	2,666	—	83.4

* 基于本文 TSS 簇的数量，不包括更高层级分类的 TSS。

† 转录本支持和 PET/CAGE 标签重合的概率，通过基因组结构校正统计计算（详见补充信息 1.3）。

‡ 只有一个标签的簇的比例。对于"已知的"这一类，计算的是含有标签支持的(25%)或所有的(74%)GENCODE 5′ 端的比例。

将基因组特征与染色质结构和转录因子结合相关联　通过检测对 DNaseI 切割的相对敏感度（详见补充信息 3.3），我们在整个 ENCODE 区域鉴定了 DNaseI 超敏位点。DHS 和 TSS 都反映了被认为是富集调控信息的基因组区域，并且很多 DHS 位于 TSS 或其附近。我们将 DHS 分为在 TSS 2.5 kb 以内的（958；46.5%）和其他位于远端的（1,102；53.5%）。然后我们通过根据相对 TSS 或 DHS 的距离将信号聚集，

as distal (1,102; 53.5%). We then cross-analysed the TSSs and DHSs with data sets relating to histone modifications, chromatin accessibility and sequence-specific transcription factor binding by summarizing these signals in aggregate relative to the distance from TSSs or DHSs. Figure 5 shows representative profiles of specific histone modifications, Pol II and selected transcription factor binding for the different categories of TSSs. Further profiles and statistical analysis of these studies can be found in Supplementary Information 3.6.

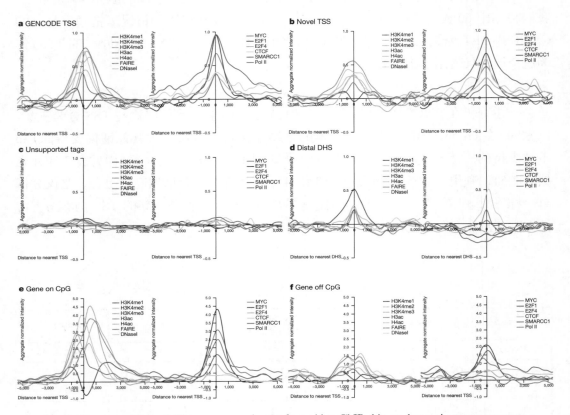

Fig. 5. Aggregate signals of tiling-array experiments from either ChIP-chip or chromatin structure assays, represented for different classes of TSSs and DHS. For each plot, the signal was first normalized with a mean of 0 and standard deviation of 1, and then the normalized scores were summed at each position for that class of TSS or DHS and smoothed using a kernel density method (see Supplementary Information section 3.6). For each class of sites there are two adjacent plots. The left plot depicts the data for general factors: FAIRE and DNaseI sensitivity as assays of chromatin accessibility and H3K4me1, H3K4me2, H3K4me3, H3ac and H4ac histone modifications (as indicated); the right plot shows the data for additional factors, namely MYC, E2F1, E2F4, CTCF, SMARCC1 and Pol II. The columns provide data for the different classes of TSS or DHS (unsmoothed data and statistical analysis shown in Supplementary Information section 3.6).

In the case of the three TSS categories (known, novel and unsupported), known and novel TSSs are both associated with similar signals for multiple factors (ranging from histone modifications through DNaseI accessibility), whereas unsupported TSSs are not. The enrichments seen with chromatin modifications and sequence-specific factors, along with the significant clustering of this evidence, indicate that the novel TSSs do not reflect false

对 TSS 和 DHS 与组蛋白修饰、染色质开放性和序列特异的转录因子结合相关的数据集进行了交叉分析。图 5 展示了特定的组蛋白修饰、Pol II 和特定转录因子结合不同类的 TSS 的代表性特征。这些研究更深入的特征和统计学分析可以在补充信息 3.6 中找到。

图 5. ChIP-chip 或染色质结构实验中的叠瓦式阵列实验的聚集信号，展示的是不同类型的 TSS 和 DHS 的情况。对于每一个图，信号先根据均值为 0、标准差为 1 被归一化，然后归一化后的值在相应类型的 TSS 或 DHS 的每一个位置求和，并利用核密度方法平滑化（详见补充信息 3.6）。对于各类位点有两个相邻的图。左图展示的是基本因子的数据：FAIRE 和 DNaseI 敏感性作为染色质开放性的检测方法，以及 H3K4me1、H3K4me2、H3K4me3、H3ac 和 H4ac 组蛋白修饰（如图所示）；右图展示的是另外的因子的数据，即 MYC、E2F1、E2F4、CTCF、SMARCC1 和 Pol II。各栏提供了不同类型的 TSS 或 DHS 的数据（未平滑的数据和统计学分析见补充信息 3.6）。

对于这三类 TSS（已知的、全新的和不被支持的），已知的和全新的 TSS 与多个因子类似的信号（从组蛋白修饰到 DNaseI 开放性）都有关联，而不被支持的 TSS 则不是这样。染色质修饰和序列特异的因子的富集，以及这些证据的明显聚集，说明全新的 TSS 并不是假阳性，可能使用和其他启动子一样的生物机制。序列特异的转

positives and probably use the same biological machinery as other promoters. Sequence-specific transcription factors show a marked increase in binding across the broad region that encompasses each TSS. This increase is notably symmetric, with binding equally likely upstream or downstream of a TSS (see Supplementary Information section 3.7 for an explanation of why this symmetrical signal is not an artefact of the analysis of the signals). Furthermore, there is enrichment of SMARCC1 binding (a member of the SWI/SNF chromatin-modifying complex), which persists across a broader extent than other factors. The broad signals with this factor indicate that the ChIP-chip results reflect both specific enrichment at the TSS and broader enrichments across ~5-kb regions (this is not due to technical issues, see Supplementary Information section 3.8).

We selected 577 GENCODE-defined TSSs at the 5' ends of a protein-coding transcript with over 3 exons, to assess expression status. Each transcript was classified as: (1) "active" (gene on) or "inactive" (gene off) on the basis of the unbiased transcript surveys, and (2) residing near a "CpG island" or not ("non-CpG island") (see Supplementary Information section 3.17). As expected, the aggregate signal of histone modifications is mainly attributable to active TSSs (Fig. 5), in particular those near CpG islands. Pronounced doublet peaks at the TSS can be seen with these large signals (similar to previous work in yeast[48]) owing to the chromatin accessibility at the TSS. Many of the histone marks and Pol II signals are now clearly asymmetrical, with a persistent level of Pol II into the genic region, as expected. However, the sequence-specific factors remain largely symmetrically distributed. TSSs near CpG islands show a broader distribution of histone marks than those not near CpG islands (see Supplementary Information section 3.6). The binding of some transcription factors (E2F1, E2F4 and MYC) is extensive in the case of active genes, and is lower (or absent) in the case of inactive genes.

Chromatin signature of distal elements. Distal DHSs show characteristic patterns of histone modification that are the inverse of TSSs, with high H3K4me1 accompanied by lower levels of H3K4Me3 and H3Ac (Fig. 5). Many factors with high occupancy at TSSs (for example, E2F4) show little enrichment at distal DHSs, whereas other factors (for example, MYC) are enriched at both TSSs and distal DHSs[49]. A particularly interesting observation is the relative enrichment of the insulator-associated factor CTCF[50] at both distal DHSs and TSSs; this contrasts with SWI/SNF components SMARCC2 and SMARCC1, which are TSS-centric. Such differential behaviour of sequence-specific factors points to distinct biological differences, mediated by transcription factors, between distal regulatory sites and TSSs.

Unbiased maps of sequence-specific regulatory factor binding. The previous section focused on specific positions defined by TSSs or DHSs. We then analysed sequence-specific transcription factor binding data in an unbiased fashion. We refer to regions with enriched binding of regulatory factors as RFBRs. RFBRs were identified on the basis of ChIP-chip data in two ways: first, each investigator developed and used their own analysis method(s) to define high-enrichment regions, and second (and independently), a stringent false discovery rate (FDR) method was applied to analyse all data using three cut-offs (1%, 5% and 10%).

录因子在包含 TSS 的较宽区域内的结合明显增加。这种增加是明显对称的，在 TSS 上游或下游结合的可能性一样（详见补充信息 3.7，其中有解释为什么这种对称的信号不是一种信号分析的假象）。另外，还有 SMARCC1 结合的富集（SWI/SNF 染色质修饰复合物的一个组分），它比其他因子分布的范围更宽。这个因子较宽的信号暗示，ChIP-chip 结果不仅反映在 TSS 特异的富集，也反映在更宽的约 5 kb 区域的富集（这不是因为技术的原因，详见补充信息 3.8）。

我们选择 577 个 GENCODE 定义的 TSS 来评价表达水平，这些 TSS 都位于蛋白质编码且含有超过三个外显子的转录本的 5′ 端。各个转录本被分为：（1）基于无偏性的转录本检测确定的"活跃的"（基因开启）或者"不活跃的"（基因关闭）和（2）位于"CpG 岛"附近或者不在附近的（"非 CpG 岛"）（详见补充信息 3.17）。正如预期的，组蛋白修饰的聚集信号主要位于活跃的 TSS（图 5），特别是那些 CpG 岛附近的。由于在 TSS 染色质的开放性，在 TSS 位置这些大的信号能看到明显的双峰（类似于之前在酵母中的发现 [48]）。正如预期的，很多组蛋白标志和 Pol II 信号现在明显是不对称的，Pol II 信号延伸到了基因区。但是，序列特异的因子仍然大部分是对称分布的。与不靠近 CpG 岛的 TSS 相比，CpG 岛附近的 TSS 呈现更宽的组蛋白标志分布（详见补充信息 3.6）。对于活跃基因，一些转录因子（E2F1、E2F4 和 MYC）广泛结合，而对于不活跃的基因，则结合水平较低（或不结合）。

远端元件的染色质标志　远端 DHS 呈现的特征性组蛋白修饰模式与 TSS 相反，高水平的 H3K4me1 伴随着低水平的 H3K4Me3 和 H3Ac（图 5）。很多在 TSS 结合水平较高的因子（如 E2F4）在远端 DHS 几乎没有富集，而其他因子（如 MYC）则在 TSS 和远端 DHS 都有富集 [49]。一个特别有意思的现象是，绝缘子相关因子 CTCF[50] 在远端 DHS 和 TSS 均有相对富集，这与 SWI/SNF 组分 SMARCC2 和 SMARCC1 明显不同，后者以 TSS 为中心。序列特异的因子的这种差异的行为表明，在远端调控位点和 TSS 之间，存在由转录因子介导的明显的生物学差异。

序列特异的调控因子结合的无偏性图谱　前面的部分聚焦于 TSS 或 DHS 定义的特定的位置。接下来我们以无偏性的方式分析序列特异的转录因子结合数据。我们称有调控因子富集结合的区域为 RFBR。基于 ChIP-chip 数据，RFBR 通过两种方式被鉴定：第一，每个研究者开发和使用他们自己的分析方法定义高富集区；第二（单独地），一种严格的错误发现率（FDR）方法被应用于分析所有的数据，它使用三个阈值（1%、5% 和 10%）。实验室特异的和基于 FDR 的方法高度相关，特别是对于

The laboratory-specific and FDR-based methods were highly correlated, particularly for regions with strong signals[10,11]. For consistency, we used the results obtained with the FDR-based method (see Supplementary Information section 3.10). These RFBRs can be used to find sequence motifs (see Supplementary Information section S3.11).

RFBRs are associated with the 5′ ends of transcripts. The distribution of RFBRs is non-random (see ref. 10) and correlates with the positions of TSSs. We examined the distribution of specific RFBRs relative to the known TSSs. Different transcription factors and histone modifications vary with respect to their association with TSSs (Fig. 6; see Supplementary Information section 3.12 for modelling of random expectation). Factors for which binding sites are most enriched at the 5′ ends of genes include histone modifications, TAF1 and RNA Pol II with a hypo-phosphorylated carboxy-terminal domain[51]—confirming previous expectations. Surprisingly, we found that E2F1, a sequence-specific factor that regulates the expression of many genes at the G1 to S transition[52], is also tightly associated with TSSs[52]; this association is as strong as that of TAF1, the well-known TATA box-binding protein associated factor 1 (ref. 53). These results suggest that E2F1 has a more general role in transcription than previously suspected, similar to that for MYC[54-56]. In contrast, the large-scale assays did not support the promoter binding that was found in smaller-scale studies (for example, on SIRT1 and SPI1 (PU1)).

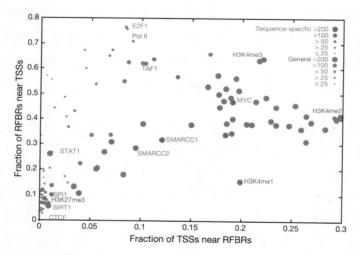

Fig 6. Distribution of RFBRs relative to GENCODE TSSs. Different RFBRs from sequence-specific factors (red) or general factors (blue) are plotted showing their relative distribution near TSSs. The x axis indicates the proportion of TSSs close (within 2.5 kb) to the specified factor. The y axis indicates the proportion of RFBRs close to TSSs. The size of the circle provides an indication of the number of RFBRs for each factor. A handful of representative factors are labelled.

Integration of data on sequence-specific factors. We expect that regulatory information is not dispersed independently across the genome, but rather is clustered into distinct regions[57]. We refer to regions that contain multiple regulatory elements as "regulatory clusters". We sought to predict the location of regulatory clusters by cross-integrating data generated using all transcription factor and histone modification assays, including

强信号区域[10,11]。为了统一性，我们使用基于 FDR 方法获得的结果（详见补充信息 3.10），这些 RFBR 可被用于发现序列模序（详见补充信息 S3.11）。

RFBR 与转录本的 5′ 端关联　RFBR 的分布不是随机的（详见参考文献 10），并且与 TSS 的位置相关。我们考察了特定 RFBR 相对已知的 TSS 的分布。不同的转录因子和组蛋白修饰在它们与 TSS 关联方面各不相同（图 6；随机期望的建模详见补充信息 3.12）。在基因 5′端最富集的与位点结合的因子包括组蛋白修饰、TAF1 和含有低磷酸化羧基端结构域的 RNA Pol II[51]——验证之前的预期。令人意外的是，我们发现 E2F1，一个在 G1 到 S 转换阶段调控很多基因表达的序列特异的因子[52]，也与 TSS 紧密关联[52]；这种关联跟 TAF1 与 TSS 的关联一样强，TAF1 即人们熟知的 TATA 框结合蛋白相关因子 1（参考文献 53）。这些结果说明相比于之前的猜测，E2F1 在转录中有着更基本的功能，这类似于 MYC[54-56] 的功能。相反，大规模的实验并不支持之前小规模研究发现的启动子的结合（如 SIRT1 和 SPI1（PU1））。

图 6. RFBR 相对 GENCODE TSS 的分布。图中展示的是源自序列特异的因子（红色）或基本因子（蓝色）的不同 RFBR 在 TSS 附近的相对分布。x 轴表示靠近（2.5 kb 以内）特定因子的 TSS 的比例。y 轴表示靠近 TSS 的 RFBR 的比例。圆圈的大小表示各个因子的 RFBR 的数量。少数几个代表性的因子被标记出来了。

序列特异的因子的数据的整合　我们预期调控信息并不是各自分散在基因组上，而是聚集在特定的区域[57]。我们称含有多个调控元件的区域为"调控簇"。利用所有转录因子和组蛋白修饰实验所产生的交叉整合的数据，包括在单个实验中低于主观阈值的结果，我们来预测调控簇的位置。特别地，我们利用了四种互为补充的

results falling below an arbitrary threshold in individual experiments. Specifically, we used four complementary methods to integrate the data from 129 ChIP-chip data sets (see Supplementary Information section 3.13 and ref. 58). These four methods detect different classes of regulatory clusters and as a whole identified 1,393 clusters. Of these, 344 were identified by all four methods, with another 500 found by three methods (see Supplementary Information section 3.13.5). 67% of the 344 regulatory clusters identified by all four methods (or 65% of the full set of 1,393) reside within 2.5 kb of a known or novel TSS (as defined above; see Table 3 and Supplementary Information section 3.14 for a breakdown by category). Restricting this analysis to previously annotated TSSs (for example, RefSeq or Ensembl) reveals that roughly 25% of the regulatory clusters are close to a previously identified TSS. These results suggest that many of the regulatory clusters identified by integrating the ChIP-chip data sets are undiscovered promoters or are somehow associated with transcription in another fashion. To test these possibilities, sets of 126 and 28 non-GENCODE-based regulatory clusters were tested for promoter activity (see Supplementary Information section 3.15) and by RACE, respectively. These studies revealed that 24.6% of the 126 tested regulatory clusters had promoter activity and that 78.6% of the 28 regulatory clusters analysed by RACE yielded products consistent with a TSS[58]. The ChIP-chip data sets were generated on a mixture of cell lines, predominantly HeLa and GM06990, and were different from the CAGE/ PET data, meaning that tissue specificity contributes to the presence of unique TSSs and regulatory clusters. The large increase in promoter proximal regulatory clusters identified by including the additional novel TSSs coupled with the positive promoter and RACE assays suggests that most of the regulatory regions identifiable by these clustering methods represent bona fide promoters (see Supplementary Information 3.16). Although the regulatory factor assays were more biased towards regions associated with promoters, many of the sites from these experiments would have previously been described as distal to promoters. This suggests that commonplace use of RefSeq- or Ensembl-based gene definition to define promoter proximity will dramatically overestimate the number of distal sites.

Predicting TSSs and transcriptional activity on the basis of chromatin structure. The strong association between TSSs and both histone modifications and DHSs prompted us to investigate whether the location and activity of TSSs could be predicted solely on the basis of chromatin structure information. We trained a support vector machine (SVM) by using histone modification data anchored around DHSs to discriminate between DHSs near TSSs and those distant from TSSs. We used a selected 2,573 DHSs, split roughly between TSS-proximal DHSs and TSS-distal DHSs, as a training set. The SVM performed well, with an accuracy of 83% (see Supplementary Information section 3.17). Using this SVM, we then predicted new TSSs using information about DHSs and histone modifications—of 110 high-scoring predicted TSSs, 81 resided within 2.5 kb of a novel TSS. As expected, these show a significant overlap to the novel TSS groups (defined above) but without a strong bias towards any particular category (see Supplementary Information section 3.17.1.5).

To investigate the relationship between chromatin structure and gene expression, we examined transcript levels in two cell lines using a transcript-tiling array. We compared

方法整合来自 129 个 ChIP-chip 数据集的数据（详见补充信息 3.13 和参考文献 58）。这四种方法检测不同类型的调控簇，合起来鉴定到 1,393 个簇。其中 344 个被四种方法都鉴定到，另外 500 个被三种方法鉴定到（详见补充信息 3.13.5）。被四种方法都鉴定到的 344 个调控簇中（或 1,393 个簇中的 65%），有 67% 位于已知的或全新的 TSS 2.5 kb 范围内（上文所定义的；按类分解情况详见表 3 和补充信息 3.14）。仅分析之前已经注释的 TSS（如 RefSeq 或者 Ensembl）发现大约 25% 的调控簇靠近之前鉴定的 TSS。这些结果说明通过整合 ChIP-chip 数据集鉴定到的调控簇中，有很多是还未被发现的启动子或者以其他的某种方式与转录存在着关联。为了检查这些可能性，启动子活性（详见补充信息 3.15）和 RACE 实验分别检测了 126 和 28 个非基于 GENCODE 的调控簇。这些研究发现 126 个被检测的调控簇中有 24.6% 具有启动子活性，28 个被 RACE 分析的调控簇中有 78.6% 产生产物，这与 TSS 一致[58]。与 CAGE/PET 数据不同，ChIP-chip 数据集产生于混合的细胞系，主要是 HeLa 和 GM06990，这意味着组织特异性也是存在独特的 TSS 和调控簇的一个原因。包括了额外全新的 TSS 以及阳性启动子和 RACE 实验后，鉴定到的启动子附近的调控簇大大增加了，这说明大部分通过这些聚类方法鉴定的调控区域代表的是真实的启动子（详见补充信息 3.16）。尽管调控因子实验更偏向启动子相关区域，很多这些实验得到的位点如果按以前的描述是远离启动子的。这说明简单地使用基于 RefSeq 或 Ensembl 定义的基因来确定是否靠近启动子会极大地高估远距离位点的数量。

基于染色质结构预测 TSS 和转录活性　　TSS 与组蛋白修饰和 DHS 的高度的相关性促使我们探究是否仅基于染色质结构信息就能预测 TSS 的位置和活性。我们使用 DHS 周围的组蛋白修饰数据训练了一个支持向量机（SVM），用来区分靠近 TSS 的 DHS 和远离 TSS 的 DHS。我们选择了 2,573 个 DHS，大体分为靠近 TSS 的 DHS 和远离 TSS 的 DHS，作为一个训练集。SVM 表现良好，准确度为 83%（详见补充信息 3.17）。使用这个 SVM，然后我们利用 DHS 和组蛋白修饰信息预测新的 TSS——110 个高分预测的 TSS 中，81 个位于全新的 TSS 的 2.5 kb 范围内。正如预期的，它们与全新 TSS 组（上文定义的）有高度的重合，不过也没有特别偏向某一类（详见补充信息 3.17.1.5）。

　　为了研究染色质结构和基因表达的关系，我们利用转录本阵列实验在两种细胞系中检测了转录本的表达水平。我们将这个转录本数据与测定 ENCODE 区域组蛋白

this transcript data with the results of ChIP-chip experiments that measured histone modifications across the ENCODE regions. From this, we developed a variety of predictors of expression status using chromatin modifications as variables; these were derived using both decision trees and SVMs (see Supplementary Information section 3.17). The best of these correctly predicts expression status (transcribed versus non-transcribed) in 91% of cases. This success rate did not decrease dramatically when the predicting algorithm incorporated the results from one cell line to predict the expression status of another cell line. Interestingly, despite the striking difference in histone modification enrichments in TSSs residing near versus those more distal to CpG islands (see Fig. 5 and Supplementary Information section 3.6), including information about the proximity to CpG islands did not improve the predictors. This suggests that despite the marked differences in histone modifications among these TSS classes, a single predictor can be made, using the interactions between the different histone modification levels.

In summary, we have integrated many data sets to provide a more complete view of regulatory information, both around specific sites (TSSs and DHSs) and in an unbiased manner. From analysing multiple data sets, we find 4,491 known and novel TSSs in the ENCODE regions, almost tenfold more than the number of established genes. This large number of TSSs might explain the extensive transcription described above; it also begins to change our perspective about regulatory information—without such a large TSS catalogue, many of the regulatory clusters would have been classified as residing distal to promoters. In addition to this revelation about the abundance of promoter-proximal regulatory elements, we also identified a considerable number of putative distal regulatory elements, particularly on the basis of the presence of DHSs. Our study of distal regulatory elements was probably most hindered by the paucity of data generated using distal-element-associated transcription factors; nevertheless, we clearly detected a set of distal-DHS-associated segments bound by CTCF or MYC. Finally, we showed that information about chromatin structure alone could be used to make effective predictions about both the location and activity of TSSs.

Replication

Overview. DNA replication must be carefully coordinated, both across the genome and with respect to development. On a larger scale, early replication in S phase is broadly correlated with gene density and transcriptional activity[59-66]; however, this relationship is not universal, as some actively transcribed genes replicate late and vice versa[61,64-68]. Importantly, the relationship between transcription and DNA replication emerges only when the signal of transcription is averaged over a large window (> 100 kb)[63], suggesting that larger-scale chromosomal architecture may be more important than the activity of specific genes[69].

The ENCODE Project provided a unique opportunity to examine whether individual histone modifications on human chromatin can be correlated with the time of replication and whether such correlations support the general relationship of active, open chromatin with early replication. Our studies also tested whether segments showing interallelic

974

修饰的 ChIP-chip 实验结果进行了比较。从中，我们以染色质修饰为变量开发了很多表达状态的预测器；这些是利用决策树和 SVM 派生的（详见补充信息 3.17）。其中最好的预测器正确预测了 91% 的表达状态（表达对不表达）。当预测算法吸收一个细胞系的结果去预测另一个细胞系的表达状态时，成功率并没有大幅降低。有趣的是，尽管组蛋白修饰富集情况在靠近 CpG 岛的 TSS 和和远离 CpG 岛的 TSS 上有很大不同（详见图 5 和补充信息 3.6），包含靠近 CpG 岛的信息后并没有对预测器有所改观。这说明尽管在这些 TSS 种类中组蛋白修饰有很大不同，利用不同组蛋白修饰水平的相互作用，仅需一个预测器即可。

　　总结一下，我们研究了很多数据集，目的是更全面地了解调控信息，不仅是特定位点（TSS 和 DHS）附近的，并且是以无偏性的方式。从多个数据集的分析中，我们在 ENCODE 区域发现了 4,491 个已知的和全新的 TSS，这几乎比已确定的基因数量多了十倍。这么大量的 TSS 可能解释了上文提到的广泛的转录，也开始改变我们关于调控信息的认识——如果没有这么一大类 TSS，很多调控簇将会被分类为远离启动子。除了揭露了靠近启动子的调控元件的丰富性外，我们还鉴定到相当数量的假定远端调控元件，特别是基于 DHS 的存在。我们关于远端调控元件的研究最可能被远端元件相关转录因子的数据的缺乏所影响，但是，我们还是清楚地检测到了一组被 CTCF 或 MYC 结合的远端 DHS 相关片段。最后，我们表明仅靠染色质结构的信息就能对 TSS 的位置和活性做出有效的预测。

复　　制

　　概况　无论是在基因组范围内，还是在发育过程中，DNA 复制必须被精确地协调。在更大的尺度下，在 S 期的早期复制与基因密度和转录活性有着广泛的相关性 [59-66]；但是，这种关系并不是普遍适用的，因为一些活跃转录的基因复制较晚，反之亦然 [61,64-68]。重要的是，只有当转录信号在一个较大的窗口（> 100 kb）中被平均时，转录与 DNA 复制之间的联系才会出现 [63]，这说明大尺度的染色体构建可能比特定基因的活性更重要 [69]。

　　ENCODE 计划提供了一个独特的机会来检验是否人类染色质上单一的组蛋白修饰可以与复制的时间相关联，以及是否这种关联支持活跃的开放染色质与早期复制

variation in the time of replication have two different types of histone modifications consistent with an interallelic variation in chromatin state.

DNA replication data set. We mapped replication timing across the ENCODE regions by analysing Brd-U-labelled fractions from synchronized HeLa cells (collected at 2 h intervals throughout S phase) on tiling arrays (see Supplementary Information section 4.1). Although the HeLa cell line has a considerably altered karyotype, correlation of these data with other cell line data (see below) suggests the results are relevant to other cell types. The results are expressed as the time at which 50% of any given genomic position is replicated (TR50), with higher values signifying later replication times. In addition to the five "activating" histone marks, we also correlated the TR50 with H3K27me3, a modification associated with polycomb-mediated transcriptional repression[70-74]. To provide a consistent comparison framework, the histone data were smoothed to 100-kb resolution, and then correlated with the TR50 data by a sliding window correlation analysis (see Supplementary Information section 4.2). The continuous profiles of the activating marks, histone H3K4 mono-, di-, and tri-methylation and histone H3 and H4 acetylation, are generally anti-correlated with the TR50 signal (Fig. 7a and Supplementary Information section 4.3). In contrast, H3K27me3 marks show a predominantly positive correlation with late-replicating segments (Fig. 7a; see Supplementary Information section 4.3 for additional analysis).

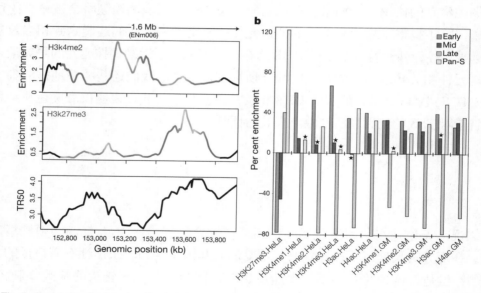

Fig. 7. Correlation between replication timing and histone modifications. **a**, Comparison of two histone modifications (H3K4me2 and H3K27me3), plotted as enrichment ratio from the Chip-chip experiments and the time for 50% of the DNA to replicate (TR50), indicated for ENCODE region ENm006. The colours on the curves reflect the correlation strength in a sliding 250-kb window. **b**, Differing levels of histone modification for different TR50 partitions. The amounts of enrichment or depletion of different histone modifications in various cell lines are depicted (indicated along the bottom as "histone mark.cell line"; GM = GM06990). Asterisks indicate enrichments/depletions that are not significant on the basis of multiple tests. Each set has four partitions on the basis of replication timing: early, mid, late and Pan-S.

的基本关系。我们的研究还检验了表现为等位基因间复制时间不同的片段是否有两种不同的组蛋白修饰，即染色质状态在等位基因间不同。

DNA 复制数据集 我们利用叠瓦式阵列分析 Brd-U 标记的同步化的 HeLa 细胞（在 S 期每隔 2h 收集），绘制 ENCODE 区域的复制时间图谱（详见补充信息 4.1）。尽管 HeLa 细胞系核型变化较大，但是利用其他细胞系数据（见下文）进行校正发现，结果跟其他细胞系是相近的。结果以任一给定基因组位置在 50% 的细胞中被复制时的时间（TR50）表示，数值越大代表复制时间越晚。除了五个"激活的"组蛋白标志，我们还将 TR50 与 H3K27me3 关联了起来，H3K27me3 是一个与多梳蛋白介导的转录抑制相关的修饰[70-74]。为了统一比较，组蛋白数据被平滑化到 100 kb 的分辨率，然后通过滑动窗口相关性分析将其与 TR50 数据关联（详见补充信息 4.2）。激活标志物组蛋白 H3K4 单、二和三甲基化以及组蛋白 H3 和 H4 乙酰化的连续图谱通常与 TR50 信号负相关（图 7a 和补充信息 4.3）。相反，H3K27me3 标志物则明显与晚期复制片段正相关（图 7a；额外的分析详见补充信息 4.3）。

图 7. 复制时间和组蛋白修饰的相关性。**a**，比较两种组蛋白修饰（H3K4m2 和 H3K27me3），以 ChIP-chip 实验得到的富集率和 50% 的 DNA 复制的时间（TR50）画图，展示的是 ENCODE 区域 ENm006。曲线的颜色表示在一个 250 kb 的滑动窗口内的相关强度。**b**，对于不同 TR50 段组蛋白修饰的不同水平。图中描绘的是不同组蛋白修饰在不同细胞系中富集或缺失的量（在底部以"组蛋白标志 . 细胞系"表示；GM = GM06990）。星号表示基于多重检验不显著的富集/缺失。基于复制时间各组含有四段：早、中、晚和 Pan-S。

Although most genomic regions replicate in a temporally specific window in S phase, other regions demonstrate an atypical pattern of replication (Pan-S) where replication signals are seen in multiple parts of S phase. We have suggested that such a pattern of replication stems from interallelic variation in the chromatin structure[59,75]. If one allele is in active chromatin and the other in repressed chromatin, both types of modified histones are expected to be enriched in the Pan-S segments. An ENCODE region was classified as non-specific (or Pan-S) regions when > 60% of the probes in a 10-kb window replicated in multiple intervals in S phase. The remaining regions were sub-classified into early-, mid- or late-replicating based on the average TR50 of the temporally specific probes within a 10-kb window[75]. For regions of each class of replication timing, we determined the relative enrichment of various histone modification peaks in HeLa cells (Fig. 7b; Supplementary Information section 4.4). The correlations of activating and repressing histone modification peaks with TR50 are confirmed by this analysis (Fig. 7b). Intriguingly, the Pan-S segments are unique in being enriched for both activating (H3K4me2, H3ac and H4ac) and repressing (H3K27me3) histones, consistent with the suggestion that the Pan-S replication pattern arises from interallelic variation in chromatin structure and time of replication[75]. This observation is also consistent with the Pan-S replication pattern seen for the H19/IGF2 locus, a known imprinted region with differential epigenetic modifications across the two alleles[76].

The extensive rearrangements in the genome of HeLa cells led us to ask whether the detected correlations between TR50 and chromatin state are seen with other cell lines. The histone modification data with GM06990 cells allowed us to test whether the time of replication of genomic segments in HeLa cells correlated with the chromatin state in GM06990 cells. Early- and late-replicating segments in HeLa cells are enriched and depleted, respectively, for activating marks in GM06990 cells (Fig. 7b). Thus, despite the presence of genomic rearrangements (see Supplementary Information section 2.12), the TR50 and chromatin state in HeLa cells are not far from a constitutive baseline also seen with a cell line from a different lineage. The enrichment of multiple activating histone modifications and the depletion of a repressive modification from segments that replicate early in S phase extends previous work in the field at a level of detail and scale not attempted before in mammalian cells. The duality of histone modification patterns in Pan-S areas of the HeLa genome, and the concordance of chromatin marks and replication time across two disparate cell lines (HeLa and GM06990) confirm the coordination of histone modifications with replication in the human genome.

Chromatin Architecture and Genomic Domains

Overview. The packaging of genomic DNA into chromatin is intimately connected with the control of gene expression and other chromosomal processes. We next examined chromatin structure over a larger scale to ascertain its relation to transcription and other processes. Large domains (50 to > 200 kb) of generalized DNaseI sensitivity have been detected around developmentally regulated gene clusters[77], prompting speculation that the genome is organized into "open" and "closed" chromatin territories that represent higher-order functional domains. We explored how different chromatin features, particularly histone

尽管大多数的基因组区域在 S 期以一种时间特异窗口复制，也有一些区域呈现非典型的复制模式（Pan-S），即复制信号出现在 S 期的多个阶段。我们已经表明这样一种复制模式源于染色质结构在等位基因间的不同 [59,75]。如果一个等位基因位于活跃的染色质而另一个位于被抑制的染色质，则这两种修饰的组蛋白都会在 Pan-S 区间富集。当一个 ENCODE 区域在 10 kb 窗口里有 >60% 的探针在 S 期的多个阶段被复制，则这个区域被归类为非特异的（或者 Pan-S）区域。基于在 10 kb 窗口内的时间特异探针的平均 TR50 值，剩下的区域被进一步分类为早、中或晚期复制 [75]。对于每一类复制时间的区域，我们确定了各种组蛋白修饰峰在 HeLa 细胞中的相对富集（图 7b；补充信息 4.4）。这个分析证实了激活和抑制的组蛋白修饰峰与 TR50 的相关性（图 7b）。有趣的是，Pan-S 区间是独特的，激活（H3K4me2、H3ac 和 H4ac）和抑制（H3K27me3）的组蛋白都有富集，这也说明 Pan-S 复制模式是由于在染色质结构和复制时间方面等位基因的差异 [75]。这种现象也与 H19/IGF2 基因座的 Pan-S 复制模式一致，该基因座是一个已知的两个等位基因不同的表观遗传学修饰印记区域。

HeLa 细胞广泛的基因组重排使我们不禁要问检测到的 TR50 和染色质状态之间的相关性是否能在其他细胞系中看到。GM06990 细胞的组蛋白修饰数据使我们能够检测是否 HeLa 细胞中基因组片段的复制时间与 GM06990 细胞中的染色质状态相关。HeLa 细胞中的早期和晚期复制片段分别在 GM06990 细胞中富集和缺失激活的标志物（图 7b）。因而，尽管存在基因组的重排（详见补充信息 2.12），HeLa 细胞中 TR50 和染色质状态差不多就是一个组成性的基准，也能在源于另一谱系的细胞系中看到。S 期早期复制片段的这种对多种激活性组蛋白修饰的富集和对抑制性修饰的缺失，以前所未有的详细度和尺度拓展了之前在哺乳动物细胞中这一领域的工作。HeLa 基因组 Pan-S 区域的组蛋白修饰模式的二元性，以及在两种不同的细胞系（HeLa 和 GM06990）中染色质标志物和复制时间的一致性，验证了人类基因组中组蛋白修饰和复制的相关性。

染色质结构和基因组结构域

概况　基因组 DNA 包装成染色质与基因表达的调控以及其他染色质过程紧密相关。接下来，我们探究更大尺度的染色质结构来确定它与转录和其他过程的关系。在发育调控的基因簇附近已经检测到广泛的 DNaseI 敏感性的大结构域（50 到 >200 kb）[77]，这促使我们猜测基因组被组成"开放"和"闭合"的染色质区域，代表着更高级的功能结构域。我们探索了不同的染色质特征，特别是组蛋白修饰，在短

modifications, correlate with chromatin structure, both over short and long distances.

Chromatin accessibility and histone modifications. We used histone modification studies and DNaseI sensitivity data sets (introduced above) to examine general chromatin accessibility without focusing on the specific DHS sites (see Supplementary Information sections 3.1, 3.3 and 3.4). A fundamental difficulty in analysing continuous data across large genomic regions is determining the appropriate scale for analysis (for example, 2 kb, 5 kb, 20 kb, and so on). To address this problem, we developed an approach based on wavelet analysis, a mathematical tool pioneered in the field of signal processing that has recently been applied to continuous-value genomic analyses. Wavelet analysis provides a means for consistently transforming continuous signals into different scales, enabling the correlation of different phenomena independently at differing scales in a consistent manner.

Global correlations of chromatin accessibility and histone modifications. We computed the regional correlation between DNaseI sensitivity and each histone modification at multiple scales using a wavelet approach (Fig. 8 and Supplementary Information section 4.2). To make quantitative comparisons between different histone modifications, we computed histograms of correlation values between DNaseI sensitivity and each histone modification at several scales and then tested these for significance at specific scales. Figure 8c shows the distribution of correlation values at a 16-kb scale, which is considerably larger than individual *cis*-acting regulatory elements. At this scale, H3K4me2, H3K4me3 and H3ac show similarly high correlation. However, they are significantly distinguished from H3K4me1 and H4ac modifications ($P < 1.5 \times 10^{-33}$; see Supplementary Information section 4.5), which show lower correlation with DNaseI sensitivity. These results suggest that larger-scale relationships between chromatin accessibility and histone modifications are dominated by sub-regions in which higher average DNaseI sensitivity is accompanied by high levels of H3K4me2, H3K4me3 and H3ac modifications.

Fig. 8. Wavelet correlations of histone marks and DNaseI sensitivity. As an example, correlations between DNaseI sensitivity and H3K4me2 (both in the GM06990 cell line) over a 1.1-Mb region on chromosome 7 (ENCODE region ENm013) are shown. **a**, The relationship between histone modification H3K4me2 (upper plot) and DNaseI sensitivity (lower plot) is shown for ENCODE region ENm013. The curves are coloured with the strength of the local correlation at the 4-kb scale (top dashed line in panel **b**). **b**, The same data as in **a** are represented as a wavelet correlation. The *y* axis shows the differing scales decomposed

距离以及长距离方面，如何与染色质结构关联。

染色质开放性和组蛋白修饰 我们使用了组蛋白修饰研究和 DNaseI 敏感性数据集（上文介绍的）来探究整体的染色质开放性，而不是聚焦于特定的 DHS 位点（详见补充信息 3.1、3.3 和 3.4）。在大的基因组区域范围内的连续数据方面，一个主要的困难是确定合适的分析尺度（如 2 kb、5 kb、20 kb 等等）。为了解决这个问题，我们基于小波分析开发了一种方法，而小波分析是主要应用于信号处理领域的一种数学工具，最近已经被应用到连续值的基因组分析当中。小波分析提供了一种可以一致地将连续信号转换为不同尺度的方法，从而能以一种一致的方式将不同的现象在不同尺度下独立地关联。

染色质开放性与组蛋白修饰的整体相关性 我们利用小波的方法，在多种尺度下计算了 DNaseI 敏感性与每一种组蛋白修饰区域的相关性（图 8 和补充信息 4.2）。为了定量比较不同的组蛋白修饰，我们计算了 DNaseI 敏感性和每一种组蛋白修饰在多个尺度下的相关性值并画了直方图，然后对其进行检验以寻找在特定的尺度下的显著性。图 8c 展示了在 16 kb 尺度下相关性值的分布，它的值明显比单个顺式调控元件的大。在这个尺度下，H3K4me2、H3K4me3 和 H3ac 表现类似，都是高度相关。但是，它们跟 H3K4me1 和 H4ac 修饰显著不同（$P < 1.5 \times 10^{-33}$；详见补充信息 4.5），后者与 DNaseI 敏感性的相关性更低。这些结果表明染色质开放性和组蛋白修饰在大尺度下的关系，主要取决于更高 DNaseI 敏感性平均值伴随着较高水平 H3K4me2、H3K4me3 和 H3ac 修饰的亚区域。

图 8. 组蛋白标志物和 DNaseI 敏感性的小波关联。作为一个例子，展示了在 7 号染色体超过 1.1 Mb 的区域内（ENCODE 区域 ENm013）DNaseI 敏感性和 H3K4me2（都是在 GM06990 细胞系）之间的相关性。**a**，展示的是 ENCODE 区域 ENm013 内组蛋白修饰 H3K4me2（上图）和 DNaseI 敏感性（下图）之间的关系。曲线的颜色是根据在 4 kb 尺度下局部相关性的强度（**b** 图中上方的虚线）。**b**，与 **a** 中同样的数据作

by the wavelet analysis from large to small scale (in kb); the colour at each point in the heatmap represents the level of correlation at the given scale, measured in a 20 kb window centred at the given position. **c**, Distribution of correlation values at the 16 kb scale between the indicated histone marks. The y axis is the density of these correlation values across ENCODE; all modifications show a peak at a positive-correlation value.

Local correlations of chromatin accessibility and histone modifications. Narrowing to a scale of ~2 kb revealed a more complex situation, in which H3K4me2 is the histone modification that is best correlated with DNaseI sensitivity. However, there is no clear combination of marks that correlate with DNaseI sensitivity in a way that is analogous to that seen at a larger scale (see Supplementary Information section 4.3). One explanation for the increased complexity at smaller scales is that there is a mixture of different classes of accessible chromatin regions, each having a different pattern of histone modifications. To examine this, we computed the degree to which local peaks in histone methylation or acetylation occur at DHSs (see Supplementary Information section 4.5.1). We found that 84%, 91% and 93% of significant peaks in H3K4 mono-, di- and tri-methylation, respectively, and 93% and 81% of significant peaks in H3ac and H4ac acetylation, respectively, coincided with DHSs (see Supplementary Information section 4.5). Conversely, a proportion of DHSs seemed not to be associated with significant peaks in H3K4 mono-, di- or tri-methylation (37%, 29% and 47%, respectively), nor with peaks in H3 or H4 acetylation (both 57%). Because only a limited number of histone modification marks were assayed, the possibility remains that some DHSs harbour other histone modifications. The absence of a more complete concordance between DHSs and peaks in histone acetylation is surprising given the widely accepted notion that histone acetylation has a central role in mediating chromatin accessibility by disrupting higher-order chromatin folding.

DNA structure at DHSs. The observation that distinctive hydroxyl radical cleavage patterns are associated with specific DNA structures[78] prompted us to investigate whether DHS subclasses differed with respect to their local DNA structure. Conversely, because different DNA sequences can give rise to similar hydroxyl radical cleavage patterns[79], genomic regions that adopt a particular local structure do not necessarily have the same nucleotide sequence. Using a Gibbs sampling algorithm on hydroxyl radical cleavage patterns of 3,150 DHSs[80], we discovered an 8-base segment with a conserved cleavage signature (CORCS; see Supplementary Information section 4.6). The underlying DNA sequences that give rise to this pattern have little primary sequence similarity despite this similar structural pattern. Furthermore, this structural element is strongly enriched in promoter-proximal DHSs (11.3-fold enrichment compared to the rest of the ENCODE regions) relative to promoter-distal DHSs (1.5-fold enrichment); this element is enriched 10.9-fold in CpG islands, but is higher still (26.4-fold) in CpG islands that overlap a DHS.

Large-scale domains in the ENCODE regions. The presence of extensive correlations seen between histone modifications, DNaseI sensitivity, replication, transcript density and protein factor binding led us to investigate whether all these features are organized systematically across the genome. To test this, we performed an unsupervised training of a two-state HMM with inputs from these different features (see Supplementary Information

为小波关联的代表。y 轴从大到小表示小波分析分解的不同尺度（单位 kb）；热图中每一个点的颜色代表在给定尺度下以给定位置为中心的 20 kb 窗口内测得的相关水平。c，在 16 kb 尺度下与相应组蛋白标志物的相关性值的分布。y 轴是这些相关性值在 ENCODE 区域的密度；所有的修饰在正相关值范围内都有一个峰。

染色质开放性和组蛋白修饰的局部相关性　将尺度缩小到约 2 kb 发现了一个更加复杂的情况，H3K4m2 是跟 DNaseI 敏感性最相关的组蛋白修饰。但是，没有明显的标志物组合与在更大尺度下看到的类似的方式与 DNaseI 敏感性相关（详见补充信息 4.3）。对于在更小尺度下增加的复杂性，一种解释是它混合了不同类型的开放染色质区域，每一类型含有不同的组蛋白修饰模式。为了研究这种可能性，我们计算了组蛋白甲基化或乙酰化中有多少局部峰是在 DHS 上（详见补充信息 4.5.1）。我们发现 H3K4 单、二和三甲基化中分别有 84%，91% 和 93% 显著的峰，以及 H3ac 和 H4ac 中分别有 93% 和 81% 的显著峰，与 DHS 是一致的（详见补充信息 4.5）。相反，一部分 DHS 则好像并不与 H3K4 单、二或三甲基化中显著的峰关联（分别为 37%、29% 和 47%），也不与 H3 或 H4 乙酰化中的峰关联（均为 57%）。因为只有有限数量的组蛋白修饰标志被检测，所以一些含有其他的组蛋白修饰的 DHS 也可能存在。鉴于广泛接受的观点是组蛋白乙酰化通过破坏更高级的染色质折叠而在介导染色质开放性方面发挥核心作用，DHS 和组蛋白乙酰化峰之间缺少更完全的一致性是出乎意料的。

DHS 处的 DNA 结构　观察到不同的羟自由基切割模式与特定的 DNA 结构[78]相关，促使我们研究 DHS 亚类是否会因它们局部的 DNA 结构而不同。反过来，因为不同的 DNA 序列能产生相似的羟自由基切割模式[79]，采用特定一种局部结构的基因组区域也未必含有相同的核苷酸序列。对 3,150 个 DHS 的羟自由基切割模式应用吉布斯采样算法，我们发现了一个 8 碱基片段含有保守的切割特征（CORCS；详见补充信息 4.6）。尽管有着这种类似的结构模式，产生这种模式的潜在 DNA 序列在一级序列上却几乎没有相似性。另外，这种结构元件在靠近启动子的 DHS（跟其他的 ENCODE 区域相比有 11.3 倍富集）比在远离启动子的 DHS 明显富集（1.5 倍富集），这种元件在 CpG 有 10.9 倍的富集，而在与 DHS 重合 CpG 到则富集倍数更高（26.4 倍）。

在 ENCODE 区域内的大尺度结构域　组蛋白修饰、DNaseI 敏感性、复制、转录本密度和蛋白质因子结合间广泛的相关性的存在，促使我们研究是否所有这些特征是在基因组范围内系统地组织起来的。为了检验这种可能性，我们输入这些不同的特征数据，无监督训练一个两态的 HMM（详见补充信息 4.7 和参考文献 81）。在

section 4.7 and ref. 81). No other information except for the experimental variables was used for the HMM training routines. We consistently found that one state ("active") generally corresponded to domains with high levels of H3ac and RNA transcription, low levels of H3K27me3 marks, and early replication timing, whereas the other state ("repressed") reflected domains with low H3ac and RNA, high H3K27me3, and late replication (see Fig. 9). In total, we identified 70 active regions spanning 11.4 Mb and 82 inactive regions spanning 17.8 Mb (median size 136 kb versus 104 kb respectively). The active domains are markedly enriched for GENCODE TSSs, CpG islands and Alu repetitive elements ($P < 0.0001$ for each), whereas repressed regions are significantly enriched for LINE1 and LTR transposons ($P < 0.001$). Taken together, these results demonstrate remarkable concordance between ENCODE functional data types and provide a view of higher-order functional domains defined by a broader range of factors at a markedly higher resolution than was previously available[82].

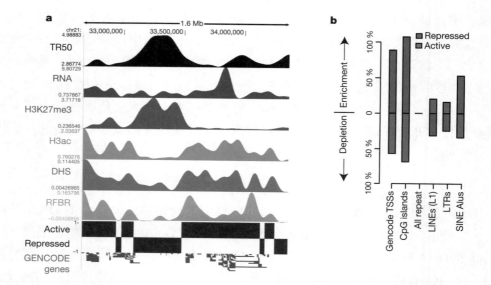

Fig. 9. Higher-order functional domains in the genome. The general concordance of multiple data types is shown for an illustrative ENCODE region (ENm005). **a**, Domains were determined by simultaneous HMM segmentation of replication time (TR50; black), bulk RNA transcription (blue), H3K27me3 (purple), H3ac (orange), DHS density (green), and RFBR density (light blue) measured continuously across the 1.6-Mb ENm005. All data were generated using HeLa cells. The histone, RNA, DHS and RFBR signals are wavelet-smoothed to an approximately 60-kb scale (see Supplementary Information section 4.7). The HMM segmentation is shown as the blocks labelled "active" and "repressed" and the structure of GENCODE genes (not used in the training) is shown at the end. **b**, Enrichment or depletion of annotated sequence features (GENCODE TSSs, CpG islands, LINE1 repeats, Alu repeats, and non-exonic constrained sequences (CSs)) in active versus repressed domains. Note the marked enrichment of TSSs, CpG islands and Alus in active domains, and the enrichment of LINE and LTRs in repressed domains.

Evolutionary Constraint and Population Variability

Overview. Functional genomic sequences can also be identified by examining evolutionary changes across multiple extant species and within the human population. Indeed, such

HMM 训练过程中，除了实验变量，没有使用其他的信息。我们不断发现一个状态（"活跃的"）通常对应于含有高水平 H3ac 和 RNA 转录、低水平 H3K27me3 标志物以及早期复制时间的结构域，而另一个状态（"抑制的"）反映的是含有低水平 H3ac 和 RNA、高水平 H3K27me3 以及晚期复制的结构域（见图 9）。总共，我们鉴定到横跨 11.4 Mb 的 70 个活跃区域和横跨 17.8 Mb 的 82 个不活跃的区域（中位数大小分别为 136 kb 和 104 kb）。活跃的结构域明显富集 GENCODE TSS、CpG 岛和 Alu 重复元件（每个都 $P < 0.0001$），而抑制的区域则明显富集 LINE1 和 LTR 转座子（$P < 0.001$）。总而言之，这些结果显示了 ENCODE 功能数据类型间显著的一致性，并且提供一个比之前已有的更高级的功能结构域图谱，该功能结构域被更广范围的因子所定义以及有着明显更高的分辨率。

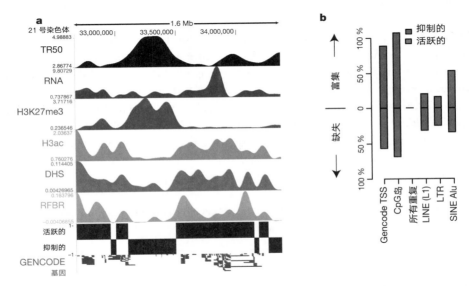

图 9. 基因组中更高级的功能结构域。本图展示的是一个用来说明 ENCODE 区域（ENm005）内多种数据类型的普遍一致性。**a**，结构域是通过对 1.6 Mb 的 ENm005 范围内对复制时间（TR50；黑色）、大量 RNA 转录（蓝色）、H3K27me3（紫色）、H3ac（橘色）、DHS 密度（绿色）和 RFBR 密度（淡蓝色）连续测量，同时进行 HMM 分段而确定的。所有的数据都是利用 HeLa 细胞产生的。组蛋白、RNA、DHS 和 RFBR 信号被小波平滑化成大约 60 kb 的尺度（详见补充信息 4.7）。HMM 分段以标为"活跃的"和"抑制的"的区块表示，最下面是 GENCODE 基因的结构（训练中没有使用）。**b**，在活跃和抑制的结构域中被注释的序列特征（GENCODE TSS、CpG 岛、LINE1 重复、Alu 重复和非外显子的限制序列（CS））的富集或缺失的比较。注意在活跃的结构域中 TSS、CpG 岛和 Alu 明显富集，以及在抑制的结构域中 LINE 和 LTR 富集。

进化的限制和群体的变异性

概况 功能性的基因组序列也能通过分析多个现存物种间和人群内部进化的变化而被鉴定。确实，这样的研究补充了鉴定特定功能元件的实验方法 [83-85]。进化的

studies complement experimental assays that identify specific functional elements[83-85]. Evolutionary constraint (that is, the rejection of mutations at a particular location) can be measured by either (i) comparing observed substitutions to neutral rates calculated from multi-sequence alignments[86-88], or (ii) determining the presence and frequency of intra-species polymorphisms. Importantly, both approaches are indifferent to any specific function that the constrained sequence might confer.

Previous studies comparing the human, mouse, rat and dog genomes examined bulk evolutionary properties of all nucleotides in the genome, and provided little insight about the precise positions of constrained bases. Interestingly, these studies indicated that the majority of constrained bases reside within the non-coding portion of the human genome. Meanwhile, increasingly rich data sets of polymorphisms across the human genome have been used extensively to establish connections between genetic variants and disease, but far fewer analyses have sought to use such data for assessing functional constraint[85].

The ENCODE Project provides an excellent opportunity for more fully exploiting inter- and intra-species sequence comparisons to examine genome function in the context of extensive experimental studies on the same regions of the genome. We consolidated the experimentally derived information about the ENCODE regions and focused our analyses on 11 major classes of genomic elements. These classes are listed in Table 4 and include two non-experimentally derived data sets: ancient repeats (ARs; mobile elements that inserted early in the mammalian lineage, have subsequently become dormant, and are assumed to be neutrally evolving) and constrained sequences (CSs; regions that evolve detectably more slowly than neutral sequences).

Table 4. Eleven classes of genomic elements subjected to evolutionary and population-genetics analyses

Abbreviation	Description
CDS	Coding exons, as annotated by GENCODE
5′UTR	5′untranslated region, as annotated by GENCODE
3′UTR	3′untranslated region, as annotated by GENCODE
Un.TxFrag	Unannotated region detected by RNA hybridization to tiling array (that is, unannotated TxFrag)
RxFrag	Region detected by RACE and analysis on tiling array
Pseudogene	Pseudogene identified by consensus pseudogene analysis
RFBR	Regulatory factor binding region identified by ChIP-chip assays
RFBR-SeqSp	Regulatory factor binding region identified only by ChIP-chip assays for factors with known sequence-specificity
DHS	DNaseI hypersensitive sites found in multiple tissues
FAIRE	Region of open chromatin identified by the FAIRE assay
TSS	Transcription start site
AR	Ancient repeat inserted early in the mammalian lineage and presumed to be neutrally evolving
CS	Constrained sequence identified by analysing multi-sequence alignments

限制(即在特定位置排斥变异)能通过(i)比较观察到的替换与多重序列比对计算得到的中性率[86-88],或者(ii)确定物种内多态性的存在和频率而被衡量。重要的是,两种方法无关乎限制序列可能发挥的任何特定功能。

之前的研究比较了人类、小鼠、大鼠和狗的基因组,分析了基因组中所有核苷酸大的进化特性,而对受限制的碱基的精确位置几乎没有了解。有意思的是,这些研究表明大部分受限制的碱基位于人类基因组的非编码部分。同时,人类基因组范围的多态性的数据集越来越丰富,并且已经被广泛地用于建立遗传变异与疾病的联系,但是目前利用这样的数据来评价功能限制的分析还很少[85]。

ENCODE 计划提供了一个很好的机会来更加全面地探索物种间和物种内的序列比较,进而结合在基因组相同区域广泛进行的实验研究来研究基因组的功能。我们统一了实验得到关于 ENCODE 区域的信息,将我们的分析聚焦于 11 个主要类别的基因组元件。这些类别在表 4 中被列出,其中包含两个非实验得到数据集:古老的重复(AR;一种可移动的元件,在早期就插入到哺乳动物谱系但自此休眠,被认为是中性进化)和受限制的序列(CS;可检测到比中性序列进化得更缓慢的区域)。

表 4. 十一类被用于进化和群体遗传学分析的基因组元件

缩写	描述
CDS	编码外显子,根据 GENCODE 注释
5′ UTR	5′非翻译区,根据 GENCODE 注释
3′ UTR	3′非翻译区,根据 GENCODE 注释
Un.TxFrag	通过 RNA 杂交到叠瓦式阵列检测到的非翻译区(即非翻译的 TxFrag)
RxFrag	通过 RACE 和叠瓦式阵列分析检测到的区域
假基因	通过共有假基因分析鉴定到的假基因
RFBR	通过 ChIP-chip 实验鉴定到的调控因子结合区域
RFBR-SeqSp	对于已知含有序列特异性的因子,仅通过 ChIP-chip 实验鉴定到的调控因子结合区域
DHS	在多种组织中发现的 DNaseI 超敏感位点
FAIRE	通过 FAIRE 实验鉴定到的开放染色质区域
TSS	转录起始位点
AR	在早期就插入到哺乳动物谱系中的古老的重复,被认为是中性进化
CS	通过多重序列比对分析鉴定到的限制序列

Comparative sequence data sets and analysis. We generated 206 Mb of genomic sequence orthologous to the ENCODE regions from 14 mammalian species using a targeted strategy that involved isolating[89] and sequencing[90] individual bacterial artificial chromosome clones. For an additional 14 vertebrate species, we used 340 Mb of orthologous genomic sequence derived from genome-wide sequencing efforts[3-8,91-93]. The orthologous sequences were aligned using three alignment programs: TBA[94], MAVID[95] and MLAGAN[96]. Four independent methods that generated highly concordant results[97] were then used to identify sequences under constraint (PhastCons[88], GERP[87], SCONE[98] and BinCons[86]). From these analyses, we developed a high-confidence set of "constrained sequences" that correspond to 4.9% of the nucleotides in the ENCODE regions. The threshold for determining constraint was set using a FDR rate of 5% (see ref. 97); this level is similar to previous estimates of the fraction of the human genome under mammalian constraint[4,86-88] but the FDR rate was not chosen to fit this result. The median length of these constrained sequences is 19 bases, with the minimum being 8 bases—roughly the size of a typical transcription factor binding site. These analyses, therefore, provide a resolution of constrained sequences that is substantially better than that currently available using only whole-genome vertebrate sequences[99-102].

Intra-species variation studies mainly used SNP data from Phases I and II, and the 10 re-sequenced regions in ENCODE regions with 48 individuals of the HapMap Project[103]; nucleotide insertion or deletion (indel) data were from the SNP Consortium and HapMap. We also examined the ENCODE regions for the presence of overlaps with known segmental duplications[104] and CNVs.

Experimentally identified functional elements and constrained sequences. We first compared the detected constrained sequences with the positions of experimentally identified functional elements. A total of 40% of the constrained bases reside within protein-coding exons and their associated untranslated regions (Fig. 10) and, in agreement with previous genome-wide estimates, the remaining constrained bases do not overlap the mature transcripts of protein-coding genes[4,5,88,105,106]. When we included the other experimental annotations, we found that an additional 20% of the constrained bases overlap experimentally identified non-coding functional regions, although far fewer of these regions overlap constrained sequences compared to coding exons (see below). Most experimental annotations are significantly different from a random expectation for both base-pair or element-level overlaps (using the GSC statistic, see Supplementary Information section 1.3), with a more striking deviation when considering elements (Fig. 11). The exceptions to this are pseudogenes, Un.TxFrags and RxFrags. The increase in significance moving from base-pair measures to the element level suggests that discrete islands of constrained sequence exist within experimentally identified functional elements, with the surrounding bases apparently not showing evolutionary constraint. This notion is discussed in greater detail in ref. 97.

可比较的序列数据集和分析。 利用包括分离[89]和测序[90]单个细菌人工染色体克隆的靶向策略，我们从 14 个哺乳动物物种中得到了 206 Mb 跟 ENCODE 区域直系同源的基因组序列。对于另外的 14 种脊椎动物，我们使用的是从全基因组测序得到的 340 Mb 直系同源的基因组序列[3-8,91-93]。我们使用三种比对程序进行直系同源序列的比对：TBA[94]、MAVID[95] 和 MLAGAN[96]。四个独立的方法（PhastCons[88]、GERP[87]、SCONE[98] 和 BinCons[86]）得到了高度一致的结果[97]，然后被用于鉴定受限制的序列。从这些分析中，我们形成了一组高度可信的"受限制的序列"，对应于 ENCODE 区域内 4.9% 的核苷酸。使用 5% 的 FDR 率作为受限制的阈值（见参考文献 97）；该水平跟之前估计的人类基因组中受哺乳动物限制的比例类似[4,86-88]，但是 FDR 率并不是为了符合这个结果。这些受限制的序列长度的中位数是 19 个碱基，最短是 8 个碱基——差不多一个典型的转录因子结合位点的长度。因而，这些分析提供的受限制的序列的分辨率明显好于目前仅利用全基因组脊椎动物序列获得的[99-102]。

物种内的变异研究主要使用来自 HapMap 计划 I 和 II 期的 SNP 数据，以及其中 48 个个体的 10 个位于 ENCODE 区域的区域的重测序数据[103]；核苷酸的插入或者缺失（插入缺失位）数据来自 SNP 协作组和 HapMap。我们也分析了 ENCODE 区域与已知的片段复制[104] 和 CNV 重合情况。

实验鉴定的功能元件和受限制的序列 我们首先将检测到的受限制的序列跟与实验鉴定到的功能元件进行了比较。总共 40% 受限制的碱基位于蛋白质编码的外显子和它们相关的非翻译区域（图 10），并且，与之前的全基因组估计一致，剩下的受限制的碱基不与蛋白质编码的基因的成熟转录本重合[4,5,88,105,106]。当包括了其他实验注释时，我们发现了 20% 额外受限制的碱基与实验鉴定到的非编码功能区域重合，尽管与受限制序列重合的这些区域要远远少于编码的外显子（见下文）。无论是碱基对还是元件水平的重合，大多数的实验注释显著不同于随机预期（利用 GSC 统计，详见补充信息 1.3），当考虑元件时差异更加明显（图 11）。其中的例外是假基因、Un.TxFrag 和 RxFrag。从碱基对测量到元件水平时显著水平升高，说明受限制序列的分离的岛存在于实验鉴定到的功能元件内，而周围的碱基则明显不具有进化上的限制。这个观点在参考文献 97 中有更详细的讨论。

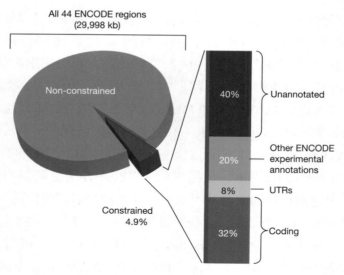

Fig. 10. Relative proportion of different annotations among constrained sequences. The 4.9% of bases in the ENCODE regions identified as constrained is subdivided into the portions that reflect known coding regions, UTRs, other experimentally annotated regions, and unannotated sequence.

Fig. 11. Overlap of constrained sequences and various experimental annotations. **a**, A schematic depiction shows the different tests used for assessing overlap between experimental annotations and constrained

图 10. 不同注释在受限制序列中的相对比例。ENCODE 区域中有 4.9% 的碱基被鉴定为受限制的，其又被进一步分为已知的编码区域、UTR、其他实验注释的区域和未注释的序列。

图 11. 受限制序列与各种实验注释的重合情况。**a**，示意图展示用于评价实验注释和受限制序列重合情况的不同检验方法，不只是对于单个碱基，而且针对整个区域。**b**，观察到的重合的比例，对于碱基和

sequences, both for individual bases and for entire regions. **b**, Observed fraction of overlap, depicted separately for bases and regions. The results are shown for selected experimental annotations. The internal bars indicate 95% confidence intervals of randomized placement of experimental elements using the GSC methodology to account for heterogeneity in the data sets. When the bar overlaps the observed value one cannot reject the hypothesis that these overlaps are consistent with random placements.

We also examined measures of human variation (heterozygosity, derived allele-frequency spectra and indel rates) within the sequences of the experimentally identified functional elements (Fig. 12). For these studies, ARs were used as a marker for neutrally evolving sequence. Most experimentally identified functional elements are associated with lower heterozygosity compared to ARs, and a few have lower indel rates compared with ARs. Striking outliers are 3′ UTRs, which have dramatically increased indel rates without an obvious cause. This is discussed in more depth in ref. 107.

Fig. 12. Relationship between heterozygosity and polymorphic indel rate for a variety of experimental annotations. 3′ UTRs are an expected outlier for the indel measures owing to the presence of low-complexity sequence (leading to a higher indel rate).

These findings indicate that the majority of the evolutionarily constrained, experimentally identified functional elements show evidence of negative selection both across mammalian species and within the human population. Furthermore, we have assigned at least one molecular function to the majority (60%) of all constrained bases in the ENCODE regions.

Conservation of regulatory elements. The relationship between individual classes of regulatory elements and constrained sequences varies considerably, ranging from cases where there is strong evolutionary constraint (for example, pan-vertebrate ultraconserved regions[108,109]) to examples of regulatory elements that are not conserved between orthologous human and mouse genes[110]. Within the ENCODE regions, 55% of RFBRs overlap the high-confidence constrained sequences. As expected, RFBRs have many unconstrained bases, presumably owing to the small size of the specific binding site. We investigated whether the binding sites in RFBRs could be further delimited using information about evolutionary constraint. For 7 out of 17 factors with either known TRANSFAC or Jaspar

区域分开展示。展示的结果是选出来的实验注释。中间的横杠表示实验元件随机排布的 95% 的置信区间，这是利用 GSC 方法得到的，目的是为了消除数据集中的异质性。当这个横杠与观察值重合时，则不能拒绝这些重合与随机排布一致的假说。

我们也分析了实验鉴定到的功能元件中人类的变异量（杂合度、衍生的等位基因频率谱和插入缺失率）（图 12）。对于这些研究，AR 被用作中性进化的标志物。与 AR 相比，大多数实验鉴定到的功能元件与更低的杂合度相关，一小部分含有比 AR 更低的插入缺失率。显著的异常情况是 3′ UTR，它含有明显更高的插入缺失率，却没有明显的原因。在参考文献 107 中有更深入的讨论。

图 12. 对于各种实验注释，杂合度与多态性的插入缺失率的关系。对于插入缺失的测量，3′ UTR 是一个符合预期的离群值，原因是低复杂序列的存在（导致更高的插入缺失率）。

这些发现表明大部分进化上受限制的实验鉴定到的功能元件呈现负选择的迹象，这不仅是在哺乳动物间，在人类群体内部也是如此。再者，我们已经将 ENCODE 区域内所有受限制碱基中的大部分（60%）至少赋予了一种分子功能。

调控元件的保守性　各种调控元件与受限制序列之间的关系差别很大，有的受到强烈的进化限制（如多个脊椎动物超保守区域[108,109]），有的调控元件则在直系同源的人和小鼠基因间不保守[110]。在 ENCODE 区域内，55% 的 RFBR 与高可信度的受限制序列重合。正如预期的，RFBR 含有很多不受限制的碱基，可能是由于特定结合位点的长度较短。利用关于进化限制的信息，我们研究了 RFBR 中的结合位点能否被进一步划分。对于含有已知的 TRANSFAC 或 Jaspar 模序的 17 个因子中的 7 个，我们的 ChIP-chip 数据发现，相比不受限制的 RFBR，在受限制的 RFBR 中明显

motifs, our ChIP-chip data revealed a marked enrichment of the appropriate motif within the constrained versus the unconstrained portions of the RFBRs (see Supplementary Information section 5.1). This enrichment was seen for levels of stringency used for defining ChIP-chip-positive sites (1% and 5% FDR level), indicating that combining sequence constraint and ChIP-chip data may provide a highly sensitive means for detecting factor binding sites in the human genome.

Experimentally identified functional elements and genetic variation. The above studies focus on purifying (negative) selection. We used nucleotide variation to detect potential signals of adaptive (positive) selection. We modified the standard McDonald–Kreitman test (MK-test[111,112]) and the Hudson–Kreitman–Aguade (HKA)[113] test (see Supplementary Information section 5.2.1), to examine whether an entire set of sequence elements shows an excess of polymorphisms or an excess of inter-species divergence. We found that constrained sequences and coding exons have an excess of polymorphisms (consistent with purifying selection), whereas 5′ UTRs show evidence of an excess of divergence (with a portion probably reflecting positive selection). In general, non-coding genomic regions show more variation, with both a large number of segments that undergo purifying selection and regions that are fast evolving.

We also examined structural variation (that is, CNVs, inversions and translocations[114]; see Supplementary Information section 5.2.2). Within these polymorphic regions, we encountered significant over-representation of CDSs, TxFrags, and intra-species constrained sequences ($P < 10^{-3}$, Fig. 13), and also detected a statistically significant under-representation of ARs ($P = 10^{-3}$). A similar overrepresentation of CDSs and intra-species constrained sequences was found within non-polymorphic segmental duplications.

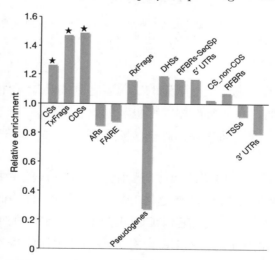

Fig. 13. CNV enrichment. The relative enrichment of different experimental annotations in the ENCODE regions associated with CNVs. CS_non-CDS are constrained sequences outside of coding regions. A value of 1 or less indicates no enrichment, and values greater than 1 show enrichment. Starred columns are cases that are significant on the basis of this enrichment being found in less than 5% of randomizations that matched each element class for length and density of features.

中

富集合适的模序（详见补充信息 5.1）。这种富集是在用于确定 ChIP-chip 阳性位点的阈值水平下看到的（1% 和 5%FDR 水平），说明结合序列的受限制和 ChIP-chip 数据可能提供一种高度敏感的方法来确定因子在人类基因组中的结合位点。

实验鉴定的功能元件和遗传变异　上述研究聚焦于纯化（负）选择。我们使用核苷酸的变异来检测潜在的适应性（正）选择信号。我们修改标准的麦克唐纳–克莱特曼检验（MK 检验[111, 112]）和赫德森–克莱特曼–阿瓜德（HKA）[113] 检验（详见补充信息 5.2.1），来检查一整套序列元件是否呈现过度的多态性或者过度的物种间差异。我们发现受限制序列和编码的外显子呈现过度的多态性（与纯化选择一致），而 5′ UTR 呈现过度的差异迹象（其中一部分可能反映了正选择）。总的来说，非编码的基因组区域呈现更多的变异，不仅大量的片段在进行纯化选择，而且有区域正在快速地进化。

我们还检查了结构变异（即 CNV，倒位和易位[114]；详见补充信息 5.2.2）。在这些多态性的区域，我们发现 CDS、TxFrag 和物种内受限制序列显著富集（$P < 10^{-3}$，图 13），还检测到有统计学差异的 AR 的缺失（$P = 10^{-3}$）。CDS 和物种内受限制序列类似的富集在非多态性的片段重复中也被发现。

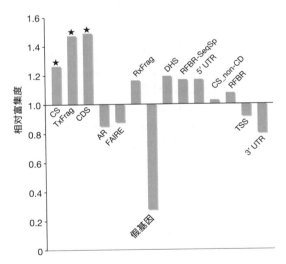

图 13. CNV 富集。在 ENCODE 区域内，与 CNV 相关的不同实验注释的相对富集程度。CS_non-CDS 是编码区域以外的受限制序列。数值为 1 或更小表示没有富集，数值大于 1 表示富集。标记星号的柱是显著的组，这种显著是基于在与相应类别元件长度和特征密度相匹配的随机组中仅有不到 5% 的富集。

Unexplained constrained sequences. Despite the wealth of complementary data, 40% of the ENCODE-region sequences identified as constrained are not associated with any experimental evidence of function. There is no evidence indicating that mutational cold spots account for this constraint; they have similar measures of constraint to experimentally identified elements and harbour equal proportions of SNPs. To characterize further the unexplained constrained sequences, we examined their clustering and phylogenetic distribution. These sequences are not uniformly distributed across most ENCODE regions, and even in most ENCODE regions the distribution is different from constrained sequences within experimentally identified functional elements (see Supplementary Information section 5.3). The large fraction of constrained sequence that does not match any experimentally identified elements is not surprising considering that only a limited set of transcription factors, cell lines and biological conditions have thus far been examined.

Unconstrained experimentally identified functional elements. In contrast, an unexpectedly large fraction of experimentally identified functional elements show no evidence of evolutionary constraint ranging from 93% for Un.TxFrags to 12% for CDS. For most types of non-coding functional elements, roughly 50% of the individual elements seemed to be unconstrained across all mammals.

There are two methodological reasons that might explain the apparent excess of unconstrained experimentally identified functional elements: the underestimation of sequence constraint or overestimation of experimentally identified functional elements. We do not believe that either of these explanations fully accounts for the large and varied levels of unconstrained experimentally functional sequences. The set of constrained bases analysed here is highly accurate and complete due to the depth of the multiple alignment. Both by bulk fitting procedures and by comparison of SNP frequencies to constraint there is clearly a proportion of constrained bases not captured in the defined 4.9% of constrained sequences, but it is small (see Supplementary Information section 5.4 and S5.5). More aggressive schemes to detect constraint only marginally increase the overlap with experimentally identified functional elements, and do so with considerably less specificity. Similarly, all experimental findings have been independently validated and, for the least constrained experimentally identified functional elements (Un.TxFrags and binding sites of sequence-specific factors), there is both internal validation and cross-validation from different experimental techniques. This suggests that there is probably not a significant overestimation of experimentally identified functional elements. Thus, these two explanations may contribute to the general observation about unconstrained functional elements, but cannot fully explain it.

Instead, we hypothesize five biological reasons to account for the presence of large amounts of unconstrained functional elements. The first two are particular to certain biological assays in which the elements being measured are connected to but do not coincide with the analysed region. An example of this is the parent transcript of an miRNA, where the current assays detect the exons (some of which are not under evolutionary selection), whereas the intronic miRNA actually harbours the constrained bases. Nevertheless, the

未解释的受限制序列　尽管有丰富的互补数据，被鉴定为受限制的 ENCODE 区域序列中仍有 40% 不与任何一项功能的实验证据有关联。没有证据表明突变冷点导致这种限制，它们与实验鉴定到的元件有类似的程度的受限制，并且含有相同比例的 SNP。为了进一步描述未解释的受限制序列的特征，我们检查了它们的聚集和系统进化分布。这些序列并非均匀分布在大多数的 ENCODE 区域，其至在大多数的 ENCODE 区域，它们的分布跟位于实验鉴定的功能元件内的受限制序列也是不同的（详见补充信息 5.3）。考虑到目前为止仅检测了有限数量的转录因子、细胞系和生物学条件，很大一部分受限制序列不与任何实验鉴定到的元件相匹配其实并不奇怪。

不受限制的实验鉴定到的功能元件　相反，出乎意料的是很大比例实验鉴定到的功能元件中没有表现出进化受限制的证据，从 Un.TxFrag 的 93% 到 CDS 的 12%。对于大多数类型的非编码功能元件，每种元件都有大约 50% 好像在所有哺乳动物中不受限制。

有两个方法学的原因可能解释这种明显过量的不受限制的实验鉴定的功能元件：低估了受限制的序列或者高估了实验鉴定的功能元件。我们不相信这些解释中的某一个能完全解释这大量且不同水平的非受限制的实验鉴定的功能序列。由于多重比对的深度，这里分析的这组受限制的碱基是高度准确而完整的。不管是通过批量拟合方法还是通过比较 SNP 频率跟受限制性，明显有一部分受限制的碱基在 4.9% 的受限制序列中没有被捕获到，但是这个数量是很小的（详见补充信息 5.4 和 S5.5）。更激进的检测受限制的策略仅仅略微增加了与实验鉴定到的功能元件的重合度，而特异性明显降低。类似地，所有实验发现已经被独立验证，对于最不受限制的实验鉴定的功能元件 (UnTxFrag 和序列特异因子的结合位点)，既有内部验证也有不同实验技术的交叉验证。这说明可能并没有显著高估实验鉴定的功能元件。因而，这两种解释可能有助于解释普遍观察到的非受限制功能元件，但是还不能完全解释它。

作为替代，我们猜测了五个生物学原因来解释大量的非受限制功能元件的存在。前两个特别针对特定的生物学实验，实验中测到的元件与分析的区域相关但是并不一致。一个这样的例子是 miRNA 的亲本转录本，现有的实验检测的是外显子 (其中一些并没有受到进化的筛选)，而位于内含子的 miRNA 实际上含有受限制的碱基。尽管如此，转录本序列还是提供了被调控的启动子与 miRNA 之间关键的耦合。转

transcript sequence provides the critical coupling between the regulated promoter and the miRNA. The sliding of transcription factors (which might bind a specific sequence but then migrate along the DNA) or the processivity of histone modifications across chromatin are more exotic examples of this. A related, second hypothesis is that delocalized behaviours of the genome, such as general chromatin accessibility, may be maintained by some biochemical processes (such as transcription of intergenic regions or specific factor binding) without the requirement for specific sequence elements. These two explanations of both connected components and diffuse components related to, but not coincident with, constrained sequences are particularly relevant for the considerable amount of unannotated and unconstrained transcripts.

The other three hypotheses may be more general—the presence of neutral (or near neutral) biochemical elements, of lineage-specific functional elements, and of functionally conserved but non-orthologous elements. We believe there is a considerable proportion of neutral biochemically active elements that do not confer a selective advantage or disadvantage to the organism. This neutral pool of sequence elements may turn over during evolutionary time emerging via certain mutations and disappearing by others. The size of the neutral pool would largely be determined by the rate of emergence and extinction through chance events; low information-content elements, such as transcription factor-binding sites[110] will have larger neutral pools. Second, from this neutral pool, some elements might occasionally acquire a biological role and so come under evolutionary selection. The acquisition of a new biological role would then create a lineage-specific element. Finally, a neutral element from the general pool could also become a peer of an existing selected functional element and either of the two elements could then be removed by chance. If the older element is removed, the newer element has, in essence, been conserved without using orthologous bases, providing a conserved function in the absence of constrained sequences. For example, a common HNF4A binding site in the human and mouse genomes may not reflect orthologous human and mouse bases, though the presence of an HNF4A site in that region was evolutionarily selected for in both lineages. Note that both the neutral turnover of elements and the "functional peering" of elements has been suggested for *cis*-acting regulatory elements in *Drosophila*[115,116] and mammals[110]. Our data support these hypotheses, and we have generalized this idea over many different functional elements. The presence of conserved function encoded by conserved orthologous bases is a commonplace assumption in comparative genomics; our findings indicate that there could be a sizable set of functionally conserved but non-orthologous elements in the human genome, and that these seem unconstrained across mammals. Functional data akin to the ENCODE Project on other related species, such as mouse, would be critical to understanding the rate of such functionally conserved but non-orthologous elements.

Conclusion

The generation and analyses of over 200 experimental data sets from studies examining the 44 ENCODE regions provide a rich source of functional information for 30 Mb of

录因子的滑动(转录因子可能结合一个特定的序列但是随后沿着 DNA 移动)或者组蛋白修饰在染色质上的延伸性则是更加异乎寻常的例子。与之相关的第二个假说是基因组不受位置限制的行为,一般的染色质开放性可能通过一些生化过程而被维持(如基因间区域的转录或者特定因子的结合)不需要特定的序列元件。这两种对相连组分和扩散组分都与受限制序列相关但又不完全一致现象的解释,与相当数量未注释且未受限制的转录本特别相关。

其他三种假说——中性(或者近中性)生化元件、谱系特异的功能元件和功能保守但非直系同源元件的存在——可能更常见。我们相信存在相当大的一部分中性的生化活跃元件,并不对机体产生选择性优势或者劣势。这种中性序列元件库可能在进化过程中发生转变,通过特定突变而出现,通过其他一些突变而消失。中性库的大小很大程度上取决于元件通过随机事件而产生和消失的速率;低信息量的元件例如转录因子结合位点 [110] 会有更大的中性库。第二,从这个中性库中,一些元件可能偶然获得一个生物学功能,因而进入进化选择。一个新的生物学功能的获得会进而产生一个谱系特异的元件。最后,普通库中的一个中性元件也能成为一个同等的已被选择的功能元件,这两个元件中的一个会随机被去除。如果更老的元件被去除,那么更新的元件即使不使用直系同源碱基,在本质上就已经是保守的,在不存在受限制序列的情况下提供了一个保守功能。例如,在人和小鼠基因组中一个共同的 HNF4A 结合位点可能并不反映直系同源的人和小鼠碱基,尽管 HNF4A 位点在那个区域的存在在两个谱系中都是被进化选择的。需要注意的是,元件的中性转换和元件的"功能等价"在果蝇 [115,116] 和哺乳动物 [110] 中都被认为是顺式调控元件。我们的数据支持这些假说,我们已经将这个观点普遍地应用于很多不同的功能元件。由保守直系同源碱基编码的保守功能的存在,在比较基因组学中是一个很平常的假设,我们的发现提示可能在人类基因组中存在相当数量的功能保守但非直系同源的元件,这些元件在哺乳动物中似乎并不受限制。类似于 ENCODE 计划的关于其他相关物种的功能数据(例如小鼠的),对于理解这种功能保守的但非直系同源元件的速率将会至关重要。

结　论

研究针对 44 个 ENCODE 区域,产生和分析了超过 200 个实验数据集,为人类

the human genome. The first conclusion of these efforts is that these data are remarkably inform-ative. Although there will be ongoing work to enhance existing assays, invent new techniques and develop new data-analysis methods, the generation of genome-wide experimental data sets akin to the ENCODE pilot phase would provide an impressive platform for future genome exploration efforts. This now seems feasible in light of throughput improvements of many of the assays and the ever-declining costs of whole-genome tiling arrays and DNA sequencing. Such genome-wide functional data should be acquired and released openly, as has been done with other large-scale genome projects, to ensure its availability as a new foundation for all biologists studying the human genome. It is these biologists who will often provide the critical link from biochemical function to biological role for the identified elements.

The scale of the pilot phase of the ENCODE Project was also sufficiently large and unbiased to reveal important principles about the organization of functional elements in the human genome. In many cases, these principles agree with current mechanistic models. For example, we observe trimethylation of H3K4 enriched near active genes, and have improved the ability to accurately predict gene activity based on this and other histone modifications. However, we also uncovered some surprises that challenge the current dogma on biological mechanisms. The generation of numerous intercalated transcripts spanning the majority of the genome has been repeatedly suggested[13,14], but this phenomenon has been met with mixed opinions about the biological importance of these transcripts. Our analyses of numerous orthogonal data sets firmly establish the presence of these transcripts, and thus the simple view of the genome as having a defined set of isolated loci transcribed independently does not seem to be accurate. Perhaps the genome encodes a network of transcripts, many of which are linked to protein-coding transcripts and to the majority of which we cannot (yet) assign a biological role. Our perspective of transcription and genes may have to evolve and also poses some interesting mechanistic questions. For example, how are splicing signals coordinated and used when there are so many overlapping primary transcripts? Similarly, to what extent does this reflect neutral turnover of reproducible transcripts with no biological role?

We gained subtler but equally important mechanistic findings relating to transcription, replication and chromatin modification. Transcription factors previously thought to primarily bind promoters bind more generally, and those which do bind to promoters are equally likely to bind downstream of a TSS as upstream. Interestingly, many elements that previously were classified as distal enhancers are, in fact, close to one of the newly identified TSSs; only about 35% of sites showing evidence of binding by multiple transcription factors are actually distal to a TSS. This need not imply that most regulatory information is confined to classic promoters, but rather it does suggest that transcription and regulation are coordinated actions beyond just the traditional promoter sequences. Meanwhile, although distal regulatory elements could be identified in the ENCODE regions, they are currently difficult to classify, in part owing to the lack of a broad set of transcription factors to use in analysing such elements. Finally, we now have a much better appreciation of how DNA replication is coordinated with histone modifications.

基因组的这 30 Mb 区域提供了一个丰富的功能信息的资源。这些工作的第一个结论是这些数据所包含的信息量是巨大的。尽管将有进一步的工作来促进现有的实验分析、发明新的技术和开发新的数据分析方法，类似于 ENCODE 先导阶段的全基因组实验数据集的产生还是会为以后的基因组研究提供一个出色的平台。现在看来这似乎是可行的，因为很多实验的通量在提升而全基因组叠瓦式阵列和 DNA 测序费用在大幅下降。就像其他大规模基因组计划一样，这种全基因组的功能数据应该开放获取，以保证它作为一个新的基础能被所有生物学家用来研究人类基因组。正是这些生物学家将会经常为鉴定到的元件提供从生化功能到生物学功能的关键联系。

ENCODE 计划先导阶段的规模也是足够大且无偏性，进而能够反映人类基因组中功能元件的重要组织原理。在很多例子中，这些原理与现有的机制模型是一致的。例如，我们观察到 H3K4 的三甲基化在活跃基因的附近富集，基于这种以及其他组蛋白修饰，我们提高了精确预测基因活性的能力。然而，我们也发现了一些意料之外的事情，对现有的生物学机制的信条提出了挑战。已经反复发现，有大量的间插性转录本的产生，这些转录本横跨大部分的基因组 [13,14]，但是对于这种现象中这些转录本的生物学意义有不同的观点。我们通过对大量的正交数据集的分析，确凿地证实了这些转录本的存在，因而简单地认为基因组含有确定的一套分离的基因座独立地被转录好像并不是准确的。也许基因组编码一个转录本的网络，很多转录本与蛋白质编码的转录本有联系，而对于大部分的转录本，我们（还）不能确定其生物学功能。我们关于转录和基因的观点可能不得不进化，另外也产生了一些有趣的关于机制的问题。例如，当有这么多重叠的原始转录本时，剪接信号是如何协调和使用的？类似地，这在多大程度上反映了没有生物学功能的重复转录本的中性转换？

我们获得了微妙但同等重要的与转录、复制和染色质修饰相关的机制方面的发现。之前认为主要结合启动子的转录因子，其实结合更广泛，那些确定结合启动子的转录因子除了结合 TSS 上游之外，同样可能结合 TSS 的下游。有趣的是，很多元件之前被划分为远端增强子，其实靠近新鉴定到的 TSS；对于有证据表明被多个转录因子结合的位点，只有大约 35% 确实远离 TSS。这不一定说明大部分的调控信息局限于经典的启动子，但是确实暗示转录和调控并不仅是传统启动子序列的协调活动。同时，尽管远端调控元件能在 ENCODE 区域中被鉴定，但是它们目前还难以分类，部分是由于缺少一套广泛的转录因子来分析这些元件。最后，目前我们对于 DNA 复制如何与组蛋白修饰协调有了更好的认识。

At the outset of the ENCODE Project, many believed that the broad collection of experimental data would nicely dovetail with the detailed evolutionary information derived from comparing multiple mammalian sequences to provide a neat "dictionary" of conserved genomic elements, each with a growing annotation about their biochemical function(s). In one sense, this was achieved; the majority of constrained bases in the ENCODE regions are now associated with at least some experimentally derived information about function. However, we have also encountered a remarkable excess of experimentally identified functional elements lacking evolutionary constraint, and these cannot be dismissed for technical reasons. This is perhaps the biggest surprise of the pilot phase of the ENCODE Project, and suggests that we take a more "neutral" view of many of the functions conferred by the genome.

Methods

The methods are described in the Supplementary Information, with more technical details for each experiment often found in the references provided in Table 1. The Supplementary Information sections are arranged in the same order as the manuscript (with similar headings to facilitate cross-referencing). The first page of Supplementary Information also has an index to aid navigation. Raw data are available in ArrayExpress, GEO or EMBL/GenBank archives as appropriate, as detailed in Supplementary Information section 1.1. Processed data are also presented in a user-friendly manner at the UCSC Genome Browser's ENCODE portal (http://genome.ucsc.edu/ENCODE/).

(**447**, 799-816; 2007)

Received 2 March; accepted 23 April 2007.

References:

1. International Human Genome Sequencing Consortium. Initial sequencing and analysis of the human genome. *Nature* **409**, 860-921 (2001).

2. Venter, J. C. *et al.* The sequence of the human genome. *Science* **291**, 1304-1351 (2001).

3. International Human Genome Sequencing Consortium. Finishing the euchromatic sequence of the human genome. *Nature* **431**, 931-945 (2004).

4. Mouse Genome Sequencing Consortium. Initial sequencing and comparative analysis of the mouse genome. *Nature* **420**, 520-562 (2002).

5. Rat Genome Sequencing Project Consortium. Genome sequence of the Brown Norway rat yields insights into mammalian evolution. *Nature* **428**, 493-521 (2004).

6. Lindblad-Toh, K. *et al.* Genome sequence, comparative analysis and haplotype structure of the domestic dog. *Nature* **438**, 803-819 (2005).

7. International Chicken Genome Sequencing Consortium. Sequence and comparative analysis of the chicken genome provide unique perspectives on vertebrate evolution. *Nature* **432**, 695-716 (2004).

8. Chimpanzee Sequencing and Analysis Consortium. Initial sequence of the chimpanzee genome and comparison with the human genome. *Nature* **437**, 69-87 (2005).

9. ENCODE Project Consortium. The ENCODE (ENCyclopedia Of DNA Elements) Project. *Science* **306**, 636-640 (2004).

10. Zhang, Z. D. *et al.* Statistical analysis of the genomic distribution and correlation of regulatory elements in the ENCODE regions. *Genome Res.* **17**, 787-797 (2007).

11. Euskirchen, G. M. *et al.* Mapping of transcription factor binding regions in mammalian cells by ChIP: comparison of array and sequencing based technologies. *Genome Res.* **17**, 898-909 (2007).

12. Willingham, A. T. & Gingeras, T. R. TUF love for "junk" DNA. *Cell* 125, 1215-1220 (2006).

13. Carninci, P. *et al.* Genome-wide analysis of mammalian promoter architecture and evolution. *Nature Genet.* **38**, 626-635 (2006).

14. Cheng, J. *et al.* Transcriptional maps of 10 human chromosomes at 5-nucleotide resolution. *Science* **308**, 1149-1154 (2005).

15. Bertone, P. *et al.* Global identification of human transcribed sequences with genome tiling arrays. *Science* **306**, 2242-2246 (2004).

16. Guigó, R. *et al.* EGASP: the human ENCODE Genome Annotation Assessment Project. *Genome Biol.* 7, (Suppl. 1; S2) 1-31 (2006).

在 ENCODE 计划的开始时，很多人认为广泛收集的实验数据将会完美吻合来自比较多种哺乳动物序列得到的详细进化信息，进而提供一个纯粹的保守基因组元件的"词典"，每一个元件含有更多的关于它们生化功能的注释。在某种意义上，这已经达到了。在 ENCODE 区域中，大部分的受限制碱基现在至少与某些实验得到的功能信息相关联。但是，我们也遇到了大量多余的实验鉴定到的功能元件，它们缺少进化的限制，又不能因为技术原因而摒弃。这可能是 ENCODE 计划先导阶段最大的意外，提示我们要更加"中性"地看待很多基因组赋予的功能。

方　　法

在补充信息中对方法进行了介绍，对于各个实验，更多的技术细节大多能在表 1 中提供的参考文献中找到。补充信息部分跟正文排列顺序相同（使用类似的标题以便于交叉参考）。补充信息的第一页也有一个索引以便于查找。原始数据可在 ArrayExpress、GEO 或者 EMBL/GenBank 档案文件获得，详见补充信息 1.1。处理过的数据也以用户友好的方式在 UCSC 基因组浏览器的 ENCODE 入口呈现（http://genome.ucsc.edu/ENCODE/）。

（李平 翻译；于军 审稿）

17. Denoeud, F. *et al.* Prominent use of distal 5′ transcription start sites and discovery of a large number of additional exons in ENCODE regions. *Genome Res.* **17**, 746-759 (2007).

18. Tress, M. L. *et al.* The implications of alternative splicing in the ENCODE protein complement. *Proc. Natl Acad. Sci. USA* **104**, 5495-5500 (2007).

19. Rozowsky, J. *et al.* The DART classification of unannotated transcription within ENCODE regions: Associating transcription with known and novel loci. *Genome Res.* **17**, 732-745 (2007).

20. Kapranov, P. *et al.* Examples of the complex architecture of the human transcriptome revealed by RACE and high-density tiling arrays. *Genome Res.* **15**, 987-997 (2005).

21. Balakirev, E. S. & Ayala, F. J. Pseudogenes: are they "junk" or functional DNA? *Annu. Rev. Genet.* **37**, 123-151 (2003).

22. Mighell, A. J., Smith, N. R., Robinson, P. A. & Markham, A. F. Vertebrate pseudogenes. *FEBS Lett.* **468**, 109-114 (2000).

23. Zheng, D. *et al.* Pseudogenes in the ENCODE regions: Consensus annotation, analysis of transcription and evolution. *Genome Res.* **17**, 839-851 (2007).

24. Zheng, D. *et al.* Integrated pseudogene annotation for human chromosome 22: evidence for transcription. *J. Mol. Biol.* **349**, 27-45 (2005).

25. Harrison, P. M., Zheng, D., Zhang, Z., Carriero, N. & Gerstein, M. Transcribed processed pseudogenes in the human genome: an intermediate form of expressed retrosequence lacking protein-coding ability. *Nucleic Acids Res.* **33**, 2374-2383 (2005).

26. Washietl, S. *et al.* Structured RNAs in the ENCODE selected regions of the human genome. *Genome Res.* **17**, 852-864 (2007).

27. Carninci, P. *et al.* The transcriptional landscape of the mammalian genome. *Science* **309**, 1559-1563 (2005).

28. Runte, M. *et al.* The IC-*SNURF–SNRPN* transcript serves as a host for multiple small nucleolar RNA species and as an antisense RNA for *UBE3A*. *Hum. Mol. Genet.* **10**, 2687-2700 (2001).

29. Seidl, C. I., Stricker, S. H. & Barlow, D. P. The imprinted *Air* ncRNA is an atypical RNAPII transcript that evades splicing and escapes nuclear export. *EMBO J.* **25**, 3565-3575 (2006).

30. Parra, G. *et al.* Tandem chimerism as a means to increase protein complexity in the human genome. *Genome Res.* **16**, 37-44 (2006).

31. Maston, G. A., Evans, S. K. & Green, M. R. Transcriptional regulatory elements in the human genome. *Annu. Rev. Genomics Hum. Genet.* **7**, 29-59 (2006).

32. Trinklein, N. D., Aldred, S. J., Saldanha, A. J. & Myers, R. M. Identification and functional analysis of human transcriptional promoters. *Genome Res.* **13**, 308-312 (2003).

33. Cooper, S. J., Trinklein, N. D., Anton, E. D., Nguyen, L. & Myers, R. M. Comprehensive analysis of transcriptional promoter structure and function in 1% of the human genome. *Genome Res.* **16**, 1-10 (2006).

34. Cawley, S. *et al.* Unbiased mapping of transcription factor binding sites along human chromosomes 21 and 22 points to widespread regulation of noncoding RNAs. *Cell* **116**, 499-509 (2004).

35. Yelin, R. *et al.* Widespread occurrence of antisense transcription in the human genome. *Nature Biotechnol.* **21**, 379-386 (2003).

36. Katayama, S. *et al.* Antisense transcription in the mammalian transcriptome. *Science* **309**, 1564-1566 (2005).

37. Ren, B. *et al.* Genome-wide location and function of DNA binding proteins. *Science* **290**, 2306-2309 (2000).

38. Iyer, V. R. *et al.* Genomic binding sites of the yeast cell-cycle transcription factors SBF and MBF. *Nature* **409**, 533-538 (2001).

39. Horak, C. E. *et al.* GATA-1 binding sites mapped in the β-globin locus by using mammalian chIp-chip analysis. *Proc. Natl Acad. Sci. USA* **99**, 2924-2929 (2002).

40. Wei, C. L. *et al.* A global map of p53 transcription-factor binding sites in the human genome. *Cell* **124**, 207-219 (2006).

41. Kim, J., Bhinge, A. A., Morgan, X. C. & Iyer, V. R. Mapping DNA–protein interactions in large genomes by sequence tag analysis of genomic enrichment. *Nature Methods* **2**, 47-53 (2005).

42. Dorschner, M. O. *et al.* High-throughput localization of functional elements by quantitative chromatin profiling. *Nature Methods* **1**, 219-225 (2004).

43. Sabo, P. J. *et al.* Genome-scale mapping of DNase I sensitivity *in vivo* using tiling DNA microarrays. *Nature Methods* **3**, 511-518 (2006).

44. Crawford, G. E. *et al.* DNase-chip: a high-resolution method to identify DNase I hypersensitive sites using tiled microarrays. *Nature Methods* **3**, 503-509 (2006).

45. Hogan, G. J., Lee, C. K. & Lieb, J. D. Cell cycle-specified fluctuation of nucleosome occupancy at gene promoters. *PLoS Genet.* **2**, e158 (2006).

46. Koch, C. M. *et al.* The landscape of histone modifications across 1% of the human genome in five human cell lines. *Genome Res.* **17**, 691-707 (2007).

47. Smale, S. T. & Kadonaga, J. T. The RNA polymerase II core promoter. *Annu. Rev. Biochem.* **72**, 449-479 (2003).

48. Mito, Y., Henikoff, J. G. & Henikoff, S. Genome-scale profiling of histone H3.3 replacement patterns. *Nature Genet.* **37**, 1090-1097 (2005).

49. Heintzman, N. D. *et al.* Distinct and predictive chromatin signatures of transcriptional promoters and enhancers in the human genome. *Nature Genet.* **39**, 311-318 (2007).

50. Yusufzai, T. M., Tagami, H., Nakatani, Y. & Felsenfeld, G. CTCF tethers an insulator to subnuclear sites, suggesting shared insulator mechanisms across species. *Mol. Cell* **13**, 291-298 (2004).

51. Kim, T. H. *et al.* Direct isolation and identification of promoters in the human genome. *Genome Res.* **15**, 830-839 (2005).

52. Bieda, M., Xu, X., Singer, M. A., Green, R. & Farnham, P. J. Unbiased location analysis of E2F1-binding sites suggests a widespread role for E2F1 in the human genome. *Genome Res.* **16**, 595-605 (2006).

53. Ruppert, S., Wang, E. H. & Tjian, R. Cloning and expression of human TAF$_{II}$250: a TBP-associated factor implicated in cell-cycle regulation. *Nature* **362**, 175-179 (1993).

54. Fernandez, P. C. *et al.* Genomic targets of the human c-Myc protein. *Genes Dev.* **17**, 1115-1129 (2003).

55. Li, Z. *et al.* A global transcriptional regulatory role for c-Myc in Burkitt's lymphoma cells. *Proc. Natl Acad. Sci. USA* **100**, 8164-8169 (2003).

56. Orian, A. *et al.* Genomic binding by the *Drosophila* Myc, Max, Mad/Mnt transcription factor network. *Genes Dev.* **17**, 1101-1114 (2003).

57. de Laat, W. & Grosveld, F. Spatial organization of gene expression: the active chromatin hub. *Chromosome Res.* **11**, 447-459 (2003).

58. Trinklein, N. D. *et al.* Integrated analysis of experimental datasets reveals many novel promoters in 1% of the human genome. *Genome Res.* **17**, 720-731 (2007).

59. Jeon, Y. *et al.* Temporal profile of replication of human chromosomes. *Proc. Natl Acad. Sci. USA* **102**, 6419-6424 (2005).

60. Woodfine, K. *et al.* Replication timing of the human genome. *Hum. Mol. Genet.* **13**, 191-202 (2004).

61. White, E. J. *et al.* DNA replication-timing analysis of human chromosome 22 at high resolution and different developmental states. *Proc. Natl Acad. Sci. USA* **101**, 17771-17776 (2004).

62. Schubeler, D. *et al.* Genome-wide DNA replication profile for *Drosophila melanogaster*: a link between transcription and replication timing. *Nature Genet.* **32**, 438-442 (2002).

63. MacAlpine, D. M., Rodriguez, H. K. & Bell, S. P. Coordination of replication and transcription along a *Drosophila* chromosome. *Genes Dev.* **18**, 3094-3105 (2004).

64. Gilbert, D. M. Replication timing and transcriptional control: beyond cause and effect. *Curr. Opin. Cell Biol.* **14**, 377-383 (2002).

65. Schwaiger, M. & Schubeler, D. A question of timing: emerging links between transcription and replication. *Curr. Opin. Genet. Dev.* **16**, 177-183 (2006).

66. Hatton, K. S. *et al.* Replication program of active and inactive multigene families in mammalian cells. *Mol. Cell. Biol.* **8**, 2149-2158 (1988).

67. Gartler, S. M., Goldstein, L., Tyler-Freer, S. E. & Hansen, R. S. The timing of *XIST* replication: dominance of the domain. *Hum. Mol. Genet.* **8**, 1085-1089 (1999).

68. Azuara, V. *et al.* Heritable gene silencing in lymphocytes delays chromatid resolution without affecting the timing of DNA replication. *Nature Cell Biol.* **5**, 668-674 (2003).

69. Cohen, S. M., Furey, T. S., Doggett, N. A. & Kaufman, D. G. Genome-wide sequence and functional analysis of early replicating DNA in normal human fibroblasts. *BMC Genomics* **7**, 301 (2006).

70. Cao, R. *et al.* Role of histone H3 lysine 27 methylation in Polycomb-group silencing. *Science* **298**, 1039-1043 (2002).

71. Muller, J. *et al.* Histone methyltransferase activity of a *Drosophila* Polycomb group repressor complex. *Cell* **111**, 197-208 (2002).

72. Bracken, A. P., Dietrich, N., Pasini, D., Hansen, K. H. & Helin, K. Genome-wide mapping of Polycomb target genes unravels their roles in cell fate transitions. *Genes Dev.* **20**, 1123-1136 (2006).

73. Kirmizis, A. *et al.* Silencing of human polycomb target genes is associated with methylation of histone H3 Lys 27. *Genes Dev.* **18**, 1592-1605 (2004).

74. Lee, T. I. *et al.* Control of developmental regulators by Polycomb in human embryonic stem cells. *Cell* **125**, 301-313 (2006).

75. Karnani, N., Taylor, C., Malhotra, A. & Dutta, A. Pan-S replication patterns and chromosomal domains defined by genome tiling arrays of human chromosomes. *Genome Res.* **17**, 865-876 (2007).

76. Delaval, K., Wagschal, A. & Feil, R. Epigenetic deregulation of imprinting in congenital diseases of aberrant growth. *Bioessays* **28**, 453-459 (2006).

77. Dillon, N. Gene regulation and large-scale chromatin organization in the nucleus. *Chromosome Res.* **14**, 117-126 (2006).

78. Burkhoff, A. M. & Tullius, T. D. Structural details of an adenine tract that does not cause DNA to bend. *Nature* **331**, 455-457 (1988).

79. Price, M. A. & Tullius, T. D. How the structure of an adenine tract depends on sequence context: a new model for the structure of T_nA_n DNA sequences. *Biochemistry* **32**, 127-136 (1993).

80. Greenbaum, J. A., Parker, S. C. J. & Tullius, T. D. Detection of DNA structural motifs in functional genomic elements. *Genome Res.* **17**, 940-946 (2007).

81. Thurman, R. E., Day, N., Noble, W. S. & Stamatoyannopoulos, J. A. Identification of higher-order functional domains in the human ENCODE regions. *Genome Res.* **17**, 917-927 (2007).

82. Gilbert, N. *et al.* Chromatin architecture of the human genome: gene-rich domains are enriched in open chromatin fibers. *Cell* **118**, 555-566 (2004).

83. Nobrega, M. A., Ovcharenko, I., Afzal, V. & Rubin, E. M. Scanning human gene deserts for long-range enhancers. *Science* **302**, 413 (2003).

84. Woolfe, A. *et al.* Highly conserved non-coding sequences are associated with vertebrate development. *PLoS Biol.* **3**, e7 (2005).

85. Drake, J. A. *et al.* Conserved noncoding sequences are selectively constrained and not mutation cold spots. *Nature Genet.* **38**, 223-227 (2006).

86. Margulies, E. H., Blanchette, M., NISC Comparative Sequencing Program, Haussler D. & Green, E. D. Identification and characterization of multi-species conserved sequences. *Genome Res.* **13**, 2507-2518 (2003).

87. Cooper, G. M. *et al.* Distribution and intensity of constraint in mammalian genomic sequence. *Genome Res.* **15**, 901-913 (2005).

88. Siepel, A. *et al.* Evolutionarily conserved elements in vertebrate, insect, worm, and yeast genomes. *Genome Res.* **15**, 1034-1050 (2005).

89. Thomas, J. W. *et al.* Parallel construction of orthologous sequence-ready clone contig maps in multiple species. *Genome Res.* **12**, 1277-1285 (2002).

90. Blakesley, R. W. *et al.* An intermediate grade of finished genomic sequence suitable for comparative analyses. *Genome Res.* **14**, 2235-2244 (2004).

91. Aparicio, S. *et al.* Whole-genome shotgun assembly and analysis of the genome of *Fugu rubripes*. *Science* **297**, 1301-1310 (2002).

92. Jaillon, O. *et al.* Genome duplication in the teleost fish *Tetraodon nigroviridis* reveals the early vertebrate proto-karyotype. *Nature* **431**, 946-957 (2004).

93. Margulies, E. H. *et al.* An initial strategy for the systematic identification of functional elements in the human genome by low-redundancy comparative sequencing. *Proc. Natl Acad. Sci. USA* **102**, 4795-4800 (2005).

94. Blanchette, M. *et al.* Aligning multiple genomic sequences with the threaded blockset aligner. *Genome Res.* **14**, 708-715 (2004).

95. Bray, N. & Pachter, L. MAVID: constrained ancestral alignment of multiple sequences. *Genome Res.* **14**, 693-699 (2004).

96. Brudno, M. *et al.* LAGAN and Multi-LAGAN: efficient tools for large-scale multiple alignment of genomic DNA. *Genome Res.* **13**, 721-731 (2003).

97. Margulies, E. H. *et al.* Relationship between evolutionary constraint and genome function for 1% of the human genome. *Genome Res.* **17**, 760-774 (2007).

98. Asthana, S., Roytberg, M., Stamatoyannopoulos, J. A. & Sunyaev, S. Analysis of sequence conservation at nucleotide resolution. *PLoS Comp. Biol.* (submitted).

99. Cooper, G. M., Brudno, M., Green, E. D., Batzoglou, S. & Sidow, A. Quantitative estimates of sequence divergence for comparative analyses of mammalian genomes. *Genome Res.* **13**, 813-820 (2003).

100. Eddy, S. R. A model of the statistical power of comparative genome sequence analysis. *PLoS Biol.* **3**, e10 (2005).

101. Stone, E. A., Cooper, G. M. & Sidow, A. Trade-offs in detecting evolutionarily constrained sequence by comparative genomics. *Annu. Rev. Genomics Hum. Genet.* **6**, 143-164 (2005).

102. McAuliffe, J. D., Jordan, M. I. & Pachter, L. Subtree power analysis and species selection for comparative genomics. *Proc. Natl Acad. Sci. USA* **102**, 7900-7905 (2005).

103. International HapMap Consortium. A haplotype map of the human genome. *Nature* **437**, 1299-1320 (2005).

104. Cheng, Z. *et al.* A genome-wide comparison of recent chimpanzee and human segmental duplications. *Nature* **437**, 88-93 (2005).

105. Cooper, G. M. *et al.* Characterization of evolutionary rates and constraints in three Mammalian genomes. *Genome Res.* **14**, 539-548 (2004).

106. Dermitzakis, E. T., Reymond, A. & Antonarakis, S. E. Conserved non-genic sequences - an unexpected feature of mammalian genomes. *Nature Rev. Genet.* **6**, 151-157 (2005).

107. Clark, T. G. *et al.* Small insertions/deletions and functional constraint in the ENCODE regions. *Genome Biol.* (submitted) (2007).

108. Bejerano, G. *et al.* Ultraconserved elements in the human genome. *Science* **304**, 1321-1325 (2004).

109. Woolfe, A. *et al.* Highly conserved non-coding sequences are associated with vertebrate development. *PLoS Biol.* **3**, e7 (2005).

110. Dermitzakis, E. T. & Clark, A. G. Evolution of transcription factor binding sites in Mammalian gene regulatory regions: conservation and turnover. *Mol. Biol. Evol.* **19**, 1114-1121 (2002).

111. McDonald, J. H. & Kreitman, M. Adaptive protein evolution at the *Adh* locus in *Drosophila. Nature* **351**, 652-654 (1991).

112. Andolfatto, P. Adaptive evolution of non-coding DNA in *Drosophila. Nature* **437**, 1149-1152 (2005).

113. Hudson, R. R., Kreitman, M. & Aguade, M. A test of neutral molecular evolution based on nucleotide data. *Genetics* **116**, 153-159 (1987).

114. Feuk, L., Carson, A. R. & Scherer, S. W. Structural variation in the human genome. *Nature Rev. Genet.* **7**, 85-97 (2006).

115. Ludwig, M. Z. *et al.* Functional evolution of a *cis*-regulatory module. *PLoS Biol.* **3**, e93 (2005).

116. Ludwig, M. Z. & Kreitman, M. Evolutionary dynamics of the enhancer region of even-skipped in *Drosophila. Mol. Biol. Evol.* **12**, 1002-1011 (1995).

117. Harrow, J. *et al.* GENCODE: producing a reference annotation for ENCODE. *Genome Biol.* **7**, (Suppl. 1; S4) 1-9 (2006).

118. Emanuelsson, O. *et al.* Assessing the performance of different high-density tiling microarray strategies for mapping transcribed regions of the human genome. *Genome Res.* advance online publication, doi: 10.1101/gr.5014606 (21 November 2006).

119. Kapranov, P. *et al.* Large-scale transcriptional activity in chromosomes 21 and 22. Science 296, 916-919 (2002).

120. Bhinge, A. A., Kim, J., Euskirchen, G., Snyder, M. & Iyer, V. R. Mapping the chromosomal targets of STAT1 by Sequence Tag Analysis of Genomic Enrichment (STAGE). *Genome Res.* **17**, 910-916 (2007).

121. Ng, P. *et al.* Gene identification signature (GIS) analysis for transcriptome characterization and genome annotation. *Nature Methods* **2**, 105-111 (2005).

122. Giresi, P. G., Kim, J., McDaniell, R. M., Iyer, V. R. & Lieb, J. D. FAIRE (Formaldehyde-Assisted Isolation of Regulatory Elements) isolates active regulatory elements from human chromatin. *Genome Res.* **17**, 877-885 (2006).

123. Rada-Iglesias, A. *et al.* Binding sites for metabolic disease related transcription factors inferred at base pair resolution by chromatin immunoprecipitation and genomic microarrays. *Hum. Mol. Genet.* **14**, 3435-3447 (2005).

124. Kim, T. H. *et al.* A high-resolution map of active promoters in the human genome. *Nature* **436**, 876-880 (2005).

125. Halees, A. S. & Weng, Z. PromoSer: improvements to the algorithm, visualization and accessibility. *Nucleic Acids Res.* **32**, W191-W194 (2004).

126. Bajic, V. B. *et al.* Performance assessment of promoter predictions on ENCODE regions in the EGASP experiment. *Genome Biol.* **7**, (Suppl 1; S3) 1-13 (2006).

127. Zheng, D. & Gerstein, M. B. A computational approach for identifying pseudogenes in the ENCODE regions. *Genome Biol.* **7**, S13.1-S13.10 (2006).

128. Stranger, B. E. *et al.* Genome-wide associations of gene expression variation in humans. *PLoS Genet* **1**, e78 (2005).

129. Turner, B. M. Reading signals on the nucleosome with a new nomenclature for modified histones. *Nature Struct. Mol. Biol.* **12**, 110-112 (2005).

Supplementary Information is linked to the online version of the paper at www.nature.com/nature.

Acknowledgements. We thank D. Leja for providing graphical expertise and support. Funding support is acknowledged from the following sources: National Institutes of Health, The European Union BioSapiens NoE, Affymetrix, Swiss National Science Foundation, the Spanish Ministerio de Educación y Ciencia, Spanish Ministry of Education and Science, CIBERESP, Genome Spain and Generalitat de Catalunya, Ministry of Education, Culture, Sports, Science and Technology of Japan, the NCCR Frontiers in Genetics, the Jérôme Lejeune Foundation, the Childcare Foundation, the Novartis Foundations, the Danish Research Council, the Swedish Research Council, the Knut and Alice Wallenberg Foundation, the Wellcome Trust, the Howard Hughes Medical Institute, the Bio-X Institute, the RIKEN Institute, the US Army, National Science Foundation, the Deutsche Forschungsgemeinschaft, the Austrian Gen-AU program, the BBSRC and The European Molecular Biology Laboratory. We thank the Barcelona SuperComputing Center and the NIH Biowulf cluster for computer facilities. The Consortium thanks the ENCODE Scientific Advisory Panel for their advice on the project: G. Weinstock, M. Cherry, G. Churchill, M. Eisen, S. Elgin, J. Lis, J. Rine, M. Vidal and P. Zamore.

Author Information. Reprints and permissions information is available at www.nature.com/reprints. The authors declare no competing financial interests. The list of individual authors is divided among the six main analysis groups and five organizational groups. Correspondence and requests for materials should be addressed to the co-chairs of the ENCODE analysis groups (listed in the Analysis Coordination group) E. Birney (birney@ebi.ac.uk); J. A. Stamatoyannopoulos (jstam@u.washington.edu); A. Dutta (ad8q@virginia.edu); R. Guigó (rguigo@imim.es); T. R. Gingeras (Tom_Gingeras@affymetrix.com); E. H. Margulies (elliott@nhgri.nih.gov); Z. Weng (zhiping@bu.edu); M. Snyder (michael.snyder@yale.edu); E. T. Dermitzakis (md4@sanger.ac.uk) or collectively (encode_chairs@ebi.ac.uk).

Generation of Germline-competent Induced Pluripotent Stem Cells

K. Okita *et al.*

Editor's Note

In 2006, Japanese cell biologist Shinya Yamanaka claimed to have made stem cell-like cells by inserting a handful of genes into mouse fibroblasts. The so-called induced pluripotent stem (iPS) cells displayed many of the hallmarks of true stem cells, but failed one acid test: they were unable to contribute to live animals when injected into early embryonic mice. In this paper, Yamanaka and colleagues overcome this problem, tweaking their methodology to produce iPS cells that appear completely reprogrammed and truly stem cell-like. Two other papers, published at the same time, describe a similar feat and iPS cells remain the focus of great attention, offering the potential to make therapeutically useful stem cells from a person's own cells without the need for a donated egg or embryo.

We have previously shown that pluripotent stem cells can be induced from mouse fibroblasts by retroviral introduction of Oct3/4 (also called Pou5f1), Sox2, c-Myc and Klf4, and subsequent selection for *Fbx15* (also called *Fbxo15*) expression. These induced pluripotent stem (iPS) cells (hereafter called Fbx15 iPS cells) are similar to embryonic stem (ES) cells in morphology, proliferation and teratoma formation; however, they are different with regards to gene expression and DNA methylation patterns, and fail to produce adult chimaeras. Here we show that selection for *Nanog* expression results in germline-competent iPS cells with increased ES-cell-like gene expression and DNA methylation patterns compared with Fbx15 iPS cells. The four transgenes (*Oct3/4*, *Sox2*, *c-myc* and *Klf4*) were strongly silenced in Nanog iPS cells. We obtained adult chimaeras from seven Nanog iPS cell clones, with one clone being transmitted through the germ line to the next generation. Approximately 20% of the offspring developed tumours attributable to reactivation of the c-*myc* transgene. Thus, iPS cells competent for germline chimaeras can be obtained from fibroblasts, but retroviral introduction of c-Myc should be avoided for clinical application.

ALTHOUGH ES cells are promising donor sources in cell transplantation therapies[1], they face immune rejection after transplantation and there are ethical issues regarding the usage of human embryos. These concerns may be overcome if pluripotent stem cells can be directly derived from patients' somatic cells[2]. We have previously shown that iPS cells can be generated from mouse fibroblasts by retrovirus-mediated introduction of four transcription factors (Oct3/4 (refs 3, 4), Sox2 (ref. 5), c-Myc (ref. 6) and Klf4 (ref. 7)) and by selection for *Fbx15* expression[8]. Fbx15 iPS cells, however, have different gene

具有种系功能的诱导
多能干细胞的产生

冲田奎介等

编者按

在 2006 年，日本细胞生物学家山中伸弥声称通过在小鼠成纤维细胞中插入少量基因制造出了干细胞样细胞。所谓的诱导多能干细胞（iPS 细胞）显示出真正干细胞的许多特征，但尚未通过一项严格的测试：当被注射到早期胚胎小鼠时，它们无法培养成为活体动物。在本文中，山中及其同事克服了这个问题，他们调整了实验方法，产生的 iPS 细胞呈现完全重编程和真正干细胞样。同时发表的另外两篇论文描述了类似的壮举。iPS 细胞仍然是人们关注的重点，因为它可以从一个人自己的细胞中制造出可用于治疗的干细胞而不需要捐赠的卵子或胚胎。

先前我们已经发现，通过逆转录病毒导入 Oct3/4（又称 Pou5f1）、Sox2、c-Myc 和 Klf4 并随后选择 *Fbx15*（又称 *Fbxo15*）表达，可以从小鼠成纤维细胞中诱导产生多能干细胞。这些诱导多能干细胞（iPS 细胞）（以下称为 Fbx15 iPS 细胞）与胚胎干细胞（ES 细胞）在形态、增殖和形成畸胎瘤方面类似；但是，它们在基因表达和 DNA 甲基化模式上是不同的，并不能形成成熟的嵌合体。这里我们发现选择 *Nanog* 基因的表达可以产生具有种系功能的 iPS 细胞，与 Fbx15 iPS 细胞相比增加了 ES 细胞样基因的表达和 DNA 甲基化模式。这四个转基因（*Oct3/4*、*Sox2*、*c-myc* 和 *Klf4*）在 Nanog iPS 细胞中极度沉默。我们从 7 个 Nanog iPS 细胞克隆中获得了成熟的嵌合体，其中一个克隆还通过种系培养到了下一代。由于重新激活了 *c-myc* 转基因，大约 20% 的后代出现了肿瘤。总之，具有产生种系嵌合体功能的 iPS 细胞能够从成纤维细胞中诱导获得，但是通过逆转录病毒导入 c-Myc 在临床应用时应该被避免。

尽管胚胎干细胞是细胞移植治疗很有前途的材料来源[1]，它们仍存在移植后免疫排斥的问题，而且还存在与使用人类胚胎有关的伦理学问题。如果多能干细胞能够直接来源于病人的体细胞，那么这些问题就都可以被解决[2]。先前我们已经发现 iPS 细胞能够从小鼠成纤维细胞通过逆转录病毒导入四个转录因子（Oct3/4（文献 3，4）、Sox2（文献 5）、c-Myc（文献 6）和 Klf4（文献 7））并继以选择 *Fbx15* 表达而产生[8]。但是，Fbx15 iPS 细胞具有与 ES 细胞不同的基因表达和 DNA 甲基化模式，

expression and DNA methylation patterns compared with ES cells and do not contribute to adult chimaeras. We proposed that the incomplete reprogramming might be due to the selection for *Fbx15* expression, and that by using better selection markers, we might be able to generate more ES-cell-like iPS cells. We decided to use *Nanog* as a candidate of such markers.

Although both *Fbx15* and *Nanog* are targets of Oct3/4 and Sox2 (refs 9–11), Nanog is more tightly associated with pluripotency. In contrast to *Fbx15*-null mice and ES cells that barely show abnormal phenotypes[9], disruption of *Nanog* in mice results in loss of the pluripotent epiblast[12]. *Nanog*-null ES cells can be established, but they tend to differentiate spontaneously[12]. Forced expression of *Nanog* renders ES cells independent of leukaemia inhibitory factor (LIF) for self-renewal[12,13] and confers increased reprogramming efficiency after fusion with somatic cells[14]. These results prompted us to propose that if we use *Nanog* as a selection marker, we might be able to obtain iPS cells displaying a greater similarity to ES cells.

Generation of Nanog iPS Cells

To establish a selection system for *Nanog* expression, we began by isolating a bacterial artificial chromosome (BAC, ~200 kilobases) containing the mouse *Nanog* gene in its centre. By using recombineering technology[15,16], we inserted a green fluorescent protein (GFP)-internal ribosome entry site (IRES)-puromycin resistance gene (Puro[r]) cassette into the 5' untranslated region (UTR; Fig. 1a). ES cells that had stably incorporated the modified BAC were positive for GFP, but became negative when differentiation was induced (not shown). By introducing these ES cells into blastocysts, we obtained chimaeric mice and then transgenic mice containing the Nanog-GFP-IRES-Puro[r] reporter construct. In transgenic mouse blastocysts, GFP was specifically observed in the inner cell mass (Fig. 1b). In 9.5 days post coitum (d.p.c.) embryos, only migrating primordial germ cells (PGCs) showed GFP signal. In 13.5 d.p.c. embryos, GFP was specifically detected in the genital ridges of both sexes. After removing the brain, visceral tissues and genital ridges, we isolated mouse embryonic fibroblasts (MEFs) from 13.5 d.p.c. male embryos. Flow cytometry analyses showed that these MEFs did not contain GFP-positive cells, whereas ~1% of cells isolated from genital ridges showed GFP signals (Fig. 1c).

在成年鼠中无嵌合。我们认为这种不完全的重编程可能是由于通过 *Fbx15* 表达来选择细胞，因此如果选用更好的选择标记物，我们可能能够产生更加像 ES 细胞的 iPS 细胞。我们计划使用 *Nanog* 作为这种标记物的候选者。

尽管 *Fbx15* 和 *Nanog* 都是 Oct3/4 和 Sox2 的靶目标（文献 9～11），但 Nanog 与多能性的关系更加密切。与几乎没有异常表型的 *Fbx15* 敲除小鼠以及 ES 细胞[9] 相反，小鼠中 *Nanog* 基因的紊乱可以导致多能上胚层的丧失[12]。可以建立敲除 *Nanog* 的 ES 细胞，但是它们倾向于发生自发分化[12]。强制表达 *Nanog* 可以使 ES 细胞的自我更新不依赖于白血病抑制因子(LIF)[12,13]，而且在体细胞融合后赋予其更高的重编程效率[14]。这些结果促使我们假设如果使用 *Nanog* 作为选择标记物，我们可能能够获得更像 ES 细胞的 iPS 细胞。

Nanog iPS 细胞的产生

为了建立 *Nanog* 表达的选择系统，我们首先分离了在中心含有小鼠 *Nanog* 基因的细菌人工染色体(BAC，约 200 个千碱基)。通过使用重组工程技术[15,16]，我们将一个绿色荧光蛋白(GFP)–内部核糖体进入位点(IRES)–嘌呤霉素抗性基因(Puro^r)盒插入 5′ 非翻译区(UTR，图 1a)。那些和修饰过的 BAC 稳定整合的 ES 细胞就含有 GFP，但是如果诱导分化，就变为 GFP 阴性(没有显示)。通过将这些 ES 细胞导入胚泡，我们就获得了嵌合小鼠，然后获得含有 Nanog-GFP-IRES-Puro^r 报告基团的转基因小鼠。在转基因的小鼠胚泡中，GFP 特有地出现在内细胞团中(图 1b)。在交配后第 9.5 天的胚胎中，只有迁移的原始生殖细胞(PGC)发出 GFP 信号。在交配后第 13.5 天，GFP 特定地出现在两种性别的生殖嵴上。去除大脑、内脏组织和生殖嵴后，我们从交配后 13.5 天的雄性胚胎中分离出小鼠胚胎成纤维细胞(MEF)。流式细胞分析显示这些 MEF 不含有 GFP 阳性的细胞，然而约 1% 从生殖嵴分离出的细胞显示 GFP 信号(图 1c)。

Fig. 1. Nanog-GFP-IRES-Puro[r] transgenic mice. **a**, Modified BAC construct. White boxes indicate the 5′ and 3′ UTRs of the mouse *Nanog* gene. Black boxes indicate the open reading frame. **b**, GFP expression in Nanog-GFP transgenic mouse embryos. Whole embryos (top panels) and isolated genital ridges (bottom panels) from 13.5 d.p.c. mice are shown. **c**, Histogram showing GFP fluorescence in cells isolated from genital ridges of a 13.5 d.p.c. Nanog-GFP transgenic mouse embryo (left) or in MEFs isolated from the same embryo (right).

Next, we introduced the four previously described factors (Oct3/4, Sox2, Klf4 and the c-Myc mutant c-Myc(T58A)) into Nanog-GFP-IRES-Puro[r] MEFs cultured on SNL feeder cells with the use of retroviral vectors. Three, five, or seven days after retroviral infection, we started puromycin selection in ES cell medium. GFP-positive cells first became apparent ~7 days after infection. Twelve days after infection, a few hundred colonies appeared, regardless of the timing of puromycin selection (Fig. 2a). By contrast, no colonies emerged from MEFs transfected with mock DNA. Among puromycin-resistant colonies, ~5% were positive for GFP (Fig. 2b). When the puromycin selection was started at 7 days after infection, we

图 1. Nanog-GFP-IRES-Puro^r 转基因小鼠。**a**，修饰的 BAC 结构。白框表示小鼠 *Nanog* 基因的 5′ 和 3′ UTR。黑框代表可读框。**b**，Nanog-GFP 转基因小鼠胚胎中的 GFP 表达。图中显示了交配后 13.5 天小鼠的整个胚胎（上部）和分离的生殖嵴（下部）。**c**，图中显示从交配后 13.5 天的 Nanog-GFP 转基因小鼠胚胎的生殖嵴中分离的细胞的 GFP 荧光（左）和从相同胚胎中分离出来的 MEF 的 GFP 荧光（右）。

然后，我们将先前所述的四种因子(Oct3/4、Sox2、Klf4 和 c-Myc 突变体 c-Myc(T58A))利用逆转录病毒载体导入到培养在 SNL 饲养细胞中的 Nanog-GFP-IRES-Puro^r MEF 内。逆转录病毒感染后的 3 天、5 天和 7 天，我们分别在 ES 细胞基质中进行嘌呤霉素选择。感染后约 7 天 GFP 阳性的细胞开始出现。感染后 12 天出现了数百个集落，并且不受嘌呤霉素选择时间的影响（图 2a）。相反地，用对照 DNA 进行转染的 MEF 没有出现集落。在嘌呤霉素抗性集落中，大约 5% 是 GFP 阳性的（图 2b）。感染 7 天后当嘌呤霉素选择开始时，我们获得了 GFP 阳性最高的集

obtained the most GFP-positive colonies. Because we used the GFP-IRES-Puro^r cassette, it is unclear why we obtained GFP-negative colonies. With increased concentrations of puromycin, we obtained fewer GFP-negative colonies (Fig. 2c). With any combination of three of the four factors, we did not obtain any GFP-positive colonies (Supplementary Fig. 1).

Fig. 2. Generation of iPS cells from MEFs of Nanog-GFP-IRES-Puro^r transgenic mice. **a**, Puromycin-resistant colonies. Puromycin selection was initiated at 3, 5, or 7 days after retroviral transduction. Numbers indicate GFP-positive colonies/total colonies. **b**, GFP fluorescence in resulting colonies. Phase contrast (top row) and fluorescence (bottom row) micrographs are shown. iPS cells were also generated from Fbx15 β-geo knockin MEFs. **c**, Effect of increasing concentrations of puromycin. Numbers of GFP-positive colonies/total colonies are shown on the right. **d**, Morphology of established Nanog iPS cells (clone 20D17). Phase contrast (left) and fluorescence (right) micrographs are shown.

By continuing cultivation of these GFP-positive colonies, we obtained cells that were morphologically indistinguishable from ES cells (Fig. 2d). These cells also demonstrated ES-like proliferation, with slightly longer doubling times than that of ES cells (Fig. 3a). Subcutaneous transplantation of these cells into nude mice resulted in tumours that consisted of various tissues of all three germ layers, indicating that these cells are pluripotent (Fig. 3b and Supplementary Fig. 2). We therefore refer to these cells as Nanog iPS cells in the remainder of this manuscript. Induced pluripotent stem cells were established from Fbx15 β-geo MEFs in parallel and are referred to as Fbx15 iPS cells.

落。因为我们插入的是 GFP-IRES-Puro' 盒，所以不清楚为什么会出现 GFP 阴性的集落。随着嘌呤霉素浓度的增加，我们得到 GFP 阴性的集落越少（图 2c）。这四个因子中的任意三个组合都不能出现 GFP 阳性的集落（补充信息图 1）。

图 2. 从 Nanog-GFP-IRES-Puro' 转基因小鼠 MEF 中生成 iPS 细胞。**a**，嘌呤霉素抗性集落。嘌呤霉素筛选开始于逆转录病毒转导后的 3、5 和 7 天。数字代表 GFP 阳性集落/总集落。**b**，集落中的 GFP 荧光。图片为相差（顶行）和荧光（底行）显微图。iPS 细胞也从 Fbx15 β-geo 基因敲入 MEF 中产生。**c**，嘌呤霉素浓度增加的影响。右边显示 GFP 阳性集落/总集落的数目。**d**，已建立的 Nanog iPS 细胞的形态（克隆20D17）。图片是相差（左）和荧光（右）显微图。

通过继续培养这些 GFP 阳性的集落，我们获得了形态上与 ES 细胞无法区分的细胞（图 2d）。这些细胞可以出现 ES 样的增殖，倍增时间略长于 ES 细胞（图 3a）。将这些细胞皮下移植到裸鼠中可以产生含有全部三个胚层各种组织的肿瘤，提示这些细胞是多能的（图 3b 和补充信息图 2）。因此在本文的剩余部分我们称这些细胞为 Nanog iPS 细胞。我们平行建立了来源于 Fbx15 β-geo MEF 的诱导多能干细胞，称为 Fbx15 iPS 细胞。

Fig. 3. Characterization of Nanog iPS cells. **a**, Proliferation. ES cells, Nanog iPS cells (clones 20D16, 20D17 and 20D18) and Fbx15 iPS cells (clones 10 and 15) were passaged every 3 days (3×10^5 cells per each well of a 6-well plate). Calculated doubling times are indicated. **b**, Teratomas. ES cells or Nanog iPS cells (clone 20D17, 1×10^6 cells) were subcutaneously transplanted into nude mice. After 8 weeks, teratomas were photographed (left) and analysed histologically with haematoxylin and eosin staining (right).

Similarity between Nanog iPS Cells and ES Cells

Polymerase chain reaction with reverse transcription (RT–PCR) showed that Nanog iPS cells expressed most ES cell marker genes, including *Nanog*, at higher and more consistent levels compared with Fbx15 iPS cells (Fig. 4a). DNA microarray analyses confirmed that Nanog iPS cells had greater ES-cell-like gene expression compared with Fbx15 iPS cells (Fig. 4b). The expression level of *Rex1* (also called *Zfp42*) in Nanog iPS cells was higher compared with Fbx15 iPS cells, but still lower than in ES cells. Thus, Nanog iPS cells show greater gene expression similarity to ES cells (without being identical) than do Fbx15 iPS cells.

图 3. Nanog iPS 细胞的特征。**a**，增殖。ES 细胞、Nanog iPS 细胞（克隆 20D16、20D17 和 20D18）以及 Fbx15 iPS 细胞（克隆 10 和 15）每 3 天都进行传代（6 孔板上每孔 3×10^5 个细胞）。图中显示了计算出的倍增时间。**b**，畸胎瘤。ES 细胞或者 Nanog iPS 细胞（克隆 20D17，1×10^6 个细胞）皮下移植到裸鼠上。8 周以后，进行畸胎瘤照相（左图）并用苏木精–伊红染色观察组织学结构（右图）。

Nanog iPS 细胞和 ES 细胞间的相似性

反转录聚合酶链反应（RT–PCR）显示 Nanog iPS 细胞表达包括 *Nanog* 在内的大部分 ES 细胞标志物基因，而且与 Fbx15 iPS 细胞相比，Nanog iPS 细胞表达水平更高、更符合 ES 细胞（图 4a）。DNA 微阵列分析确证了 Nanog iPS 细胞与 Fbx15 iPS 细胞相比表达更多的 ES 细胞样基因（图 4b）。Nanog iPS 细胞中 *Rex1*（又称 *Zfp42*）的表达水平高于 Fbx15 iPS 细胞，但是仍然低于 ES 细胞。因此，Nanog iPS 细胞与 ES 细胞的基因表达相似程度（不是完全一致）要超过 Fbx15 iPS 细胞。

Fig. 4. Gene expression in Nanog iPS cells. **a**, RT–PCR. Total RNA was isolated from six clones of Nanog iPS cells (clones 20D1, 20D2, 20D6, 20D16, 20D17 and 20D18), six clones of Fbx15 iPS cells (clones 1, 4, 5, 10, 15 and 16), MEFs and ES cells. **b**, Scatter plots showing comparison of global gene expression between ES cells and Nanog iPS cells (right), and between ES cells and Fbx15 iPS cells (left), as determined by DNA microarrays. **c**, Expression levels of the four transcription factors. Total RNA was isolated from six clones of Nanog iPS cells (clones 20D1, 20D2, 20D6, 20D16, 20D17 and 20D18), six clones of Fbx15 iPS cells (clones 1, 4, 5, 10, 15 and 16), MEFs and ES cells. RT–PCR analyses were performed with primers that amplified the coding regions of the four factors (Total), endogenous transcripts only (Endo.), and transgene transcripts only (tg).

RT–PCR showed that Nanog iPS cells have significantly lower expression levels of the four transgenes than Fbx15 iPS cells (Fig. 4c). Real-time PCR confirmed that transgene expression was very low in Nanog iPS cells (Supplementary Fig. 4a–d). In contrast, Southern blot analyses showed similar copy numbers of retroviral integration in Nanog

图 4. Nanog iPS 细胞的基因表达。**a**，RT-PCR。从 6 个 Nanog iPS 细胞克隆（克隆 20D1、20D2、20D6、20D16、20D17 和 20D18）、6 个 Fbx15 iPS 细胞克隆（克隆 1、4、5、10、15 和 16）、MEF 和 ES 细胞中分离出总 RNA。**b**，散点图显示了使用 DNA 微阵列得出的 ES 细胞和 Nanog iPS 细胞（右图）以及 ES 细胞和 Fbx15 iPS 细胞（左图）之间的整体基因表达的对比。**c**，四个转录因子的表达水平。从 6 个 Nanog iPS 细胞克隆（克隆 20D1、20D2、20D6、20D16、20D17 和 20D18）、6 个 Fbx15 iPS 细胞克隆（克隆 1、4、5、10、15 和 16）、MEF 和 ES 细胞中分离出总 RNA。然后进行 RT-PCR 分析，使用的引物分别扩增四个因子的编码区（Total）、仅内源转录物（Endo.）和仅转基因转录物（tg）。

RT-PCR 显示 Nanog iPS 细胞中四个转基因的表达水平远远低于 Fbx15 iPS 细胞（图 4c）。实时 PCR 确证了 Nanog iPS 细胞中转基因的表达非常低（补充信息图 4a～4d）。相反，Southern 印迹分析显示 Nanog iPS 细胞和 Fbx15 iPS 细胞中逆转录

iPS cells and Fbx15 iPS cells (Supplementary Fig. 5). These data indicate that retroviral transgene expression is largely silenced in Nanog iPS cells, as has been shown in ES cells[17]. The expression levels of the transgenes are reversely correlated with *Dnmt3a2* expression, suggesting that *de novo* methyltransferase[18] may be involved in the retroviral silencing observed in iPS cells (Supplementary Fig. 6).

Bisulphite genomic sequencing analyses also revealed similarities between Nanog iPS cells and ES cells (Fig. 5). The promoter regions of *Nanog*, *Oct3/4* and *Fbx15* were largely unmethylated in Nanog iPS cells. This is in marked contrast to Fbx15 iPS cells in which the promoters of *Nanog* and *Oct3/4* were only partially unmethylated[8]. Differentially methylated regions of imprinting genes *H19* and *Igf2r* were partially methylated in Nanog iPS cells. During PGC development, imprinting is erased by 12.5 d.p.c.[19-21]. The loss of imprinting is maintained in embryonic germ cells derived from 12.5 d.p.c. PGCs[22] and cloned embryos derived from 12.5–16.5 d.p.c. PGCs[23,24]. ES cells, by contrast, showed normal imprinting patterns[25]. Thus, Nanog iPS cells show greater similarity in the methylation patterns of imprinting genes to ES cells than to embryonic germ cells.

Fig. 5. DNA methylation of ES-cell-specific genes and imprinting genes. White circles indicate unmethylated CpG dinucleotides, whereas black circles indicate methylated CpG dinucleotides.

Simple sequence length polymorphism (SSLP) analyses showed that Nanog iPS cells are largely of the DBA background but also have some contribution from the C57BL/6 and 129S4 backgrounds (Supplementary Fig. 3). This result is consistent with the genetic background of the MEFs, which was 75% DBA, 12.5% C57BL/6 and 12.5% 129S4. This result also confirms that Nanog iPS cells are not a contamination of ES cells that exists in our laboratory, which are either pure 129S4 or C57BL/6.

We next compared the stability of Nanog iPS cells and Fbx15 iPS cells (Supplementary Fig. 7). Cells were cultivated in the presence of the selection drug for up to 22–26 passages.

病毒整合的拷贝数目相似（补充信息图 5）。这些数据提示 Nanog iPS 细胞中逆转录病毒转基因的表达大量地被抑制，这和 ES 细胞中出现的情况一样[17]。转基因的表达水平与 *Dnmt3a2* 的表达呈负相关，说明新生的甲基转移酶[18] 可能参与了 iPS 细胞内逆转录病毒被抑制的过程（补充信息图 6）。

亚硫酸氢盐基因组测序分析也揭示了 Nanog iPS 细胞与 ES 细胞间的相似性（图 5）。Nanog iPS 细胞内的 *Nanog*、*Oct3/4* 和 *Fbx15* 的启动子区域大部分都是未甲基化的。这与 Fbx15 iPS 细胞明显相反，后者的 *Nanog* 和 *Oct3/4* 启动子仅仅是部分未甲基化[8]。印记基因 *H19* 和 *Igf2r* 的差异甲基化区域在 Nanog iPS 细胞中部分被甲基化。在 PGC 的发育过程中，印记在交配后 12.5 天消除[19-21]。这种印记消除的现象在交配后 12.5 天的 PGC 来源的胚胎生殖细胞以及交配后 12.5～16.5 天的 PGC 来源的克隆胚胎中保持[23,24]。相反，ES 细胞具有正常的印记分布[25]。因此，Nanog iPS 细胞在印记基因的甲基化分布方面与 ES 细胞的相似程度比胚胎生殖细胞更高。

图 5. ES 细胞特异性基因和印记基因的 DNA 甲基化。白圈代表未甲基化的 CpG 二核苷酸，而黑圈代表甲基化的 CpG 二核苷酸。

简单序列长度多态性（SSLP）分析显示 Nanog iPS 细胞大部分是来源于 DBA 背景的，但是也有一部分来源于 C57BL/6 和 129S4 背景（补充信息图 3）。这个结果与 MEF 的基因背景相一致，即 75% DBA、12.5% C57BL/6 和 12.5% 129S4。该结果也证实了 Nanog iPS 细胞不是存在于我们实验室中的 ES 细胞的污染，因为那些 ES 细胞都是纯的 129S4 或者 C57BL/6 来源的。

我们接下来比较了 Nanog iPS 细胞和 Fbx15 iPS 细胞的稳定性（补充信息图 7）。

Morphologically, we did not observe significant changes over the long-term culture course. However, RT–PCR showed that Fbx15 iPS cells lost the expression of ES cell marker genes after prolonged culture. By contrast, Nanog iPS cells maintained relatively high expression levels of the ES cell marker genes. These data demonstrate that Nanog iPS cells are more stable than Fbx15 iPS cells.

We also compared the induction efficiency of Nanog iPS cells and Fbx15 iPS cells. In independent experiments, we obtained 4–125 GFP-positive colonies from 8×10^5 Nanog-reporter MEFs transfected with the four transcription factors. Because ~50% of transfected MEFs are supposed to express all four factors[8], the induction efficiency is approximately 0.001–0.03%. In contrast, from the same number of Fbx15-reporter MEFs, we obtained 47–1,800 G418-resistant colonies, with the induction efficiency of approximately 0.01–0.5%. Thus, the efficiency of Nanog iPS cell induction is approximately one-tenth that of Fbx15 iPS cells.

We then compared the responses of Nanog iPS cells and Fbx15 iPS cells to LIF or retinoic acid (Supplementary Fig. 8). As we have shown previously[8], Fbx15 iPS cells do not remain undifferentiated when cultured without feeder cells, even in the presence of LIF. Furthermore, Fbx15 iPS cells formed compact colonies when cultured without feeder cells in the presence of retinoic acid. In contrast, LIF maintained the undifferentiated state of Nanog iPS cells cultured without feeder cells. Retinoic acid induced the differentiation of Nanog iPS cells. Thus, Nanog iPS cells are similar to ES cells in their response to LIF and retinoic acid.

Initially we used the T58A mutant of c-Myc to induce Nanog iPS cells. We also tested wild-type c-Myc for Nanog iPS cell induction. We obtained a similar number of colonies with both wild-type c-Myc and the T58A mutant. Nanog iPS cells established with wild-type c-Myc were indistinguishable from those established with the T58A mutant with regards to morphology, gene expression (analysed via microarrays), teratoma formation (Supplementary Fig. 2) and stability under puromycin selection (Supplementary Fig. 9). Without puromycin selection, Nanog iPS cells induced by wild-type c-Myc were more stable (Supplementary Fig. 9).

Germline Chimaeras from Nanog iPS Cells

We next examined the ability of Nanog iPS cells to produce adult chimaeras. We injected 15–20 male Nanog iPS cells (five clones with the T58A mutant and three with wild-type c-Myc) into C57BL/6-derived blastocysts, which we then transplanted into the uteri of pseudo-pregnant mice. We obtained adult chimaeras from seven clones (four clones with the T58A mutant and three with wild-type c-Myc) as determined by coat colour (Fig. 6a and Supplementary Table 1). SSLP analyses showed that Nanog iPS cells contributed to various organs, with the level of chimaerism ranging from 10% to 90%. Chimeras from clone 20D17 showed highest iPS cell contribution in the testes. From clone 20D18, we

细胞在存在选择药物的环境中培养 22～26 代。在这段长时间的培养过程中，我们没有发现形态学上明显的改变。但是，RT–PCR 提示经过延长培养后 Fbx15 iPS 细胞丢失了 ES 细胞标志基因的表达。相反，Nanog iPS 细胞保持着相对高水平的 ES 细胞标志基因表达。这些数据说明 Nanog iPS 细胞比 Fbx15 iPS 细胞更加稳定。

我们还比较了 Nanog iPS 细胞和 Fbx15 iPS 细胞的诱导效率。在独立的实验中，我们从 8×10^5 个转染了 4 个转录因子的 Nanog 报告基因 MEF 中获得了 4～125 个 GFP 阳性的集落。因为大约 50% 的转染 MEF 被认为会表达所有的四个因子[8]，诱导效率约为 0.001%～0.03%。相反，从同样数量的 Fbx15 报告基因 MEF 中，我们获得了 47～1,800 个 G418 抗性集落，诱导效率大约是 0.01%～0.5%。因此，Nanog iPS 细胞的诱导效率大约是 Fbx15 iPS 细胞的十分之一。

然后我们比较了 Nanog iPS 细胞和 Fbx15 iPS 细胞对 LIF 或者视黄酸的响应（补充信息图 8）。正如我们之前所示[8]，即便是存在 LIF，Fbx15 iPS 细胞在没有饲养细胞的情况下也不会保持未分化状态。此外，Fbx15 iPS 细胞在存在视黄酸和没有饲养细胞的情况下也形成紧致的集落。相反，没有饲养细胞存在时，LIF 能保持 Nanog iPS 细胞的未分化状态。视黄酸诱导 Nanog iPS 细胞的分化。因此，Nanog iPS 细胞在对 LIF 和视黄酸的反应方面与 ES 细胞相似。

起初我们使用 c-Myc 的 T58A 突变体来诱导 Nanog iPS 细胞。我们也实验了野生型 c-Myc 诱导 Nanog iPS 细胞。两种情况下我们获得的集落数相似。在形态、基因表达（通过微阵列分析）、畸胎瘤形成（补充信息图 2）和嘌呤霉素选择下的稳定性（补充信息图 9）等方面，无法区分用野生型 c-Myc 诱导的与 T58A 突变体诱导的 Nanog iPS 细胞。没有嘌呤霉素选择的话，野生型 c-Myc 诱导的 Nanog iPS 细胞更加稳定（补充信息图 9）。

Nanog iPS 细胞来源的种系嵌合体

我们接下来检验了 Nanog iPS 细胞产生成熟嵌合体的能力。我们将 15～20 个雄性 Nanog iPS 细胞（5 个 T58A 突变体诱导的克隆和 3 个野生型 c-Myc 诱导的克隆）注射到 C57BL/6 来源的胚泡中，然后将胚泡移植到假孕小鼠的子宫内。根据毛色，我们得到了 7 个克隆的成熟嵌合体（4 个 T58A 突变体诱导的克隆和 3 个野生型 c-Myc 诱导的克隆）（图 6a 和补充信息表 1）。SSLP 分析显示 Nanog iPS 细胞参与生成多个器官，嵌合水平从 10% 到 90% 不等。克隆 20D17 来源的嵌合体在睾丸内出现最高的 iPS 细胞嵌合。对于克隆 20D18，我们仅从感染后胚泡中获得少量非嵌合

obtained only a few nonchimaeric pups from infected blastocysts; thus, whether this clone has competency for producing adult chimaeras remained to be determined. These data demonstrate that most Nanog iPS clones are competent for adult chimaeric mice.

Fig. 6. Germline chimaeras from Nanog iPS cells. **a**, Tissue distribution of iPS cells in chimaeras. Genomic DNA was isolated from the indicated organs of chimaeras derived from three Nanog iPS cell clones (20D17, 38C2 and 38D2). SSLP analyses were performed for D6Mit15. **b**, PCR analyses showing the presence of the GFP cassette and retroviral transgenes in F_1 mice obtained from the intercross between a chimaeric male and a C57BL/6 female. **c**, Coat colours of F_2 mice obtained from F_1 intercrosses. **d**, Sperm contribution of iPS cells in chimaeric mice. Spermatozoa were isolated from the epididymides of chimaeric mice derived from three Nanog iPS cell clones (20D17, 38D2 and 38C2). iPS cell contribution was determined by SSLP of D6Mit15.

We then crossed three of the chimaeras from clone 20D17—for which the highest iPS cell contribution was in the testes—with C57BL/6 females. Whereas all F_1 mice showed black coat colour, all contained retroviral integration of the four transcription factors and approximately half contained the GFP-IRES-Puro^r cassette (Fig. 6b), indicating germline transmission. Furthermore, approximately half of the F_2 mice born from F_1 intercrosses showed agouti coat colour, confirming germline transmission of Nanog-iPS-20D17 (Fig. 6c).

We also examined germline competency for two other clones that produced adult chimaeras. In one chimaeric mouse from Nanog-iPS-38C2 cell line, PCR analysis detected iPS cell contribution in isolated spermatozoa (Fig. 6d), suggesting that germline competency

型幼仔。因此，该克隆是否具有产生成熟嵌合体的能力还有待确定。这些数据提示大部分 Nanog iPS 细胞具有产生成熟嵌合体小鼠的能力。

图 6. Nanog iPS 细胞来源的种系嵌合体。**a**，嵌合体中 iPS 细胞的组织分布。基因组 DNA 从三个 Nanog iPS 细胞克隆（20D17、38C2 和 38D2）来源的嵌合体的所示器官中分离出来。对 D6Mit15 进行 SSLP 分析。**b**，PCR 分析显示嵌合体雄鼠和 C57BL/6 雌鼠交配生成的 F₁ 代小鼠中存在 GFP 盒和逆转录病毒转基因。**c**，F₁ 代互交产生的 F₂ 代小鼠的毛色。**d**，嵌合体小鼠中 iPS 细胞对精子生成的贡献。从三个 Nanog iPS 细胞克隆（20D17、38D2 和 38C2）来源的嵌合体小鼠的附睾中分离出精子。通过 D6Mit15 的 SSLP 分析确定 iPS 细胞的嵌合。

我们然后用克隆 20D17 来源的 3 只嵌合体（在这些嵌合体中，iPS 细胞在睾丸中贡献最大）与 C57BL/6 雌性小鼠杂交。所有的 F₁ 代小鼠显示黑色的毛色，且都含有逆转录病毒整合的这四个转录因子，几乎一半含有 GFP-IRES-Puroʳ 盒（图 6b），这标志着发生了种系的传递。此外，F₁ 代互交产生的几乎一半的 F₂ 代小鼠显示刺豚鼠样的毛色，证实了发生 Nanog-iPS-20D17 的种系传递（图 6c）。

我们还检测了产生成熟嵌合体的另两个克隆的种系产生能力。在一个 Nanog-iPS-38C2 细胞系来源的嵌合型小鼠中，PCR 分析检测到分离的精子中有 iPS 细胞来源（图 6d），表明其种系能力并不局限于克隆 20D17。但是，克隆 38C2 中 iPS 细

is not confined to clone 20D17. However, the iPS cell contribution to sperm of clone 38C2 is much smaller than that of clone 20D17, and no iPS-cell-derived offspring were found for 119 mice born from the cross between the 38C2 chimaera and C57BL/6 female mice. Most male mice with a high degree of chimaerism from the Nanog-iPS-38D2 cell line showed small testes and aspermatogenesis (Supplementary Fig. 13). The testes of some chimaeras from Nanog-iPS-38D2 contained mature sperm, but no iPS cell contribution was detected by PCR (Fig. 6d).

Tumour Formation by *c-myc* Reactivation

Out of 121 F_1 mice (aged 8–41 weeks) derived from the Nanog-iPS-20D17 cell line, 24 died or were killed because of weakness, wheezing or paralysis. Necropsy of 17 mice identified neck tumours (Supplementary Fig. 10) in 13 mice and other tumours in five mice, including two mice with neck tumours. Histological examination of one neck tumour showed that it was a ganglioneuroblastoma with follicular carcinoma of the thyroid gland (not shown). In these tumours, retroviral expression of *c-myc*, but not *Oct3/4*, *Sox2*, or *Klf4*, is reactivated (Supplementary Fig. 11). In contrast, transgene expression of all four transcription factors remained low in normal tissues, except for *c-myc* in muscle in one mouse (Supplementary Fig. 12). These data indicate that reactivation of *c-myc* retrovirus is attributable to tumour formation.

Discussion

Our results demonstrate that Nanog selection allows the generation of high-quality iPS cells that are comparable to ES cells in morphology, proliferation, teratoma formation, gene expression and competency for adult chimaeras. Nearly all Nanog iPS clones showed these properties, indicating that Nanog is a major determinant of quality in cellular pluripotency. However, germline competence was variable among Nanog iPS clones, indicating the existence of other important determinants of germline competency in addition to Nanog. The high quality of Nanog iPS cells underscores the possibility of using this technology to generate patient-specific pluripotent stem cells. In a separate study, we found that germline-competent iPS cells can also be obtained from adult mouse somatic cells (T. Aoi and S.Y., unpublished data). The current study, however, also reveals that reactivation of *c-myc* retrovirus may result in tumour formation. There may be ways to overcome this problem. Strong silencing of the four retroviruses in Nanog iPS cells indicates that they are only required for the induction, but not the maintenance, of pluripotency. Therefore, the retrovirus-mediated system might be eventually replaced by transient expression, such as the adenovirus-mediated system. Alternatively, high-throughput screening of chemical libraries might identify small molecules that can replace the four genes. These are crucial research areas in order to apply iPS cells to regenerative medicine.

We found that the efficiency of Nanog iPS cell induction is less than 0.1%. The low

胞产生精子的比例要远远少于克隆 20D17，而且 38C2 嵌合体与 C57BL/6 雌性小鼠间交配生出的 119 只小鼠中没有发现 iPS 细胞来源的后代。大部分具有高嵌合度 Nanog-iPS-38D2 细胞系来源的雄性小鼠都表现为小睾丸和无精子发生（补充信息图 13）。Nanog-iPS-38D2 细胞系来源的另一些嵌合型小鼠的睾丸内含有成熟的精子，但是 PCR 没有检测到其中有来源于 iPS 细胞的（图 6d）。

c-myc 再激活后的肿瘤形成

Nanog-iPS-20D17 细胞系来源的 121 只 F_1 小鼠中（年龄 8～41 周），24 只因为虚弱、喘鸣或者瘫痪而死亡或者被杀死。对 17 只小鼠进行尸检发现其中 13 只小鼠有颈部肿瘤（补充信息图 10），五只小鼠有其他肿瘤（其中两只有颈部肿瘤）。对一个颈部肿瘤进行组织学检查显示，它是滤泡性甲状腺癌的成神经节细胞瘤（未显示）。在这些肿瘤中，只有逆转录病毒的基因 c-myc 被重新激活，而 Oct3/4、Sox2 或者 Klf4 并没有（补充信息图 11）。相反，除了一只小鼠肌肉中的 c-myc 外，正常组织中所有四个转录因子的转基因表达都非常低（补充信息图 12）。这些数据提示逆转录病毒 c-myc 基因的再激活导致了肿瘤的生成。

讨　论

我们的结果显示 Nanog 选择可以产生高质量的 iPS 细胞，其在形态、增殖、畸胎瘤形成、基因表达和成熟嵌合体形成能力上与 ES 细胞相似。几乎所有的 Nanog iPS 克隆都有这些特性，表明 Nanog 是细胞多能性质量的主要决定因素。但是，Nanog iPS 克隆间的种系形成能力有差别，这提示除了 Nanog 外还存在其他重要的决定因素。Nanog iPS 细胞的这种高性能使得应用该技术产生病人特异性的多能干细胞成为可能。在另一个研究中，我们发现具有种系形成功能的 iPS 细胞也能从成年小鼠的体细胞中产生（青井贵之和山中伸弥，未发表的数据）。但是，目前的研究也揭示了 c-myc 基因的再激活可能导致肿瘤的形成。可能有解决这个问题的方法。Nanog iPS 细胞中这四个逆转录病毒基因的高度沉默说明，它们仅是诱导而非维持多能性所必需的。因此，逆转录病毒介导的系统可能最终被瞬时表达取代，比如腺病毒介导的系统。或者，高通量筛选化合物库可能会发现能够替代这四个基因的小分子。这是将 iPS 细胞应用于再生医学的关键研究领域。

我们发现 Nanog iPS 细胞诱导的效率低于 0.1%。这种低效率表明 iPS 细胞的起

efficiency suggests that the origin of iPS cells might be rare stem cells co-existing in MEF culture. Alternatively, activation of additional genes by retroviral integration might be required for iPS cell generation in addition to the four transcription factors. This is relevant to the fact that we have been able to obtain iPS cells only with retroviral transduction. Identification of such factor(s) may lead to the generation of iPS cells with higher efficiency, and without the need for retroviruses.

Methods Summary

To generate Nanog-reporter mice, we isolated a BAC clone containing the mouse *Nanog* gene in its centre. By using the RED/ET recombination technique (Gene Bridges), we inserted a GFP-IRES-Puro[r] cassette into the 5′ UTR of the mouse *Nanog* gene. We introduced the modified BAC into RF8 ES cells by electroporation[26]. We then microinjected transgenic ES cells into C57BL/6 blastocysts to generate Nanog-reporter mice containing the modified BAC. MEFs were isolated from 13.5 d.p.c. male embryos after removing genital ridges. Generation of Nanog iPS cells was performed as described[8], except that puromycin was used instead of G418 as a selection antibiotic. Retroviruses (pMXs) were generated with Plat-E packaging cells[27]. RF8 ES cells[26] and iPS cells were cultured on SNL feeder cells[28]. Analyses of iPS cells, such as RT–PCR, real-time PCR, bisulphite genomic sequencing, SSLP analyses, DNA microarrays, teratoma formation, and microinjection into C57BL/6 blastocysts, were performed as described[8]. Contribution of iPS cells in chimaeric mice was determined by PCR for the SSLP marker D6Mit15.

Full Methods and any associated references are available in the online version of the paper at www.nature.com/nature.

(**448**, 313-317; 2007)

Keisuke Okita[1], Tomoko Ichisaka[1,2] & Shinya Yamanaka[1,2]
[1] Department of Stem Cell Biology, Institute for Frontier Medical Sciences, Kyoto University, Kyoto 606-8507, Japan
[2] CREST, Japan Science and Technology Agency, Kawaguchi 332-0012, Japan

Received 6 February; accepted 22 May 2007. Published online 6 June 2007.

References:

1. Thomson, J. A. *et al.* Embryonic stem cell lines derived from human blastocysts. *Science* **282**, 1145-1147 (1998).

2. Hochedlinger, K. & Jaenisch, R. Nuclear reprogramming and pluripotency. *Nature* **441**, 1061-1067 (2006).

3. Niwa, H., Miyazaki, J. & Smith, A. G. Quantitative expression of Oct-3/4 defines differentiation, dedifferentiation or self-renewal of ES cells. *Nature Genet.* **24**, 372-376 (2000).

4. Nichols, J. *et al.* Formation of pluripotent stem cells in the mammalian embryo depends on the POU transcription factor Oct4. *Cell* **95**, 379-391 (1998).

5. Avilion, A. A. *et al.* Multipotent cell lineages in early mouse development depend on SOX2 function. *Genes Dev.* **17**, 126-140 (2003).

6. Cartwright, P. *et al.* LIF/STAT3 controls ES cell self-renewal and pluripotency by a Myc-dependent mechanism. *Development* **132**, 885-896 (2005).

7. Li, Y. *et al.* Murine embryonic stem cell differentiation is promoted by SOCS-3 and inhibited by the zinc finger transcription factor Klf4. *Blood* **105**, 635-637 (2005).

8. Takahashi, K. & Yamanaka, S. Induction of pluripotent stem cells from mouse embryonic and adult fibroblast cultures by defined factors. *Cell* **126**, 663-676 (2006).

9. Tokuzawa, Y. *et al.* Fbx15 is a novel target of Oct3/4 but is dispensable for embryonic stem cell self-renewal and mouse development. *Mol. Cell. Biol.* **23**, 2699-2708 (2003).

源可能是 MEF 培养物中共存的少量干细胞。或者，在 iPS 细胞的生成过程中除了这四个转录因子外，可能还需要通过逆转录病毒整合激活额外的基因。这与我们只能够通过逆转录病毒转导才能产生 iPS 细胞的事实相关。鉴定这些因子可能有助于更高效率地产生 iPS 细胞，而且可能不再需要借助逆转录病毒。

方法概述

为了产生 Nanog 报告小鼠，我们分离了一个在中心含有小鼠 Nanog 基因的 BAC 克隆。通过使用 RED/ET 重组技术（基因桥），我们将一个 GFP-IRES-Puro^r 盒插入小鼠 Nanog 基因的 5′UTR 区。我们通过电穿孔技术将修饰的 BAC 转到 RF8 ES 细胞内[26]。然后我们将转基因的 ES 细胞微注射到 C57BL/6 胚泡中以产生含有修饰 BAC 的 Nanog 报告小鼠。在交配后 13.5 天的雄性胚胎中移除生殖嵴后分离出 MEF。Nanog iPS 细胞的产生如文献所述[8]，但是我们用嘌呤霉素代替 G418 作为选择抗生素。逆转录病毒（pMX）用 Plat-E 包装细胞产生[27]。RF8 ES 细胞[26] 和 iPS 细胞都在 SNL 饲养细胞上培养[28]。对 iPS 细胞的分析，比如 RT–PCR、实时 PCR、亚硫酸氢盐基因组测序、SSLP 分析、DNA 微阵列、畸胎瘤形成和微注射到 C57BL/6 胚泡中等，都如文献所述进行[8]。通过 SSLP 标记物 D6Mit15 的 PCR 确定嵌合体小鼠中 iPS 细胞的嵌合。

完整的方法和相关的文献可在本文的网上版本中获得。

（毛晨晖 翻译；王宇 审稿）

10. Kuroda, T. *et al.* Octamer and Sox elements are required for transcriptional cis regulation of Nanog gene expression. *Mol. Cell. Biol.* **25**, 2475-2485 (2005).

11. Rodda, D. J. *et al.* Transcriptional regulation of Nanog by OCT4 and SOX2. *J. Biol. Chem.* **280**, 24731-24737 (2005).

12. Mitsui, K. *et al.* The homeoprotein Nanog is required for maintenance of pluripotency in mouse epiblast and ES cells. *Cell* **113**, 631-642 (2003).

13. Chambers, I. *et al.* Functional expression cloning of nanog, a pluripotency sustaining factor in embryonic stem cells. *Cell* **113**, 643-655 (2003).

14. Silva, J., Chambers, I., Pollard, S. & Smith, A. Nanog promotes transfer of pluripotency after cell fusion. *Nature* **441**, 997-1001 (2006).

15. Copeland, N. G., Jenkins, N. A. & Court, D. L. Recombineering: a powerful new tool for mouse functional genomics. *Nature Rev. Genet.* **2**, 769-779 (2001).

16. Testa, G. *et al.* Engineering the mouse genome with bacterial artificial chromosomes to create multipurpose alleles. *Nature Biotechnol.* **21**, 443-447 (2003).

17. Cherry, S. R., Biniszkiewicz, D., van Parijs, L., Baltimore, D. & Jaenisch, R. Retroviral expression in embryonic stem cells and hematopoietic stem cells. *Mol. Cell. Biol.* **20**, 7419-7426 (2000).

18. Chen, T., Ueda, Y., Xie, S. & Li, E. A novel Dnmt3a isoform produced from an alternative promoter localizes to euchromatin and its expression correlates with active de novo methylation. *J. Biol. Chem.* **277**, 38746-38754 (2002).

19. Davis, T. L., Yang, G. J., McCarrey, J. R. & Bartolomei, M. S. The H19 methylation imprint is erased and re-established differentially on the parental alleles during male germ cell development. *Hum. Mol. Genet.* **9**, 2885-2894 (2000).

20. Sato, S., Yoshimizu, T., Sato, E. & Matsui, Y. Erasure of methylation imprinting of Igf2r during mouse primordial germ-cell development. *Mol. Reprod. Dev.* **65**, 41-50 (2003).

21. Brandeis, M. *et al.* The ontogeny of allele-specific methylation associated with imprinted genes in the mouse. *EMBO J.* **12**, 3669-3677 (1993).

22. Labosky, P. A., Barlow, D. P. & Hogan, B. L. Mouse embryonic germ (EG) cell lines: transmission through the germline and differences in the methylation imprint of insulin-like growth factor 2 receptor (Igf2r) gene compared with embryonic stem (ES) cell lines. *Development* **120**, 3197-3204 (1994).

23. Kato, Y. *et al.* Developmental potential of mouse primordial germ cells. *Development* **126**, 1823-1832 (1999).

24. Lee, J. *et al.* Erasing genomic imprinting memory in mouse clone embryos produced from day 11.5 primordial germ cells. *Development* **129**, 1807-1817 (2002).

25. Geijsen, N. *et al.* Derivation of embryonic germ cells and male gametes from embryonic stem cells. *Nature* **427**, 148-154 (2004).

26. Meiner, V. L. *et al.* Disruption of the acyl-CoA:cholesterol acyltransferase gene in mice: evidence suggesting multiple cholesterol esterification enzymes in mammals. *Proc. Natl Acad. Sci. USA* **93**, 14041-14046 (1996).

27. Morita, S., Kojima, T. & Kitamura, T. Plat-E: an efficient and stable system for transient packaging of retroviruses. *Gene Ther.* **7**, 1063-1066 (2000).

28. McMahon, A. P. & Bradley, A. The Wnt-1 (int-1) proto-oncogene is required for development of a large region of the mouse brain. *Cell* **62**, 1073-1085 (1990).

Supplementary Information is linked to the online version of the paper at www.nature.com/nature.

Acknowledgements. We thank K. Takahashi, M. Nakagawa and T. Aoi for scientific discussion; M. Maeda for histological analyses; M. Narita, J. Iida, H. Miyachi and S. Kitano for technical assistance; and R. Kato, R. Iyama and Y. Ohuchi for administrative assistance. We also thank T. Kitamura for Plat-E cells and pMXs retroviral vectors, and R. Farese for RF8 ES cells. This study was supported in part by a grant from the Uehara Memorial Foundation, the Program for Promotion of Fundamental Studies in Health Sciences of NIBIO, a grant from the Leading Project of MEXT, and Grants-in-Aid for Scientific Research of JSPS and MEXT (to S.Y.). K.O. is a JSPS research fellow.

Author Contributions. K.O. conducted most of the experiments in this study. T.I. performed manipulation of mouse embryos to generate Nanog-GFP transgenic mice. T.I. also maintained the mouse lines. S.Y. designed and supervised the study, and prepared the manuscript. S.Y. also performed computer analyses of DNA microarray data.

Author Information. The microarray data are deposited in GEO under accession number GSE7841. Reprints and permissions information is available at www.nature.com/reprints. The authors declare no competing financial interests. Correspondence and requests for materials should be addressed to S.Y. (yamanaka@frontier.kyoto-u.ac.jp).

In Vitro Reprogramming of Fibroblasts into a Pluripotent ES-cell-like State

M. Wernig *et al.*

Editor's Note

Here, American cell biologist Rudolf Jaenisch and colleagues manage to convert mature mouse fibroblasts into stem-like cells called induced pluripotent stem (iPS) cells. The study builds on the work of Japanese cell biologist Shinya Yamanaka who showed, the previous year, that turning on the expression of just four genes in adult mouse cells could partially reprogram them to become stem cell-like. Jaenisch tweaked Yamanaka's egg- and embryo-free "recipe" to produce cells that could contribute to a whole organism—a key hallmark of a true stem cell. Yamanaka simultaneously published an essentially identical study, as did a third group of scientists based in America. Jaenisch's group has since made dopamine-producing neurons from iPS cells derived from patients with Parkinson's disease, highlighting the potential of these cells for reproductive medicine.

Nuclear transplantation can reprogramme a somatic genome back into an embryonic epigenetic state, and the reprogrammed nucleus can create a cloned animal or produce pluripotent embryonic stem cells. One potential use of the nuclear cloning approach is the derivation of "customized" embryonic stem (ES) cells for patient-specific cell treatment, but technical and ethical considerations impede the therapeutic application of this technology. Reprogramming of fibroblasts to a pluripotent state can be induced *in vitro* through ectopic expression of the four transcription factors Oct4 (also called Oct3/4 or Pou5f1), Sox2, c-Myc and Klf4. Here we show that DNA methylation, gene expression and chromatin state of such induced reprogrammed stem cells are similar to those of ES cells. Notably, the cells—derived from mouse fibroblasts—can form viable chimaeras, can contribute to the germ line and can generate live late-term embryos when injected into tetraploid blastocysts. Our results show that the biological potency and epigenetic state of *in-vitro*-reprogrammed induced pluripotent stem cells are indistinguishable from those of ES cells.

EPIGENETIC reprogramming of somatic cells into ES cells has attracted much attention because of the potential for customized transplantation therapy, as cellular derivatives of reprogrammed cells will not be rejected by the donor[1,2]. Thus far, somatic cell nuclear transfer and fusion of fibroblasts with ES cells have been shown to promote the epigenetic reprogramming of the donor genome to an embryonic state[3-5]. However, the therapeutic application of either approach has been hindered by technical complications as well as ethical objections[6]. Recently, a major breakthrough was reported whereby

体外重编程技术将成纤维细胞诱导到
ES 样细胞的多能性状态

沃尼格等

编者按

在本文中，美国细胞生物学家鲁道夫·耶尼施和他的同事们成功地将成熟的小鼠成纤维细胞转化为干细胞样细胞，称为"诱导多能性干细胞"（iPS）。这项研究建立在日本细胞生物学家山中伸弥工作的基础上。山中伸弥在前一年的研究中发现，在胎鼠或者成年小鼠的成纤维中，只要激活四个转录因子的表达，就能将它们部分重编程，使其变成干细胞样的细胞。耶尼施调整了山中伸弥的不直接操作卵子和胚胎的"配方"，从而产生了可以形成整个个体的细胞——这是真正干细胞的一个关键特征。山中伸弥和美国的第三组科学家同时发表了一项基本相同的研究。自那以后，耶尼施的团队从帕金森病患者的 iPS 细胞分化得到能够形成多巴胺的神经元，凸显了这些细胞在再生医学上的潜力。

核移植能够将体细胞的基因组重新编程回到胚胎表观遗传状态，而重新编程的细胞核能够形成克隆动物或者产生多能性胚胎干细胞。这种核克隆方法的一个潜在应用价值就是衍生出"定制的"胚胎干（ES）细胞，用于患者的特异性的细胞治疗，但是技术和伦理学方面的考虑限制了该技术的治疗应用。成纤维细胞能够在体外通过四个转录因子 Oct4（又称 Oct3/4 或 Pou5f1）、Sox2、c-Myc 和 Klf4 的异位表达诱导至多能性状态。在此，我们证明了这些诱导多能性干细胞在 DNA 甲基化、基因表达和染色质状态上都与 ES 细胞相似。尤为重要的是，这些来自小鼠成纤维细胞的细胞可以形成可存活的嵌合体，促进生殖系的发育，并可以在注射到四倍体囊胚时产生活的晚期胚胎。我们的结果显示了体外重编程得到的诱导多能性干细胞在生物学功能和表观遗传状态上与 ES 细胞没有明显区别。

由于重编程得到的细胞衍生物不会被供体排斥，体细胞经过表观遗传重编程形成的 ES 细胞具有定制移植治疗的潜力，因此引起了广泛关注[1,2]。到目前为止，体细胞核转移以及成纤维细胞与 ES 细胞的融合被证实能够促进供体基因组的表观遗传重编程，使其处于胚胎状态[3-5]。但是，这两种方法的治疗应用都受到技术并发症以及伦理问题的阻碍[6]。最近，有一个重大的突破，即转录因子 Oct4、Sox2、 expression of the transcription factors Oct4, Sox2, c-Myc and Klf4 was shown to induce fibroblasts to become pluripotent stem cells (designated as induced pluripotent stem (iPS) cells), although with a low efficiency[7]. The iPS cells were isolated by selection for activation of *Fbx15* (also called *Fbxo15*), which is a downstream gene of *Oct4*. This important study left a number of questions unresolved: (1) although iPS cells were pluripotent they were not identical to ES cells (for example, iPS cells injected into blastocysts generated abnormal chimaeric embryos that did not survive to term); (2) gene expression profiling revealed major differences between iPS cells and ES cells; (3) because the four transcription factors were transduced by constitutively expressed retroviral vectors it was unclear why the cells could be induced to differentiate and whether continuous vector expression was required for the maintenance of the pluripotent state; and (4) the epigenetic state of the endogenous pluripotency genes *Oct4* and *Nanog* was incompletely reprogrammed, raising questions about the stability of the pluripotent state.

Here we used activation of the endogenous *Oct4* or *Nanog* genes as a more stringent selection strategy for the isolation of reprogrammed cells. We infected fibroblasts with retroviral vectors transducing the four factors, and selected for the activation of the endogenous *Oct4* or *Nanog* genes. Positive colonies resembled ES cells and assumed an epigenetic state characteristic of ES cells. When injected into blastocysts the reprogrammed cells generated viable chimaeras and contributed to the germ line. Our results establish that somatic cells can be reprogrammed to a pluripotent state that is similar, if not identical, to that of normal ES cells.

Selection of Fibroblasts for *Oct4* or *Nanog* Activation

Using homologous recombination in ES cells we generated mouse embryonic fibroblasts (MEFs) and tail-tip fibroblasts (TTFs) that carried a neomycin-resistance marker inserted into either the endogenous *Oct4* (Oct4-neo) or *Nanog* locus (Nanog-neo) (Fig. 1a). These cultures were sensitive to G418, indicating that the *Oct4* and *Nanog* loci were, as expected, silenced in somatic cells. These MEFs or TTFs were infected with Oct4-, Sox2-, c-Myc- and Klf4-expressing retroviral vectors and G418 was added to the cultures 3, 6 or 9 days later. The number of drug-resistant colonies increased substantially when analysed at day 20 (Fig. 1i). Most colonies had a flat morphology (Fig. 1h, right) and between 11% and 25% of the colonies were "ES-like" (Fig. 1h, left) when selection was applied early (Fig. 1k), a percentage that increased at later time points. At day 20, ES-like colonies were picked, dissociated and propagated in G418-containing media. They gave rise to ES-like cell lines (designated as Oct4 iPS or Nanog iPS cells, respectively) that could be propagated without drug selection, displayed homogenous Nanog, SSEA1 and alkaline phosphatase expression (Fig. 1b–g and Supplementary Figs 1 and 5), and formed undifferentiated colonies when seeded at clonal density on gelatincoated dishes (see inset in Fig. 1b). Four out of five analysed lines had a normal karyotype (Supplementary Table 1).

c-Myc 和 Klf4 的表达可以诱导成纤维细胞成为诱导多能性干细胞，尽管其效率很低[7]。这些 iPS 细胞是通过选择激活 Oct4 的下游基因 *Fbx15*（又称 *Fbxo15*）而分离出来的。这个重要的研究遗留了一系列没有解决的问题：(1) 尽管 iPS 细胞具有多能性，但是它们与 ES 细胞并不相同（比如，注射到囊胚中的 iPS 细胞产生异常的嵌合体胚胎，无法长久存活）；(2) 基因表达分析显示 iPS 细胞和 ES 细胞之间存在较大差异；(3) 由于这四个转录因子是通过组成性表达的逆转录病毒载体转导的，目前尚不清楚为什么可以诱导细胞分化，以及是否需要持续的载体表达才能维持这种多能状态；(4) 内源性多能基因 *Oct4* 和 *Nanog* 的表观遗传状态并不是被完全重编程的，研究者们对多能状态的稳定性提出了质疑。

在这里，我们使用内源性基因 *Oct4* 或 *Nanog* 的激活作为更加严格的选择策略来分离重编程的细胞。我们用转导这四个因子的逆转录病毒感染成纤维细胞，并选择激活内源性基因 *Oct4* 或 *Nanog* 的细胞。阳性克隆酷似 ES 细胞，呈现出 ES 细胞的表观遗传特性。当被注射到囊胚中后，这些重编程的细胞能够形成存活的嵌合体并对生殖系的形成具有贡献。我们的研究结果证明体细胞能够被重编程成与 ES 细胞相似（尽管不是完全一致）的多能性状态。

选择用于 *Oct4* 或 *Nanog* 激活的成纤维细胞

通过在 ES 细胞中进行同源重组，我们得到了小鼠胚胎成纤维细胞（MEF）和尾尖纤维母细胞（TTF），这些成纤维细胞携带新霉素耐药标记物，并将其插入到内源性 *Oct4*（Oct4-neo）或者 *Nanog*（Nanog-neo）位点中（图 1a）。这些细胞对 G418 敏感，表明 *Oct4* 和 *Nanog* 位点在体细胞中如预期的那样沉默。分别用表达 Oct4、Sox2、c-Myc 和 Klf4 的逆转录病毒载体包装得到的病毒感染 MEF 或 TTF，然后分别在第3、6、9 天后加入 G418 进行培养。第 20 天进行分析时，耐药克隆的数量显著增加（图 1i）。大部分克隆的形态都是扁平的（图 1h，右侧），当早期进行选择时（图 1k），大约 11%～25% 的克隆形态像 ES 细胞（图 1h，左侧），这个比例随着药物处理时间延长而增加。在第 20 天，挑出 ES 样的克隆，将其消化后用含有 G418 的培养基进行培养。它们能够形成 ES 样的细胞系（分别称为 Oct4 iPS 细胞或者 Nanog iPS 细胞），而且这些细胞系能够在没有药物选择的情况下繁殖，展示出均质的 Nanog、SSEA1 和碱性磷酸酶的表达（图 1b～g 和补充信息图 1 和 5），当在明胶包被的培养皿上克隆密接种时，这些细胞能够形成未分化的克隆（见图 1b 插图）。进行分析的细胞系中有五分之四具有正常的核型（补充信息表 1）。

Fig. 1. Generation of Oct4- and Nanog-selected iPS cells. **a**, Targeting strategy to generate an Oct4-IRES-GFPneo allele. The resulting GFPneo fusion protein has sufficient neomycin-resistance activity in ES cells; GFP fluorescence, however, is not visible. **b**, Phase-contrast micrograph of Oct4 iPS cells (clone 18) grown on irradiated MEFs. Inset: an ES-cell-like colony 5 days after seeding in clonal density without feeder cells. iPS clone 18 cells exhibited strong alkaline phosphatase activity (**c**) and were homogenously labelled with antibodies against SSEA1 (**d, e**) and Nanog (**f, g**). **h**, One example of an ES-like colony 16 days after infection (left). Most G418-resistant colonies, however, consisted of flat non-ES-like cells (right): **b**, 10 × ; **c–g**, 20 × ; **h**, 4 × . **i**, Gradual activation of the Nanog and Oct4-neo alleles. Shown are the total colony numbers of one experiment at day 20 after infection starting neomycin selection at day 3, 6 and 9. **j**, Fraction of total selected cells expressing alkaline phosphatase, SSEA1 and Nanog 0, 14, and 20 days after infection (counted were more than ten visual fields containing $n > 1,000$ total cells for every time point; error bars indicate s.d.). **k**, Estimated reprogramming efficiency of Oct4 selection and Nanog selection ($n = 3$ different experiments; s.e.m. is shown). Indicated are the total number of drug-resistant colonies per 100,000 plated MEFs 20 days after infection; the fraction of ES-like colonies per total number of colonies; the fraction of iPS cell lines that could be established from picked ES-like colonies as defined by homogenous alkaline phosphatase, SSEA1 and Nanog expression. After determining the fraction of *Sox2*- (83.4%), *Oct4*- (53.2%) and *c-myc*- (46.3%) infected MEFs 2 days after infection by immunofluorescence and assuming 50% were infected by *Klf4* viruses, we estimated the overall reprogramming efficiency as the ratio of quadruple-infected cells and the extrapolated total number of iPS cell lines that could be established with G418 selection starting at day 6 after infection.

Although the timing and appearance of colonies were similar between the Oct4 and Nanog selection, we noticed pronounced quantitative differences between the two

图 1. 选择性表达 *Oct4* 和 *Nanog* 的 iPS 细胞的产生。**a**，产生 Oct4-IRES-GFPneo 等位基因的靶向策略。得到的 GFPneo 融合蛋白在 ES 细胞内具有足够的新霉素抗性活性；但是看不到 GFP 荧光。**b**，生长在辐射过的 MEF 上的 Oct4 iPS 细胞（克隆 18）的相差显微镜图像。插图：在没有饲养细胞的情况下，将细胞以克隆的密度接种 5 天后形成的 ES 细胞样克隆。iPS 克隆 18 的细胞表现出强烈的碱性磷酸酶活性（**c**），并用抗 SSEA1（**d,e**）和 Nanog（**f,g**）的抗体均匀标记。**h**，感染 16 天后的 ES 样克隆的一个例子（左图）。然而，大多数 G418 耐药细胞集落都由扁平的非 ES 样细胞组成（右图）：**b**，10×；**c~g**，20×；**h**，4×。**i**，Nanog 和 Oct4-neo 等位基因的逐渐激活。图为在第 3、6 和 9 天开始用新霉素进行筛选，病毒感染后第 20 天，一个实验的克隆总数。**j**，感染后第 0 天、第 14 天和第 20 天表达碱性磷酸酶、SSEA1 和 Nanog 的细胞的比例（每个时间点只有超过 10 个视野含有 $n > 1{,}000$ 个总细胞的才计数，误差条指代 s.d.）。**k**，估算 *Oct4* 和 *Nanog* 选择的重建效率（$n = 3$ 个不同的实验，s.e.m. 如图所示）。图中表示的是感染 20 天后每 100,000 个 MEF 重编程得到的总数；ES 样克隆占克隆总数的百分比；从挑取的 ES 样克隆中能够均质表达碱性磷酸酶、SSEA1 和 Nanog 的 iPS 克隆比例。通过免疫荧光确定了感染 2 天后 *Sox2*（83.4%）、*Oct4*（53.2%）和 *c-myc*（46.3%）感染 MEF 的比例后，并且假设 50% 受到 *Klf4* 病毒的感染，我们估计总体的重建效率为四倍感染的细胞的比例，并推算出在感染后第 6 天用 G418 选择获得的 iPS 细胞系的总数。

虽然 *Oct4* 和 *Nanog* 选择性表达的克隆出现的时间和外观相似，但我们注意到这两种选择策略之间存在明显的数量差异：*Oct4* 选择性表达的 MEF 能够形成的克

selection strategies: whereas Oct4-selected MEF cultures had 3- to 10-fold fewer colonies, the fraction of ES-like colonies was 2- to 3-fold higher than in Nanog-selected cultures. Accordingly, approximately four times more Oct4-selected ES-like colonies gave rise to stable and homogenous iPS cell lines compared with Nanog-selected ES-like colonies (Fig. 1k). This suggests that although the *Nanog* locus was easier to activate, a higher fraction of the drug-resistant colonies in Oct4-neo cultures was reprogrammed to a pluripotent state. Therefore, the overall estimated efficiency of 0.05–0.1% to establish iPS cell lines from MEFs was similar between Oct4 selection and Nanog selection, despite the larger number of total Nanog-neo resistant colonies (Fig. 1k). Next we investigated the time course of reprogramming by studying the fraction of alkaline-phosphatase-, SSEA1- and Nanog-positive cells in Oct4-selected MEF cultures. Fourteen days after infection some cells had already initiated alkaline phosphatase activity and SSEA1 expression, but lacked detectable amounts of Nanog protein (Fig. 1j), whereas by day 20, alkaline phosphatase and SSEA1 expression had increased and ~8% of the cells were Nanog-positive. Thus, the reprogramming induced by the four transcription factors (Oct4, Sox2, c-Myc and Klf4) is a gradual and slow process.

Expression and DNA Methylation

To characterize the reprogrammed cells on a molecular level we used quantitative polymerase chain reaction with reverse transcription (qRT–PCR) to measure the expression of ES-cell- and fibroblast- specific genes. Figure 2a shows that in Oct4 iPS cells the total level of Nanog and Oct4 was similar to that in ES cells but decreased on differentiation to embryoid bodies. MEFs did not express either gene. Using specific primers for endogenous or total *Sox2* transcripts showed that most *Sox2* transcripts originated from the endogenous locus rather than the viral vector (Fig. 2b). In contrast, *Hoxa9* and *Zfpm2* were highly expressed in MEFs but were expressed at very low levels in iPS or ES cells (Fig. 2c). Western blot analysis showed that multiple iPS clones expressed Nanog and Oct4 proteins at similar levels compared to ES cells (Fig. 2d). Finally, we used microarray technology to compare gene expression patterns on a global level. Figure 2f shows that the iPS cells clustered with ES cells in contrast to wild-type or donor MEFs.

To investigate the DNA methylation level of the *Oct4* and *Nanog* promoters we performed bisulphite sequencing and combined bisulphite restriction analysis (COBRA) with DNA isolated from ES cells, iPS cells and MEFs. As shown in Fig. 2g, both loci were demethylated in ES and iPS cells and fully methylated in MEFs. To assess whether the maintenance of genomic imprinting was compromised we assessed the methylation status of the four imprinted genes *H19*, *Peg1* (also called *Mest*), *Peg3* and *Snrpn*. As shown in Fig. 2e, bands corresponding to an unmethylated and methylated allele were detected for each gene in MEFs, iPS cells and TTFs. In contrast, embryonic germ cells, which have erased all imprints[8], were unmethylated. Our results indicate that the epigenetic state of the *Oct4* and *Nanog* genes was reprogrammed from a transcriptionally repressed (somatic) to an active (embryonic) state and that the pattern of somatic imprinting was maintained in iPS cells.

隆是 *Nanog* 选择性表达的 1/3 ~ 1/10，但是其能够形成 ES 样克隆的比例却是 *Nanog* 选择性表达的 MEF 的 2 ~ 3 倍。因此，与 *Nanog* 选择性表达的 ES 样克隆相比，*Oct4* 选择性表达的 ES 样克隆能够产生的稳定且均质的 iPS 细胞系的数量约是前者的 4 倍（图 1k）。这表明，尽管 *Nanog* 的基因位点更加容易被激活，但是 Oct4-neo 的细胞能够被重编程到多能性状态的比例更高。因此，尽管 Nanog-neo 的细胞总数更多（图 1k），但从 *Oct4* 选择性表达和 *Nanog* 选择性表达的 MEF 重编程获得 iPS 克隆的比例几乎都是 0.05 ~ 0.1（图 1k）。接下来，我们通过研究 *Oct4* 选择性表达的 MEF 重编程后获得的碱性磷酸酶、SSEA1 和 Nanog 阳性克隆的比例，研究重编程的时间进程。感染后 14 天，部分细胞已经出现了碱性磷酸酶活性和 SSEA1 表达，但检测不到 Nanog 的蛋白表达（图 1j），而到了第 20 天左右，碱性磷酸酶和 SSEA1 的表达增加了，大约 8% 的细胞是 Nanog 阳性的。因此，这四种转录因子（Oct4、Sox2、c-Myc 和 Klf4）诱导的重编程是一个渐进而缓慢的过程。

基因表达和 DNA 甲基化

为了在分子水平描述重编程后细胞的特征，我们使用定量反转录聚合酶链式反应（qRT–PCR）测量 ES 细胞和成纤维细胞特异性表达的基因。图 2a 显示了在 Oct4 iPS 细胞中，*Nanog* 和 *Oct4* 的总水平与 ES 细胞中相似，但分化成 EB 球后表达量就减少了。MEF 不表达这两个基因。使用内源或者总 *Sox2* 转录的特异性引物进行检测基因的表达，结果显示大部分 *Sox2* 转录起源于内源性位点而不是病毒载体（图 2b）。相反，*Hoxa9* 和 *Zfpm2* 在 MEF 中高表达，但是在 iPS 或者 ES 细胞中表达水平很低（图 2c）。Western bolt 分析显示多个 iPS 克隆表达的 Nanog 和 Oct4 蛋白水平与 ES 细胞相近（图 2d）。最后，我们使用微阵列技术在整体水平上比较了基因表达模式。图 2f 显示了 iPS 细胞与 ES 细胞聚集在一起，而不是与野生型或者供者 MEF 聚集在一起。

为了研究 *Oct4* 和 *Nanog* 启动子的 DNA 甲基化水平，我们对从 ES 细胞、iPS 细胞和 MEF 中分离出的 DNA 进行了亚硫酸氢盐测序和联合亚硫酸氢盐限制分析（COBRA）。如图 2g 所示，两个位点在 ES 和 iPS 细胞中都去甲基化，而在 MEF 中完全甲基化。为了评估基因组印迹的维持是否受到损害，我们评价了 4 个印记基因 *H19*、*Peg1*（又称为 *Mest*）、*Peg3* 和 *Snrpn* 的甲基化状态。如图 2e 所示，在 MEF、iPS 细胞和 TTF 中，每个基因都检测到与未甲基化和甲基化等位基因对应的条带。相反，已经消除所有印记的胚胎生殖细胞[8] 没有甲基化。我们的结果表明，*Oct4* 和 *Nanog* 基因的表观遗传状态从转录抑制（体细胞）状态被重编辑为活跃（胚胎）状态，

Furthermore, the presence of imprints suggests a non-embryonic-germ-cell origin of iPS cells.

Fig. 2. Expression and promoter methylation analysis of iPS cells. **a–c**, qRT–PCR analysis ($n = 3$ independent PCR reactions; error bars indicate s.d.) of Oct4 iPS clone 18, subclone 18.1, 2-week-old embryoid bodies (EBs) derived from clone 18, V6.5 ES cells and Oct4-neo MEFs shows similar Nanog (red bars) and total Oct4 (blue bars) levels as in ES cells (**a**); slightly lower total Sox2 levels (filled red bars), mostly due to expression of endogenous Sox2 transcripts (open red bars, **b**); and strong downregulation of Hoxa9 (red) and Zfpm2 (blue) transcripts in iPS cells (**c**). Transcript levels were normalized to Gapdh expression, with expression levels in ES cells (**a**, **b**) and MEFs (**c**) set as 1. **d**, Western blot analysis for Oct4 and Nanog expression of different Oct4 iPS clones (6, 9, 10, 16, 18) and a GFP-labelled subclone of clone 18 (18.1). **e**, COBRA methylation analysis[32] of imprinted genes *H19* (maternally expressed), *Peg1* (paternally expressed), *Peg3* (paternally expressed) and *Snrpn* (paternally expressed). Upper band, unmethylated (U); lower band, methylated (M). **f**, Unsupervised hierarchical clustering of averaged global transcriptional profiles obtained from Oct4-neo iPS clone 18, Nanog-neo iPS clone 8, genetically matched ES cells (V6.5;129SvJae/C57Bl/6), Oct4-neo MEFs (O), Nanog-neo MEFs (N) and wild-type 129/B6 F1 MEFs (WT). **g**, Analysis of the methylation state of the *Oct4* and *Nanog* promoters using bisulphite sequencing. Open circles indicate unmethylated and filled circles methylated CpG dinucleotides. Shown are eight representative sequenced clones from ES cells (V6.5), Oct4-neo MEFs and Oct4-neo iPS clone 18.

并在 iPS 细胞中保持了体细胞印记的模式。此外，印记基因的存在进一步表明 iPS 细胞的非胚胎生殖细胞起源。

图 2. iPS 细胞的基因表达和启动子甲基化分析。**a ~ c**，对 Oct4 iPS 克隆 18、亚克隆 18.1、来源于克隆 18 的 2 周龄胚胎体、V6.5 ES 细胞和 Oct4-neo MEF 进行 qRT–PCR 分析（$n = 3$ 个独立 PCR 反应，误差条表示 s.d.），显示 Nanog（红条）和总 Oct4（蓝条）水平与 ES 细胞（**a**）相似；Sox2 总水平略低（实心红条），主要是由于内源性 Sox2 转录本的表达（空心红条，**b**）；以及 iPS 细胞中 Hoxa9（红）和 Zfpm2（蓝）转录本的明显下调（**c**）。转录本水平根据 Gapdh 的表达进行了标化，即将 ES 细胞（**a,b**）和 MEF 细胞（**c**）内的表达水平设置为 1。**d**，不同 Oct4 iPS 克隆（6、9、10、16、18）和 GFP 标记的克隆 18 的亚克隆（18.1）中 Oct4 和 Nanog 表达的 Western 印迹分析。**e**，印记基因 H19（母方表达）、Peg1（父方表达）、Peg3（父方表达）和 Snrpn（父方表达）的 COBRA 甲基化分析 [32]。上面的条带，未甲基化（U）；下面的条带，甲基化（M）。**f**，Oct4-neo iPS 克隆 18、Nanog-neo iPS 克隆 8、与之遗传信息匹配的 ES 细胞（V6.5；129SvJae/C57BL/6）、Oct4-neo MEF（O）、Nanog-neo MEF（N）和野生型 129/B6 F1 MEF（WT）中的平均整体转录情况的自发分级集合。**g**，使用亚硫酸氢盐测序分析 Oct4 和 Nanog 启动子的甲基化状态。空圈表示未甲基化，实圈表示甲基化的 CpG 二核苷酸。图中所示的是 ES 细胞（V6.5）、Oct4-neo MEF 和 Oct4-neo iPS 克隆 18 中的 8 个代表性的测序方法。

Chromatin Modifications

Recently, downstream target genes of *Oct4*, *Nanog* and *Sox2* have been defined in ES cells by genome-wide location analyses[9,10]. These targets include many important developmental regulators, a proportion of which is also bound and repressed by PcG (Polycomb-Group) complexes[11,12]. Notably, the chromatin at many of these non-expressed target genes adopts a bivalent conformation in ES cells, carrying both the "active" histone H3 lysine 4 (H3K4) methylation mark and the "repressive" histone H3 lysine 27 (H3K27) methylation mark[13,14]. In differentiated cells, those genes tend instead to carry either H3K4 or H3K27 methylation depending on their expression state. We used chromatin immunoprecipitation (ChIP) and real-time PCR to quantify H3K4 and H3K27 methylation for a set of genes reported to be bivalent in pluripotent ES cells[13]. Figure 3a shows that the fibroblast-specific genes *Zfpm2* and *Hoxa9* carried stronger H3K4 methylation than H3K27 methylation in the donor MEFs, whereas the silent genes *Nkx2.2*, *Sox1*, *Lbx1* and *Pax5* primarily carried H3K27 methylation. In contrast, in the Oct4 iPS cells, all of these genes showed comparable enrichment for both histone modifications, similar to normal ES cells (Fig. 3a). Identical results were obtained in Nanog iPS clones selected from Nanog-neo MEFs (Supplementary Fig. 2). These data suggest that the chromatin configuration of somatic cells is re-set to one that is characteristic of ES cells.

Fig. 3. Reprogrammed MEFs acquire an ES-cell-like epigenetic state. **a**, Real-time PCR after chromatin immunoprecipitation using antibodies against tri-methylated histone H3K4 and H3K27. Shown are the

染色质修饰

最近，通过全基因组的定位分析[9,10]，在 ES 细胞中发现了 *Oct4*、*Nanog* 和 *Sox2* 的下游目的基因。这些目的基因包括了许多重要的发育调节因子，其中一部分还受到 PcG(多聚硫) 复合物的限制和抑制[11,12]。值得注意的是，这些未表达的目的基因中的染色质状态在 ES 细胞中形成双标构型，同时携带激活基因表达的组蛋白 3 赖氨酸 4(H3K4) 甲基化标志和抑制基因表达的组蛋白 3 赖氨酸 27(H3K27) 甲基化标志[13,14]。在分化的细胞中，这些基因根据倾向于携带 H3K4 或 H3K27 甲基化，这取决于它们的表达状态。我们用染色质免疫沉淀法(ChIP)和实时 PCR 对多能 ES 细胞内一系列被认为是双标基因的 H3K4 和 H3K27 甲基化进行了定量分析[13]。图 3a 显示了在供体 MEF 中成纤维细胞中特异性表达的基因 *Zfpm2* 和 *Hoxa9* 携带的 H3K4 甲基化水平强于 H3K27，而沉默基因 *Nkx2.2*、*Sox1*、*Lbx1* 和 *Pax5* 主要带有 H3K27 甲基化标志。相反，在 Oct4 iPS 细胞内，所有这些基因在两种组蛋白修饰上都表现出类似于正常 ES 细胞的相似富集(图 3a)。从 Nanog-neo MEF 中获得的 Nanog iPS 克隆得到了相同的结果(补充信息图 2)。这些数据表明，体细胞的染色质结构被重置成了具有 ES 细胞特征的模式。

图 3. 重编程的 MEF 获得了 ES 细胞样的表观遗传状态。**a**，用三甲基化组蛋白 H3K4 和 H3K27 抗体进行染色质免疫沉淀后的实时 PCR。图中所示的是先前报道的 ES 细胞中数个"双标"位点的 log₂ 富集

log$_2$ enrichments for several previously reported "bivalent" loci in ES cells ($n = 3$ experiments; error bars indicate s.d.). *Zfpm2* and *Hoxa9* show enrichment for the active (H3K4) mark in MEFs and are expressed (Fig. 1c and microarray data), whereas the other tested genes remain silent (microarray data). All loci tested in iPS clone O18 show enrichment for both H3K4 and H3K27 tri-methylation ("bivalent"), as seen in ES cells (V6.5). (See Supplementary Fig. 2 for H3K4 and H3K27 tri-methylation analysis of a subclone (clone O18.1) and Nanog-neo iPS clone N8.) **b**, Experimental design to de- and remethylate genomic DNA. Clone O18 was infected with the *Dnmt1*-hairpin-containing lentiviral vector pSicoR-GFP. The shRNA and GFP marker in the pSicoR vector are flanked by *loxP* sites[18]. Green colonies were expanded and passaged four times. Tat-Cre protein transduction was used to remove the shRNA[33]. **c**, Southern blot analysis of the minor satellite repeats using a methylation-sensitive restriction enzyme (*Hpa*II) and its methyl-insensitive isoschizomer (*Msp*I) as a control. Loss of methylation in two different clones (lanes 6 and 7) is comparable to Dnmt1 knockout ES cells (lane 2). After Cre-mediated recombination, complete remethylation (lane 8) of the repeats is observed within four passages. **d**, **e**, Successful loop out after Tat-Cre treatment was identified by disappearance of EGFP fluorescence (arrow) and verified by PCR analysis (**e**). **f**, COBRA assay of the imprinted genes *Peg3* and *Snrpn* and a random intergenic region close to the *Otx2* locus (Intergenic), demonstrating the expected resistance to *de novo* methylation of imprinted genes in contrast to non-imprinted intergenic sequences. U, unmethylated band; M, methylated band.

iPS Cells Tolerate Genomic Demethylation

Tolerance of genomic demethylation is a unique property of ES cells in contrast to somatic cells, which undergo rapid apoptosis on loss of the DNA methyltransferase Dnmt1 (refs 15–17). We investigated whether iPS cells would be resistant to global demethylation after Dnmt1 inhibition and would be able to re-establish global methylation patterns after restoration of Dnmt1 activity. To this end, we used a conditional lentiviral vector harbouring a *Dnmt1*-targeting short hairpin (sh)RNA and a green fluorescence protein (GFP) reporter gene (Fig. 3b and ref. 18). Infected iPS cells were plated at low density and GFP-positive colonies were picked and expanded. Southern blot analysis using *Hpa*II-digested genomic DNA showed that global demethylation of infected iPS cells (Fig. 3c, lanes 6, 7) was similar to *Dnmt1$^{-/-}$* ES cells (lane 2). In contrast, uninfected iPS cells or MEFs (lanes 4, 5) displayed normal methylation levels. Morphologically, the GFP-positive cells were indistinguishable from the parental line or from uninfected sister subclones, indicating that iPS cells tolerate global DNA demethylation. In a second step, the *Dnmt1* shRNA was excised through Cre-mediated recombination and GFP-negative clones were picked (Fig. 3d). The cells had excised the shRNA vector (Fig. 3e) and normal DNA methylation levels were restored (Fig. 3c, lane 8) and were able to generate chimaeras (see below, Table 1), as has been reported previously for ES cells[19]. These observations imply that the *de novo* methyltransferases Dnmt3a and Dnmt3b were reactivated in iPS cells[20], leading to restoration of global methylation levels. As expected[19], the imprinted genes *Snrpn* and *Peg3* were unmethylated and resistant to remethylation (Fig. 3f).

（n＝3 个实验，误差条表示 s.d.）。*Zfpm2* 和 *Hoxa9* 显示了 MEF 中活性（H3K4）标记的富集和表达（图 1c 和微阵列数据），而其他被检测的基因都保持沉默（微阵列数据）。iPS 克隆 O18 中检测的所有位点都显示 H3K4 和 H3K27 三甲基化的富集（双标性），与 ES 细胞（V6.5）一样。（亚克隆（克隆 18.1）和 Nanog-neo iPS 克隆 N8 的 H3K4 和 H3K27 三甲基化分析见补充信息图 2）。**b**，基因组 DNA 去甲基化和再甲基化的实验。克隆 O18 感染了含有 *Dnmt1* 发夹结构的慢病毒载体 pSicoR-GFP。pSicoR 载体中 shRNA 和 GFP 标记物的两侧是 *loxP* 位点[18]。绿色的克隆进行扩增并且传代四次。Tat-Cre 蛋白转导被用于去除 shRNA[33]。**c**，用甲基化敏感的限制性内切酶（*Hpa*II）进行小卫星重复序列的 Southern 印迹分析，以甲基化不敏感型异构酶（*Msp*I）作为对照。两个不同的克隆（泳道 6 和 7）中甲基化的缺失与 Dnmt1 敲除的 ES 细胞（泳道 2）相似。Cre 介导的重组之后，在四代内观察到了重复序列的完全再甲基化（泳道 8）。**d**，**e**，通过 EGFP 荧光的消失（箭头）验证了 Tat-Cre 处理后成功的消除作用，并用 PCR 进行验证（**e**）。**f**，印记基因 *Peg3* 和 *Snrpn* 以及邻近 *Otx2* 位点的随机基因间区域（基因间的）的 COBRA 实验，说明印记基因相对于非印记的基因间序列而言具有预期的对从头合成甲基化的耐受作用。U，未甲基化条带；M，甲基化条带。

iPS 细胞耐受基因组去甲基化

与体细胞不同，基因组去甲基化的耐受是 ES 细胞的特有性质，而体细胞在 DNA 甲基转移酶 Dnmt1 缺失后迅速凋亡（参考文献 15～17）。我们研究了在 Dnmt1 抑制后，iPS 细胞是否会对全面去甲基化产生耐药性，以及在 Dnmt1 活性恢复后能否重建甲基化模式。为此，我们使用了条件慢病毒载体，它含有一个 *Dnmt1* 靶向短发夹（sh）RNA 和一个绿色荧光蛋白（GFP）报告基因（图 3b 和参考文献 18）。将感染后的 iPS 细胞以较低的密度种下，并挑出 GFP 阳性克隆进行扩增。使用 *Hpa*II 消化的基因组 DNA 进行的 Southern 印迹分析显示，感染后 iPS 细胞的整体去甲基化状态（图 3c，6，7 道）与 *Dnmt1*−/− 的 ES 细胞相似（2 道）。相反，未感染的 iPS 细胞或者 MEF（4，5 道）显示正常的甲基化水平。形态学上，GFP 阳性的细胞与其父代或者未受感染的姐妹亚克隆无明显区别，表明 iPS 细胞能够耐受整体的 DNA 去甲基化。第二步，通过 Cre 介导的重组将 *Dnmt1* shRNA 去除，并选择 GFP 阴性克隆（图 3d）。这些细胞已经去除了 shRNA 载体（图 3e），并恢复了正常的 DNA 甲基化水平（图 3c，8 道），能够产生嵌合体（见下，表 1），正和之前报道的 ES 细胞性质相同[19]。这些观察结果表明，在 iPS 细胞中从头合成甲基转移酶 Dnmt3a 和 Dnmt3b 被重新激活[20]，导致了整体甲基化水平的恢复。如预期所示[19]，印记基因 *Snrpn* 和 *Peg3* 未发生甲基化，并且能够抵御再甲基化（图 3f）。

Table 1. Summary of blastocyst infections

Cell line	2N injections				4N injections		
	Injected blastocysts	Live chimaeras	Chimaerism (%)	Germ line	Injected blastocysts	Dead embryos (arrested)	Live embryos (analysed)
O6	ND	ND	ND	ND	13	0	2 (E12.5)
O9	30	5	30–70	Yes	90	3 (E11–13.5)	12 (E10–12.5)
O16	15	3	10–30	Yes	ND	ND	ND
O18	95	8	5–50	No	134	7 (E9–11.5)	4* (E10–12.5)
O3-2	ND	ND	ND	ND	25	2 (E8,11.5)	0
O4-16	ND	ND	ND	ND	35	4 (E11–13.5)	3 (E14.5)
N7	30	1	30	ND	ND	ND	ND
N8	90	14	5–50	No	118	9 (E9–11.5)	1* (E12.5)
N14	30	5	5–20	ND	46	2 (E8,11.5)	1 (E12.5)
TT-O25	50	2	30†	ND	39	3 (E9.5)	0
O18 rem/3.1	25	1	30	ND	ND	ND	ND

The extent of chimaerism was estimated on the basis of coat colour or EGFP expression. ND, not determined. 4N injected blastocysts were analysed between embryonic day E10.5 and E14.5.

"Analysed" indicates the day of embryonic development analysed; "arrested" indicates the estimated stage of development of dead embryos.

* Developmentally retarded or abnormal. O18 rem/3.1 is a de- and remethylated iPS clone (Fig. 3c).

† On the basis of GFP fluorescence.

Maintenance of the Pluripotent State

Southern blot analysis indicated that Oct4-neo iPS clone 18 carried four to six copies of the *Oct4*, *c-myc* and *Klf4* retroviral vectors and only one copy of the *Sox2* retroviral vector (Fig. 4a). Because these four factors were under the control of the constitutively expressed retroviral long terminal repeat, it was unclear in a previous study why iPS cells could be induced to differentiate[7]. To address this question, we designed primers specific for the four viral-encoded transcription factor transcripts and compared expression levels by qRT–PCR in MEFs 2 days after infection in iPS cells, in embryoid bodies derived from iPS cells, and in demethylated and remethylated iPS cells (Fig. 4b). Although the MEFs represented a heterogeneous population composed of uninfected and infected cells, virally encoded RNA levels of *Oct4*, *Sox2* and *Klf4* RNA were 5-fold higher and of *c-myc* more than 10-fold higher than in iPS cells. This suggests silencing of the viral long terminal repeat by *de novo* methylation during the reprogramming process. Accordingly, the total *Sox2* and *Oct4* RNA levels in iPS cells were similar to those in wild-type ES cells, and the *Sox2* transcripts in iPS cells were mostly, if not exclusively, transcribed from the endogenous gene (compare Fig. 2b). On differentiation to embryoid bodies, both viral and endogenous transcripts were downregulated. All viral *Sox2*, *Oct4* and *Klf4* transcripts were upregulated by approximately twofold in Dnmt1 knockdown iPS cells, and again downregulated on restoration of Dnmt1 activity. This is consistent with previous data that Moloney virus is efficiently *de*

表 1. 囊胚感染总结

细胞系	2N 注射				4N 注射		
	注射的囊胚	活的嵌合体	嵌合率 %	胚系	注射的囊胚	死胚胎（停止）	活胚胎（已分析）
O6	ND	ND	ND	ND	13	0	2(E12.5)
O9	30	5	30 ~ 70	Yes	90	3(E11 ~ 13.5)	12(E10 ~ 12.5)
O16	15	3	10 ~ 30	Yes	ND	ND	ND
O18	95	8	5 ~ 50	No	134	7(E9 ~ 11.5)	4*(E10 ~ 12.5)
O3-2	ND	ND	ND	ND	25	2(E8,11.5)	0
O4-16	ND	ND	ND	ND	35	4(E11 ~ 13.5)	3(E14.5)
N7	30	1	30	ND	ND	ND	ND
N8	90	14	5 ~ 50	No	118	9(E9 ~ 11.5)	1*(E12.5)
N14	30	5	5 ~ 20	ND	46	2(E8,11.5)	1(E12.5)
TT-O25	50	2	30†	ND	39	3(E9.5)	0
O18 rem/3.1	25	1	30	ND	ND	ND	ND

嵌合的程度根据毛色或者 EGFP 的表达估计。ND：不确定。4N 注射的囊胚在胚胎发育的 E10.5 到 E14.5 天之间进行了分析。

"已分析"表示已分析的胚胎发育天数；"停止"表示死亡胚胎的估计发育阶段。

* 发育迟缓或者异常。O18rem/3.1 是一个去甲基化和再甲基化的 iPS 克隆（图 3c）。

† 基于 GFP 荧光。

多能状态的保持

Southern 印迹分析显示 Oct4-neo iPS 克隆 18 带有 4 到 6 个拷贝的 *Oct4*、*c-Myc* 和 *Klf4* 逆转录病毒载体，只带有一个拷贝的 *Sox2* 逆转录病毒载体（图 4a）。因为这四个因子都是在组成性表达的逆转录病毒长末端重复的控制之下，所以在以前的研究中并不清楚 iPS 细胞能够被诱导分化的原因[7]。为了解决这个问题，我们设计了针对这四个病毒编码转录因子特异性的引物，并用 qRT–PCR 比较 iPS 细胞感染后 2 天的 MEF、iPS 细胞衍生的 EB 球、去甲基化和再甲基化的 iPS 细胞中的表达水平（图 4b）。虽然 MEF 是由未感染和感染细胞组成的异质性群体，但 *Oct4*、*Sox2* 和 *Klf4* RNA 的病毒编码 RNA 水平是 iPS 细胞的 5 倍，*c-Myc* 则是 10 倍以上。这表明在重编程的过程中发生了新的甲基化使病毒的长末端重复沉默。因此，iPS 细胞内的 *Sox2* 和 *Oct4* RNA 的总水平与野生型 ES 细胞内相似，而且 iPS 细胞内的 *Sox2* 转录本不完全是大部分来源于内源性基因（对照图 2b）。在向 EB 球分化的过程中，病毒和内源性的转录产物都发生了下调。在 Dnmt1 敲降的 iPS 细胞中，所有的病毒 *Sox2*、*Oct4* 和 *Klf4* 转录本都上调至原来的将近 2 倍，而在 Dnmt1 功能恢复时又下调回来。这与先前的数据一致，在胚胎中莫洛尼病毒能够有效地被甲基化和沉默，

novo methylated and silenced in embryonic but not in somatic cells[21,22]. Transcript levels of *c-myc* were about 20-fold lower in iPS cells than in infected MEFs, and did not change on differentiation or demethylation.

Fig. 4. Efficient silencing of retroviral transcripts in induced pluripotent cells. **a**, Southern blot analysis of proviral integrations in iPS clone O18 (left lanes) for the four retroviral vectors. Uninfected ES cells (right lanes) show only one or two bands corresponding to the endogenous gene (marked by an asterisk). **b**, Quantitative RT–PCR using primers specifically detecting the four viral transcripts. Shown are Oct4-neo iPS clone 18 and a GFP-labelled subclone, Oct4-neo MEFs, 2-week-old embryoid bodies generated from clone 18, two demethylated clones (18 dem/1 and 18 dem/3), a remethylated clone (18 rem/3.1), and Oct4-neo MEFs 2 days after infection with all four viruses but not selected with G418 (*n* = 3 independent experiments; error bars indicate s.d.). **c**, Viral transcript levels at various time points in cell populations after infection and Oct4 selection and in the two Oct4 iPS cell lines O1.3 and O9 (*n* = 3 independent experiments; error bars indicate s.d.). **d–f**, Paraffin sections of a teratoma 26 days after subcutaneous injection of Oct4 iPS clone 18 cells into SCID mice. H&E, haematoxylin and eosin. Nanog (**e**) and Oct4 (**f**) expression was confined to undifferentiated cell types as indicated an immunohistochemical analysis.

To follow the kinetics of vector inactivation during the reprogramming process, we isolated RNA from drug-resistant cell populations at different times after infection. Figure 4c shows that the viral-vector-encoded transcripts were gradually silenced during the transition from MEFs to iPS cells with a time course that corresponded to the gradual appearance of pluripotency markers (compare Fig. 1j). Finally, to visualize directly Oct4 and Nanog expression during differentiation, we injected Oct4 iPS cells into SCID mice to induce teratoma formation (Fig. 4d). Immunostaining revealed that Oct4 and Nanog were expressed in the centrally located undifferentiated cells but were silenced in the differentiated parts of the teratoma (Fig. 4e, f). Our results suggest that the retroviral vectors

而在体细胞中不行 [21,22]。iPS 细胞中的 *c-Myc* 转录本水平大约为感染的 MEF 的二十分之一，而且在分化或者去甲基化过程中没有变化。

图 4. 诱导的多能细胞中逆转录病毒转录本的有效沉默。**a**，iPS 克隆 O18（左侧泳道）中四个逆转录病毒载体的前病毒整合的 Southern 印迹分析。未感染的 ES 细胞（右侧泳道）只显示与内源性基因对应的一条或者两条带（星号标记）。**b**，使用识别四个病毒转录子的引物进行的定量 RT–PCR。显示的分别是 Oct4-neo iPS 克隆 18 和 GFP 标记的亚克隆，OCT4-neo MEF，来源于克隆 18 的 2 周龄胚胎体，两个去甲基化的克隆（18dem/1 和 18dem/3），一个再甲基化的克隆（18dem/3.1）和用所有四种病毒感染 2 天后但是不用 G418 进行选择得到的 OCT4-neo MEF（*n* = 3 独立的实验，误差条表示 s.d.）。**c**，经过感染和 Oct4 选择的细胞群以及两个 Oct4 iPS 细胞系 O1.3 和 O9 在不同时间点的病毒转录子水平（*n* = 3 独立的实验，误差条表示 s.d.）。**d~f**，皮下注射 Oct4 iPS 克隆 18 到 SCID 小鼠中 26 天后形成的畸胎瘤的石蜡切片。H&E，苏木精和伊红。免疫组化分析显示，Nanog（**e**）和 Oct4（**f**）表达仅限于未分化的细胞类型。

为了研究重编程过程中外源基因失活的动力学，我们从感染后不同时间的耐药细胞中分离出 RNA。图 4c 显示了从 MEF 向 iPS 转化的过程中，病毒载体编码的转录本逐渐沉默，这一过程与多能性标志物的逐渐出现相对应（对照图 1j）。最后，为了直接观察 Oct4 和 Nanog 在分化过程中的表达，我们将 Oct4 iPS 细胞注射到 SCID 小鼠体内诱导畸胎瘤形成（图 4d）。免疫染色显示 Oct4 和 Nanog 在中心位置的未分化细胞中表达，但在畸胎瘤的已分化部分沉默（图 4e、f）。我们的结果表明，在重

are subject to gradual silencing by *de novo* methylation during the reprogramming process. The maintenance of the pluripotent state and induction of differentiation strictly depends on the expression and normal regulation of the endogenous *Oct4* and *Nanog* genes.

Developmental Potency

We determined the developmental potential of iPS cells by teratoma and chimaera formation. Histological and immunohistochemical analysis of Oct4- or Nanog-iPS-cell-induced teratomas revealed that the cells had differentiated into cell types representing all three embryonic germ layers (Supplementary Figs 3 and 4). To assess more stringently their developmental potential, various iPS cell lines were injected into diploid (2N) or tetraploid (4N) blastocysts. After injection into 2N blastocysts both Nanog iPS and Oct4 iPS clones derived from MEFs (Fig. 5a) or from TTFs (Fig. 5b, c), as well as iPS cells that had been subjected to a consecutive cycle of demethylation and remethylation (compare Fig. 3b, c), efficiently generated viable high-contribution chimaeras (summarized in Table 1). To test for germline transmission, chimaeras derived from two different iPS lines (Oct4 iPS O9 and O16) were mated with normal females, and blastocysts were isolated and genotyped by three different PCR reactions for the presence of the multiple viral *Oct4* and *c-myc* genes and for the single-copy GFPneo sequences inserted into the *Oct4* locus of the donor cell (Fig. 1a). Figure 5f shows that 9 out of 16 embryos from two chimaeras were positive for the viral copies. As expected, only half of the viral-positive blastocysts contained the GFPneo sequences (5 out of 9 embryos, Fig. 5f, left panel). When embryonic day (E)10 embryos derived from an Oct4 iPS line O16 chimaera were genotyped, three out of eight tested embryos were transgenic (Fig. 5f, right panel). Finally, we injected iPS cells into 4N blastocysts as this represents the most rigorous test for developmental potency, because the resulting embryos are composed only of the injected donor cells ("all ES embryo"). Figure 5d, e shows that both Oct4 and Nanog iPS cells could generate mid- and late-gestation "all iPS embryos" (summarized in Table 1). These findings indicate that iPS cells can establish all lineages of the embryo and thus have a similar developmental potential as ES cells.

建的过程中逆转录病毒载体通过从头合成甲基化逐渐沉默。保持多能状态和诱导分化严格依赖于内源性 *Oct4* 和 *Nanog* 基因的表达和正常调控。

发育潜力

我们用畸胎瘤和嵌合体的形成来确定 iPS 细胞的发育潜力。对 Oct4 或 Nanog iPS 细胞诱导的畸胎瘤进行组织学和免疫组化分析显示，这些细胞已经分化成代表三个胚层（补充信息图 3 和 4）的细胞类型。为了更加严格地评估其发育潜力，不同的 iPS 细胞系被注射到二倍体（2N）或者四倍体（4N）囊胚中。注射到 2N 囊胚后，来源于 MEF（图 5a）或者 TTF（图 5b、c）的 Nanog iPS 和 Oct4 iPS 细胞克隆以及经过连续去甲基化和再甲基化循环的 iPS 细胞（对照图 3b、c）都有效地产生高度嵌合的嵌合体（总结见表 1）。为了检验胚系传递的能力，来源于两个不同 iPS 细胞系（Oct4 iPS O9 和 O16）的嵌合体与正常雌性小鼠进行交配，分离出囊胚并用三种不同的 PCR 反应进行基因分型，验证是否存在多种病毒 *Oct4* 和 *c-Myc* 基因以及为了将单拷贝 GFPneo 序列插入到供者细胞 *Oct4* 位点内（图 1a）。图 5f 显示两个嵌合体共 16 个胚胎中的 9 个含有病毒拷贝。正如所期望的，只有一半的病毒阳性囊胚含有 GFPneo 序列（9 个胚胎中有 5 个，图 5f，左侧栏）。当对 Oct4 iPS 细胞系 O16 嵌合体的 10 个胚胎进行基因型鉴定时，8 个被测胚胎中有 3 个是转基因的（图 5f，右侧栏）。最后，我们将 iPS 细胞注射到 4N 囊胚中，这代表了发育潜力最严格的检测，因为得到的胚胎仅仅由注射的供者细胞组成（全 ES 胚胎）。图 5d、e 显示了 Oct4 和 Nanog iPS 细胞都能够产生孕中期和孕晚期的全 iPS 胚胎（总结见表 1）。这些结果表明 iPS 细胞能够建立胚胎的所有细胞系，因此具有与 ES 细胞类似的发育潜力。

Fig. 5. Developmental pluripotency of reprogrammed fibroblasts. **a**, A 6-week-old chimaeric mouse. Agouti-coloured hairs originated from Oct4 iPS cell line O18.1. **b**, **c**, Two live pups after 2N blastocyst injection, one of which shows a high contribution (**c**) of the TTF-derived Oct4 iPS cell line TT-O25, which had been GFP-labelled with a lentiviral ubiquitin-EGFP vector. **d**, "All iPS cell embryos" were generated by injection of iPS cells into 4N blastocysts[34]. Live E12.5 embryos generated from Oct4 iPS line O6 (left), from Nanog iPS line N14 (middle) and from V.6.5 ES cells (right) are shown. **e**, A normally developed E14.5 embryo was derived from Oct4 iPS cell line O4-16 after tetraploid complementation and was isolated by screening MEFs for activation of GFP inserted into the *Oct4* locus. **f**, Germline contribution of Oct4 iPS clones O9 and O16. Genotyping of blastocysts from females mated with three chimaeric males demonstrated the presence of *Oct4* and *c-myc* virus integrations and the Oct4-IRES-GFPneo allele (left panel). Because of the multiple integrations (Fig. 4a) all embryos with iPS cell contribution are expected to be positive for proviral sequences in this assay. In contrast, the single-copy Oct4-IRES-GFPneo allele segregated into only 5 of the 9 virus-positive embryos. All six blastocysts from O9 chimaera 1 were iPS-cell-derived, suggesting that this chimaera was a pseudo-male. Additional genotyping identified 13 out of 72 tested blastocysts derived from iPS line O9 and 4 out of 13 blastocysts derived from iPS line O16 chimaeras carrying the viral transgenes. The right panel shows that 3 out of 8 tested E.10 mid-gestation embryos were sired by a chimaera derived from the donor iPS line O16. +, positive control; –, negative control.

Discussion

The results presented here demonstrate that the four transcription factors Oct4, Sox2, c-myc and Klf4 can induce epigenetic reprogramming of a somatic genome to an embryonic pluripotent state. In contrast to selection for Fbx15 activation[7], fibroblasts that had reactivated the endogenous *Oct4* (Oct4-neo) or *Nanog* (Nanog-neo) loci grew independently of feeder cells, expressed normal Oct4, Nanog and Sox2 RNA and protein levels, were epigenetically identical to ES cells by a number of criteria, and were able to generate viable chimaeras, contribute to the germ line and generate viable late-gestation embryos after

图 5. 重编程后成纤维细胞的发育多能性。**a**，一只 6 周龄的嵌合体小鼠。刺豚鼠样的毛色来源于 Oct4 iPS 细胞系 O18.1。**b, c**，2N 囊胚注射后的两只活幼鼠，其中一只显示了高比例 (**c**) 的 TTF 来源的 Oct4 iPS 细胞系 TT-O25，该细胞系已被慢病毒泛素化 -EGFP 进行 GFP 标记。**d**，所有的 iPS 细胞胚胎都是通过将 iPS 细胞注入 4N 囊胚生成的 [34]。图中显示了来源于 Oct4 iPS 细胞系 O6 (左侧)、Nanog iPS 细胞系 N14 (中间) 和 V.6.5 ES 细胞 (右侧) 的活的 E12.5 胚胎。**e**，经过四倍体互补后，从 Oct4 iPS 细胞系 O4-16 中获得一个正常发育的 E14.5 胚胎，通过筛选插入到 Oct4 位点的 MEF，激活 GFP，将其分离出来。**f**，Oct4 iPS 克隆 O9 和 O16 的生殖系嵌合贡献。对雌鼠和三只嵌合体雄鼠交配产生的囊胚进行基因型鉴定，显示存在 Oct4 和 c-Myc 病毒整合以及 Oct4-TRES-GFP 等位基因 (左侧泳道)。由于多重整合 (图 4a)，在本实验中，所有含有 iPS 细胞成分的胚胎的前病毒序列均呈阳性。相反，9 只病毒阳性的胚胎中只有 5 只具有单拷贝 Oct4-TRES-GFPneo 等位基因。O9 嵌合体 1 的 6 个囊胚都是 iPS 细胞来源，表明该嵌合体是假雄性。另外的基因分型在 72 个测试的囊胚中鉴定出 13 个来自 iPS 细胞系 O9，在 13 个来自携带病毒转基因的 iPS 系 O16 嵌合体的囊胚中鉴定出 4 个。右侧泳道显示了 8 个检测的 E10 孕中期胚胎中有 3 个来源于供体 iPS 细胞系 O16 的嵌合体。+，阳性对照；-，阴性对照。

讨　论

　　本研究表明，Oct4、Sox2、c-Myc 和 Klf4 这四个转录因子能够诱导体细胞基因组的表观遗传重编程成胚胎多能状态。相对于 *Fbx15* 活化选择 [7]，激活内源性 *Oct4* (Oct4-neo) 或者 *Nanog*(Nanog-neo) 位点的成纤维细胞可以不依赖饲养细胞而独立生长，能够表达正常的 *Oct4*、*Nanog* 和 *Sox2* RNA 和蛋白水平。在许多标准下，成纤维细胞与 ES 细胞在表观遗传学上是相同的，它能够产生可以存活的嵌合体，在注

injection into tetraploid blastocysts. Transduction of the four factors generated significantly more drug-resistant cells from Nanog-neo than from Oct4-neo fibroblasts but a higher fraction of Oct4-selected cells had all the characteristics of pluripotent ES cells, suggesting that *Nanog* activation is a less stringent criterion for pluripotency than *Oct4* activation.

Our data suggest that the pluripotent state of Oct4 iPS and Nanog iPS cells is induced by the virally transduced factors but is largely maintained by the activity of the endogenous pluripotency factors including Oct4, Nanog and Sox2, because the viral-controlled transcripts, although expressed highly in MEFs, become mostly silenced in iPS cells. The total levels of Oct4, Nanog and Sox2 were similar in iPS and wild-type ES cells. Consistent with the conclusion that the pluripotent state is maintained by the endogenous pluripotency genes is the finding that the *Oct4* and the *Nanog* genes became hypomethylated in iPS cells as in ES cells, and that the bivalent histone modifications of developmental regulators were re-established. Furthermore, iPS cells were resistant to global demethylation induced by inactivation of Dnmt1, similar to ES cells but in contrast to somatic cells. Re-expression of Dnmt1 in the hypomethylated ES cells resulted in global remethylation, indicating that the iPS cells had also reactivated the *de novo* methyltransferases Dnmt3a and Dnmt3b. All these observations are consistent with the conclusion that the iPS cells have gained an epigenetic state that is similar to that of normal ES cells. This conclusion is further supported by the recent observation that female iPS cells, similar to ES cells, reactivate the somatically silenced X chromosome[23].

Expression of the four transcription factors proved to be a robust method to induce reprogramming of somatic cells to a pluripotent state. However, the use of retrovirus-transduced oncogenes represents a serious barrier to the eventual use of reprogrammed cells for therapeutic application. Much work is needed to understand the molecular pathways of reprogramming and to eventually find small molecules that could achieve reprogramming without gene transfer of potentially harmful genes.

Methods Summary

Cell culture, gene targeting and viral infections. ES and iPS cells were cultivated on irradiated MEFs. Using homologous recombination we generated ES cells carrying an IRES-GFPneo fusion cassette downstream of *Oct4* exon 5 (Fig. 1a). The *Nanog* gene was targeted as described[24]. Transgenic MEFs were isolated and selected from E13.5 chimaeric embryos after blastocyst injection of Oct4-IRES-GFPneo- or Nanog-neo-targeted ES cells. MEFs were infected overnight with the Moloney-based retroviral vector pLIB (Clontech) containing the murine complementary DNAs of *Oct4*, *Sox2*, *Klf4* and *c-myc*.

Southern blot, methylation and chromatin analyses. To assess the levels of DNA methylation, genomic DNA was digested with *Hpa*II and hybridized to a probe for the minor satellite repeats[25] or with an IAP probe[26]. Bisulphite treatment was performed with the Qiagen EpiTect Kit. For the methylation status of *Oct4* and *Nanog* promoters, bisulphite sequencing analysis was performed

射到四倍体囊胚中后，对生殖系的形成有促进作用，能够产生孕晚期的胚胎。这四个因子的转导使 Nanog-neo 成纤维细胞中的耐药细胞明显比 Oct4-neo 成纤维细胞中的多，但 *Oct4* 选择性表达的细胞中具有多能 ES 细胞所有的特征的比例较高，这表明 *Nanog* 活化是比 *Oct4* 活化更加不严格的多能性标准。

我们的数据表明 Oct4 iPS 和 Nanog iPS 细胞的多能状态是通过病毒转导的因子诱导的，但大部分是由内源多能性因子包括 *Oct4*、*Nanog* 和 *Sox2* 的活性来维持的，因为病毒控制的转录子尽管在 MEF 中高度表达，却在 iPS 细胞内大部分都沉默了。iPS 细胞和野生型 ES 细胞中的 *Oct4*、*Nanog* 和 *Sox2* 总水平相似。与内源性多能基因保持多能状态的结论相一致的是发现了 *Oct4* 和 *Nanog* 基因在 iPS 细胞内与在 ES 细胞一样低甲基化，而且发育调节因子的双标组蛋白修饰发生了重建。此外，iPS 细胞对 Dnmt1 失活诱导的整体去甲基化具有抗性，这与 ES 细胞相似但与体细胞相反。Dnmt1 在低甲基化 ES 细胞中的重新表达导致了整体的再甲基化，这表明 iPS 细胞也重新激活了从头合成甲基转移酶 Dnmt3a 和 Dnmt3b。所有的这些发现与 iPS 细胞已经获得了类似于正常 ES 细胞的表观遗传状态的结论相一致。最近的发现进一步支持了这一结论，即雌性 iPS 细胞，类似于 ES 细胞，能够重新激活体细胞中沉默的 X 染色体 [23]。

四个转录因子的表达被证实是一种能将体细胞重编程成多能状态的可靠的方法。但是，使用逆转录病毒转导的致癌基因意味着最终将重编程的细胞用于临床治疗存在严重的障碍。我们需要做更多的工作来了解重编程的分子机制，并最终找到小分子物质，可以在没有潜在有害基因的基因转移情况下实现重编程。

方法概述

细胞培养、基因靶向和病毒感染 在辐射过的 MEF 上进行 ES 和 iPS 细胞培养。通过同源重组，我们获得了在 *Oct4* 的 5 号外显子下游产生携带 IRES-GFPneo 融合盒的 ES 细胞系（图 1a）。*Nanog* 基因如所描述的是靶向的 [24]。将 Oct4-IRES-GFPneo 或者 Nanog-neo 靶向 ES 细胞注入囊胚后，从 E13.5 嵌合体胚胎中选择和分离出转基因 MEF。MEF 用含有 *Oct4*、*Sox2*、*c-Myc* 和 *Klf4* 的小鼠互补 DNA 的莫洛尼逆转录病毒载体 pLIB（Clontech）产生的病毒感染过夜。

Southern 印迹、甲基化和染色质分析 为了评估 DNA 甲基化水平，基因组 DNA 用 *Hpa*II 进行消化，并与小卫星重复序列探针 [25] 或者 IAP 探针 [26] 进行杂交。用 Qiagen EpiTect 试剂盒进行亚硫酸氢盐处理。如先前所述的用亚硫酸氢盐序列分析法研究 *Oct4* 和 *Nanog* 启

as described previously[27]. For imprinted genes, a COBRA assay was performed. PCR primers and conditions were as described previously[28]. The status of bivalent domains was determined by chromatin immunoprecipitation followed by quantitative PCR analysis, as described previously[12].

Expression analysis. Total RNA was reverse-transcribed and quantified using the QuantTtect SYBR green RT–PCR Kit (Qiagen) on a 7000 ABI detection system. Western blot and immunofluorescence analysis was performed as described[29,30]. Microarray targets from 2 μg total RNA were synthesized and labelled using the Low RNA Input Linear Amp Kit (Agilent), hybridized to Agilent whole-mouse genome oligonucleotide arrays (G4122F) and analysed as previously described[31].

Full Methods and any associated references are available in the online version of the paper at www.nature.com/nature.

(**448**, 318-324; 2007)

Marius Wernig[1]*, Alexander Meissner[1]*, Ruth Foreman[1,2]*, Tobias Brambrink[1]*, Manching Ku[3]*, Konrad Hochedlinger[1]†, Bradley E. Bernstein[3,4,5] & Rudolf Jaenisch[1,2]

[1]Whitehead Institute for Biomedical Research and [2]Department of Biology, Massachusetts Institute of Technology, Cambridge, Massachusetts 02142, USA

[3]Molecular Pathology Unit and Center for Cancer Research, Massachusetts General Hospital, Charlestown, Massachusetts 02129, USA

[4]Broad Institute of Harvard and MIT, Cambridge, Massachusetts 02142, USA

[5]Department of Pathology, Harvard Medical School, Boston, Massachusetts 02115, USA

†Present address: Center for Regenerative Medicine and Cancer Center, Massachusetts General Hospital, Harvard Medical School and Harvard Stem Cell Institute, Boston, Massachusetts 02414, USA

*These authors contributed equally to this work

Received 27 February; accepted 22 May 2007. Published online 6 June 2007.

References:

1. Hochedlinger, K. & Jaenisch, R. Nuclear transplantation, embryonic stem cells, and the potential for cell therapy. *N. Engl. J. Med.* **349**, 275-286 (2003).

2. Yang, X. *et al.* Nuclear reprogramming of cloned embryos and its implications for therapeutic cloning. *Nature Genet.* **39**, 295-302 (2007).

3. Hochedlinger, K. & Jaenisch, R. Nuclear reprogramming and pluripotency. *Nature* **441**, 1061-1067 (2006).

4. Tada, M., Takahama, Y., Abe, K., Nakatsuji, N. & Tada, T. Nuclear reprogramming of somatic cells by *in vitro* hybridization with ES cells. *Curr. Biol.* **11**, 1553-1558 (2001).

5. Cowan, C. A., Atienza, J., Melton, D. A. & Eggan, K. Nuclear reprogramming of somatic cells after fusion with human embryonic stem cells. *Science* **309**, 1369-1373 (2005).

6. Jaenisch, R. Human cloning—the science and ethics of nuclear transplantation. *N. Engl. J. Med.* **351**, 2787-2791 (2004).

7. Takahashi, K. & Yamanaka, S. Induction of pluripotent stem cells from mouse embryonic and adult fibroblast cultures by defined factors. *Cell* **126**, 663-676 (2006).

8. Labosky, P. A., Barlow, D. P. & Hogan, B. L. Mouse embryonic germ (EG) cell lines: transmission through the germline and differences in the methylation imprint of insulin-like growth factor 2 receptor (*Igf2r*) gene compared with embryonic stem (ES) cell lines. *Development* **120**, 3197-3204 (1994).

9. Boyer, L. A. *et al.* Core transcriptional regulatory circuitry in human embryonic stem cells. *Cell* **122**, 947-956 (2005).

10. Loh, Y. H. *et al.* The Oct4 and Nanog transcription network regulates pluripotency in mouse embryonic stem cells. *Nature Genet.* **38**, 431-440 (2006).

11. Lee, T. I. *et al.* Control of developmental regulators by Polycomb in human embryonic stem cells. *Cell* **125**, 301-313 (2006).

12. Boyer, L. A. *et al.* Polycomb complexes repress developmental regulators in murine embryonic stem cells. *Nature* **441**, 349-353 (2006).

13. Bernstein, B. E. *et al.* A bivalent chromatin structure marks key developmental genes in embryonic stem cells. *Cell* **125**, 315-326 (2006).

14. Azuara, V. *et al.* Chromatin signatures of pluripotent cell lines. *Nature Cell Biol.* **8**, 532-538 (2006).

15. Jackson-Grusby, L. *et al.* Loss of genomic methylation causes p53-dependent apoptosis and epigenetic deregulation. *Nature Genet.* **27**, 31-39 (2001).

16. Li, E., Bestor, T. H. & Jaenisch, R. Targeted mutation of the DNA methyltransferase gene results in embryonic lethality. *Cell* **69**, 915-926 (1992).

1056

动子的甲基化水平 [27]。对于印记基因，进行 COBRA 实验。PCR 引物和条件如前所述 [28]。通过染色质免疫沉淀然后通过 PCR 分析确定双标结构域的状态 [12]。

基因表达分析　用 QuantTtect SYBR green RT–PCR 试剂盒（Qiagen）将总 RNA 进行反转录，之后再通过 7000ABI 检测系统完成定量检测。按照上述方法进行 Western 印迹和免疫荧光分析 [29,30]。基因微阵列的靶标用 Law RNA Input Linear Amp 试剂盒，由 2μg 总的 RNA 合成，并进行标记，然后与 Agilent 全鼠基因组寡核苷酸阵列（G4122F）进行杂交和分析 [31]。

完整的方法和相关的文献可在本文的网上版本中获得。

（毛晨晖 翻译；裴端卿 审稿）

17. Meissner, A. *et al.* Reduced representation bisulfite sequencing for comparative high-resolution DNA methylation analysis. *Nucleic Acids Res.* **33**, 5868-5877 (2005).

18. Ventura, A. *et al.* Cre-lox-regulated conditional RNA interference from transgenes. *Proc. Natl Acad. Sci. USA* **101**, 10380-10385 (2004).

19. Holm, T. M. *et al.* Global loss of imprinting leads to widespread tumorigenesis in adult mice. *Cancer Cell* **8**, 275-285 (2005).

20. Okano, M., Bell, D. W., Haber, D. A. & Li, E. DNA methyltransferases Dnmt3a and Dnmt3b are essential for *de novo* methylation and mammalian development. *Cell* **99**, 247-257 (1999).

21. Stewart, C. L., Stuhlmann, H., Jähner, D. & Jaenisch, R. *De novo* methylation, expression, and infectivity of retroviral genomes introduced into embryonal carcinoma cells. *Proc. Natl Acad. Sci. USA* **79**, 4098-4102 (1982).

22. Jähner, D. *et al. De novo* methylation and expression of retroviral genomes during mouse embryogenesis. *Nature* **298**, 623-628 (1982).

23. Maherali, N. *et al.* Global epigenetic remodeling in directly reprogrammed fibroblasts. *Cell Stem Cells* (in the press).

24. Mitsui, K. *et al.* The homeoprotein Nanog is required for maintenance of pluripotency in mouse epiblast and ES cells. *Cell* **113**, 631-642 (2003).

25. Chapman, V., Forrester, L., Sanford, J., Hastie, N. & Rossant, J. Cell lineage specific undermethylation of mouse repetitive DNA. *Nature* **307**, 284-286 (1984).

26. Walsh, C. P., Chaillet, J. R. & Bestor, T. H. Transcription of IAP endogenous retroviruses is constrained by cytosine methylation. *Nature Genet.* **20**, 116-117 (1998).

27. Blelloch, R. *et al.* Reprogramming efficiency following somatic cell nuclear transfer is influenced by the differentiation and methylation state of the donor nucleus. *Stem Cells* **24**, 2007-2013 (2006).

28. Lucifero, D., Mertineit, C., Clarke, H. J., Bestor, T. H. & Trasler, J. M. Methylation dynamics of imprinted genes in mouse germ cells. *Genomics* **79**, 530-538 (2002).

29. Hochedlinger, K., Yamada, Y., Beard, C. & Jaenisch, R. Ectopic expression of Oct-4 blocks progenitor-cell differentiation and causes dysplasia in epithelial tissues. *Cell* **121**, 465-477 (2005).

30. Wernig, M. *et al.* Functional integration of embryonic stem cell-derived neurons *in vivo. J. Neurosci.* **24**, 5258-5268 (2004).

31. Brambrink, T., Hochedlinger, K., Bell, G. & Jaenisch, R. ES cells derived from cloned and fertilized blastocysts are transcriptionally and functionally indistinguishable. *Proc. Natl Acad. Sci. USA* **103**, 933-938 (2006).

32. Eads, C. A. & Laird, P. W. Combined bisulfite restriction analysis (COBRA). *Methods Mol. Biol.* **200**, 71-85 (2002).

33. Peitz, M., Pfannkuche, K., Rajewsky, K. & Edenhofer, F. Ability of the hydrophobic FGF and basic TAT peptides to promote cellular uptake of recombinant Cre recombinase: a tool for efficient genetic engineering of mammalian genomes. *Proc. Natl Acad. Sci. USA* **99**, 4489-4494 (2002).

34. Eggan, K. *et al.* Hybrid vigor, fetal overgrowth, and viability of mice derived by nuclear cloning and tetraploid embryo complementation. *Proc. Natl Acad. Sci. USA* **98**, 6209-6214 (2001).

35. Naviaux, R. K., Costanzi, E., Haas, M. & Verma, I. M. The pCL vector system: rapid production of helper-free, high-titer, recombinant retroviruses. *J. Virol.* **70**, 5701-5705 (1996).

Supplementary Information is linked to the online version of the paper at www.nature.com/nature.

Acknowledgements. We thank H. Suh, D. Fu and J. Dausman for technical assistance; J. Love for help with the microarray analysis; S. Markoulaki for help with blastocyst injections; F. Edenhofer for a gift of Tat-Cre; and S. Yamanaka for the Nanog-neo construct. We acknowledge L. Zagachin in the MGH Nucleic Acid Quantitation core for assistance with real-time PCR. We also thank C. Lengner, C. Beard and M. Creyghton for constructive criticism. M.W. was supported in part by fellowships from the Human Frontiers Science Organization Program and the Ellison Foundation; B.B. by grants from the Burroughs Wellcome Fund, the Harvard Stem Cell Institute and the NIH; and R.J. by grants from the NIH.

Author Contributions. M.W., A.M. and R.J. conceived and designed the experiments and wrote the manuscript; M.W. derived all iPS lines; M.W. and A.M. performed the *in vitro* and *in vivo* characterization of the iPS lines (teratoma, 2N and 4N injections and IHC) and the conditional Dnmt1 experiment; A.M. investigated the promoter and imprinting methylation; M.K. and B.B. performed and analysed the real-time PCRs and ChIP experiments; R.F. and K.H. generated the selectable MEFs and TTFs; R.F. performed western blot and PCR analyses; and T.B. performed the microarray analysis and the proviral integration Southern blots.

Author Information. All microarray data from this study are available from Array Express at the EBI (http://www.ebi.ac.uk/arrayexpress) under the accession number E-MEXP-1037. Reprints and permissions information is available at www.nature.com/reprints. The authors declare no competing financial interests. Correspondence and requests for materials should be addressed to R.J. (jaenisch@wi.mit.edu).

.

Appendix: Index by Subject
附录：学科分类目录

Physics
物理学

Chemistry
化学

Biology
生物学

Astronomy
天文学

Geoscience
地球科学